C000145685

Springer Series in Statistics

Springer Series in Statistics

D. J. Daley   D. Vere-Jones

An Introduction to the
Theory of Point Processes

Springer-Verlag
New York Berlin Heidelberg
London Paris Tokyo

D. J. Daley
Department of Statistics
Institute for Advanced Study
Australian National University
Canberra, ACT 2601 Australia

D. Vere-Jones
Department of Statistics
Victoria University
Private Bag
Wellington, New Zealand

Mathematics Subject Classification (1980): 60G55, 60-01

Library of Congress Cataloging-in-Publication Data
Daley, Daryl J.
  An introduction to the theory of point
processes.
  (Springer series in statistics)
  Includes bibliographies.
  1. Point processes.   I. Vere-Jones, D.
II. Title.   III. Series.
QA274.42.D35   1988   519.2'3   87-32097

With 1 Illustration

Typeset by Asco Trade Typesetting Ltd., North Point, Hong Kong.
Printed and bound by R. R. Donnelley & Sons, Harrisonburg, Virginia.
Printed in the United States of America.

9 8 7 6 5 4 3 2 1

ISBN 0-387-96666-8 Springer-Verlag New York Berlin Heidelberg
ISBN 3-540-96666-8 Springer-Verlag Berlin Heidelberg New York

To Mary and Nola

Preface

This book has developed over many years—too many, as our colleagues and families would doubtless aver. It was conceived as a sequel to the review paper that we wrote for the Point Process Conference organized by Peter Lewis in 1971. Since that time the subject has kept running away from us faster than we could organize our attempts to set it down on paper. The last two decades have seen the rise and rapid development of martingale methods, the surge of interest in stochastic geometry following Rollo Davidson's work, and the forging of close links between point processes and equilibrium problems in statistical mechanics.

Our intention at the beginning was to write a text that would provide a survey of point process *theory* accessible to beginning graduate students and workers in applied fields. With this in mind we adopted a partly historical approach, starting with an informal introduction followed by a more detailed discussion of the most familiar and important examples, and then moving gradually into topics of increased abstraction and generality. This is still the basic pattern of the book. Chapters 1–4 provide historical background and treat fundamental special cases (Poisson processes, stationary processes on the line, and renewal processes). Chapter 5, on finite point processes, has a bridging character, while Chapters 6–14 develop aspects of the general theory.

The main difficulty we had with this approach was to decide when and how far to introduce the abstract concepts of functional analysis. With some regret, we finally decided that it was idle to pretend that a general treatment of point processes could be developed without this background, mainly because the problems of existence and convergence lead inexorably to the theory of measures on metric spaces. This being so, one might as well take advantage of the metric space framework from the outset and let the point process itself be defined on a space of this character: at least this obviates the tedium of having continually to specify the dimension of the Euclidean space, while in the context of complete separable metric spaces—and this is the greatest generality we contemplate—intuitive spatial notions still provide a reasonable guide to basic properties. For these reasons the general results from Chapter 6 onward are couched in the language of this setting, although the examples continue to be drawn mainly from the one- or two-dimensional Euclidean spaces $\mathbb{R}^1$ and $\mathbb{R}^2$. Two appendices collect together the main results we need from measure theory and the theory of measures on metric spaces. We hope that their inclusion will help to make the book more readily usable by applied workers who wish to understand the main ideas of the general theory without themselves becoming experts in these fields. Chapter 13, on the martingale approach, is a special case. Here the context is again the real line, but we added a third appendix that attempts to summarize the main ideas needed from martingale theory and the general theory of processes. Such special treatment seems to us warranted by the exceptional importance of these ideas in handling the problems of inference for point processes.

In style, our guiding star has been the texts of Feller, however many light-years we may be from achieving that goal. In particular, we have tried to follow his format of motivating and illustrating the general theory with a range of examples, sometimes didactical in character, but more often taken from real applications of importance. In this sense we have tried to strike a mean between the rigorous, abstract treatments of texts such as those by Matthes, Kerstan, and Mecke (1974/1978/1982) and Kallenberg (1975, 1983), and practically motivated but informal treatments such as Cox and Lewis (1966) and Cox and Isham (1980).

Numbering Conventions. Each chapter is divided into sections, with consecutive labelling within each of equations, statements (encompassing Definitions, Conditions, Lemmas, Propositions, Theorems), examples, and the exercises collected at the end of each section. Thus, in Section 1.2, (1.2.3) is the third equation, **Statement 1.2.III** is the third statement, EXAMPLE 1.2(c) is the third example, and Exercise 1.2.3 is the third exercise. The exercises are varied in both content and intention and form a significant part of this text. Usually, they indicate extensions or applications (or both) of the theory and examples developed in the main text, elaborated by hints or references intended to help the reader seeking to make use of them. The symbol □ denotes the end of a proof. Instead of a name index, the listed references carry page number(s) where they are cited. A general outline of the notation used has been included before the main text.

It remains to acknowledge our indebtedness to many persons and institutions. Any reader familiar with the development of point process theory over the last two decades will have no difficulty in appreciating our dependence on the fundamental monographs already noted by Matthes, Kerstan, and Mecke in its three editions (our use of the abbreviation MKM for the 1978 English edition is as much a mark of respect as convenience) and Kallenberg in its two editions. We have been very conscious of their generous interest in our efforts from the outset and are grateful to Olav Kallenberg in particular for saving us from some major blunders. A number of other colleagues, notably David Brillinger, David Cox, Klaus Krickeberg, Robin Milne, Dietrich Stoyan, Mark Westcott, and Deng Yonglu, have also provided valuable comments and advice for which we are very grateful. Our two universities have responded generously to a seemingly unending stream of requests to visit one another at various stages during more intensive periods of writing the manuscript. We also note visits to the University of California at Berkeley, to the Centre for Stochastic Processes at the University of North Carolina at Chapel Hill, and to Zhongshan University at Guangzhou. For secretarial assistance we wish to thank particularly Beryl Cranston, Sue Watson, June Wilson, Ann Milligan, and Shelley Carlyle for their excellent and painstaking typing of difficult manuscript.

Finally, we must acknowledge the long-enduring support of our families, and especially our wives, throughout: they are not alone in welcoming the speed and efficiency of Springer-Verlag in completing this project.

Canberra, Australia   D. J. Daley
Wellington, New Zealand   D. Vere-Jones

Contents

Principal Notation

Very little of the general notation used in the Appendices is given below. Also, notation that is largely confined to one or two sections of the same chapter is mostly excluded, so that neither all the symbols used nor all uses of the symbols shown are given. The repeated use of some symbols occurs as a result of point process theory embracing a variety of topics from the theory of stochastic processes. Generally, the particular interpretation of symbols with more than one use is clear from the context. Throughout the lists below,

N	signifies a point process
ξ	signifies a random measure
$\xi(t)$	signifies a cumulative process on $(0, \infty)$ (see p. 514)

Spaces

$\mathbb{C}$	complex numbers
$\mathbb{R}^d$	d-dimensional euclidean space
$\mathbb{R} = \mathbb{R}^1$	real line
$\mathbb{R}_+$	nonnegative numbers
$\mathbb{S}$	circle group and its representation as $(0, 2\pi]$ [p. 378]
U_α^d	d-dimensional cube of side length α [p. 341]
$\mathsf{U}^d = \mathsf{U}_1^d$	unit cube in $\mathbb{R}^d$
$\mathbb{Z}, \mathbb{Z}_+$	integers of $\mathbb{R}, \mathbb{R}_+$
$\mathcal{X}$	state space of N or ξ; often $\mathcal{X} = \mathbb{R}^d$; always $\mathcal{X}$ is c.s.m.s. (complete separable metric space)

Ω	space of probability elements ω
$\varnothing, \varnothing(\cdot)$	null set, null measure
$\mathscr{E}$	measurable sets in probability space
$(\Omega, \mathscr{E}, \mathscr{P})$	basic probability space on which N and ξ are defined [p. 154]
$\mathscr{X}^{(n)}$	n-fold product space $\mathscr{X} \times \cdots \times \mathscr{X}$ [p. 121]
$\mathscr{X}^{\cup}$	$= \mathscr{X}^{(0)} \cup \mathscr{X}^{(1)} \cup \cdots$ [p. 126]
$\mathscr{B}(\cdot)$	Borel σ-field on $\cdot$ [p. 148]
$\mathscr{B}(\mathscr{X})$	Borel σ-field generated by open spheres of c.s.m.s. $\mathscr{X}$ [p. 32]
$\mathscr{B}_{\mathscr{X}}$	$= \mathscr{B}(\mathscr{X}), \mathscr{B} = \mathscr{B}_{\mathbb{R}} = \mathscr{B}(\mathbb{R})$ [p. 32]
$\mathscr{B}_{\mathscr{X}}^{(n)} = \mathscr{B}(\mathscr{X}^{(n)})$	product σ-field on product space $\mathscr{X}^{(n)}$ [p. 126]
$BM(\mathscr{X}), BM_+(\mathscr{X})$	measurable (resp., measurable nonnegative) functions of bounded support [p. 182]
$\overline{BM_+}(X)$	limits of monotone sequences from $BM_+(\mathscr{X})$ [p. 192]
$\mathscr{K}$	mark space for marked point process [p. 204]
$\mathscr{M}_{\mathscr{X}}, \hat{\mathscr{M}}_{\mathscr{X}}$	totally (resp., boundedly) finite measures on c.s.m.s. $\mathscr{X}$ [pp. 153, 622]
$\mathscr{N}_{\mathscr{X}}, \hat{\mathscr{N}}_{\mathscr{X}}$	totally (resp., boundedly) finite counting measures on c.s.m.s. $\mathscr{X}$ [p. 197]
$\hat{\mathscr{N}}_0(\mathscr{X}) = \hat{\mathscr{N}}_{\mathscr{X}} \backslash \{N(\mathscr{X}) = 0\}$	support of KLM measures [p. 258]
$\hat{\mathscr{N}}_{\mathscr{X}}^*$	simple counting measures N^* on c.s.m.s. $\mathscr{X}$ [p. 197]
$\hat{\mathscr{N}}_{\mathscr{X}}^0 = \hat{\mathscr{N}}_{\mathscr{X}} \cap \{N(\{0\}) \geq 1\}$	counting measures with mass at origin [p. 470]
$\mathscr{P}^+$	p.p.d. (positive positive-definite) measures [p. 402]
$\mathscr{S}$	infinitely differentiable functions of rapid decay
$\mathscr{S}^+$	doubly infinite sequences of positive numbers $\{t_0, t_{\pm 1}, t_{\pm 2}, \ldots\}$ with $\sum_{n=1}^{\infty} t_n = \sum_{n=1}^{\infty} t_{-n} = \infty$ [p. 200]
$\mathscr{U}$	complex-valued Borel measurable functions on $\mathscr{X}$ of modulus ≤ 1 [p. 140]
$\mathscr{U} = \{(x, N): N \in \hat{\mathscr{N}}_{\mathscr{X}}, \ N(\{x\}) \geq 1\}$	carrier space of Campbell measure $C_{\mathscr{P}}$ of N [p. 469]
$\mathscr{U}_0 = \mathscr{U} \cap \{N: N(\{0\}) \geq 1\}$	carrier space of $\mathscr{P}_0(\cdot)$ for stationary N [p. 469]
$\mathscr{U} \otimes \mathscr{V}$	product topology on product space $\mathscr{X} \times \mathscr{Y}$ of topological spaces $(\mathscr{X}, \mathscr{U}), (\mathscr{Y}, \mathscr{V})$ [p. 602]
$\mathscr{V} = \mathscr{V}(\mathscr{X})$	$[0, 1]$-valued measurable functions with bounded support in $\mathscr{X}$ [p. 220]
$\mathscr{V}_0(\mathscr{X})$	$= \{h \in \mathscr{V}(\mathscr{X}): \inf_x h(x) > 0\}$ (hence $-\log h \in BM_+(\mathscr{X})$) [p. 221]
$\overline{\mathscr{V}}(\mathscr{X})$	limits of monotone sequences from $\mathscr{V}(\mathscr{X})$ [p. 222]

General

Unless otherwise specified, $A \in \mathcal{B}_{\mathcal{X}}, k$ and $n \in \mathbb{Z}_+, t$ and $x \in \mathbb{R}, h \in \mathcal{V}(\mathcal{X}), z \in \mathbb{C}$.

$\sim$	$\tilde{v}, \tilde{F}$ = Fourier–Stieltjes transforms of measure v or d.f. F [pp. 400, 637]; $\tilde{\phi}$ = Fourier transform of Lebesgue integrable function ϕ for counting measures [pp. 400, 636]; $\tilde{N} \in \mathcal{N}_{\tilde{\mathcal{X}}}^0$ which supports KLM measure $\tilde{Q}$ of infinitely divisible N [p. 258]
$\wedge$	reduced (ordinary or factorial) (moment or cumulant) measure [p. 357]; extension of concept from totally to boundedly finite measure space [p. 627]
$\|\mu\|$	variation norm of measure μ [p. 598]
$\|y\|$	$= \rho(0, y)$ for $y \in \mathbb{R}^d$ with metric $\rho(\cdot, \cdot)$
$A^{(n)}$	n-fold product set $A \times \cdots \times A$ [pp. 121, 127]
$A(\cdot) = A^{\mathscr{F}}(\cdot)$	$\mathscr{F}$-compensator for $\xi(t)$ [pp. 516, 519]
$\{A_n\}$	convex averaging sequence [p. 332]
$\mathscr{A}$	family of sets generating $\mathscr{B}$; more generally, semiring of bounded Borel sets generating $\mathscr{B}_{\mathcal{X}}$ [pp. 29, 155]
$B^c N = N(\cdot \cap B^c)$	point process exterior to bounded Borel set B [p. 578]
B_u	backward recurrence time at u [p. 56]
$c_k, c_{[k]}$	kth, kth factorial cumulants of distribution $\{p_n\}$ [p. 114]
$c(x) = c(y, y + x)$	covariance density of stationary mean square continuous process on $\mathbb{R}^d$ [p. 401]
$\hat{c}_2(x) = m\delta(x) + \hat{c}_{[2]}(x)$	complete covariance density of stationary N [p. 364]
$C_{[k]}(\cdot), c_{[k]}(\cdot)$	factorial cumulant measure and density [p. 146]
$C_2(A \times B)$ $= \text{cov}(\xi(A), \xi(B))$	covariance measure of ξ [p. 191]
$\hat{C}_{[2]}(\cdot)$	reduced covariance measure of stationary ξ [pp. 246, 357]
$C_{\mathscr{P}}$	Campbell measure of N or ξ [p. 453]
$\hat{C}_{\mathscr{P}}(\cdot)$	Palm measure of first-order stationary ξ (cf. $\mathscr{P}_0(\cdot)$) [p. 462]
$C_{\mathscr{P}}^*$	modified Campbell measure [p. 578]
$D_a^{(k)}$	diagonal shift operator: $D_a^{(k)} y = y + a\mathbf{1}$ [p. 357]
$\delta(\cdot)$	Dirac delta function

$\delta_x(A)$ — Dirac measure, $= \int_A \delta(u - x)\,du, = I_A(x)$ [p. 610]

$\Delta F(x) = F(x) - F(x-)$ — jump at x in right-continuous function F [p. 104]

$e_\lambda(x)$
$= (\lambda/2)^d \exp(-\lambda \sum_{i=1}^d |x_i|)$ — two-sided exponential density [p. 402]

F — renewal process lifetime d.f. [p. 64]

F^{n*} — n-fold convolution power of measure or d.f. F [p. 52]

$F_k(\cdot\,;\,\cdot)$ — fidi (finite-dimensional) distribution [p. 167]

$\mathscr{F}$ — history [p. 514]

$\Phi[\cdot]$ — characteristic functional [p. 186]

$G[h]$ — p.g.fl. of N [pp. 15, 141]; extended p.g.fl. [p. 222]

$G[h|x]$ — measurable family of p.g.fl.s [p. 235]

$G_c[\cdot], G_m[\cdot\,|x]$ — p.g.fl.s of cluster centre and member processes $N_c, N(\cdot\,|x)$ [p. 237]

$\Gamma(\cdot), \gamma(\cdot)$ — Bartlett spectrum, its density when it exists [p. 411]

$\Gamma(d\theta|r)$ — $= M_1(dr \times d\theta)/K_1(dr)$ directional rose of planar N or ξ [p. 379]

$H(\mathscr{P};\mu)$ — generalized entropy [p. 564]

H, H_I — entropy rate (resp., rate per interval) of stationary N on $\mathbb{R}$ [p. 569]

$\mathscr{H}, \mathscr{H}^*$ — internal history of $\xi(t)$ on $\mathbb{R}_+, \mathbb{R}$ [p. 514]

$I_A(x) = \delta_x(A)$ — indicator function of set A [p. 402]

$I_n(x)$ — modified Bessel function of order n [p. 68]

$\mathscr{I}$ — σ-field of events invariant under shift operator S_u [p. 330]

$J_n(A_1 \times \cdots \times A_n)$ — Janossy measure [p. 122]

$j_n(x_1, \ldots, x_1)$ — Janossy density [p. 122]

$J_n(\cdot\,|A)$ — local Janossy measure [p. 230]

K — compact set [pp. 595, 611]

$K_n(\cdot), k_n(\cdot)$ — Khinchin measure and density [p. 144]

$K_1(r) = EN(S(0; r)),$
$\qquad K_{[2]}(dr_1 \times dr_2)$ — radial components of first and second factorial moment measures of rotationally invariant planar N or ξ [p.380]

$\ell(A)$ — Lebesgue measure of A in $\mathscr{B}(\mathbb{R}^d)$, Haar measure on σ-group [pp. 29, 634]

$L_u = B_u + T_u$ — current lifetime of point process on $\mathbb{R}$ [p. 73]

$L[f]\,(f \in BM_+(\mathscr{X}))$ — Laplace functional, extended Laplace functional [pp. 164, 192]

$L_\xi[1 - h]\,(h \in \mathscr{V}(\mathscr{X}))$ — p.g.fl. of Cox process directed by ξ [p. 262]

$L[f; x]\,(f \in BM_+(\mathscr{X}))$ — Laplace functional of local Palm distribution $\mathscr{P}_0(x, \cdot)$ [p. 457]

$L_2(\xi^0), L_2(\Gamma)$ — Hilbert spaces of square integrable r.v.s ξ^0 or functions   [p. 419]

$L_A(x_1, \ldots, x_N)$
$\quad = j_N(x_1, \ldots, x_N | A)$ — likelihood and local Janossy density, $N \equiv N(A)$ [pp. 21, 497]

L_A^* — likelihood for nonstationary Poisson process [499]

λ — rate of N, especially intensity of stationary N [pp. 3, 44]

$\lambda(A) = M^*(A) = EN^*(A)$ — intensity measure of N [p. 209]

$\lambda^*(t) \, (t \in \mathbb{R}_+)$ — conditional intensity function of regular N on $\mathbb{R}_+$ [p. 503]

$\lambda^{\mathscr{F}}$ — $\mathscr{F}$-intensity for $\xi(t)$ [p. 530]

$\lambda^+(t) \, (t \in \mathbb{R}_+)$ — internal conditional intensity of N or ξ defined on $\mathbb{R}$ [p. 565]

$\lambda^*(t) \, (t \in \mathbb{R})$ — complete intensity function of N on $\mathbb{R}$, $= \mathscr{H}^*$-conditional intensity   [p. 559]

$m_{[k]}, m_k, m'_k$ — kth factorial, kth, and kth central moment of distribution $\{p_n\}$ [p. 112]

$m = M((0, 1]), = M(\mathbb{U}^d)$ — mean density of stationary N or ξ on $\mathbb{R}$, $\mathbb{R}^d$ [pp. 43, 356]

$M(x) = EN(0, x], m(x)$ — first moment function, its density, for ξ or N on $\mathbb{R}$ [p. 43]

$M_2(x) = M_2((0, x])$
$\quad = E(N^2(0, x])$ — second moment function for N or ξ on $\mathbb{R}$ [p. 58]

$M(A) = E\xi(A)$ — expectation measure of ξ or N [p. 188]

$M_k(A_1 \times \cdots \times A_k)$
$\quad = E[N(A_1) \cdots N(A_k)]$,
$\qquad m_k(\cdot)$ — kth moment measure, density   [p. 129]

$M_{[k]}(A_1 \times \cdots \times A_k), m_{[k]}(\cdot)$ — kth factorial moment measure, density   [p. 129]

$M_k(A) = E(\xi^{(k)}(A))$ — kth order moment measure of $\xi(\cdot)$ [p. 188]

$M^c, M(\cdot | x), M_{[k]}^c, M_{[k]}(\cdot | x)$ — expectation and kth factorial moment measures of N_c and $N(\cdot | x)$ of cluster process   [p. 238]

$\hat{m}_k$ — density of reduced moment measure $\hat{M}_k$, $\hat{m}_k(x_2 - x_1, \ldots, x_k - x_1) = m_k(x_1, \ldots, x_k)$ for stationary ξ [p. 358]

$\mathring{M}_k(\cdot) = m^{-1}\hat{M}_{k+1}(\cdot)$ — kth moment measure of Palm distribution [p. 464]

$M(t) \, (t \in \mathbb{R}_+)$ — $\mathscr{F}$-martingale in Doob–Meyer decomposition $\xi(t) = M(t) + A(t)$ [p. 522]

$\mu(\cdot), \tilde{\mu}(\cdot)$ — infectivity function and Fourier transform in Hawkes process   [p. 151]

$n^{[k]}$ — factorial power of n: $n^{[k+1]} = (n - k)n^{[k]}, n^{[0]} = 1$ [p. 112]

$N(A)$ — number of points in A [p. 39]

$N(a, b] = N((a, b])$ number of points in half-open interval $(a, b]$ [p. 18]

$N(t)$ $= N(0, t] = N((0, t])$ [p. 39]

N^*, N_k^* support point processes for N and for batches of size k in N [p. 199]

$N_c, N(\cdot | x)$ cluster centre (resp., member or component) process   [p. 236]

$N_{\mathscr{X}}(A)$ marginal point process $N(A \times \mathscr{K})$ of marked point process on $\mathscr{X} \times \mathscr{K}$ [p. 204]

$\{(p_n, \Pi_n)\}$ elements of probability measure for finite point process   [p. 121]

$P(z)$ p.g.f. (probability generating function) of distribution $\{p_n\}$ [p. 10]

$P(x, A)$ Markov transition kernel   [p. 107]

$P_0(A)$ avoidance function   [pp. 132, 215]

$P_k(x), p_k(x)$ $\mathscr{P}\{N(0, x] \le k\}, \mathscr{P}\{N(0, x] = k\}$ [p. 53]

$P_k(\cdot; \cdot)$ fidi distribution of N [p. 202]

$\mathscr{P}_{jk}$ set of j-partitions of $\{1, \ldots, k\}$ [p. 118]

$\mathscr{P}$ probability measure of stationary N on $\mathbb{R}$ [p. 50]; more generally, probability measure of N or ξ on c.s.m.s. $\mathscr{X}$ [p. 154]

$\{\mathscr{P}_0(x, U): x \in \mathscr{X},$ Palm kernel of local Palm distributions $\mathscr{P}_0(x, \cdot)$
$U \in \mathscr{B}(\hat{\mathscr{M}}_{\mathscr{X}})\}$ [p. 455]

$\mathscr{P}_0(\cdot) = m^{-1}\hat{C}_{\mathscr{P}}(\cdot)$ regular local Palm distribution of stationary N
$\quad = \mathscr{P}_0(x, S_{-x}(\cdot))$ or ξ with finite mean density   [p. 463]

$\{\pi_k\}$ batch-size distribution   [pp. 27, 48]

$\Pi^{\text{sym}}(\cdot)$ symmetrized set function (exclusion probabilities)   [p. 122]

$\Pi(\cdot)$ directional rose for line process   [p. 388]

$\Psi^{\mathscr{F}}$ $\mathscr{F}$-predictable σ-algebra   [p. 524]

$q(x) = f(x)/(1 - F(x))$ hazard function associated with lifetime d.f. F [p. 2]

$Q(z)$ $= -\log P(z)$ [p. 26]

$Q(t)$ IHF (integrated hazard function)   [p. 106]

$\tilde{Q}$ KLM measure   [p. 258]

$\rho(A|N)$ first-order Papangelou kernel   [p. 580]

$\rho(x, y)$ metric for x, y in metric space   [p. 594]

$\{S_n\}$ random walk, sequence of partial sums   [p. 64]

$S(x) = 1 - F(x)$ survivor function of d.f. F [p. 2]

$S(x; r)$ sphere in metric space $\mathscr{X}$ with centre at x, radius r [pp. 198, 401]

$S_{\varepsilon, x}$ $S(x, \varepsilon)$ [p. 33]

$\hat{S}_u: \hat{S}_u \mathscr{P}(B)$ shift operator on measures on $\mathscr{B}(\hat{\mathscr{M}}_{\mathscr{X}})$ [p.
$\quad = \mathscr{P}(S_u B) \ (B \in \mathscr{B}(\hat{\mathscr{M}}_{\mathscr{X}}))$ 318]

$\sigma\{X_1, X_2, \ldots\}$ σ-field generated by r.v.s $X_1\ X_2, \ldots$ [p. 483]

$S_u\colon (S_u\mu)(A) = \mu(T_u A)$ shift operator on $\hat{\mathcal{M}}_{\mathscr{X}}$ [p. 317]

$t(x) = \prod_{i=1}^d (1 - |x_i|)_+$ triangular density   [p. 402]

T_u forward recurrence time at u [p. 55]

$T_u\colon T_u x = x + u$ shift operator on $\mathbb{R}^d$ [p. 317]

$T_n = T_n(\omega)$
$\quad = \sup\{t\colon \xi(t, \omega) < n\}$ stopping time of $\xi(t)$ [p. 515]

$\mathscr{T} = \{S_1(\mathscr{T}), \ldots, S_j(\mathscr{T})\}$ a j-partition of k [p. 118]

$\mathscr{T} = \{\mathscr{T}_n\} = \{\{A_{ni}\}\}$ dissecting system of nested partitions   [pp. 157, 171, 608]

$\mathscr{T}$ tail σ-algebra of process in $\mathbb{R}^d$ [p. 343]

$U(A) = EN(A)$ renewal measure, $= \sum_{n=0}^{\infty} F^{n*}(A)$ [p. 64]

$U(x) = U([0, x])$ renewal function   [p. 64]

$V(A) = \operatorname{var} N(A)$ or
$\qquad\qquad \operatorname{var} \xi(A)$ variance function   [p. 365]

$V(x) = V((0, x])$ variance function for stationary N or ξ on $\mathbb{R}$ [p. 77]

$x^*(N)$ point closest to origin of N on $\mathbb{R}^d$ [p. 479]

$\xi = \xi(\cdot) = \xi(\cdot, \omega)$ random measure   [p. 154]

$\xi^{(k)}(A_1 \times \cdots \times A_k)$
$\quad = \xi(A_1) \cdots \xi(A_k)$ product random measure (after extension)   [p. 188]

$\xi^0(\cdot) = \xi(\cdot) - \ell(\cdot)$ mean-corrected second-order random measure   [p. 418]

$\{X_n\}$ components of $\{S_n\}$ [p. 64]; intervals of Wold process   [p. 89]

CHAPTER 1

Early History

The ancient origins of the modern theory of point processes are not easy to trace, nor is it our aim to give here an account with claims to being definitive. But any retrospective survey of a subject must inevitably give some focus on those past activities that can be seen to embody concepts common with the modern theory. Accordingly, this first chapter is a historical indulgence, but with the added benefit of describing certain fundamental concepts informally and in a heuristic fashion prior to possibly obscuring them with a plethora of mathematical jargon and techniques. These essentially simple ideas appear to have emerged from four distinguishable strands of enquiry—although our division of material may sometimes be a little arbitrary. These are

(i) life tables and the theory of self-renewing aggregates;
(ii) counting problems;
(iii) particle physics and population processes; and
(iv) communication engineering.

The first two of these strands can be discerned in centuries past and are discussed in the first two sections. The remaining two essentially belong to the present century, and our comments are briefer in the remaining section.

1.1. Life Tables and Renewal Theory

Of all the threads that go to make up the modern theory of point processes, the one with the longest history is that associated with intervals between events. This includes, in particular, renewal theory, which could be defined in a narrow sense as the study of the sequence of intervals between successive replacements of a component that is liable to failure and is replaced by a new component every time a failure occurs. As such, it is a subject that developed during the 1930s and reached a definitive stage with the work of Feller, Smith, and others in the period following World War II. But its roots extend back much further than this, through the study of "self-renewing aggregates" to problems of statistical demography, insurance, and mortality tables—in short, to one of the founding impulses of probability theory itself. It is not easy to point with confidence to any intermediate stage in this chronicle that recommends itself as the natural starting point either of renewal theory or of point process theory more generally. Accordingly, we start from the beginning, with a brief discussion of life tables themselves. The connection with point processes may seem distant at first sight, but in fact the theory of life tables provides not only the source of much current terminology but also the setting for a range of problems concerning the evolution of populations in time and space, which, in their full complexity, are only now coming within the scope of current mathematical techniques.

In its basic form, a life table consists of a list of the numbers of individuals, usually from an initial group of 1000 individuals so that the numbers are effectively proportions, who survive to a given age in a given population. The most important parameters are the number l_x surviving to age x; the number d_x dying between the ages x and $x + 1$ ($d_x = l_x - l_{x+1}$); and the number q_x of those surviving to age x who die before reaching age $x + 1$ ($q_x = d_x/l_x$). In practice, the tables are given for discrete ages, with the unit of time usually taken as 1 year. For our purposes it is more appropriate to replace the discrete time parameter by a continuous one and to replace numbers by probabilities for a single individual. Corresponding to l_x we have then the *survivor function*

$$S(x) = \Pr\{\text{lifetime} > x\}.$$

To d_x corresponds $f(x)$, the density of the lifetime distribution function, where

$$f(x)dx = \Pr\{\text{lifetime terminates between } x, x + dx\},$$

while to q_x corresponds $h(x)$, the *hazard function*, where

$$q(x)dx = \Pr\{\text{lifetime terminates between } x, x + dx \text{ given it does not terminate before } x\}.$$

Denoting the lifetime distribution function itself by $F(x)$, we have the following important relations between the above functions:

$$(1.1.1) \qquad S(x) = 1 - F(x) = \int_x^\infty f(y)\,dy = \exp\left(-\int_0^x q(y)\,dy\right),$$

$$(1.1.2) \qquad f(x) = \frac{dF}{dx} = -\frac{dS}{dx},$$

$$(1.1.3) \qquad q(x) = \frac{f(x)}{S(x)} = -\frac{d}{dx}[\log S(x)] = -\frac{d}{dx}\{\log[1 - F(x)]\}.$$

The first life table appeared, in a rather crude form, in John Graunt's *Observations on the London Bills of Mortality*. This work, which appeared in 1662, is a landmark in the early history of statistics, much as the famous correspondence between Pascal and Fermat, which took place in 1654 but was not published until 1679, is a landmark in the early history of formal probability. The coincidence in dates lends weight to the thesis (e.g., see Maistrov, 1967) that mathematical scholars studied games of chance not only for their own interest, but for the opportunity they gave for clarifying the basic notions of chance, frequency, and expectation, already actively in use in mortality, insurance, and population movement contexts.

An improved life table was constructed in 1693 by the astronomer Halley, using data from the smaller city of Breslau, which was not subject to the same problems of disease, immigration, and incomplete records with which Graunt struggled in the London data. Graunt's table was also discussed by Huyghens (1629–1695), to whom the notion of expected length of life is due. A. de Moivre (1667–1754) suggested that for human populations the function $S(x)$ could be taken to decrease with equal yearly decrements between the ages 22 and 86. This corresponds to a uniform density over this period and a hazard function that increases to infinity as x approaches 86. The analysis leading to (1.1.1) and (1.1.2), with further elaborations to take into account different sources of mortality, would appear to be due to Laplace (1747–1829). It is interesting that in *A Philosophical Essay on Probabilities* (1814), where the classical definition of probability based on equiprobable events is laid down, Laplace gave a discussion of mortality tables in terms of probabilities of a totally different kind. Euler (1707–1783) also studied a variety of problems of statistical demography.

From the mathematical point of view, the paradigm distribution function for lifetimes is the exponential function, which has a constant hazard independent of age: for $x > 0$ we have

$$(1.1.4) \quad f(x) = \lambda e^{-\lambda x}, \quad q(x) = \lambda, \quad S(x) = e^{-\lambda x}, \quad F(x) = 1 - e^{-\lambda x}.$$

The usefulness of this distribution, particularly as an approximation for purposes of interpolation, was stressed by Gompertz (1779–1865), who also suggested, as a closer approximation, the distribution function corresponding to a power law hazard of the form

$$(1.1.5) \qquad\qquad q(x) = Ae^{\alpha x} \qquad (A > 0, \alpha > 0, x > 0).$$

With the addition of a further constant $[q(x) = B + Ae^{\alpha x}]$, this is known in demography as the *Gompertz–Makeham law* and is possibly still the most widely used function for interpolating or graduating a life table.

Other forms commonly used for modelling the lifetime distribution in different contexts are the *Weibull, gamma,* and *lognormal* distributions, corresponding, respectively, to the formulae

$$(1.1.6) \quad q(x) = \beta\lambda x^{\beta-1} \quad \text{with } S(x) = \exp(-\lambda x^\beta) \qquad (\lambda > 0, \beta > 0),$$

(1.1.7) $f(x) = \lambda \alpha x^{\alpha-1} e^{-\lambda x}/\Gamma(\alpha),$

(1.1.8) $f(x) = (\sigma x \sqrt{2\pi})^{-1} e^{-[(\log x - \mu)/\sigma]^2/2}.$

The Weibull distribution was introduced by Weibull (1939a, b) as a model for brittle fracture. Both this and the preceding distribution have an interpretation in terms of extreme value theory (e.g., see Exercise 1.1.2), but it should be emphasized that as a general rule the same distribution may arise from several models (cf. Exercise 1.1.3).

The gamma distribution has a long history and arises in many different contexts. When $\alpha = k/2$ and $\lambda = \frac{1}{2}$, it is nothing other than the chi-squared distribution with k degrees of freedom, with well-known applications in mathematical statistics. When $\alpha = 1$ it reduces to the exponential distribution, and when $\alpha = \frac{3}{2}$ it reduces to the Maxwell distribution for the distribution of energies of molecules in a perfect gas. The most important special cases in the context of life tables arise when α is a positive integer, say $\alpha = k$. It then has an interpretation as the sum of k independent random variables each having an exponential distribution. Although commonly known as the Erlang distributions, after the Danish engineer and mathematician who introduced it as a model for telephone service and intercall distributions in the 1920s, this special form and its derivation were known much earlier. One of the earliest derivations, if not the first, is due to the English mathematician R. C. Ellis (1817–1859) in a remarkable paper in 1844 that could well be hailed as one of the early landmarks in stochastic process theory, although in fact it is very little quoted. In addition to establishing the above-mentioned result as a special case, Ellis studied a general renewal process and in that context established the asymptotic normality of the sum of a number of independent nonnegative random variables. It is particularly remarkable in that he used Fourier methods, in other words essentially the modern characteristic function proof (with a few lacunae from a modern standpoint) of the central limit theorem.

An equally interesting aspect of Ellis' paper is the problem that inspired the study. This takes us back a century and a half, to an even less familiar statistician in the guise of Sir Isaac Newton (1642–1728). For much of his later life, Newton's spare time was devoted to theological problems, one of which was to reconcile the ancient Greek and Hebrew chronologies. In both chronologies, periods of unknown length are spanned by a list of successive rulers. Newton proposed to estimate such periods, and hence to relate the two chronologies, by supposing each ruler to reign for a standard period of 22 years. This figure was obtained by a judicious comparison of averages from a miscellany of historical data for which more or less reliable lengths of reigns were known. It is a statistical inference in the same sense as many of Graunt's inferences from the London Bills of Mortality; a plausible value based on the best or only evidence available and supported by as many cross-checks as can be devised. How far it was explicitly present in Newton's mind that he was dealing with a statistical problem and whether he made any attempts to assess the likely errors of his results himself are questions we have not been able to answer with any certainty. In an informal summary of his work, he commented (1728): "I do not pretend to be exact to a year: there may be errors of five or ten years, and sometimes twenty, and not much above." However, it appears unlikely that these figures were obtained by any theory of compounding of errors. It is tempting to conjecture that he may have discussed the problems with such friends and Fellows of the Royal Society as Halley, whose paper to the Royal Society would have been presented while Newton was president, and de Moivre, who dedicated the first edition of *The Doctrine of Chances* to Newton, but if records of such discussions exist, we have not found them.

Up until the middle of the nineteenth century, as will be clear even from the brief review presented above, mathematical problems deriving from life tables not only occupied a major place in the subject matter of probability and statistics but also attracted the attention of many leading mathematicians of the time. From the middle of the nineteenth century onward, however, actuarial mathematics (together, it may be added, with many other probabilistic notions), while important in providing employment for mathematicians, became somewhat disreputable mathematically, a situation from which it has not fully recovered. (How many elementary textbooks in statistics, for example, even mention life tables, let alone such useful descriptive tools as the hazard function?) The result was that when, as was inevitably the case, new applications arose that made use of the same basic concepts, the links with earlier work were lost or only partially recognized. Moreover, the new developments themselves often took place independently or with only a partial realization of the extent of common material.

In the present century, at least three such areas of application may be distinguished. The first, historically, was queueing theory, more specifically the theory of telephone trunking problems. Erlang's first paper on this subject appeared in 1909 and contained a derivation of the Poisson distribution for the numbers of calls in a fixed time interval. It is evident from his comments that even before that time the possibility of using probabilistic methods in that context was being considered by engineers in several countries. The work here appears to be quite independent of earlier contributions. In later work the analysis was extended to cover queueing systems with more general input and service distributions.

Mathematical interest in actuarial problems as such reemerged in the 1910s and 1920s, in connection with the differential and integral equations of population growth. Here at least there is a bridge between the classical theory of life tables on the one hand and the modern treatments of renewal processes on the other. It is provided by the theory of "self-renewing aggregates" [to borrow a phrase from the review by Lotka (1939), which provides a useful survey of early work in this field], a term that refers to a population (portfolio in the insurance context) of individuals subject to death but also able to regenerate themselves so that a stable population can be achieved.

As a typical illustration, consider the evolution of a human population for which it is assumed that each female of age x has a probability $\phi(x)dt$ of giving birth to a daughter in a time interval of length dt, independently of the behaviour of other females in the population and also of any previous children she may have had. Let $S(x)$ denote the survivor function for the (female) life distribution and $n(t)$ the expected female birth rate at time t. Then $n(t)$ satisfies the integral equation

$$n(t) = \int_0^t n(t - x)S(x)\phi(x)dx,$$

which represents a breakdown of the total female birth rate by age of parent. If the population is started at time zero with an initial age distribution having density $r(x)$, the equation can be rewritten in the form

$$n(t) = n_0(t) + \int_0^t n(t - x)S(x)\phi(x)dx,$$

where

$$n_0(t) = \int_0^\infty r(x)\frac{S(t + x)}{S(x)}\phi(t + x)dx$$

is the contribution to the birth rate at time t from the initial population. In this form the analogy with the integral equation of renewal theory is clear. Indeed, the latter equation corresponds to the special case where at death each individual is replaced by another of age zero, and no other "births" are possible. The population size then remains constant, and it is enough to consider a population with just one member. In place of $n(t)$ we have then the *renewal density* $m(t)$, with $m(t)dt$ representing the probability that a replacement will be required in the small time interval $(t, t + dt)$; also $\phi(x)$ becomes the hazard function $h(x)$ for the life distribution, and the combination $S(x)h(x)$ can be replaced by the probability density function $f(x)$ as at (1.1.3). Thus, we obtain the renewal equation in the form

$$m(t) = n_0(t) + \int_0^t m(t - u)f(u)du.$$

If, finally, the process is started with a new component in place at time 0, then $n_0(t) = f(t)$ and we have the standard form

$$m_s(t) = f(t) + \int_0^t m_s(t - u)f(u)\,du.$$

The third field to mention is reliability theory. A few problems in this field, including Weibull's discussion of brittle fracture, appeared before World War II, but its systematic development relates to the post-war period and the rapid growth of the electronics industry. Typical problems are the calculation of lifetime distributions of systems of elements connected in series ("weakest link" model) or in parallel. Weibull's analysis is an example of the first type of model, which typically leads to an extreme value distribution with a long right tail. An early example of a parallel model is Daniels' (1945) treatment of the failure of fibre bundles; the distributions in this case have an asymptotically normal character. In between and extending these two primary cases lie an infinite variety of further failure models, in all of which the concepts and terminology invented to cover the life table problem play a central role.

In retrospect, it is easy to see that the three fields referred to are closely interconnected. Together, they provide one of the main areas of application and development of point process theory. Of course they do not represent the only fields where life table methods have been applied with success. An early paper by Watanabe (1933) gives a life table analysis of the times between major earthquake disasters, a technique that has been resurrected by several more recent writers under the name of *theory of durability*. An important recent field of application has been the study of trains of nerve impulses in neurophysiology. In fact, the tools are available and relevant for any phenomenon in which the events occur along a time axis and the intervals between the time points are important and meaningful quantities.

Exercises

1.1.1. A nonnegative random variable (r.v.) X with distribution function (d.f.) F has an *increasing failure rate* (abbreviated to IFR) if the conditional d.f.s

$$F_x(u) = \Pr\{X \le x + u | X > x\} = \frac{F(x+u) - F(x)}{1 - F(x)} \qquad (u, x \ge 0)$$

are increasing functions of x for every fixed u in $0 < u < \infty$. It has a *decreasing mean residual life* (DMRL) if $E(X - x | X > x)$ decreases with increasing x, and it is *new-better-than-used in expectation* (NBUE) if $E(X - x | X > x) \le EX$ (all $x > 0$). Show that IFR implies DMRL, DMRL implies NBUE, and NBUE implies that var $X \le (EX)^2$ [cf. Stoyan (1983, §1.6)].

1.1.2. Let $X_1, X_2, \ldots$, be a sequence of independent identically distributed r.v.s with d.f. $F(\cdot)$. Then for any fixed nonnegative integer n,

$$\Pr\left\{ \max_{1 \le j \le n} X_j \le u \right\} = (F(u))^n.$$

Replacing n by a Poisson distributed r.v. N with mean μ yields

$$G(u) \equiv \Pr\left\{ \max_{1 \le j \le N} X_j \le u \right\} \equiv e^{-\mu} \sum_{k=0}^{\infty} \mu^k (k!)^{-1} (F(u))^k$$

$$= e^{-\mu(1 - F(u))}.$$

When $F(u) = 1 - e^{-\lambda u}$, G is the Gumbel d.f., while when $F(u) = 1 - \lambda u^{-\alpha}$, G is the Weibull d.f. [In the forms indicated, these extreme value distributions include location and/or scale parameters; for example, see Johnson and Kotz (1970, p. 272).]

1.1.3. Let $X_1, X_2, \ldots$ be as in the previous exercise with $F(u) = 1 - e^{-\lambda u}$. Show that $Y \equiv \max(X_1, \ldots, X_n)$ has the same distribution as $\sum_{j=1}^{n} X_j / j$. [*Hint*: Regard X_1,

..., X_n as lifetimes in a linear death process with death rate λ, so that Y is the time to extinction of the process. Exercise 2.1.2 gives more general properties.]

1.1.4. Suppose that the lifetimes of rulers are independent r.v.s with common d.f. F and that conditional on reaching age 21 years, a ruler has a son (with lifetime d.f.s F) every 2 years for up to six sons, with the eldest surviving son succeeding him. Conditional on there being a succession, what is the d.f. of the age at succession and the expected time that successor reigns (assuming a reign terminated by death from natural causes)?

What types of error would be involved in matching chronologies from a knowledge of the orders of two sets of ruler (cf. reference to Newton's work in the text)? How would such chronologies be matched in the light of developments in statistical techniques subsequent to Newton?

1.1.5. Investigate the integral equation for the stationary age distribution in a super-critical age-dependent branching process. Using a suitable metric, evaluate the difference between this stationary age distribution and the backward recurrence time distribution of a stationary renewal process with the same lifetime distribution, as a function of the mean of the offspring distribution. Note that Euler worked on the age distribution in exponentially growing populations.

1.2. Counting Problems

The other basic approach to point process phenomena, and the only systematic approach yet available in spaces of higher dimension, is to count the numbers of events in intervals or regions of various types. In this approach the machinery of discrete distributions plays a central role. Since in probability theory discrete problems are usually easier to handle than continuous problems, it might be thought that the development of general models for a discrete distribution would precede those for a continuous distribution, but in fact the reverse seems to be the case. Although particular examples, such as the Bernoulli distribution and the negative binomial distribution, occurred at a very early stage in the discussion of games of chance, there seems to be no discussion of discrete distributions as such until well into the nineteenth century. We may take as a starting point the text of Poisson (1837), which included a derivation of the Poisson distribution by passage to the limit from the binomial (the claim that he was anticipated in this by de Moivre is a little exaggerated in our view: it is true de Moivre appends a limit result to the discussion of a certain card problem, but it can hardly be said that the resulting formula was considered by de Moivre *as a distribution*, which may be the key point). Even Poisson's result does not seem to have been widely noted at the time, and it is not derived in a counting process context. The first discussions of counting problems known to us are by Seidel (1876) and Abbé (1879) who treated the occurrence of thunderstorms and the numbers of blood cells in haemocytometer squares, respectively, and both apparently independently of Poisson's work. Indeed, Poisson's discovery of the distribution seems to have been lost sight of until attention was drawn to it in Von Bortkiewicz's (1898) monograph *Das Gesetz der kleinen Zahlen*, which includes a systematic account of phenomena that fit the Poisson distribution, including, of course, the famous example of the numbers of deaths from horse kicks in the Prussian army.

Lyon and Thoma (1881) on Abbé's data and Student (1907) gave further discussions of the blood cell problem, the latter paper being famous as one of the earliest applications of the χ^2 test of goodness of fit. Shortly afterward the Poisson process arose simultaneously in two very important contexts. Erlang (1909) derived the Poisson distribution for the number of incoming calls to a telephone trunking system by supposing the numbers in disjoint intervals to be independent and considering the limit behaviour when the interval of observation is divided into an increasing number of equally sized subintervals. This effectively reproduces the Poisson distribution as the limit of the binomial, but Erlang was not aware of Poisson's work at the time, although he corrected the omission in later papers. Then in 1910 Bateman, brought in as mathematical consultant by Rutherford and Geiger in connection with their classical experiment on the counting of α particles, obtained the Poisson probabilities as solutions to the family of differential equations

$$p_n'(t) = -\lambda p_n(t) + p_{n-1}(t) \qquad (n \geq 1)$$

$$p_0'(t) = -\lambda p_0(t).$$

[Concerning the relation $p_0(t) = e^{-\lambda t}$, Bateman (1910) commented that it "has been known for some time (Whitworth's *Choice and Chance*, 4th Ed., Proposition LI)," while Haight (1967) mentioned the result as a theorem of Boltzmann (1868) and quoted the reference to Whitworth who does not indicate the sources of his result.]

These equations represent a formulation in terms of a pure birth process and the first step in the rapid development of the theory of birth and death processes during the next two decades, with notable early papers by McKendrick (1914, 1926) and Yule (1924). This work preceded the general formulation of birth and death processes as Markov processes (themselves first studied by Markov more than a decade earlier) in the 1930s and is not of immediate concern, despite the close connection with point process problems. A similar remark can be made in respect of branching processes, studied first by Bienaymé (see Heyde and Seneta, 1977) and of course by Galton and Watson (1874). There are close links with point processes, particularly in the general case, but the early studies used special techniques that again lie a little outside the scope of our present discussion, and it was only from the 1940s onward that the links became important.

Closer in line with our immediate interests is the work on alternatives to the Poisson distribution. In many problems in ecology and elsewhere, it is found that the observed distribution of counts frequently shows a higher dispersion (i.e., a higher variance for a given value of the mean) than can be accounted for satisfactorily by the Poisson distribution, for which the variance/mean ratio is identically unity. The earliest and perhaps still the most widely used alternative is the *negative binomial distribution*, which figures in early papers by Student (1907), McKendrick (1914), and others. A particularly important paper for the sequel was the study by Greenwood and Yule (1920) of accident statistics, which provided an important model for the negative binomial, and in so doing sparked a controversy, still not entirely resolved, concerning the identifiability of the model describing accident occurrence. Since the accident process is a kind of point process in time, and since shades of the same controversy will appear in our own models, we briefly paraphrase their derivation. Before doing so, however, it is convenient to summarize some of the machinery for handling discrete distributions.

The principal tool is the *probability generating function* (p.g.f.) defined for nonnegative integer-valued random variables X by the equation

$$P(z) = \sum_0^\infty p_n z^n,$$

where $p_n = \Pr\{X = n\}$. It is worth mentioning that although generating functions have been used in connection with difference equations at least since the time of Laplace, their application to this kind of problem in the 1920s and 1930s was hailed as something of a technological breakthrough.

In Chapter 5, relations between the p.g.f., factorial moments, and cumulants are discussed. For the present, we content ourselves with the observation that the negative binomial distribution can be characterized by the form of its p.g.f.,

$$(1.2.1) \qquad P(z) = \left(\frac{\mu}{1 + \mu - z}\right)^\alpha \qquad (\alpha > 0, \mu > 0),$$

corresponding to values of the probabilities themselves

$$p_n = \frac{(\alpha - 1 + n)!}{(\alpha - 1)! \, n!} \left(\frac{\mu}{1 + \mu}\right)^\alpha \left(\frac{1}{1 + \mu}\right)^n.$$

Greenwood and Yule derived this distribution as an example of what we call a *mixed Poisson*[†] distribution; that is, it can be obtained from a Poisson distribution $p_n = e^{-\lambda}\lambda^n/n!$ by treating the parameter λ as a random variable. If, in particular, λ is assumed to have the gamma distribution

$$dF(\lambda) = \mu^\alpha \lambda^{\alpha-1}(\Gamma(\alpha))^{-1} e^{-\mu\lambda} \, d\lambda,$$

then the resultant discrete distribution has p.g.f.

[†] Note that there is a lack of agreement on terminology: other authors, for example, Johnson and Kotz (1969), would label this as a compound Poisson and would call the distribution we treat below under that name a *generalized* Poisson. The terminology we use is perhaps more common in texts on probability and stochastic processes; the alternative terminology is more common in the statistical literature.

$$P(z) = \int_0^\infty e^{\lambda(z-1)} \, dF(\lambda) = \left(\frac{\mu}{1 + \mu - z} \right)^\alpha,$$

$e^{\lambda(z-1)}$ being the p.g.f. of the Poisson distribution with parameter λ.

It is not difficult to verify that the mean and variance of this negative binomial distribution equal α/μ and $(\alpha/\mu)(1 + \mu^{-1})$, so that the variance/mean ratio of the distribution equals $1 + \mu^{-1}$, exceeding by μ^{-1} the corresponding ratio for a Poisson distribution. Greenwood and Yule interpreted the variable parameter λ of the underlying Poisson distribution as a measure of individual "accident proneness," which was then averaged over all individuals in the population.

The difficulty for the sequel is that, as was soon recognized, many other models also give rise to the negative binomial, and these may have quite contradictory interpretations in regard to accidents. Lüders (1934) showed that the same distribution could be derived as an example of a *compound* Poisson distribution, meaning a random sum of independent random variables in which the number of terms in the sum has a Poisson distribution. If each term is itself discrete and has a *logarithmic distribution* with p.g.f.

(1.2.2)
$$P(z) = \frac{\log(1 + \mu - z)}{\log(\mu)},$$

and if the number of terms has a Poisson distribution with parameter α, then the resultant distribution has the identical p.g.f. (1.2.1) for the negative binomial (see Exercise 1.2.1). The interpretation here would be that all individuals are identical but subject to accidents in batches. Even before this, Eggenberger and Pólya (1923) and Pólya (1931) had introduced a whole family of distributions, for which they coined the term "contagious distributions," to describe situations where the occurrence of a number of events enhances the probability of the occurrence of a further event, and had shown that the negative binomial distribution could be obtained in this way. If the mixed and compound models can be distinguished in principle by examining the joint distributions of the numbers of accidents in nonoverlapping intervals of a person's life, Cane (1974, 1977) has shown that there is no way in which the mixed Poisson and Polya models can be distinguished from observations on individual case histories, for they lead to identical conditional distributions (see Exercise 1.2.2).

Another important contribution in this field is the work of Neyman (1939), who introduced a further family of discrete distributions, derived from consideration of a cluster model. Specifically, Neyman was concerned with distributions of beetle larvae in space, supposing these to have crawled some small distance from their initial locations in clusters of eggs. Further analysis of this problem resulted in a series of papers, written by Neyman in collaboration with E. L. Scott and other writers, which treated many different statistical questions relating to clustering processes in ecology, astronomy, and other subjects (e.g., see Neyman and Scott, 1958).

Many of these questions can be treated most conveniently by the use of generating functionals and moment densities, a theory that had been developing simultaneously as a tool for describing the evolution of particle showers and related problems in theoretical physics. The beginnings of such a general theory appear in the work of the French physicist Yvon (1935), but the main developments relate to the post-war period, and we therefore defer a further discussion to the following section.

Exercises

1.2.1. Verify that if $X_1, X_2, \ldots$, are independent r.v.s with the logarithmic distribution whose p.g.f. is at (1.2.2), and if N, independent of $X_1, X_2, \ldots$, is a Poisson r.v. with mean α, then $X_1 + \cdots + X_N$ has the negative binomial distribution at (1.2.1).

1.2.2. (Compare Cane, 1974.) Suppose that an individual has n accidents in the time interval $(0, T)$ at $t_1 < t_2 < \cdots < t_n$. Evaluate the likelihood function for these n times for the two models:
   (i) accidents occur at the epochs of a Poisson process at rate λ (where λ is fixed for each individual but may vary between individuals);
   (ii) conditional on having experienced j accidents in $(0, t)$, an individual has probability $(k + j)\mu \, dt/(1 + \mu t)$ of an accident in $(t, t + dt)$, independent of the occurrence times of the j accidents in $(0, t)$; each individual has probability $k\mu \, dt$ of an accident in $(0, dt)$.
   Show that the probabilities of n events in $(0, T)$ are Poisson and negative binomial, respectively, and deduce that the conditional likelihood, given n, is the same for (i) and (ii).

1.2.3. The negative binomial distribution can also arise as the limit of the Pólya–Eggenberger distribution defined for integers n and $\alpha, \beta > 0$ by

$$p_k = \binom{n}{k} \frac{\Gamma(\alpha + k)\Gamma(\beta + n - k)\Gamma(\alpha + \beta)}{\Gamma(\alpha + \beta + n)\Gamma(\alpha)\Gamma(\beta)} = \binom{-\alpha}{k} \frac{\Gamma(\alpha + \beta)n!\,\Gamma(\beta + n - k)}{\Gamma(\beta)(n - k)!\,\Gamma(\beta + n + \alpha)}.$$

When β and $n \to \infty$ with $n/\beta \to \mu$, a constant, and α fixed, show that $\{p_k\}$ has the p.g.f. at (1.2.1). [For further properties see Johnson and Kotz (1969) and the papers cited in the text.]

1.2.4. Neyman's Type A distribution (see Johnson and Kotz, 1969) has a p.g.f. of the form

$$\exp\left[\mu\left(\sum_i \alpha_i \exp[-\lambda_i(1 - z)] - 1\right)\right],$$

where $\alpha_i \geq 0$, $\sum_i \alpha_i = 1$, $\lambda_i > 0$, and $\mu > 0$, and arises as a cluster model. Give such a cluster model interpretation for the simplest case $\alpha_i = 1$ for $i = 1$, $\alpha_i = 0$ otherwise, and general $\lambda \equiv \lambda_1$ and μ.

1.2.5. Suppose that a (large) population evolves according to a one-type Galton–Watson branching process in which the distribution of the number of children has p.g.f. $P(z)$. Choose an individual at random in a particular generation. Show that the distribution of the number of sibs (sisters, say) of this randomly chosen individual has p.g.f. $P'(z)/P'(1)$ and that this is the same as for the number of aunts, or nth great-aunts, of this individual. [Attempting to estimate the off-spring distribution by using the observed family size distribution, when based on sampling via the children, leads to the distribution with p.g.f. $zP'(z)/P(1)$ and is an example of length-biased sampling that underlies the waiting-time paradox referred to in Sections 3.2 and 3.4. The p.g.f. for the number of great-aunts is used in Section 9.4.]

1.3. Some More Recent Developments

The Period during and following World War II saw an explosive growth in theory and applications of stochastic processes. On the one hand, many new applications were introduced and existing fields of application were extended and deepened; on the other hand, there was also an attempt to unify the subject by defining more clearly the basic theoretical concepts. The monographs by Feller (1950) and Bartlett (1955) (preceded by mimeographed lecture notes from 1947) played an important role in stressing common techniques and exploring the mathematical similarities in different applications; both remain remarkably succinct and wide-ranging surveys.

From such a busy scene it is difficult to pick out clearly marked lines of development, and any selection of topics is bound to be influenced by personal preferences. Bearing such reservations in mind, we can attempt to follow through some of the more important themes into the post-war period.

On the queueing theory side, a paper of fundamental importance is C. Palm's (1943) study of intensity fluctuations in traffic theory, a title that embraces topics ranging from the foundation of a general theory of the input stream to the detailed analysis of particular telephone trunking systems. Three of his themes, in particular, were important for the future of point processes. The first is the systematic description of properties of a renewal process, as a first generalization of the Poisson process as input to a service system. The notion of *regeneration point*, a time instant at which the system reverts to a specified state with the property that the future evolution is independent of how the state was reached, has proved exceptionally fruitful in many different applications. In Palm's terminology, the Poisson process is characterized by the property that every instant is a regeneration point, whereas for a general renewal process only those instants at which a new interval is started form regeneration points. Hence, he called a Poisson process a process *without aftereffects* and a renewal process a process with *limited aftereffects*. Another important idea was his realization that two types of distribution function are important in describing a stationary point process—the distribution of the time to the next event from a fixed but arbitrary origin and the distribution of the time to the next event from an arbitrary event of the process. The relations between the two sets of distributions are given by a set of equations now commonly called the Palm–Khinchin equations, Palm himself having exhibited only the simplest special case. A third important contribution was his (incomplete) proof of the first limit theorem for point processes, namely, that superposition of a large number of independent sparse renewal processes leads to a Poisson process in the limit. Finally, it may be worth mentioning that it was in Palm's paper that the term "point processes" (Punktprozesse) was first used as such—at least to the best of our knowledge.

All these ideas have led to important further development. H. Wold (1948, 1949), also a Swedish mathematician, was one of the first to take up Palm's work, studying processes with Markov dependent intervals that, he suggested, would form the next most complex alternative to the renewal model. Bartlett (1954) reviewed some of this early work. Of the reworkings of Palm's theory, however, the most influential was the monograph by Khinchin (1955), which provided a more complete and rigorous account of Palm's work, notably extended it in several directions, and had the very important effect of bringing the subject to the attention of pure mathematicians. Thus, Khinchin's book became the inspiration of much theoretical work, particularly in the Soviet Union and Eastern Europe. Ryll-Nardzewski's (1961) paper set out fundamental properties of point processes and provided a new and more general approach to Palm probabilities. Starting in the early 1960s, Matthes and co-workers developed many aspects concerned with infinitely divisible point processes and related questions. The book by Kerstan, Matthes, and Mecke (1974) represented the culmination of the first decade of such work; extensive revisions and new material were incorporated into the later editions in English (1978) (referred to as MKM in this book) and in Russian (1982).

In applications, these ideas have been useful not only in queueing theory [for continuing development in this field see the monographs of Franken et al. (1981) and Brémaud (1981)] but also in the study of level-crossing problems. Here the pioneering work was due to Rice (1944) and McFadden (1956, 1958). More rigorous treatments, using some of the Palm–Khinchin theory, were given by Leadbetter and other writers [e.g., see Leadbetter (1972) and the monographs by Cramér and Leadbetter (1967) and Leadbetter, Lindgren, and Rootzen (1983)].

On a personal note in respect of much of this work, it is appropriate to remark that Belyaev, Franken, Grigelionis, König, Matthes, and one of us, among others, were affected by the lectures and personal influence of Gnedenko, who was a student of Khinchin.

Meanwhile, there was also rapid development on the theoretical physics front. The principal ideas here were the characteristic and generating functionals and product densities. As early as 1935, Kolmogorov suggested the use of the *characteristic functional*

$$\Phi(\xi) = E(e^{i\langle X, \xi \rangle})$$

as a tool in the study of random elements X from a linear space L; ξ is then an element from the space of linear functionals on L. The study of probability measures on abstract spaces remained a favourite theme of the Russian school of probability theory and led to the development of the weak convergence theory for measures on metric spaces by Prohorov (1956) and others, which in turn preceded the general study of random measures [e.g., Jirina (1966) and later writers including the Swedish mathematicians Jagers (1974) and Kallenberg (1975)]. After the war, the characteristic functional was discussed by Le Cam (1947) for stochastic processes and Bochner (1947) for random interval functions. Bochner's (1955) monograph, in particular, contains many original ideas that have only partially been followed up, for example, by Brillinger (1972). Kendall (1949) and Bartlett and Kendall (1951) appear to be the first to have used the characteristic functional in the study of specific population models.

Of more immediate relevance to point processes is the related concept of a *probability generating functional* (p.g.fl.) defined by

$$G[h] = E\left[\prod_i h(x_i)\right] = E[e^{\int \log h(x) N(dx)}],$$

where $h(x)$ is a suitable test function and the x_i are the points at which population members are located, that is, the atoms of the counting measures $N(\cdot)$. The p.g.fl. is the natural extension of the p.g.f., and, like the p.g.f., it has an expansion, when the total population is finite, in terms of the probabilities of the number of particles in the population and the probability densities of their locations. There is also an expansion, analogous to the expansion of the p.g.f. in terms of factorial moments, in terms of certain factorial moment density functions, or *product densities* as they are commonly called in the physical literature. Following the early work of Yvon noted at the end of Section 2, the p.g.fl. and product densities were used by Bogoliubov (1946), while properties of product densities were further explored in important papers by Bhabha (1950) and Ramakrishnan (1950). Ramakrishnan, in particular, gave formulae expressing the moments of the number of particles in a given set in terms of the product densities and Stirling numbers. Later, these ideas were considerably extended by Ramakrishnan, Janossy, Srinivasan, and others; an extensive literature exists on their application to cosmic ray showers summarized in the monographs by Janossy (1948) and Srinivasan (1969, 1974).

This brings us to another key point in the mathematical theory of point processes, namely, the fundamental paper by Moyal (1962a). Drawing principally on the physical and ecological contexts, Moyal for the first time set out clearly the mathematical constructs needed for a theory of point processes on a general state space, clarifying the relations between such quantities as the product densities, finite-dimensional distributions, and probability generating functionals and pointing out a number of important applications. Independently, Harris (1963) set out similar ideas in his monograph on branching processes, subsequently (Harris, 1968, 1971) contributing important ideas to the general theory of point processes and the more complex subject of interacting particle systems.

In principle, the same techniques are applicable to other contexts where population models are important, but in practice the discussions in such contexts have tended to use more elementary, ad hoc tools. In forestry, for example, a key problem is the assessment of the number of diseased or other special kinds of tree in a given region. Since a complete count may be physically very difficult to carry out and expensive, emphasis has been on statistical sampling techniques, particularly of transects (line segments drawn through the region) and nearest-neighbour distances. Matérn's (1960) monograph brought together many ideas, models, and statistical techniques of importance in such fields and includes an account of point process aspects. Ripley's (1981) monograph covers some more recent developments.

On the statistical side, Cox's (1955) paper contained seeds leading to the treatment of many statistical questions concerning data generated by point processes, as well as discussing various models including the important class of doubly stochastic Poisson processes. A further range of techniques was introduced by Bartlett (1963), who showed how to adapt methods of time series analysis to a point process context and brought together a variety of different models. This work was extended to processes in higher dimensions in a second paper (Bartlett, 1964). Lewis (1964a) used similar techniques to discuss the instants of failure of a computer. The subsequent monograph by Cox and Lewis (1966) was a further important development that, perhaps for the first time, showed clearly the wide range of applications of point processes, as well as extending many of the probabilistic and statistical aspects of such processes.

In the last decade, perhaps the most important development has been the rapid growth of interest in point processes in communications engineering (e.g., see Snyder, 1975). It is a remarkable fact that in nature, for example, in nerve systems, the transfer of information is more often effected by pulse signals than by continuous signals. This fact seems to be associated with the high signal/noise ratios which it is possible to achieve by these means; for the same reason, pulse techniques are becoming increasingly important in communication applications. For such processes, just as for continuous processes, it is meaningful to pose questions concerning the prediction, interpolation, and estimation of signals, and the detection of signals against background noise (in this context, of random pulses). Since the signals are intrinsically nonnegative, the distributions cannot be Gaussian, so that linear models are not in general appropriate. Thus, the development of a suitable theory for point processes is closely linked to the development of nonlinear techniques in other branches of stochastic process theory. As in the applications to processes of diffusion type, martingale methods provide a powerful tool in the discussion of these problems, yielding, for example, structural information about the process and its likelihood function, as well as more technical convergence results. Developments in this area have been surveyed in several recent books including Liptser and Shiryayev (1974), Brémaud (1981), Jacobsen (1982), and others.

The one drawback of these methods is that they are restricted to processes of an evolutionary type, for which a time-like variable is an essential ingredient. While this covers a great many of the practically important applications, it is less satisfactory as a general theory, and perhaps one of the important problems for future study is the development of a related theory that can be applied both to point processes on a general state space and to the study of other geometrical objects as addressed in stochastic geometry [e.g., see Harding and Kendall (1974), Stoyan, Kendall, and Mecke (1987), and the discussion on stochastic geometry in Volume 50 of the *Bulletin of the International Statistical Institute*].

CHAPTER 2

Basic Properties of the Poisson Process

The archetypal point processes are the Poisson and renewal processes. Their importance is so great, not only historically but also in illustrating and motivating more general results, that we prefer to give an account of some of their more elementary properties in this and the next two chapters, before proceeding to the general theory of point processes.

For our present purposes, we shall understand by a point process some method of randomly allocating points to intervals of the real line or (occasionally) to rectangles or hyper-rectangles in a d-dimensional Euclidean space $\mathbb{R}^d$. It is intuitively clear and will be made rigorous in Chapters 5–7 that a point process is completely defined if the joint probability distributions are known for the numbers of events in all finite families of disjoint intervals (or rectangles, etc.).

2.1. The Stationary Poisson Process

With the understanding just enunciated, the stationary Poisson process on the line is completely defined by the following equation, in which we use $N(a_i, b_i]$ to denote the number of events of the process falling in the half-open interval $(a_i, b_i]$ with $a_i < b_i \le a_{i+1}$:

$$(2.1.1) \quad \Pr\{N(a_i, b_i] = n_i, i = 1, \ldots, k\} = \prod_{i=1}^{k} \frac{[\lambda(b_i - a_i)]^{n_i}}{n_i!} e^{-\lambda(b_i - a_i)}.$$

This definition embodies three important features:

(i) the numbers of points in each finite interval $(a_i, b_i]$ has a Poisson distribution;

(ii) the numbers of points in disjoint intervals are independent random variables; and
(iii) the distributions are stationary: they depend only on the lengths $b_i - a_i$ of the intervals.

Thus, the joint distributions are multivariate Poisson of the special type in which the variates are independent.

Let us first summarize a number of properties that follow directly from (2.1.1). The mean $M(a, b]$ and variance $V(a, b]$ of the number of points falling in the interval $(a, b]$ are given by

$$(2.1.2) \qquad M(a, b] = \lambda(b - a) = V(a, b].$$

The equality of mean and variance and the fact that both are proportional to the length of the interval provide a useful diagnostic test for the stationary Poisson process: estimate the variance $V(a, b]$ for intervals of different length, and plot the ratios $V(a, b]/(b - a)$. The estimates should be approximately constant for a stationary Poisson process and equal to the mean rate. Any systematic departure from this constant value indicates some departure either from the Poisson assumption or from stationarity [see Exercise 2.1.1 and Cox and Lewis (1966, §6.3) for more discussion].

Note also from (2.1.2) that λ can be interpreted as the *mean rate* or *mean density* of points of the process.

Now consider the relation, following directly from (2.1.1), that

$$(2.1.3) \qquad \Pr\{N(0, \tau] = 0\} = e^{-\lambda \tau}$$

is the probability of finding no points in an interval of length τ. This may also be interpreted as the probability that the random interval extending from the origin to the point first appearing to the right of the origin has length exceeding τ. In other words, it gives nothing other than the *survivor function* for the length of this interval. Equation (2.1.3) therefore shows that the interval under consideration has an exponential distribution. From stationarity, the same result applies to the length of the interval to the first point of the process to the right of any arbitrarily chosen origin and then equally to the interval to the first point to the left of any arbitrarily chosen origin. In queueing terminology, these two intervals are referred to as the *forward* and *backward recurrence times*; thus, for a Poisson process both forward and backward recurrence times have an exponential distribution with parameter λ.

Using the independence property, we can extend this result to the distribution of the time interval between any two consecutive points of the process, for the conditional distribution of the time to the next point to the right of the origin, given a point in $(-\Delta, 0]$, has the same exponential form, which, being independent of Δ, is therefore the limiting form of this conditional distribution as $\Delta \to 0$. When such a unique limiting form exists, it can be identified with the distribution of the time interval between two arbitrary points of the process (see also Section 3.4 of the following chapter). Similarly, by considering the limiting forms of more complicated joint distributions, we can show that successive intervals are independently distributed as well as having exponential distributions (see Exercises 2.1.4 and 2.1.5).

On the other hand, the particular interval containing the origin is *not* exponentially distributed. Indeed, since it is equal to the sum of the forward and backward recurrence times, and each of these has an exponential distribution and is independent of the other, its distribution must have an Erlang (or gamma) distribution with density $\lambda^2 x e^{-\lambda x}$. This result has been referred to as the "waiting-time paradox" because it describes the predicament of a passenger arriving at a bus stop when the bus service follows a Poisson pattern. The intuitive explanation is that since the position of the origin (the passenger's arrival) is unrelated to the process governing the buses, it may be treated as effectively uniform over any given time interval; hence, it is more likely to fall in a large rather than a small interval. See Sections 3.2 and 3.4 for more detail and references.

Now let t_k, $k = 1, 2, \ldots$, denote the time from the origin $t_0 = 0$ to the kth point of the process to the right of the origin. Then we have

(2.1.4) $\{t_k \geq x\} = \{N(0, x] \leq k\}$

in the sense that the expressions in braces describe identical events. Hence, in particular, their probabilities are equal. But the probability of the event on the right is given directly by (2.1.1), so we have

(2.1.5) $\Pr\{t_k \geq x\} = \Pr\{N(0, x] \leq k\} = \sum_{j=0}^{k} \frac{(\lambda x)^j}{j!} e^{-\lambda x}.$

Differentiating this expression, which gives the survivor function for the time to the kth point, we obtain the corresponding density function

(2.1.6) $f_k(x) = \frac{\lambda^{k+1} x^k}{k!} e^{-\lambda x},$

which is again an Erlang distribution. Since the time to the kth event can be considered as the sum of the lengths of the k random intervals $(t_0, t_1]$, $(t_1, t_2]$, $\ldots$, $(t_{k-1}, t_k]$, which as above are independently and exponentially distributed, this provides an indirect proof of the result that the sum of k independent exponential random variables has the Erlang distribution.

In much the same vein, we can obtain the *likelihood* of a finite realization of a Poisson process. This may be defined as the probability of obtaining the given number of observations in the observation period, times the joint conditional density for the positions of those observations, given their number. Suppose that there are N observations on $(0, T]$, at time points $t_1, \ldots, t_N$. From (2.1.1) we can write down immediately the probability of obtaining single events in $(t_i - \Delta, t_i]$ and no points on the remaining part of $(0, T]$: it is just

$$e^{-\lambda T} \prod_{j=1}^{N} \lambda \Delta.$$

Dividing by Δ^N and letting $\Delta \to 0$, to obtain the density, we find as the required likelihood function

(2.1.7) $$L_{(0,T]}(N; t_1, \ldots, t_N) = \lambda^N e^{-\lambda T}.$$

Since the probability of obtaining precisely N events in $(0, T]$ is equal to $[(\lambda T)^N/N!]e^{-\lambda T}$, this implies, *inter alia*, that the conditional density of obtaining points at $(t_1, \ldots, t_N)$, given N points in the interval, is just $N!/T^N$, corresponding to a uniform distribution over the hyperoctant

$$0 \leq t_1 \leq \cdots \leq t_N \leq T.$$

One point about this result is worth stressing. It corresponds to treating the points as *indistinguishable* apart from their locations. In physical contexts, however, we may be concerned with the positions of N physically distinguishable particles. The factor $N!$, which arises in the first instance as the volume of the unit hyperoctant, can then be interpreted also as the combinatorial factor representing the number of ways the N distinct particles can be allocated to the N distinct time points. The individual particles are then to be thought of as uniformly and independently distributed over $(0, T]$. It is in this sense that the conditional distributions for the Poisson process are said to correspond to the distributions of N particles laid down uniformly at random on the interval $(0, T]$. Furthermore, either from this result or directly from (2.1.1), we obtain

(2.1.8) $$\Pr\{N(0, x] = k | N(0, T] = N\} = \frac{\Pr\{N(0, x] = k, N(x, T] = N - k\}}{\Pr\{N(0, T] = N\}}$$

$$= \binom{N}{k}\left(\frac{x}{T}\right)^k\left(1 - \frac{x}{T}\right)^{N-k},$$

representing a binomial distribution for the number in the subinterval $(0, x]$, given the number in the larger interval $(0, T]$.

Most of the results in this section extend both to higher dimensions and to nonstationary processes. The extensions to higher dimensions are discussed in Exercise 2.1.7 and Section 2.4. Let us conclude the present section by mentioning the simple but important extension to a Poisson processs with time varying rate $\lambda(t)$, commonly called the nonhomogeneous or inhomogeneous Poisson process. The process can be defined exactly as in (2.1.1), with the quantities $\lambda(b_i - a_i)$ replaced wherever they occur by quantities

$$\Lambda(a_i, b_i] = \int_{a_i}^{b_i} \lambda(x)dx.$$

Thus, the joint distributions are still Poisson, and the independence property still holds. Furthermore, conditional distributions now correspond to particles independently distributed on $(0, T]$ with a common distribution having density function $\lambda(x)/\Lambda(0, T]$ $(0 \leq x \leq T)$. The construction of sample realizations is described in Exercise 2.1.6, while the likelihood function takes the more general form

(2.1.9) $L_{(0,T]}(N; t_1, \ldots, t_N) = e^{-\Lambda(0,T]} \prod_{i=1}^{N} \lambda(t_i)$

$$= \exp\left(-\int_0^T \lambda(t)dt + \int_0^T \log \lambda(t) N(dt)\right).$$

From this expression it can be seen that results for the nonstationary Poisson process can be derived from those for the stationary case by a deterministic time change $t \to u(t) \equiv \Lambda(0, t]$. In other words, if we write $N(t) = N(0, t]$ (all $t \geq 0$) and define a new point process by

$$\tilde{N}(t) = N(u^{-1}(t))$$

then $\tilde{N}(t)$ is a stationary Poisson process.

In Chapter 13, we meet a remarkable extension of this last result, due to Papangelou (1972a): any point process satisfying a simple continuity condition can be transformed into a Poisson process if we allow a random time change in which $\Lambda[0, t]$ depends on the past of the process up to time t. Papangelou's result also implies that (2.1.9) represents the typical form of the likelihood for a point process: in the general case all that is needed is to replace the absolute rate $\lambda(t)$ in (2.1.9) by a conditional rate that is allowed to depend on the past of the process.

Other extensions lead to the class of mixed Poisson processes (see Exercise 2.1.8) and Cox processes treated in Chapter 8.

Exercises

2.1.1. Let $N_1, \ldots, N_n$ be i.i.d. like the Poisson r.v. N with mean $\mu = EN$, and write $\bar{N} = (N_1 + \cdots + N_n)/n$ for the sample mean. When μ is sufficiently large, indicate why the sample index of dispersion

$$Z = \sum_{j=1}^{n} \frac{(N_j - \bar{N})^2}{\bar{N}}$$

has a distribution approximating that of a χ^2_{n-1} r.v. Darwin (1957) found approximations to the distribution of Z for a general distribution for N based on its cumulants, illustrating his work via the Neyman, negative binomial, and Thomas distributions (see also Kathirgamatamby, 1953).

2.1.2. *Exponential distribution order properties.* Let $X_1, \ldots, X_n$ be i.i.d. exponential r.v.s on $(0, \infty)$ with

$$\Pr\{X_1 > x\} = e^{-\lambda x} \qquad (x \geq 0)$$

for some positive finite λ.
(a) Let $X_{(1)} < \cdots < X_{(n)}$ be the order statistics of $X_1, \ldots, X_n$. Then $(X_{(1)}, \ldots, X_{(n)})$ has the same distribution as the vector whose kth component is

$$\frac{X_n}{n} + \frac{X_{n-1}}{n-1} + \cdots + \frac{X_{n-k+1}}{n-k+1}.$$

(b) Write $Y = X_1 + \cdots + X_n$ and set $Y_{(k)} = (X_1 + \cdots + X_k)/Y$. Then $Y_{(1)}, \ldots,$ $Y_{(n-1)}$ are the order statistics of $n - 1$ i.i.d. r.v.s uniformly distributed on $(0, 1)$.

2.1.3. *Exponential r.v.s have no memory.* Let X be exponentially distributed as in Exercise 2.1.2, and for any nonnegative r.v. Y that is independent of X, define a r.v. X_Y as any r.v. whose d.f. has as its tail

$$R(z) \equiv \Pr\{X_Y > z\} = \Pr\{X > Y + z | X > Y\}.$$

Then X_Y and X have the same d.f. [There exist innumerable characterizations of exponential r.v.s via their lack of memory properties; many are surveyed in Galambos and Kotz (1978).]

2.1.4. A process satisfying (2.1.1) has

$$\Pr\{N(t - x - \Delta, t - \Delta] = 0, N(t - \Delta, t] = 1, N(t, t + y] = 0 | N(t - \Delta, t] > 0\}$$
$$\to e^{-\lambda x} e^{-\lambda y} \quad (\Delta \to 0),$$

showing the stochastic independence of successive intervals between points of the process.

2.1.5. The distance X of the point closest to the origin of a Poisson process in $\mathbb{R}^d$ with rate λ satisfies

$$\Pr\{X > y\} = \exp(-\lambda v_k(y)),$$

where $v_d(y) = y^d v_d(1)$ is the volume of a sphere of radius y in $\mathbb{R}^d$. In particular,
  (i) in $\mathbb{R}^1$, $\Pr\{X > y\} = e^{-2\lambda y}$;
  (ii) in $\mathbb{R}^2$, $\Pr\{X > y\} = e^{-\pi\lambda y^2}$;
  (iii) in $\mathbb{R}^3$, $\Pr\{X > y\} = e^{-(4\pi/3)\lambda y^3}$.
These same expressions also hold for the nearest-neighbour distance of an arbitrarily chosen point of the process.

2.1.6. To construct a realization on $(0, T]$ of an inhomogeneous Poisson process Π_1 for which the local intensity $\lambda(\cdot)$ satisfies $0 \le \lambda(u) \le \lambda_{\max}$ $(0 < u \le T)$ for some finite positive constant $\lambda_{\max}$, first construct a realization of a stationary Poisson process with rate $\lambda_{\max}$ (using the fact that successive intervals are i.i.d. exponential r.v.s with mean $1/\lambda_{\max}$), yielding the points $0 < t_1 < t_2 < \cdots$, say. Then, independently for each $k = 1, 2, \ldots$, retain t_k as a point of Π_1 with probability $\lambda(t_k)/\lambda_{\max}$ and otherwise delete it. Verify that the residual set of points satisfies the independence axiom and that

$$E(\#\{j: 0 < t_j < u, t_j \in \Pi_1\}) = \int_0^u \lambda(v) dv.$$

[See also Lewis and Shedler (1976) and Example 13.1(g).]

2.1.7. Using the notation of Exercise 2.1.5, we can construct a realization of a Poisson process Π_d in a neighbourhood of the origin in $\mathbb{R}^d$ by adapting Exercises 2.1.5 and 2.1.6 to give an inhomogeneous Poisson process on $(0, T)$ with intensity $\lambda(d/dy)v_d(y)$ and then, denoting these points by $r_1, r_2, \ldots$, taking the points of Π_d as having polar coordinates (r_j, θ_j), where θ_j are points independently and uniformly distributed over the surface of the unit sphere in $\mathbb{R}^d$. [An alternative construction for r_j is to use the fact that $\lambda(v_d(r_j) - v_d(r_{j-1}))$, with $r_0 = 0$, are i.i.d. exponential r.v.s with unit mean.]

2.1.8. (a) A point process whose fidi distributions are given by integrating λ in the right-hand side of (2.1.1) with respect to some d.f. defines a *mixed Poisson process*, since the distributions come from regarding λ as a r.v. Verify that

$$N(0, t]/t \xrightarrow{\text{a.s.}} \lambda \qquad (t \to \infty),$$

$$EN(0, t] = (E\lambda)t,$$

$$\text{var } N(0, t] = (E\lambda)t + (\text{var } \lambda)t^2 \geq EN(0, t],$$

with strict inequality unless var $\lambda = 0$.

(b) Let $Y, Y_1, Y_2, \ldots$, be i.i.d. nonnegative integer-valued r.v.s with probability generating function $g(s) = Es^Y(|s| \leq 1)$, and let them be independent of a Poisson process N° at rate λ with $N^\circ(t) = N^\circ(0, t]$. Then

$$N(0, t] \equiv \sum_{i=1}^{N^\circ(t)} Y_i$$

defines the counting function of a *compound Poisson process* for which

$$Ez^{N(0,t]} = \exp[-\lambda t(1 - g(z))],$$

$$EN(0, t] = \lambda(EY)t,$$

$$\text{var } N(0, t] = \lambda(\text{var } Y)t + \lambda(EY)^2 t$$

$$= [EN^\circ(t)](\text{var } Y) + [\text{var } N^\circ(t)](EY)^2 \geq EN(0, t],$$

with strict inequality unless $EY(Y - 1) = 0$. [Both the mixed and compound Poisson processes are in general overdispersed compared with a Poisson process in the sense of having var $N(0, t]/EN(0, t] \geq 1$ with equality holding only in the exceptional cases as noted.]

2.1.9. For a Poisson process with cyclic intensity function

$$\lambda(t) = \lambda \exp[\kappa \sin(\omega_0 t + \theta)]/I_0(\kappa) \qquad (\kappa \geq 0, \omega_0 > 0, 0 \leq \theta < 2\pi, \lambda > 0),$$

where $I_0(\kappa) = \int_0^{2\pi} \exp(\kappa \sin u)du$ is the modified Bessel function of the first kind of zero order, the likelihood [see (2.1.9) above] of the realization $t_1, \ldots, t_N$ on the interval $(0, T)$ where, for convenience of simplifying the integral below, T is a multiple of the period $2\pi/\omega_0$, equals

$$\exp\left(-\int_0^T \lambda \exp[\kappa \sin(\omega_0 t + \theta)](I_0(\kappa))^{-1} dt\right)\left(\frac{\lambda}{I_0(\kappa)}\right)^N \exp\left(\kappa \sum_{i=1}^N \sin(\omega_0 t_i + \theta)\right)$$

$$= e^{-\lambda T/2\pi}\left(\frac{\lambda}{I_0(\kappa)}\right)^N \exp\left(\kappa \sum_{i=1}^N \sin(\omega_0 t_i + \theta)\right).$$

Consequently, N is a sufficient statistic for λ, and, when the frequency ω_0 is known,

$$\left(N, \sum_{i=1}^N \sin \omega_0 t_i, \sum_{i=1}^N \cos \omega_0 t_i\right) \equiv (N, S, C) \quad \text{say,}$$

are jointly sufficient statistics for the parameters $(\lambda, \kappa, \theta)$, the maximum likelihood estimates $(\hat{\lambda}, \hat{\kappa}, \hat{\theta})$ being determined by $\hat{\lambda} = 2\pi N/T$, $\tan \hat{\theta} = C/S$ and $(d/d\kappa) \log I_0(\kappa)|_{\kappa=\hat{\kappa}} = S/N \cos \hat{\theta} = (S^2 + C^2)^{1/2}/N$ (the constraints that $\hat{\kappa} \geq 0$ and that S and $\cos \theta$ are of the same sign determine which root $\hat{\theta}$ is taken). [See Lewis (1970) and Kutoyants (1984b, Chap. 4) for more detail.]

2.2. Characterizations of the Stationary Poisson Process: I. Complete Randomness

In applications, the Poisson process is sometimes referred to simply as a *random* distribution of points on a line (as if there were no alternative random processes!) or slightly more specifically as a *purely random* or *completely random* process. In all these terminologies, what is in view is the fundamental independence property referred to in (ii) under (2.1.1). We start our discussion of characterizations by examining how far this property alone is capable of characterizing the Poisson process. More precisely, let us assume that we are given a point process satisfying the assumptions below, and examine how far the distributions are determined by them.

Assumptions 2.2.I

   (i) *The number of points in any finite interval is finite and not identically zero.*
  (ii) *The numbers in disjoint intervals are independent random variables.*
 (iii) *The distribution of $N(a + t, b + t]$ is independent of t.*

For brevity we speak of a process satisfying (i) as *boundedly finite and nonnull*, while propety (ii) may be referred to as *complete independence* and (iii) as *(crude) stationarity*.

Theorem 2.2.II. *Under Assumptions 2.2.I the probability generating function (p.g.f.)*

$$P(z, \tau) = E(z^{N(0, \tau]})$$

can be written uniquely in the form

(2.2.1) $$P(z, \tau) = e^{\lambda\tau(\Pi(z)-1)},$$

where λ is a positive constant and $\Pi(z) = \sum_1^\infty \pi_n z^n$ is the p.g.f. of a discrete distribution having no zero term.

Remark. From the stationarity and independence assumptions, all the joint distributions can be written down once the form of (2.2.1) is given, so that (2.2.1) is in fact sufficient to specify the process completely. Hence, the assumption of crude stationarity suffices in the case of the Poisson process to ensure its complete stationarity (see Definition 3.2.I below).

PROOF. Since $N(a, b]$ is a monotonic increasing function of b, it is clear that $P(z, \tau)$ is a monotonic *decreasing* function of τ for any fixed z with $0 \le z \le 1$, while $Q(z, \tau) = -\log P(z, \tau)$, finite because of Assumption 2.2.I(i), is a monotonic *increasing* nonnegative function of τ. Also, since

$$N(0, \tau_1 + \tau_2] = N(0, \tau_1] + N(\tau_1, \tau_1 + \tau_2],$$

it follows from the stationarity and independence assumptions that

$$P(z, \tau_1 + \tau_2) = P(z, \tau_1)P(z, \tau_2),$$

(2.2.2)

$$Q(z, \tau_1 + \tau_2) = Q(z, \tau_1) + Q(z, \tau_2).$$

Now it is well known (e.g., see Lemma 3.6.III) that the only monotonic solutions of the functional equation (2.2.2) are of the form

$$Q(z, \tau) = \text{constant} \times \tau,$$

where in this case the constant is a function of z, say $C(z)$. Thus, for all $\tau > 0$ we can write

(2.2.3) $$P(z, \tau) = e^{-\tau C(z)}$$

for some uniquely determined function $C(z)$.

Consider first the case $z = 0$. From Assumption 2.2.I(i), $N(0, \tau] \not\equiv 0$, so $P(0, \tau) \not\equiv 1$, and hence $C(0) \ne 0$. Now

$$\{N(0, 1] \ge n\} \supseteq \bigcup_{k=1}^{n} \{N((k-1)/n, k/n] \ge 1\},$$

so using the independence assumption and (2.2.3) we have

$$\Pr\{N(0, 1] \ge n\} \ge (\Pr\{N(0, 1/n] \ge 1\})^n = (1 - e^{-C(0)/n})^n.$$

If now $C(0) = \infty$, then $\Pr\{N(0, 1] \ge n\} = 1$ (all $n = 1, 2, \ldots$), contradicting Assumption 2.2.I(i) that $N(0, 1]$ is a.s. finite. Thus, we conclude that

(2.2.4) $$0 < C(0) < \infty.$$

Define quantities λ and $\Pi(z)$ by

$$\lambda = C(0),$$

$$\Pi(z) = \frac{C(0) - C(z)}{C(0)} = \frac{\log P(z, \tau) - \log P(0, \tau)}{\log P(0, \tau)},$$

the finiteness and nonnegativity of $\Pi(z)$ on $0 \le z \le 1$ being ensured by the monotonicity in z of $P(z, \cdot)$. From (2.2.3) and (2.2.4) it follows that $P(z, \tau) \to 1$ $(\tau \to 0)$ for every fixed z in $0 \le z \le 1$, and so from (2.2.3) we have

$$\tau C(z) = 1 - P(z, \tau) + o(\tau) \qquad (\tau \downarrow 0),$$

from which we have

$$\Pi(z) = \lim_{\tau \downarrow 0} \frac{P(z, \tau) - P(0, \tau)}{1 - P(0, \tau)}.$$

This representation expresses $\Pi(\cdot)$ as the limit of p.g.f.s, namely, the p.g.f.s of the conditional probabilities

$$\pi_{k|\tau} \equiv \Pr\{N(0, \tau] = k | N(0, \tau] > 0\}.$$

The definition of $\Pi(z)$ shows that it inherits from $P(z, \tau)$ the property of continuity as $z \uparrow 1$, and therefore the continuity theorem for p.g.f.s [e.g., see Feller (1968, §XI.6)] ensures that $\Pi(z)$ must also be a p.g.f., $\Pi(z) = \sum \pi_k z^k$ say, where

(2.2.5) $$\pi_k = \lim_{\tau \downarrow 0} \pi_{k|\tau} = \lim_{\tau \downarrow 0} \Pr\{N(0, \tau] = k | N(0, \tau] > 0\}.$$

In particular, $\pi_0 = \Pi(0) = 0$.

We have thus established the required form of the representation at (2.2.1). Uniqueness follows from the uniqueness of $P(z, \tau)$, which defines $C(z)$ by (2.2.3), and $C(z)$ in turn defines λ and $\Pi(z)$. □

The process defined by Assumptions 2.2.I is clearly more general than the Poisson process, to which it reduces only in the case $\pi_1 = 1$, $\pi_k = 0$ $(k \neq 1)$. The clue to its interpretation comes from the limit relation (2.2.5), which suggests that $\{\pi_k\}$ should be interpreted as a "batch-size" distribution, where "batch" refers to a collection of points of the process located at the same time point. None of our initial assumptions precludes the possibility of such batches. The distribution of the *number* of such batches in $(0, 1)$ is found by replacing $\Pi(z)$ by z in (2.2.1), and therefore it is Poisson with rate λ. Thus, the general process defined by Assumptions 2.2.I can be described as consisting of a succession of batches, the successive batch sizes or *multiplicities* being independent random variables [as follows readily from Assumption 2.2.I(ii)] having the common distribution $\{\pi_k\}$, and the number of batches following a Poisson process with constant rate λ. Recognizing that (2.2.1) specifies the p.g.f. of a compound Poisson distribution, we refer to the process as the *compound Poisson process* [see footnote below (1.2.1) regarding terminology].

Processes with batches represent an extension of the intuitive notion of a point process as a random placing of points over a region. They are variously referred to as nonorderly processes, processes with multiple points, compound processes, processes with positive integer marks, and so on. For a general proof of the existence of a batch-size distribution for stationary point processes, see Proposition 3.3.VII.

It should be noted that the uniqueness of the representation (2.2.1) breaks down once we drop the convention $\pi_0 = 0$. Indeed, given any p.g.f. $\Pi(\cdot)$ as at (2.2.1), let π_0^* be any number in $0 \leq \pi_0^* < 1$, and define $\lambda^* = \lambda/(1 - \pi_0^*)$, $\pi_n^* = (1 - \pi_0^*)\pi_n$. Then $\Pi^*(z) \equiv \sum_{n=0}^{\infty} \pi_n^* z^n = \pi_0^* + (1 - \pi_0^*)\Pi(z)$, and

$$\lambda^*(1 - \Pi^*(z)) = \lambda(1 - \pi_0^*)^{-1}\{(1 - \pi_0^*)[1 - \Pi(z)]\} = \lambda(1 - \Pi(z)).$$

The interpretation of this nonuniqueness is that if we increase the rate of occurrence of batches, we may compensate for this increase by observing only those batches with nonzero batch size.

An alternative interpretation of the process can be obtained by writing (2.2.1) in the form

$$P(z, \tau) = \prod_{k=1}^{\infty} \exp[-\lambda \pi_k \tau (1 - z^k)],$$

corresponding to a representation of the total as the sum of independent contributions from a countable family of simpler processes, the kth of which may be regarded as a modified Poisson process in which the rate of occurrence of points is equal to $\lambda \pi_k$ and each such point is treated as a batch of fixed size k. In this representation, the process is regarded as a superposition of independent component processes, each of Poisson type, but with fixed batch size. Since both interpretations lead to the same finite distributions, and hence to the same probability structures, they must be regarded as equivalent.

Theorem 2.2.II may also be regarded as a special case of the more general theorem of Lévy [e.g., see Loève (1963, §37)] on the structure of processes with stationary independent increments. In our case there can be no Gaussian component (since the realizations are monotonic), no drift component (since the realizations are integer-valued), and the Poisson components must have positive integral jumps. Because a process has independent increments if and only if the distributions of the increment over any finite interval are infinitely divisible, (2.2.1) also gives the general form of an infinitely divisible distribution taking values only on the nonnegative integers [see Exercise 2.2.2 and Feller (1968, §XII.2)].

Analytically, the condition corresponding to the requirement of no batches, or points occurring one at a time, is clearly $\pi_1 = 1$, or equivalently

(2.2.6) $\Pr\{N(0, \tau] > 1\} = o(\Pr\{N(0, \tau] > 0\})$

$$= o(1 - e^{-\lambda \tau})$$

$$= o(\tau) \quad \text{for } \tau \downarrow 0.$$

More generally, a stationary process satisfying this condition was called by Khinchin (1955) an *orderly* process (Russian ординарний) and we follow this terminology for the time being, as contrasted with the sample path terminology of a *simple* point process. The relations between analytical and sample path properties are discussed later in Section 3.3 and Chapter 7: for the present, suffice it to be noted that the analytical condition (2.2.6) is equivalent to the absence of batches with probability 1 (see Exercise 2.2.4). Using the notion of an orderly process, we obtain the following characterization of the Poisson process as a corollary to Theorem 2.2.II.

Theorem 2.2.III. *A stationary point process satisfying Assumption 2.2.I(i) is a Poisson process if and only if (a) it has the complete independence property 2.2.I(ii) and (b) it is orderly.*

Exercises

2.2.1. At Equation (2.2.3), $P(z, \tau) \to 1$ $(z \to 1)$ for every finite τ (why?), and Equation (2.2.2) and $\lambda\tau > 0$ suffice to check that $\Pi(1) = 1$. [A general proof, using only stationarity and not the Poisson assumption, is given in Proposition 3.3.VIII below.]

2.2.2. Call the p.g.f. $P(z)$ *infinitely divisible* when for $0 \le z \le 1$ its uniquely defined nonnegative kth root $P_{1/k}(z) \equiv (P(z))^{1/k}$ is a p.g.f. for every positive integer. Then show that unless $P(z) \equiv 1$ for all $0 \le z \le 1$:
(a) $p_0 = P(0) > 0$;
(b) $(P(z)/p_0)^{1/k} \to 1$ $(k \to \infty)$;
(c) $\dfrac{\log P(z) - \log P(0)}{-\log P(0)} = \lim_{k \uparrow \infty} \dfrac{P_{1/k}(z) - P_{1/k}(0)}{1 - P_{1/k}(0)}$;
(d) the left-hand side of (c) represents a p.g.f. on $\{1, 2, \ldots\}$.
Hence deduce that every nontrivial infinitely divisible p.g.f. is of the form $\exp[-\lambda(1 - \Pi(z))]$ for finite λ (in fact, $p_0 = e^{-\lambda}$), and p.g.f. $\Pi(z) = \sum_{n=1}^{\infty} \pi_n z^n$ [for details see, e.g., Feller (1968, §XII.2)].

2.2.3. (Continuation) Show that an r-variate p.g.f. $P(z_1, \ldots, z_r)$, which is nontrivial in the sense that $P(z_1, \ldots, z_r) \not\equiv 1$ in $\sum_{j=1}^{r} |1 - z_j| > 0$, is infinitely divisible if and only if it is expressible in the form $\exp[-\lambda(1 - \Pi(z_1, \ldots, z_r))]$ for some p.g.f.

$$\Pi(z_1, \ldots, z_r) = \sum_{n_1=0}^{\infty} \cdots \sum_{n_r=0}^{\infty} \pi_{n_1, \ldots, n_r} z_1^{n_1} \cdots z_r^{n_r}$$

for which $\pi_{0 \cdots 0} = 0$.

2.2.4. If a point process N has $N((k-1)/n, k/n] \le 1$ for $k = 1, \ldots, n$, then there can be no batches on $(0, 1]$. Use the complete independence property at Assumption 2.2.I(ii) and the fact that $(1 - o(1/n))^n \to 1$ $(n \to \infty)$ to show that a Poisson process satisfying the analytic orderliness property at (2.2.6) has a.s. no batches on the unit interval, and hence on $\mathbb{R}$.

2.3. Characterizations of the Stationary Poisson Process: II. The Form of the Distribution

The discussion to this point has stressed the independence property, and it has been shown that the *Poisson* character of the finite-dimensional distributions is really a consequence of this property. To what extent is it possible to work in the opposite direction and derive the independence property from the Poisson form of the distributions? Following Renyi (1967) we pose the question in the following form. Suppose we are given a stationary point process, satisfying the finiteness Assumption 2.2.I(i), and are told in addition that, for a certain family $\mathscr{A}$ generating the Borel sets, the distribution of $N(A)$, $A \in \mathscr{A}$, is Poisson with parameter $\lambda \ell(A)$, where $\ell(A)$ denotes the Lebesgue measure of the set A. Is it possible to deduce from this information that the process is Poisson, and if so, what is the smallest class of sets $\mathscr{A}$ that will suffice for this purpose?

There are two remarkable results in this direction. The first is that there does exist such a family $\mathscr{A}$—in fact it is enough to take $\mathscr{A}$ to be the class of all finite unions of disjoint intervals. The second is that it is *not* enough to take $\mathscr{A}$ to be the class of unions of any *fixed* number of intervals: in particular, it is not enough to know that $N(A)$ has a Poisson distribution for all single intervals $A = [a, b]$. The first result is due to Renyi and is given below. The second was established in a series of counterexamples provided by Shepp in Goldman (1967), Moran (1967, 1976a, b), Lee (1968), Szasz (1970), and Oakes (1974); one such counterexample is described in Exercise 2.3.1.

Theorem 2.3.I. *In order that $N(\cdot)$ be a stationary Poisson process, it is necessary and sufficient that $N(A)$ have a Poisson distribution, with parameter $\lambda \ell(A)$ for each set A that can be represented as a finite union of finite intervals.*

PROOF. The theorem is a consequence of the following lemma. $\square$

Lemma 2.3.II. *Let $X_1, \ldots, X_N$ and Z be jointly distributed random variables with Poisson marginals, such that $Z = \sum_1^N X_i$. Then $X_1, \ldots, X_N$ are independent.*

PROOF OF LEMMA. For simplicity we treat the case $N = 2$; the general case can be handled in a similar way.

Since $X_1 + X_2 = Z$ and X_1, X_2 are nonnegative, it follows that $X_1 \le Z$, $X_2 \le Z$. Hence, for all $m, n \ge 0$, $E(X_1^m X_2^n) \le E(Z^{m+n})$. Now Z has a moment generating function $\exp[\lambda(e^{i\zeta} - 1)]$ that is analytic at $\zeta = 0$, and this implies the same property for the bivariate m.g.f. of X_1, X_2. Therefore, the logarithm $Q(z_1, z_2)$ of the bivariate p.g.f. of X_1, X_2 is defined and analytic in a neighbourhood of $(z_1, z_2) = (1, 1)$, and thus we have an expansion of the form

$$Q(1 + v_1, 1 + v_2) = \sum_1^\infty c_{[k]}^{(1)} v_1^k + \sum_1^\infty c_{[k]}^{(2)} v_2^k + \sum_{j \ge 1} \sum_{k \ge 1} c_{[j, k]} v_1^j v_2^k.$$

We are told that X_1 is Poisson, so $c_{[k]}^{(1)} = 0$ for $k \ge 2$, and similarly $c_{[k]}^{(2)} = 0$ for $k \ge 2$. Also, the relation $X_1 + X_2 = Z$ implies $Q(1 + v, 1 + v) = c_{[1]} v$ for some constant $c_{[1]}$, so $c_{[j, k]} = 0$ for $j \ge 1, k \ge 1$ and we find

$$Q(z_1, z_2) = c_{[1]}^{(1)}(z_1 - 1) + c_{[1]}^{(2)}(z_2 - 1),$$

which corresponds to the joint distribution of two independent Poisson variables.

Applying this lemma to the situation described in the theorem, we deduce that the joint distribution for the numbers in any finite family of disjoint intervals has the independent form given by (2.1.1). Hence, the process is a stationary Poisson process. $\square$

In fact Renyi gives an even more remarkable weakening of the condition in Theorem 2.3.I, for he shows that it is not even necessary to assume the distribution of $N(A)$; if the process is assumed to be orderly, it is enough to know the form of $P_0(A) = \Pr\{N(A) = 0\}$. This is a corollary of a more general result, proved at Theorem 7.3.II, that for any orderly point process, the finite-dimensional distributions are fully determined by knowing the set function $P_0(A)$ for all sets A as in Theorem 2.3.I. For completeness we express this as a final theorem (see also Exercise 2.3.3).

Theorem 2.3.III. *Let N be an orderly point process. Then for N to be a stationary Poisson process it is necessary and sufficient that*

$$(2.3.1) \qquad\qquad P_0(A) = e^{-\lambda\ell(A)}$$

for all sets A that can be represented as the union of a finite number of finite intervals.

Exercises

2.3.1. (Compare Theorem 2.3.I.) Let $N(\cdot)$ be a point process on $\mathbb{R}$ having as its fidi distributions those of a stationary Poisson process of unit rate except for the following eight probabilities relating to the interval $(0, 4]$:

$$p_{0010} = p_{0101} = p_{1011} = p_{1100} = e^{-4} + \varepsilon,$$

$$p_{0100} = p_{1010} = p_{1101} = p_{0011} = e^{-4} - \varepsilon$$

where $p_{ijkl} = \Pr\{N(0, 1] = i, N(1, 2] = j, N(2, 3] = k, N(3, 4] = l\}, 0 < \varepsilon < e^{-4}$, and, conditional on $N(a, a + 1] = 1$ for $a = 0, 1, 2, 3$, that point is uniformly distributed over that unit interval. Show that $N(I)$ is Poisson distributed for any interval I, notwithstanding the fact that $N(\cdot)$ is not a Poisson process (Lee, 1968).

2.3.2. (a) Suppose Z is a Poisson r.v. expressible as the sum $Z = X + Y$ of independent nondegenerate, nonnegative r.v.s X and Y. Then X and Y are Poisson r.v.s [this is Raikov's theorem; e.g., see Loève (1963, §19.2) or Moran (1968, p. 408)].

   (b) Let N be a Poisson process for which $N = N' + N''$ for nontrivial independent point processes N', N''. Show that each of N' and N'' is a Poisson process.

2.3.3. (Compare Theorem 2.3.III.) Suppose a stationary orderly point process satisfies (2.3.1). Since orderliness implies that

$$\Pr\{N((0, 1]\setminus((k - 1)/n, k/n]) = 0\} - \Pr\{N(0, 1] = 0\}$$

$$= \Pr\{N((0, 1]\setminus((k - 1)/n, k/n]) = 0, N((k - 1)/n, k/n] = 1\} + o(1/n),$$

deduce that $\Pr\{N(0, 1] = 1\} = \lim_{n\to\infty} n(e^{-\lambda(1-1/n)} - e^{-\lambda} - o(1/n)) = \lambda e^{-\lambda}$.

2.3.4. (a) *Random thinning.* Let $N(\cdot)$ be an orderly nonhomogeneous Poisson process on $\mathbb{R}^d$ with rate $\lambda(\cdot)$. Form a new process $N'(\cdot)$ by treating each point of a realization $\{x_i\}$ independently of all other points, and $(*)$ retaining x_i with probability $p(x_i)$ and deleting it with probability $1 - p(x_i)$, where $p(\cdot)$ is a measurable function with $0 \leq p(x) \leq 1$ for all x. Show that $N'(\cdot)$ is a Poisson process with rate $p(x)\lambda(x)$.

    (b) *Random translation.* Repeat part (a) but with (∗) replaced by translating x_i to $x_i + Y_i$, where Y_i are independent identically distributed random variables with distribution function $F(\cdot)$. Show that the resulting point process, $N''(\cdot)$ say, is Poisson with rate $\int_{\mathbb{R}^d} \lambda(x - y)F(dy)$.

    (c) What conditions on λ and p make $N'(\cdot)$ stationary? What conditions are needed for $N''(\cdot)$ to be stationary?

2.4. The General Poisson Process

We suppose in this section that the point process takes its values in a complete separable metric space $\mathscr{X}$, thereby anticipating the context of Chapter 6. The cases of frequent occurrence are those in which $\mathscr{X}$ is two- or three-dimensional Euclidean space, but some slightly more complex examples are given at the end of the chapter.

    We suppose throughout that $N(A)$ (the number of points in the set A) is defined and finite for every bounded set A in the Borel σ-field $\mathscr{B}_{\mathscr{X}}$ generated by the open spheres of $\mathscr{X}$. We may express this more succinctly by saying that (with probability 1) the trajectories $N(\cdot)$ are *boundedly finite* [recall Assumption 2.2.I(i)]. The Poisson process can then be defined by assuming that there exists a boundedly finite Borel measure $\Lambda(\cdot)$ such that for every finite family of disjoint bounded Borel sets $\{A_i, i = 1, \ldots, k\}$

$$(2.4.1) \qquad \Pr\{N(A_i) = n_i, i = 1, \ldots, k\} = \prod_{i=1}^{k} \frac{\Lambda(A_i)^{n_i}}{n_i!} e^{-\Lambda(A_i)}.$$

The measure $\Lambda(\cdot)$ is called the *parameter measure* of the process. It should be noted that, when $\mathscr{X}$ is the real line, (2.4.1) includes as special cases the two examples given in Section 2.1: for the homogeneous process $\Lambda(A) = \lambda \ell(A)$, and for the nonhomogeneous, $\Lambda(A) = \int_A \lambda(x)dx$. Equation (2.4.1) embraces a nontrivial increase in generality because, in general, the parameter measure may have both a discrete (or, atomic) component and a continuous singular component.

    Returning to the general case, we first clarify the role of the discrete component of $\Lambda(\cdot)$. Suppose, in particular, that $\Lambda(\cdot)$ has an atom of mass λ_0 at the point x_0. Since the single-point set $\{x_0\}$ is a Borel set, it follows at once from (2.4.1) that $N\{x_0\}$ must have a Poisson distribution with parameter λ_0. We say that any point x_0 with the property $\Pr\{N(\{x_0\}) > 0\} > 0$ is a *fixed atom* of the process. Thus, we conclude that every atom of $\Lambda(\cdot)$ is a fixed atom of $N(\cdot)$. Conversely, if x_0 is a fixed atom of $N(\cdot)$, then $N\{x_0\}$ must have a Poisson distribution with nonzero parameter λ_0 say. From this it follows that x_0 is an atom of $\Lambda(\cdot)$ with mass λ_0. Hence, the following is true.

Lemma 2.4.I. *The point x_0 is an atom of the parameter measure Λ if and only if it is a fixed atom of the process.*

Note that whether a given point x_0 represents a fixed atom of the process is not discernible from a single realization: any point of the process is an atom of its particular realization. For x_0 to constitute a fixed atom, there must be positive probability of it recurring over a whole family of realizations. Thus, the fixed atoms relate to the probability structure of the process, not to the structure of individual realizations.

In the Poisson case the fixed atoms are also the key to the question of *orderliness*. The definition given earlier at (2.2.6) is most naturally extended to the present context by requiring

$$(2.4.2) \qquad \Pr\{N(S_{\varepsilon,x}) > 1\} = o(\Pr\{N(S_{\varepsilon,x}) > 0\}), \qquad \varepsilon \to 0,$$

for each $x \in \mathcal{X}$, where $S_{\varepsilon,x}$ denotes the open sphere with radius ε and center x. In the case of a Poisson process, $N(S_{\varepsilon,x})$ has a Poisson distribution, with parameter $\Lambda(S_{\varepsilon,x}) = \Lambda_\varepsilon$ say, so that

$$\Pr\{N(S_{\varepsilon,x}) > 0\} = 1 - e^{-\Lambda_\varepsilon},$$

$$\Pr\{N(S_{\varepsilon,x}) > 1\} = 1 - e^{-\Lambda_\varepsilon} - \Lambda_\varepsilon e^{-\Lambda_\varepsilon}.$$

Now if x is a fixed atom of Λ, $\Lambda_\varepsilon \to \Lambda_0 = \Lambda\{x\} > 0$ as $\varepsilon \downarrow 0$, whereas if x is not a fixed atom, $\Lambda_\varepsilon \to 0$. In the first case the ratio $\Pr\{N(S_{\varepsilon,x}) > 1\}/\Pr\{N(S_{\varepsilon,x}) > 0\}$ tends to the positive constant $1 - \Lambda_0/(e^{\Lambda_0} - 1)$, whereas in the second case it tends to zero. Thus, the process is orderly, in the sense of (2.4.2), if and only if $\Lambda(\cdot)$ has no atoms.

Theorem 2.4.II. *The Poisson process defined by (2.4.1) is orderly if and only if it has no fixed atoms, equivalently if and only if the parameter measure has no discrete component.*

When $\mathcal{X}$ is the real line, the distribution function $F_\Lambda(x) \equiv \Lambda(0, x]$ is continuous if and only Λ has no discrete component, so in this case Λ itself could be called continuous. One should beware of claiming any such conclusions for more general $\mathcal{X}$, however, for even though $\Lambda(\cdot)$ may have no atoms, it may well have concentrations on lines, surfaces, or other lower-dimensional subsets that may cause an associated distribution function to be discontinuous. In such situations, in contrast to the case of a homogeneous Poisson process, there will be positive probability of points of the process appearing on such lines, surfaces, and so on.

The next two theorems generalize in an obvious way the characterizations in Theorems 2.3.I and 2.3.III. The first is proved by reference to the same Lemma 2.3.II; the second follows by appealing to the general Theorem 7.3.II that we quoted in respect of the proof of Theorem 2.3.III.

Theorem 2.4.III. *In order for $N(\cdot)$ to be a Poisson process, it is necessary and sufficient that there exist a boundedly finite measure Λ on the Borel sets $\mathcal{B}_\mathcal{X}$ such that $N(A)$ has a Poisson distribution with parameter $\Lambda(A)$ for each bounded Borel set $A \in \mathcal{B}_\mathcal{X}$.*

Theorem 2.4.IV. *Let $N(\cdot)$ be an orderly process in the sense of (2.4.2). For $N(\cdot)$ to be Poisson it is necessary and sufficient that there exist a boundedly finite nonatomic measure Λ on $\mathscr{B}_{\mathscr{X}}$ such that for each $A \in \mathscr{B}_{\mathscr{X}}$,*

$$P_0(A) = e^{-\Lambda(A)}.$$

We turn next to the slightly more difficult problem of extending the characterizations based on the complete independence property stated below.

Assumption 2.4.V. *For each finite family of bounded, disjoint, Borel sets $\{A_i, i = 1, \ldots, k\}$, the random variables $N(A_1), \ldots, N(A_k)$ are mutually independent.*

The most important result is contained in the following lemma.

Lemma 2.4.VI. *Suppose (i) N is boundedly finite a.s. and has no fixed atoms and (ii) N has the complete independence property of Assumption 2.4.V. Then there exists a boundedly finite nonatomic Borel measure $\Lambda(\cdot)$ such that*

$$P_0(A) = \Pr\{N(A) = 0\} = e^{-\Lambda(A)}$$

for all bounded Borel sets A.

PROOF. Set $Q(A) = -\log P_0(A)$, observing immediately that $Q(A) \geq 0$ and that by (ii) it is finitely additive. Countable additivity is equivalent to having $Q(A_n) \to 0$ for any decreasing sequence $\{A_n\}$ of bounded Borel sets for which $Q(A_n) < \infty$ and $A_n \downarrow \varnothing$. For $A_n \downarrow \varnothing$, we must have $N(A_n) \to 0$ a.s., and thus $e^{-Q(A_n)} = P_0(A_n) = \Pr\{N(A_n) = 0\} \to 1$, establishing $Q(A_n) \to 0$ as required. To show that $Q(\cdot)$ is nonatomic, observe that, by (i),

$$0 = \Pr\{N\{x\} > 0\} = 1 - e^{-Q(\{x\})}$$

so that $Q(\{x\}) = 0$ for every x.

It remains to show that $Q(\cdot)$ is boundedly finite, which is equivalent to $P_0(A) > 0$ for any bounded Borel set A. Suppose the contrary for some set A, which without loss of generality we may assume to be closed, for if not, $0 \leq P_0(\bar{A}) \leq P_0(A) = 0$, whence $P_0(\bar{A}) = 0$. Since $\mathscr{X}$ is separable, A can be covered by a countable number of disjoint Borel sets A_n, each with diameter less than 1, so $A = \bigcup_1^\infty A_n$. Let $p_n = \Pr\{N(A_n) > 0\}$, so that $N(A) = 0$ only if $N(A_n) = 0$ for all n, and thus $0 = P_0(A) = \prod_1^\infty (1 - p_n)$. This infinite product vanishes only if $p_n = 1$ for some n, or else $\sum p_n$ diverges. In the latter event, the Borel–Cantelli lemma implies that a.s. infinitely many $N(A_n)$ are nonzero, and hence $N(A) = \infty$ a.s., contradicting the assumption that $N(\cdot)$ is boundedly finite. Consequently, we must have $p_n = 1$ for some set A_n, $A_{(1)}$ say, and $A_{(1)}$ has diameter less than 1, and as with A may be assumed to be closed. By repeating the argument, we can find a closed set $A_{(2)}$ with diameter less than 2^{-1} such that $P_0(A_{(2)}) = 0$. Proceeding by induction, a sequence $\{A_{(n)}\}$ of nested closed sets is constructed with diameters $\to 0$, and $P_0(A_{(n)}) = 0$ (all n). Choose $x_n \in A_{(n)}$, so that $\{x_n\}$ is a Cauchy sequence, $x_n \to x_0$ say, and, each

$A_{(n)}$ being closed, $x_0 \in A_{(n)}$, and therefore $A_n \downarrow \{x_0\}$. Then $N(A_{(n)}) \downarrow N(\{x_0\})$, and by monotone convergence, $P_0(\{x_0\}) = \lim P_0(A_{(n)}) = 0$. Equivalently, $\Pr\{N\{x_0\} > 0\} = 1$, so that x_0 is a fixed atom of the process, contradicting (i).   □

Now suppose that the process is orderly, in addition to satisfying the conditions of Lemma 2.4.VI. Then it follows from Theorem 2.4.IV that we have a Poisson process without fixed atoms. Thus, the following theorem, due to Prekopa (1957a, b), is true.

Theorem 2.4.VII. *Let $N(\cdot)$ be a.s. boundedly finite and without fixed atoms. Then $N(\cdot)$ is a Poisson process if and only if*

(i) *it is orderly, and*
(ii) *it has the complete independence property of Assumption 2.4.V.*

To extend this result to the nonorderly case, consider for fixed real z in $0 \le z \le 1$, the set function

$$Q_z(A) \equiv -\log E(z^{N(A)}) \equiv -\log P_z(A)$$

defined over the Borel sets A. It follows immediately that

$$0 \le Q_z(A) < Q(A),$$

and using also the argument of Lemma 2.4.VI it follows that $Q_z(\cdot)$ is a measure, absolutely continuous with respect to $Q(\cdot)$. Consequently, there exists a density, $q_z(x)$ say, such that

(2.4.3) $$Q_z(A) = \int_A q_z(x)Q(dx)$$

and for Q-almost all x [cf. (2.4.2) for $S_{\varepsilon,x}$]

$$q_z(x) = \lim_{\varepsilon \downarrow 0} \frac{Q_z(S_{\varepsilon,x})}{Q(S_{\varepsilon,x})}$$

(e.g., see Exercise 2.4.1 for a discussion of this property of Radon–Nikodym derivatives). If we continue to assume that the process has no fixed atoms, $Q(S_{\varepsilon,x})$ and hence also $Q_z(S_{\varepsilon,x})$ both $\to 0$ as $\varepsilon \to 0$, for then $S_{\varepsilon,x} \to \{x\}$. We can then imitate the argument leading to Theorem 2.2.II and write for Q-almost all x,

(2.4.4) $$\Pi_z(x) = 1 - q_z(x) = \lim_{\varepsilon \downarrow 0} \frac{P_z(S_{\varepsilon,x}) - P_0(S_{\varepsilon,x})}{1 - P_0(S_{\varepsilon,x})}.$$

Now for fixed A, $Q_z(A)$ is monotone decreasing in z for $0 \le z \le 1$, so by taking a countably dense set of z values in $[0,1]$, (2.4.4) holds for such z except possibly on a Q-null set formed by the union of the Q-null sets where it may fail for the separate values of z.

For each ε, (2.4.4) is the p.g.f. of the conditional distribution $\Pr\{N(S_{\varepsilon, x}) = k | N(S_{\varepsilon, x}) > 0\}$. Now a sequence of p.g.f.s converging on a countably dense set of z values in $[0, 1)$ converges for all $0 \le z < 1$, with the limit being a p.g.f. of a possibly dishonest distribution. In the present case, the limit is in fact Q-almost everywhere honest, because by monotone convergence, and (2.4.3),

$$0 = \log P_1(A) = \lim_{z \uparrow 1} Q_z(A) = \int_A \left(\lim_{z \to 1} q_z(x) \right) Q(dx),$$

implying that $\lim_{z \to 1} q_z(x) = 0$ Q-almost everywhere.

Consequently, except for a Q-null set, (2.4.4) holds for all $0 \le z \le 1$, and for the limit $q_z(x)$, $1 - q_z(x)$ is the p.g.f. of a proper distribution $\{\pi_k(x)\}$ say, for which

$$\pi_0(x) = 0, \qquad \Pi_z(x) = \sum_1^\infty \pi_k(x) z^k,$$

and

(2.4.5) $$P_z(A) = \exp\left(-\int_A [1 - \Pi_z(x)] Q(dx) \right).$$

There is the alternative form for (2.4.5),

$$P_z(A) = \exp\{-Q(A)[1 - \Pi_z(A)]\},$$

in which there appears the p.g.f. $\Pi_z(A)$ of the "averaged" probabilities

$$\pi_k(A) = (Q(A))^{-1} \int_A \pi_k(x) Q(dx).$$

Thus, the distributions in this process still have the compound Poisson form.

Finally, suppose we reinstate the fixed atoms of the process. Note that these are also atoms of $Q(\cdot)$ and can therefore be at most countable in number, and also that the numbers of points of the process at each fixed atom must be a discrete random variable independent of the rest of the process. We thus arrive at the following structure theorem for the general point process satisfying the complete independence property.

Theorem 2.4.VIII. *Let $N(\cdot)$ be a point process that is a.s. boundedly finite and has the complete independence property of Assumption 2.4.V. Then $N(\cdot)$ can be written in the form of a superposition $N = N_1 + N_2$ where N_1 and N_2 are independent, and*

(i) *N_1 consists of a finite or countable family of fixed atoms, $\{x_1, x_2 \ldots\}$, where for each i, $N_1(\{x_i\})$ has a proper, discrete distribution and is independent of the rest of the process; and*

(ii) *N_2 is a process without fixed atoms, which can be represented in the compound Poisson form (2.4.5), where $Q(\cdot)$ is a fixed, boundedly finite, nonatomic measure, and for Q-almost-all x, $\Pi_z(x)$ is the p.g.f. of a proper discrete distribution, satisfying $\Pi_0(x) = 0$.*

We remark that, analogously to the situation described by Theorem 2.2.II the realizations of N_2 consist a.s. of random batches of points, where the number of batches is governed by a Poisson process with parameter measure $Q(\cdot)$, and, conditional on a batch occurring at x, its probability distribution is given by $\{\pi_k(x)\}$. These sample-path results can be established directly for this special case, but we prefer to treat them as special cases of the theorems established in Chapter 3.

Exercises

2.4.1. [Compare Loève (1963, §24).] For each $n = 1, 2, \ldots$, let $\{A_{ni}: i = 1, \ldots, n\}$ be a partition of the bounded set $A \subseteq \mathcal{X}$ on which the measure v is absolutely continuous with respect to the measure μ and for which

$$\inf_i \mu(A_{ni}) > 0 \qquad \text{(each } n\text{)},$$

$$\sup_i \mu(A_{ni}) \to 0 \qquad (n \to \infty).$$

Prove that the sequence of simple functions

$$f_n(x) = v(A_{ni})/\mu(A_{ni}) \qquad (x \in A_{ni}),$$

defined on A, converges there a.e. μ to the Radon–Nikodym derivative $dv/d\mu$.

2.4.2. Let N_1, N_2 be independent Poisson processes with parameter measures Λ_1, Λ_2. Show that $N_1 + N_2$ is a Poisson process with parameter measure $\Lambda_1 + \Lambda_2$.

CHAPTER 3

Simple Results for Stationary Point Processes on the Line

The object of this chapter is to give an account of some of the distinctive aspects of stationary point processes on the line without falling back on the measure-theoretic foundations that are given in Chapters 6 and 7. Some aspects that are intuitively reasonable and that can in fact be given a rigorous basis are taken at face value, in order that the basic ideas may be exposed without the burden of too much mathematical detail. Thus, the results presented in this chapter may be regarded as being made logically complete when combined with the results of Chapters 6 and 7.

3.1. Specification of a Point Process on the Line

A point process on the line may be taken as modelling the occurrences of some phenomenon at the time epochs $\{t_i\}$ with i in some suitable index set. For such a process there are four equivalent descriptions of the sample paths:

  (i) counting measures;
  (ii) nondecreasing integer-valued step functions;
  (iii) sequences of points; and
  (iv) sequences of intervals.

In describing a point process as a counting measure, it does not matter that the process is on the real line. However, for the other three methods of describing the process, the order properties of the reals are used in an essential way. While the methods of description may be capable of extension into higher dimensions, they become less natural and [in the case of (iv)] decidedly artificial.

In Chapters 1 and 2 we mostly used the intuitive notion of a point process as a counting measure. To make this notion precise, take any subset A of the real line and let $N(A)$ denote the number of occurrences of the process in the set A; that is,

(3.1.1) $N(A)$ = number of indices i for which t_i lies in A

$$= \#\{i: t_i \in A\}.$$

When A is expressed as the union of the disjoint sets $A_1, \ldots, A_r$, say, that is,

$$A = \bigcup_{i=1}^{r} A_i \quad \text{with } A_i \cap A_j = \varnothing \quad \text{for} \quad i \neq j,$$

it is a consequence of (3.1.1) that

(3.1.2) $N\left(\bigcup_{i=1}^{r} A_i\right) = \sum_{i=1}^{r} N(A_i)$ *for mutually disjoint* $A_1, \ldots, A_r$.

It also follows from (3.1.1) that

(3.1.3) $N(A)$ *is nonnegative integer- (possibly ∞-) valued.*

In order that we may operate conveniently on $N(A)$ for different sets A, in particular, in order that the probability of events specified in terms of $N(A)$ may be well defined, we must impose a restriction on the sets A that we are prepared to consider. Since we want to include intervals and unions thereof, the usual constraint is that

(3.1.4) $N(A)$ *is defined for all Borel subsets A of the real line.*

Finally, in order to exclude the possibility of "too many" points occurring "too close" together, we insist that, for the point processes we consider,

(3.1.5) $N(A)$ *is finite for bounded sets A.*

The assumptions at (3.1.2)–(3.1.5) with (3.1.2) extended to allow $r = \infty$ are precisely those that make $N(\cdot)$ a counting measure on the σ-field $\mathscr{B}$ of all Borel subsets of the real line. The constraint in (3.1.3) that $N(\cdot)$ be integer-valued distinguishes it from other more general nonnegative measures as a *counting measure*.

To be consistent with $N(\cdot)$ being a set function, we ought to write, for example, $N((a, b])$ when A is the half-open interval $(a, b]$; our preference for the less cumbersome abbreviation $N(a, b]$ should lead to no confusion.

We have already used in Chapters 1 and 2 the further contraction

(3.1.6) $N(t) = N(0, t] = N((0, t])$ $(0 < t \leq \infty)$;

the difference in argument should suffice to distinguish the real function $N(t)$ $(t > 0)$ from the set function $N(A)$. This function $N(t)$ is nondecreasing, right-continuous, and integer-valued, hence a step function. For point processes on the positive half-line, knowledge of $N(t)$ for all $t \geq 0$ suffices to determine $N(A)$

for Borel sets $A \subset (0, \infty)$ in precisely the same manner as a distribution function determines a probability measure on Borel sets. When the point process is defined on the whole line, we extend the definition (3.1.6) to

$$(3.1.7) \qquad N(t) = \begin{cases} N((0, t]) & (t > 0), \\ 0 & (t = 0), \\ -N((t, 0]) & (t < 0). \end{cases}$$

In this way, $N(t)$ retains the properties of being a right-continuous integer-valued function on the whole line. Moreover, $N(t)$ determines $N(A)$ for all Borel sets A and hence describes the point process via a step function. Thus, instead of starting with $N(A)$ (all $A \in \mathcal{B}$), we could just as well have specified the sample path as a right-continuous function $N(t)$ $(-\infty < t < \infty)$ that is nonnegative and integer-valued for $t > 0$, nonpositive and integer-valued for $t < 0$, and has $N(0) = 0$.

The simplest case of the third method listed above occurs where the process is defined on the half-line $t > 0$. Setting

$$(3.1.8) \qquad t_i = \inf\{t > 0: N(t) \geq i\} \qquad (i = 1, 2, \ldots),$$

it follows that for $i = 1, 2, \ldots$, we have the seemingly obvious but most important relation

$$(3.1.9) \qquad t_i \leq t \text{ if and only if } N(t) \geq i.$$

This relation makes it clear that specifying the sequence of points $\{t_i\}$ is equivalent to specifying the function $N(t)$ in the case that $N(-\infty, 0] = 0$. It should be noted that the set of points $\{t_i\}$ at (3.1.8) is in increasing order; such a restriction is not necessarily implied in talking of a set of time epochs $\{t_i\}$ as at the beginning of the present section.

If the point process has points on the whole line and not just the positive axis, the simplest extension consistent with (3.1.8) is obtained by defining

$$(3.1.10) \quad t_i = \inf\{t: N(t) \geq i\}$$
$$= \begin{cases} \inf\{t > 0: N(0, t] \geq i\} & (i = 1, 2, \ldots), \\ -\inf\{t > 0: N(-t, 0] \geq -i + 1\} & (i = 0, -1, \ldots). \end{cases}$$

Such a doubly infinite sequence of points has the properties that

$$(3.1.11) \qquad t_i \leq t_{i+1} \text{ (all } i) \quad and \quad t_0 \leq 0 < t_1.$$

Finally, by setting

$$(3.1.12) \qquad \tau_i = t_i - t_{i-1} \quad \text{with } \{t_i\} \text{ as at } (3.1.10)$$

[or else, in the case of only a half-line as at (3.1.8), with the added conventions that $t_0 = 0$, and τ_i is defined only for $i = 1, 2, \ldots$], the process is fully described by the sequence of *intervals* $\{\tau_i\}$ and one of the points $\{t_i\}$, usually t_0. Observe that $\tau_i \geq 0$, and that if $N(t) \to \infty$ ($t \to \infty$) then $\sum_{i=1}^{n} \tau_i \to \infty$ ($n \to \infty$), while if $N(t) \not\to \infty$ ($t \to \infty$) then τ_i is not defined for $i > \lim_{t \to \infty} N(t)$.

We now make the intuitively plausible assumption that there exists a probability space on which the functions $N(A)$, $N(t)$, t_i, τ_i are well-defined random variables and furthermore that we can impose various constraints on these random variables in a manner consistent with that assumption. The question of the existence of such a probability space is discussed in Sections 6.2 and 7.1.

Exercises

3.1.1. Suppose that the r.v.s $\{t_i\}$ at (3.1.8) are such that $\Pr\{t_{i+1} > t_i\} = 1$, and define

$$G_i(x) = \Pr\{t_i \leq x\}.$$

(a) Show that $\lim_{x \to 0} G_i(x) = 0$ for all integers $i > 0$.
(b) Show that the assumption at (3.1.5) of $N(\cdot)$ being boundedly finite implies that for all real $x > 0$,

$$\lim_{i \to \infty} G_i(x) = 0.$$

3.1.2. (Continuation) Show that for $x > 0$, $M(x) \equiv EN(x) = \sum_{i=1}^{\infty} G_i(x)$, and, more generally, that

$$E((N(x)^r) = \sum_{i=1}^{\infty} (i^r - (i-1)^r) G_i(x)$$

$$= \sum_{i=1}^{\infty} i^r (G_i(x) - G_{i+1}(x))$$

in the sense that either both sides are infinite, or, if one is finite, so is the other and the two sides are equal.

3.1.3. (Continuation) Show that for $|z| \leq 1$, and $x > 0$,

$$P(x; z) \equiv Ez^{N(x)} = 1 + (z-1) \sum_{i=0}^{\infty} G_{i+1}(x) z^i.$$

3.2. Stationarity: Definitions

The notion of stationarity of a point process at first sight appears to be a simple matter: at the very least it means that the distribution of the number of points lying in an interval depends on its length but not its location; that is,

(3.2.1) $\qquad p_k(x) \equiv \Pr\{N(t, t+x] = k\} \qquad (x > 0, k = 0, 1, \dots)$

depends on the length x but not the location t. Lawrance (1970) called this property *simple stationarity*, while we follow Chung (1972) in calling it *crude stationarity*. It is in fact weaker than the full force of the definition below (see Exercise 3.2.1).

Definition 3.2.I. A point process is *stationary* when for every $r = 1, 2, \ldots,$ and all bounded Borel subsets $A_1, \ldots, A_r$ of the real line the joint distribution of

$$\{N(A_1 + t), \ldots, N(A_r + t)\}$$

does not depend on $t \, (-\infty < t < \infty)$.

In the case that the point process is defined only on the positive half-line, the sets A_i must be Borel subsets of $(0, \infty)$ and we require $t > 0$.

There is also the intuitive feeling that the intervals $\{\tau_i\}$ should be stationary, and accordingly we introduce the following definition.

Definition 3.2.II. A point process is *interval stationary* when for every $r = 1,$ $2, \ldots,$ and all integers $i_i, \ldots, i_r$ the joint distribution of $\{\tau_{i_1+k}, \ldots, \tau_{i_r+k}\}$ does not depend on $k \, (k = 0, \pm 1, \ldots)$.

Note that this definition makes no reference to the point t_0 required to complete the specification of a sample path as below (3.1.12). It is most natural to take $t_0 = 0$ [cf. (3.1.11)]. Such processes may then be regarded as a generalization of renewal processes in that the intervals between occurrences, instead of being mutually independent and identically distributed, constitute merely a stationary sequence.

The relation that exists between the probability distributions for interval stationarity on the one hand and stationarity on the other is taken up in Section 3.4 and elsewhere, notably Chapter 12, under its usual heading of Palm–Khinchin theory.

Some authors speak of *arbitrary times* and *arbitrary points* in connection with point processes. A probability distribution with respect to an arbitrary time epoch of a stationary point process is one that is stationary as under Definition 3.2.I; a probability distribution with respect to an arbitrary point of a point process is one determined by the interval stationary distributions as under Definition 3.2.II.

The importance of maintaining a distinction between interval stationarity and ordinary stationarity is underlined by the waiting-time paradox. If in some town buses run exactly on schedule every Δ minutes and a stranger arrives at a random time to wait for the next bus, then his expected waiting time EW is $\Delta/2$ minutes. If, on the other hand, buses run haphazardly according to a Poisson process with an average time Δ between buses then the expected waiting time of the same stranger is Δ. The core of the (so called) paradox lies in the use of Δ as an average interval length from the arrival of one bus to the next, and the waiting time EW being half the mean interval between bus arrivals when the probabilities of different intervals being chosen are proportional to their lengths. In renewal theory, the resolution of the paradox is known as *length-biased sampling* [see Feller (1966, §I.4), Exercise 1.2.5, and (3.4.17) below].

Exercise

3.2.1. (a) Construct an example of a crudely stationary point process that is not stationary (for one example, see Exercise 2.3.1).
(b) Let $N(\cdot)$ be crudely stationary. Is it necessarily true that

$$\Pr\{N(\{t\}) \geq 2 \text{ for some } t \text{ in } (-1, 0]\}$$
$$= \Pr\{N(\{t\}) \geq 2 \text{ for some } t \text{ in } (0, 1]\}$$

(cf. the proof of Proposition 3.3.VI, where equality is shown to hold when the expressions are zero)?

3.3. Mean Density, Intensity, and Batch-Size Distribution

A natural way of measuring the average density of points of a point process is via its mean, or in the case of a stationary point process, its *mean density*, which we define as

(3.3.1) $$m = E(N(0, 1]).$$

Defining the function

(3.3.2) $$M(x) = E(N(0, x]),$$

it is a consequence of the additivity properties of $N(\cdot)$ as at (3.1.2) and of expectations of sums, and of the crude stationarity property at (3.2.1), that for $x, y \geq 0$,

$$M(x + y) = E(N(0, x + y])$$
$$= E(N(0, x] + N(x, x + y])$$
$$= E(N(0, x]) + E(N(x, x + y])$$
$$= E(N(0, x]) + E(N(0, y])$$
$$= M(x) + M(y).$$

In other words, $M(\cdot)$ is a nonnegative function satisfying Cauchy's functional equation

$$M(x + y) = M(x) + M(y) \qquad (0 \leq x, y < \infty).$$

Consequently, by Lemma 3.6.III,

(3.3.3) $$M(x) = M(1)x = mx \qquad (0 \leq x < \infty),$$

irrespective of whether $M(x)$ is finite or infinite for finite $x > 0$.

There is another natural way of measuring the rate of occurrence of points of a stationary point process, due originally to Khinchin (1955).

Proposition 3.3.I (Khinchin's Existence Theorem). *For a stationary (or even crudely stationary) point process the limit*

$$(3.3.4) \qquad \lambda = \lim_{h \downarrow 0} \Pr\{N(0, h] > 0\}/h$$

exists, though it may be infinite.

PROOF. Introduce the function

$$(3.3.5) \qquad \phi(x) = \Pr\{N(0, x] > 0\}.$$

Then $\phi(x) \downarrow 0$ $(x \downarrow 0)$, and $\phi(\cdot)$ is subadditive on $(0, \infty)$ because for $x, y > 0$,

$$\phi(x + y) = \Pr\{N(0, x + y] > 0\}$$
$$= \Pr\{N(0, x] > 0\} + \Pr\{N(0, x] = 0, N(x, x + y] > 0\}$$
$$\leq \Pr\{N(0, x] > 0\} + \Pr\{N(x, x + y] > 0\}$$
$$= \phi(x) + \phi(y).$$

The assertion of the proposition now follows from the subadditive function lemma 3.6.I. □

The parameter λ is called the *intensity* of the point process, for when it is finite, it makes sense to rewrite (3.3.4) as

$$(3.3.6) \quad \Pr\{N(x, x + h] > 0\} = \Pr\{\text{there is at least one point in } (x, x + h]\}$$
$$= \lambda h + o(h) \qquad (h \downarrow 0).$$

Examples of a point process with $\lambda = \infty$ are given in Exercises 3.3.2 and 3.3.3.

These two measures of the "rate" of a stationary point process coincide when the point process has the following property.

Definition 3.3.II. A point process is *simple* when

$$(3.3.7) \qquad \Pr\{N(\{t\}) = 0 \text{ or } 1 \text{ (all } t)\} = 1.$$

Daley (1974) called this sample-path property *almost sure orderliness* to contrast it with the following analytic property introduced by Khinchin (1955).

Definition 3.3.III. A crudely stationary point process is *orderly* when

$$(3.3.8) \qquad \Pr\{N(0, h] \geq 2\} = o(h) \qquad (h \downarrow 0).$$

It is to be noted that stationarity plays no role in the definition of a simple point process nor does it matter whether the point process is defined on the real line or even a Euclidean space. While orderliness can be defined for point processes that either are nonstationary or are on some space different from the real line, the defining equation (3.3.8) must then be suitably amended [see Exercise 3.3.1, Section 7.2, and Daley (1974) for further discussion and references].

It is a consequence of Korolyuk's theorem and Dobrushin's lemma, given below, that for stationary point processes with finite intensity, Definitions 3.3.II and 3.3.III coincide.

Proposition 3.3.IV (Korolyuk's Theorem). *For a crudely stationary simple point process,*

$$(3.3.9) \qquad\qquad \lambda = m, \text{ finite or infinite.}$$

Remark. In Khinchin's (1955, §11) original statement of this proposition, the point process was assumed to be orderly rather than simple. In view of the possible generalizations of the result to nonstationary point processes and to processes on spaces other than the real line where any definition of orderliness may be more cumbersome, it seems sensible to follow Leadbetter (1972) in connecting the present result with Korolyuk's name.

PROOF. For any positive integer n and $i = 1, \ldots, n$, define indicator random variables

$$(3.3.10) \qquad\qquad \chi_{ni} = \begin{cases} 1 & \text{if } N((i-1)/n, i/n] > 0, \\ 0 & \text{if } N((i-1)/n, i/n] = 0. \end{cases}$$

Then as $n \to \infty$ through the integers 2^p, $p = 1, 2, \ldots$,

$$(3.3.11) \qquad\qquad \sum_{i=1}^{n} \chi_{ni} \uparrow N(0, 1]$$

for those realizations $N(\cdot)$ for which $N(0, 1] < \infty$ and $N(\{t\}) = 0$ or 1 for all $0 < t \leq 1$; that is, in view of (3.1.5) and (3.3.7), (3.3.11) holds a.s. Then

$$m = E(N(0, 1])$$

$$= E\left(\lim_{n \to \infty} \sum_{i=1}^{n} \chi_{ni} \right)$$

$$= \lim_{n \to \infty} E\left(\sum_{i=1}^{n} \chi_{ni} \right) \quad \text{by Lebesgue's monotone convergence theorem,}$$

$$= \lim_{n \to \infty} n\phi(n^{-1}) \quad \text{by (3.3.5), (3.3.10), and crude stationarity,}$$

$$= \lambda \quad \text{by Khinchin's existence theorem.} \qquad\qquad \square$$

Proposition 3.3.V (Dobrushin's Lemma). *A crudely stationary simple point process of finite intensity is orderly.*

PROOF. For any positive integer n, $E(N(0, 1]) = nE(N(0, n^{-1}])$ by crude stationarity, so

(3.3.12) $m = E(N(0, 1]) = n \sum_{j=1}^{\infty} \Pr\{N(0, n^{-1}] \geq j\}$

$$\geq n\phi(n^{-1}) + n \Pr\{N(0, n^{-1}] \geq 2\}.$$

Under the given assumptions, both Khinchin's existence theorem and Korolyuk's theorem apply; that is, $n\phi(n^{-1}) \to \lambda = m \ (n \to \infty)$, so $n \Pr\{N(0, n^{-1}] \geq 2\} \to 0$ $(n \to \infty)$, which by (3.3.8) is equivalent to orderliness.   □

Dobrushin's lemma is a partial converse of the following result in which there is no finiteness restriction on the intensity.

Proposition 3.3.VI. *A crudely stationary orderly point process is simple.*

PROOF. Simpleness is equivalent to

$$0 = \sum_{r=-\infty}^{\infty} \Pr\{N(\{t\}) \geq 2 \text{ for some } t \text{ in } (r, r+1]\},$$

which in turn is equivalent to

(3.3.13) $0 = \Pr\{N(\{t\}) \geq 2 \text{ for some } t \text{ in } (r, r+1]\}, \qquad r = 0, \pm 1, \ldots$

For every positive integer n,

$$\Pr\{N(\{t\}) \geq 2 \text{ for some } t \text{ in } (0, 1]\}$$

$$\leq \sum_{i=1}^{n} \Pr\{N((i-1)/n, i/n] \geq 2\}$$

$$= n \Pr\{N(0, n^{-1}] \geq 2\} \quad \text{by crude stationarity,}$$

$$\to 0 \ (n \to \infty) \quad \text{when } N(\cdot) \text{ is orderly,}$$

so (3.3.13) holds for $r = 0$, and by trite changes, for all r.   □

In the results just given, a prominent role is played by orderliness, which stems from the notion that the points $\{t_i\}$ can indeed be ordered; that is, in the notation of (3.1.10), we have $t_i < t_{i+1}$ for all i. Without orderliness, we are led to the idea of batches of points: we proceed as follows.

Proposition 3.3.VII. *For a crudely stationary point process, the limits*

(3.3.14) $\lambda_k = \lim_{h \downarrow 0} \Pr\{0 < N(0, h] \leq k\}/h$

exist for $k = 1, 2, \ldots$, and

(3.3.15) $\lambda_k \uparrow \lambda \ (k \to \infty) \quad$ *finite or infinite;*

when λ is finite,

(3.3.16) $\pi_k \equiv (\lambda_k - \lambda_{k-1})/\lambda = \lim_{h \downarrow 0} \Pr\{N(0, h] = k \,|\, N(0, h] > 0\}$

is a probability distribution on $k = 1, 2, \ldots$.

PROOF. Define, by analogy with (3.3.5),

(3.3.17) $\phi_k(x) = \Pr\{0 < N(0, x] \le k\}$ $(x > 0, k = 1, 2, \ldots)$.

Then, like $\phi(\cdot)$, $\phi_k(x) \to 0$ for $x \downarrow 0$ and it is subadditive on $(0, \infty)$ because for $x, y > 0$,

$$\phi_k(x + y) = \Pr\{0 < N(0, x] \le k, N(x, x + y] = 0\}$$
$$+ \Pr\{N(0, x] \le k - N(x, x + y], 0 < N(x, x + y] \le k\}$$
$$\le \Pr\{0 < N(0, x] \le k\} + \Pr\{0 < N(x, x + y] \le k\}$$
$$= \phi_k(x) + \phi_k(y),$$

invoking crude stationarity at the last step. So (3.3.14) follows from the subadditive function lemma, which is also invoked in writing

$$\lambda = \sup_{h>0} \sup_{k>0} \phi_k(h)/h$$
$$= \sup_{k>0} \sup_{h>0} \phi_k(h)/h = \sup_{k>0} \lambda_k.$$

The monotonicity of λ_k in k is obvious from (3.3.14), so (3.3.15) is now proved. Equation (3.3.16) follows from (3.3.14), (3.3.15), and (3.3.17).   □

The limit of the conditional probability at (3.3.16) can be rewritten in the form

(3.3.18) $\Pr\{N(0, h] = k\} = \lambda \pi_k h + o(h)$ $(h \downarrow 0, k = 1, 2, \ldots)$.

This equation and (3.3.16) suggest that the points $\{t_i\}$ of sample paths occur in batches of size $k = 1, 2, \ldots$ with respective intensities $\lambda \pi_k$. To make this idea precise, recall that for bounded Borel sets A we have asssumed $N(A)$ to be integer-valued and finite so that we can define

$$N_k(A) = \#\{\text{distinct } t \in A: N(\{t\}) = k\}   (k = 1, 2, \ldots),$$

and thereby express $N(A)$ as

(3.3.19) $$N(A) = \sum_{k=1}^{\infty} k N_k(A).$$

By definition, these point processes $N_k(\cdot)$ are simple and stationary, and for them we can define indicator random variables χ_{ni}^k, analogous to χ_{ni} at (3.3.10), by

(3.3.20) $$\chi_{ni}^k = \begin{cases} 1 & \text{if } N((i-1)/n, i/n] = k \\ 0 & \text{otherwise.} \end{cases}$$

By letting $n \to \infty$ through $n = 2^p, p = 1, 2, \ldots$, it follows from (3.3.20) and the construction of $N_k(\cdot)$ that

(3.3.21) $$N_k(0, 1] = \lim_{n \to \infty} \sum_{i=1}^{n} \chi_{ni}^k \quad \text{a.s.}$$

Now $\chi_{ni}^k \leq \chi_{ni}$, so when $\lambda < \infty$, it follows from (3.3.21) by using dominated convergence that $E(N_k(0, 1]) < \infty$, being given by

(3.3.22) $$E(N_k(0, 1]) = \lim_{n \to \infty} E\left(\sum_{i=1}^n \chi_{ni}^k\right)$$

$$= \lim_{n \to \infty} n(\phi_k(n^{-1}) - \phi_{k-1}(n^{-1}))$$

$$= \lambda \pi_k.$$

The sample-path definition of $N_k(\cdot)$ having intensity $\lambda \pi_k$ as at (3.3.22) warrants the use of the term *batch-size distribution* for the probability distribution $\{\pi_k\}$. Note that a stationary orderly point process has the degenerate batch-size distribution for which $\pi_1 = 1$, $\pi_k = 0$ (all $k \neq 1$). Otherwise, the sample paths are appropriately described as having *multiple points*; this terminology is reflected in the frequently used description of a simple point process as one *without multiple points*.

The moments of the distribution $\{\pi_k\}$ can be related to those of $N(\cdot)$ as in the next two propositions in which we call Equation (3.3.23) a *generalized Korolyuk equation*.

Proposition 3.3.VIII. *For a crudely stationary point process of finite intensity,*

(3.3.23) $$m = E(N(0, 1]) = \lambda \sum_{k=1}^\infty k\pi_k \quad \text{finite or infinite.}$$

PROOF. Take expectations in (3.3.19) with $A = (0, 1]$ and use Fubini's theorem and (3.3.22) to deduce (3.3.23). $\qquad\qquad\qquad\qquad\qquad\qquad\qquad\qquad\square$

Proposition 3.3.IX. *For a crudely stationary point process of finite intensity λ and finite γth moment, $\gamma \geq 1$,*

(3.3.24) $$\lim_{h \downarrow 0} E(N^\gamma(0, h])/h \text{ exists and equals } \lambda \sum_{k=1}^\infty k^\gamma \pi_k.$$

PROOF. Introduce

$$M_\gamma(x) = E(N^\gamma(0, x]),$$

and observe that for $x, y > 0$, using $\gamma \geq 1$,

$$M_\gamma(x + y) = E((N(0, x] + N(x, x + y])^\gamma)$$

$$\geq E(N^\gamma(0, x]) + E(N^\gamma(x, x + y])$$

$$= M_\gamma(x) + M_\gamma(y);$$

that is, the function $M_\gamma(x)$ is superadditive for $x > 0$. When $M_\gamma(x)$ is finite for $0 < x < \infty$, $M_\gamma(x) \to 0$ $(x \downarrow 0)$, so the subadditive function lemma applied to $-M_\gamma(x)$ proves the existence part of (3.3.24). Since

$$N^\gamma(0, 1] \geq \sum_{i=1}^{n} \left(\sum_{k=1}^{\infty} k^\gamma \chi_{ni}^k \right) \to \sum_{k=1}^{\infty} k^\gamma N_k(0, 1] \quad \text{a.s.} \quad (n \to \infty),$$

we can use dominated convergence and crude stationarity to conclude that

$$\lim_{n \to \infty} n M_y(n^{-1}) = E \left(\sum_{k=1}^{\infty} k^\gamma N_k(0, 1] \right) = \lambda \sum_{k=1}^{\infty} k^\gamma \pi_k. \qquad \square$$

Exercises

3.3.1. Verify that a simple point process (Definition 3.3.II) can be defined equivalently as one for which the distances between points of a realization are a.s. positive. [*Hint*: When the realization consists of the points $\{t_n\}$, (3.3.7) is equivalent (Vasil'ev, 1965) to the relation

$$\Pr\{|t_i - t_j| > 0 \text{ (all } i \neq j)\} = 1.]$$

3.3.2. Show that a mixed Poisson process for which

$$\Pr\{N(0, t] = j\} = \int_1^\infty e^{-\lambda t} (\lambda t)^j (j!)^{-1} \tfrac{1}{2} \lambda^{-3/2} \, d\lambda$$

is simple but not orderly. A mixed Poisson process with

$$\Pr\{N(0, t] = j\} = \int_1^\infty e^{-\lambda t} (\lambda t)^j (j!)^{-1} \lambda^{-2} \, d\lambda$$

also has infinite intensity, but it does satisfy the orderliness property (3.3.8).

3.3.3. (a) Let the r.v. X be distributed on $(0, \infty)$ with distribution function $F(\cdot)$ and, conditional on X, let the r.v. Y be uniformly distributed on $(0, X)$. Now define a point process to consist of the set of points $\{nX + Y: n = 0, \pm 1, \ldots\}$. Verify that such a process is stationary and that

$$\Pr\{N(0, h] = 0\} = \int_h^\infty \left(1 - \frac{h}{x} \right) dF(x) = 1 - h \int_h^\infty x^{-2} F(x) dx,$$

$$\Pr\{N(0, h] \geq 2\} = h \int_{(1/2)h}^h x^{-2} F(x) dx.$$

When $F(x) = x$ $(0 < x < 1)$, show that (i) the intensity $\lambda = \infty$; (ii) the process is not orderly; and (iii) it has the Khinchin orderliness property [(Khinchin (1956); see also Leadbetter (1972) and Daley (1974)]

(*) $\Pr\{N(0, h] \geq 2 | N(0, h] \geq 1\} \to 0 \qquad (h \to 0).$

(b) Let the realizations of a stationary point process come, with probability $\frac{1}{2}$ each, either from a process of doublets consisting of two points at each of $\{n + Y: n = 0, \pm 1, \ldots\}$, where Y is uniformly distributed on $(0, 1)$, or from a simple point process as in part (a). Then $\Pr\{N(\{t\}) \leq 1 \text{ for all } t\} = \frac{1}{2}$, so the process is not simple, but it does have the Khinchin orderliness property (*).

3.3.4. Suppose that $N(\cdot)$ is a simple point process on $(0, \infty)$ with finite first moment $M(x) = EN(x)$, and suppose that $M(\cdot)$ is absolutely continuous in the sense that

$$M(x) = \int_0^x m(y)dy \qquad (x > 0)$$

for some density function $m(\cdot)$. Show that the distribution functions $G_i(\cdot)$ of Exercise 3.1.1 are also absolutely continuous with density functions $g_i(\cdot)$, where

$$G_i(x) = \int_0^x g_i(y)dy,$$

$$m(x) = \sum_{i=1}^{\infty} g_i(x) \quad \text{a.e.}$$

3.3.5. (Continuation) Now define $G_i(x; t)$ as the d.f. of the ith forward recurrence time after t [i.e., $G_i(x; t)$ is the d.f. of $\inf\{u > t: N(t, u] \geq i\}$]. Supposing that $N(\cdot)$ has finite first moment and is absolutely continuous in the sense of the previous exercise, show that when $N(\cdot)$ is simple,

$$g_1(0; t) = m(t), \quad g_i(0; t) = 0 \qquad (i \geq 2).$$

Use these results to give an alternative proof of Korolyuk's theorem 3.3.IV.
   Show also that when the rth moment of $N(\cdot)$ is finite, that

$$\lim_{h \downarrow 0} h^{-1}E(N(t, t + h])^r = m(t).$$

3.3.6. Given any point process with sample realizations N, define another point process with sample realization N^* by means of

$$N^*(A) = \#\{\text{distinct } x \in A: N(\{x\}) \geq 1\} \quad \text{(all Borel sets } A).$$

Show that if for any real finite $s > 0$,

$$E(e^{-sN(A)}) \geq E(e^{-sN^*(A)}) \quad \text{(all Borel sets } A),$$

then N is simple. Irrespective of whether or not it is simple, $N(A) = 0$ iff $N^*(A) = 0$.
   Show that if N is a compound Poisson process as in Theorem 2.2.II, then N^* is a stationary Poisson process with rate λ.

3.3.7. Consider a compound Poisson process as in Theorem 2.2.II, and suppose that the mean batch size $\Pi'(1) = \sum k\pi_k$ is infinite. Let the points of the process be subject to independent shifts with a common distribution that has no atoms. The resulting process is no longer Poisson, is simple, and has infinite intensity.
   When the shifts are i.i.d. and uniform on $(0, 1)$, show that for $0 < h < 1$,

$$\Pr\{N(0, h] = 0\} = \exp\{-\lambda(1 + h) + \lambda(1 - h)\Pi(1 - h) + 2\lambda \int_0^h \Pi(1 - u)du\}.$$

3.4. Palm–Khinchin Equations

Throughout this section we use $\mathscr{P}$ to denote the probability measure of a stationary point process (Definition 3.2.I). Our aim is to describe an elementary approach to the problem raised by the intuitively reasonable idea that the stationarity of a point process as at Definition 3.2.I should imply some equivalent interval stationarity property as in Definition 3.2.II. For example, for positive x and y and small positive h, stationarity of the point process $N(\cdot)$ implies that

$$(3.4.1) \quad \mathscr{P}\{N(t, t + h] = N(t + x, t + x + h] =$$
$$N(t + x + y, t + x + y + h] = 1, N(t, t + x + y + h] = 3\}$$
$$= \mathscr{P}\{N(-h, 0] = N(x - h, x] = N(x + y - h, x + y] = 1,$$
$$N(-h, x + y] = 3\}$$
$$\equiv \mathscr{P}\{A_{x,y,h}\}, \quad \text{say}.$$

Now the event $A_{x,y,h}$ describes a sample path with a point near the origin and intervals of about x and y, respectively, to the next two points. Our intuition suggests that, as far as the dependence on the variables x and y is concerned, $\mathscr{P}\{A_{x,y,h}\}$ should be related to the probability measure $\mathscr{P}_0(\cdot)$ for an interval stationary point process; that is, there should be a simple relation between $\mathscr{P}\{A_{x,y,h}\}$ and $\mathscr{P}_0\{\tau_1 \simeq x, \tau_2 \simeq y\}$. We proceed to describe the partial solution that has its roots in Khinchin's monograph (1955) and that connects $\mathscr{P}\{N(0, x] \leq j\}$ to what we shall show is a distribution function

$$(3.4.2) \quad R_j(x) = \lim_{h \downarrow 0} \mathscr{P}\{N(0, x] \geq j \mid N(-h, 0] > 0\} \qquad (j = 1, 2, \ldots).$$

What emerges from the deeper considerations of Chapter 12 is that, granted orderliness, there exists an interval stationary point process $\{\tau_j\}$ with probability measure $\mathscr{P}_0$, so $\mathscr{P}_0\{t_0 = 0\} = 1$, for which we can indeed set

$$\mathscr{P}_0(\cdot) = \lim_{h \downarrow 0} \mathscr{P}(\cdot \mid N(-h, 0] > 0).$$

It then follows, for example, that

$$(3.4.3) \qquad \mathscr{P}_0\{\tau_1 + \cdots + \tau_j \leq x\} = R_j(x)$$

[cf. (3.4.2) and (3.1.9)], thereby identifying the random variable of which $R_j(\cdot)$ is the distribution function.

Instead of the expression at (3.4.1), we consider first the probability

$$(3.4.4) \qquad \psi_j(x, h) \equiv \mathscr{P}\{N(0, x] \leq j, N(-h, 0] > 0\},$$

and prove the following proposition.

Proposition 3.4.I. *For a stationary point process of finite intensity the limit*

$$(3.4.5) \qquad Q_j(x) = \lim_{h \downarrow 0} \mathscr{P}\{N(0, x] \leq j \mid N(-h, 0] > 0\}$$

exists for $x > 0$ and $j = 0, 1, \ldots$, being right-continuous and nonincreasing in x with $Q_j(0) = 1$.

PROOF. Observe that for $u, v > 0$,

$$\psi_j(x, u + v) = \mathscr{P}\{N(0, x] \le j, N(-u, 0] > 0\}$$
$$+ \mathscr{P}\{N(0, x] \le j, N(-u, 0] = 0, N(-u - v, -u] > 0\}.$$

In the last term,

$$\{N(0, x] \le j, N(-u, 0] = 0\} = \{N(-u, x] \le j, N(-u, 0] = 0\}$$
$$\subseteq \{N(-u, x] \le j\}$$
$$\subseteq \{N(-u, x - u] \le j\},$$

and then using stationarity of $\mathscr{P}(\cdot)$, we have

$$\psi_j(x, u + v) \le \psi_j(x, u) + \psi_j(x, v).$$

Consequently, the subadditivity lemma implies that the limit as $h \to 0$ of $\psi_j(x, h)/h$ exists, being bounded by λ [because $\psi_j(x, h) \le \phi(h)$]; so by writing

$$\mathscr{P}\{N(0, x] \le j | N(-h, 0] > 0\} = \frac{\psi_j(x, h)}{\phi(h)} = \frac{\psi_j(x, h)/h}{\phi(h)/h},$$

we can let $h \to 0$ to prove the assertion at (3.4.5) concerning existence. By subadditivity, and right-continuity and monotonicity in x of $\psi_j(x, h)$,

$$Q_j(x) = \sup_{h > 0} \psi_j(x, h)/\lambda h = \sup_{h > 0} \sup_{y > x} \psi_j(y, h)/\lambda h$$
$$= \sup_{y > x} Q_j(y),$$

so $Q_j(x)$ is right-continuous and nonincreasing in x, with $Q_j(0) = 1$ since $\psi_j(0, h) = \phi(h)$.   □

It follows from this result that

(3.4.6) $R_j(x) \equiv 1 - Q_{j-1}(x)$ $(j = 1, 2, \ldots)$

is a d.f. on $(0, \infty)$ except for the possibility, to be excluded later under the conditions of Theorem 3.4.II, that $\lim_{x \to \infty} R_j(x)$ may be less than 1. The plausible interpretation of (3.4.5), or equivalently, of (3.4.6), is that $R_j(x)$ represents the conditional probability (in which the conditioning event has zero probability)

(3.4.7) $\mathscr{P}\{N(0, x] \ge j | N(\{0\}) > 0\} = \mathscr{P}\{\tau_1 + \cdots + \tau_j \le x | t_0 = 0, t_1 > 0\}.$

EXAMPLE 3.4(a) *Renewal process*. Consistent with (3.4.7), for a renewal process starting at 0 with lifetime d.f. F for which $F(0+) = 0$, $R_j(x) = F^{j*}(x)$, where $F^{n*}(\cdot)$ is the n-fold convolution of F. In this case then, $R_j(\cdot)$ is the d.f. of the sum of j random variables that are not merely stationary but also independent. On the other hand, if we have a renewal process with a point at 0 and having lifetime d.f. F for which $0 < F(0+) < 1$, then the constraint at (3.4.7) that $\tau_1 = t_1 - t_0 > 0$ means that τ_1 has d.f. $F_+(x) = (F(x) - F(0+))/(1 - F(0+))$, while $\tau_2, \tau_3, \ldots$ have d.f. F and

$$R_j(x) = \int_0^x F^{(j-1)*}(x - u)dF_+(u) \qquad (j = 1, 2, \ldots).$$

Thus, $R_j(x)$ is here the d.f. of the sum of nonstationary r.v.s, and so for a renewal process we have the stationarity property at (3.4.3) only when $F(0+) = 0$, that is, when the process is orderly (equivalently, simple).

This last assumption is also what enables us to proceed simply in general [but note the remarks around (3.4.12) below].

Theorem 3.4.II. *For an orderly stationary point process of finite intensity λ and such that*

(3.4.8) $$\mathscr{P}\{N(-\infty, 0] = N(0, \infty) = \infty\} = 1,$$

(3.4.9) $$\mathscr{P}\{N(0, x] \le j\} = \lambda \int_x^\infty q_j(u)du, \qquad j = 0, 1, \ldots,$$

where

(3.4.10) $$q_j(x) = \lim_{h \downarrow 0} \mathscr{P}\{N(0, x] = j \mid N(-h, 0] > 0\},$$

and $R_j(x) = 1 - \sum_{k=0}^{j-1} q_k(x)$ is a distribution function on $(0, \infty)$ with mean $j\lambda^{-1}$ for each $j = 1, 2, \ldots$.

PROOF. Set

$$P_j(x) = \mathscr{P}\{N(0, x] \le j\}$$

and observe by Proposition 3.4.I and the assumption of orderliness that

$$P_j(x + h) = \sum_{i=0}^j \mathscr{P}\{N(0, x] \le j - i, N(-h, 0] = i\}$$

$$= \mathscr{P}\{N(0, x] \le j\} - \mathscr{P}\{N(0, x] \le j, N(-h, 0] > 0\}$$

$$+ \mathscr{P}\{N(0, x] \le j - 1, N(-h, 0] = 1\} + o(h).$$

Thus,

$$P_j(x + h) - P_j(x) = \mathscr{P}\{N(0, x] \le j - 1, N(-h, 0] \ge 1\}$$

$$- \mathscr{P}\{N(0, x] \le j, N(-h, 0] > 0\} + o(h)$$

$$= -\lambda h q_j(x) + o(h),$$

where the existence of $q_j(x)$ at (3.4.10) is assured by (3.4.5) directly for $j = 0$ and then by induction for $j = 1, 2, \ldots$. Using D_+ to denote the right-hand derivative operator, it follows that

$$D_+ P_j(x) = -\lambda q_j(x).$$

Setting $Q_{-1}(x) \equiv 0$, the nonnegative function $q_j(x) = Q_j(x) - Q_{j-1}(x)$ is the difference of two bounded nonincreasing functions and hence is integrable on bounded intervals with

(3.4.11) $$P_j(x) - P_j(y) = \lambda \int_x^y q_j(u)du.$$

The assumption at (3.4.8) implies that $P_j(y) \to 0$ for $y \to \infty$, so (3.4.9) now follows from (3.4.11).

Letting $x \downarrow 0$ in (3.4.9) it follows that

$$\lambda^{-1} = \int_0^\infty q_j(u)du \qquad (j = 0, 1, \ldots),$$

and hence, using (3.4.6) as well, that for $j = 1, 2, \ldots$,

$$\int_0^\infty (1 - R_j(u))du = \int_0^\infty Q_{j-1}(u)du = j\lambda^{-1}. \qquad \square$$

There is a most instructive heuristic derivation of (3.4.9) as follows. By virtue of (3.4.8), if we look backward from a point x, there will always be some point $u < x$ for which $N(u, x] \le j$ and $N[u, x] > j$. In fact, because of orderliness, we can write (with probability 1)

$$\{N(0, x] \le j\} = \bigcup_{u \le 0} \{N(u, x] = j, N(\{u\}) = 1\},$$

in which we observe that the right-hand side is the union of the mutually exclusive events that the $(j + 1)$th point of $N(\cdot)$ looking backward from x occurs at some $u \le 0$. Consequently, we can add their "probabilities," which by (3.4.7), (3.3.4), and orderliness equal $q_j(x - u)\lambda\, du$, yielding the Palm–Khinchin equation (3.4.9) in the form

$$P_j(x) = \lambda \int_{-\infty}^0 q_j(x - u)du.$$

Without the orderliness assumption, made from (3.4.8) onward above, we can proceed as follows. First (cf. Proposition 3.4.I), we show that the function

(3.4.12) $$\psi_{j|i}(x, h) \equiv \mathscr{P}\{N(0, x] \le j, 0 < N(-h, 0] \le i\}$$

is subadditive in h, and so we deduce that for those i for which $\pi_i > 0$ [see (3.3.16)], there exists the limit

(3.4.13) $$Q_{j|i}(x) = \lim_{h \downarrow 0} \mathscr{P}\{N(0, x] \le j | N(-h, 0] = i\},$$

with

$$\mathscr{P}\{N(0, x] \le j, N(-h, 0] = i\} = \lambda\pi_i Q_{j|i}(x)h + o(h) \qquad (h \downarrow 0)$$

irrespective of $\pi_i >$ or $= 0$ by setting $Q_{j|i}(x) \equiv 0$ when $\pi_i = 0$. Then the argument of the proof of Theorem 3.4.II can be mimicked in establishing that

$$(3.4.14) \qquad P_j(x) = \lambda \int_x^\infty \sum_{i=1}^\infty \pi_i [Q_{j|i}(u) - Q_{j-i|i}(u)] du,$$

setting $Q_{k|i}(u) \equiv 0$ for $k < 0$, and it can also be shown that, when $\pi_i > 0$,

$$R_{j|i}(x) \equiv 1 - Q_{j-1|i}(x) \equiv 1 - \sum_{k=0}^{j-1} q_{k|i}(x)$$

is a proper distribution function on $(0, \infty)$.

For any point process N, the random variable

$$(3.4.15) \qquad T_u \equiv \inf\{t > 0 : N(u, y + t] > 0\}$$

is the *forward recurrence time r.v.* For a stationary point process, $T_u =_d T_0$ for all u, and we can study its distribution via the Palm–Khinchin equations, since $\{T_0 > x\} = \{N(0, x] = 0\}$. Assuming that (3.4.8) holds,

$$(3.4.16) \qquad \mathscr{P}\{T_0 > x\} = \lambda \int_x^\infty q_0(u) du$$

when $N(\cdot)$ is orderly as in Theorem 3.4.II. Recall that $q_0(\cdot)$ is the tail of the d.f. $R_1(\cdot)$, which can be interpreted as the d.f. of the length τ_1 of an arbitrarily chosen interval. Then, still assuming that (3.4.8) holds,

$$(3.4.17) \qquad ET_0 = \int_0^\infty \mathscr{P}\{T_0 > x\} dx = \lambda \int_0^\infty u q_0(u) du$$

$$= \lambda \int_0^\infty u(1 - R_1(u)) du$$

$$= \lambda (E\tau_1^2)/2.$$

When all intervals are of the same length Δ say, $\lambda = \Delta^{-1}$ and $ET_0 = \Delta/2$, whereas for a Poisson process, τ_1 has mean Δ and second moment $E\tau_1^2 = 2\Delta^2$, so then $ET_0 = \Delta$. These remarks amplify the comments on the waiting-time paradox at the end of Section 3.2.

In both Theorem 3.4.II and the discussion of the forward recurrence time r.v. T_u, the caveat that $\mathscr{P}\{N(0, \infty) = \infty\} = 1$ has been added. This is because stationary point processes on the real line $\mathbb{R}$ have the property that

$$(3.4.18) \qquad \mathscr{P}\{N(0, \infty) = \infty = N(-\infty, 0)\} = 1 - \mathscr{P}\{N(\mathbb{R}) = 0\},$$

which is equivalent to

$$(3.4.19) \qquad \mathscr{P}\{0 < N(\mathbb{R}) < \infty\} = 0;$$

the property is proved in a more general setting at Proposition 10.1.IV.

Inspection of the statements onward from (3.4.8) shows that they are either conditional probability statements (including limits of such statements), which in view of (3.4.18) reduce to being conditional also on $\{N(\mathbb{R}) = \infty\}$, or unconditional statements, which without (3.4.8) need further elaboration. This is quickly given: (3.4.8) is equivalent by (3.4.18) to $\mathscr{P}\{T_0 < \infty\} = 1$, and without (3.4.8), Equations (3.4.16) and (3.4.17) must be replaced by assertions of the form

$$(3.4.20) \qquad \mathscr{P}\{T_0 > x\} = \lambda\varpi \int_x^\infty q_0(u)du + 1 - \varpi,$$

$$(3.4.21) \qquad E(T_0 | T_0 < \infty) = \lambda E(\tau_1^2)/2,$$

where $\varpi = \mathscr{P}\{N(\mathbb{R}) = \infty\} = \mathscr{P}\{T_0 < \infty\}$.

Exercises

3.4.1. Analogously to (3.4.15), define a *backward recurrence time* r.v. $B_u \equiv \inf\{t > 0: N(u - t, u] > 0\}$ (assuming this to be finite a.s.). Show that for a stationary point process, N, $B_u =_d B_0 =_d T_0$. The r.v. $L_u = B_u + T_u$ denotes the *current lifetime* r.v.; when N is orderly and stationary, show that $EL_0 = (E\tau_1^2)/(E\tau_1)$, [cf. (3.4.16)] and that

$$\mathscr{P}\{L_0 < x\} = \lambda \int_0^x [q_0(u) - q_0(x)]du = \lambda \int_0^x uR_1(du).$$

3.4.2. Use Palm–Khinchin equations to show that the hazard functions q and r of the r.v.s τ_1 and T_0 are related by

$$r(x) = q(x) + r'(x)/r(x) \qquad (x > 0)$$

(assuming the density function r' exists).

3.4.3. Show that for an orderly point process,

$$EN(0, 1] = \int_0^1 \mathscr{P}\{N(dx) \geq 1\},$$

where the right-hand side is to be interpreted as a Burkill integral [see Fieger (1971) for further details].

3.4.4. For a point process N on $\mathbb{R}$ define the event

$$B_k \equiv B_k((x_i, j_i): i = 1, \ldots, k) = \{N(0, x_i] \leq j_i \ (i = 1, \ldots, k)\}$$

for positive x_i, nonnegative integers j_i $(i = 1, \ldots, k)$, and any fixed finite positive integer k.
(a) When N is stationary with finite intensity λ,

$$\psi(B_k, h) \equiv \mathscr{P}(B_k \cap \{N(-h, 0] > 0\})$$

is subadditive in $h > 0$, the limit

$$Q(B_k) \equiv \lim_{h\downarrow 0} \mathscr{P}(B_k | \{N(-h, 0] > 0\})$$

exists finite, is right-continuous and nonincreasing in each x_i and nondecreasing in j_i, is invariant under permutations of $(x_1, j_1), \ldots, (x_k, j_k)$, with

$$Q(B_k) = \lim_{h \downarrow 0} \psi(B_k, h)/\lambda h = \sup_{h > 0} \psi(B_k, h)/\lambda h,$$

and

$$Q(B_k) = Q(B_{k+1}((0, j_{k+1}), (x_i, j_i) \, (i = 1, \ldots, k)))$$
$$= Q(B_{k+1}((x_{k+1}, \infty), (x_i, j_i) \, (i = 1, \ldots, k)).$$

(b) Define a shift operator S_h $(h > 0)$ and a difference operator Δ on B_k by

$$S_h B_k = B_k((x_i + h, j_i) \, (i = 1, \ldots, k)),$$
$$\Delta B_k = B_k((x_i, j_i - 1) \, (i = 1, \ldots, k)),$$

and put $q(B_k) = Q(B_k) - Q(\Delta B_k)$, with the convention that if any $j_i = 0$, then ΔB_k is a null set with $Q(\Delta B_k) = 0$. Under the condition (3.4.8) of Theorem 3.4.II, the right-hand derivative $D_+ \mathscr{P}(B_k)$ exists in the sense that $D_+ \mathscr{P}(S_h B_k)|_{h=0} = -\lambda q(B_k)$, and

$$\mathscr{P}(B_k) - \mathscr{P}(S_x B_k) = \lambda \int_0^x q(S_u B_k) du.$$

[Compare Daley and Vere-Jones (1972, §7) and Slivnyak (1962, 1966). Slivnyak used a slightly different operator S_h^0 defined by

$$S_h^0 B_k = B_{k+1}((h, 0), (x_i + h, j_i) \, (i = 1, \ldots, k)),$$

so that $\psi(B_k, h) = \mathscr{P}(B_k) - \mathscr{P}(S_h^0 B_k)$, and deduced the existence of a derivative in h of $\mathscr{P}(S_h^0 B_k)$ from the convexity in h of this function assuming stationarity of N but not necessarily that it has finite intensity.]

3.4.5. Prove that (3.4.18) and (3.4.19) are equivalent when $\mathscr{P}\{N(\mathbb{R}) \geq 0\} = 1$.

3.5. Ergodicity and an Elementary Renewal Theorem Analogue

Let $N(\cdot)$ be a stationary point process with finite mean density $m = EN(0, 1]$. Then the sequence $\{X_n\}$ of random variables defined by

$$X_n = N(n - 1, n] \qquad (n = 0, \pm 1, \ldots)$$

is stationary with finite first moment $m = EX_n$ (all n), and by the strong law for stationary random sequences,

$$N(0, n]/n = (X_1 + \cdots + X_n)/n \to \xi \quad \text{a.s.}$$

for some random variable ξ for which $E\xi = m$. Using $[x]$ to denote the largest integer $\leq x$, it then follows on letting $x \to \infty$ in the inequalities

$$\frac{N(0, [x]]}{[x]} \cdot \frac{[x]}{x} \leq \frac{N(0, x]}{x} \leq \frac{N(0, [x] + 1]}{[x] + 1} \cdot \frac{[x] + 1}{x} \qquad (x \geq 1)$$

that we have proved the following proposition.

Proposition 3.5.I. *For a stationary point process with finite mean density* $m = EN(0, 1]$, $\xi \equiv \lim_{x \to \infty} N(0, x]/x$ *exists a.s. and is a random variable with* $E\xi = m$.

In our discussion of limit properties of stationary point processes we shall have cause to use various concepts of ergodicity; for the present we simply use the following definition.

Definition 3.5.II. A stationary point process with finite mean density m is *ergodic* when

$$\mathscr{P}\{N(0, x]/x \to m \ (x \to \infty)\} = 1.$$

Suppose that in addition to being ergodic, the second moment $EN^2(0, 1]$ is finite, so by stationarity and the Cauchy–Schwarz inequality, $EN^2(0, x] < \infty$ for all finite positive x. Then we can use an argument similar to that leading to Proposition 3.5.I to deduce from the convergence in mean square of $(X_1 + \cdots + X_n)/n = N(0, n]/n$ to the same limit [e.g., see (2.15) of Doob (1953, p. 471)] that

$$(3.5.1) \qquad \text{var}(N(0, x]/x) = E(N(0, x]/x - m)^2 \to 0 \qquad (x \to \infty)$$

when $N(\cdot)$ is ergodic with finite second moment. This is one of the key probabilistic steps in the proof of the next theorem in which the asymptotic result at (3.5.3), combined with the remarks that follows, is an analogue of the elementary renewal theorem. The function $U(\cdot)$, called the *expectation function* in Daley (1971), is the analogue of the renewal function.

Theorem 3.5.III. *For a stationary ergodic point process with finite second moment and mean density m, the second moment function*

$$(3.5.2) \qquad M_2(x) \equiv EN^2(0, x] = \int_0^x (2U(u) - 1)m \, du$$

for some nondecreasing function $U(\cdot)$ *for which*

$$(3.5.3) \qquad U(x)/x \to m \qquad (x \to \infty),$$

and when the process is orderly,

$$(3.5.4) \qquad U(x) = \sum_{j=0}^{\infty} R_j(x).$$

Remark. It is consistent with the interpretation of $R_j(\cdot)$ at (3.4.3) as the d.f. of the sum $S_j = \tau_1 + \cdots + \tau_j$ that

$$U(x) = \lim_{h \downarrow 0} E(N(0, x] + 1 | N(-h, 0] > 0)$$

in the case that $N(\cdot)$ is orderly. In the nonorderly case, it emerges that, given an ergodic stationary sequence $\{\tau_j\}$ of nonnegative random variables with

$E\tau_j = 1/m$ and partial sums $\{S_n\}$ given by $S_0 = 0$ and

$$S_n = \tau_1 + \cdots + \tau_n, \quad S_{-n} = -(\tau_0 + \cdots + \tau_{-(n-1)}) \qquad (n = 1, 2, \ldots),$$

we can interpret $U(\cdot)$ as

(3.5.5) $\quad 2U(x) - 1 = E \# \{n = 0, \pm 1, \ldots : |S_n| \leq x\} = \sum_{-\infty}^{\infty} \Pr\{|S_n| \leq x\}.$

In the case that the random variables $\{\tau_j\}$ are independent and identically distributed,

(3.5.6) $$U(x) = \sum_{0}^{\infty} F^{n*}(x)$$

and hence $U(\cdot)$ is then the renewal function.

PROOF OF THEOREM 3.5.III. By definition at (3.5.2),

$$M_2(x) = EN^2(x) = \operatorname{var} N(x) + (EN(x))^2$$
$$= x^2(\operatorname{var}(N(x)/x) + m^2)$$
$$\sim m^2 x^2 \qquad (x \to \infty)$$

when $N(\cdot)$ is ergodic, by (3.5.1). If we can assume that $M_2(\cdot)$ is absolutely continuous and that the function $U(\cdot)$, which can then be defined as at (3.5.2), is monotonic nondecreasing, we can appeal to a Tauberian theorem [e.g., Feller (1966, p. 421)] and conclude that (3.5.3) holds.

It remains then to establish (3.5.2), for which purpose we assume first that $N(\cdot)$ is orderly so that the representation (3.4.9) is at our disposal. It is a matter of elementary algebra that

$$M_2(x) + mx = E(N(x)(N(x) + 1)) = \sum_{j=1}^{\infty} j(j+1)\mathscr{P}\{N(x) = j\}$$

$$= 2 \sum_{k=1}^{\infty} k\mathscr{P}\{N(x) \geq k\} = 2 \sum_{k=0}^{\infty} (k+1)(1 - P_k(x))$$

$$= 2 \sum_{k=0}^{\infty} (k+1) \int_0^x q_k(u)\lambda \, du$$

$$= 2 \int_0^x \left(1 + \sum_{j=0}^{\infty} (1 - Q_j(u))\right) \lambda \, du = 2 \int_0^x \sum_{j=0}^{\infty} R_j(u)\lambda \, du,$$

where $R_0(u) \equiv 1$. Thus, we have (3.5.2) in the case of orderly $N(\cdot)$ with the additional identification that

(3.5.7) $$U(x) = \sum_{j=0}^{\infty} R_j(x)$$

of which (3.5.6) is a special case. Note in (3.5.7) that the nondecreasing nature of each $R_j(\cdot)$ ensures the same property for $U(\cdot)$.

When $N(\cdot)$ is no longer orderly, we must appeal to (3.4.14) in writing

$$(3.5.8) \quad M_2(x) + mx = 2 \sum_{k=0}^{\infty} (k+1)(1 - P_k(x))$$

$$= 2 \sum_{k=0}^{\infty} (k+1) \int_0^x \sum_{i=1}^{\infty} \pi_i(Q_{k|i}(u) - Q_{k-i|i}(u)) \lambda \, du.$$

Without loss of generality we may set

$$Q_{k|i}(x) \equiv 1 \text{ when } \pi_i = 0.$$

Fubini's theorem is then applicable as before in the manipulations below:

$$(3.5.9) \quad 2 \sum_{k=0}^{\infty} (k+1) \sum_{i=1}^{\infty}{}' \pi_i \sum_{j=(k-i+1)_+}^{k} q_{j|i}(u)$$

$$= 2 \sum_{i=1}^{\infty} \pi_i \sum_{k=0}^{\infty} (k+1) \sum_{j=(k-i+1)_+}^{k} q_{j|i}(u)$$

$$= \sum_{i=1}^{\infty} \pi_i \sum_{j=0}^{\infty} i(2j + i + 1) q_{j|i}(u)$$

$$= \sum_{i=0}^{\infty} i\pi_i \left(i + 1 + 2 \sum_{j=0}^{\infty} (1 - Q_{j|i}(u)) \right).$$

Substituting (3.5.9) in (3.5.8) and recalling that $Q_{j|i}(u)$ is nonincreasing now suffice to establish the existence of nondecreasing $U(\cdot)$ at (3.5.2) as required. ☐

Exercises

3.5.1. (Compare Theorem 3.5.III.) Use the Cauchy–Schwarz inequality to show that, when $M_2(x) \equiv EN^2(0, x] < \infty$ for finite x, $(M_2(x))^{1/2}$ is subadditive in $x > 0$ and hence that there is then a finite constant $\lambda_2 \geq \mu^2$ such that $M_2(x) \sim \lambda_2 x^2$ $(x \to \infty)$.

3.5.2. Let $N(\cdot)$ be a stationary mixed Poisson process with $\mathscr{P}\{N(0, t] = j\} = \frac{1}{2}e^{-t}t^j/j! + \frac{1}{2}e^{-2t}(2t)^j/j!$. Show that $\lambda = \frac{3}{2} = m < U(t)/t = \frac{5}{3}$ (all $t > 0$) (cf. Theorem 3.5.III; this process is not ergodic) and that $N(0, t]/t \to \xi$ $(t \to \infty)$, where $\xi = 1$ or 2 with probability $\frac{1}{2}$ each.

3.6. Sub- and Superadditive Functions

We have referred earlier in this chapter to properties of sub- and superadditive functions, and for convenience we now establish these properties in a suitable form. For a more extensive discussion of such functions see Hille and Phillips (1957).

A function $g(x)$ defined for $0 \leq x < a \leq \infty$ is *subadditive* when

(3.6.1) $$g(x + y) \leq g(x) + g(y)$$

holds throughout its domain of definition; similarly, a function $h(x)$ for which

(3.6.2) $$h(x + y) \geq h(x) + h(y)$$

holds is *superadditive*. A function $f(x)$ for which

(3.6.3) $$f(x + y) = f(x) + f(y)$$

holds is *additive*, and (3.6.3) is known as Cauchy's functional equation or [see Feller (1966, §IV.4)] the Hamel equation.

Lemma 3.6.I. *For a subadditive function $g(\cdot)$ that is bounded on finite intervals, $\mu \equiv \inf_{x>0} g(x)/x$ is finite or $-\infty$, and*

(3.6.4) $$g(x)/x \to \mu \text{ as } x \to \infty.$$

PROOF. There exists y for which $g(y)/y < \mu'$ for any $\mu' > \mu$. Given any x, there is a unique integer n for which $x = ny + \eta$, where $0 \leq \eta < y$, and $n \to \infty$ as $x \to \infty$. Then

$$\frac{g(x)}{x} \leq \frac{g(ny) + g(\eta)}{x} \leq \frac{ng(y)}{ny + \eta} + \frac{g(\eta)}{x}$$

$$= \frac{g(y)}{y + \eta/n} + \frac{g(\eta)}{x} \to \frac{g(y)}{y} \quad \text{as } x \to \infty.$$

Thus, $\limsup_{x\to\infty} g(x)/x \leq \mu'$, and μ' being an arbitrary quantity $> \mu$, this proves the lemma.   □

The function $-h(x)$ is subadditive when $h(\cdot)$ is superadditive, and an additive function is both sub- and superadditive, so Lemma 3.6.I implies both of the following results.

Lemma 3.6.II. *For a superadditive function $h(\cdot)$ that is bounded on finite intervals, $\mu \equiv \sup_{x>0} h(x)/x$ is finite or $+\infty$ and*

(3.6.5) $$h(x)/x \to \mu \text{ as } x \to \infty.$$

Lemma 3.6.III. *An additive function $f(\cdot)$ that is bounded on finite intervals satisfies*

(3.6.6) $$f(x) = f(1)x \quad (0 \leq x < \infty).$$

In passing, note that there do exist additive functions that do not have the linearity property (3.6.6): they are unbounded on every finite interval and moreover are not measurable (e.g., see Hewitt and Zuckerman, 1969).

Observe also that nonnegative additive functions satisfy (3.6.6) with the understanding that $f(1) = \infty$ is allowed.

The behaviour near 0 of sub- and superadditive functions requires the stronger condition of continuity at 0 in order to derive a useful result [a counterexample when $f(\cdot)$ is not continuous at 0 is indicated in Hille and Phillips (1957, §7.11)].

Lemma 3.6.IV. *Let $g(x)$ be subadditive on $[0, a]$ for some $a > 0$, and let $g(x) \to 0$ as $x \to 0$. Then $\lambda \equiv \sup_{x>0} g(x)/x$ is finite or $+\infty$, and*

$$(3.6.7) \qquad\qquad g(x)/x \to \lambda \text{ as } x \to 0.$$

PROOF. The finiteness of $g(x)$ for some $x > 0$ precludes the possibility that $\lambda = -\infty$. Consider first the case that $0 < \lambda < \infty$, and suppose that $g(a_n)/a_n < \lambda - 2\varepsilon$ for some $\varepsilon > 0$ for all members of a sequence $\{a_n\}$ with $a_n \to 0$ as $n \to \infty$. For any given $x > 0$, we can find a_n sufficiently small that $\sup_{0 \le \delta < a_n} g(\delta) < \varepsilon x$. Write $x = k_n a_n + \delta_n$ for some nonnegative integer k_n and $0 \le \delta_n < a_n$. Then

$$\frac{g(x)}{x} \le \frac{k_n g(a_n) + g(\delta_n)}{k_n a_n + \delta_n} \le \frac{g(a_n)/a_n}{1 + (\delta_n/a_n)/k_n} + \frac{g(\delta_n)}{x}$$

$$\le \lambda - \varepsilon \text{ for all } n \text{ sufficiently large.}$$

Thus, $\sup_{x>0} g(x)/x \le \lambda - \varepsilon$, contradicting the definition of λ. The case $-\infty < \lambda \le 0$ is established by considering $g_1(x) \equiv g(x) + \lambda' x$ for some finite $\lambda' > -\lambda$. Finally, the case $\lambda = \infty$ is proved by contradiction starting from the supposition that $g(a_n)/a_n \to \lambda'' < \infty$ for some $\{a_n\}$ with $a_n \to 0$. $\qquad\square$

Lemma 3.6.V. *Let $h(x)$ be superadditive on $[0, a]$ for some $a > 0$, and let $h(x) \to 0$ as $x \to 0$, Then $\lambda \equiv \inf_{x>0} h(x)/x$ is finite or $-\infty$, and*

$$(3.6.8) \qquad\qquad h(x)/x \to \lambda \quad \text{as } x \to 0.$$

CHAPTER 4

Renewal Processes

The renewal process and variants of it have been the subject of much study, both as a model in many fields of application (e.g., see Cox, 1962; Cox and Lewis, 1966; Cox and Isham, 1980) and as a source of important theoretical problems. It is not the aim of this chapter to repeat much of the material that is available, for example, in Volume II of Feller (1966); rather, we have selected some features that either are complementary to Feller's treatment or are relevant to more general point processes.

The first two sections are concerned with basic properties, setting these where possible into a point process context. The third section is concerned with some characterization theorems, and the fourth with aspects of the renewal theorem, a topic so important and with such far-reaching applications that it can hardly be omitted. Two versions of the theorem are discussed, corresponding to different forms of convergence of the renewal measure to Lebesgue measure. Some small indication of the range of applications is given in Section 4.5, which is concerned with "neighbours" of the renewal process, notably the Wold process of correlated intervals.

A final section is concerned with the concept of a hazard measure for the lifetime distribution, a topic that is of interest in its own right and of central importance to the discussion of compensators and conditional intensity functions in Chapter 13.

4.1. Basic Properties

Let $X, X_1, X_2, \ldots$ be independent identically distributed nonnegative random variables, and define the partial sums

(4.1.1) $S_0 = 0,$ $S_n = S_{n-1} + X_n = X_1 + \cdots + X_n$ $(n = 1, 2, \ldots).$

For Borel subsets A of $(0, \infty)$ we attempt to define the counting measure of a point process by setting

(4.1.2) $N(A) = \#\{n: S_n \in A\}.$

Even if we exclude the trivial case $X \equiv 0$, as we do throughout this chapter, it may not be completely obvious that (4.1.2) is finite. To see that this is so, observe that for $X \not\equiv 0$ there must exist positive ε, δ such that

$$\Pr\{X > \varepsilon\} > \delta$$

so that with probability 1 the event $\{X_n > \varepsilon\}$ must occur infinitely often (by the Borel–Cantelli lemmas) and hence $S_n \to \infty$ (a.s.). It follows that the right-hand side of (4.1.2) is a.s. finite whenever A is bounded, thus justifying the definition (4.1.2). [Here we ignore measurability aspects, for which see Example 7.1(b).] The process so defined is the *renewal process*.

In the notation and terminology of Chapter 3, provided $X_1 > 0$, we have $t_i = S_i$ and $\tau_i = X_i$ for $i = 1, 2, \ldots$, while the assumption that the $\{X_n\}$ are i.i.d. implies that $N(\cdot)$ is interval stationary. *Orderliness* of the process here means $S_{n+1} > S_n$ for $n = 0, 1, 2, \ldots$; that is, $X_n > 0$ for all $n \geq 0$, all with probability 1. But the probability that $X_n > 0$ for $n = 0, 1, \ldots, N - 1$ is equal to $(\Pr\{X > 0\})^N \to 0$ as $N \to \infty$ unless $\Pr\{X > 0\} = 1$. Thus, the process is orderly if and only if $\Pr\{X > 0\} = 1$, that is, if and only if the lifetime distribution has zero mass at the origin.

Taking expectations of (4.1.2) yields the *renewal measure*

(4.1.3) $U(A) = E(\#\{n: S_n \in A, n = 0, 1, 2, \ldots\}) = E(N(A)),$

an equation that remains valid even if A includes the origin. $U(A)$ is just the *first moment* or *expectation measure* of N.

Writing $F(\cdot)$ for the common lifetime distribution, and F^{k*} for its k-fold convolution (which is thus the distribution function for S_k), and immediately abusing the notation by writing $F(\cdot)$ for the measure induced on the Borel sets of $\mathcal{B}(\mathbb{R})$ by F, we have

(4.1.4) $U(A) = E\left(\sum_{k=0}^{\infty} I_{\{S_k \in A\}} \right) = \delta_0(A) + \sum_{k=1}^{\infty} F^{k*}(A).$

We note in passing that the higher moments of $N(A)$ can also be expressed in terms of U (see Exercise 4.1.2). The quantity most commonly studied is the cumulative function, commonly called the *renewal function*,

(4.1.5) $U(x) \equiv U([0, x]) = 1 + \sum_{k=1}^{\infty} F^{k*}(x)$ $(x \geq 0).$

Again, $U(x)$ is always finite. To see this, choose any $\delta > 0$ for which $F(\delta) < 1$ (possible since we exclude the case $X \equiv 0$). Then since $F(0-) = 0$, we have for any positive integers i, j and $x, y > 0$,

$$1 - F^{(i+j)*}(x + y) \geq (1 - F^{i*}(x))(1 - F^{j*}(y)),$$

and for $0 < y < x$,

$$F^{i*}(x - y)F^{j*}(y) \leq F^{(i+j)*}(x) \leq F^{i*}(x)F^{j*}(x).$$

Thus, $F^{k*}(\delta) \leq (F(\delta))^k < 1$, and therefore the series in (4.1.5) certainly converges for $x < \delta$. For general x in $0 < x < \infty$, there exists finite positive k for which $x/k < \delta$. For given x and such k, $1 - F^{k*}(x) > (1 - F(x/k))^k > 0$, and so

$$U(x) \leq (1 + F(x) + \cdots + F^{(k-1)*}(x)) \sum_{n=0}^{\infty} F^{nk*}(x)$$

$$\leq (1 + F(x) + \cdots + F^{(k-1)*}(x))/(1 - F^{k*}(x)) < \infty.$$

Thus, (4.1.5) converges for all $x > 0$.

Taking Laplace–Stieltjes transforms in (4.1.5), we have for $\mathrm{Re}(\theta) > 0$

$$(4.1.6) \qquad \chi(\theta) \equiv \int_0^{\infty} e^{-\theta x} \, dU(x) = \sum_{k=0}^{\infty} (\psi(\theta))^k = \frac{1}{1 - \psi(\theta)},$$

where $\psi(\theta) = \int_0^{\infty} e^{-\theta x} \, dF(x)$. Equivalently, for $\mathrm{Re}(\theta) > 0$,

$$\psi(\theta) = 1 - 1/\chi(\theta),$$

which shows (using the uniqueness theorem for Laplace transforms) that U determines F uniquely and hence that there is a $1:1$ correspondence between lifetime distributions F and renewal functions U.

From (4.1.5) we have for $x > 0$

$$(4.1.7) \qquad U(x) = 1 + \int_0^x U(x - y) dF(y),$$

this being the most important special case of the *general renewal equation*

$$(4.1.8) \qquad Z(x) = z(x) + \int_0^x Z(x - y) dF(y) \qquad (x > 0),$$

where the solution function Z is generated by the initial function z. If the function $z(x)$ is measurable and bounded on finite intervals, one solution to (4.1.8) is given by

$$(4.1.9) \quad Z_0(x) = z(x) + \sum_{k=1}^{\infty} \int_0^x z(x - y) dF^{k*}(y) = \int_0^x z(x - y) dU(y),$$

the convergence of the series in the middle member being justified by comparison with (4.1.5).

Using the monotonicity of the relation $z \to Z_0$, we easily see that if $z \geq 0$, (4.1.9) is the minimal nonnegative solution to (4.1.8). In fact, considerably more is true, for if $z(x)$ is merely measurable and bounded on finite intervals, the difference $D(x)$ between any two solutions of (4.1.8) with the same property satisfies

$$D(x) = \int_0^x D(x - y)dF^{k*}(y) \quad \text{for each } k = 1, 2, \ldots;$$

hence, $D(x) \equiv 0$ from the fact that $F^{k*}(x) \to 0$ as $k \to \infty$ and the assumed boundedness of D. Thus, if $z(x)$ is measurable and bounded on finite intervals, (4.1.9) represents the unique measurable solution of (4.1.8), which is also bounded on finite intervals. In particular, $U(x)$ is the unique monotonic and finite-valued solution of (4.1.7).

EXAMPLE 4.1(a) Exponential intervals. The lack of memory property of the exponential distribution bequeaths on the renewal process that it generates the additional independence properties of the Poisson process. Suppose specifically that

$$F(x) = 1 - e^{-\lambda x} \quad (\lambda > 0).$$

The renewal function for the corresponding Poisson process is $U(x) = 1 + \lambda x$, as can be checked either by using the transform equation in (4.1.6), or by summing the convolution powers as at (4.1.5), or by direct verification in the integral equation at (4.1.7).

EXAMPLE 4.1(b) Forward recurrence time. We gave below (3.4.15) an expression for the distribution of the forward recurrence time r.v. T_u of a stationary point process. The definition at (3.4.15) does not require stationarity, and in the present case of a renewal process it can be written as

$$T_u = \inf\{S_n: S_n > u\} - u = \inf\{S_n - u: S_n - u > 0\}$$
$$= \begin{cases} X_1 - u & \text{if } X_1 > u, \\ \inf\{S_n - X_1: S_n - X_1 > u - X_1\} - (u - X_1) & \text{otherwise.} \end{cases}$$

Now when $X_1 \leq u$, T_u has the same distribution as the forward recurrence time r.v. T'_{u-X_1} defined on the renewal process with lifetime r.v.s $\{X'_n\} \equiv \{X_{n+1}\}$, so

(4.1.10) $\Pr\{T_u > y\} = \Pr\{X_1 > y + u\} + \int_0^u \Pr\{T_{u-v} > y\}dF(v).$

But this equation is of the form (4.1.8), with $z(x) = \Pr\{X_1 > y + x\} = 1 - F(y + x)$, so by (4.1.9)

(4.1.11) $\Pr\{T_u > y\} = \int_{0-}^u (1 - F(y + u - v))dU(v).$

In particular, putting $y = 0$, we recover the identity that is implicit in (4.1.5),

(4.1.12) $1 = \int_{0-}^x (1 - F(x - v))dU(v) \quad (\text{all } x \geq 0).$

EXAMPLE 4.1(c) Renewal equation with linear solution. As another important application of (4.1.8), consider the generator $z(\cdot)$ that corresponds to the solution $Z(x) = \lambda x$ (all $x > 0$), assuming such a solution function exists, and that $\lambda^{-1} = EX_n = \int_0^\infty (1 - F(x))dx$ is finite. Rearranging (4.1.8) yields

$$z(x) = \lambda x - \lambda \int_0^x (x - y)dF(y) = \lambda \int_0^x (1 - F(y))dy.$$

We may recognize in this expression the distribution function of the forward recurrence time of a stationary point process. The argument just given shows that this is the only initial distribution for which the renewal function is linear.

We conclude this section with a few brief remarks concerning the more general case that the random variables X_n are not necessarily nonnegative, or even one-dimensional; thus we admit the possibility that the X_n are d-dimensional vectors for some integer $d > 1$. In such cases, the sequence $\{S_n\}$ constitutes a *random walk*. Such a walk is said to be *transient* if (4.1.2) is finite for all bounded Borel sets A, otherwise *recurrent*, in which case the walk revisits any open set infinitely often. Thus, it is only for transient random walks that (4.1.2) can be used to define a point process, which we shall call the *random walk point process*. In $\mathbb{R}^1$ it is known that a random walk is transient if the mean $E(X)$ is finite and nonzero; if $E(X)$ exists but $E(X) = 0$ the random walk is recurrent. If the expectation is not defined (the integral diverges), examples of both kinds can occur. In $\mathbb{R}^2$ the random walk can be transient even if $E(X) = 0$, but only if the variance is infinite. In higher dimensions every random walk is transient unless perhaps it is concentrated on a one- or two-dimensional subspace. Proofs and further details are given, for example, in Feller (1966).

Most of the renewal equation results also carry over to this context with only nominal changes of statement, but often more difficult proofs. Thus, the expectation or renewal measure may still be defined as at (4.1.4), namely,

$$(4.1.4') \qquad\qquad U(A) = \delta_0(A) + \sum_{k=1}^\infty F^{k*}\{A\},$$

and is finite for bounded Borel sets whenever the random walk is transient (but not otherwise, at least if A has nonempty interior). Furthermore, if $z(x)$ is bounded, measurable, and vanishes outside a bounded set, we may consider the function

$$(4.1.13)\quad Z_0(x) = z(x) + \sum_{k=1}^\infty \int_{\mathbb{R}^d} z(x - y)F^{k*}(dy) = \int_{\mathbb{R}^d} z(x - y)U(dy),$$

which is then a solution, bounded on finite intervals, of the *generalized renewal equation*

$$(4.1.14) \qquad\qquad Z(x) = z(x) + \int_{\mathbb{R}^d} Z(x - y)F(dy).$$

Note that in (4.1.8) we were constrained not only to distributions $F(\cdot)$ concentrated on the half-line but also to functions $z(x)$ and solutions $Z(x)$ that could be taken as zero for $x < 0$. Without such constraints the proof of uniqueness becomes considerably more subtle: one possible approach is outlined in Exercise 4.1.4. Note too that both (4.1.13) and (4.1.14) remain valid on replacing the argument x by a bounded Borel set A, provided $Z(\cdot)$ is then a set function uniformly bounded under translation for such A.

EXAMPLE 4.1(d) *Random walks with symmetric stable distributions.* Here we define the symmetric stable distributions to be those distribution in $\mathbb{R}$ with characteristic functions of the form

$$\phi_\alpha(s) = \exp(-c|s|^\alpha) \qquad 0 < \alpha \le 2.$$

Let us consider the associated random walks for the cases $\alpha \le 1$ for which the first moment does not exist. The case $\alpha = 1$ corresponds to the Cauchy distribution with density function for some finite positive c

$$f(x) = \frac{c}{\pi(c^2 + x^2)} \qquad (-\infty < x < \infty).$$

The nth convolution is again a Cauchy distribution with parameter $c_n = nc$. If the renewal measure were well defined, we should expect it to have a *renewal density*

$$u(x) = \sum_{n=1}^{\infty} f^{n*}(x) = \pi^{-1} \sum_{n=1}^{\infty} \frac{cn}{c^2 n^2 + x^2}.$$

The individual terms are $O(n^{-1})$ as $n \to \infty$, and so the series diverges. It follows readily that the first moment measure is infinite and so the associated random walk is *recurrent*.

For $\alpha < 1$ it is difficult to obtain a convenient explicit form for the density, but standard results for stable distributions imply that f^{n*} and f differ only by a scale factor:

$$f_\alpha^{n*}(x) = n^{-(1/\alpha)} f_\alpha(xn^{-(1/\alpha)}),$$

so that, assuming f_α is continuous at zero,

$$f_\alpha^{n*}(x) \sim xn^{-(1/\alpha)} f_\alpha(0).$$

Thus, the series is convergent for $(1/\alpha) > 1$, that is, for $\alpha < 1$, and divergent otherwise; so it is only for $\alpha < 1$ that the associated random walk is transient.

EXAMPLE 4.1(e) *A renewal process in two dimensions.* We consider independent pairs (X_n, Y_n) where each pair has a bivariate exponential distribution with density vanishing except for $x \ge 0$, $y \ge 0$, where

$$f(x, y) = \frac{\lambda_1 \lambda_2}{1 - \rho} \exp\left(-\frac{\lambda_1 x + \lambda_2 y}{1 - \rho}\right) I_0\left(\frac{2(\rho \lambda_1 \lambda_2 xy)^{1/2}}{1 - \rho}\right),$$

λ_1, λ_2, and ρ are positive constants, $0 \le \rho < 1$, and $I_n(x)$ is the modified Bessel function of order n defined by the series

$$I_n(x) = \sum_{k=0}^{\infty} [k!(k+n)!]^{-1}(x/2)^{2k+n}.$$

The marginal distributions are exponential with parameters λ_1, λ_2; ρ is the correlation between X_1 and Y_1; and the joint distribution has bivariate Laplace–Stieltjes transform

$$\psi(\theta, \phi) = \{(1 + \theta/\lambda_1)(1 + \phi/\lambda_2) - \rho\theta\phi/\lambda_1\lambda_2\}^{-1}.$$

Much as in the one-dimensional case, the renewal function can be defined as

$$U(x, y) = E(\# \{n: S_n \le x, T_n \le y\}),$$

where $S_n = \sum_{k=1}^{n} X_k$ and $T_n = \sum_{k=1}^{n} Y_k$, and has Laplace–Stieltjes transform $\chi(\theta, \phi)$ given by

$$\chi(\theta, \phi) = \frac{1}{1 - \psi(\theta, \phi)}.$$

Substituting for $\psi(\theta, \phi)$ and simplifying, we obtain

$$\chi(\theta, \phi) - 1 = [\theta/\lambda_1 + \phi/\lambda_2 + (1 - \rho)\theta\phi/\lambda_1\lambda_2]^{-1},$$

corresponding to the renewal density

$$u(x, y) = \frac{\lambda_1\lambda_2}{1 - \rho}\exp\left(-\frac{\lambda_1 x + \lambda_2 y}{1 - \rho}\right)I_0\left(\frac{2(\lambda_1\lambda_2 xy)^{1/2}}{1 - \rho}\right) \qquad (x > 0, y > 0).$$

It should be noted that while the renewal density has uniform marginals, corresponding to the fact that each marginal process is Poisson, the bivariate renewal density is far from uniform and in fact as $x \to \infty$, $y \to \infty$ becomes relatively more and more intensely peaked around the line $\lambda_1 x = \lambda_2 y$, as one might anticipate from the central limit theorem.

The example is taken from Hunter (1974a, b), where more general results can be found, together with a bibliography of earlier papers on bivariate renewal processes. See also Exercise 4.1.5.

Exercises

4.1.1. (a) Using a sandwich argument and the strong law of large numbers for the i.i.d. sequence of lifetimes, prove that $N(x)/x \to \lambda$ (a.s.) as $x \to \infty$.
   (b) Deduce from (a) the *elementary renewal theorem*: $U(x)/x \to \lambda$ as $x \to \infty$.
   (c) Similarly, if the lifetime distribution has finite second moment with variance σ^2, deduce from the central limit theorem for the X_n that $(N(x) - \lambda x)/\lambda\sigma\sqrt{\lambda x}$ converges in distribution as $x \to \infty$ to a standard $N(0, 1)$ random variable.

4.1.2. *Higher moments of the number of renewals.*
   (a) Show that for $0 < x < y < \infty$,

$$E[N(dx)N(dy)] = U(dx)U(dy - x),$$

where U is the renewal measure. Similarly, for any finite sequence $0 < x_1 < x_2 < \cdots < x_k < \infty$

$$E[N(dx_1)\cdots N(dx_k)] = U(dx_1)U(dx_2 - x_1)\cdots U(dx_k - x_{k-1}).$$

[These are differential forms for the moment measures; that is, they are moment or product densities as discussed in Chapter 5; see in particular Example 5.4(a).]
(b) Prove directly that $E(N(0, x]^{[k]}) \leq k!(U_0(x))^k < \infty$, where $n^{[k]} = n(n-1)\cdots$ $(n-k+1)$ and $U_0(x) = U(x) - 1$.
(c) In terms of the renewal function $U(x)$, use (a) to show that

$$E(N[0, x]^2) = U(x) + 2\int_{0-}^{x} U_0(x - y)dU(y).$$

Verify that for the special case of a Poisson process

$$E(N[0, x]^2) = 1 + 3\lambda x + \lambda^2 x^2.$$

4.1.3. Let $Q(z; x) = \sum_{n=0}^{\infty} z^n \Pr\{N[0, x] \geq n\}$. Show that

$$Q(z; x) = 1 + z\int_0^x Q(z; x - y)dF(y)$$

and hence that the Laplace–Stieltjes transform is given by

$$\tilde{Q}(z; \theta) = \int_{0-}^{\infty} e^{-\theta x}d_x Q(z; x) = \frac{1}{1 - z\psi(\theta)},$$

where $\psi(\theta)$ is the Laplace–Stieltjes transform of F. Obtain corresponding results for the p.g.f. $P(z; x) = \sum_{n=0}^{\infty} z^n \Pr\{N[0, x] = n\}$. Deduce an expression for the Laplace–Stieltjes transform of the factorial moment $E(N[0, x]^{[k]})$.

4.1.4. For the one-dimensional random walk with nonlattice step distribution F, prove that the only bounded measurable solutions of the equation

$$D(x) = \int_{-\infty}^{\infty} D(x - y)F(dy)$$

are constant. An outline of one method is as follows.
    (i) Let $Y_n = D(-S_n)$, where $S_n = \sum_{i=1}^{n} X_i$. Use the equation to show that for any bounded measurable solution D, the random variables $\{Y_n\}$ constitute a bounded martingale (see Appendix 3) and hence converge a.s. to some limit random variable Y_∞.
    (ii) Since Y_∞ is defined on the tail σ-algebra of the i.i.d. sequence $\{X_n\}$, it must be degenerate, $Y_\infty = c$ for some finite real number c.
    (iii) Since for all X_1' independent of S_n, $D(-X_1' - S_n) =_d D(-S_{n+1}) \to c$ a.s., deduce that

$$E(D(-X_1' - S_n)|X_1') \to c$$

and hence, using the equation again, that $D(-X_1') = c$ a.s., whence also $D(-S_n) = c$ a.s. for $n = 1, 2, \ldots$. Thus, finally, $D(x) = c$ a.e. whenever X has a nonlattice distribution. [see Doob, Snell, and Williamson (1960); for an alternative proof see Feller (1966, §XI. 2), and for a recent review, see Rao and Shanbhag (1986).]

4.1.5. *Two-dimensional renewal process.* In the context of Example 4.1(e), let $N(x, y) = \#\{n: S_n \le x, T_n \le y\}$, where $S_n = \sum_{i=1}^{n} X_i$ and $T_n = \sum_{i=1}^{n} Y_i$, and put

$$Q(z; x, y) = \sum_{n=0}^{n} z^n \Pr\{N(x, y) \ge n\},$$

$$P(z; x, y) = \sum_{n=0}^{\infty} z^n \Pr\{N(x, y) = n\}.$$

Extend the result of Exercise 4.1.3 to show that the double Laplace–Stieltjes transform of $P(z; x, y)$ is given by

$$\tilde{P}(z; \theta, \phi) = \frac{1 - \psi(\theta, \phi)}{1 - z\psi(\theta, \phi)}, \qquad \psi(\theta, \phi) = \int_0^{\infty} \int_0^{\infty} e^{-\theta x - \phi y} d_{x, y} F(x, y).$$

For the particular bivariate exponential distribution in Example 4.1(e), the renewal measure has the density $\sum_{n=1}^{\infty} f^{n*}$, where for $x, y > 0$,

$$f^{n*}(x, y) = f(x, y)(\zeta/\rho)^{n-1} I_{n-1}(2\zeta/(1 - \rho))/I_0(2\zeta/(1 - \rho)), \qquad \zeta = \sqrt{\rho \lambda_1 \lambda_2 xy}.$$

4.2. Stationarity and Recurrence Times

A *modified* or *delayed renewal process*, $\{S_n'\}$ say, is defined much as at (4.1.1), but with X_1 replaced by X_1', which is independent of, but not necessarily identically distributed with, the remaining variables $X_2, X_3, \ldots$. The most important delayed renewal process arises when X_1' has the probability density function

(4.2.1) $f_1(x) = \lambda(1 - F(x)) \qquad (x \ge 0, \lambda^{-1} = E(X)),$

for then the resulting point process in $(0, \infty)$, with counting measure

$$N'(A) = \#\{n: S_n' \in A\},$$

is stationary, as we might anticipate from (3.4.16) and Example 4.1(c). Note that here we are dealing with stationarity on the half-line, in the sense that Definition 3.2.I is required to hold only for Borel subsets of $(0, \infty)$ and for shifts $t \ge 0$.

To establish this stationarity property more formally, introduce the forward recurrence time variable T_u', associated with the sequence S_n', by setting

$$T_u' = \inf\{S_n': S_n' > u\} - u,$$

and define a new point process by taking the origin at u, setting $X_1'' = T_u'$, and following X_1'' by a further sequence of i.i.d. random variables with common d.f. F. Denoting by $\{S_n''\}$ the points of this new process, stationarity will follow if we can show that, for all u, the distributions of the two sequences $\{S_n'\}$ and $\{S_n''\}$ coincide. From the assumed independence and distributional properties, this will hold whenever the distributions of the two initial intervals X_1' and X_1'' coincide, that is, if we can show that

(4.2.2) $\Pr\{T'_u \le x\} = \Pr\{X'_1 \le x\} = \lambda \int_0^x (1 - F(v))dv.$

To show that T'_u has such a distributional property, note that

$$T'_u = \begin{cases} X'_1 & \text{if } X'_1 > u, \\ T_{u-X'_1} & \text{if } X'_1 \le u, \end{cases}$$

and therefore, much as at (4.1.10),

(4.2.3) $\Pr\{T'_u > y\} = \lambda \int_{y+u}^{\infty} (1 - F(v))dv + \int_0^u \lambda(1 - F(v))dv$

$$\times \int_0^{u-v} (1 - F(y + u - v - w))dU(w).$$

The last term here equals

$$\lambda \int_{0-}^u dU(w) \int_0^{u-w} (1 - F(v))(1 - F(y + u - v - w))dv$$

$$= \lambda \int_{0-}^u dU(w) \int_0^{u-w} (1 - F(u - w - v))(1 - F(y + v))dv$$

$$= \lambda \int_0^u (1 - F(y + v))dv \int_{0-}^{u-v} (1 - F(u - v - w))dU(w)$$

$$= \lambda \int_0^u (1 - F(y + v))dv, \quad \text{using (4.1.11)}.$$

Substituting back in the expression for $\Pr\{T'_u > y\}$ and simplifying, we obtain (4.2.2) as required.

These remarks lead to the following proposition.

Proposition 4.2.I. *If the lifetime d.f. has finite first moment λ^{-1}, then the delayed renewal process with initial density (4.2.1) is stationary, and for all $u > 0$ this density coincides with that of the forward recurrence time T_u. If the mean of the lifetime distribution is infinite, then no stationary version of the renewal process can exist.*

PROOF. Only the last statement of the proposition needs elaboration. By it we mean that if $\lambda^{-1} = \infty$, then there does not exist any initial distribution F_1 such that the resulting delayed renewal process is stationary. To show that this is so, it is enough to show that no stationary form can exist for the forward recurrence time distributions. This in turn is an easy corollary of the key renewal theorem, proved later at Proposition 4.4.II, from which we obtain that for all y we should have

$$F_u(y) = \Pr\{T_u \le y\} \to 0 \qquad (u \to \infty)$$

[see Example 4.4(a)].

To extend this result to an arbitrary initial distribution, we consider the general form of (4.1.10); that is, for general F_1,

$$(4.2.4) \qquad \Pr\{T_u' > y\} = 1 - F_1(y + u) + \int_0^u (1 - F_{u-v}(y))dF_1(v).$$

Since for every fixed y and v, $1 - F_{u-v}(y) \to 1$ for $u \to \infty$, it follows by dominated convergence that then $\Pr\{T_u' > y\} \to 1$. Thus, no stationary form for the distribution can exist. $\qquad\qquad\qquad\qquad\qquad\qquad\qquad\qquad\square$

The intuitive interpretation of the last somewhat paradoxical limit statement is that if $\lambda^{-1} = \infty$, we shall spend an ever greater proportion of time traversing intervals of exceptional length and of finding ourselves in a situation where the current interval has a length greater than y still to run.

Now recall from Exercise 3.4.1 the definition of a *backward recurrence time* r.v. B_u as a companion to the forward recurrence time r.v. T_u:

$$(4.2.5) \quad T_u = \inf\{y: N(u, u + y] > 0\}, \qquad B_u = \inf\{x: N(u - x, u] > 0\}.$$

Note that there is an asymmetry in the definitions of B_u and T_u: because $N(\cdot)$ is a.s. finite on bounded intervals, $T_u > 0$ a.s. but it is quite possible to have $\Pr\{B_u = 0\} > 0$. The current lifetime r.v. L_u can then be defined by

$$L_u \equiv B_u + T_u.$$

The joint distribution of any two of these r.v.s thus gives the distribution of all three: the simplest is that of B_u and T_u for which, when $N(\cdot)$ is stationary and orderly,

$$
\begin{aligned}
(4.2.6) \quad \Pr\{B_u > x, T_u > y\} &= \Pr\{N(u - x, u + y] = 0\} \\
&= \Pr\{N(u, u + x + y] = 0\} \\
&= \Pr\{T_u > x + y\} = \lambda \int_{x+y}^{\infty} (1 - F(v))dv.
\end{aligned}
$$

Note that under stationarity and orderliness, B_u has the same marginal d.f. as T_u, while

$$
\begin{aligned}
(4.2.7)\, \Pr\{L_u > z\} &= \int_0^z \Pr\{T_u > z - x, B_u \in (x, x + dx)\} + \Pr\{B_u > z\} \\
&= \int_0^z \lambda(1 - F(x + z - x))dx + \int_z^{\infty} \lambda(1 - F(v))dv \\
&= \lambda \int_0^{\infty} (1 - F(\max(v, z)))dv.
\end{aligned}
$$

Thus,

$$(4.2.8) \qquad EL_u = 2ET_u = 2EB_u = \lambda EX^2 = EX^2/EX \geq EX,$$

with equality only in the case that $X = EX$ a.s.; that is, all lifetimes are equal to the same constant, when the renewal process is variously called a *deterministic renewal process* or a *process of equidistant points*.

By identifying $1 - F(\cdot)$ with $q_0(\cdot)$ in (3.4.9), Equations (4.2.6)–(4.2.8) continue to hold for any stationary orderly point process as discussed in Section 3.4.

Without the assumption of stationarity, we may use the alternative definition for B_u

$$B_u = u - \sup\{S_n: S_n \le u\} \qquad (u \ge 0).$$

Arguing as in (4.1.10), it is not difficult to show (see Exercise 4.2.1) that for the basic renewal process $\{S_n\}$,

(4.2.9) $\Pr\{B_u > x, T_u > y\} = \displaystyle\int_0^{(u-x)_+} (1 - F(u + y - v))dU(v).$

In the case of a Poisson process, we have $F(x) = 1 - e^{-\lambda x}$, and it is then not difficult to check from these relations that

(4.2.10a) $EX < \infty$ *and the distribution of T_u is independent of u;*

(4.2.10b) $EX < \infty$ *and B_u and T_u are independent for each $u > 0$;*

(4.2.10c) $ET_u < \infty$ *(all u) and is independent of u.*

Properties like (4.2.10) have been used to characterize the Poisson process among renewal processes, as detailed in part in Galambos and Kotz (1978). For example, when $ET_u < \infty$, integration of (4.1.10) shows that

$$ET_u = \int_u^\infty (1 - F(y))dy + \int_0^u E(T_{u-v})dF(v),$$

so that when (4.2.10c) holds,

$$(1 - F(u))ET_u = (1 - F(u))ET_0 = \int_u^\infty (1 - F(y))dy \qquad \text{(all } u > 0).$$

Thus, $F(y) = 1 - ce^{-\lambda y}$ for some constant $c = 1 - F(0+)$, $= 1$ for an orderly renewal process. The proof of the rest of Proposition 4.2.II is indicated in Exercises 4.2.2 and 4.2.3.

Proposition 4.2.II. *Any one of the statements* (4.2.10a), (4.2.10b), *and* (4.2.10c) *suffices to characterize the Poisson process among orderly renewal processes.*

Exercises

4.2.1. By following the argument leading to (4.2.4), show that for an orderly renewal process $N(\cdot)$ for which $N(\{0\}) = 1$ a.s.,

$$P\{B_u > x, T_u > y\} = P\{N(u - x, u + y] = 0\}$$

$$= \int_{0-}^{(u-x)_+} (1 - F(y + u - v))dU(v),$$

$$P\{L_u > z\} = \int_{0-}^{u} (1 - F(\max(z, u - v)))dU(v).$$

4.2.2. Use (4.1.10) to show that (4.2.10a) characterizes the Poisson process among orderly renewal processes.

4.2.3. Use (4.2.9) with $x \uparrow u$ to deduce that when (4.2.10b) holds,

$$P\{T_u > y\} = \frac{1 - F(y + u)}{1 - F(u)}$$

for each u and $y \geq 0$. Consequently, for all v in the support of $U(\cdot)$,

$$(1 - F(0+))(1 - F(y + v)) = (1 - F(y))(1 - F(v)),$$

so that $F(\cdot)$ is either geometric or exponential. If $F(x)$ is constant for $0 < x < \delta$, then B_u and T_u cannot be independent—hence the characterization in Proposition 4.2.II via (4.2.10b).

4.2.4. For a renewal process with lifetime d.f. $F(x) = 1 - (1 + \mu x)e^{-\mu x}$, evaluate the renewal function as

$$U(x) = 1 + \mu x/2 - (1 - e^{-2\mu x})/4,$$

and hence derive the d.f.s of the forward and backward recurrence time r.v.s T_u and B_u. Verify their asymptotic properties for $u \to \infty$.

4.3. Some Simple Operations Involving Renewal Processes and Characterizations

Because a single d.f. F suffices to describe a renewal or stationary renewal process, it is of interest to ask in various contexts involving the manipulation of point processes what conditions lead again to a renewal process as a result of the transformation or operation concerned. More often than not, the solution to such a question is a characterization of the Poisson process, which conclusion can be disappointing when it might otherwise be hoped that more general renewal processes could be realized. Roughly speaking, when such a Poisson process characterization solution holds, it indicates that the interval independence property of a renewal process can be preserved only as a corollary of the stronger lack-of-memory property of the Poisson process.

We have already given an example of a characterization of the Poisson process in Proposition 4.2.II. The three operations considered in this section concern thinning, superposition, and infinite divisibility.

EXAMPLE 4.3(a) *Thinning of renewal processes.* Given a renewal process $\{S_n\}$, let each point S_n for $n = 1, 2, \ldots$ be omitted from the sequence with probability

$1 - \alpha$ and retained with probability α for some constant α in $0 < \alpha < 1$, each such point S_n being treated independently. This independence property means that if $\{S_{n(r)}, r = 1, 2, \ldots\}$ is the sequence of retained points with $0 = n(0) < n(1) < n(2) < \cdots$, then $N_r \equiv n(r) - n(r - 1)$ is a family of i.i.d. positive integer-valued r.v.s with $\Pr\{N_r = j\} = \alpha(1 - \alpha)^{j-1} (j = 1, 2, \ldots)$, and hence

(4.3.1) $$\{Y_r\} \equiv \{S_{n(r)} - S_{n(r-1)}\}$$

is a family of i.i.d. r.v.s with d.f.

$$\Pr\{Y_r \le x\} = \sum_{j=1}^{\infty} \alpha(1 - \alpha)^{j-1} F^{j*}(x).$$

Consequently, $\{S_{n(r)}\}$ is still a renewal process, and it is not hard to verify that its renewal function, U_α say, is related to that of $\{S_n\}$ via

(4.3.2) $$U_\alpha(x) - 1 = \alpha(U(x) - 1).$$

It is readily seen that whenever $\{N_r\}$ here is a family of i.i.d. positive integer-valued r.v.s, $\{S_{n(r)}\}$ is a renewal process, but it is only for the geometric distribution for N_r that Equation (4.3.2) holds. In connection with this equation, the converse question can be asked as to when it can be taken as defining a renewal function for $\alpha > 1$. In general, for a given renewal function U, there is a finite largest $\alpha \ge 1$ for which $1 + \alpha(U(x) - 1)$ is a renewal function, although there is a class of lifetime d.f.s, including the exponential and others besides, for which $1 + \alpha(U(x) - 1)$ is a renewal function for all finite positive α [Daley (1965); see also van Haan (1978) and Exercise 4.3.1].

Any renewal function U satisfies $U(x)/\lambda x \to 1$ $(x \to \infty)$, and consequently the renewal function U_α of the thinned renewal process $\{S_{n(r)}\}$, when rescaled so as to have the same mean lifetime, becomes U_α^s, say, defined by

$$U_\alpha^s(x) - 1 = \alpha(U(x/\alpha) - 1) \to \lambda x \qquad (\alpha \downarrow 0).$$

Consequently, when U_α^s is independent of α, it must equal the renewal function of a Poisson process, which is thus the only renewal process whose renewal function is preserved under thinning and rescaling [i.e., $U_\alpha^s = U$ (all $0 < \alpha < 1$)].

EXAMPLE 4.3(b) *Superposition of renewal processes.* Let $N_1, \ldots, N_r$ be independent nontrivial stationary renewal processes. When is the superposed process

(4.3.3) $$N = N_1 + \cdots + N_r$$

again a renewal process? Certainly, N is a renewal process (indeed a Poisson process) when each of the components $N_1, \ldots, N_r$ is a Poisson process. Conversely, since by Raikov's theorem (e.g., Lukacs, 1970) independent random variables can have their sum Poisson distributed only if every component of the sum is Poisson distributed also, it follows from writing $N(A) = N_1(A) + \cdots + N_r(A)$ (all Borel sets A) and appealing to Renyi's characterization at

Theorem 2.3.I that if N is a Poisson process, then so also is each N_j. Because a renewal process is characterized by its renewal function, and this is linear only if the process is Poisson, one way of attempting to establish the following assertions is to show that the renewal function concerned is linear.

Proposition 4.3.I. *A stationary renewal process is the superposition of two independent nontrivial stationary renewal processes only if the processes are Poisson.*

Proposition 4.3.II. *A stationary renewal process is the superposition of $r \geq 2$ independent identically distributed stationary renewal processes only if the processes are Poisson.*

PROOF. We start by allowing the renewal processes N_j to have possibly different lifetime d.f.s F_j, denoting each mean by λ_j^{-1}, so by Proposition 4.1.I, each λ_j is finite and positive. Write $\lambda = \lambda_1 + \cdots + \lambda_r$, $p_j = \lambda_j/\lambda$, $\pi_j = F(0+)$, and $\pi = F(0+)$, where F is the lifetime d.f. of the superposed process N. For any such renewal process we have, for small $h > 0$ and $|z| \leq 1$,

$$Ez^{N(0,h)} = 1 - \frac{\lambda h(1-z)}{(1-\pi)(1-z\pi)} + o(h)$$

$$= \prod_{j=1}^{r} Ez^{N_j(0,h)} = \prod_{j=1}^{r} \left(1 - \frac{\lambda_j h(1-z)}{(1-\pi_j)(1-z\pi_j)} + o(h)\right).$$

It follows by equating powers of z that for $i = 1, 2, \ldots$,

$$\lim_{h\downarrow 0} \Pr\{N(0, h] = i \,|\, N(0, h] > 0\} = \pi^{i-1}(1-\pi) = (1-\pi)\lambda^{-1}\sum_{j=1}^{r} \lambda_j \pi_j^{i-1}.$$

These equations can hold for nonzero π and π_j (and nonzero λ_j) only if $\pi = \pi_j$ for $j = 1, \ldots, r$, that is, only if all renewal processes concerned have the same probability of zero lifetimes. Consequently, it is enough to establish the propositions in the orderly case, which we assume to hold from here on.

In place of the renewal function U at (4.1.5), we use

(4.3.4)
$$H(x) = \sum_{n=1}^{\infty} F^{n*}(x)$$

$$= \lambda x \quad \text{for a Poisson process.}$$

Then from (3.5.3), for a stationary renewal process N,

$$\text{var } N(0, x) = \text{var } N(0, x] = \lambda \int_0^x (2H(u) + 1)du - (\lambda x)^2$$

$$= \lambda \int_0^x (2(H(u) - \lambda u) + 1)du \equiv V(x)$$

and thus

$$\text{cov}(N[-x, 0), N(0, y]) = \tfrac{1}{2}(V(x + y) - V(x) - V(y))$$

$$= \lambda \int_0^y (G(x + u) - G(u))du,$$

where $G(x) = H(x) - \lambda x$. It will also be convenient to write, for events A and r.v.s X for which the limits exist,

$$\Pr\{A|N(\{0\}) > 0\} = \lim_{h\downarrow 0} \Pr\{A|N(0, h] > 0\},$$

$$E(X|N(\{0\}) > 0) = \lim_{h\downarrow 0} E(X|N(0, h] > 0).$$

Then since $p_j = \lim_{h\downarrow 0} \Pr\{N_j(0, h] > 0|N(0, h] > 0\}$,

$$H(x) = E(N(0, x]|N(\{0\}) > 0) = \sum_{j=1}^r E\left(\sum_{i=1}^r N_i(0, x]|N_j(\{0\}) > 0\right)p_j$$

(4.3.5)
$$= \sum_{j=1}^r \left(p_j H_j(x) + p_j \sum_{i \neq j} \lambda_i x\right),$$

so $G(x) = \sum_{j=1}^r p_j G_j(x)$. Similar, somewhat lengthier, algebra leads to

(4.3.6) $G(x, y) \equiv E((N(-x, 0) - \lambda x)(N(0, y) - \lambda y)|N(\{0\}) > 0)$

$$= \sum_{j=1}^r p_j G_j(x, y) + \lambda \int_0^y \left(G(x + u) - G(u)\right.$$

$$\left. - \sum_{j=1}^r p_j^2 (G_j(x + u) - G_j(u))\right) du.$$

Consequently, when $N_1, \ldots, N_r$ are identically distributed, $p_j = 1/r$ and $G_j(x) = G_1(x)$ (all j), $= G(x)$. Also, for a renewal process, $G(x, y) = G(x)G(y)$, so

$$G(x)G(y) = G(x)G(y) + \lambda(1 - 1/r) \int_0^y (G(x + u) - G(u))du.$$

It follows that $G(x + y) = G(y) = G(0)$ (all $x, y > 0$). Thus, $H(x) = \lambda x$, and Proposition 4.3.II is proved.

On the other hand, for $r = 2$ and possibly different F_1 and F_2, replacing $G(x, y)$ by $G(x)G(y)$ with $G(x) = p_1 G_1(x) + p_2 G_2(x)$, $p_1 + p_2 = 1$, leads to

$$-p_1 p_2 (G_1(x) - G_2(x))(G_1(y) - G_2(y))$$

$$= \lambda p_1 p_2 \int_0^y (G_1(x + u) + G_2(x + u) - G_1(u) - G_2(u))du.$$

The function $K(y) \equiv G_1(y) - G_2(y)$ thus has a right-derivative $k(\cdot)$ given by

$$-K(x)k(y) = \lambda(G_1(x + y) + G_2(x + y) - G_1(y) - G_2(y)).$$

Either $K(x) = 0$, in which case $G_1 = G_2$ and the earlier argument shows that $G(x) = 0$, or else by letting $y \downarrow 0$ and using $G_1(0) = G_2(0) = 0$ it follows that $G_1(x)$ is proportional to $G_2(x)$, with $G_1(x)$ having the derivative $g_1(x)$ say. Consequently,

$$g_1(x)g_1(y) = \alpha g_1(x + y)$$

for some nonzero α, so that $g_1(x) = \alpha e^{-\beta x}$ for some $0 < \beta < \infty$ because $G_1(x)/x \to 0$ as $x \to \infty$. Transform calculus now shows that each $1 - F_j(u) = e^{-b_j u}$.

$\square$

An earlier version of Proposition 4.3.I is in McFadden and Weissblum (1963), and a different proof is in Mecke (1969). Another argument is used in Mecke (1967a) to prove the following result (the proof is omitted here).

Proposition 4.3.III. *Let the stationary renewal process N be the superposition of the independent stationary point processes N_1 and N_2 with N_1 renewal. If the lifetime d.f.s F and F_1 of N and N_1 have continuous density functions on $(0, \infty)$ (and right-continuous at the origin), then N_1 is a Poisson process.*

By taking N_1 to be Poisson with rate parameter λ and N_2 to be an alternating renewal process with exponential distributions for the alternating lifetime d.f.s, their parameters α and β being such that $\lambda^2 = \alpha\beta$, Daley (1973) furnished an example showing that Mecke's result cannot characterize N_2 as a Poisson process. If only the differentiability assumptions could be omitted, the restriction in Proposition 4.3.II that the components N_j of the sum N at (4.3.3) should be identically distributed, could be dropped.

EXAMPLE 4.3(c) *Infinite divisibility.* A natural complement to the work of the last example is to discuss whether there are any stationary renewal processes other than the Poisson that are infinitely divisible. In this example we ask whether for (any or all) integers r, the stationary renewal process N at (4.3.3) is expressible as the superposition of the i.i.d. stationary point processes N_1, ..., N_r. On the assumption that the lifetime distribution concerned has a density function, Häberlund (1975) proved that the Poisson process is the only one, while under the additional assumption of the existence of density functions for all the joint distributions of the component process N_1, Ito (1980) has asserted the stronger result that if N is expressible as $N = N_1 + \cdots + N_r$ for one integer $r \geq 2$, then it is Poisson and hence infinitely divisible.

Exercise

4.3.1. (a) When $F(x) = 1 - (1 + x)e^{-x}$, show (e.g., by using Laplace–Stieltjes transforms) that $1 + \alpha(U(x) - 1)$ is a renewal function if and only if $0 < \alpha \leq 1$.
(b) Let $\{X(t): t \geq 0\}$ be a stochastic process with $X(0) = 0$ and stationary nonnegative independent increments, with Lévy–Khinchin representation $E(e^{-\theta X(t)}) = e^{t\psi(\theta)}$, where

$$\psi(\theta) = -\theta\mu_0 + \int_{(0, \infty)} (e^{-\theta x} - 1)\mu(dx),$$

$\mu_0 \geq 0$, and $\mu(\cdot)$ a nonnegative measure on $(0, \infty)$ for which $\int_{(0, \infty)} \times \min(x, 1)\mu(dx) < \infty$ and $\mu(0, \infty) = \infty$ if $\mu_0 = 0$. Let $0 = t_0 < t_1 < \cdots$ be the successive epochs of a Poisson process in $(0, \infty)$ with unit intensity, so that the r.v.s. $X(t_n) - X(t_{n-1})$ are i.i.d. with d.f. $F(x) = \int_0^\infty F(x, t)e^{-t} dt$, where $F(x, t) = \Pr\{X(t) \leq x\}$. Show that with $U(\cdot)$ the renewal function corresponding to F, $1 + \alpha(U(x) - 1)$ is a renewal function for all $0 < \alpha < \infty$.

4.4. Renewal Theorems

Considerable effort has been expended in the mathematics of renewal theory on establishing Theorem 4.4.I below and its equivalents. It is variously known as Blackwell's renewal theorem or the key renewal theorem, depending basically on how it is formulated.

Theorem 4.4.I (Blackwell's Theorem). *For fixed positive y, restricted to finite multiples of the span of the lattice when the lifetime d.f. is lattice, and otherwise arbitrary,*

$$(4.4.1) \qquad\qquad U(x + y) - U(x) \to \lambda y \qquad (x \to \infty).$$

Before proving this result, observe that it is much stronger than the asymptotic linearity property of U known as the elementary renewal theorem (see Exercise 4.1.1; Theorem 3.5.III extends that result to general stationary point processes). Rather, (4.4.1) says roughly that the renewal measure ultimately behaves like Lebesgue measure.

To make this more precise, let $U(\cdot)$ denote the renewal measure and $S_t U$ its shifted version, so that

$$S_t U(A) = U(t + A).$$

Then (4.4.1) implies that on any finite interval $(0, M)$, $S_t U$ converges weakly to the multiple $\lambda \ell$ of Lebesgue measure $\ell(\cdot)$ (or, equivalently, $S_t U$ as a whole converges vaguely to $\lambda \ell$; see Section A2.3 for definitions and discussions of weak and vague convergence). Blackwell's theorem represents the "set" form of the criterion for weak convergence, while the key renewal theorem below represents a strengthened version of the corresponding "function" form, the strengthening taking advantage of the special character of the limit measure and its approximants.

On the other hand, the theorem is not so strong as to assert anything concerning a density $u(\cdot)$ for U. Such results require further assumptions about the lifetime distributions and will be explored, together with further strengthenings of Blackwell's theorem, following Theorem 4.4.II.

PROOF OF THEOREM 4.4.I. The proof given here is probabilistic and uses a coupling method [see Lindvall (1977) for further references]. We compare each sample path $\{S_n\}$ with the sample path $\{S'_n\}$ of a stationary renewal process as defined in Section 4.2, $\{S_n\}$ and $\{S'_n\}$ being defined on a common probability space $(\Omega, \mathscr{F}, P)$ so as to be mutually independent. For each $\omega \in \Omega$, and every integer $i \geq 0$, define for $\{S'_n\}$ the forward recurrence time r.v.s. $Z_i(\omega) = T'_{S_i(\omega)}$ so that

$$Z_i(\omega) = \min\{S'_j(\omega) - S_i(\omega): S'_j(\omega) > S_i(\omega)\}.$$

Because the sequence $\{S_{i+n} - S_i\}$ has a distribution independent of i and is independent of $\{S'_n\}$, and because T'_u is stationary, it follows that the sequence $\{Z_i\}$ is also stationary. Thus, the events

$$A_i \equiv \{Z_j < \delta \text{ for some } j \geq i\},$$

which we define for any fixed $\delta > 0$, have the same probability for each $i = 0$, $1, \ldots$, and in particular therefore $P(A_0) = P(A_\infty)$, where

$$A_0 \supseteq A_1 \supseteq \cdots \supseteq A_\infty \equiv \bigcap_{i=0}^{\infty} A_i = \{Z_i < \delta \text{ i.o.}\}.$$

Now A_∞ is a tail event on the conditional σ-field (namely, conditional on X'_1) of the i.i.d. r.v.s $\{X_1, X'_2, X_2, X'_3, X_3, \ldots\}$, and therefore by the zero-one law for tail events [e.g., see Feller (1966, §IV.6)],

$$P(A_\infty | X'_1 = x) = 0 \text{ or } 1 \qquad (0 < x < \infty).$$

Because F is nonlattice, $P\{u - x < S'_j - X'_1 < u - x + \delta \text{ for some } j\}$ is positive for all sufficiently large u for fixed $\delta > 0$ [cf. Lemma 2 of Section V.4a of Feller (1966)], and hence $P(A_0 | X'_1 = x) > 0$ for every x. Thus, the equations

$$0 < \lambda \int_0^\infty P(A_0 | X'_1 = x)(1 - F(x))dx = P(A_0)$$

$$= P(A_\infty) = \lambda \int_0^\infty P(A_\infty | X'_1 = x)(1 - F(x))dx$$

force $P(A_\infty | X'_1 = x) = 1$ for every x for which $F(x) < 1$. Hence, $P(A_\infty) = 1 = P(A_0)$, so that

$$P\{Z_i < \delta \text{ for some } i\} = 1$$

for every $\delta > 0$.

To establish (4.4.1) it is enough to show that for any $\delta > 0$, we can find x_0 such that $x \geq x_0$ implies that $|EN(x, x + y] - \lambda y| \leq \delta$. Observe that $\lambda y = EN'(x, x + y]$, where N' is the counting function for the stationary renewal process with intervals $\{X'_n\}$. Let $I_\delta = \inf\{i: Z_i < \delta\}$, so that $P\{I_\delta < \infty\} = 1$. Defining

$$J \equiv \inf\{j: S'_j(\omega) > S_{I_\delta}(\omega)\},$$

we then have

$$0 < Z_{I_\delta}(\omega) = S'_J(\omega) - S_{I_\delta}(\omega) < \delta.$$

Define a new point process by means of the sequence of intervals

$$\{X_1, \ldots, X_{I_\delta}, X'_{J+1}, X'_{J+2}, \ldots\}.$$

Denote its counting function by N'' so that for any Borel set A,

$$N''(A) = N(A \cap (0, S_{I_\delta})) + N'((A + Z_{I_\delta}) \cap (S'_J, \infty))$$
$$= N(A \cap (0, S_{I_\delta})) + N'(A + Z_{I_\delta}) - N'((A + Z_{I_\delta}) \cap (0, S'_J)).$$

When A is the interval $(x, x + y]$, the shifted interval $A + Z_{I_\delta}$ has $EN'(A + Z_{I_\delta})$ lying between $\lambda(y - \delta)$ and $\lambda(y + \delta)$ because

$$(x + \delta, x + y] \subseteq (x + Z_{I_\delta}, x + y + Z_{I_\delta}] \subseteq (x, x + y + \delta].$$

For every x the r.v.s. $N(x, x + y]$ are stochastically dominated by the r.v. $1 + N(0, y]$, and since this has finite expectation, $\{N(x, x + y]: x \geq 0\}$ is a uniformly integrable family of r.v.s. This ensures that

$$E(N(x, x + y]I_{\{x < S_{I_\delta}\}}) \to 0 \quad \text{as } x \to \infty$$

since then $P\{x < S_{I_\delta}\} \to 0$. Similarly, $N'(x + Z_{I_\delta}, x + y + Z_{I_\delta}]$ is stochastically dominated by $1 + N(0, y]$ and $P\{x < S'_j\} \to 0$ as $x \to \infty$, so $E(N'(x + Z_{I_\delta}, x + y + Z_{I_\delta}]I_{\{x < S'_j\}}) \to 0$. Consequently, $U(x + y) - U(x) = EN''(x, x + y]$ is arbitrarily close to $EN'(A + Z_{I_\delta})$ for x sufficiently large, and since δ is arbitrary positive, (4.4.1) is established.   □

We now turn to an equivalent but very important form of Theorem 4.4.I for nonlattice lifetimes. A function $g(\cdot)$ defined on $[0, \infty)$ is *directly Riemann integrable* there when for any $h > 0$, the normalized sums

$$h \sum_{n=1}^{\infty} g^h_-(nh) \quad \text{and} \quad h \sum_{n=1}^{\infty} g^h_+(nh)$$

converge to a common finite limit as $h \to 0$; here,

$$g^h_-(x) = \inf_{0 \leq \delta \leq h} g(x - \delta), \qquad g^h_+(x) = \sup_{0 \leq \delta \leq h} g(x - \delta).$$

For such a function, with $U(x) \equiv 0$ for $x < 0$ and monotonic increasing on $x \geq 0$,

$$\int_0^x g(x - y)dU(y) \lessgtr \sum_{n=1}^{\infty} g^h_\pm(nh)(U(x - (n - 1)h) - U(x - nh)).$$

These sums can be truncated to finite sums with truncation error bounded by

$$\int_0^{x-C} |g(x - y)|dU(y)$$

$$\leq \sum_{n=1}^{[x-C]} |g|^1_+(C + n)(U(x + 1 - C - n) - U(x - C - n))$$

$$\leq U(1) \sum_{n=1}^{\infty} |g|^1_+(C + n),$$

which can be made arbitrarily small, uniformly in $x > 0$, by taking C sufficiently large. Thus, the sums are approximated by

$$\int_{x-C}^{x} g(x - y)dU(y) \lessgtr \sum_{n=1}^{[C/h]} g_{\pm}^{h}(nh)[U(x - nh + h) - U(x - nh)]$$

$$\to \lambda h \sum_{n=1}^{[C/h]} g_{\pm}^{h}(nh) \qquad (x \to \infty)$$

$$\to \lambda \int_{0}^{C} g(u)du \qquad (h \to 0).$$

The following equivalent form of Theorem 4.4.I can now be given.

Theorem 4.4.II (Key Renewal Theorem). *For nonlattice lifetime distributions and directly Riemann integrable functions $g(\cdot)$.*

$$(4.4.2) \qquad \int_{0}^{x} g(x - y)dU(y) \to \lambda \int_{0}^{\infty} g(y)dy \qquad (x \to \infty).$$

The following examples may serve as prototypes for the application of the renewal theorem to problems of convergence to equilibrium.

EXAMPLE 4.4(a) *Convergence of the forward recurrence time distribution.* Our starting point is (4.1.11), which after subtracting from (4.1.12) can be written

$$(4.4.3) \quad F_u(y) \equiv \Pr\{T_u \le y\} = \int_{0-}^{u} [F(y + u - v) - F(u - v)]dU(v).$$

This is in the form (4.4.2) with

$$g(x) = F(y + x) - F(x).$$

This function is integrable and of bounded variation over the whole half-line; it then follows easily (see Exercise 4.4.1) that the function is directly Riemann integrable, so that the theorem can be applied. It asserts that, provided the lifetime distribution is nonlattice,

$$F_u(y) \to \lambda \int_{0}^{\infty} [F(y + x) - F(x)]dx$$

$$= \lambda \int_{0}^{y} [1 - F(u)]du.$$

If $\lambda^{-1} < \infty$, this is the usual form of the *length-biased distribution* associated with F, the fact that the distribution is proper following from the identity

$$\lambda^{-1} = \int_{0}^{\infty} (1 - F(u))du.$$

In this case, (4.4.2) asserts directly that the forward recurrence time distribution converges weakly to its limit form. The extension of this result to a delayed renewal process with arbitrary initial distribution follows then from (4.2.4).

In the case $\lambda^{-1} = \infty$, $F_u(y) \to 0$ for all y and no stationary form can exist.

EXAMPLE 4.4(b) *Convergence of the renewal density.* As a further corollary, we shall prove [see Feller (1966, §XI.4)] that *if the lifetime distribution F has finite mean and bounded density $f(t)$, then $U(t)$ has density $u(t)$ such that*

$$(4.4.4) \qquad\qquad u(t) - f(t) \to \lambda.$$

This follows from the fact that $u(t)$, when it exists, satisfies the renewal equation in its traditional form

$$u(t) = f(t) + \int_0^t u(t - x)f(x)dx.$$

[To check this, observe that by (4.1.9) the solution has the form $u(s) = \int_0^s f(s - x)dU(x)$, which on integrating yields $\int_0^t u(s)ds = U(t) - 1$.] Furthermore, the function

$$u(t) - f(t) = \sum_{k=2}^{\infty} f^{k*}(t)$$

satisfies the renewal equation

$$(4.4.5) \qquad u(t) - f(t) = f^{2*}(t) + \int_0^t [u(t - x) - f(t - x)]f(x)dx.$$

Now if $f(t)$ is bounded, $f^{2*}(t)$ is directly Riemann integrable. Indeed, as the convolution of a bounded and an integrable function, it is uniformly continuous (Exercise 4.4.2) while the inequality

$$f^{2*}(t) = \int_0^{t/2} f(t - y)f(y)dy + \int_{t/2}^t f(t - y)f(y)dy$$

$$= 2\int_0^{t/2} f(t - y)f(y)dy$$

$$\leq 2C[1 - F(\tfrac{1}{2}t)],$$

where $C = \sup|f(t)|$, shows that when $\mu = \lambda^{-1} < \infty$, $f^{2*}(t)$ is also bounded above by a monotonic integrable function and is therefore directly Riemann integrable (see Exercise 4.4.1). Thus, Proposition 4.4.II applies and yields (4.4.4).

The argument can be extended to the case where, if not f itself, at least one of its convolution powers has bounded density (see Exercise 4.4.3).

Even a partial assumption of absolute continuity allows the conclusions of the renewal theorems to be substantially strengthened—for example, from local weak convergence of the renewal measure to local convergence in variation norm, namely,

(4.4.6) $$\|S_t U - \lambda \ell\|_M \to 0,$$

where $\|\mu\|_M$ is the variation norm of the (signed) measure μ over $[0, M]$. Equation (4.4.6) would imply that, in Blackwell's theorem, $U(t + A) \to \lambda \ell(A)$ not only for A an interval, as in (4.4.1), but for any bounded Borel A, a strengthening considered by Breiman (1965) [see Feller (1966, §XI.1) for counterexamples].

An appropriate condition is embodied in the following definition.

Definition 4.4.III. A probability distribution F is *spread out* if there exists a positive integer n_0 such that F^{n_0*} has a nonzero absolutely continuous component with respect to Lebesgue measure.

The definition implies that F^{n_0*} can be written in the form

(4.4.7) $$F^{n_0*} = \Sigma + A,$$

where Σ is singular and A is absolutely continuous with respect to Lebesgue measure, and A has a nonzero density $a(x)$, so that

$$\sigma = \|\Sigma\| = 1 - \int_0^\infty a(x)dx < 1.$$

Since the convolution of A with any power of F or Σ is again absolutely continuous, it follows that the total masses of the absolutely continuous components F^{n*} can only increase as $n \to \infty$, and in fact must approach 1, since $\|\Sigma^{k*}\| = \sigma^k \to 0$. Thus, we might anticipate that the asymptotic behaviour of the renewal measure for a spread out distribution would approximate the behaviour to be expected when a density exists. This is the broad content of the following proposition of Stone (1966), from which our further results will follow as corollaries.

Proposition 4.4.IV. *Let F be spread out, U the renewal measure associated with F, and $U_G = G * U$ the renewal measure associated with the corresponding delayed renewal process with initial distribution G. Then U_G can be written in the form*

(4.4.8) $$U_G = U_{1G} + U_{2G}$$

where U_{1G} is absolutely continuous with density $u_{1G}(x)$ satisfying

(4.4.9) $$u_{1G}(x) \to \lambda, \qquad \lambda^{-1} = \int_0^\infty x \, dF(x)$$

and U_{2G} is totally finite.

PROOF. Consider first the ordinary renewal measure U associated with F. Since the convolution of A with itself can always be taken to dominate a uniformly continuous function (Exercise 4.4.2), there is no loss of generality in supposing that the density $a(x)$ of A in (4.4.6) is continuous, bounded, and vanishes outside some finite interval $(0, M)$.

With this understanding let U_3 denote the renewal measure associated with the distribution F^{n_0*}, so that we may write

$$U_3 = \delta_0 + F^{n_0*} + F^{2n_0*} + \cdots$$

and

$$U = [\delta_0 + F + F^{2*} + \cdots + F^{(n_0-1)*}] * U_3 = \rho * U_3,$$

where ρ has total mass n_0. Also, since U_3 satisfies the renewal equation

$$U_3 = \delta_0 + F^{n_0*} * U_3 = \delta_0 + (\Sigma + A) * U_3,$$

we have

$$U_3 * (\delta_0 - \Sigma) = \delta_0 + A * U_3.$$

Since $\delta_0 - \Sigma$ has total mass less than unity, this factor may be inverted to yield

$$U_3 = U_\sigma + A * U_\sigma * U_3,$$

where

$$U_\sigma = \delta_0 + \Sigma + \Sigma^{2*} + \cdots$$

has total mass $(1 - \sigma)^{-1}$. Thus, we obtain for U, and then for U_G,

$$U_G = G * \rho * U_\sigma + A * G * \rho * U_\sigma * U_3.$$

This will serve as the required decomposition, with $U_{2G} = G * \rho * U_\sigma$ totally finite and

$$U_{1G} = A * G * \rho * U_\sigma * U_3$$

absolutely continuous, since it is a convolution in which one of the terms is absolutely continuous. To show that its density has the required properties, we note first that the key renewal theorem applies to U_3 in the form

$$(U_3 * g)(t) \rightarrow \frac{\lambda}{n_0} \int_0^\infty g(x)dx$$

whenever g is directly Riemann integrable. But then a similar result applies also to $H = G * \rho * U_\sigma * U_3$, which is simply a type of delayed renewal measure in which the initial "distribution" $G * \rho * U_\sigma$ has total mass $1 \times n_0 \times (1 - \sigma)^{-1}$, so that

$$(H * g)(t) \rightarrow \lambda(1 - \sigma)^{-1} \int_0^\infty g(x)dx \qquad (t \rightarrow \infty).$$

Finally, since the density of A is continuous and vanishes outside a bounded set, we can take $g(t) = a(t)$, in which case the left side of the last equation reduces to $u_{1G}(t)$ and we obtain

$$u_{1G}(t) \rightarrow \lambda(1 - \sigma)^{-1} \int_0^\infty a(x)dx = \lambda. \qquad \square$$

We obtain the following corollary (see Arjas, Nummelin, and Tweedie, 1978).

Corollary 4.4.V. *If F is spread out and $g \geq 0$ is bounded, integrable, and satisfies $g(x) \to 0$ as $x \to \infty$, then*

$$(4.4.10) \qquad \lim_{\substack{t \to \infty \\ |f| \leq g}} \sup \left| (U_G * f)(t) - \lambda \int_0^\infty f(x)dx \right| \to 0.$$

PROOF. We consider separately the convolution of g with each of the two components in the decomposition (4.4.8) of U_G. Taking first the a.c. component, and setting $u_G(x) = 0$ for $x < 0$, we have

$$\sup_{|f| \leq g} \left| \int_0^t u_{1G}(t - x)f(x)dx - \lambda \int_0^\infty f(x)dx \right| \leq \int_0^\infty |u_{1G}(t - x) - \lambda| g(x)dx.$$

Now $u_{1G}(t) \to \lambda$ so it is bounded for sufficiently large t, $|u_{1G}(t) - \lambda| \leq C$ say for $t > T$, and we can write the last integral as

$$\int_0^{t-T} g(x)|u_{1G}(t - x) - \lambda|dx + \int_0^T |u_{1G}(s) - \lambda|g(t - s)ds,$$

where the first integral tends to zero by dominated convergence since $|u_{1G}(t - x) - \lambda|$ is bounded, $u_{1G}(t - x) \to \lambda$ for each fixed x, and $g(x)$ is integrable, while the second tends to zero by dominated convergence since $|u_{1G}(s) - \lambda|$ has finite total mass over $(0, T)$ and by assumption $g(t - s) \to 0$ for each fixed s.

Similarly, the integral against the second component is dominated for all $|f| \leq g$ by

$$\int_0^t g(t - x)dU_{2G}(x),$$

where again the integrand is bounded and tends to zero for each fixed x, while U_{2G} has finite total mass, so the integral tends to zero by dominated convergence. $\qquad \square$

Corollary 4.4.VI. *If F is spread out, then for each finite interval $(0, M)$*

$$\|S_t U_G - \lambda \ell\|_M \to 0.$$

The version of the renewal theorem summarized by these results has the double advantage of not only strengthening the form of convergence but also replacing the rather awkward condition of direct Riemann integrability by the simpler conditions of Proposition 4.4.IV. Further variants are discussed in Exercise 4.4.4 and in the paper by Arjas et al. (1978). With further conditions on the lifetime distributions, for example, the existence of moments, it is possible to obtain bounds on the rate of convergence in the renewal theorem. For results of this type see Stone (1966), Schäl (1971), and Bretagnolle and Dacunha-Castelle (1967); for a very simple case, see Exercise 4.4.5.

Exercises

4.4.1. *Conditions for direct Riemann integrability.* Let $z(x)$ be a measurable function defined on $[0, \infty)$. Show that each of the following conditions is sufficient to make $z(\cdot)$ directly Riemann integrable (see also Feller, 1966).
   (i) $z(x)$ is nonnegative, monotone decreasing, and Lebesgue integrable.
   (ii) $z(x)$ is continuous, and setting $\alpha_n = \sup_{n < x \le n+1} |z(x)|$, $\Sigma \alpha_n < \infty$. [*Hint*: $z(x)$ is Riemann integrable on any finite interval, and the remainder term outside this interval provides a contribution that tends to zero.]
   (iii) $z(x) \ge 0$, $z(x)$ is uniformly continuous and bounded above by a monotonic decreasing integrable function.

4.4.2. (a) If g is bounded and continuous, f integrable, then $f * g = \int_{\mathbb{R}} g(t - x)f(x)dx$ is uniformly continuous.
   (b) Extend this to the case where g is any bounded measurable function by approximating g by bounded continuous functions. In particular therefore, $\int_A f(t - x)dx$ is uniformly continuous whenever A is a measurable set.
   (c) Let F have a.c. component f; show from (b) that $F * F$ has a.c. component f_2, which dominates a uniformly continuous function and hence a bounded function that vanishes outside a bounded set and is twice continuously differentiable.

4.4.3. Apply the key renewal theorem as around (4.4.5) to show that if F has density f with f^{k*} bounded, and if $\lambda^{-1} < \infty$, then the renewal density $u(x)$ exists and satisfies

$$u(x) - \sum_{j=1}^{2k-1} f^{j*}(x) \to \lambda.$$

[*Hint*: $u(x) - \sum_{j=1}^{2k-1} f^{j*}(x) = \sum_{j=2k}^{\infty} f^{j*}(x)$ satisfies the renewal equation with $z(x) = f^{2k*}(x)$, which is uniformly continuous and bounded above by an integrable function. Necessary and sufficient conditions for $u(x)$ itself to converge are given in Smith (1962); see also Feller (1966 §XI.4).]

4.4.4. *Strong convergence of the forward recurrence time distribution.* Let G_u denote the distribution of the forward recurrence time at $t = u$ and G_∞ its limit form, supposing $\mu = \lambda^{-1} < \infty$. Show that, without any further assumptions on the lifetime distributions other than it is nonlattice, $\|G_u - G_\infty\| \to 0$. [*Hint*: For any bounded measurable $h \ge 0$,

$$\int_{\mathbb{R}_+} h(x)dG_u(x) = \int_0^u dU(u - t) \int_t^\infty h(y - t)dF(y),$$

where the function $\int_t^\infty h(y - t)dF(y)$ is uniformly continuous and bounded above by the integrable function $C(1 - F(t))$ for $C < \infty$, and hence directly Riemann integrable.]

4.4.5. *Rate of convergence in renewal theorems.*
   (a) Set $z(t) = \lambda \int_t^\infty (1 - F(y))dy$, where F has second moment $\sigma^2 + \mu^2$. By considering the associated $Z(t)$ show that for $0 \le t \to \infty$,

$$0 \le U(t) - \lambda t \to \lambda^2(\sigma^2 + \mu^2)/2.$$

(b) Let the r.v.s T_1, T_2 be independent with $\Pr\{T_i > t\} = z(t)$ as in (a). Use the subadditivity of the renewal function $U(\cdot)$ to give, for all $t \geq 0$,

$$U(2t) \leq 2EU(t + T_1 - T_2),$$

and hence deduce from $EU(t - T_1) = \lambda t$ [cf. Example 4.1(c) and Proposition 4.2.I] that

$$2\lambda t \leq U(2t) \leq 2\lambda t + \lambda^2 \sigma^2 + 1.$$

[See Carlsson and Nerman (1986) for earlier references.]

4.5. Neighbours of the Renewal Process: Wold Processes

The specification of a renewal process via independent identically distributed intervals raises the possibility of specifying other point processes via intervals that are one step removed from independence. In this section we consider point processes for which the successive intervals $\{X_n\}$ form a Markov chain, so that the distribution of X_{n+1} given $X_n, X_{n-1}, \ldots$ in fact depends only on X_n. Such processes seem first to have been considered by Wold (1948) and we call them *Wold processes* accordingly.

EXAMPLE 4.5(a) *A first-order exponential autoregressive process.* Suppose that the family $\{X_n\}$ of intervals satisfy the relation

(4.5.1) $$X_{n+1} = \rho X_n + \varepsilon_n$$

for some $0 \leq \rho < 1$ and family $\{\varepsilon_n\}$ of i.i.d. nonnegative random variables (note $\{X_n\}$ is itself i.i.d. if $\rho = 0$). For the particular distribution given by

$$\Pr\{\varepsilon_n > y\} = (1 - \rho)e^{-y} \qquad (y > 0),$$

$$\Pr\{\varepsilon_n = 0\} = \rho,$$

taking Laplace transforms of (4.5.1) shows that if a stationary sequence of intervals is to exist, the common distribution F of the $\{X_n\}$ must have its Laplace–Stieltjes transform $\tilde{F}$ satisfying the functional equation

$$\tilde{F}(s) = \tilde{F}(\rho s)(1 + \rho s)/(1 + s).$$

The only solution of this equation for which $\tilde{F}(0) = \tilde{F}(0+) = 1$ is $\tilde{F}(s) = (1 + s)^{-1}$. Thus, a stationary version of the Markov chain exists, for which the intervals have the same exponential distribution as a Poisson process. The parameter ρ controls the degree of association between the intervals. For $\rho > 0$, a realization of the process consists of a sequence of intervals each one of which is an exact fraction of the preceding one, followed by an interval independently chosen from the same exponential distribution. The construction can be extended to more general types of gamma distribution and has been studied extensively by P. A. Lewis and co-authors: see, for example, Gaver and Lewis (1980). They have advocated its use as an alternative to the Poisson process, partly on the grounds of the very simple behaviour of the spectrum of the interval process. Other aspects are more intractable, however, and from a point process viewpoint its partly deterministic behaviour gives it a rather special character (see Exercises 4.5.2 and 4.5.9).

In general, the interval structure of a Wold process is determined by a Markov transition kernel $P(x, A)$, that is, a family $\{P(x, \cdot), 0 \le x < \infty\}$ of probability measures in $[0, \infty)$, and the distribution, $P_0(\cdot)$ say, of the initial interval X_0, with $P(\cdot, A)$ measurable for each fixed Borel set $A \subseteq [0, \infty)$. When the chain $\{X_n\}$ is irreducible [e.g., see Harris (1956) or Orey (1971) for discussions of the precise meaning of irreducibility] and admits a stationary distribution $\pi(\cdot)$ say, so that for all Borel subsets A

$$(4.5.2) \qquad \pi(A) = \int_{0-}^{\infty} P(x, A)\pi(dx),$$

a stationary interval sequence $\{X_n\}$ can be specified. The following construction then leads to a counting process $N(\cdot)$, stationary in the sense of Definition 3.2.I.

First, let $\{X_0, X_1, \ldots\}$ be a realization of the Markov chain for which X_0 has the initial distribution

$$(4.5.3) \qquad P_0(dx) \equiv \Pr\{X_0 \in (x, x + dx)\} = \frac{x\pi(dx)}{\int_{0-}^{\infty} u\pi(du)},$$

where we suppose the normalizing factor

$$\lambda^{-1} \equiv \int_{0-}^{\infty} x\pi(dx) = \int_{0-}^{\infty} \pi(u, \infty)\, du$$

is finite and that $\pi\{0\} = 0$. Next, conditional on X_0, let X_0' be uniformly distributed on $(0, X_0)$, and determine N by

$$N(0, x] = \#\{n: S_n' \le x\},$$

where

$$S_1' = X_0', \qquad S_{n+1}' = S_n' + X_n \qquad (n = 1, 2, \ldots).$$

The relation (4.5.3), in conjunction with the definition of S_n', states that the origin is located uniformly at random within an interval selected according to the length-biased distribution with increment around x proportional to $x\pi(dx)$. Since $\pi\{0\} = 0$, the normalizing constant λ is just the intensity of the process. Note that the distributions here are consistent with the relations found in Exercise 3.4.1 for the stationary distributions for the forward recurrence time and the length of the current interval. Indeed, the construction here can be rephrased usefully in terms of the bivariate, continuous time Markov process

(4.5.4) $$\mathbf{X}(t) = (L(t), R(t)),$$

where $L(t)$ is the length of the interval containing t and $R(t)$ is the forward recurrence time at time t. The Markovian character of $\mathbf{X}(t)$ follows readily from that of the sequence of intervals. Moreover, it is clear that the process $N(t)$ is uniquely determined by $\mathbf{X}(t)$ and vice versa. By starting the Markov process with its stationary distribution, we ensure that it remains stationary in its further evolution, and the same property then holds for the point process.

An immediate point of contrast to the ordinary point process is that it is not necessary, in (4.5.2), to have $\int_{\mathbb{R}_+} \pi(dx) < \infty$. If the underlying Markov chain is null recurrent, a stationary regime can exist for the point process (though not for its intervals) in which, because of the dependence between the lengths of successive intervals, long runs of very short intervals intervene between the occurrences of longer intervals; in such situations, divergence of $\int_{\mathbb{R}_+} \pi(dx)$ can coexist with convergence of $\int_{\mathbb{R}_+} x\pi(dx)$ (i.e., near the origin, π may integrate x, but note 1). This leads to the possibility of constructing stationary Wold processes with infinite intensity but finite mean interval length. One such construction is given in Daley (1982a); another is outlined in Exercise 4.5.1.

With such examples to bear in mind, it is evident that the problem of formulating analogues of the renewal theorems for the Wold process will need to be approached with some care. One possible approach is through the family of renewal measures

$$U(A|x) = E[\# \{n: S_n \in A\}|X_0 = x]$$

and their associated cumulative processes $U(t|x) \equiv U([0, t]|x)$. The latter functions satisfy the renewal-type equations

(4.5.5) $$U(t|x) = I_{\{t \geq x\}}(t) + \int_0^\infty U(t - x|y)P(x, dy).$$

Unfortunately, these equations seem rather intractable in general. The analogy with the renewal equations of Section 4.4 becomes clearer on taking Laplace–Stieltjes transforms of (4.5.5) with respect to t. Introducing the integral operator T_θ with kernel

$$t_\theta(dy, x) = e^{-\theta x}P(x, dy),$$

the transformed versions of Equations (4.5.5) become

$$U_\theta(x) = e^{-\theta x} + (T_\theta U_\theta)(x) \qquad \left(U_\theta(x) = \int e^{-\theta t} U(dt|x)\right)$$

with the formal solution

$$U_\theta = (I - T_\theta)^{-1} e_\theta, \qquad (e_\theta)(x) \equiv e^{-\theta x},$$

which may be compared to Equation (4.1.6).

EXAMPLE 4.5(b) *Discrete Wold processes.* Consider a simple point process ({0, 1}-valued process) on the lattice of integers {0, 1, 2, ... }; the kernel $P(x, dy)$ here becomes a matrix p_{ij} and in place of the cumulative form at (4.5.5) it is more natural to consider the renewal functions $u(j|i) = \Pr\{N\{j\} = 1|X_0 = i\}$. Then

$$u(j|i) = \delta_{ij} + \sum_{k=1}^{\infty} p_{ik}u(j-i|k),$$

taking the right-hand side here to be zero for $j < i$. By introducing the transforms $u_i(z) = \sum_{k=i}^{\infty} z^k u(k|i)$, these become

$$u_i(z) = z^i + \sum_{k=1}^{\infty} p_{ik}z^i u_k(z),$$

or in matrix-vector form

$$\mathbf{u}(z) = \boldsymbol{\zeta} + \mathbf{P}_z\mathbf{u}(z),$$

where $\mathbf{P}_z = \{p_{ik}z^i\}$, $\mathbf{u}(z) = \{u_i(z)\}$, and $\boldsymbol{\zeta} = (1, z, z^2, ...)$. The asymptotic behaviour of $u(j|i)$ as $j \to \infty$ is therefore related to the behaviour of the resolvent-type matrix $(\mathbf{I} - \mathbf{P}_z)^{-1}$ as $z \to 1$. When $\mathbf{P}$ is finite this can be discussed in classical eigenvector/eigenvalue terms; see Exercise 4.5.4 and for further details Vere-Jones (1975a). A particular question that arises relates to *periodicity* of the process: nonzero values of $u(j|i)$ may be restricted to a sublattice of the integers. This phenomenon is *not* directly related to periodicity of the underlying Markov chain; again, see Exercise 4.5.4 for some examples.

A more general approach, which can be extended to the denumerable case and anticipates the general discussion to be given below, is to consider the discrete version of the Markov chain $\mathbf{X}(t)$ at (4.5.4). When this bivariate chain is aperiodic and recurrent, returns to any given state pair—for example, time points at which an interval of specified length i_0 is just commencing—constitute an imbedded renewal process for $\mathbf{X}(t)$ and allow the standard renewal theory results to be applied.

EXAMPLE 4.5(c) *Transition kernels specified by a diagonal expansion.* Lancaster (1963) has investigated the class of bivariate probability densities that can be represented by an expansion of the kind

$$f(x, y) = f_X(x)f_Y(y)\left(1 + \sum_{n=1}^{\infty} \rho_n L_n(x)M_n(y)\right),$$

where $f_X(\cdot)$, $f_Y(\cdot)$ are the marginal densities, and $L_n(x)$, $M_n(y)$ are families of complete orthonormal functions defined on the marginal distributions $f_X(\cdot)$, $f_Y(\cdot)$, respectively. When f_X and f_Y coincide (so $L_n = M_n$), the bivariate density can be used to define the density of the transition kernel of a stationary Markov chain with specified stationary distribution $f_X(x)$; we simply put

$$p(x, y) = \frac{f(x, y)}{f_X(x)} = f_X(y)\left(1 + \sum_{n=1}^{\infty} \rho_n L_n(x)L_n(y)\right).$$

For many of the standard distributions, this leads to expansions in terms of classical orthogonal polynomials (e.g., see Tyan and Thomas, 1975). In particular, when $f_X(x)$ and $f_Y(y)$ are both taken as gamma distributions, say

$$f_X(x) = x^{\alpha-1} e^{-x} / \Gamma(\alpha),$$

the $L_n(x)$ become the Laguerre polynomials of order α. The bivariate exponential density of Example 4.1(e) is a case in point, when $\alpha = 1$ and $\rho_n = \rho^n$. The resulting Wold process then has exponential intervals, but in contrast to Example 4.5(a) the realizations have no deterministic properties but simply appear as clustered groups of small or large intervals, the degree of clustering being controlled by the parameter ρ. Lampard (1968) describes an electrical counter system that produces correlated exponential intervals. More generally, when $\alpha = d/2$, such correlated gamma distributions can be simulated from bivariate normal distributions with random variables in common; this leads to the possibility of simulating Wold processes with correlated gamma intervals starting from a sequence of i.i.d. normal variates (see Exercise 4.5.7).

Even in such a favourable situation, the analytic study of the renewal functions remains relatively intractable. Lai (1978) has studied the exponential case in detail and provides a perturbation expansion for the renewal function and (count) spectral density of the process in terms of the parameter ρ.

As such examples illustrate, explicit computations for the Wold process are often surprisingly difficult. However, a useful and general approach to the asymptotic results can be developed by identifying a sequence of regeneration points within the evolution of the process and by applying to this sequence the renewal theorems of Section 4.4. It is by no means obvious that any such sequence of regeneration points exists, but the "splitting" techniques developed for Markov chains with general state space by Nummelin (1978) and Athreya and Ney (1978) allow such a sequence to be constructed for a wide class of examples. The essence of this idea is to identify a particular set A_0 in the state space and a particular distribution ϕ on A_0 such that whenever the process enters A_0, it has a certain probability of doing so "according to ϕ", when its future evolution will be just the same as when it last entered A_0 "according to ϕ." In effect, returns to A_0 according to ϕ can be treated as if they were returns to a fixed atom in the state space and provide the sought for regeneration points. The following conditions summarize the requirements on the transition kernel for this to be possible (see Athreya and Ney, 1978).

Conditions 4.5.I. (Regenerative homing set conditions). *For the Markov chain* $\{X_n\}$ *on state space* $S \subseteq [0, \infty) \equiv \mathbb{R}_+$, *there exists a homing set* $A_0 \in \mathcal{B}(\mathbb{R}_+)$, $A_0 \subseteq S$, *a probability measure* ϕ *on* A_0, *and a positive constant* c *such that*

(i) $\Pr\{X_n \in A_0 \text{ for some } n = 1, 2, \dots | X_0 = x\} = 1 \ (x \in S)$;
(ii) *for every Borel subset* B *of* A_0,

$$P(x, B) \geq c\phi(B) \qquad (x \in S).$$

The first of these conditions embodies a rather strong recurrence condition;

indeed Athreya and Ney call a chain satisfying 4.5.I "strongly aperiodic recurrent" since the conditions imply aperiodicity as well as recurrence. The second condition is more akin to an absolute continuity requirement on the transition kernel. In particular, it is satisfied whenever the following simpler but more stringent condition holds.

Condition 4.5.I. (ii)′ *For all* $x \in A_0$, $P(x, B)$ *has density* $p(x, y)$ *on* A_0 *with respect to* ϕ *such that* $p(x, y) \geq c > 0$ $(x \in A_0, y \in A_0)$.

Typically, A_0 will be a set with positive Lebesgue measure and ϕ the uniform distribution on A_0 (i.e., Lebesgue measure renormalized to give A_0 total mass unity). In the discrete case, 4.5.I(ii) is equivalent to the assumption that the matrix of transition probabilities has at least one positive diagonal element.

Conditions 4.5.I are trivially satisfied in the independent (renewal) case, if we take S to be the support of the lifetime distribution F and put $A_0 = S$, $\phi = F$, and $c = 1$.

Under Conditions 4.5.I, Athreya and Ney (1978) show that the chain is recurrent in the sense of Harris (1956) and admits a unique finite invariant measure $\pi(\cdot)$. The important feature for our purposes is not so much the existence of the invariant measure as its relation to the sequence $\{v_k\}$ of "returns to A_0 according to ϕ." This aspect is made explicit in the following proposition, for proof of which we refer to Athreya and Ney (1978) and Nummelin (1978).

Proposition 4.5.II. *Conditions* 4.5.I *imply that for the Markov chain* $\{X_n\}$:
   (a) *there exists a stopping time* $v \geq 1$ *with respect to the* σ-*fields generated by* $\{X_n\}$ *such that for Borel subsets* B *of* A_0

$$(4.5.6) \qquad \Pr\{X_v \in B | X_0 \cdots X_{v-1}; v\} = \phi(B);$$

   (b) $\{X_n\}$ *has an invariant measure* $\pi(\cdot)$ *related to* ϕ *by*

$$(4.5.7) \qquad \pi(B) = E_\phi\left(\sum_{n=0}^{v-1} I_B(X_n)\right) \qquad (B \in \mathscr{B}(\mathbb{R}_+))$$

where E_ϕ *refers to expectations under the initial condition that* X_0 *has distribution* ϕ *on* A_0; *that is* $\Pr\{X_0 \in B\} = \phi(B \cap A_0)$ $(B \in \mathscr{B}(\mathbb{R}_+))$.

Equation (4.5.7) can be extended by linearity and approximation by simple functions to

$$(4.5.8) \qquad \int_{\mathbb{R}_+} f(x)\pi(dx) = E_\phi\left(\sum_{n=0}^{v-1} f(X_n)\right)$$

whenever f is Borel-measurable and either nonnegative or π-integrable. Special cases of (4.5.8) include

(4.5.9a)
$$E_\phi(v) = \int_{\mathbb{R}_+} \pi(dx)$$

and

(4.5.9b)
$$E_\phi(X_0 + X_1 + \cdots + X_{v-1}) = \int_{\mathbb{R}_+} x\pi(dx).$$

Now let $S_n = \sum_{i=1}^n X_i$, and let $\{T_k\} = \{S_{v_k} - 1\}$ denote the sequence of times at which the process returns to A_0 according to ϕ. These T_k form the regeneration points that we seek. If $G(\cdot)$ denotes the distribution function of the successive differences $T_k - T_{k-1}$, so that in particular

(4.5.10)
$$G(u) = E_\phi\{I_{S_{v-1}} \le u\} = \Pr_\phi\{S_{v-1} \le u\},$$

then the T_k form the instants of a renewal process with lifetime distribution G. We apply this fact, with the theorems of Section 4.4, to determine the asymptotic behaviour of the Wold process.

The results are stated for the renewal function

(4.5.11)
$$U_\phi(C \times T_t B) = E_\phi \# \{n: X_n \in C, S_n \in T_t B\},$$

where $T_t B$ is the translate of B through time t. If the process is started from a general distribution κ for X_0, we write $U_\kappa(\cdot)$ for the corresponding renewal function. The analogue of Blackwell's renewal theorem for this function reads, for $B = (0, h)$,

$$U_\phi(C \times T_t B) \to \lambda\pi(C)\ell(B) \qquad \left(\lambda^{-1} = \int_{\mathbb{R}_+} x\pi(dx)\right).$$

We approach these results through an extended version of the key renewal theorem, fixing a bounded measurable function $h(x, y)$ with support in the positive quadrant $x \ge 0$, $y \ge 0$, and setting for $t > 0$

(4.5.12)
$$Z(t) = E_\phi\left(\sum_{n=0}^{N(t)} h(X_n, t - S_n)\right)$$
$$= \int_0^\infty \int_0^t h(x, t - u)U_\phi(dx \times du).$$

Considering the time T_1 to the first return to A_0 according to ϕ, we find that $Z(t)$ satisfies the renewal equation

$$Z(t) = z(t) + \int_0^t Z(t - u)dG(x),$$

where

(4.5.13)
$$z(t) = E_\phi\left(\sum_{n=0}^{v-1} h(X_n, t - S_n)\right) = E_\phi\left(\int_0^T h(X_{N(u)}, t - u)dN(u)\right).$$

If then we can show that $z(t)$ satisfies the condition of direct Riemann integrability (for Feller's form of the key renewal theorem, 4.4.II), or the conditions of 4.4.III for the Breiman form of the theorem, we shall be able to assert that

$$Z(t) \to \lambda \int_0^\infty z(t)dt \qquad (t \to \infty).$$

To evaluate the integral we make use of (4.5.8), so that formally

$$(4.5.14) \qquad \int_0^\infty z(t)dt = \int_0^\infty E_\phi \left(\sum_{n=0}^{\nu-1} h(X_n, t - S_n) \right) dt$$

$$= E_\phi \left(\sum_{n=0}^{\nu-1} \int_{S_n}^\infty h(X_n, t - S_n)dt \right)$$

$$= E_\phi \left(\sum_{n=0}^{\nu-1} \int_0^\infty h(X_n, u)du \right)$$

$$= \int_0^\infty \int_0^\infty h(x, t)\pi(dx)dt,$$

the formal operations being justified by Fubini's theorem whenever $h \geq 0$ or h is $\pi \times \ell$ integrable.

Direct Riemann integrability can be established directly in simple cases, to which we add the following general sufficient condition. For $\delta > 0$, any α in $0 \leq \alpha < \delta$, and $I_j(\delta) \equiv (j\delta, (j + 1)\delta]$, define

$$\bar{m}_\delta(x, \alpha) = \sum_{j=0}^\infty \sup_{t \in I_j(\delta)} h(x, t),$$

$$\bar{m}_\delta(x) = \sup_{0 \leq \alpha < \delta} \bar{m}_\delta(x, \alpha),$$

and similarly $\underline{m}_\delta(x, \alpha)$ and $\underline{m}_\delta(x)$ by replacing sup by inf. For any y, there is a unique $\alpha_\delta(y)$ in $[0, \delta)$ such that $y = j'\delta + \alpha_\delta(y)$ for some integer j'. Then

$$\sum_{j=0}^\infty \sup_{t \in I_j(\delta)} h(x, t - y) = \bar{m}_\delta(x, \alpha_\delta(y)).$$

Using first Fatou's lemma and then Fubini's theorem,

$$\sum_{j=0}^\infty \sup_{t \in I_j(\delta)} z(t) \leq E_\phi \left(\sum_{n=0}^{\nu-1} \bar{m}_\delta(X_n, \alpha_\delta(-S_n)) \right)$$

$$\leq E_\phi \left(\sum_{n=0}^{\nu-1} \bar{m}_\delta(X_n) \right)$$

$$= \int_0^\infty \bar{m}_\delta(x)\pi(dx).$$

A similar lower bound with sup and $\bar{m}_\delta$ replaced by inf and $\underline{m}_\delta$, respectively, holds. Thus, a sufficient condition for the direct Riemann integrability of $z(t)$ is that, as $\delta \downarrow 0$,

$$(4.5.15) \qquad \delta \int_0^\infty [\bar{m}_\delta(x) - \underline{m}_\delta(x)] \pi(dx) \to 0.$$

If, alternatively, G is spread out, then it is enough to show that $z(t)$ is integrable and tends to zero as $t \to \infty$. Simple sufficient conditions for the latter (not the most general possible) are that

$$(4.5.16a) \qquad h(x, t) \to 0 \quad \text{as } t \to \infty \text{ for each fixed } x,$$

and

$$(4.5.16b) \qquad |h(x, t)| \le h_0(x),$$

where $h_0(x)$ is π-integrable. This follows readily from (4.5.13) and an application of the dominated convergence theorem.

Summarizing these results, we have the following theorem.

Theorem 4.5.III. *Suppose that the Markov transition kernel associated with a Wold process satisfies the regenerative homing set Conditions 4.5.I and that its invariant measure π satisfies*

$$\lambda^{-1} = \int_{\mathbb{R}_+} x\pi(dx) < \infty.$$

Also let $h(x, t)$ be a fixed measurable function, vanishing outside the positive quadrant in $\mathbb{R}^2$ and $\pi \times \ell$ integrable in $\mathbb{R}_+ \times \mathbb{R}_+$, and define $G, U_\phi, Z_\phi,$ and z_ϕ by (4.5.10)–(4.5.13), respectively.

(i) If G is nonlattice and z_ϕ is directly Riemann integrable [hence in particular if (4.5.15) holds], then

$$(4.5.17) \qquad Z_\phi(t) = \int_0^\infty \int_0^t h(x, t - u)U_\phi(dx \times du)$$

$$\to \lambda \int_0^\infty \int_0^\infty h(x, u)\pi(dx)du \qquad (t \to \infty).$$

(ii) Equation (4.5.17) also holds if, alternatively, G is spread out and $z(t)$ is bounded and $\to 0$ as $t \to \infty$ [hence in particular if (4.5.16) holds].

We now apply this theorem to some important special cases. Consider first the Blackwell-type result, where

$$h(x, t) = I_A(x)I_{(0, h)}(t).$$

In general, we shall only have $h(x, t) \pi \times \ell$ integrable if A is bounded away from zero. Then since $I_{(0, h)}(t)$ has only two points of discontinuity, each of unit height, it is easy to see that for all $x \in \mathbb{R}_+$,

$$\bar{m}_\delta(x) - \underline{m}_\delta(x) \le 2I_A(x),$$

so that both (4.5.15) and (4.5.16) are satisfied. Equation (4.5.16) also holds if the interval $(0, h)$ is replaced by any bounded Borel set B. Finally, if $\pi(\cdot)$ is totally finite, the condition on A can be dropped and the same results hold. Thus, we have the following corollary.

Corollary 4.5.IV. *Let A, B be Borel subsets of $\mathbb{R}_+$, and suppose first that G is nonlattice. Then*

$$(4.5.18) \qquad U_\phi(A \times T_t B) \to \lambda\pi(A)\ell(B) \qquad (t \to \infty)$$

whenever B is a finite interval $(0, h)$ and $A \subseteq [\varepsilon, \infty)$ for some $\varepsilon > 0$. If G is spread out, the same result holds for B any bounded Borel set, while if $\pi(\cdot)$ is totally finite the same results hold without any further condition on A.

We next extend the results to an arbitrary initial distribution, κ say, for X_0. If we denote the corresponding renewal functions by U_κ, Z_κ, then Z_κ satisfies

$$(4.5.19) \qquad Z_\kappa(t) = z_\kappa(t) + \int_0^t Z_\phi(t - u)G(du)$$

with

$$(4.5.20) \qquad z_\kappa(t) = E_\kappa\left(\sum_{n=0}^{v'-1} h(X'_n, t - S'_n) \right),$$

where X'_n, S'_n refer to the sequence of interval lengths and renewals for the process with initial distribution κ, and v' is the time of the first entry to A_0 according to ϕ, again starting from X_0 distributed according to κ. It follows from the first of the Conditions 4.5.I that this entry is certain, so v' is finite with probability 1. It then follows from (4.5.19) that

$$Z_\kappa(t) - Z_\phi(t) = z_\kappa(t) - z_\phi(t)$$

so that we need conditions to ensure the convergence of the right-hand side to zero. This will follow from (4.5.20) if $E_\kappa(v') < \infty$ and h is bounded and satisfies (4.5.16a).

Corollary 4.5.V. *Suppose that (4.5.17) holds for U_ϕ and that κ is an arbitrary initial distribution for X_0. Then (4.5.17) continues to hold with U_κ in place of U_ϕ if and only if $z_\kappa(t) - z_\phi(t) \to 0$, in particular if h is bounded and satisfies (4.5.16a), and $E_\kappa(v') < \infty$, $E_\phi(v) = \int_{\mathbb{R}_+} \pi(dx) < \infty$.*

Finally, we turn to the question of the weak convergence of the process $\mathbf{X}(t)$. It somewhat simplifies the algebraic details to work with the bivariate process $\mathbf{Y}(t) = (L(t), L(t) - R(t))$, that is, with the backward in place of the forward recurrence time. If then $\xi(x, y)$ is any bounded continuous function of x, y in $\mathbb{R}_+ \times \mathbb{R}_+$, we consider $\xi(\mathbf{Y}(t))$, which we may write in the form

$$\xi(\mathbf{Y}(t)) = \sum_{n=0}^{\infty} h(L_n, t - S_n),$$

where

$$h(x, t) = \begin{cases} \xi(x, t) & (0 \le t \le x), \\ 0 & (t > x), \end{cases}$$

since in fact only the term with $n = N(t)$ contributes to the sum.

Suppose first that G is nonlattice, and define the *modulus of continuity* $\omega(x, \delta)$ of $h(\cdot)$ by

$$\omega(x, \delta) = \sup_{0 \le t \le x - \delta} \sup_{0 \le u \le \delta} |h(x, t) - h(x, t + u)|.$$

Then for the particular choice of h given above,

$$\bar{m}_\delta(x) - \underline{m}_\delta(x) \le (x/\delta)\omega(x, \delta)$$

so that

$$\delta \int_{\mathbb{R}_+} [\bar{m}_\delta(x) - \underline{m}_\delta(x)]\pi(dx) \le \int_{\mathbb{R}_+} x\omega(x, \delta)\pi(dx).$$

For each fixed $x > 0$, $h(x, t)$ is continuous and nonvanishing on a finite closed interval, hence uniformly continuous, so $\omega(x, \delta) \to 0$. Also, $\omega(x, \delta)$ is uniformly bounded in x and δ, so by dominated convergence the integral on the right converges to zero as $\delta \to 0$; that is, (4.5.15) holds. Also,

$$|z_\kappa(t)| \le E_\kappa[|\xi(\mathbf{Y}(t))|; T > t] \le CP_\kappa\{T > t\},$$

where the last term tends to zero from the recurrence property assumed in Condition 4.5.I(i). Consequently, the conditions for Corollary 4.5.V hold. If, furthermore, G is spread out, then this result alone is sufficient to ensure the truth of the Riemann-type theorem. This means the continuity condition on ξ can be dropped, implying that the weak convergence of $\mathbf{Y}(t)$ to its limit can be replaced by convergence in variation norm.

Proposition 4.5.VI. *Let $P_{\kappa,t}$ denote the distribution of $\mathbf{X}(t)$ supposing X_0 has initial distribution κ and π_∞ is the stationary distribution for $\mathbf{X}(t)$ with elementary mass $\lambda\pi(dx)dy$ over the region $0 \le y \le x < \infty$. Then if G is nonlattice and $\lambda^{-1} = \int_{\mathbb{R}_+} x\pi(dx) < \infty$, $P_{\kappa,t} \to \pi_\infty$ weakly. If, furthermore, G is spread out, $P_{\kappa,t} \to \pi_\infty$ in variation norm.*

Throughout the discussion we have assumed that the mean $\lambda = \int_{\mathbb{R}_+} x\pi(dx)$ is finite. When λ is infinite, further types of behaviour are possible, some of which are sketched in Athreya, Tweedie, and Vere-Jones (1980).

Exercises

4.5.1. *A Wold process with infinite intensity.* Consider a symmetric random walk $\{X_n\}$ with reflecting barrier at the origin, supposing the walk to have density and be null recurrent [e.g., the single-step distribution could be $N(0, 1)$]. Then the invariant measure for X_n is Lebesgue measure on $(0, \infty)$. Now transform the state space by setting $Y_n = T(X_n)$, where

$$x = T^{-1}(y) = y^{-\beta}(1 + y)^{-\alpha} \qquad (\alpha > 0, \beta > 0).$$

(Note that under T the origin is mapped into the point at infinity and vice versa.) Then the transformed process Y_n is Markovian with invariant measure having density $\pi(y)$, where near the origin $\pi(y) \sim y^{-(1+\beta)}$ and near infinity $\pi(y) \sim y^{-(\alpha+\beta+1)}$. Choosing $0 < \beta < 1, \alpha + \beta > 1, \int_0^\infty y\pi(y)dy < \infty$ but $\int_0^\varepsilon \pi(y)dy$ diverges. Show that the construction of a stationary version of the corresponding Wold process, through the joint distribution of the current interval and forward recurrence time, can be completed as indicated in the text.

4.5.2. *Infinitely divisible autoregressive process.* Let $X \geq 0$ have an infinitely divisible distribution with representation of the form

$$\psi(\theta) = E(e^{-\theta X}) = \exp\left(\int_0^\infty (e^{-\theta x} - 1)M(dx)\right) \qquad (\mathrm{Re}(\theta) > 0),$$

where M integrates x at the origin and integrates 1 at infinity. Show that there exists a stationary sequence $\{X_n\}$, satisfying the autoregressive equation

$$X_{n+1} = \rho X_n + \varepsilon_n \qquad (\varepsilon_n \text{ independent of } X_n)$$

and having marginal distribution with Laplace–Stieltjes transform $\psi(\theta)$, whenever M is absolutely continuous with monotonic decreasing density $m(x)$, hence in particular whenever the X_n are gamma distributed. [*Hint:* If ε_n is also infinitely divisible, its Laplace–Stieltjes transform, $\phi(\theta)$ say, must satisfy

$$\phi(\theta) = \frac{\psi(\theta)}{\psi(\rho\theta)} = \exp\left(\int_0^\infty (e^{-\theta x} - 1)[M(dx) - M(\rho^{-1} dx)]\right).$$

4.5.3. Let $F(t; x, y)$ be the distribution function of the bivariate process $\{(L(t), L(t) - R(t))\}$, conditional on an event at the origin and $L(0-) = s$. Then if F has a density $f(t; x, y) \equiv f(t; x, y \mid s)$ it satisfies for $0 < y < \min(x, t)$

$$\frac{\partial F}{\partial t} + \frac{\partial F}{\partial y} = \int_0^t f(t; u, u)P(u, (0, x])du - \int_0^y f(t; u, u)du,$$

and if also the density function is sufficiently regular, then for the same x, y, t,

$$\frac{\partial f}{\partial t} + \frac{\partial f}{\partial y} = 0.$$

Argue on probabilistic grounds that $f(t; x, y) = f(t - v; x, y - v)$ for $0 < y - v < \min(x, t - v)$, so $f(t; x, x) = f(t - x; x, 0+)$ for $0 < x < t$, and that

$$(*) \qquad f(t; x, 0+) = p(s, t)p(t, x) + \int_0^t f(t; u, u)p(u, x)du.$$

When the p.d.f.s $p(u, x)$ are independent of u, this reduces to the renewal density function equation.

Assuming that the conditions for the limits of Theorem 4.5.III and its corollaries are satisfied, identify $f(x, y) \equiv \lim_{t\to\infty} f(t; x, y)$ with the density function $\pi(x)$ for the stationary measure $\pi(\cdot)$ of the theorem, and deduce the density version of Equation (4.5.2) by taking the limit in $(*)$.

Now let $L(0-)$ be a r.v. with p.d.f. $\lambda s\pi(s)$ with λ as in the theorem. Interpret $\int_0^t dx \int_0^\infty yf(t; x, y|s)\lambda s\pi(s)ds$ as the density of the expectation function $U(\cdot)$ of the Wold process. [Lai (1978) has other discussion and references.]

4.5.4. *Discrete Wold processes.*
(a) Suppose integer-valued intervals are generated by a finite Markov chain on $\{1, 2, 3\}$ with transition matrices of the forms

$$\text{(i)} \quad P = \begin{pmatrix} 0 & 1 & 0 \\ 0 & 0 & 1 \\ 1 & 0 & 0 \end{pmatrix}; \quad \text{(ii)} \quad P = \begin{pmatrix} 0 & 0 & 1 \\ \frac{1}{2} & \frac{1}{2} & 0 \\ \frac{1}{2} & \frac{1}{2} & 0 \end{pmatrix}; \quad \text{(iii)} \quad P = \begin{pmatrix} 0 & \frac{1}{2} & \frac{1}{2} \\ 1 & 0 & 0 \\ 1 & 0 & 0 \end{pmatrix}.$$

For which of these P do the corresponding Wold processes show lattice behaviour? What is the relation of periodicity of P to lattice behaviour of the associated Wold process?

(b) Define $m_{ij}(n) = \Pr\{\text{interval of length } j \text{ starts at } n | X_0 = i\}$ and show that for $n \ge 0$,

$$m_{ij}(n) = \delta_{ij}\delta_{0n} + \sum_k m_{ik}(n - k)p_{kj} = \delta_{ij}\delta_{0n} + \sum_k p_{ik}m_{kj}(n - i),$$

where we interpret $m_{ij}(n) = 0$ for $n < 0$. In matrix form, the p.g.f.s are given by

$$\mathbf{M}(z) = \{\tilde{m}_{ij}(z)\} \equiv \left\{\sum_{n=0}^\infty m_{ij}(n)z^n\right\} = (\mathbf{I} - \mathbf{H}(z))^{-1},$$

where

$$\mathbf{H}(z) = (h_{ij}(z)) \equiv (z^i p_{ij}).$$

(c) If the Wold process is nonlattice and P is irreducible,

$$(1 - z)[\mathbf{I} - \mathbf{H}(z)]^{-1} = \lambda\mathbf{\Pi} + (1 - z)\mathbf{Q}(z),$$

where $\mathbf{\Pi}$ is the one-dimensional projection onto the null space of $\mathbf{I} - \mathbf{P}$, and $\mathbf{Q}(z)$ is analytic within some disk $|z| \le 1 + \varepsilon$, $\varepsilon > 0$ (see Vere-Jones, 1975a).

4.5.5. *Denumerable discrete Wold processes.* Consider the bivariate process $\mathbf{X}(n) = (L(n), R(n))$ [or $\mathbf{Y}(n) = (L(n), L(n) - R(n))$] as a Markov chain with an augmented space. Show that the Wold process is nonlattice if and only if this augmented chain is aperiodic, and that if the original Markov chain is positive recurrent with stationary distribution $\{\pi_j\}$, having finite mean, the augmented chain $\mathbf{X}(n)$ is positive recurrent with stationary distributions

$$\pi(h, j) = \Pr\{L_n = j, R_n = h\} = \lambda\pi_j \quad (h = 1, 2, \ldots, j),$$

$$= 0 \quad \text{(otherwise)},$$

where as before $\lambda^{-1} = \sum j\pi_j < \infty$.

4.5.6. *Markov chains with kernels generated by a power diagonal expansion.*
(a) If $\{X_n\}$ is generated by a kernel with the structure

$$p(x, y) = f(y) \sum_{n=0}^\infty \rho^n L_n(x)L_n(y)$$

for an orthogonal family of functions $L_n(\cdot)$, then the m-step transition kernel $p^{(m)}(x, y)$ is generated by a kernel with similar structure and ρ replaced by $\rho_m = \rho^m$.

(b) In the particular case that $f(\cdot)$ is exponential and the $\{L_n(x)\}$ are Laguerre polynomials, a key role is played by the Hille–Hardy formula

$$\sum_{n=0}^{\infty} L_n(x)L_n(y)\rho^n = (1 - \rho)^{-1} \exp\left(-\frac{(x + y)\rho}{(1 + \rho)}\right) I_0\left(\frac{2\sqrt{xy\rho}}{1 - \rho}\right).$$

Use this to show the following:

(i) The convergence to the stationary limit as $m \to \infty$ is *not* uniform in x.

(ii) For every $x > 0$, the conditional distribution functions $F(h|x) = \int_0^h p(x, y)dy$ are bounded by a common function $\alpha(h)$, where $\alpha(h) < 1$ for $h < \infty$.

(iii) If $A(\theta)$ is the integral operator on $L_1[0, \infty)$ with kernel $p(x, y)e^{-\theta x}$, then for all θ with $\mathrm{Re}(\theta) \ge 0$, $\theta \ne 0$, $\|A^2(\theta)\| < 1$ and so the inverse $[I - A(\theta)]^{-1}$ exists and is defined by an absolutely convergent series of powers of $A(\theta)$. [For details see Lai (1978).]

4.5.7. *Simulation of Wold process with χ^2 interval distribution.* Starting from a sequence $Z_0, Z_1, \ldots$ of i.i.d. $N(0, \sigma^2)$ variables, form successively $Y_1 = Z_0/\sqrt{1 - \rho^2}$ and $Y_{i+1} = \rho Y_1 + Z_i$ $(i = 1, 2, \ldots)$. Then the Y_i form a stationary sequence of normal r.v.s with first-order autoregressive structure. Construct d independent realizations of such autocorrelated normal series, $\{Y_{1i}, \ldots, Y_{di}; i = 1, 2, \ldots\}$ say, and generate a stationary sequence of autocorrelated gamma r.v.s $\{X_i\}$ by setting

$$X_i = \sum_{k=1}^{d} Y_{ki}^2.$$

These X_i can be used as the intervals of a point process, but the process so obtained is not initially stationary: to obtain a stationary version, the length-biased distribution may be approximated by choosing $T \gg \lambda^{-1}$, selecting a time origin uniformly on $(0, T)$ and taking the initial interval to be the one containing the origin so selected, and the subsequent intervals to be X_1, X_2, and so on.

4.5.8. *Wold processes generated by conditionally exponential random variables.* Take $p(x, y)$ of the form $\lambda(x)e^{-\lambda(x)y}$.

(a) If $\lambda(x) = \lambda x^{-1/2}$, then the marginal density $\pi(x)$ can be found via Mellin transforms (Wold, 1948).

(b) If $\lambda(x) = \lambda + \alpha x$, then the density $\pi(x)$ is given by

$$\pi(x) = c(\lambda + \alpha x)^{-1} e^{-\lambda x}$$

[see Cox (1955), Cox and Isham (1980), and Daley (1982a); the model has a simple form of likelihood function and has been used to illustrate problems of inference for Poisson processes when the alternative is a Wold process, in particular of the type under discussion].

4.5.9. *Time reversed exponential autoregression.* Let the intervals Y_n of a point process be stationary and satisfy

$$Y_{n+1} = \min(Y_n/\rho, \eta_n)$$

for i.i.d. nonnegative η_n and $0 < \rho < 1$. Show that when η_n is exponentially distributed, so also is Y_n, with $\text{corr}(Y_0, Y_n) = \rho^{|n|}$. Furthermore, $\{Y_n\} =_d \{X_{-n}\}$, where X_n are as in Example 4.5(a) with $\Pr\{\varepsilon_n > y\} = (1 - \rho)e^{-y}$ [see Chernick et al. (1988), where it is also shown that this identification of $\{X_n\}$ as the time reversed process of $\{Y_n\}$ characterizes the exponential distribution].

4.5.10. *Lampard's reversible counter system* [see Lampard (1968) and Takacs (1976)]. Consider a system with two counters, one of which is initially empty but accumulates particles according to a Poisson process of rate λ, the other of which has an initial content $\xi_0 + r$ particles and loses particles according to a Poisson process of rate μ until it is empty. At that point the roles of the two counters are reversed; an additional r particles are added to the number ξ_1 accumulated in the first counter, which then begins to lose particles at rate μ, while the second counter begins to accumulate particles again at rate λ. We take X_0, X_1, X_2 to be the intervals between successive reversals of the counters. Then the $\{X_i\}$ form a Markov chain that has a stationary distribution if and only if $\mu > \lambda$.

4.5.11. *mth-order dependence.* Suppose that the intervals form an *m*th-order Markov chain. Then in place of the process $\mathbf{X}(t) = (L(t), R(t))$ we may consider the process $\mathbf{X}(t) = (L_{-m+1}(t), \ldots, L_{-1}(t), L(t), R(t))$, where the state is defined as the set of $(m - 1)$ preceding intervals, the current interval, and the forward recurrence time. The regenerative homing set conditions can be applied to the discrete time vector process with state $\mathbf{U}_n = (X_{n-m+1}, \ldots, X_{n-1}, X_n)$, which is Markovian in the simple sense. Establish analogues to Theorem 4.5.III and its corollaries [see Chong (1981) for details].

4.6. Hazard Measures and Conditional Intensities

When the lifetime distribution function $F(\cdot)$ is absolutely continuous with density $f(\cdot)$, an important role is played by the hazard function $q(x) = f(x)/S(x)$ [cf. (1.1.3)], particularly in applications relating to risk.

In this section we develop some properties of hazard functions and their extensions to *hazard measures* in the nonabsolutely continuous case. In the case of a renewal or Wold process, a point process can be entirely characterized by the hazard measure. It is the central concept also in estimating the time to the next renewal. This section may also be regarded as a forerunner of the general discussion of conditional intensities and compensators in Chapter 13.

It is convenient to start with statements of two results for Lebesgue–Stieltjes integrals. The first is just the formula for integration by parts in the Lebesgue–Stieltjes calculus. The second is much more remarkable: it is the *exponential formula*, which has been used mainly in connection with martingale theory without its being in any sense a martingale result; it is in fact a straightforward (if unexpected) theorem in classical real analysis.

Lemma 4.6.I (Integration by Parts Formula). *Let $F(x)$, $G(x)$ be monotonic increasing right-continuous functions of $x \in \mathbb{R}$. Then*

$$(4.6.1) \qquad \int_a^b F(x)dG(x) = F(b)G(b) - F(a)G(a) - \int_a^b G(x-)dF(x).$$

This is a standard result on Lebesgue–Stieltjes integrals; it can be proved directly from first principles, or as an application of Fubini's theorem [e.g., see Brémaud (1981, p. 336)]. Note in particular the intervention of the left-continuous function $G(x-)$ in the last term of (4.6.1), and the convention for Lebesgue–Stieltjes integrals that

$$\int_a^b u(x)dG(x) = \int_{-\infty}^{\infty} I_{(a,b]}(x)u(x)dG(x);$$

if it is desired to incorporate the contribution from a jump of G at a itself, the integral would have to be written

$$\int_{a-}^b u(x)dG(x);$$

similarly,

$$\int_a^{b-} u(x)dG(x)$$

would exclude the contribution from any jump of G at b.

It is also important to note that *the lemma extends immediately to the situation where F and G are right-continuous functions of bounded variation.* This is because any such function can be written as the difference of two monotonic increasing right-continuous functions, $F = F_1 - F_2$ say; hence, the extended version of (4.6.1) follows by linearity.

Lemma 4.6.II (Exponential Formula). *Suppose $F(x)$ is a monotonic increasing right-continuous function of $x \in \mathbb{R}$ and that $u(x)$ is a measurable function for which $\int_0^t |u(x)|dF(x) < \infty$ for each $t > 0$. Writing $\{x_i\}$ for the set of discontinuities of F in $[0, \infty)$, $\Delta F(x_i) = F(x_i) - F(x_i-)$, and $F_c(x) = F(x) - \sum_{0 < x_i \leq t} \Delta F(x_i)$ for the continuous part of $F(\cdot)$, the function*

$$(4.6.2) \qquad H(t) = H(0)\exp\left(\int_0^t u(x)dF_c(x)\right) \prod_{0 < x_i \leq t} (1 + u(x_i)\Delta F(x_i))$$

is the unique solution in $t \geq 0$ of the integral equation

$$(4.6.3) \qquad \qquad H(t) = H(0) + \int_0^t H(x-)u(x)dF(x)$$

satisfying $\sup_{0 \leq s \leq t} |H(s)| < \infty$ for each $t > 0$.

A sketch proof may be outlined as follows [cf. Bremaud (1981, pp. 336–339)]. Write

$$G_1(t) = H(0) \prod_{0 < x_i \leq t} (1 + u(x_i))\Delta F(x_i)$$

and

$$G_2(t) = \exp\left(\int_0^t u(x)dF_c(x)\right);$$

then the relation between (4.6.2) and (4.6.3) can be seen as an application of the integration by parts formula to obtain an expression for $G_1(t)G_2(t)$, noting that $G_1(\cdot)$ increases by jumps only at the points $t = x_i$, where in fact the jump is equal to

$$G_1(x_i) - G_1(x_i-) = (1 + u(x_i))G_1(x_i-) - G_1(x_i-) = u(x_i)G_1(x_i-).$$

To show that (4.6.2) is the unique bounded solution to (4.6.3), let

$$D(t) = H_1(t) - H_2(t)$$

be the difference between any two bounded solutions. Then $D(t)$ itself is bounded in every finite interval, and we can form the estimate, using (4.6.3) and fixing finite s and t with $0 < s < t$,

$$|D(s)| \leq \int_0^s |D(x-)||u(x)|dF(x) \leq M \int_0^s |u(x)|dF(x),$$

where

$$M = \sup_{0 \leq s \leq t} |D(s)|.$$

Now feeding this estimate back into (4.6.3) we obtain

$$|D(s)| \leq M \int_0^s \left(\int_0^x |u(y)|dF(y)\right)|u(x)|dF(x)$$

$$\leq \frac{M}{2}\left(\int_0^s |u(x)|dF(x)\right)^2.$$

Evidently this iteration may be continued and yields for general $n \geq 1$

$$|D(s)| \leq \frac{M}{n!}\left(\int_0^s |u(x)|dF(x)\right)^n.$$

This last expression converges to zero as $n \to \infty$, so $D(s) \equiv 0$.

Again, *the argument can be extended to the case that F is a function of bounded variation*, for it depends only on the use of the formula for integration by parts and the estimate, for any bounded interval A,

$$\left| \int_A u(x)dF(x) \right| \le \int_A |u(x)| dV_F(x),$$

where V_F is the total variation of F.

We now specialize these results to the case that F is a distribution function of a positive random variable [so $F(0+) = 0$, $F(\infty) = \lim_{x \to \infty} F(x) \le 1$].

Definition 4.6.III. The *hazard measure* $Q(\cdot)$ associated with the distribution F on $[0, \infty)$ is the measure on $[0, \infty)$ for which

$$Q(dx) = \frac{F(dx)}{S(x-)};$$

in integrated form, the *integrated hazard function* (IHF) is the function

$$Q(t) = \int_0^t (1 - F(x-))^{-1} \, dF(x).$$

In the case that F has a density f, we have simply

$$Q(t) = \int_0^t q(x)dx = -\log S(t),$$

where $q(x)$ is the hazard function and $S(x) = 1 - F(x)$ is the survivor function of F. However, this logarithmic relation holds only in the continuous case; in the discrete case, it must be replaced by a relation analogous to (4.6.2) (Kotz and Shanbhag, 1980).

Proposition 4.6.IV. *The IHF of a right-continuous d.f. F is monotonic increasing and right continuous, and at each discontinuity x_i of F it has a jump of height*

$$\Delta Q(x_i) = \frac{\Delta F(x_i)}{S(x_i-)} \le 1.$$

Conversely, any monotonic increasing right-continuous nonnegative function Q with discontinuities of magnitude < 1, save perhaps for a final discontinuity of size 1, can be the IHF of some d.f. F given by the inversion formula

$$(4.6.4) \qquad S(t) = 1 - F(t) = \prod_{0 \le x_i \le t} (1 - \Delta Q(x_i)) \exp\left(-\int_0^t dQ_c(x) \right),$$

where $\Delta Q(x_i)$ is the jump of Q at its discontinuity x_i and Q_c is the continuous part of Q.

PROOF. Given a d.f. F on $[0, \infty)$, observe first that when F has a jump $\Delta F(x_i)$ at the discontinuity x_i, the corresponding jump in the IHF is $\Delta F(x_i)/S(x_i-)$ by Definition 4.6.III. Since $\Delta F(x_i) = F(x_i) - F(x_i-) \le 1 - F(x_i-) = S(x_i-)$ with equality if and only if $F(x_i) = 1$, that is, x_i is a discontinuity of F and is the supremum of the support of F, we must have $\Delta Q(x_i) \le 1$ with equality possible only for such x_i.

The inversion formula (4.6.4) is an immediate application of the exponential formula. To see this, we have from Definition 4.6.III

$$dF(x_i) = S(x_i-)dQ(x_i)$$

with

$$S(t) = 1 - F(t) = 1 - \int_0^t dF(x) = 1 - \int_0^t S(x-)dQ(x).$$

Taking $u(x) = -1$ in (4.6.3), $S(\cdot)$ is the unique solution of the equation satisfying $\int_0^t |S(x)|dQ(x) < \infty$ for $t < \infty$, so (4.6.4) holds. $\qquad \square$

Corollary 4.6.V. *The distribution F is uniquely determined by its IHF and conversely.*

The important interpretation of the hazard function in the context of a renewal process is that it represents the risk of an event occurring in the next short time interval, given the time elapsed since the last renewal; that is, $q(x)dt = \Pr\{\text{event in } t, t + dt | \text{ last event at } t - x\}$. For a stationary Poisson process, the risk is everywhere constant. If the lifetime distribution has a jump at x, then we should think of the risk as having a delta function component at x, the weight associated with the delta function being given by $\Delta Q(x)$ as above. In a Wold process, the risk has to be conditioned not only by the time since the last event but also by the length of the most recently observed complete interval.

EXAMPLE 4.6(a) *Wold process with exponential conditional distributions.* Wold (1948) and Cox (1955) both considered processes with Markov dependent intervals, where the transition kernel has the form

$$P(x, dy) = p(x, y)dy = \lambda(x)\exp[-\lambda(x)y]dy \qquad (x, y > 0),$$

corresponding to the assumption that conditionally on the length of the previous interval, the current interval is exponentially distributed with parameter $\lambda(x)$, x being the length of the previous interval.

   In this case, if we observe the process at time t and the length of the last completed interval x, the risk is constant at $\lambda(x)$ until the occurrence of the next event. As a stochastic process, the conditional risk appears as a step function, constant over intervals, the constant for any one interval being a function of the length of the preceding interval.

   See also Exercise 4.5.8.

EXAMPLE 4.6(b) *Prediction of the time to the next event in a renewal process.* Suppose that the lifetime distribution of a renewal process is absolutely continuous with hazard function $q(x)$, and that we observe the process at time t with x the time back to the last event. Then the distribution of the time to the next event has hazard function

$$q_x(y) = q(x + y) \qquad (y \geq 0)$$

with corresponding distribution function

$$F_x(y) = 1 - \exp\left(-\int_0^y q(x + u)du\right).$$

In general, the distribution of the time to the next event will be given by the corresponding modification of (4.6.4), namely,

$$S_x(y) = \prod_{x \leq x_i \leq x+y} (1 - \Delta Q(x_i)) \exp\left(-\int_x^{x+y} dQ_c(u)\right).$$

Clearly, the ideas in these two examples can be generalized to situations where the dependence on the past extends to more than just the time since the last event or the length of the last completed interval. Taken in full generality, they lead to the concept of the conditional intensity function explored in Chapter 13.

CHAPTER 5

Finite Point Processes

The Poisson process can be generalized in many directions. We have already discussed some consequences of relaxing the independency assumptions while retaining those of stationarity and orderliness of a point process on the line. In this chapter we examine generalizations in another direction, stemming from the observation in Chapter 2 that, for a Poisson process, conditional on the total number of points in a bounded region of time or space, the individual points can be treated as independently and identically distributed over the region. This prompts an alternative approach to specifying the structure of point processes in a bounded domain or, more generally, of *any point process in which the total number of points is finite with probability 1*. Such a process is called a *finite point process*.

The approach suggested is first to specify the distribution of the total number N of points and then, given N, to specify the joint distribution of the N points over the region. This stepwise approach leads to the problem of finding, in terms of these initial specifications, the distributions, correlations, and so on of the numbers of points falling into various subregions.

Such finite point processes arise naturally as models for populations of animals, insects, and plants in the ecological field and as models for particle processes in physics, which was also the context of the first general theory of point processes given by Moyal (1962a) following earlier work by Yvon (1935), Bogoliubov (1946), Janossy (1950), Bhabha (1950), and Ramakrishnan (1950).

In this chapter we give a somewhat informal introduction to structure theorems and applications of finite point processes. In contrast to the methods of the previous two chapters, the order properties of the real line play no role in the present discussion, and the theory can be developed as easily for a general state space as it can for the real line. On the other hand, a special feature of this work is its dependence on combinatorial arguments. The reader may find it helpful to brush up on the definitions of binomial and multinomial coefficients and their relation to the numbers of ways of sorting n objects into various subsets. Closely related to these ideas are the results collected together in Section 5.2, concerning some basic tools for handling discrete distributions: factorial moments and cumulants and their relation with probability generating functions. The importance of this material for the theory of point processes would be hard to overemphasize; not only the results of this chapter, but also the general theory presented in subsequent chapters, with all the apparatus of moment measures and generating functionals, may be seen as extensions of the results for discrete distributions summarized below.

5.1. An Elementary Example: Independently and Identically Distributed Clusters

We start with an elementary example that may help to illustrate and motivate the more general discussion. Let a random number N of particles be independently and identically distributed (i.i.d.) over a Euclidean space $\mathscr{X}$ according to some common probability measure $F(\cdot)$ on the Borel sets of $\mathscr{X}$. Then, given N, the number of particles in any subregion A is found by "binomial sampling:" with probability $p = F(A)$, each particle may fall in A, independently of the others, so that, conditional on N, the number of particles in A has the binomial distribution

$$p(n; A | N) = \binom{N}{n} (F(A))^n (1 - F(A))^{N-n}.$$

Similarly, given any finite partition $A_1, \ldots, A_k$ of $\mathscr{X}$, the joint distribution of the numbers of particles is given by

$$p(n_1, \ldots, n_k; A_1, \ldots, A_k | N) = \binom{N}{n_1 \ldots n_k} (F(A_1))^{n_1} \ldots (F(A_k))^{n_k}.$$

Unconditionally, the joint distribution of the numbers $N(A_1), \ldots, N(A_k)$ of particles in $A_1, \ldots, A_k$ is found by averaging over N:

$$\Pr\{N(A_i) = n_i \, (i = 1, \ldots, k)\} = \sum_{n=0}^{\infty} \Pr\{N = n\} p(n_1, \ldots, n_k; A_1, \ldots, A_k | n).$$

The procedure just outlined is most readily carried out in terms of generating functions. Let $P_N(z) = E(z^N)$ and write for convenience $p_i = F(A_i)$. Then the joint p.g.f. of $N(A_i) \, (i = 1, \ldots, k)$ is

(5.1.1) $$P(A_1, \ldots, A_k; z_1, \ldots, z_k) \equiv E(z_1^{N(A_1)} \cdots z_k^{N(A_k)})$$

$$= P_N(p_1 z_1 + \cdots + p_k z_k).$$

If $\{A_1, \ldots, A_k\}$ is not a partition but still a set of mutually disjoint subregions, then

(5.1.2)

$$P(A_1, \ldots, A_k; z_1, \ldots, z_k) = P_N(p_1 z_1 + \cdots + p_k z_k + (1 - p_1 - \cdots - p_k));$$

in effect we have introduced a further subset $A_{k+1} = (A_1 \cup \cdots \cup A_k)^c$ and set $z_{k+1} = 1$ on A_{k+1}.

As special cases, when N is Poisson distributed with parameter λ, the $N(A_i)$ are independent Poisson random variables with parameters $\lambda F(A_i)$. In this case (5.1.1) reduces to the identity

$$P(A_1, \ldots, A_k; z_1, \ldots, z_k) = \exp\left(\lambda\left[\sum_1^k z_i F(A_i) - 1\right]\right)$$

$$= \prod_1^k \exp(\lambda F(A_i)(z_i - 1)).$$

When N has a negative binomial distribution on $\{0, 1, \ldots\}$ so that $P_N(z) = (1 + \mu(1 - z))^{-\alpha}$ for some μ, $\alpha > 0$, $\{N(A_i)\}$ is a set of mutually correlated negative binomial random variables with joint p.g.f.

$$P(A_1, \ldots, A_k; z_1, \ldots, z_k) = \left(1 + \mu\sum_1^k F(A_i)(1 - z_i)\right)^{-\alpha}.$$

In particular, from (5.1.2), the distribution of $N(A_i)$ itself has the p.g.f.

$$P(A_i; z) = [1 + \mu F(A_i)(1 - z)]^{-\alpha}$$

and is again negative binomial with parameters $\mu F(A_i)$, α.

It is not only the distributions of the $N(A_i)$ that may be of interest, but also their moments. Consider, for example, the problem of finding the covariance of the numbers of points in two complementary subsets A_1, $A_2 = A_1^c$. For any given N, we have from the binomial sampling property that

$$E[N(A_1)N(A_2)|N] = N(N - 1)F(A_1)(1 - F(A_1)) = N(N - 1)F(A_1)F(A_2).$$

Hence,

(5.1.3) $$E(N(A_1)N(A_2)) = m_{[2]}F(A_1)F(A_2)$$

and

(5.1.4) $$\text{Cov}(N(A_1), N(A_2)) = c_{[2]}F(A_1)F(A_2),$$

where $m_{[2]}$ is the second factorial moment, and $c_{[2]}$ the second factorial cumulant, of the total number N of points. In the Poisson case, the covariance is zero, and in the negative binomial case it is positive: both contrast with the more familiar case of fixed N when the covariance is clearly negative.

Note that both the second moment and the covariance have the form of a measure evaluated on the product set $A_1 \times A_2$. This is also the case in general and anticipates the introduction of factorial moment and cumulant measures in Section 5.4.

5.2. Factorial Moments, Cumulants, and Generating Function Relations for Discrete Distributions

Factorial moments and cumulants are natural tools for handling nonnegative, integer-valued random variables, a characteristic they bequeath to their off-spring, the factorial moment and cumulant measures, in the point process context. We begin by recalling some basic definitions.

For any integers n and r, the *factorial powers* of n, written $n^{[r]}$, may be defined by

$$n^{[r]} = \begin{cases} n(n-1)\cdots(n-r+1) & r = 0, \ldots, n, \\ 0 & r > n. \end{cases}$$

We then have the following definition.

Definition 5.2.I. For $r = 0, 1, \ldots,$ the rth *factorial moment* $m_{[r]}$ of the non-negative integer-valued random variable N is $m_{[r]} \equiv E(N^{[r]})$.

Thus, when N has probability distribution $\{p_n\} = \{\Pr\{N = n\}\}$,

$$(5.2.1) \qquad\qquad m_{[r]} = \sum_{n=0}^{\infty} n^{[r]} p_n.$$

Consequently, when the distribution is concentrated on a finite range $0, 1, \ldots,$ n_0, all factorial moments of order larger than n_0 are zero.

It is useful to be able to convert from factorial moments to ordinary moments and back again. The coefficients that arise in these conversions are the *Stirling numbers of the first and second kinds*, defined, respectively, as the coefficients arising in the expansion of $x^{[r]}$ and x^r in powers or factorial powers of x, where, by analogy with the definition of $n^{[r]}$,

$$x^{[r]} = x(x - 1)\cdots(x - r + 1)$$

for any real x and positive integer r. We follow the notation of David and Barton (1962) in denoting them by $D_{j,r}$ and $\Delta_{j,r}$.

Definition 5.2.II. The Stirling numbers of the first kind $D_{j,r}$ and second kind $\Delta_{j,r}$ are defined by the relations

$$(5.2.2) \qquad\qquad n^{[r]} = \sum_{j=1}^{r} D_{j,r} n^j (-1)^{r-j} \qquad (n \geq r),$$

$$(5.2.3) \qquad\qquad n^r = \sum_{j=1}^{r} \Delta_{j,r} n^{[j]} \qquad (n \geq r).$$

Replacing n in (5.2.2) and (5.2.3) by the random variable N and taking expectations, we obtain the corresponding relations between moments:

$$(5.2.4) \qquad\qquad m_{[r]} = \sum_{j=1}^{r} D_{j,r} m_j (-1)^{r-j},$$

$$(5.2.5) \qquad m_r \equiv EN^r = \sum_{j=1}^{r} \Delta_{j,r} m_{[j]}.$$

It is clear that for a nonnegative random variable the rth factorial moment is finite if and only if the ordinary rth moment is finite.

Some useful recurrence relations for the Stirling numbers are given in Exercise 5.2.1. For further properties, relation to Bernoulli numbers, and so on, we refer to David and Barton (1962, Chap. 15) and texts on finite differences.

The factorial moments of the random variable N are related to the Taylor series expansion of the p.g.f.

$$P(z) = E(z^N) \qquad (|z| \leq 1)$$

about $z = 1$ in much the same way as the ordinary moments arise in the expansion of the characteristic or moment generating function about the origin.

Proposition 5.2.III. *For a nonnegative integer-valued random variable N whose kth factorial moment is finite, the p.g.f. is expressible as*

$$(5.2.6) \qquad P(1 + \eta) = 1 + \sum_{r=1}^{k} \frac{m_{[r]} \eta^r}{r!} + o(\eta^k)$$

for all η such that $|1 + \eta| \leq 1$. The complete Taylor series expansion of the p.g.f.,

$$(5.2.7) \qquad P(1 + \eta) = 1 + \sum_{r=1}^{\infty} \frac{m_{[r]} \eta^r}{r!}$$

is valid for some nonzero η if and only if all moments exist and the series at (5.2.7) has nonzero radius of convergence in η; equivalently, if and only if the p.g.f. $P(z)$ is analytic in a disk $|z| < 1 + \varepsilon$ for some $\varepsilon > 0$. Equation (5.2.7) then holds for $|\eta| < \varepsilon$.

PROOF. To establish (5.2.6), write

$$(1 + \eta)^N = 1 + \sum_{r=1}^{k} \frac{N^{[r]} \eta^r}{r!} + R_k(N, \eta) \qquad (k = 1, 2, \ldots)$$

for some remainder term $R_k(N, \eta)$, which we proceed to investigate. For $k = 0$, set

$$R_0(N, \eta) = (1 + \eta)^N - 1$$

and observe that $|R_0(N, \eta)| \leq 2$ under the condition of the theorem that $|1 + \eta| \leq 1$. For general $k = 1, 2, \ldots$, repeated integration of $R_0(N, \cdot)$ shows that

$$|R_k(N, \eta)/\eta^k| \leq 2N^{[k]}/k! \qquad (|1 + \eta| \leq 1).$$

Since the left-hand side of this inequality $\to 0$ $(\eta \to 0)$ for each fixed N, and the right-hand side has finite expectation under the assumption of the theorem, it follows by dominated convergence that $E(R_k(N, \eta)) = o(\eta^k)$, which is the result required.

To establish (5.2.7), consider the binomial expansion

$$(1 + \eta)^N = 1 + \sum_{r=1}^{\infty} \frac{N^{[r]}\eta^r}{r!}.$$

For $\eta > 0$, the finiteness of the expectation on the left is equivalent to requiring the p.g.f. to be analytic for $|z| < 1 + \eta$. When this condition is satisfied, it follows from Fubini's theorem that for such η the expectation can be taken inside the summation on the right, leading to the right-hand side of (5.2.7).

Conversely, suppose all moments exist and that the sum on the right-hand side of (5.2.7) is at least conditionally convergent for some nonzero η_0. Then $m_{[r]}\eta_0^r/r! \to 0$ as $r \to \infty$, and it follows from a standard power series argument that the series at (5.2.7) is absolutely convergent for $|\eta| < |\eta_0|$ and so defines an analytic function of η there. Since each $m_{[r]} = EN^{[r]}$ is nonnegative we can now take any positive $\eta < |\eta_0|$ and use Fubini's theorem to reverse the argument used earlier to deduce that because (5.2.7) holds for all $0 \le \eta < |\eta_0|$, $P(z)$, being a power series with nonnegative terms, has its first singularity on the positive half-line outside $|z| < 1 + |\eta_0|$.   □

In the sequel we also require the version of Proposition 5.2.III in which the remainder term is bounded by a term proportional to the $(k + 1)$th moment. The proof, which is along similar lines, is left as an exercise. An alternative approach is indicated in Exercise 5.2.2.

A similar expansion holds for $\log P(1 + \eta)$, the coefficients of $\eta^r/r!$ being the *factorial cumulants* $c_{[r]}$ $(r = 1, 2, \ldots)$. If $P(\cdot)$ is analytic in a disk as below (5.2.7), then the infinite expansion

$$(5.2.8a) \qquad\qquad \log P(1 + \eta) = \sum_{r=1}^{\infty} \frac{c_{[r]}\eta^r}{r!}$$

is valid, while under the more limited assumption that $m_k < \infty$, we have the finite Taylor series expansion

$$(5.2.8b) \qquad \log P(1 + \eta) = \sum_{r=1}^{k} \frac{c_{[r]}\eta^r}{r!} + o(\eta^k) \qquad (\eta \to 0)$$

valid for $|1 + \eta| < 1$: verification is left to the reader.

The factorial cumulants are related to the factorial moments by the same relations as hold between ordinary cumulants and moments. The first few relations between the ordinary cumulants c_r, central moments m_r', and factorial moments and cumulants are useful to list, as below:

$$(5.2.9a) \quad c_{[1]} = c_1 = \mu = m_{[1]},$$

$$(5.2.9b) \quad c_{[2]} = c_2 - c_1 = \sigma^2 - \mu = m_{[2]} - m_{[1]}^2,$$

$$(5.2.9c) \quad c_{[3]} = c_3 - 3c_2 + 2c_1 = m_3' - 3\sigma^2 + 2\mu = m_{[3]} - 3m_{[2]}m_{[1]} + 2m_{[1]}^2.$$

Generally, the factorial moments and cumulants provide a much simpler description of the moment properties of a discrete distribution than do the ordinary moments. In particular, for the Poisson distribution $\{p_n(\lambda)\}$,

$$m_{[r]} = \lambda^r, \quad c_{[1]} = \lambda, \quad c_{[r]} = 0 \quad (r = 2, 3, \ldots).$$

This vanishing of the factorial cumulants of the Poisson distribution is reminiscent of the vanishing of the ordinary cumulants of the normal distribution and is perhaps one indication of why the Poisson process plays such an outstanding role in the theory of point processes.

There are in fact four expansions of the p.g.f. of possible interest, according to whether we expand $P(z)$ itself or its logarithm, and whether the expansion is about $z = 0$ or $z = 1$. The expansions about $z = 1$ yield the factorial moments and factorial cumulants, and the expansion of $P(z)$ about $z = 0$ yields the probability distribution $\{p_n\}$. This leaves the expansion of $\log P(z)$ about $z = 0$, an expansion that, while rarely used, has an important interpretation in the case of an infinitely divisible (compound Poisson) distribution. Since the analogous expansion for the p.g.fl. ($\equiv$ probability generating functional) of a point process is also important, again in the context of infinite divisibility, we now consider this last case in some detail.

Proposition 5.2.IV. *If $p_0 > 0$, the p.g.f. $P(\cdot)$ can be written in the form*

$$(5.2.10) \qquad \log P(z) = -q_0 + \sum_{n=1}^{\infty} q_n z^n \qquad (|z| < R)$$

where $p_0 = e^{-q_0}$ and R is the distance from the origin to the nearest zero or singularity of $P(z)$. When $P(\cdot)$ is the p.g.f. of a compound Poisson distribution, the terms q_n are nonnegative and $q_0 = \sum_{n=1}^{\infty} q_n$, so the sequence $\{\pi_n: n = 1, 2, \ldots\} \equiv \{q_n/q_0\}$ can be interpreted as the probability distribution of the cluster size, given that the cluster is nonempty; in this case (5.2.10) can be rewritten as

$$\log P(z) = -q_0 \sum_{n=1}^{\infty} \pi_n(1 - z^n) \qquad (|z| < R).$$

PROOF. The structure of the compound Poisson distribution follows from the analysis in Chapter 2 (see Theorem 2.2.II and Exercise 2.2.2). The other remarks are standard properties of power series expansions of analytic functions. $\square$

EXAMPLE 5.2(a). To illustrate these various expansions consider the negative binomial distribution p.g.f.

$$P(z) = (1 + \mu(1 - z))^{-\alpha} \qquad (\mu > 0, \alpha > 0, |z| \leq 1).$$

Putting $z = 1 + \eta$, we find

$$P(1 + \eta) = (1 - \mu\eta)^{-\alpha} = 1 + \sum_{r=1}^{\infty} \binom{\alpha + r - 1}{r} \mu^r \eta^r$$

so that

$$m_{[r]} = \alpha(\alpha + 1)\cdots(\alpha + r - 1)\mu^r.$$

Taking logarithms,

$$\log P(1 + \eta) = -\alpha \log(1 - \mu\eta) = \alpha \sum_{r=1}^{\infty} \frac{\mu^r\eta^r}{r}$$

so that

$$c_{[r]} = (r - 1)!\,\alpha\mu^r.$$

For the expansions about $z = 0$ we have

$$P(z) = (1 + \mu)^{-\alpha}\left(1 - \frac{\mu z}{1 + \mu}\right)^{-\alpha} = (1 + \mu)^{-\alpha} \sum_{n=0}^{\infty} \binom{\alpha + n - 1}{n}\left(\frac{\mu z}{1 + \mu}\right)^n,$$

so

$$p_n = \binom{\alpha + n - 1}{n}(1 + \mu)^{-\alpha}\left(\frac{\mu}{1 + \mu}\right)^n,$$

and

$$\log P(z) = -\alpha \log(1 + \mu) - \alpha \log\left(1 - \frac{\mu z}{1 + \mu}\right)$$

$$= -[\alpha \log(1 + \mu)]\left(1 - \sum_{n=1}^{\infty} \pi_n z^n\right),$$

where $\pi_n = [n \log(1 + \mu)]^{-1}[\mu/(1 + \mu)]^n$. Clearly, these $\{\pi_n\}$ constitute a probability distribution, namely, the logarithmic distribution, illustrating the well-known fact that the negative binomial is infinitely divisible and hence must be expressible as a compound Poisson distribution.

Corresponding to the four possible expansions referred to above, there are 12 sets of conversion relations between the different coefficients. One of these, the expression for factorial moments in terms of the probabilities, is a matter of definition: what can be said about the others?

Formally, either expansion about $z = 1$ can be converted to an expansion about $z = 0$ by a change of variable and expansion, for example, in (formally) expressing the probabilities in terms of the factorial moments via

$$P(z) = 1 + \sum_{r=1}^{\infty} \frac{m_{[r]}(z - 1)^r}{r!};$$

expanding $(z - 1)^r$ and equating coefficients of z^n, we obtain

$$p_n = \sum_{r \geq n} (-1)^{r-n} \frac{m_{[r]}}{r!}\binom{r}{n},$$

or, in the more symmetrical form,

$$(5.2.11) \qquad n! \, p_n = \sum_{r=n}^{\infty} (-1)^{r-n} \frac{m_{[r]}}{(r-n)!} = \sum_{r=0}^{\infty} (-1)^r \frac{m_{[n+r]}}{r!}.$$

This relation may be compared with its converse

$$(5.2.12) \qquad m_{[r]} = \sum_{n=r}^{\infty} n^{[r]} p_n = \sum_{n=0}^{\infty} \frac{J_{r+n}}{n!},$$

where $J_{n+r} = (n+r)! \, P_{n+r}$. Thus, to display the symmetry in these (formal) relations to best advantage we need to use the quantities J_n, which are analogues of the Janossy measures to be introduced in Section 5.3.

Under what circumstances can the converse relation (5.2.11) be established rigorously? In general, for the derivation above we must be able to expand $P(z)$ about $z = 1$ in a disk $|z - 1| < 1 + \varepsilon$ for some $\varepsilon > 0$, requiring $P(z)$ itself to be analytic at all points on the line segment $(-\varepsilon, 2 + \varepsilon)$. Since $P(z)$ has nonnegative coefficients, its radius of convergence is determined by the first singularity on the positive real axis. Consequently, it suffices in order for (5.2.II) to hold for all $r = 0, 1, \ldots$ that $P(z)$ should be analytic in the disk $|z| < 2 + \varepsilon$ for some $\varepsilon > 0$.

A finite version of (5.2.11) with remainder term is due to Fréchet (1940); extensions are given in Takacs (1967) and Galambos (1975) (see also Daley and Narayan, 1980). We give a simple result in the theorem below, with some extensions left to the Exercises 5.2.2–5.2.4.

Proposition 5.2.V. *If the distribution $\{p_n\}$ has all its moments finite and its p.g.f. $P(z)$ is convergent in a disk $|z| < 2 + \varepsilon$ for some $\varepsilon > 0$, then (5.2.11) holds. Without assuming such analyticity, the finiteness of $m_{[k]}$ ensures that for integers $n = 0, 1, \ldots, k - 1$,*

$$(5.2.13a) \qquad n! \, p_n = \sum_{r=n}^{k-1} (-1)^{r-n} \frac{m_{[r]}}{(r-n)!} + R_k^{(n)},$$

where

$$(5.2.13b) \qquad 0 \le (-1)^{k-n} R_k^{(n)} \le m_{[k]}/(k-n)!,$$

while if all moments are finite and for some integer n_0

$$(5.2.14a) \qquad m_{[k]} = o((k - n_0)!) \qquad (k \to \infty),$$

then

$$(5.2.14b) \qquad \lim_{k \to \infty} \sum_{r=n}^{k} (-1)^{r-n} \frac{m_{[r]}}{(r-n)!}$$

exists for $n = 0, \ldots, n_0$ and the formal relation (5.2.11) holds for such n.

PROOF. When $P(z)$ is analytic for $|z| < 2 + \varepsilon$, the expansion

$$P(z) = \sum_{r=0}^{\infty} \frac{m_{[r]}(z-1)^r}{r!}$$

is valid for $|z - 1| < 1 + \varepsilon$, within which region, and at $z = 0$ in particular, it can be differentiated n times, leading at once to (5.2.11).

Under the weaker condition that $m_{[k]} < \infty$, n-fold differentiation in the definition $P(z) = E(z^N)$ is possible for all $|z| \le 1$ for $n = 1, \ldots, k$, leading to $P^{(n)}(z) = E(N^{[n]}z^{N-n})$. Now $P^{(n)}(z)$ is differentiable in $|z| \le 1$ $k - n$ times, and so the Taylor series expansion

$$P^{(n)}(z) = \sum_{r=0}^{k-n-1} \frac{(z - 1)^r P^{(n+r)}(1)}{r!} + \frac{(z - 1)^{k-n} P^{(k)}(1 + (z - 1)v)}{(k - n)!}$$

holds for real z in $|z| \le 1$ for some $v \equiv v(z)$ in $(0, 1)$. In particular, (5.2.13a) results on putting $z = 0$ with

$$R_k^{(n)} = (-1)^{k-n} \frac{E(N^{[k]}(1 - v)^{N-k})}{(k - n)!},$$

from which relation the inequalities at (5.2.13b) follow. When (5.2.14) holds, $R_k^{(n)} \to 0$ $(k \to \infty)$ for each fixed n, and hence (5.2.11) holds in the sense indicated.   □

The Bonferroni inequalities result as special cases of (5.2.13) as indicated in Exercise 5.2.5.

Similar relations can be obtained between the factorial cumulants and the quantities π_n of Proposition 5.2.IV. Thus, when $\log P(z)$ is analytic in a disk $|z| < 1 + \varepsilon$ for some $\varepsilon > 0$, r-fold differentiation of (5.2.10) and setting $z = 1$ yield

(5.2.15) $c_{[r]} = \sum_{n=r}^{\infty} q_n n^{[r]} = q_0 \mu_{[r]},$

where $\mu_{[r]}$ in the case of a compound Poisson process is the rth factorial moment of the cluster-size distribution. Reversing the exercise, when $\log P(z)$ is analytic in the disk $|z| < 2 + \varepsilon$, we have [cf. the derivation of (5.2.11)]

(5.2.16) $n! \, q_n = \sum_{r=n}^{\infty} (-1)^{r-n} \frac{c_{[r]}}{(r - n)!}.$

The most difficult relations to treat in a general form are those between the moments and cumulants, or between the $\{p_n\}$ and the $\{q_n\}$, which arise from taking exponentials or logarithms of a given series and expanding it by formal manipulation. The feature of these relations is that they involve partitions. For given positive integers j and k with $j \le k$ we define a j-partition of k as a partition of the set of k numbers $\{1, \ldots, k\}$ into j nonempty subsets. We use $\mathscr{P}_{jk}$ to denote the collection of all such j-partitions, and write $\mathscr{T} = \{S_1(\mathscr{T}), \ldots, S_j(\mathscr{T})\}$ for an element of $\mathscr{P}_{jk}$, noting that the order in which the subsets $S_i(\mathscr{T})$ are labelled or written is immaterial. Thus, for example, the collection of sets $\{1, 2, 4\}, \{3, 5\}, \{6, 8\}, \{7\}$ is a 4-partition of 8 and is the same as $\{1, 2, 4\}, \{6, 8\}, \{7\}, \{3, 5\}$. The following lemma is basic (e.g., see Andrews, 1976); in it, $|S_i(\mathcal{T})|$ denotes the number of elements in $S_i(\mathcal{T}) \subset \{1, \ldots, k\}$.

Lemma 5.2.VI. *Let $\{c_j; j = 1, 2, \ldots\}$ be a sequence of numbers with $\sum_{j=1}^{\infty} |c_j|/j! < \infty$. Then for all z with $|z| \le 1$,*

$$(5.2.17) \qquad \exp\left(\sum_{j=1}^{\infty} \frac{c_j z^j}{j!}\right) = \sum_{k=0}^{\infty} \frac{d_k z^k}{k!},$$

where $d_0 = 1$ and for $k = 1, 2, \ldots,$

$$(5.2.18) \qquad d_k = \sum_{j=1}^{k} \sum_{\mathcal{T} \in \mathscr{P}_{jk}} \prod_{i=1}^{j} c_{|S_i(\mathcal{T})|},$$

$$(5.2.19) \qquad c_k = \sum_{j=1}^{k} (-1)^{j-1}(j-1)! \sum_{\mathcal{T} \in \mathscr{P}_{jk}} \prod_{i=1}^{j} d_{|S_i(\mathcal{T})|}.$$

PROOF. Establishing (5.2.18) and (5.2.19) is essentially a matter of counting terms. For (5.2.18) consider the expansion $1 + \Sigma + \Sigma^2/2! + \cdots$ of the exponential in (5.2.17) (here, $\Sigma = \sum_{j=1}^{\infty} c_j z^j/j!$), and concentrate attention on all the terms in a specified product of coefficients such as $c_3 c_2^2 c_1$. Observe first that such terms involve z to the power of the sum of the indices, here $3 + 2 + 2 + 1 = 8$, and thus they contribute to the term d_8. Second, if we transfer the coefficient $1/k!$ of $d_k z^k$ to the multiplier $k!$ on the opposite side, each particular term $c_3 c_2^2 c_1$ is then multiplied by the ratio of factorials $8!/3! 2! 2! 1!$ arising from the factorials associated with the c_j and d_k. Third, the number of such terms obtained from expanding Σ^4 equals the multinomial coefficient $4!/1! 2! 1!$, which on division by the factorial $4!$ from the expansion of $\exp(\Sigma)$ leaves the factor $1/1! 2! 1!$. Thus, altogether the contribution of the coefficient of $c_3 c_2^2 c_1$ to d_8 is $8!/\{(3! 2! 2! 1!)(1! 2! 1!)\}$. On the other hand, in the expression asserted for d_k at (5.2.18), we have to look at 4-partitions of 8 into subsets of sizes 3, 2, 2, 1. The numbers of such subsets is just $8!/3! 2! 2! 1!$, which must be divided by 2! because there are two subsets of size 2. Thus, the coefficient of $c_3 c_2^2 c_1$ is of the form implied by (5.2.18).

Arguing this way in general establishes (5.2.18), and a similar kind of argument leads to (5.2.19). $\qquad\square$

We remark that the advantage of working with j-partitions, rather than with additive partitions as in David and Barton (1962), is that the counting procedure automatically takes into account repeated terms, without requiring explicit notation for the numbers of repetitions; such notation would make (5.2.18) and (5.2.19) appear much more cumbersome. Examples of full expansions are given in Exercises 5.2.6–5.2.8.

Corollary 5.2.VII. *(a) Factorial moments $m_{[k]}$ and factorial cumulants $c_{[k]}$ are related as at (5.2.18) and (5.2.19) via the substitutions $c_j = c_{[j]}$ and $d_k = m_{[k]}$.*

(b) In Equation (5.2.10) the probabilities p_n and q_n are also related as at (5.2.18) and (5.2.19) with $c_j = j!\, q_j/(-\log p_0)$, $d_k = k!\, p_k/p_0$.

Exercises

5.2.1. *Recurrence relations for Stirling numbers.* By using $n^{[r+1]} = (n - r)n^{[r]}$ show that

$$\Delta_{j,r+1} = j\Delta_{j,r} + \Delta_{j-1,r}, \quad \Delta_{1r} = 1 \quad (r \geq 1), \quad \Delta_{j0} = 0 \quad (j \geq 1),$$

$$D_{j,r+1} = rD_{j,r} + D_{j-1,r}, \quad D_{0r} = 0 \quad (r \geq 1), \quad D_{11} = 1, D_{j1} = 0 \quad (r \geq 2).$$

5.2.2. Show that when $P(z)$ is any p.g.f. with finite first moment $P'(1)$, the function $(1 - P(z))/P'(1)(1 - z)$ is also a p.g.f. Use this fact in an induction argument to show that (cf. Lemma 5.2.VI) when $m_{[k]} = P^{(k)}(1) < \infty$, the function $m_k(z)$ in the expansion

$$P(z) = 1 + \sum_{r=1}^{k-1} \frac{(z - 1)^r m_{[r]}}{r!} + \frac{(z - 1)^k m_k(z)}{k!}$$

equals $m_{[k]}$ times a p.g.f. Since $m_k(z) = m_{[k]} + o(1)$ as $z \to 1$ through values $|z| \leq 1$, (5.2.6) follows, as well as the alternative version with remainder bounded by $m_{[k]}$. Equations (5.2.13) can also be derived by n-fold differentiation of an expansion to $k - n$ terms (e.g., see Daley and Narayan, 1980).

5.2.3. Let the nonnegative integer-valued r.v. N have all factorial moments $m_{[r]}$ finite and $\lim \sup_{r \to \infty} (m_{[r]}/r!)^{1/r} = 1/\varepsilon$ for some $\varepsilon > 0$. Show that the p.g.f. $P(z)$ of N has radius of convergence $1 + \varepsilon$, and hence deduce that the moments $\{m_{[r]}\}$ determine the distribution of N uniquely. By relating the p.g.f. to the moment generating function, deduce that ε is related to $1/\varepsilon' \equiv \lim \sup_{r \to \infty} (m_r/r!)^{1/r}$ by $\varepsilon' = \log(1 + \varepsilon)$.

5.2.4. (Continuation) By using an analytic continuation technique (see Takács, 1965) it can be shown that when $\varepsilon > 0$,

$$p_n = \sum_{r=n}^{\infty} \binom{r}{n}(1 + z)^{-(r+1)} \sum_{s=n}^{r} (-1)^{s-n} \binom{r - n}{s - n} z^{r-s} \frac{m_{[s]}}{s!}$$

for any nonnegative $z > \varepsilon^{-2} - 1$.

5.2.5. *Bonferroni inequalities.* Let the r.v. N count the number of occurrences among a given set of v events $A_1, \ldots, A_v$. Show that

$$S_r \equiv \sum_{(r)} \Pr(A_i \cap A_j \cap \cdots) = E(N^{[r]})/r!,$$

where the summation $\sum_{(r)}$ extends over all $\binom{v}{r}$ distinct subsets $\{i, j, \ldots\}$ of size r from the index set $\{1, \ldots, v\}$. [*Hint:* Using indicator r.v.s, write

$$N^{[r]} = r! \sum_{(r)} I(A_i \cap A_j \cap \cdots),$$

where the $r!$ term arises from the $r!$ ordered subsets of $\{1, \ldots, v\}$ yielding the same (unordered) subset $\{i, j, \ldots\}$ containing r indices.] Deduce from (5.2.13) the Bonferroni inequalities

$$0 \leq S_n - \binom{n + 1}{1}S_{n+1} + \cdots + \binom{n + k}{k}S_{n+k} - p_n \leq \binom{n + k + 1}{k + 1}S_{n+k+1},$$

where k is an even integer [e.g., see Moran (1968, pp. 25–31)].

5.2.6. For given positive integers j and k with $j \leq k$, define $\mathscr{P}(j, k) = \{$positive integers $\{r_1, \ldots, r_p\}$ and $\{\pi_1, \ldots, \pi_p\}$ such that $\sum_{i=1}^{p} \pi_i = j$, $\sum_{i=1}^{p} \pi_i r_i = k\} = $ set of all j-partitions of k. Write the series (5.2.7) in the form $P = 1 + \Sigma$ so that

$$\log P(z) = \Sigma - \Sigma^2/2 + \Sigma^3/3 - \cdots,$$

and expand the series Σ^n as a multinomial expansion. By equating coefficients of z^k, show formally that the factorial cumulants in (5.2.8) are given by

$$c_{[k]} = k! \sum_{j=1}^{k} (-1)^{j-1}(j-1)! \sum_{\mathscr{P}(j,k)} (\pi_1! \cdots \pi_p!)^{-1} \left(\frac{m_{[r_1]}}{r_1!}\right)^{\pi_1} \cdots \left(\frac{m_{[r_p]}}{r_p!}\right)^{\pi_p}.$$

5.2.7. Apply Lemma 5.2.VI to show that

$$c_{[4]} = m_{[4]} - 4m_{[3]}m_{[1]} - 3m_{[2]}^2 + 12m_{[2]}m_{[1]}^2 - 6m_{[1]}^4,$$

$$m_{[4]} = c_{[4]} + 4c_{[3]}c_{[1]} + 3c_{[2]}^2 + 6c_{[2]}c_{[1]}^2 + c_{[1]}^4.$$

5.2.8. Investigate the use of Lemma 5.2.VI in deriving explicit expressions for probabilities of
  (i) the "doubly Poisson" compound Poisson distribution with p.g.f. $P(z) = \exp\{\mu[\exp(\lambda(z-1)) - 1]\}$;
  (ii) the Hermite distribution with p.g.f. $P(z) = \exp(az + bz^2)$ for appropriate constants a and b (cf. Milne and Westcott, 1988).

5.3. The General Finite Point Process: Definitions and Distributions

We now drop any special assumptions and suppose only that the following conditions hold concerning a finite point process.

Conditions 5.3.I. *(a) The points are located in a complete separable metric space (c.s.m.s.) $\mathscr{X}$, as, for example, $\mathscr{X} = R^d$. (b) A distribution $\{p_n\}$ $(n = 0, 1, \ldots)$ is given determining the total number of points in the population, with $\sum_{n=0}^{\infty} p_n = 1$. (c) For each integer $n \geq 1$, a probability distribution $\Pi_n(\cdot)$ is given on the Borel sets of $\mathscr{X}^{(n)} \equiv \mathscr{X} \times \cdots \times \mathscr{X}$, and it determines the joint distribution of the positions of the points of the process, given that their total number is n.*

Such a definition is both natural and powerful. In particular, it provides a *constructive* definition that could be used to simulate the process: first, generate a random number N according to the distribution $\{p_n\}$ (and note that $\Pr\{0 \leq N < \infty\} = 1$), and then, supposing $N = n$ and excepting the case $n = 0$ in which case there is nothing else to do, generate a random vector $(x_1, \ldots, x_n)$ according to the distribution $\Pi_n(\cdot)$.

At this stage the distinction between ordered and unordered sets of points should be clarified. In talking of stochastic point processes, we make the tacit assumption that we are dealing with *unordered* sets of points; that is, we talk of the probability of finding a given number k of points in a set A: we do not give names to the individual points and ask for the probability of finding k

specified individuals within the set A. Nevertheless, this latter approach is quite possible (indeed, natural) in contexts where the points refer to individual particles, animals, plants, and so on. Moreover, it is actually this latter point of view that is implicit in the above conditions, for as yet there is nothing in them to prevent x_1 say, that is, the first point or particle named, from taking its place preferentially in some part of the space, leaving the other particles to distribute themselves elsewhere.

To be consistent with treating point processes as a theory of unordered sets, we stipulate that the distributions $\Pi_n(\cdot)$ should give equal weight to all $n!$ permutations of the coordinates of $(x_1, \ldots, x_n)$, or in other words, $\Pi_n(\cdot)$ should be symmetric. If this is not already the case in Condition 5.3.I(c) it is easily achieved by introducing the symmetrized form for any partition $(A_1, \ldots, A_n)$ of $\mathcal{X}$

$$(5.3.1) \qquad \Pi_n^{\text{sym}}(A_1 \times \cdots \times A_n) = (n!)^{-1} \sum_{\text{perm}} \Pi_n(A_{i_1} \times \cdots \times A_{i_n}),$$

where the summation $\sum_{\text{perm}}$ is taken over all $n!$ permutations $(i_1, \ldots, i_n)$ of the integers $(1, \ldots, n)$ and the normalizing factor $(n!)^{-1}$ ensures that the resulting measure still has total mass unity.

An alternative notation, which has some advantages in simplifying combinatorial formulae, utilizes the nonprobability measures

$$(5.3.2) \qquad J_n(A_1 \times \cdots \times A_n) = p_n \sum_{\text{perm}} \Pi_n(A_{i_1} \times \cdots \times A_{i_n})$$

$$= n! \, p_n \Pi_n^{\text{sym}}(A_1 \times \cdots \times A_n).$$

We follow Srinivasan (1969) in referring to these as *Janossy measures* after their introduction by Janossy (1950) in the context of particle showers. By contrast, Yvon (1935), Bogoliubov (1946), and Bhabha (1950) worked with the form (5.3.1), as have Macchi (1975) and co-workers in more recent work in which quantities like $\Pi_n^{\text{sym}}(\cdot)$ at (5.3.1) are referred to as *exclusion probabilities*.

A further advantage of the Janossy measures is their simple interpretation when derivatives exist. If $\mathcal{X} = \mathbb{R}^d$ and $j_n(x_1, \ldots, x_n)$ denotes the density of $J_n(\cdot)$ with respect to Lebesgue measure on $(\mathbb{R}^d)^{(n)}$ with $x_i \neq x_j$ for $i \neq j$, then

$$j_n(x_1, \ldots, x_n)dx_1 \cdots dx_n = \text{Pr}\{\text{there are exactly } n \text{ points in the}$$
$$\text{process, one in each of the } n$$
$$\text{distinct infinitesimal regions}$$
$$(x_i, x_i + dx_i)\}.$$

EXAMPLE 5.3(a) *I.i.d. clusters* (continued from Section 5.1). In this case $\mathcal{X} = \mathbb{R}^d$ and, assuming $F(A) = \int_A f(x)dx$ for some density function $f(\cdot)$, the joint density function for the ordered sequence of n points at $x_1, \ldots, x_n$ is

$$\pi_n(x_1, \ldots, x_n) = f(x_1) \cdots f(x_n)$$

which is already in symmetric form. Here

$$j_n(x_1, \ldots, x_n) = p_n n! \, f(x_1) \cdots f(x_n)$$

and it is $j_n(\cdots)$, not $\pi_n(\cdots)$, that gives the probability density of finding one particle at each of the n points $(x_1, \ldots, x_n)$, the factorial giving the number of ways the particles can be allocated to these locations.

EXAMPLE 5.3(b) *Finite renewal processes and random walks.* Suppose $\mathscr{X} = \mathbb{R}^1$ and that, given $N = n$, the points of the process are determined by the successive points $S_1, \ldots, S_n$ of a simple renewal process for which the common distribution of the lifetimes $S_j - S_{j-1}$ (where $S_0 \equiv 0$ and $j = 1, \ldots, n$) has a density function $f(\cdot)$. Then

$$(5.3.3) \qquad \pi_n(S_1, \ldots, S_n) = \prod_{j=1}^{n} f(S_j - S_{j-1}).$$

In moving to the symmetrized form some care is needed. For any $x_1, \ldots, x_n$ we have, formally,

$$\pi_n^{\text{sym}}(x_1, \ldots, x_n) = (n!)^{-1} \sum_{\text{perm}} f(x_{i_1}) f(x_{i_2} - x_{i_1}) \cdots f(x_{i_n} - x_{i_{n-1}}).$$

Let $x_{(1)}, \ldots, x_{(n)}$ denote the set $\{x_1, \ldots, x_n\}$ in ascending order. Then at least one term in each product in the sum $\sum_{\text{perm}}$ will vanish (since $f(x) = 0$ for $x < 0$) unless we already have $x_1, \ldots, x_n$ ordered; that is, $x_j = x_{(j)}$ for $j = 1, \ldots, n$. Hence,

$$(5.3.4) \quad \pi_n^{\text{sym}}(x_1, \ldots, x_n) = (n!)^{-1} f(x_{(1)}) f(x_{(2)} - x_{(1)}) \cdots f(x_{(n)} - x_{(n-1)}).$$

Comparing (5.3.3) and (5.3.4), $(n!)^{-1}$ in the latter is seemingly a discrepant factor. The reconciliation lies in the fact that (5.3.3) vanishes outside the hyperoctant $x_1 \le x_2 \cdots \le x_n$, whereas (5.3.4) repeats itself symmetrically in all $n!$ hyperoctants.

Finally, the Janossy densities are given by

$$(5.3.5a) \quad j_n(x_1, \ldots, x_n) = p_n f(x_{(1)}) f(x_{(2)} - x_{(1)}) \cdots f(x_{(n)} - x_{(n-1)}),$$

where as before p_n is the probability that the process contains just n points. Again it is to be noted that (5.3.3) vanishes outside the first hyperoctant, whereas (5.3.5) gives positive measure to all hyperoctants.

Once the unidirectional character of each step is lost, these simplifications do not occur, and for a general random walk only the forms (5.3.3) and the corresponding expression

$$(5.3.5b) \quad j_n(x_1, \ldots, x_n) = p_n \sum_{\text{perm}} f(x_{i_1}) f(x_{i_2} - x_{i_1}) \cdots f(x_{i_n} - x_{i_{n-1}})$$

are available.

The simplest renewal example occurs when f has an exponential density. The joint density (5.3.3) then reduces to

$$\pi_n(x_1, \ldots, x_n) = \begin{cases} \lambda^n \exp(-\lambda x_n) & 0 \le x_1 < \cdots < x_n, \\ 0 & \text{otherwise,} \end{cases}$$

or in terms of (5.3.5)

$$j_n(x_1, \ldots, x_n) = p_n \lambda^n \exp(-\lambda x_{(n)}).$$

Remarkably, the joint distribution depends only on the position of the extreme $x_{(n)}$; given this value the other points are distributed uniformly over $(0, x_{(n)})$.

The simplest example of a symmetric random walk is probably that for which the individual steps are normally distributed $N(0, 1)$. The successive S_i are then the partial sums of a sequence of independent normal variates

$$S_i = \sum_{j=1}^{i} Z_j$$

and for any given n are therefore jointly normally distributed with zero mean vector and covariance matrix having elements

$$\sigma_{ij} = \min(i, j) \qquad (1 \le i, j \le n).$$

No dramatic simplifications seem possible, but some further details are given in Exercise 5.3.1.

EXAMPLE 5.3(c) *Gibbs processes or processes generated by interaction potentials.* A fundamental class of point processes arising in statistical physics is described by means of forces acting on and between particles. The total potential energy corresponding to a given configuration of particles is assumed to be decomposable into terms representing the interactions between the particles taken in pairs, triples, and so on; first-order terms representing the potential energies of the individual particles due to the action of an external force field may also be included. This leads to a representation of the total potential energy for a configuration of n particles at $x_1, \ldots, x_n$ by a series of the form

$$U(x_1, \ldots, x_n) = \sum_{r=1}^{n} \sum_{1 \le i_1 < \cdots < i_r \le n} \psi_r(x_{i_1}, \ldots, x_{i_r}),$$

where $\psi_r(\cdot)$ is the rth-order interaction potential. Frequently, it is supposed that only the first and second terms need be included, so that the process is determined by the *point pair potentials*, and

$$U(x_1, \ldots, x_n) = \sum_{i=1}^{n} \psi_1(x_i) + \sum_{i=1}^{n-1} \sum_{j=i+1}^{n} \psi_2(x_i, x_j).$$

It is then one of the fundamental principles of statistical mechanics that in equilibrium the probability density of a particular configuration is inversely proportional to the exponential of the potential energy. In terms of Janossy densities, this means that

(5.3.6) $$j_n(x_1, \ldots, x_n) = C(\theta) \exp[-\theta U(x_1, \ldots, x_n)]$$

for some constant of proportionality $C(\theta)$ and parameter θ related to the temperature of the system. The normalizing constant is referred to as the *partition function*. The major difficulty in handling processes of this type lies in expressing the partition function as a function of θ (or, indeed, any other parameters that may occur in the description of the system).

In fact, two slightly different situations may be considered. In the first of these, the *canonical ensemble*, the number n of particles is regarded as fixed and the normalizing constant chosen so as to satisfy

$$[C(\theta)]^{-1} = \int_{\mathscr{X}^{(n)}} \exp\{-\theta U(x_1, \ldots, x_n)\} dx_1 \cdots dx_n.$$

In the second, the *grand canonical ensemble*, both the number of particles and their locations are regarded as variable, and the partition function has to be chosen so as to satisfy (5.3.7) below.

We examine two special cases.

(i) *No interactions (ideal gas).* Here,

$$j_n(x_1, \ldots, x_n) = C(\theta) \exp\left(-\theta \sum_{i=1}^n \psi(x_i)\right) = C(\theta) \prod_{i=1}^n \exp[-\theta \psi(x_i)].$$

Integrating over $(x_1, \ldots, x_n) \in \mathscr{X}^{(n)}$ and summing, using (5.3.7), we obtain

$$C(\theta) \sum_{n=0}^{\infty} \frac{[\Lambda(\theta)]^n}{n!} = C(\theta) e^{\Lambda(\theta)},$$

where we have set $j_0 = J_0 = C(\theta)$ and $\Lambda(\theta) = \int_{\mathscr{X}} e^{-\theta \psi(x)} dx$. Thus, $C(\theta) = e^{-\Lambda(\theta)}$ and the process is nothing but an inhomogeneous Poisson process with intensity $e^{-\theta \psi(x)}$.

(ii) *Repulsive interactions.* Consider next the case of a homogeneous process in which the potential is specified entirely by the pairwise interactions $\psi_2(x, y)$, which are assumed to be a function $\phi(r)$ of the distance $r = \|x - y\|$ between the point pair. A large variety of special forms have been considered for the function $\phi(\cdot)$ both in the statistical mechanical literature (e.g., Ruelle, 1969; Preston, 1976) and more recently as models for spatial point processes in other contexts (e.g., see Ripley, 1977; Ogata and Tanemura, 1984). Typical examples include

$$\phi_1(r) = -\log(1 - \exp[-(r/\sigma)^2]),$$

$$\phi_2(r) = (\sigma/|r|)^n \qquad (n = 4, 6, \text{etc.})$$

$$\phi_3(r) = \infty \text{ or } 0 \quad \text{as } r \leq \text{ or } > \sigma.$$

The function $\phi_1(\cdot)$ represents relatively weak repulsive forces, even for r near zero, and it is therefore described as a "soft core" model. $\phi_3(\cdot)$ corresponds to the "hard core" model: every point pair has a separation $> \sigma$, and no other interaction occurs. The second model is of intermediate type, approximating the behaviour of the hard core model for large n. None of these models is easy to handle analytically, and special expansion techniques have been developed to approximate the partition function.

For the subsequent discussions, we mainly make use of the Janossy measures. In this formulation the normalization condition $\sum p_n = 1$ takes the form

$$(5.3.7) \qquad \sum_{n=0}^{\infty} (n!)^{-1} J_n(\mathscr{X}^{(n)}) = 1,$$

since we may interpret $J_0(\mathcal{X}^{(0)}) = p_0$ and, for $n \geq 1$, we have

$$J_n(\mathcal{X}^{(n)}) = p_n \sum_{\text{perm}} \Pi_n(\mathcal{X}^{(n)}) = p_n n!.$$

It is clear that from any family of symmetric measures $J_n(\cdot)$ satisfying (5.3.7), we can construct a probability distribution $\{p_n\}$ and a set of symmetric probability measures $\{\Pi_n^{\text{sym}}(\cdot)\}$ satisfying Conditions 5.3.I, and conversely. Either specification is equivalent to specifying a global probability measure $\mathscr{P}$ on the Borel sets $\mathscr{A}$ of the countable union (with $\mathcal{X}^{(0)}$ interpreted as an isolated point)

(5.3.8) $$\mathcal{X}^{\cup} = \mathcal{X}^{(0)} \cup \mathcal{X}^{(1)} \cup \mathcal{X}^{(2)} \cup \cdots;$$

Moyal (1962a) takes $(\mathcal{X}^{\cup}, \mathscr{P})$ as the canonical probability space of a finite point process. Given such a measure $\mathscr{P}$, the measure $p_n \Pi_n^{\text{sym}}$, or equivalently, $(n!)^{-1} J_n$, appears as the restriction of $\mathscr{P}$ to the component $\mathcal{X}^{(n)}$. The situation is summarized in the following proposition.

Proposition 5.3.II. *Let $\mathcal{X}$ be a complete separable metric space, and let $\mathscr{B}_{\mathcal{X}}^{(n)}$ be the product σ-field on $\mathcal{X}^{(n)}$. Then the following specifications are equivalent, and each suffices to define a finite point process on $\mathcal{X}$:*

(i) *A probability distribution $\{p_n\}$ on the nonnegative integers and a family of symmetric probability distributions $\Pi_n^{\text{sym}}(\cdot)$ on $\mathscr{B}_{\mathcal{X}}^{(n)}$, $n \geq 1$, with the added convention $\Pi_n^{\text{sym}}(\mathcal{X}^{(0)}) = p_0$ and the set $\mathcal{X}^{(0)}$ denotes an ideal point such that $\mathcal{X}^{(0)} \times \mathcal{X} = \mathcal{X} = \mathcal{X} \times \mathcal{X}^{(0)}$.*

(ii) *A family of nonnegative symmetric measures $J_n(\cdot)$ on $\mathscr{B}_{\mathcal{X}}^{(n)}$, $n \geq 1$, satisfying the normalization condition (5.3.7) and with $J_0(\mathcal{X}^{(0)}) = p_0$, a nonnegative scalar.*

(iii) *A probability measure $\mathscr{P}$ on the Borel sets of the countable union at (5.3.8).*

There is one point of principle to be noted here concerning the canonical choice of state space for a finite point process. To be consistent with treating a point process as a set of *unordered* points, a realization with, say, k points should be thought of not as a point in $\mathcal{X}^{(k)}$ but as a point in the quotient space of $\mathcal{X}^{(k)}$ with respect to the group of permutations among the k coordinates. For example, when $\mathcal{X} = \mathbb{R}$ and $k = 2$, then in place of all pairs (x_1, x_2), with (x_1, x_2) and (x_2, x_1) being treated as equivalent, we should consider some representation of the quotient space such as the set $\{(x_1, x_2): x_1 \leq x_2\}$. The difficulty with this approach in general is that it is often hard to find a convenient concrete representation of the quotient space (e.g., consider the case just cited with $\mathbb{R}$ replaced by the unit circle or sphere), with the attendant problems of visualizing the results and bringing geometric intuition to bear. We have therefore preferred the redundant representation, which allows a distinction between the points but then gives all permutations among the labelling of the points equal weight in the measure. It must be borne in mind that there is then a many–one relation between the points in the space $\mathcal{X}^{\cup}$

and the set of all totally finite counting measures. Furthermore, any event defined on the point process represents a symmetrical set in $\mathscr{X}^{\cup}$ (i.e., a set invariant under permutation of the axes of the components $\mathscr{X}^{(k)}$ of $\mathscr{X}^{\cup}$), and thus the natural σ-algebra to use in discussing point process properties is this σ-algebra of symmetric sets. We do not emphasize this approach, because our main development in Chapters 6 and 7 is given in terms of counting measures; we merely refer the reader seeking details to Moyal (1962a) and Macchi (1975) (see also Exercises 5.3.2–5.3.3).

Now let us turn to the problem of expressing in terms of the Janossy measures (or one of their equivalents) the probability distributions of the random variables $N(A_i)$. If $(A_1, \ldots, A_k)$ represents a finite partition of $\mathscr{X}$, the probability of finding exactly n_i points in A_i ($i = 1, \ldots, k$) can be written, with $n_1 + \cdots + n_k = n$, as

$$(5.3.9) \quad P_k(A_1, \ldots, A_k; n_1, \ldots, n_k) = (n_1! \cdots n_k!)^{-1} J_n(A_1^{(n_1)} \times \cdots \times A_k^{(n_k)})$$

$$= p_n \binom{n}{n_1 \cdots n_k} \Pi_n^{\text{sym}}(A_1^{(n_1)} \times \cdots \times A_k^{(n_k)}),$$

where the multinomial coefficient can be interpreted as the number of ways of grouping the n points so that n_i lie in A_i ($i = 1, \ldots, k$).

It is important in (5.3.9) that the sets A_i both are disjoint and have union $\mathscr{X}$. If any of the n_i are zero, the corresponding set is omitted from the right-hand side.

From (5.3.9) it follows in particular that the probability of finding n points in A, irrespective of the number in its complement A^c, is given by

$$(5.3.10) \quad n! \, P_1(A; n) = \sum_{r=0}^{\infty} (r!)^{-1} J_{n+r}(A^{(n)} \times (A^c)^{(r)}).$$

Similarly, if $A_1, \ldots, A_k$ are any k disjoint Borel sets, $C = (A_1 \cup \cdots \cup A_k)^c$, and $n = n_1 + \cdots + n_k$, the probability of finding just n_i points in A_i, $i = 1, \ldots, k$ is given by

$$(5.3.11) \quad n_1! \cdots n_k! \, P_k(A_1, \ldots, A_k; n_1, \ldots, n_k)$$

$$= \sum_{r=0}^{\infty} (r!)^{-1} J_{n+r}(A_1^{(n_1)} \times \cdots \times A_k^{(n_k)} \times C^{(r)}).$$

These probabilities are in fact the joint distributions of the random variables $N(A_i)$, $i = 1, \ldots, k$. The fact that they do form a *consistent* set of finite-dimensional distributions is implicit in their derivation, but it can also be verified directly, as we show following the discussion of such conditions in Chapter 6 [see Example 6.4(c)].

An alternative approach, following Moyal (1962a), starts from the observation that each realization can be represented as a random vector $Y \in \mathscr{X}^{(n)}$ for some $n \geq 0$. Any such vector defines a counting measure on $\mathscr{X}$, through

$$N(A) = \#\{i: y_i \in A\},$$

where the y_i are the components of the random vector Y. The random vector thus gives rise to a mapping from $\mathscr{X}^{(n)}$ into the space $\mathscr{N}_{\mathscr{X}}$ of all counting measures on $\mathscr{X}$. It is easy to see [Example 7.1(a)] that this mapping is measurable, and so defines a point process. This being true for every n, the whole process is a point process, and since (5.3.11) are its fidi distributions, they are necessarily consistent. As Moyal pointed out, this approach to the existence of finite point processes can be extended to more general cases by considering the restrictions of the process to an increasing family of Borel sets (say spheres) chosen so that they expand to fill the whole space but with probability 1 have only a finite number of points in each. The main difficulty with this approach from our point of view is that it does not extend readily to random measures, which we require for their own sake and for applications in later chapters.

We conclude this section with a lemma that will play a useful role in simplifying the relations among various measures introduced in the sequel. It is needed in particular in checking that the distributions defined by (5.3.11) satisfy the consistency conditions of Chapter 6.

Lemma 5.3.III. *Let A be a Borel subset of $\mathscr{X}$ and S a symmetric measure defined on $\mathscr{X}^{(n)}$ for some $n > 0$. Then for any partition $\{A_1, \ldots, A_k\}$ of A,*

$$(5.3.12) \qquad S(A^{(n)}) = \sum \binom{n}{j_1 \cdots j_k} S(A_1^{(j_1)} \times \cdots \times A_k^{(j_k)}),$$

where the summation extends over all nonnegative integers $j_1, \ldots, j_k$ for which $j_1 + \cdots + j_k = n$.

PROOF. Equation (5.3.12) expresses the fact that the partitioning of A induces a partitioning of $A^{(n)}$ into k^n subsets, which are grouped together into classes that are identified by vectors $(j_1, \ldots, j_k)$: within any given class, each constituent subset has A_i appearing as a coordinate or "edge" j_i times. The symmetry of S implies that all subsets in the same class have the same S measure; hence, (5.3.12) follows. $\square$

Exercises

5.3.1. [Compare Example 5.3(b).] For a finite random walk with normally distributed $N(0, 1)$ steps, show that

$$\pi_2^{\text{sym}}(x, y) = (4\pi)^{-1}(e^{-x^2/2} + e^{-y^2/2})e^{-(x-y)^2/2},$$

and that

$$\pi_3^{\text{sym}}(x, y, z) = (12\pi(2\pi)^{1/2})^{-1}(f(x, y, z) + f(y, z, x) + f(z, x, y)),$$

where $f(x, y, z) = e^{-(x^2+(y-z)^2)/2}(e^{-(y-x)^2/2} + e^{-(z-x)^2/2})$.

5.3.2. Check Proposition 5.3.II in detail.

5.3.3. Show that, by a suitable choice of metric, $\mathscr{X}^{\cup}$ at (5.3.8) becomes a c.s.m.s. [recall the assumption, made in Condition 5.3.I(a), that $\mathscr{X}$ is a c.s.m.s.].

5.3.4. Let $A^{(k)}$ denote the k-fold product set $A \times \cdots \times A$. Show that a symmetric measure on the Borel sets of $\mathscr{X}^{(2)}$ is determined by its values on sets of the form $A^{(2)}$ but that the corresponding statement for $\mathscr{X}^{(k)}$ with $k \geq 3$ is false. [*Hint:* Consider first $\mathscr{X} = \{1, 2\}$ and $k = 2, 3$.]

5.3.5. (Continuation) Let $\mathscr{B}_{\text{sym}}^{(k)}$ be the smallest σ-algebra containing the sets $A^{(k)}$ for Borel subsets A of $\mathscr{X}$. Show that $\mathscr{B}_{\text{sym}}^{(k)}$ consists of all symmetric Borel subsets of $\mathscr{X}^{(k)}$ and that any symmetric measure on $\mathscr{B}^{(k)}$ is completely determined by its values on $\mathscr{B}_{\text{sym}}^{(k)}$. Show also that a symmetric measure μ on $\mathscr{B}^{(k)}$ is completely determined by integrals of the form

$$\int_{\mathscr{X}^{(k)}} \zeta(x_1) \cdots \zeta(x_k) \mu(dx_1 \times \cdots \times dx_k)$$

for functions ζ in the class $\mathscr{U}$ of Definition 5.5.I.

5.3.6. Let $\mathscr{X}_0^{(n)}$ denote the quotient space $\mathscr{X}^{(n)}/\mathscr{P}^{(n)}$, where $\mathscr{P}^{(n)}$ is the permutation group over the coordinates of a point in $\mathscr{X}^{(n)}$. Prove that there is a one-to-one correspondence between measures on the Borel subsets of $\mathscr{X}_0^{(n)}$ and symmetric measures on the Borel subsets of $\mathscr{X}^{(n)}$ [cf. Macchi (1975) who uses $\bigcup_{n=0}^{\infty} \mathscr{X}_0^{(n)}$ in place of $\mathscr{X}^{\cup}$ at (5.3.8) as the sample space for finite point processes].

5.3.7. Let $\{j_k(\cdot): k = 1, 2, \ldots\}$ be a family of positive Janossy densities for an a.s. finite point process. Define functions $\psi_1(x) = -\log j_1(x)$,

$$\psi_k(x_1, \ldots, x_k) = -\log j_k(x_1, \ldots, x_k) - \sum_{r=1}^{k-1} \sum_{1 \leq i_1 < \cdots < i_r \leq k} \psi_r(x_{i_1}, \ldots, x_{i_r}).$$

Show that $j_k(\cdot)$ thereby defines recursively a unique family of interaction potentials for a Gibbs process [cf. Example 5.3(c), especially (5.3.6)].

5.3.8. Let $f(\cdot)$ be a bounded or nonnegative functional of an a.s. finite point process with Janossy measures $J_n(\cdot)$. Show that

$$E(f(N)) = \sum_{n=0}^{\infty} (n!)^{-1} \int_{\mathscr{X}} \cdots \int_{\mathscr{X}} f(\delta_{x_1} + \cdots + \delta_{x_n}) J_n(dx_1 \times \cdots \times dx_n).$$

5.4. Moment Measures and Product Densities

We now investigate the moment structure of finite point processes, extending to counting measures the notions of ordinary and factorial moments and cumulants developed for nonnegative integer-valued r.v.s in Section 5.2. In fact, because we require a general point process to be finite a.s. on bounded sets, the definitions can be extended almost immediately to the general case (these extensions are treated in Section 7.4).

Suppose then that the total population has finite kth moment $\mu_k = E(N(\mathscr{X})^k)$ for some $k = 1, 2, \ldots$. Then for any Borel set $A \in \mathscr{B}_{\mathscr{X}}$ we define

(5.4.1) $$M_k(A^{(k)}) = E(N(A)^k),$$

where we choose to regard the left side as the value on the product set $A^{(k)}$ of a set function defined on the product σ-field $\mathscr{B}_{\mathscr{X}}^{(k)}$ in $\mathscr{X}^{(k)}$. In particular, if the total population has finite mean $\mu_1 = E(N(\mathscr{X}))$, we can define the *expectation measure* $M(\cdot)$ by

(5.4.2) $M(A) \equiv M_1(A) = E(N(A))$ $A \in \mathscr{B}_{\mathscr{X}}$.

Here it is clear from Fubini's theorem that $M(\cdot)$ inherits countable additivity from $N(\cdot)$, so that it does in fact define a measure on $\mathscr{B}_{\mathscr{X}}$.

For $k > 1$ we can extend the definition of M_k to arbitrary rectangle sets of the form

$$A_1^{(k_1)} \times \cdots \times A_r^{(k_r)},$$

where $\{k_1, \ldots, k_r\}$ is a partition of k (so $k_i \geq 1$ and $k_1 + \cdots + k_r = k$) and the A_i are disjoint sets of $\mathscr{B}_{\mathscr{X}}$, by setting

(5.4.3) $M_k(A_1^{(k_1)} \times \cdots \times A_r^{(k_r)}) = E(N(A_1)^{k_1} \cdots N(A_r)^{k_r}).$

It is not difficult to check that M_k is countably additive on these k-dimensional rectangle sets and hence can be extended to a measure on the Borel sets $\mathscr{B}_{\mathscr{X}}^{(k)}$. In fact, M_k can be regarded as the expectation measure of a point process on $\mathscr{X}^{(k)}$: the point process consists of all k-tuples (allowing repetitions and distinguishing the order in this k-tuple) of points from the original realization; that is, it consists of the k-fold product $N^{(k)}$ of N with itself. Thus, M_k gives the expected number of such k-tuples in arbitrary sets from $\mathscr{B}_{\mathscr{X}}^{(k)}$. Since $N^{(k)}$ is a *symmetric* measure on $\mathscr{X}^{(k)}$, so too is its expectation measure M_k. We call M_k the kth *moment measure* of N.

Similarly, we can introduce the kth *factorial moment measure* $M_{[k]}$. Here, $M_{[1]} = M_1 = M$, and for $k > 1$ the ordinary powers inside the expectation at (5.4.3) are replaced by factorial powers: with A_i and k_i as at (5.4.3), we set

(5.4.4) $M_{[k]}(A_1^{(k_1)} \times \cdots \times A_r^{(k_r)}) = E(N(A_1)^{[k_1]} \cdots N(A_r)^{[k_r]}).$

As for M_k, the set function on the left-hand side of this defining relation is countably additive on rectangle sets in $\mathscr{X}^{(k)}$ and can be interpreted as the expectation measure of a certain point process in $\mathscr{X}^{(k)}$. In this case, the realizations of the new process consist of all k-tuples of *distinct* points from the original process, still distinguishing the order within the k-tuple but not allowing repetitions. (Note that if the original process N has multiple points, each such point is to be enumerated according to its multiplicity: for example, a double point of N should be regarded as two distinct points having the same coordinates when constructing the k-tuples.) Then $M_{[k]}(A)$ represents the expected number of such k-tuples falling in $A \in \mathscr{B}_{\mathscr{X}}^{(k)}$.

Proposition 5.4.I. *If $\mu_k = E(N(\mathscr{X})^k) < \infty$, the set functions M_k and $M_{[k]}$ defined by (5.4.3) and (5.4.4) are countably additive on rectangle sets and have unique extensions to symmetric measures M_k and $M_{[k]}$, respectively, on $\mathscr{B}_{\mathscr{X}}^{(k)}$.*

Using the identities (5.2.2) and (5.2.3) that relate ordinary and factorial powers, it is possible to write down explicit expressions for M_k on certain sets in terms of $\{M_{[j]}, j = 1, \ldots, k\}$ and for $M_{[k]}$ in terms of $\{M_j, j = 1, \ldots, k\}$.

Directly from (5.2.5) we have the important special case

$$(5.4.5) \qquad E(N(A)^k) = M_k(A^{(k)}) = \sum_{j=1}^{k} \Delta_{j,k} M_{[j]}(A^{(j)}).$$

Such relations are particularly useful when the factorial moment measures are absolutely continuous so that the right-hand side of (5.4.5) can be expressed as a sum of integrals of the product densities introduced below Lemma 5.4.III. Note also relations such as

$$(5.4.6) \qquad M_{[2]}(A \times B) = E(N(A)N(B)) - E(N(A \cap B))$$
$$= M_2(A \times B) - M(A \cap B) \qquad (A, B \in \mathscr{B}_{\mathscr{X}})$$

(see Exercises 5.4.1–5.4.6 for a more systematic exposition of such relations).

Applications of these moment measures appear in subsequent chapters; here we explore their relation to the Janossy measures and their interpretation in terms of product densities.

Since (5.4.4) is simply the factorial moment of a fidi distribution, which, by means of (5.3.11), can be expressed in terms of the Janossy measures, we can obtain an expression for $M_{[k]}(\cdot)$ in terms of these latter measures. To examine this expression we return to the case that $A_1, \ldots, A_r$ is a partition of $\mathscr{X}$. Assuming $E(N(\mathscr{X})^{[k]}) < \infty$, we have directly from the definitions, when $k_1 + \cdots + k_r = k$, that

$$M_{[k]}(A_1^{(k_1)} \times \cdots \times A_r^{(k_r)}) = \sum_{j_i \ge k_i, i=1,\ldots,r} j_1^{[k_1]} \cdots j_r^{[k_r]} P_r(A_1, \ldots, A_r; j_1, \ldots, j_r)$$

$$= \sum_{j_i \ge k_i} \left(\prod_{i=1}^{r} (j_i - k_i)! \right)^{-1} J_{j_1 + \cdots + j_r}(A_1^{(j_1)} \times \cdots \times A_r^{(j_r)}).$$

To simplify the last sum, put $n_i = j_i - k_i$ and group together the terms for which $n_1 + \cdots + n_r = n$. Setting $k = k_1 + \cdots + k_r$, we obtain

$$M_{[k]}(A_1^{(k_1)} \times \cdots \times A_r^{(k_r)})$$

$$= \sum_{n=0}^{\infty} (n!)^{-1} \sum_{\Sigma n_i = n} \binom{n}{n_1 \cdots n_r} J_{k+n}(A_1^{(k_1+n_1)} \times \cdots \times A_r^{(k_r+n_r)}).$$

The inner sum can be reduced by Lemma 5.3.III, taking $A = \mathscr{X}$ and defining S by

$$S(B) = J_{k+n}(A_1^{(k_1)} \times \cdots \times A_r^{(k_r)} \times B) \qquad (B \in \mathscr{B}_{\mathscr{X}}^{(n)}),$$

thereby yielding the equation

$$M_{[k]}(A_1^{(k_1)} \times \cdots \times A_r^{(k_r)}) = \sum_{n=0}^{\infty} (n!)^{-1} J_{k+n}(A_1^{(k_1)} \times \cdots \times A_r^{(k_r)} \times \mathscr{X}^{(n)}).$$

Using the countable additivity of both sides, this extends to the following elegant generalization of (5.2.12),

$$(5.4.7) \qquad M_{[k]}(B) = \sum_{n=0}^{\infty} \frac{J_{k+n}(B \times \mathscr{X}^{(n)})}{n!} \qquad (\text{all } B \in \mathscr{B}_{\mathscr{X}}^{(k)}).$$

To obtain the inverse relation, suppose that all factorial moments $\mu_{[k]}$ of $N(\mathcal{X})$ exist and that the p.g.f.

(5.4.8)
$$P(1 + \eta) = \sum_{k=0}^{\infty} \frac{\mu_{[k]}\eta^k}{k!}$$

is convergent in a disk $|\eta| < 1 + \varepsilon$ for some $\varepsilon > 0$ [equivalently, that $P(z) = E(z^{N(\mathcal{X})})$ is analytic for $|z| < 2 + \varepsilon$]. Then the inverse relation (5.2.1) can be applied to yield, with the same notation as in (5.4.7) and following a parallel route,

$$J_n(A_1^{(k_1)} \times \cdots \times A_r^{(k_r)}) = \sum_{k=0}^{\infty} (-1)^k \frac{M_{[n+k]}(A_1^{(k_1)} \times \cdots \times A_r^{(k_r)} \times \mathcal{X}^{(k)})}{k!}$$

$$= \sum_{j_i \geq k_i} \left(\prod_{i=1}^{r} (-1)^{j_i - k_i} \frac{M_{[j_1 + \cdots + j_r]}(A_1^{(j_1)} \times \cdots \times A_r^{(j_r)})}{(j_i - k_i)!} \right)$$

so that for general $B \in \mathcal{B}_{\mathcal{X}}^{(n)}$

(5.4.9)
$$J_n(B) = \sum_{k=0}^{\infty} (-1)^k \frac{M_{[n+k]}(B \times \mathcal{X}^{(k)})}{k!}.$$

These results may be summarized for reference in the following theorem.

Theorem 5.4.II. *If the total population size $N(\mathcal{X})$ has finite kth moment, then the kth factorial moment measure is defined and finite and can be represented in terms of the Janossy measures by (5.4.7). Conversely, if all moments are finite and for some $\varepsilon > 0$ the p.g.f. (5.4.8) is convergent for $|\eta| < 1 + \varepsilon$, then the Janossy measures can be represented in terms of the factorial moment measures by (5.4.9).*

EXAMPLE 5.4(a) *Avoidance function.* To illustrate the application of Theorem 5.4.II, consider the set function

$$P_0(A) \equiv \Pr\{N(A) = 0\} = P_1(A; 0),$$

that is, the probability of finding no points in a given subset A of $\mathcal{X}$, or, equivalently, the probability that the support of N avoids A. Taking $n = 0$ in (5.4.9) and restricting $\mathcal{X}$ to A itself, we obtain immediately

(5.4.10)
$$P_0(A) = J_0(A) = \sum_{k=0}^{\infty} (-1)^k \frac{M_{[k]}(A^{(k)})}{k!}.$$

An important feature of (5.4.10) is that it is not necessary to know anything about the nature of the moment measure outside A to determine the probability. In the case $\mathcal{X} = \mathbb{R}$ and A equal to the interval $(0, t]$, the result at (5.4.10) gives the survivor function for the forward recurrence time in terms of the moment measures on $(0, t]$. Of course, from another point of view, (5.4.10) is just a special case of Equation (5.2.11) giving the probabilities of a discrete distribution in terms of the factorial moments.

We now turn and consider densities for the moment measures, assuming

$\mathscr{X}$ to be a real Euclidean space (or well-behaved subset thereof). Recall the standard result, which follows from Fubini's theorem, that if a totally finite measure can be represented as the superposition of a finite or countably infinite family of component measures, then it is absolutely continuous with respect to a given measure if and only if each component is absolutely continuous, the density of the superposition being represented a.e. by the sum of the densities. Applied to the representation (5.4.7) this yields immediately the following lemma.

Lemma 5.4.III. *If the kth factorial moment measure $M_{[k]}(\cdot)$ exists, then it is absolutely continuous if and only if the Janossy measures $J_n(\cdot)$ are absolutely continuous for all $n \geq k$, in which case the densities $m_{[k]}(\cdot)$ and $j_n(\cdot)$ are related by the equations*

$$(5.4.11) \quad m_{[k]}(x_1, \ldots, x_k)$$

$$= \sum_{n=0}^{\infty} (n!)^{-1} \int \cdots \int_{\mathscr{X}^{(n)}} j_{k+n}(x_1, \ldots, x_k, y_1, \ldots, y_n) dy_1 \cdots dy_n.$$

The inverse relation follows in a similar way: if all the factorial moment measures exist and are absolutely continuous, and if the series (5.4.9) is absolutely convergent, then the corresponding Janossy measure is absolutely continuous with density given by

$$(5.4.12) \quad j_n(x_1, \ldots, x_n)$$

$$= \sum_{k=0}^{\infty} (-1)^k (k!)^{-1} \int \cdots \int_{\mathscr{X}^{(k)}} m_{[n+k]}(x_1, \ldots, x_n, y_1, \ldots, y_k) dy_1 \cdots dy_k.$$

Historically, the introduction of the factorial moment densities, also referred to as *product densities* in Bhabha (1950) and Ramakrishnan (1950) and as *coincidence densities* in Macchi (1975), considerably preceded the more general treatment as above using factorial moment measures. This is easily understood in view of the simple physical interpretation of the densities: from (5.4.7) and (5.3.9) it follows that if $m_{[k]}(x_1, \ldots, x_k)$ is bounded in a neighbourhood of $(x_1, \ldots, x_k)$ then we can write

$$(5.4.13) \quad m_{[k]}(x_1, \ldots, x_k) dx_1 \cdots dx_k = \sum_{n=0}^{\infty} (n!)^{-1} J_{k+n}(dx_1 \times \cdots \times dx_k \times \mathscr{X}^{(n)})$$

$$= \Pr\{\text{one particle located in each of} \\ \text{the infinitesimal subsets} \\ dx_i \, (i = 1, \ldots, k)\},$$

where dx_i denotes both the infinitesimal set $(x_i, x_i + dx_i)$ and its Lebesgue measure. This interpretation may be contrasted with that for the density

$$(5.4.14) \quad j_k(x_1, \ldots, x_k) dx_1 \cdots dx_k = \Pr\{\text{exactly } k \text{ points in realization, one} \\ \text{in each subset } dx_i \, (i = 1, \ldots, k), \\ \text{and none elsewhere}\}.$$

From an experimental point of view, (5.4.13) can be estimated from the results of k observations at specific times or places, whereas the Janossy measure requires indefinitely many observations so as to determine the exact (total) number of occurrences. For this reason the densities (5.4.13) are in principle amenable to experimental determination (through "coincidence" experiments, hence the name *coincidence densities*) in a way in which the Janossy measures are not, at least in the particle counting context. However, as Macchi (1975) has stressed, the Janossy measures, and hence the joint distributions, can be determined by the converse relations (5.4.9) and (5.4.12).

Moment measures also have the important feature, in common with relations like (5.4.10), that they are *global* in character, in contrast to the *local* character of the Janossy measures. We mean by this that the form of the moment measures is not influenced by the nature of the region of observations: if two observation regions overlap, the moment measures coincide over their common region. On the other hand, the Janossy measures depend critically on the observation regions: just as the number of points observed in the region depends on its size and shape, so also the Janossy measures are exactly tailored to the particular region. This feature lends further importance to the converse relations (5.4.9) and (5.4.12): knowing the moment densities, the Janossy densities for any observation region A can be calculated by taking $\mathcal{X} = A$ in (5.4.12), a remark that continues to have force even when the point process is not totally finite over the whole of $\mathcal{X}$. Thus, the one set of moment measures suffices to determine the Janossy measures for as many observation regions as one cares to nominate.

The existence of densities is closely linked to the concept of orderliness, or more properly, simplicity, in the sense of Chapter 3 that with probability 1 there are no coincidences among the points. Suppose on the contrary that, for some population size n, there is a positive probability of two points coinciding. In terms of the measure $J_n(\cdot)$, the necessary and sufficient condition for this probability to be positive is that $J_n(\cdot)$ should allot nonzero mass to at least one (and hence all) of the diagonal sets $\{x_i = x_j\}$, where x_i is a point in the ith coordinate space. Thus, we have the following proposition.

Proposition 5.4.IV. *The necessary and sufficient condition for a point process to be simple is that, for all n, the associated Janossy measure $J_n(\cdot)$ allots zero mass to the "diagonals" $\{x_i = x_j\}$. In particular, when $\mathcal{X} = \mathbb{R}^d$, the process is simple if for all $n = 1, 2, \ldots$ the Janossy measures have densities $j_n(\cdot)$ with respect to nd-dimensional Lebesgue measure.*

It is more convenient to frame an analogous condition in terms of the moment measures (assuming they exist). From the preceding result and the representation (5.4.7) we have immediately the following proposition.

Proposition 5.4.V. *Suppose the second factorial moment measure $M_{[2]}(\cdot)$ exists. Then a necessary and sufficient condition for the point process to be simple is* *that $M_{[2]}(\cdot)$ allots zero mass to the "diagonal" set $\{x_1 = x_2\}$. In particular, for $\mathscr{X} = \mathbb{R}^d$, the process is simple whenever $M_{[2]}(\cdot)$ has a density $m_{[2]}(\cdot)$ with respect to 2d-dimensional Lebesgue measure.*

An alternative proof of the first part of this proposition is given at Proposition 7.4.VI: the later proof is more readily adapted to random measures (Exercise 6.4.5). The further property of simple point processes, that the diagonal concentrations of the kth-order moment measure M_k determine all moment measures of lower order, is indicated in Exercise 5.4.6.

In some applications we may wish to verify that a given family of densities constitutes the product densities of some point process. The following result gives a simple sufficient condition, which, however, is far from necessary (see remarks after the proof).

Proposition 5.4.VI. *Let $m_{[k]}(\cdot)$ on $\mathscr{X}^{(k)}$ ($k = 1, 2, \ldots$) be a family of symmetric nonnegative functions with finite total integrals*

$$\mu_{[k]} = \int_{\mathscr{X}^{(k)}} m_{[k]}(x) dx$$

and suppose that for some $\varepsilon > 0$ the series $\sum_1^\infty \mu_{[k]} z^k$ is convergent for $|z| < 1 + \varepsilon$. Then a necessary and sufficient condition for the family $\{m_{[k]}(\cdot)\}$ to be factorial moment densities of a finite point process is that the integrals at (5.4.12) should be nonnegative for every $n = 1, 2, \ldots$ and every vector $x = (x_1, \ldots, x_n)$. These factorial moment densities then determine the process uniquely.

PROOF. The integrals are convergent by assumption and clearly define a family of nonnegative symmetric functions. The only other requirement needed for them to form a set of Janossy functions is the normalization condition (5.4.9). On integrating (5.4.12) over $x_1, \ldots, x_n$, the required condition is seen to be equivalent to demanding that if we define $\{p_n\}$ by

$$n! \, p_n = \sum_{k=0}^\infty (-1)^k \frac{\mu_{[k+n]}}{k!}$$

then the $\{p_n\}$ should sum to unity. But this reduces to the condition $\mu_{[0]} = m_{[0]} = 1$, which may be assumed without loss of generality. □

Remarks. The constraint that $\sum_1^\infty \mu_{[k]} z^k$ converges for $|z| < 1 + \varepsilon$ is stronger than needed: it is enough that $\limsup_{r \to \infty} (\mu_{[r]}/r!)^{1/r} < \infty$, but a more complicated definition of p_n may be needed (see Exercises 5.2.3–5.2.4). Also, for the product densities to define a point process that is not necessarily a finite point process, it is enough for the result to hold (with either the given or modified conditions on $\{\mu_{[r]}\}$) with the state space $\mathscr{X}$ replaced by a sequence $\{A_n\}$ of bounded sets for which $A_n \uparrow \mathscr{X}$ as $n \to \infty$.

EXAMPLE 5.4(b) *Moment densities of a renewal process* (Macchi, 1971a). It is well known (see Chapter 4) that the moment properties of a renewal process are completely specified by the renewal function. Although the renewal process is not a finite point process, the machinery developed in this section can be carried over to give a particularly succinct formulation of this result in terms of the factorial moment densities, where for ease of exposition it is assumed that the renewal density exists, $u(\cdot)$ say. In these terms, and assuming stationarity, the renewal density is just a multiple of the second moment density, since for $s < t$ and with $m = m_{[1]}(0, 1]$,

$$m_{[2]}(s, t)ds\, dt = \Pr\{\text{renewals in } (s, s + ds) \text{ and } (t, t + dt)\}$$

$$= m\, ds\, u(t - s)dt.$$

Similarly, making use of the regeneration property, we have for $t_1 < \cdots < t_k$ that

$$(5.4.15) \quad m_{[k]}(t_1, \ldots, t_k)dt_1 \cdots dt_k = \Pr\{\text{renewals in } (t_i, t_i + dt_i)\, (i = 1, \ldots, k)\}$$

$$= m\, dt_1 u(t_2 - t_1)dt_2 \cdots u(t_k - t_{k-1})dt_k.$$

Thus, when the moment densities exist, a necessary condition for a point process to be a stationary renewal process is that the densities be expressible in the product form (5.4.15).

This condition is also sufficient. To see this, assume (5.4.15) holds for some constant m and some function $u(\cdot)$ for each $k = 1, 2, \ldots$. From the cases $k = 1$, 2, first the constant m and then the function $u(\cdot)$ are identified in terms of first and second moment densities. From (5.4.12) we can obtain an expression for the density of the interval distribution by taking $\mathcal{X} = [0, t]$ and requiring exactly two events, one at 0 and one at t, thus yielding for the lifetime density $f(\cdot)$ the relation

$$mf(t) = m \sum_{k=0}^{\infty} (-1)^k (k!)^{-1} \int \cdots \int_{[0,t]^{(k)}} u(x_1)u(x_2 - x_1) \cdots u(t - x_k)dx_1 \cdots dx_k$$

$$= m \sum_{k=0}^{\infty} (-1)^k \int \cdots \int_{0 < x_1 < \cdots < x_k < t} u(x_1)u(x_2 - x_1) \cdots u(t - x_k)dx_1 \cdots dx_k.$$

This identifies $f(\cdot)$ as the solution to an inverse of the renewal equation in the form

$$f = u - f * u.$$

Finally, uniqueness follows from the fact that the moment measures, which coincide with those constructed from a renewal process with this density $f(\cdot)$, determine the process uniquely.

EXAMPLE 5.4(c) *The fermion process* (Macchi, 1975). The renewal process of the previous example generally produces a spacing or "antibunching" effect, at least if its lifetime distribution has its coefficient of variation less than unity. Such behaviour is characteristic of fermions (e.g., electrons) as distinct from bosons (e.g., photons) in the elementary particle context. Benard and Macchi (1973) and Macchi (1975) developed a remarkable dual theory for both types of particles that, though derived in the first instance from quantum mechanical considerations, leads to a dual family of point processes of considerable general interest. Here we describe the first family, because it shares something of the character of a renewal process and reduces to such a process under suitable special conditions. The dual family turns out to be a doubly stochastic process and is described in Section 8.5.

Our state space $\mathscr{X}$ is a general d-dimensional Euclidean space, and we use Δ to denote a closed bounded subset (e.g., a rectangle) within $\mathscr{X}$. Let $C(x, y)$ be a covariance function defined on $\mathscr{X}$, that is, a function such that any symmetric determinant

$$C\begin{pmatrix} x_1, \ldots, x_k \\ x_1, \ldots, x_k \end{pmatrix} \equiv \det \begin{pmatrix} C(x_1, x_1) \cdots C(x_1, x_k) \\ \vdots \\ C(x_k, x_1) \cdots C(x_k, x_k) \end{pmatrix} \geq 0.$$

In general, the function may be complex-valued and therefore Hermitian so that $C(x, y) = \overline{C(x, y)}$, but for ease of writing we assume here that $C(\cdot, \cdot)$ is real.

It follows from nonnegativity that for $\lambda > 0$ the function

$$(5.4.16) \qquad m_{[k]}(x_1, \ldots, x_k) = \lambda^k C\begin{pmatrix} x_1, \ldots, x_k \\ x_1, \ldots, x_k \end{pmatrix}$$

is at least a possible candidate for the kth factorial moment density of some orderly point process on $\mathscr{X}$. To investigate whether this is a legitimate choice, we need to investigate whether the corresponding Janossy densities, given formally by (5.4.12), are well-defined and nonnegative.

In fact, the Janossy densities have a parallel representation to (5.4.16) in terms of the solution $R_\lambda(x, y)$ of the resolvent equation

$$(5.4.17) \qquad R_\lambda(x, y) - \lambda \int_\Delta C(x, u) R_\lambda(u, y) du = C(x, y).$$

It is well known in the theory of integral equations [e.g., see Pogorzelski (1966, p. 47)] that $R_\lambda(x, y)$ can be expressed as a series in λ with terms involving (5.4.16), specifically,

$$R_\lambda(x, y) = (d(\lambda))^{-1} \left\{ \lambda C(x, y) + \lambda \sum_{k=1}^\infty \int_\Delta \cdots \int_\Delta C\begin{pmatrix} x_1, \ldots, x_k \\ x_1, \ldots, x_k \end{pmatrix} dx_1 \cdots dx_k \right\},$$

where

$$d(\lambda) = 1 + \sum_{k=1}^\infty \frac{(-\lambda)^k}{k!} \int_\Delta \cdots \int_\Delta C\begin{pmatrix} u_1, \ldots, u_k \\ u_1, \ldots, u_k \end{pmatrix} du_1 \cdots du_k$$

is the Fredholm determinant associated with Equation (5.4.17). More generally, the $k \times k$ "Fredholm minor" associated with this equation, obtained by replacing C by R_λ in the basic determinant, is given by

$$(5.4.18) \quad \lambda^k R_\lambda \begin{pmatrix} x_1, \ldots, x_k \\ y_1, \ldots, y_k \end{pmatrix}$$

$$= \frac{1}{d(\lambda)} \left\{ \lambda^k C \begin{pmatrix} x_1, \ldots, x_k \\ y_1, \ldots, y_k \end{pmatrix} \right.$$

$$\left. + \lambda^k \sum_{j=1}^{\infty} \frac{(-\lambda)^j}{j!} \int_A \cdots \int_A C \begin{pmatrix} x_1, \ldots, x_k, u_1, \ldots, u_j \\ y_1, \ldots, y_k, u_1, \ldots, u_j \end{pmatrix} du_1 \cdots du_j \right\}$$

[e.g., see Pogorzelski (1966, p. 52)]. Now (5.4.18) has just the same form as (5.4.12) if we identify the factorial moment densities by (5.4.16) and the Janossy measures by

$$(5.4.19) \qquad j_k(x_1, \ldots, x_k) = \lambda^k d(\lambda) R_\lambda \begin{pmatrix} x_1, \ldots, x_k \\ x_1, \ldots, x_k \end{pmatrix}.$$

The convergence of (5.4.18) is ensured by the general theory, using the Hadamard inequality to bound the determinants appearing therein. Thus, only the nonnegativity of the functions (5.4.19) needs to be checked. While these functions will not be nonnegative in general, an appropriate sufficient condition can easily be stated in terms of λ and the eigenvalues of (5.4.17), that is, the values of λ for which the homogeneous equation corresponding to (5.4.17) (with the right-hand side set equal to zero) admits a nontrivial solution. In fact, the determinant R_λ in (5.4.19) will only be nonnegative if the function R_λ is itself a covariance function, that is, if its own eigenvalues $\mu_i(\lambda)$ are nonnegative. Since the eigenvalues of R_λ are related to those of C by the equation

$$\mu_i(\lambda) = \lambda_i - \lambda,$$

a necessary and sufficient condition for R_λ to be a covariance function is that $\lambda < \min\{\lambda_i\}$, in which case $d(\lambda)$ is also nonnegative. It is now easy to check that this condition is necessary and sufficient for the existence of a well-defined point process with factorial moments and Janossy densities given by (5.4.16) and (5.4.19).

A great virtue of this process is that it provides a rather general model for "antibunching," with repulsive rather than attractive points, for which moment and probability densities can be given explicitly, or at least be computed numerically, and which is not restricted to the state space $\mathbb{R}$.

Further details of the process, including a discussion of the corresponding discrete process in which the integral operator is replaced by a matrix, are given in Exercises 5.4.7–5.4.10.

Exercises

5.4.1. (Compare Proposition 5.4.I.) Show that for disjoint sets A and B,

$$M_{[2]}((A \cup B)^{(2)}) = M_{[2]}(A^{(2)}) + M_{[2]}(B^{(2)}) + 2M_{[2]}(A \times B).$$

5.4.2. Establish the analogues of (5.4.6)

$$M_{[3]}(A_1 \times A_2 \times A_3) = E[N(A_1)N(A_2)N(A_3)]$$
$$- \sum E[N(A_1)N(A_2 \cap A_3)] + 2E[N(A_1 \cap A_2 \cap A_3)],$$

$$M_{[4]}(A_1 \times A_2 \times A_3 \times A_4)$$
$$= E[N(A_1)N(A_2)N(A_3)N(A_4)]$$
$$- \sum E[N(A_1)N(A_2)N(A_3 \cap A_4)] + \sum E[N(A_1 \cap A_2)N(A_3 \cap A_4)]$$
$$+ 2 \sum E[N(A_1)N(A_2 \cap A_3 \cap A_4)] - 6E[N(A_1 \cap A_2 \cap A_3 \cap A_4)],$$

where each summation is over all distinct terms of like kind.

5.4.3. (Continuation) Find the generalization for $M_{[k]}(A_1 \times \cdots \times A_k)$ for general k, and discuss the relation to the Stirling numbers $D_{j,k}$. Observe that the relation is essentially one between the ordinary product counting measure $N^{(k)}$ and the modified product counting measure consisting of distinct ordered k-tuplets.

5.4.4. Establish the relation

$$M_3(dx_1 \times dx_2 \times dx_3)$$
$$= M_{[3]}(dx_1 \times dx_2 \times dx_3)$$
$$+ \sum M_{[2]}(dx_1 \times dx_2)\delta(x_2, x_3) + M_{[1]}(dx_1)\delta(x_1, x_2, x_3),$$

where $\delta(x_1, x_2)$ vanishes outside the hyperplane $x_1 = x_2$ and similarly $\delta(x_1, x_2, x_3)$ vanishes outside $x_1 = x_2 = x_3$, and the summation convention of Exercise 5.4.2 continues to hold.

5.4.5. (Continuation) Show that in general

$$M_k(dx_1 \times \cdots \times dx_k) = \sum_{j=1}^{k} \sum_{\mathscr{V}}^{k} M_{[j]}\left(\prod_{i=1}^{i} dy_i(\mathscr{V})\right)\delta(\mathscr{V}),$$

where the inner sum is taken over all partitions $\mathscr{V}$ of the k coordinates into j nonempty subsets, the $y_i(\mathscr{V})$ constitute an arbitrary selection of one coordinate from each subset, and $\delta(\mathscr{V})$ is a δ-function that equals zero unless equality holds among the coordinates in each of the nonempty subsets of $\mathscr{V}$ (cf. Krickeberg, 1974b).

5.4.6. (Continuation) Show that if a point process is simple, the moment measure M_k completely determines M_j for $j \leq k$. [Hint: Consider the representation of M_k in terms of the factorial moment measures $M_{[j]}$ with $j \leq k$. If the process is simple, each diagonal term for M_k can be identified with one of the $M_{[j]}$.] Provide a counterexample showing that for point processes that are not simple, two distinct point processes may have the same M_2 but different M_1. [cf. Theorem 3, Corollary 3 of Krickeberg (1974b)].

5.4.7. As a discrete analogue of Example 5.4(b), let $\mathscr{X}$ be a space with K points labelled $1, \ldots, K$, and for $k \geq 1$ set

$$m_k(i_1, \ldots, i_k) = E(N(i_1) \cdots N(i_k)) \equiv \lambda^k C\binom{i_1, \ldots, i_k}{i_1, \ldots, i_k},$$

where $C = (c_{ii})$ is a $K \times K$ covariance matrix. Observe that the determinant on the right vanishes if an index is repeated (and hence, in particular, if $k > K$), so that the function $m_k(\cdot)$ is nonzero only for combinations of distinct indices. Define

$$P(1 + \eta_1, \ldots, 1 + \eta_K) = 1 + \sum_{k=1}^{K} \lambda^k \sum_{\text{comb}} C\begin{pmatrix} i_1, \ldots, i_k \\ i_1, \ldots, i_k \end{pmatrix} \eta_{i_1} \cdots \eta_{i_k}$$

$$= \det(I + \lambda D_\eta C),$$

where $D_\eta = \text{diag}(\eta_i, \ldots, \eta_K)$ and $\sum_{\text{comb}}$ is taken over all distinct combinations of k indices from K.

Show that, with $z_i = 1 + \eta_i$, $P(\cdot)$ is a proper multivariate p.g.f. [*Hint*: Use the identity

$$(I + \lambda D_z R_\lambda)(I - \lambda C) = I + \lambda D_\eta C,$$

where $R_\lambda = C(I - \lambda C)^{-1}$, leading to

$$P(z_1, \ldots, z_k) = d(\lambda) \det(I + \lambda D_z R_\lambda),$$

where $d(\lambda) = \det(I - \lambda C)$ and thus

$$j_k(i_1, \ldots, i_k) = d(\lambda) \lambda^k R_\lambda \begin{pmatrix} i_1, \ldots, i_k \\ i_1, \ldots, i_k \end{pmatrix}$$

$$= \Pr\{N(i_1) = \cdots = N(i_k) = 1, N(j) = 0 \quad (j \notin \{i_1, \ldots, i_k\})\}.$$

Check that this expression is nonnegative provided $0 < \lambda < \min\{\lambda_i\}$, where the λ_i solve $d(\lambda) = 0.$]

5.4.8. (Continuation) For the process of the last exercise show the following:
   (i) the process is simple, that is, $\Pr\{N(\{j\}) = 0 \text{ or } 1 \text{ for } j = 1, \ldots, K\} = 1$;
   (ii) $E(N(i)N(j)) = \lambda^2(c_{ii}c_{jj} - |c_{ij}|^2) < \lambda^2 c_{ii} c_{jj}$

$$= EN(i)EN(j),$$

and hence that the values are negatively correlated for all i, j;
   (iii) $N(\mathcal{X})$, the total number of points on $\mathcal{X}$, has p.g.f. $d(\lambda(1 - z))$;
   (iv) $\Pr\{N(\mathcal{X}) = 0\} = d(\lambda)$.

5.4.9. Derive the results asserted in Example 5.4(b) by a passage to the limit from the discrete analogue described in the preceding exercises assuming $C(x, y)$ is bounded and continuous on Δ and imitating the proofs of the Fredholm theory approach to integral equations. Show in particular that the p.g.fl. $G[1 + \eta]$ of the fermion process is just the Fredholm determinant of the integral equation with kernel $C(x, y)\eta(y)$.

5.4.10. For the special case of Example 5.4(b) with $\mathcal{X} = \mathbb{R}$ and $C(x, y) = \rho e^{-|x-y|/L}$, the fermion process reduces to a stationary renewal process with interval distributions having density

$$f(x) = 2\rho(1 - 2\rho L)^{-1/2} e^{-x/L} \sinh((1 - 2\rho L)^{1/2}(x/L)) \qquad \text{(Macchi, 1971b)}.$$

More generally, a reduction to a renewal process is possible whenever

$$C(x_1, x_2)C(x_2, x_3) = C(x_1, x_3)C(x_2, x_2) \qquad (x_1 \leq x_2 \leq x_3).$$

5.5. Generating Functionals and Their Expansions

The factorial moment densities are closely linked, as are the factorial moments in the univariate and finite multivariate cases, to an appropriate version of the generating function concept. In the point process context the appropriate generalization is the *probability generating functional*, which we introduce as follows. Let $\zeta(\cdot)$ be any bounded complex-valued Borel measurable function; then for a realization $\{x_i (i = 1, \ldots, N)\}$ of a finite point process the (random) product $\prod_{i=1}^{N} \zeta(x_i)$ is well defined, and on imposing the further requirement that $|\zeta(x)| \le 1$ (all $x \in \mathcal{X}$) its expectation will exist and be finite. [When p.g.fl.s return in Section 7.4, they are defined first over the more restricted class of nonnegative real-valued functions h for which $1 - h$ has bounded support, that is, $h(x) = 1$ outside a bounded region; then abandoning the bounded support requirement leads to the definition of an extended p.g.fl.]

Definition 5.5.I. Let $\mathcal{U} \colon \mathcal{X} \to \mathbb{C}$ be the class of complex-valued Borel-measurable functions satisfying the condition $|\zeta(x)| \le 1$. Then for a finite point process, the *probability generating functional (p.g.fl.)* is defined for $\zeta \in \mathcal{U}$ by

(5.5.1)
$$G[\zeta] = E\left(\prod_{i=1}^{N} \zeta(x_i) \right),$$

the product being unity if $N = 0$, and zero if $N > 0$ and $\zeta(x_i) = 0$ for any i.

We can get some feel for the p.g.fl. by taking $A_1, \ldots, A_r$ to be a measurable partition of $\mathcal{X}$ and setting

(5.5.2)
$$\zeta(x) = \sum_{i=1}^{r} z_i I_{A_i}(x),$$

where $I_A(x)$ is the indicator function of the set A and $|z_i| \le 1$ for $i = 1, \ldots, r$. The function ζ at (5.5.2) belongs to $\mathcal{U}$, and substitution in (5.5.1) leads to

$$G\left[\sum_{i=1}^{r} z_i I_{A_i}(\cdot) \right] = E\left(\prod_{i=1}^{r} z_i^{N(A_i)} \right),$$

which is just the multivariate p.g.f. of the numbers of points in the sets of the given partition. The case of a general function $\zeta \in \mathcal{U}$ may be regarded as a limiting form of this result, where every infinitesimal region dx is treated as a separate set in a grand partition of B, and $\zeta(x)$ is the coefficient (z value) of the corresponding indicator function in (5.5.2). In this way, the p.g.fl. provides a portmanteau description of the p.g.f. of all possible finite or infinite families of counting r.v.s $N(\cdot)$. As in the case of an ordinary discrete distribution, the p.g.fl. provides a useful way of summarizing and illuminating the complex combinatorial results associated with the moments and a convenient formal tool for deriving relations between them.

In further analogy to the univariate case, there are two useful expansions of the p.g.fl., the first about $\zeta \equiv 0$ and the second about $\zeta \equiv 1$. The first results directly from the definition (5.5.1) when the expectation is written out in terms of the elements $\{(p_n, \Pi_n)\}$ of the point process or, equivalently, in terms of the Janossy measures $J_n(\cdot)$ [cf. Conditions 5.3.I and Equation (5.3.11)]. For all $\zeta \in \mathcal{U}$ we have

$$(5.5.3a) \quad G[\zeta] = p_0 + \sum_{n=1}^{\infty} p_n \int \cdots \int_{\mathcal{X}^{(n)}} \zeta(x_1) \cdots \zeta(x_n) \Pi_n(dx_1 \times \cdots \times dx_n)$$

$$(5.5.3b) \qquad = J_0 + \sum_{n=1}^{\infty} (n!)^{-1} \int \cdots \int_{\mathcal{X}^{(n)}} \zeta(x_1) \cdots \zeta(x_n) J_n(dx_1 \times \cdots \times dx_n).$$

The second expansion can be derived as a generalization from the case where ζ has the particular form (5.5.2) when the p.g.fl. reduces to a multivariate p.g.f., and the expansion can be expressed in terms of the multivariate factorial moments. Assuming as in (5.4.8) that the series $\sum_0^{\infty} \mu_{[k]} z^k$ is convergent for $|z| < \varepsilon$ for some $\varepsilon > 0$ and expressing the factorial moments of the counting r.v.s in terms of the factorial moment measures (5.4.4), we obtain

$$G\left[\sum_{i=1}^{r} z_i I_{A_i}\right] = G\left[1 + \sum_{i=1}^{r} (z_i - 1) I_{A_i}\right]$$

$$= 1 + \sum_{k=1}^{\infty} (k!)^{-1} \sum_{k_1 + \cdots + k_r = k} \binom{k}{k_1 \cdots k_r}$$

$$\times \prod_{i=1}^{r} (z_i - 1)^{k_i} M_{[k]}(A_1^{(k_1)} \times \cdots \times A_r^{(k_r)}).$$

The final sum can be identified with the integral of the product $\prod_{i=1}^{r} \times \{(z_i - 1)^{k_i} I_{A_i}(x_j)\}$ with respect to $M_{[k]}(\cdot)$, so that we have

$$(5.5.4) \quad G[1 + \eta]$$

$$= 1 + \sum_{k=1}^{\infty} (k!)^{-1} \int \cdots \int_{\mathcal{X}^{(k)}} \eta(x_1) \cdots \eta(x_k) M_{[k]}(dx_1 \times \cdots \times dx_k),$$

where $\eta(x) = \sum_{i=1}^{r} (z_i - 1) I_{A_i}(x)$ in the special case considered. Since any Borel measurable function can be approximated by simple functions such as η, the general result follows by familiar continuity arguments, using the dominated convergence theorem and the assumed convergence of $\sum \mu_{[k]} z^k$ in $|z| < \varepsilon$, supposing that $|\eta(x)| < \varepsilon$ for $x \in \mathcal{X}$.

EXAMPLE 5.5(a) *General branching processes; multiplicative population chains.* This basic model stimulated much of the early discussion of generating functionals and moment measure (e.g., see Bartlett and Kendall, 1951; Moyal, 1962a, b) and may be described as follows. A population evolves in discrete time or generations $t = 0, 1, \ldots$, the members of each generation being characterized by both their total number and their locations in the state space $\mathcal{X}$ in such a way that the population constituting the tth generation can be described by a finite point process on $\mathscr{X}$. The fundamental *multiplicative* property of the process expresses the fact that the population at the *(t + 1)*th generation is built up as the sum or, more properly, the superposition of the contributing processes representing the offspring from each of the members of the *t*th generation. Here we shall assume that, given the number Z_t and the locations $\{x_{ti}: i = 1, \ldots, Z_t\}$ of the members of the *t*th generation, the contributing processes to the *(t + 1)*th generation are mutually independent, and independent of both Z_t and all generations prior to *t*. This relation is then expressible in the form

$$(5.5.5) \qquad N_{t+1}(A) = \sum_{i=1}^{Z_t} N(A|x_{ti}) \qquad (A \in \mathscr{B}_{\mathscr{X}}, t = 0, 1, \ldots),$$

where the Z_t finite point processes $\{N(\cdot|x_{ti}): i = 1, \ldots, Z_t\}$ are mutually independent. The distributions of the contributing or offspring processes $N(\cdot|x)$ may depend on the location x of the parent. They can be specified by probability distributions $\{p_n(x): n = 0, 1, \ldots\}$ and symmetric distributions $\Pi_n(\cdot|x)$ as in Conditions 5.3.I with the additional requirement that for fixed values of their other arguments the $p_n(x)$ and $\Pi_n(\cdot|x)$ are all assumed to be measurable functions of x for each $n = 0, 1, \ldots$. Then the offspring p.g.fl., $G[\zeta|x]$ say, will also be a measurable function, and the relation (5.5.5) can be expressed as

$$(5.5.6) \qquad G_{t+1}[\zeta|N_t] = \prod_{i=1}^{Z_t} G[\zeta|x_{ti}],$$

where the left-hand side represents the conditional p.g.fl. for the *(t + 1)*th generation given the number and locations of the members of the *t*th generation as specified by the point process N_t. It is clear that the right-hand side is measurable function of $\{Z_t, x_{ti}(i = 1, \ldots, Z_t)\}$, and hence that the left-hand side is a measurable function of the finite process N_t. We may therefore take expectations over the left-hand side with respect to N_t, thus obtaining the relation

$$(5.5.7) \qquad G_{t+1}[\zeta] = G_t[G[\zeta|\cdot]] \qquad (t = 0, 1, \ldots),$$

where $G[\zeta|\cdot]$ is to be treated as the argument of G_t (note that $G[\zeta|\cdot] \in \mathscr{U}$ whenever $\zeta \in \mathscr{U}$). This equation (5.5.7) is a far-reaching generalization of the functional iteration relation for the p.g.f.s of the numbers of offspring in successive generations of the Galton–Watson process (see also Exercise 5.5.2).

Analogous formulas for the factorial moment measures can be established by similar conditioning arguments or else more formally by expanding the p.g.fl. in powers of ζ and equating like terms. Let us illustrate these procedures for the expectation measures, denoting by $M(\cdot|x)$ the expectation measure for the offspring process $N(\cdot|x)$ with a parent at x, and by $M_{(t)}(\cdot)$ the expectation measure for the population at the *t*th generation. Corresponding to (5.5.6) we have

$$(5.5.8) \qquad M_{(t+1)}(A|N_t) = \sum_{i=1}^{Z_t} M(A|x_{ti}) = \int_{\mathscr{X}} M(A|x)N_t(dx),$$

where again the measurability of $M(A|x)$ as a function of x is clear from the assumptions. Taking expectations with respect to N_t we then have

$$(5.5.9) \qquad\qquad M_{(t+1)}(A) = \int_{\mathscr{X}} M(A|x)M_{(t)}(dx),$$

showing that the expectation measures for successive generations are obtained by operating on $M_{(0)}(\cdot)$ by successive powers of the integral operator with kernel $M(\cdot|x)$. As in the case of a multitype Galton–Watson process (which indeed is the special case when the state space $\mathscr{X}$ consists of a finite number of discrete points), this operator governs the asymptotic behaviour of the process. In particular, its maximum eigenvalue determines the asymptotic rate of growth (or decay) of the mean population size.

These and many other properties are discussed in standard references on general branching processes (e.g., see Moyal, 1962b; Harris, 1963; Athreya and Ney, 1972; Jagers, 1975). Most attention has been given to the case where $\mathscr{X}$ is compact, which results in behaviour similar to that of the finite multitype case. New types of behaviour occur in the noncompact case: for example, $M(A|\cdot)$ may be the kernel of a transient Markov chain, in which case the total mass is preserved but, in contrast to the compact case, the population need not necessarily become extinct—it may continue "moving" indefinitely across the state space as a kind of population wave. Some further aspects and examples are taken up in the exercises [see also Chapter 12 of MKM (1978)].

For an alternative derivation of (5.5.9), write $\zeta = 1 + \eta$ in (5.5.7) and expand the two sides. We have

$$1 + \int_{\mathscr{X}} \eta(x)M_{(t+1)}(dx) + \cdots = 1 + \int_{\mathscr{X}} (G[1 + \eta|x] - 1)M_{(t)}(dx) + \cdots$$

$$= 1 + \int_{\mathscr{X}} M_{(t)}(dx)\left(\int_{\mathscr{X}} \eta(u)M(du|x) + \cdots\right) + \cdots,$$

where all terms omitted involve product terms in η. Equating the measures with respect to which η is integrated on each side of the equation, we obtain (5.5.9). This brief illustration is a typical example of the fact that the p.g.fl. acts as a portmanteau device for condensing a broad range of formulae (see also Exercise 5.5.3).

By taking logarithms of the expansions at (5.5.3) and (5.5.4), we can obtain expansions analogous to those at (5.2.10) and (5.2.8). The first of these takes the form, under the condition that $J_0 > 0$,

$$(5.5.10) \quad \log G[\zeta]$$

$$= -K_0 + \sum_{n=1}^{\infty} (n!)^{-1} \int \cdots \int_{\mathscr{X}^{(n)}} \zeta(x_1)\cdots\zeta(x_n)K_n(dx_1 \times \cdots \times dx_n),$$

where $J_0 = \exp(-K_0)$ and $K_n(\cdot)$ for $n = 1, 2, \ldots$ are symmetric signed measures, which, following Bol'shakov (1969), we call *Khinchin measures*. This expansion is important when the point process is infinitely divisible and can be given a cluster interpretation generalizing that of the compound Poisson distribution (see Chapter 8). Here we note that in this case the measures $K_n(\cdot)/K_0$ can be identified as the Janossy measures of the process characterizing the clusters, so $K_0 = \sum_{n=1}^{\infty} K_n(\mathcal{X}^{(n)})/n!$, and the expansion can be rewritten in the form

(5.5.11) $\log G[\zeta]$

$$= \sum_{n=1}^{\infty} (n!)^{-1} \int \cdots \int_{\mathcal{X}^{(n)}} (\zeta(x_1)\cdots\zeta(x_n) - 1)K_n(dx_1 \times \cdots \times dx_n).$$

EXAMPLE 5.5(b) *I.i.d. clusters* (continued from Section 5.1 and Example 5.3(a)). Returning to our initial example, we see that Equation (5.1.1) is a special case of the general form for the p.g.fl.

(5.5.12) $$G[\zeta] = P_N\left(\int_{\mathcal{X}} \zeta(x)F(dx)\right),$$

where as before $P_N(x)$ is a p.g.f. of the cluster size and $F(\cdot)$ is the distribution of the individual cluster members about the origin.

The case that $P_N(\cdot)$ has the compound Poisson form

$$P_N(z) = e^{-\lambda(1-\Pi(z))}$$

(see Theorem 2.2.II), where $\Pi(z)$ is the p.g.f. of the compounding distribution, is of interest. Expanding $\log G[\zeta]$, we have

$$\log G[\zeta] = -\lambda\left\{1 - \Pi\left(\int_{\mathcal{X}} \zeta(x)F(dx)\right)\right\}$$

$$= \lambda \sum_{n=1}^{\infty} \pi_n\left\{\left(\int_{\mathcal{X}} \zeta(x)F(dx)\right)^n - 1\right\};$$

hence, $K_0 = \lambda$ and for $n = 1, 2, \ldots,$

$$K_n(dx_1 \times \cdots \times dx_n) = \lambda\pi_n n!\, F(dx_1)\cdots F(dx_n).$$

This can be compared with the form for the Janossy measures for which $J_0 = e^{-\lambda}$ and for $n = 1, 2, \ldots,$

$$J_n(dx_1 \times \cdots \times dx_n) = p_n n!\, F(dx_1)\cdots F(dx_n),$$

the interpretation being as follows. The process can be regarded as the superposition of ν i.i.d. nonempty subclusters, where ν has a Poisson distribution with mean λ, and for each subcluster, $K_n(dx_1 \times \cdots \times dx_n)/K_0$ is the probability that the subcluster consists of n points and that they are located at $\{x_1, \ldots, x_n\}$. The Janossy measure yields as $J_n(dx_1 \times \cdots \times dx_n)$ the probability that the superposition of the ν subclusters results in n points in all with these points being located at $\{x_1, \ldots, x_n\}$.

   In this particular case, the measures $J_n(\cdot)$ and $K_n(\cdot)$ for $n = 1, 2, \ldots$ differ only by a scalar factor (that depends on n): this is a consequence of the i.i.d. nature of the locations of the points. In the more complex examples studied in Chapter 8 this no longer need hold [see also Example 13.1(b)].

   Taking logarithms of the expansion (5.5.4) leads to a development in terms of *factorial cumulant measures* $C_{[k]}$, namely,

(5.5.13)

$$\log G[1 + \eta] = \sum_{k=1}^{\infty} (k!)^{-1} \int \cdots \int_{\mathscr{X}^{(k)}} \eta(x_1) \cdots \eta(x_k) C_{[k]}(dx_1 \times \cdots \times dx_k).$$

This expansion converges under the same conditions as (5.5.4) itself, namely, that the factorial moments $\mu_{[k]}$ of the total population size should satisfy $\sum \mu_{[k]} \varepsilon^k < \infty$ for some $\varepsilon > 0$, or equivalently that the p.g.f. of the total population size should be analytic within a disk $|z| < 1 + \varepsilon$. Note that the scope of application of these results can be increased considerably if it is borne in mind that $\mathscr{X}$ itself can be deliberately restricted to a subspace such as a finite interval or rectangle of the original space in which the process may not even be finite.
   Relations between the factorial cumulant measures and factorial moment measures can be derived from the expansions (5.5.4) and (5.5.13) by formal substitution or by recalling that the measures appearing in those expansions are symmetric: without this restriction they are not uniquely defined by integral representations such as (5.5.13). For example, by comparing the linear and quadratic terms of ζ we have

(5.5.14a) $$\int \zeta(x_1) C_{[1]}(dx_1) = \int \zeta(x_1) M_{[1]}(dx_1),$$

(5.5.14b) $$\int \int \zeta(x_1) \zeta(x_2) C_{[2]}(dx_1 \times dx_2)$$
$$= \int \int \zeta(x_1) \zeta(x_2) M_{[2]}(dx_1 \times dx_2)$$
$$- \int \zeta(x_1) M_{[1]}(dx_1) \int \zeta(x_2) M_{[1]}(dx_2),$$

which can be abbreviated to

(5.5.14c) $$C_{[1]}(dx_1) = M_{[1]}(dx_1),$$

(5.5.14d) $$C_{[2]}(dx_1 \times dx_2) = M_{[2]}(dx_1 \times dx_2) - M_{[1]}(dx_1) M_{[1]}(dx_2).$$

The latter statement follows because any Borel measure on $\mathscr{X}^{(2)}$ is determined by its values on rectangles $A \times B$, which in the case of a symmetric measure may be taken to be squares $A \times A$, for which the indicator functions have the form $\zeta(x_1) \zeta(x_2)$. In the sequel we repeatedly use such infinitesimal notation to represent equality of measures on product spaces. Using this notation, the general relation between $C_{[k]}$ and the factorial moment measures $M_{[j]}$ for $j \leq k$, is most conveniently written in the form, analogous to (5.2.19),

(5.5.15) $\quad C_{[k]}(dx_1 \times \cdots \times dx_k)$

$$= \sum_{j=1}^{k} (-1)^{j-1}(j-1)! \sum_{\mathcal{T} \in \mathcal{P}_{jk}} \prod_{i=1}^{j} M_{[|S_i(\mathcal{T})|]}(dx_{i,1} \times \cdots \times dx_{i,|S_i(\mathcal{T})|}).$$

To check that (5.5.15) holds, apply Lemma 5.2.VI to the expansions (5.5.4) for the p.g.fl. and (5.5.13) for its logarithm. Note that in (5.5.15), unlike (5.2.19), we must here take explicit note of the elements $x_{i,1}, \ldots, x_{i,|S_i(\mathcal{T})|}$ of each constituent set $S_i(\mathcal{T})$ in each partition $\mathcal{T}$ in $\mathcal{P}_{jk}$.

In practice, it is convenient to group together those partitions $\mathcal{T}$ in $\mathcal{P}_{jk}$ that have common numbers of elements in their subsets: using Σ^* to denote summation over such groups, (5.5.15) then yields, for example, when $k = 4$,

(5.5.16) $\quad C_{[4]}(dx_1 \times \cdots \times dx_4) = M_{[4]}(dx_1 \times \cdots \times dx_4)$

$$- \sum{}^* M_{[1]}(dx_1)M_{[3]}(dx_2 \times dx_3 \times dx_4)$$

$$- \sum{}^* M_{[2]}(dx_1 \times dx_2)M_{[2]}(dx_3 \times dx_4)$$

$$+ 2 \sum{}^* M_{[1]}(dx_1)M_{[1]}(dx_2)M_{[2]}(dx_3 \times dx_4)$$

$$- 6M_{[1]}(dx_1)\cdots M_{[1]}(dx_4).$$

Here, the first two $\sum^*$ terms come from $\mathcal{P}_{24}$, with four terms in the former sum and three terms in the latter, while the other $\sum^*$ term comes from $\mathcal{P}_{34}$ and has six terms. This expression then compares immediately with the relation in Exercise 5.2.7.

Inverse relations can be derived in the same way and take the form

(5.5.17) $\qquad M_{[k]}(dx_1 \times \cdots \times dx_k)$

$$= \sum_{j=1}^{k} \sum_{\mathcal{T} \in \mathcal{P}_{jk}} \prod_{i=1}^{j} C_{[|S_i(\mathcal{T})|]}(dx_{i,1} \times \cdots \times dx_{i,|S_i(\mathcal{T})|}).$$

Just as with integer-valued r.v.s, expansions such as (5.4.9) and (5.5.17) can in principle be combined to provide expressions for the Janossy measures in terms of the factorial cumulant measures and vice versa. While they may appear to be too clumsy to be of any great practical value, when one or more of the entities concerned has a relatively simple structure as occurs, for example, with the Poisson process, they can in fact provide a usable theoretical tool (see Proposition 13.1.III for an example). Similar comments apply to the relations between the Khinchin measures and the factorial moment measures.

For ease of reference we conclude this section with a summary of the various expansions of the p.g.fl. $G[\cdot]$ of an a.s. finite point process N, together with the corresponding relations between the associated families of measures. For brevity of notation, the latter are written in density form: they can easily be translated into measure notation, for example, as at (5.5.17), which corresponds to an analogue of (5.5.26) both for measure notation and analogous expansions. Recall also the comments following (5.4.14) about applying the expansions to point processes for which $\mathscr{P}\{N(\mathscr{X}) = \infty\} > 0$ by looking instead at the process $N(\cdot \cap A)$ for some bounded $A \in \mathscr{B}_{\mathscr{X}}$.

Some statements below have already been proved; proofs of the rest are left to the reader.

(I) G[h]	(II) G[1 + η]
Janossy measures	Factorial moment measures

(III) log G[h]	(IV) log G[1 + η]
Khinchin measures	Factorial cumulant measures

(A) Definitions, Range of Validity

For suitable measurable functions h and family of measures $\{\mu_n\colon n = 0, 1, 2, \ldots\}$ with μ_0 a constant and μ_n defined on $\mathscr{B}(\mathscr{X}^{(n)})$, write

$$(5.5.18) \quad Y[h, \{\mu_n\}] = \sum_{n=1}^{\infty} (n!)^{-1} \int_{\mathscr{X}^{(n)}} h(x_1)\cdots h(x_n)\mu_n(dx_1 \times \cdots \times dx_n).$$

$\mathscr{V}$ denotes the class of measurable functions $h\colon \mathscr{X} \to [0, 1]$ such that $h(x) = 1$ for x outside some bounded Borel set. R denotes the radius of convergence of the p.g.f. $P(z) = \sum_{n=0}^{\infty} p_n z^n = E(z^{N(\mathscr{X})})$. Always, $R \geq 1$.

(I) *Janossy Measures* $\{J_n\}$

$$(5.5.19) \qquad\qquad G[h] = J_0 + Y[h, \{J_n\}],$$

valid for $h \in \mathscr{V}$, and $\{J_n\}$ satisfying the normalizing condition

$$(5.5.20) \qquad\qquad 1 = G[1] = J_0 + \sum_{n=1}^{\infty} \frac{J_n(\mathscr{X}^{(n)})}{n!}.$$

$\{J_n(\cdot)/n!\}$ is a probability measure on $\mathscr{X}^{\cup} = \bigcup_{n=0}^{\infty} \mathscr{X}^{(n)}$, with $p_n = J_n(\mathscr{X}^{(n)})/n!$ $(n = 0, 1, \ldots)$.

(II) *Factorial Moment Measures* $\{M_{[n]}\}$

$$(5.5.21) \qquad\qquad G[1 + \eta] = 1 + Y[\eta, \{M_{[n]}\}],$$

valid for $|1 + \eta| \in \mathscr{V}$ for which $|\eta(x)| < \varepsilon$ (all x) provided $R \geq 1 + \varepsilon > 1$, imply that all $M_{[n]}(\mathscr{X}^{(n)}) < \infty$. $M_{[0]} = 1$.

(III) *Khinchin Measures* $\{K_n\}$

(5.5.22) $$\log G[h] = -K_0 + Y[h, \{K_n\}],$$

valid for $h \in \mathcal{V}$ with $K_0 > 0$ and $\{K_n\}$ satisfying the normalizing condition

(5.5.23) $$K_0 = \sum_{n=1}^{\infty} \frac{K_n(\mathcal{X}^{(n)})}{n!}.$$

For $n \geq 1$, $K_n(\cdot)$ are not necessarily nonnegative; every $K_n(\cdot) \geq 0$ implies that N is infinitely divisible.

(IV) *Factorial Cumulant Measures* $\{C_{[n]}\}$

(5.5.24) $$\log G[1 + \eta] = Y[\eta, \{C_{[n]}\}],$$

valid for η as in (II), with $R \geq 1 + \varepsilon > 1$ implying that $|C_{[n]}(\mathcal{X}^{(n)})| < \infty$ for all n. $C_{[0]} = 0$.

(B) Relations Between Measures in Different Expansions

The conditions given for validity are sufficient but not always necessary.

$(I) \rightarrow (II)$. This is a matter of definition! For n such that $M_{[n]}(\mathcal{X}^{(n)}) < \infty$,

(5.5.25) $m_{[n]}(x_1, \ldots, x_n)$

$$= \sum_{r=0}^{\infty} (r!)^{-1} \int_{\mathcal{X}^{(r)}} j_{n+r}(x_1, \ldots, x_n, y_1, \ldots, y_r) dy_1 \cdots dy_r.$$

$(II) \rightarrow (I)$. For $R > 2$,

(5.5.26) $j_n(x_1, \ldots, x_n)$

$$= \sum_{r=0}^{\infty} (-1)^r (r!)^{-1} \int_{\mathcal{X}^{(r)}} m_{[n+r]}(x_1, \ldots, x_n, y_1, \ldots, y_r) dy_1 \cdots dy_r.$$

$(I) \rightarrow (III)$. $K_0 = -\log J_0$ (hence, need $J_0 > 0$) and $R > 1$,

(5.5.27) $k_n(x_1, \ldots, x_n)$

$$= \sum_{r=1}^{n} (-1)^{r-1} (r-1)! \sum_{\mathcal{T} \in \mathcal{P}_{rn}} \prod_{i=1}^{r} j_{|S_i(\mathcal{T})|}(x_{i,1}, \ldots, x_{i,|S_i(\mathcal{T})|}),$$

with partition notation as in (5.5.15).

$(III) \rightarrow (I)$. $J_0 = \exp(-K_0)$ (hence, need $K_0 < \infty$) and $R > 1$,

(5.5.28) $j_n(x_1, \ldots, x_n) = J_0 \left(\sum_{r=1}^{n} \sum_{\mathcal{T} \in \mathcal{P}_{rn}} \prod_{i=1}^{r} k_{|S_i(\mathcal{T})|}(x_{i,1}, \ldots, x_{i,|S_i(\mathcal{T})|}) \right).$

$(III) \rightarrow (IV)$ and $(IV) \rightarrow (III)$. These are direct analogues of the relations between (I) and (II), noting that $C_{[0]} = 0$. Valid for $R > 2$.

$(II) \rightarrow (IV)$ and $(IV) \rightarrow (II)$. These are the direct analogues of the relations between (I) and (III), noting that $M_{[0]} = 1$. Valid for $R > 2$.

Exercises

5.5.1. [Compare Section 5.1 and Examples 5.3(a) and 5.5(b).] Derive (5.1.1) from (5.5.12) by putting $\xi(x) = \sum_{i=1}^{j} z_i I_{A_i}(x)$, where $\{A_1, \ldots, A_j\}$ is a finite partition of $\mathcal{X}$. Put $\xi = 1 + \eta$ to establish the formal relation

$$G[1 + \eta] = 1 + \sum_{k=1}^{\infty} \left(\frac{\mu_{[k]}}{k!}\right) \int_{\mathcal{X}} \cdots \int_{\mathcal{X}} \eta(x_1) \cdots \eta(x_k) \Pi(dx_1) \cdots \Pi(dx_k),$$

and hence, when $\mu_{[k]} = E(N^{[k]}) < \infty$, that

$$M_{[k]}(dx_1 \times \cdots \times dx_k) = \mu_{[k]} \Pi(dx_1) \cdots \Pi(dx_k),$$

of which the case $k = 2$ appears at (5.1.3).

5.5.2. In the branching process of Example 5.5(a), let $G_t[\zeta|x]$ be the p.g.fl. for the population, $N_t(\cdot|x)$ say, of the tth generation starting from a single ancestor at x, so $G_1[\zeta|x] = G[\zeta|x]$. Show that for all $k = 1, \ldots, t - 1$,

$$G_t[\zeta|x] = G_{t-k}[G_k[\zeta|\cdot]|x] = G^{(t)}[\zeta|x],$$

where $G^{(t)}[\cdot|x]$ is the tth functional iterate of $G[\cdot|\cdot]$ [cf. (5.5.7)].

5.5.3. (Continuation) Let $q_t(x)$ denote the probability of extinction within t generations starting from a single ancestor at x, so that $q_t(x) = \Pr\{N_t(\mathcal{X}|x) = 0\}$. Show that for each fixed $x \in \mathcal{X}$, $\{q_t(x): t = 0, 1, \ldots\}$ is a monotonic nondecreasing sequence, and that for $k = 1, \ldots, t - 1$,

$$q_t(x) = G_{t-k}[q_k(\cdot)|x],$$

so in particular

$$q_{t+1}(x) = G[q_t(\cdot)|x].$$

Deduce that the probability of ultimate extinction starting from an initial ancestor at x, $q(x)$ say, is the smallest nonnegative solution of the equation $q(x) = G[q(\cdot)|x]$.

5.5.4. (Continuation) Show that the first moment measure $M^{(t)}(\cdot|x)$ of $N_t(\cdot|x)$ and the second factorial cumulant measure, $C_{[2]}^{(t)}(A \times B|x)$ say, of $N_t(\cdot|x)$ satisfy the recurrence relations (with $M \equiv M^{(1)}$)

$$M^{(t+1)}(A|x) = \int_{\mathcal{X}} M^{(t)}(A|y) M(dy|x),$$

$$C_{[2]}^{(t+1)}(A \times B|x) = \int_{\mathcal{X}^{(2)}} M^{(t)}(A|y) M^{(t)}(B|z) C_{[2]}(dy \times dz)$$

$$+ \int_{\mathcal{X}} C_{[2]}^{(t)}(A \times B|y) M(dy|x).$$

[*Hint*: Use $N_{t+1}(A|x) =_d \sum_{x_i} N_t(A|x_i)$, where the $\{x_i\}$ denote the individuals of the first generation; cf. also Proposition 8.2.IV.]

5.5.5. (Continuation) Let $H_t[\zeta|x]$ denote the p.g.fl. for all individuals up to and including those in the tth generation starting from an initial ancestor at x. Show that these p.g.fl.s satisfy the recurrence relations

$$H_{t+1}[\zeta|x] = \zeta(x)G[H_t[\zeta|\cdot]|x].$$

Show also that, if extinction is certain, the total population over all generations has p.g.fl. $H[\zeta|\cdot]$, which for $0 < \zeta < 1$ is the smallest nonnegative solution to the functional equation

$$H[\zeta|x] = \zeta(x)G[H[\zeta|\cdot]|x],$$

and find equations for the corresponding first two moment measures.

5.5.6. *Model for the spread of infection.* Take $\mathscr{X} = \mathbb{R}^d$, and suppose that any individual infected at x in turn gives rise to infected individuals according to a Poisson process with parameter measure $\mu(\cdot|x) = \mu(\cdot - x|0) \equiv \mu(\cdot - x)$, where $\int_{\mathscr{X}} \mu(du) = v < 1$. Show that the total number $N(\mathscr{X}|0)$ of infected individuals, starting from one individual infected at 0, is finite with probability 1 and that the p.g.fl. $H[\cdot|\cdot]$ for the entire population of infected individuals satisfies the functional equation

$$H[\zeta|0] = \zeta(0)\exp\left(-\int_{\mathscr{X}}(1 - H[\zeta|u])\mu(du)\right),$$

where $H[\zeta|u] = H[T_u\zeta|0]$.
    Deduce, in particular, the following:
(i) The p.g.f. of $N(\mathscr{X}|0)$ satisfies $f(z) \equiv Ez^{N(\mathscr{X}|0)} = ze^{v(f(z)-1)}$.
(ii) The expectation measure $M(\cdot|0)$ for the total population of infected individuals, given an initial infected individual at the origin, satisfies

$$M(A|0) = \delta_0(A) + \int_{\mathscr{X}} M(A - \mu|0)\mu(du)$$

$$= \delta_0(A) + \mu(A) + \mu^{2*}(A) + \cdots.$$

(iii) The second factorial moment measure $M_{[2]}(A \times B|0)$ of $N(\cdot|0)$ satisfies

$$M_{[2]}(A \times B|0) = M(A|0)M(B|0)$$

$$+ \int_{\mathscr{X}} M_{[2]}(A - u, B - u|0)\mu(du) - \delta_0(A)\delta_0(B).$$

(iv) The Fourier transforms for $M(\cdot|0)$ and $M_{[2]}(\cdot|0)$ are given by

$$\tilde{M}(\theta|0) = \int_{\mathscr{X}} e^{i\theta \cdot x} M(dx|0) = (1 - \tilde{\mu}(\theta))^{-1},$$

$$\tilde{M}_{[2]}(\theta, \phi|0) \equiv \int\int e^{i(\theta \cdot x + \phi \cdot y)} M_{[2]}(dx \times dy|0)$$

$$= (\tilde{M}(\theta|0)\tilde{M}(\phi|0) - 1)(1 - \tilde{\mu}(\theta + \phi))^{-1},$$

where $\tilde{\mu}(\theta) = \int_{\mathscr{X}} e^{i\theta \cdot x}\mu(dx)$.

5.5.7. *Age-dependent branching process.*
   (a) Take $\mathscr{X} = \mathbb{R}$, and suppose that an individual born at time u produces offspring according to a Poisson process with parameter measure $\mu(\cdot\,|u) = \mu(\cdot - u|0) \equiv \mu(\cdot - u)$ for some boundedly finite measure $\mu(\cdot)$ that vanishes on $(-\infty, 0]$. Let $G_t[h|0]$ denote the p.g.fl. for the *ages* of individuals present in the population at time t starting from a single newly born individual at time 0. Show that G_t satisfies the equation

$$G_t[h|0] = h(t)\exp\left(-\int_0^t (1 - G_t[h|u])\mu(du)\right),$$

   where $G_t[h|u] = G_{t-u}[h|0]$ $(0 < u < t)$.
   (b) When $\mu(A) = \mu\ell(A \cap \mathbb{R}_+)$, show that

$$G_t[h|0] = h(t)\left(1 + \mu\int_0^t [1 - h(u)]e^{\mu(t-u)}du\right)^{-1}.$$

5.5.8. Equation (5.5.26) expresses Janossy densities in terms of factorial moment densities when $R > 2$. Investigate whether the relation in Exercise 5.2.4 has an analogue for densities valid when only $R > 1$.

CHAPTER 6

Introduction to the General Theory of Random Measures

In this chapter we set out the main basic features of a general theory of random measures. This approach encompasses the study of point processes as counting measures and is best suited for handling point processes in the plane and more general spaces. While results for random measures are of interest in their own right, the unified context allows us to appreciate more clearly the features that are peculiar to point processes. Discussion of such features is deferred to Chapter 7.

We have chosen to develop the theory in the context of a complete separable metric space (c.s.m.s. throughout this chapter) rather than in the more restricted context of Euclidean spaces or locally compact spaces. Critical to this choice of context is the existence of a well-developed theory of measures on metric spaces, as set out, for example, in Parthasarathy (1967) or Billingsley (1968). We use this theory at two levels. First, we establish results concerning the structure of the space $\mathcal{M}_{\mathscr{X}}$ of realizations of the process, showing in particular that a crucial role is played by the result that $\mathcal{M}_{\mathscr{X}}$ can itself be regarded as a c.s.m.s. Second, it provides the framework for the discussion of convergence of random measures. The fact that the same theory appears at both levels lends a pleasing unity and economy to the development.

This context generalizes two of the principal features that are crucial to the theory of measures on the real line: the existence of a concept of distance, which can be used to define convergence and continuity, and the concept of a rational number, which can be used in various ways to reduce the statement of most important properties to statements concerning countable families (sequences) of points or operations. It does not generalize the third crucial property, embodied in Bolzano's assertion that any sequence drawn from a closed bounded set must contain a convergent subsequence. Since this property hinges on the finite dimensionality of the Euclidean spaces, it is not shared by (for example) infinite-dimensional Hilbert space, but when it does hold it leads to elegant proofs as, for example, in the theory of measures on locally compact spaces. Proofs for the metric space context are generally clumsier, but arguably more direct, and have the advantage mentioned earlier that only the one theory is needed to make the development self-contained.

Nevertheless, it will be clear that this chapter, and also most of the subsequent development, cannot be understood well without more knowledge of measure theory and topology than we have required hitherto. To help with this aspect, two appendices are provided at the end of the book. The first reviews elementary concepts from topology, measure theory, and real analysis. The second provides a brief but essentially self-contained account of the main results needed from the theory of measures on metric spaces.

6.1. Definitions and Examples

Let $\mathscr{X}$ be an arbitrary c.s.m.s. In our earlier discussions of point processes we required the counting measures to allot only finitely many points to bounded sets (so that, in particular, they have no finite accumulation points). Extending this property to more general measures we arrive at the following definition.

Definition 6.1.I. A Borel measure μ on the c.s.m.s. $\mathscr{X}$ is *boundedly finite* if $\mu(A) < \infty$ for every bounded Borel set A.

Basic properties of the space $\hat{\mathscr{M}}_{\mathscr{X}}$ of all boundedly finite Borel measures on the c.s.m.s. $\mathscr{X}$ are set out in Section A.2.6 of Appendix 2. Summarizing that discussion, the key points for our immediate purposes are

(i) there is a natural distance function on $\hat{\mathscr{M}}_{\mathscr{X}}$ allowing it to be treated as a c.s.m.s. in its own right; and
(ii) the corresponding Borel σ-algebra, $\mathscr{B}(\hat{\mathscr{M}}_{\mathscr{X}})$ say, is the smallest σ-algebra on $\hat{\mathscr{M}}_{\mathscr{X}}$ with respect to which the mappings $\mu \to \mu(A)$ are measurable for all $A \in \mathscr{B}_{\mathscr{X}}$.

The first property opens the way to defining a random measure as a measurable mapping; the second leads to simple characterization of random measures.

Definition 6.1.II. A random measure ξ with phase or state space $\mathscr{X}$, is a measurable mapping from a probability space $(\Omega, \mathscr{E}, \mathscr{P})$ into $(\hat{\mathscr{M}}_{\mathscr{X}}, \mathscr{B}(\hat{\mathscr{M}}_{\mathscr{X}}))$.

Thus, with every sample point $\omega \in \Omega$, we associate a particular *realization* that is a boundedly finite Borel measure on $\mathscr{X}$: it may be denoted by $\xi(\cdot, \omega)$ or just $\xi(\cdot)$ (or even ξ) when we have no need to draw attention to the

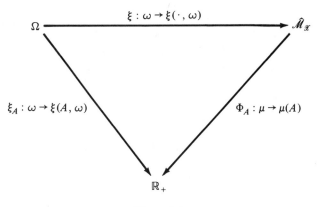

Figure 6.1

underlying probability space. Such a realization has the value $\xi(A, \omega)$ [or we may write just $\xi(A)$] on the Borel set $A \in \mathscr{B}_{\mathscr{X}}$. Note that for each fixed A, $\xi_A \equiv \xi(A, \cdot)$ is a function mapping Ω into $\mathbb{R}_+$, and thus it is a candidate for a nonnegative random variable: that it is indeed such is shown in the following proposition.

Proposition 6.1.III. *Let ξ be a mapping from a probability space into $\hat{\mathscr{M}}_{\mathscr{X}}$ and $\mathscr{A}$ a semiring of bounded Borel sets generating $\mathscr{B}_{\mathscr{X}}$. Then ξ is a random measure if and only if ξ_A is a random variable for each $A \in \mathscr{A}$.*

PROOF. Let $\mathscr{U}$ be the σ-algebra of subsets of $\hat{\mathscr{M}}_{\mathscr{X}}$ whose inverse images under ξ are events, and let Φ_A denote the mapping taking a measure $\mu \in \hat{\mathscr{M}}_{\mathscr{X}}$ into $\mu(A)$ [hence, in particular, $\Phi_A: \xi(\cdot, \omega) \to \xi(A, \omega)$]. Since $\xi_A(\omega) = \xi(A, \omega) = \Phi_A[\xi(\cdot, \omega)]$ as in Figure 6.1, we have for any $B \in \mathscr{B}$

$$\xi^{-1}(\Phi_A^{-1}(B)) = (\xi_A)^{-1}(B).$$

When ξ_A is a random variable, $(\xi_A)^{-1}(B) \in \mathscr{E}$, and then by definition we have $\Phi_A^{-1}(B) \in \mathscr{U}$. It now follows from Theorem A2.6.III that $\mathscr{B}(\hat{\mathscr{M}}_{\mathscr{X}}) \subseteq \mathscr{U}$ and hence that ξ is a random measure.

Conversely, by definition of $\mathscr{B}(\hat{\mathscr{M}}_{\mathscr{X}})$, $\Phi_A^{-1}(B) \in \mathscr{B}(\hat{\mathscr{M}}_{\mathscr{X}})$, and then when ξ is a random measure, $\xi^{-1}(\Phi_A^{-1}(B)) \in \mathscr{E}$. Consequently, ξ_A is then a random variable. □

Taking for $\mathscr{A}$ the semiring of all bounded sets in $\mathscr{B}_{\mathscr{X}}$ we obtain the following corollary.

Corollary 6.1.IV. $\xi: \Omega \to \hat{\mathscr{M}}_{\mathscr{X}}$ *is a random measure if and only if $\xi(A)$ is a random variable for each bounded $A \in \mathscr{B}_{\mathscr{X}}$.*

One practical consequence of Proposition 6.1.III is that we may justifiably use $\xi(A)$ to denote the random variable ξ_A as well as the value $\xi(A, \omega)$ of the realization of the random measure ξ.

Definition 6.1.II on its own does not lend itself easily to the construction of particular random measures: for this the most powerful tool is the existence theorem of Section 6.2. Nevertheless, using the proposition or corollary above, we can handle a number of examples.

EXAMPLE 6.1(a) *Uniform random measure.* Let $\mathscr{X}$ be the real line, or more generally any Euclidean space $\mathbb{R}^d$, and define

$$\xi(A) = \Theta \ell(A)$$

where $\ell(\cdot)$ denotes Lebesgue measure on $\mathscr{X}$ and Θ is a random multiplier that is nonnegative. To set this up formally, take Ω to be a half-line $[0, \infty)$, $\mathscr{E}$ the Borel σ-algebra on Ω, and $\mathscr{P}$ any probability measure on Ω, for example, the measure with gamma density $x^\alpha e^{-x}/\Gamma(\alpha)$. This serves as the distribution of Θ. For each particular value of Θ, the corresponding realization of the random measure is the Θ multiple of Lebesgue measure. (Note that this process is only random in a rather artificial sense. Given only one realization of the process, we would have no means of knowing it was random. Randomness would only appear if we were privileged to observe many realizations. In the language of Chapter 10, the process is stationary but not ergodic.)

We are left with one task, to verify that the mapping in $(\mathscr{M}_{\mathscr{X}}, \mathscr{B}(\mathscr{M}_{\mathscr{X}}))$ is indeed measurable. By Proposition 6.1.III, it is sufficient to verify that the mappings $\xi(A)$ are random variables for each fixed bounded $A \in \mathscr{B}_{\mathscr{X}}$. In our case, $\xi(A)$ is a multiple of the random variable Θ, so the verification is trivial. Thus, we have an example of a random measure.

EXAMPLE 6.1(b) *Random measures with χ^2 density; "quadratic" random measures.* An interesting class of random measures, closely associated with the "negative binomial" processes studied by Barndorff–Nielsen and Yeo (1969), can be obtained from the following construction. Take $\mathscr{X} = \mathbb{R}$, and choose any Gaussian process $Z(t, \omega)$ with a.s. continuous trajectories. [Sufficient conditions for this can be expressed in terms of the covariance function: for example, it is enough for $Z(\cdot)$ to be stationary with covariance function $c(u)$ that is continuous at $u = 0$. Cramér and Leadbetter (1967) give further results of this kind.] Then set

$$(6.1.1) \qquad \xi(A) = \begin{cases} \displaystyle\int_A Z^2(t)dt & \text{for continuous } Z(\cdot, \omega), \\ 0 & \text{otherwise.} \end{cases}$$

Since $Z^2(t) \geq 0$, it is clear that $\xi(A) \geq 0$, while countable additivity is a standard property of indefinite integrals. Moreover, since $Z^2(\cdot)$ is a.s. continuous, it is bounded on bounded sets, and so $\xi(\cdot)$ is boundedly finite. For almost all ω, therefore, $\xi(\cdot, \omega)$ is a boundedly finite Borel measure. To complete the proof that $\xi(\cdot)$ is a random measure it is easiest to check the condition of Proposition 6.1.III. Suppose that A is any finite half-open (left-open right-closed for definiteness) interval, and let

(6.1.2) $$\mathcal{T}_n = \{A_{ni}: i = 1, \ldots, k_n\}$$

be a sequence of partitions of A into subintervals with lengths $1/n$ or less. If t_{ni} is a representative point from A_{ni}, it follows from standard properties of the Riemann integral that

$$\xi_n(A) \equiv \sum_{i=1}^{k_n} Z^2(t_{ni})\ell(A_{ni}) \to \int_A Z^2(t)dt = \xi(A) \quad \text{a.s.}$$

Since by assumption each $Z(t)$ is a random variable, so is $\xi_n(A)$ (as a linear combination of random variables) and $\xi(A)$ (as the limit of a sequence of random variables). It is therefore clear that $\xi(A)$ is a random variable for every set A in the semiring of finite unions of left-open right-closed intervals. It now follows from the proposition that $\xi(\cdot)$ is a random measure.

If $Z(\cdot)$ is stationary and has zero mean, the mean and variance properties of $\xi(A)$ follow immediately from the results $E(Z^2(u)) = \sigma^2$, $\text{Cov}(Z^2(t), Z^2(u)) = 2(c(t-u))^2$. Thus, we find

(6.1.3a) $$E(\xi(A)) = \sigma^2 \ell(A),$$

(6.1.3b) $$\text{cov}(\xi(A), \xi(B)) = 2 \int_A \int_B c^2(u-t)du\, dt.$$

The distributions of $\xi(A)$ are nearly but not quite of -gamma form: each particular value $Z^2(t)$ has a gamma distribution and is proportional to a χ^2 random variable with one degree of freedom, so that the integral $\xi(A)$ behaves like a linear combination of gamma variables. Its characteristic function can be obtained in the form of an infinite product of rational factors each associated with a characteristic root of the integral operator with kernel $c^2(u-t)$ on $A \times A$.

This example is discussed further in Example 6.4(c); see also Exercise 6.1.1.

EXAMPLE 6.1(c) *Processes with nonnegative increments.* Let $\mathcal{X} = \mathbb{R}$. It seems obvious that any stochastic process $X(t)$, defined for $t \in \mathbb{R}$ and possessing a.s. finite-valued monotonic increasing trajectories, should define a random measure through the relation

(6.1.4) $$\xi(a, b] = X(b) - X(a).$$

Let us show that this is the case at least when $X(t)$ is also a.s. right-continuous. In any case, (6.1.4) certainly induces, for each realization, a finitely additive set function on the ring of finite unions of half-open intervals. Right-continuity enters as the condition required to secure countable additivity on this ring (compare the conditions in Lemmas A.2.2.VI and A.2.2.VII). Then the set function defined by (6.1.4) can be extended a.s. to a boundedly finite measure, which we may continue to denote by ξ on $\mathscr{B}(\mathbb{R})$. ξ now represents a mapping from the probability space into $\mathscr{M}_{\mathbb{R}}$. Since $X(t)$ is a stochastic process, (6.1.4) is a random variable for each half-open interval $(a, b]$. It then follows from Proposition 6.1.III that ξ is a random measure.

The condition of right continuity can always be assumed when $X(t)$ is *stochastically continuous*, that is, whenever for each $\varepsilon > 0$,

$$(6.1.5) \qquad \Pr\{|X(t + h) - X(t)| > \varepsilon\} \to 0 \quad \text{as } h \to 0,$$

because we may then define a new process by setting

$$X^*(t) = X(t + 0)$$

and it is easy to verify that $X^*(t)$ is a *version* of $X(t)$, in the sense that it has the same fidi distributions. This condition is satisfied in particular by processes with stationary independent increments, giving rise to stationary random measures with the "completely random" property of Section 2.2 (see also Section 6.3). The following example illustrates the type of behaviour to be expected.

EXAMPLE 6.1(d) *Gamma random measures—stationary case.* Suppose that the random variables $\xi(\cdot)$ in (6.1.4) are independent for disjoint intervals and have gamma distributions with Laplace transforms

$$\psi((a, b]; s) = (1 + \lambda s)^{-\alpha(b-a)} \qquad (\lambda > 0, \alpha > 0, b > a, \operatorname{Re}(s) \geq 0).$$

Clearly, $\psi((a, b]; s) \to 1$ as $(b - a) \to 0$, showing that the process is stochastically continuous, so we can assume right-continuity of the sample paths. It is clear then that the extension to a random measure, guaranteed by the discussion above, will have distributions given by the Laplace transforms

$$(6.1.6) \qquad \psi(A; s) = E(e^{-s\xi(A)}) = (1 + \lambda s)^{-\alpha\ell(A)}.$$

Note that

$$E(\xi(A)) = \lambda\alpha\ell(A),$$

$$\operatorname{var}(\xi(A)) = \lambda^2\alpha\ell(A),$$

both functions being additive over disjoint sets, as we should anticipate from the completely random character of the process.

Despite the condition of stochastic continuity, the measures $\xi(\cdot)$ here are not absolutely continuous, but on the contrary have a purely atomic character. This follows from the Lévy representation theorem [e.g., see Feller (1966, §XVII.2)] for processes with independent increments, which represents every such process as the sum of a shift, a Gaussian component, and an integral of Poisson components indexed according to the heights of the jumps with which they are associated. The existence of a Gaussian component is ruled out by the monotonic character of the realizations, which also implies that the jumps are all positive. Thus, the random measure can be represented as a superposition of Poisson processes, in the same kind of way as the compound Poisson process of Section 2.2. In the present case, however, the random measure has a countable rather than a finite number of atoms in any finite interval, most atoms being so small that the total mass in such an interval is still a.s. finite. In Section 6.3 we provide a similar description of the sample-path behaviour for arbitrary completely random measures.

The general gamma random measure is described in Exercise 6.1.2. Several other constructions of particular random measures are also given in the exercises.

A random measure may be regarded as a family of random variables indexed by the Borel sets of $\mathscr{X}$, but it is considerably more than this. The additivity and continuity properties of measures require at least the truth of

$$(6.1.7) \qquad \xi(A_1 \cup A_2) = \xi(A_1) + \xi(A_2) \quad \text{a.s.}$$

for all pairs of disjoint Borel sets A_1, A_2 in $\mathscr{X}$, and

$$(6.1.8) \qquad \xi(A_n) \to 0 \quad \text{a.s.}$$

for all sequences of bounded Borel sets A_n such that $A_n \downarrow \varnothing$. It is not quite trivial to prove, but fundamental for the resulting theory, that these conditions are in fact sufficient for the family to form a random measure. The difficulty is associated with the exceptional sets of measure zero: because there is an uncountable family of relations (6.1.7) and (6.1.8), it is not clear that the exceptional sets can be combined to form a single set that is still of measure zero. The next lemma indicates one way round the difficulty.

Lemma 6.1.V. *Let $\mathscr{A}$ be a countable ring of bounded Borel sets with the self-approximating property of Definition A2.2.VIII, and $\xi_A(\omega)$ a family of nonnegative random variables indexed by the sets $A \in \mathscr{A}$. In order that, with probability 1, the $\xi_A(\omega)$ should admit an extension to a measure on $\sigma(\mathscr{A})$, it is necessary and sufficient that (6.1.7) hold for all disjoint pairs (A_1, A_2) of sets in $\mathscr{A}$ and that (6.1.8) hold for all sequences $\{A_n\}$ of sets in $\mathscr{A}$ with $A_n \downarrow \varnothing$.*

PROOF. The number of sets in $\mathscr{A}$ being countable, it follows immediately that (6.1.7) implies that the $\xi_A(\omega)$ are a.s. finitely additive there. To establish countable additivity, we use the covering property of Lemma A2.2.IX, from which it follows that it is enough to know that

$$(6.1.9) \qquad \lim_{n \to \infty} \xi \left(\bigcup_{i=1}^{n} F_i(A; 1/k) \right) = \xi(A)$$

simultaneously for all sets $A \in \mathscr{A}$ and integers $k < \infty$. Since each such relation holds a.s. from (6.1.8), and since the number of sets $A \in \mathscr{A}$ and integers $k < \infty$ is countable, this requirement is satisfied almost surely. Then Lemma A2.2.IX implies that the ξ_A can be a.s. extended to a measure on $\sigma(\mathscr{A})$.

The necessity of both conditions follows directly from the additivity and continuity properties of a measure.   □

As an immediate corollary we obtain the following theorem.

Theorem 6.1.VI. *Let $\{\xi_A(\omega)\}$ be a family of nonnegative random variables indexed by the sets of $\mathcal{B}_{\mathscr{X}}$ and a.s. finite-valued on bounded Borel sets. In order that there exist a random measure $\xi^*(A, \omega)$ such that, for all $A \in \mathcal{B}_{\mathscr{X}}$,*

(6.1.10) $$\xi^*(A, \omega) = \xi_A(\omega) \quad \text{a.s.,}$$

it is necessary and sufficient that (6.1.7) hold for all pairs (A_1, A_2) of disjoint, bounded Borel sets and that (6.1.8) hold for all sequences $\{A_n\}$ of bounded Borel sets with $A_n \downarrow \varnothing$.

PROOF. Let $\mathscr{A}$ be any countable, generating ring of bounded Borel sets with the self-approximating property of Definition A2.2.VIII, as, for example, the ring $\mathscr{C}$ following Lemma A2.2.IX. If (6.1.7) and (6.1.8) hold for Borel sets in general, they certainly hold for sets in $\mathscr{A}$. Thus, the conditions of Lemma 6.1.V are satisfied, and we can assert that with probability 1 the $\xi_A(\omega)$, initially defined for $A \in \mathscr{A}$, can be extended to measures $\xi^*(A, \omega)$ defined for all $A \in \sigma(\mathscr{A}) = \mathcal{B}_{\mathscr{X}}$. For ω in the $\mathscr{P}$-null set, U say, where (6.1.7) and (6.1.8) may fail, set $\xi^*(A, \omega) \equiv 0$.

It is not immediately obvious, nor indeed is it necessarily true, that the extensions $\xi^*(A, \omega)$ coincide with the original random variables $\xi_A(\omega)$ for $A \notin \mathscr{A}$, even outside the exceptional set U of probability zero where the extension may fail. The best we can do is to show that they are a.s. equal for each particular Borel set A. The exceptional sets may be different for different As, and we do not claim that they can be combined into a single exceptional set of measure zero.

Consider the class of sets on which ξ^* and ξ coincide a.s. This class includes $\mathscr{A}$, and from the relations (6.1.8) it is closed under monotone limits. By the monotone class theorem it therefore includes $\sigma(A)$, which by assumption is $\mathcal{B}_{\mathscr{X}}$. This proves (6.1.10).

It remains to check that ξ^* is a random measure. Note first that the exceptional set U where the extension fails can be taken to be an event, that is, an element of $\mathscr{E}$ in the underlying probability space $(\Omega, \mathscr{E}, \mathscr{P})$. This follows from the fact that the set where the additivity relation fails for a given pair $A, B \in \mathscr{A}$ can be represented as a countable union of events $\{|\xi_A + \xi_B - \xi_{A \cup B}| > 1/n\}$; similarly, the set where the continuity condition fails for any given sequence of sets in $\mathscr{A}$ is an event; and hence U, being the countable union of all these events, is itself an event. Consequently, we can write for all $A \in \mathscr{A}$

$$\xi^*(A) = \xi_A I_{U^c} + 0 \cdot I_U,$$

which represents $\xi^*(A)$ in terms of a product of random variables, and for such A, $\xi^*(A)$ is a r.v. Since $\xi^*(\cdot, \omega)$ is a measure for all $\omega \in \Omega$ by construction, it now follows from Proposition 6.1.III that ξ^* is a random measure.

This completes the proof of the sufficiency part of the theorem; necessity is an easy corollary of the additivity and continuity properties of a measure. $\square$

As an example of the application of the theorem we give the following result.

Proposition 6.1.VII. *Let ξ be a random measure defined on the probability space $(\Omega, \mathscr{E}, \mathscr{P})$ with some c.s.m.s. $\mathscr{X}$ as state space, and let $\mathscr{F}$ be a sub-σ-algebra of $\mathscr{E}$. Then there exists a version of the conditional expectation*

$$\eta(A, \omega) = E(\xi(A)|\mathscr{F})(\omega)$$

such that

(i) *for each $A \in \mathscr{B}_{\mathscr{X}}$, $\eta(A, \cdot)$ is an $\mathscr{F}$-measurable r.v.; and*
(ii) *η is a random measure with state space $\mathscr{X}$.*

PROOF. It is easy to see from standard properties of conditional expectations that the additivity and consistency relations (6.1.7) and (6.1.8) are both satisfied for the conditional expectations $\eta(A, \omega)$. Furthermore, we may take the probability space here to be $(\Omega, \mathscr{F}, \mathscr{P}_{\mathscr{F}})$ rather than $(\Omega, \mathscr{F}, \mathscr{P})$, where $\mathscr{P}_{\mathscr{F}}$ denotes the restriction of $\mathscr{P}$ to sets of $\mathscr{F}$, since by definition the conditional expectations are all $\mathscr{F}$-measurable. It now follows directly from Theorem 6.1.VI that there exists an $\mathscr{F}$-measurable random measure η^* such that $\eta^*(A) = \eta(A)$ a.s. $\square$

An almost identical argument leads to the classical result on the existence of regular conditional distributions given a σ-algebra (see Exercise 6.1.7 for variants on this theme).

It is important to emphasize that the truth of Proposition 6.1.III and Theorem 6.1.VI depends *essentially* on the assumption of nonnegativity. Corresponding statements for random signed measures are false in general, as the following example shows.

EXAMPLE 6.1(e) *Wiener's homogeneous chaos.* For $A \in \mathscr{B}_{\mathscr{X}}$, let $\xi(A)$ have a normal $N(0, \mu(A))$ distribution, where $\mu(A)$ is a fixed, boundedly finite, Borel measure on $\mathscr{X}$, and suppose that the $\xi(A)$ are independent for disjoint sets. These two requirements immediately allow the joint distributions of finite families $\xi(A_1), \ldots, \xi(A_k)$ to be written down, and it is easy to check that these joint distributions satisfy the consistency requirements of the Kolmogorov theorem. Thus, there does exist a probability space Ω on which the $\xi(A)$ may be simultaneously defined as random variables.

Now consider the random variable

$$W = \xi(A_1 \cup A_2) - \xi(A_1) - \xi(A_2),$$

where A_1, A_2 are disjoint bounded Borel sets. It is readily checked that

$$E(W) = 0,$$

$$\text{var}(W) = \mu(A_1 \cup A_2) + \mu(A_1) + \mu(A_2) - 2\mu(A_1) - 2\mu(A_2) = 0.$$

Thus, $W = 0$ a.s. Next consider a sequence $\{A_j\}$ of disjoint bounded Borel sets with $A = \bigcup_1^\infty A_j$, where A is also bounded, and set

$$W_n \equiv \xi \left(\bigcup_1^n A_j \right) = \sum_1^n \xi(A_j) \quad \text{a.s.,}$$

where the last equality follows by induction from the previous result.

$$\text{var}(W_n) = \mu \left(\bigcup_1^n A_j \right) = \sum_1^n \mu(A_j),$$

and if $W = \xi(\bigcup_1^\infty A_j)$, we must have

$$\text{var}(W - W_n) \to 0.$$

This shows that

$$\sum_1^n \xi(A_j) \to \xi(A)$$

in quadratic mean, and since the $\xi(A_j)$ are independent, the partial sums converge to $\xi(A)$ almost surely as well [e.g., see Theorem 8.24 in Moran (1968)]. We have shown that the family $\{\xi(A_j)\}$ satisfies both (6.1.7) and (6.1.8).

On the other hand it is *not* true that for almost all ω the realization are signed measures. To see this, let $\{A_1, \ldots, A_n\}$ be a finite partition of A and set

$$Y_n = \sum_1^n |\xi(A_j)|.$$

If the realizations $\xi(\cdot)$ were signed measures, the Y_n would remain uniformly bounded a.s. over all possible partitions. But

$$E(Y_n) = \sum_1^n E|\xi(A_j)| = \left(\frac{2}{\pi} \right)^{1/2} \sum_1^n (\mu(A_j))^{1/2},$$

and

$$\sum_1^n (\mu(A_j))^{1/2} \geq \sum_1^n \mu(A_j) \Big/ \max_{1 \leq j \leq n} (\mu(A_j))^{1/2}$$

$$= \frac{\mu(A)}{\max_{1 \leq j \leq n} (\mu(A_j))^{1/2}},$$

so EY_n can be made arbitrarily large by choosing a partition for which $\max_{1 \leq j \leq n} \mu(A_j)$ is sufficiently small. Since $\text{var } Y_n \leq \mu(A)$ for every partition, an application of Chebyshev's inequality shows that for any given finite y, a partition can be found for which $\Pr\{Y_n \geq y\}$ can be made arbitrarily close to 1. This is impossible if the Y_n are a.s. bounded.

To conclude this section, let us emphasize that by choosing the state space $\mathscr{X}$ appropriately, Definition 6.1.II can be made to include not only a number of important special cases but also a number of apparent generalizations. In the case $\mathscr{X} = \mathbb{R}$, discussion of *one-dimensional random measures* is essentially equivalent, as we have seen, to the discussion of processes with nonnegative increments. The cases $\mathscr{X} = \mathbb{R}^d$ correspond to *multidimensional random measures*. If $\mathscr{X}$ has the product form $\mathscr{X}_1 \times \mathscr{X}_2$, where $\mathscr{X}_2$ is a finite set, $\{1, \ldots, d\}$ say, and we define distance in $\mathscr{X}_1 \times \mathscr{X}_2$ by (for example)

$$d((x, i), (y, j)) = \rho(x, y) + |i - j|,$$

the resulting process is a *multivariate random measure*, with d components each a random measure on $\mathscr{X}_1$. Any *point process* defines a random measure by setting $\xi(A) = N(A)$, while a *marked point process* (see around Definition 7.1.X for more detail), with real marks, defines a random measure through the relation

$$\xi(A) = \sum_{i=1}^{N(A)} \kappa(x_i),$$

where $\{x_i\}$ is an enumeration of the points in A and $\{\kappa(x_i)\}$ specifies the associated marks.

Exercises

6.1.1. Let $\{X(t): t \in \mathbb{R}\}$ be a measurable nonnegative stochastic process on $(\Omega, \mathscr{E}, \mathscr{P})$. Show that, when the integrals concerned are finite, the relation

$$\xi(A, \omega) = \int_A X(t, \omega)dt \qquad (\text{bounded } A \in \mathscr{B}_\mathbb{R})$$

defines a random measure $\xi: \Omega \to \mathscr{M}_\mathbb{R}$. [*Hint*: Consider first $X(t, \omega)$ of the form $\sum c_j I_{A_j}(t) I_{E_j}(\omega)$.]

6.1.2. The general *gamma random measure* on the c.s.m.s. $\mathscr{X}$ can be constructed as a process with independent nonnegative increments for which the increment $\xi(A)$ on the bounded Borel set A has a gamma distribution with Laplace transform

$$E(e^{-s\xi(A)}) = (1 + \lambda s)^{-\alpha(A)},$$

where the *scale* parameter λ is finite and positive and the *shape* parameter measure $\alpha(\cdot)$ is a boundedly finite measure on $\mathscr{B}_\mathscr{X}$.
(a) Verify that these marginal distributions, coupled with the independent increment property, lead to a well-defined random measure.
(b) (Compare also Section 6.3.) In the case $\mathscr{X} = \mathbb{R}$, show that $\xi(\cdot)$ may be regarded as the increments of an underlying nondecreasing stochastic process $X(t)$, which with positive probability is discontinuous at t if and only if $\alpha(\{t\}) > 0$.

(c) (Compare Section 6.4.) Show that ξ has as its Laplace functional

$$L[f] = \exp\left(-\int_{\mathscr{X}} \log(1 + \lambda f(x))\alpha(dx)\right),$$

where $f \in BM_+(\mathscr{X})$.

6.1.3. Let N be a well-defined point process on $\mathscr{X} = \mathbb{R}^2$, and with each point x_i in a realization of N associate a geometric object in one of the following ways.
  (a) Construct a disk $S(x_i, r)$ with centre x_i and radius r, and let

$$\xi_S(A) = \sum_i \ell(A \cap S(x_i, r))$$

represent the total area of disks intersecting any Borel set A. Use Proposition 6.1.III to verify that ξ_S is a well-defined random measure on $\mathbb{R}^2$.
  (b) If the radius of $S(x_i, r)$ is also a random variable, leading to $S(x_i, R_i)$ say, a conditioning argument as in Section 8.1, coupled with some condition ensuring the a.s. finiteness of the defining sum $\sum \ell(A \cap S(x_i, R_i))$, is needed.
  (c) In place of the disks, let x_i be the end point of a finite line segment L_i of length d and random orientation θ_i say, for some independent identically distributed random variables $\{\theta_i\}$ on $(0, 2\pi]$. For any Borel set $A \subset \mathbb{R}^2$ let $\ell(A \cap L)$ now denote the Lebesgue measure (in $\mathbb{R}^1$) of the intersect of a line L with A. Again use a conditioning argument to show that

$$\xi_L(A) \equiv \sum_i \ell(A \cap L_i) \qquad (\text{bounded } A \in \mathscr{B}(\mathbb{R}^2))$$

is a well-defined random measure.

6.1.4. *Random probability distributions* play an important role in the theory of statistical inference, in particular, as prior distributions in nonparametric inference. In this and the next two exercises, we indicate some of the methods that have been proposed for constructing such distributions.
  (a) Suppose given a random measure ξ on the c.s.m.s. $\mathscr{X}$, with ξ a.s. totally finite and nonzero, and define

$$\zeta(A) = \xi(A)/\xi(\mathscr{X}) \qquad (A \in \mathscr{B}_{\mathscr{X}}).$$

Show that ζ is a random measure.
  (b) When ξ is a completely random measure with gamma distributions governed by the totally finite measure $\alpha(\cdot)$ (cf. Section 6.3 and Exercise 6.1.2 above), ζ defines the *Dirichlet process* $\mathscr{D}_\alpha$ say. Show that $\zeta(A)$ has a beta distribution and, more generally, that the fidi distributions of $\zeta(A_i)$ over disjoint sets A_i, $i = 1, \ldots, r$, are multivariate beta distributions.
  (c) In the case $\mathscr{X} = \mathbb{R}$, write $F_\zeta(\cdot)$ for the random d.f. associated with the random probability distribution ζ and show that the joint distribution of $Z_i = F_\zeta(x_i) - F_\zeta(x_{i-1})$, $i = 1, \ldots, r$, where $-\infty = x_0 < x_1 < \cdots < x_{r-1} < x_r = \infty$, has, when each $\alpha_i \equiv \alpha((x_{i-1}, x_i]) > 0$, a joint distribution that is singular with respect to r-dimensional Lebesgue measure but absolutely continuous with respect to $(r-1)$-dimensional Lebesgue measure on the simplex $\{(z_1, \ldots, z_{r-1}): z_i \geq 0, z_1 + \cdots + z_{r-1} \equiv 1 - z_r \leq 1\}$, where it has the density function

$$f(z_1, \ldots, z_{r-1}|\alpha_1, \ldots, \alpha_r) = \Gamma\left(\sum_{i=1}^r \alpha_i\right)\prod_{i=1}^r \left(\frac{z_i^{\alpha_i-1}}{\Gamma(\alpha_i)}\right).$$

(d) Suppose the (unobserved) realization ζ of $\mathscr{D}_\alpha$ governs independent observation $X_1, \ldots, X_n$. Given the parameter α of the prior distribution of ζ, show that, conditional on $(X_1, \ldots, X_n) = (x_1, \ldots, x_n)$, the posterior distribution of ζ is again that of a Dirichlet process but has parameter $\alpha + \sum_{i=1}^n \delta_{x_i}$ [cf. Ferguson (1973) for details].

(e) Use the representation in (6.3.12) to show that the realizations of ζ are a.s. purely atomic, that is, equivalently, that the possible d.f.s are a.s. purely discrete.

6.1.5. (a) Let ξ be a boundedly finite but not totally finite measure on $\mathbb{R}_+$, and from the distribution function

$$F_\eta(x) \equiv 1 - \exp(-\xi[0, x])$$

define a measure η on $\mathbb{R}_+$, with $\eta(\mathbb{R}_+) = 1$. Show that when ξ is a random measure, η is a random probability measure on $\mathbb{R}_+$.

(b) When ξ is completely random, η is a "neutral process" in the terminology of Doksum (1974). Show that when ξ has no deterministic component (see Section 6.3), the distribution η is a.s. purely discrete.

6.1.6. A sequence $\{F_n(\cdot)\}$ of distribution functions is defined on $(0, 1]$ by the following construction: $F_n(0) = 0$, $F_n(1) = 1$ $(n = 1, 2, \ldots)$, $F_1(\tfrac{1}{2}) = F_n(\tfrac{1}{2}) = U_{11}$, and for $k = 1, 3, \ldots, 2^n - 1$ and integers $n = 1, 2, \ldots,$

$$F_n(k/2^n) = (1 - U_{nk})F_{n-1}((k - 1)/2^n) + U_{nk}F_{n-1}((k + 1)/2^n),$$

$$= F_{n+r}(k/2^n) \qquad (r = 1, 2, \ldots),$$

where $\mathscr{U}_n \equiv \{U_{nk}: k = 1, \ldots, 2^n - 1\}$ is a family of i.i.d. $(0, 1)$-valued r.v.s with $EU_{nk} = \tfrac{1}{2}$ and $\sigma_n^2 = \mathrm{var}(U_{nk})$, the families $\{\mathscr{U}_n\}$ are mutually independent, and $F_n(x)$ is obtained by linear interpolation between $F_n(j_n(x)/2^n)$ and $F_n((j_n(x) + 1)/2^n)$, where $j_n(x) = $ largest integer $\leq 2^n x$. With $F_n(x)$ so defined on $0 \leq x \leq 1$, the derivative $f_n(\cdot)$ of $F_n(\cdot)$ is well defined except at $x = a_{nj} \equiv j/2^n$ $(j = 0, 1, \ldots, 2^n)$, where we adopt the convention that $f(a_{nj}) = 1$ (all n, all a_{nj}).

(a) Show that there is a d.f. F on $0 \leq x \leq 1$ such that

$$\Pr\{F_n(x) \to F(x) \ (0 \leq x \leq 1) \text{ as } n \to \infty\} = 1.$$

(b) Provided the U_{nj} are sufficiently likely to be close to $\tfrac{1}{2}$—a sufficient condition is that $\sum \sigma_n^2 < \infty$—show that

$$\Pr\{f_n(x) \to f(x) \text{ for } 0 < x < 1\} = 1$$

for some density function $f(\cdot)$ for which

$$F(x) = \int_0^x f(u)\,du \quad \text{a.s.} \qquad (0 < x < 1).$$

Thus, the random d.f. $F(\cdot)$ is a.s. absolutely continuous with respect to Lebesgue measure. [*Hint*: Let the r.v. W be uniformly distributed on $[0, 1]$ and independent of $\{\mathscr{U}_n\}$. Show that $\{f_n(W)\}$ is a martingale, and assuming $\sum \sigma_n^2 < \infty$, use the mean square martingale convergence theorem to deduce that $f_n(W)$ converges a.s. and that F is the integral of its limit.]

(c) Investigate other conditions such as $\liminf_{n\to\infty} \sigma_n^2 < \tfrac{1}{4}$ or $\sum_{n=1}^\infty \Pr\{|2U_{ni} - 1| < 1 - \varepsilon\} = \infty$ for some $\varepsilon > 0$ that may be sufficient to imply either that $F(\cdot)$ is continuous on $(0, 1)$ or else that $F(\cdot)$ has jumps.

[*Remarks*: For constructions related to the above by Kraft (1964), see Dubins and Freedman (1967)—the random d.f.s they construct on [0, 1] are a.s. singular continuous—and Métivier (1971) where the construction leads to random d.f.s on [0, 1] that are a.s. absolutely continuous.]

6.1.7. (a) Use Theorem 6.1.VI to establish the existence of *regular conditional probabilities* on a product space $\mathscr{X} \times \mathscr{Y}$, where $(\mathscr{X}, \mathscr{E})$ is an arbitrary measurable space and $\mathscr{Y}$ is a c.s.m.s. (cf. Proposition A1.5.III). [*Hint*: Let π be a probability measure on the product space and $\pi_{\mathscr{X}}$ the marginal distribution on $(\mathscr{X}, \mathscr{E})$. For fixed disjoint $A, B \in \mathscr{B}_{\mathscr{Y}}$ show the existence of Radon–Nikodym derivatives $Q(A|x), Q(B|x), Q(A \cup B|x)$ such that

$$Q(A \cup B|x) = Q(A|x) + Q(B|x) \qquad (\pi_{\mathscr{X}}\text{-a.e. } x).$$

Now identify $Q(A|x)$ with $\xi_A(\omega)$ of the theorem and verify the continuity condition (6.1.8). For alternative approaches see Ash (1972, §6.6) and Feller (1966, p. 158).]

(b) Extend the above argument to the case of μ, a boundedly finite measure on $\mathscr{X} \times \mathscr{Y}$, where $\mathscr{X}, \mathscr{Y}$ are c.s.m.s. and there exists a boundedly finite measure λ on $\mathscr{B}_{\mathscr{X}}$ such that $\mu(\cdot \times B)$ is absolutely continuous with respect to λ for bounded sets $B \in \mathscr{B}_{\mathscr{Y}}$; that is, establish the existence of a family of measures $\mu(\cdot|x)$ on $\mathscr{B}_{\mathscr{Y}}$ for all $x \in \mathscr{X}$ such that $\mu(B|\cdot)$ is measurable for each bounded $B \in \mathscr{B}_{\mathscr{Y}}$, and for bounded sets $A \in \mathscr{B}_{\mathscr{X}}, B \in \mathscr{B}_{\mathscr{Y}}$,

$$\mu(A \times B) = \int_A \mu(B|x)\lambda(dx).$$

[*Hint*: Normalize λ so that it is a probability measure on A.]

6.2. Finite-Dimensional Distributions and the Existence Theorem

Only statements about the distributions of a process are amenable, via frequency counts and the like, to direct comparison with observations. This is some justification for the view that the theory of random measures can be reduced to the study of the measures they induce on $(\hat{\mathscr{M}}_{\mathscr{X}}, \mathscr{B}(\hat{\mathscr{M}}_{\mathscr{X}}))$.

Definition 6.2.I. The distribution of a random measure is the probability measure it induces on $(\hat{\mathscr{M}}_{\mathscr{X}}, \mathscr{B}(\hat{\mathscr{M}}_{\mathscr{X}}))$.

The properties of such probability measures are most easily approached through their finite-dimensional distributions.

Definition 6.2.II. The *finite-dimensional distributions* (*fidi* distributions for short) of a random measure ξ are the joint distributions, for all finite families of bounded Borel sets $A_1, \ldots, A_k$, of the random variables $\xi(A_1), \ldots, \xi(A_k)$, that is, the family of proper distribution functions

(6.2.1) $F_k(A_1, \ldots, A_k; x_1, \ldots, x_k) = \mathcal{P}\{\xi(A_i) \le x_i, i = 1, \ldots, k\}.$

Analogously to Theorem A2.6.III and Proposition 6.1.III, we have the following result, in which we say the distribution of a random measure is *completely determined* by some quantities ψ if, whenever two random measures give the same values for ψ, their distributions coincide.

Proposition 6.2.III. *The distribution of a random measure is completely determined by the fidi distributions* (6.2.1) *for all finite families* $(A_1, \ldots, A_k)$ *of disjoint sets from a semiring $\mathscr{A}$ of bounded sets generating $\mathscr{B}_{\mathscr{X}}$.*

PROOF. Let $\mathscr{R}$ denote the ring generated by $\mathscr{A}$. Then any element A of $\mathscr{R}$ can be represented as the finite union of disjoint sets from $\mathscr{A}$, $A = \bigcup_{i=1}^k A_i$ say, and thus, since

(6.2.2) $$\xi(A) = \sum_1^k \xi(A_i),$$

the distribution of $\xi(A)$ can be written down in terms of (6.2.1) for disjoint A_i. A similar result holds for the joint distributions of the $\xi(A)$ for any finite family of sets in $\mathscr{R}$. Thus, we may suppose (6.2.1) given for all finite families of sets A_i in $\mathscr{R}$.

Now consider the class of subsets of $\hat{\mathscr{M}}_{\mathscr{X}}$ of the form of *cylinder sets*,

(6.2.3) $\{\xi: \xi(A_i) \in B_i, i = 1, \ldots, k\},$

where the A_i are chosen from $\mathscr{R}$, and the B_i are Borel sets of the real line $\mathbb{R}$. These cylinder sets form a ring, and it follows from Theorem A2.5.III that this ring generates $\mathscr{B}(\hat{\mathscr{M}}_{\mathscr{X}})$. But the probabilities of all such sets can be determined from the joint distributions (6.2.1). Thus, the distribution of ξ is known on a ring generating $\mathscr{B}(\hat{\mathscr{M}}_{\mathscr{X}})$ and it follows from Proposition A1.3.I(b) that it is determined uniquely.   □

In the terminology of Billingsley (1968), Proposition 6.2.III asserts that finite families of disjoint sets from a semiring $\mathscr{A}$ generating $\mathscr{B}_{\mathscr{X}}$ form a *determining class* for random measures on $(\mathscr{X}, \mathscr{B}_{\mathscr{X}})$. Of course we also have the following corollary.

Corollary 6.2.IV. *The distribution of a random measure is completely determined by its fidi distributions.*

We turn now to the main problem of this section, to find necessary and sufficient conditions on a set of distribution functions (6.2.1) that will ensure that they are the fidi distributions of a random measure. The conditions fall into two groups: first the consistency requirements of the Kolmogorov existence theorem, and then the supplementary requirements of additivity and continuity needed to ensure that the realizations are measures.

Conditions 6.2.V (Kolmogorov Consistency Conditions).

(a) Invariance under index permutations. *For all integers $k > 0$ and all permutations $i_1, \ldots, i_k$ of the integers $1, \ldots, k$*

$$F_k(A_1, \ldots, A_k; x_1, \ldots, x_k) = F_k(A_{i_1}, \ldots, A_{i_k}; x_{i_1}, \ldots, x_{i_k}).$$

(b) Consistency of marginals. *For all $k \geq 1$*

$$F_{k+1}(A_1, \ldots, A_k, A_{k+1}; x_1, \ldots, x_k, \infty) = F_k(A_1, \ldots, A_k; x_1, \ldots, x_k).$$

The first of these is something like a notational requirement, reflecting the fact that the quantity $F_k(A_1, \ldots, A_k; x_1, \ldots, x_k)$ measures the probability of an event

$$\{\omega: \xi(A_i) \leq x_i; i = 1, 2, \ldots, k\},$$

which is independent of the order in which the random variables are written down. The second embodies the essential requirement that must be satisfied if there is to exist a single probability space Ω on which the random variables can be jointly defined.

The other group of conditions captures in distribution function terms the conditions (6.1.7) and (6.1.8), which express the fact that the random variables so produced must fit together as measures.

Condition 6.2.VI (Measure Requirements).

(a) *For every pair A_1, A_2 of disjoint Borel sets from $\mathcal{B}_{\mathcal{X}}$, the distribution $F_3(A_1, A_2; A_1 \cup A_2; x_1, x_2, x_3)$ is concentrated on the diagonal $x_1 + x_2 = x_3$.*
(b) *For every sequence $\{A_n; n \geq 1\}$ of bounded Borel sets decreasing to $\emptyset$, and all $\varepsilon > 0$,*

$$(6.2.4) \qquad\qquad 1 - F_1(A_n, \varepsilon) \to 0 \quad \text{as } n \to \infty.$$

Conditions 6.2.V imply the existence of a probability space on which random variables $\xi(A)$, $A \in \mathcal{B}_{\mathcal{X}}$, can be jointly defined. Then Condition 6.2.VI(a) implies

$$(6.2.5) \qquad\qquad \mathcal{P}\{\xi(A_1) + \xi(A_2) = \xi(A_1 \cup A_2)\} = 1.$$

It follows by induction that a similar relation holds for the members of any finite family of Borel sets. For any given sequence of sets, Condition 6.2.VI(a) implies a.s. finite additivity, and then Condition 6.2.VI(b) allows this finite additivity to be extended to countable additivity.

This leads us to the existence theorem itself, which asserts that, in the case of nonnegative realizations, the Conditions 6.2.V and 6.2.VI are not only necessary but also sufficient to ensure that the fidi distributions can be associated with a random measure. Note that Example 6.1(e) implies that without nonnegativity, the sufficiency argument breaks down. It appears to be an open problem to find necessary and sufficient conditions on the fidi distributions, which will ensure that they belong to a random signed measure.

Theorem 6.2.VII. *Let $F_k(\cdot\,;\,\cdot)$ be a family of distributions satisfying the consistency conditions 6.2.V. In order that the $F_k(\cdot)$ be the fidi distributions of a random measure, it is necessary and sufficient that*

(i) *the distributions $F_k(\cdot)$ be supported by the nonnegative half-line;*
(ii) *the $F_k(\cdot)$ satisfy Conditions 6.2.VI.*

PROOF. Since necessity is clear from the necessity part of Theorem 6.1.VI, let us proceed to sufficiency. Since the $F_k(\cdot)$ satisfy the Kolmogorov conditions, there exists a probability space $(\Omega, \mathscr{E}, \mathscr{P})$, and a family of random variables ξ_A indexed by the bounded Borel sets, such that they are related to the given fidi distributions by (6.2.1). Condition (i) above implies $\xi_A \geq 0$ a.s., and condition (ii) that the random variables ξ_A satisfy (6.1.7) for each fixed pair of bounded Borel sets. Since the random variables are a.s. monotonic decreasing, (6.2.4) implies the truth of (6.1.8) for each fixed sequence of bounded Borel sets A_n with $A_n \downarrow \varnothing$. As in earlier discussions, the whole difficulty of the proof evolves around the fact that in general there is an uncountable number of conditions to be checked, so that even though each individual condition is satisfied with probability 1, it cannot be concluded from this that the set on which they are simultaneously satisfied also has probability 1. To overcome this difficulty, we invoke Theorem 6.1.VI. It is clear from the earlier discussion that both conditions of Theorem 6.1.VI are satisfied, so that we can deduce the existence of a random measure ξ^* such that $\xi^*(A)$ and ξ_A coincide a.s. for every Borel set A. But this implies that ξ^* and ξ have the same fidi distributions, and so completes the proof.   □

Corollary 6.2.VIII. *There is a one-to-one correspondence between probability measures on $\mathscr{B}(\mathcal{M}_{\mathcal{X}})$ and families of fidi distributions satisfying Conditions 6.2.V and 6.2.VI.*

In practice, the fidi distributions are given most often for disjoint sets, so that Condition 6.2.VI(a) cannot be verified directly. In this situation it is important to know what conditions on the joint distributions of the $\xi(A)$ for disjoint sets will allow such distributions to be extended to a family satisfying Condition 6.2.VI(a).

Lemma 6.2.IX. *Let F_k be the family of fidi distributions defined for finite families of disjoint Borel sets and satisfying for such families the Kolmogorov conditions 6.2.V. In order for there to exist an extension (necessarily unique) to a full set of finite distributions satisfying Conditions 6.2.VI(a) as well as 6.2.V, it is necessary and sufficient that for all integers $k \geq 2$, and finite families* *of disjoint Borel sets* $\{A_1, A_2, \ldots, A_k\}$,

(6.2.6) $\qquad \int_0^z F_k(A_1, A_2, A_3, \ldots, A_k; dx_1, z - x_1, x_3, \ldots, x_k)$

$\qquad\qquad = F_{k-1}(A_1 \cup A_2, A_3, \ldots, A_k; z, x_3, \ldots, x_k).$

PROOF. The condition (6.2.6) is clearly a corollary of Condition 6.2.VI(a) and therefore necessary. We shall show that it is also sufficient. Let us first point out how the extension from disjoint to arbitrary families of sets can be made. Let $\{B_1, \ldots, B_n\}$ be any such arbitrary family. Then there exists a minimal family $\{A_1, \ldots, A_k\}$ of disjoint sets (formed from the intersections of the B_i) such that each B_i can be represented as a finite union of some of the A_j. The joint distribution $F_k(A_1, \ldots, A_k; x_1, \ldots, x_k)$ will be among those originally specified. Using this distribution, together with the representation of each $\xi(B_i)$ as a sum of the corresponding $\xi(A_j)$, we can write down the joint distribution of any combination of the $\xi(B_i)$ in terms of F_k. It is clear from the construction that the resultant joint distributions will satisfy Condition 6.2.VI(a) and that only this construction will satisfy this requirement. To complete the proof it is necessary to check that the extended family of distributions continues to satisfy Condition 6.2.V(b). We shall establish this by induction on the index k of the minimal family of disjoint sets generating the given fidi distribution. Suppose first that there are just two sets A_1, A_2 in this family. The new distributions defined by our construction are $F_2(A_1, A_1 \cup A_2)$, $F_2(A_2, A_1 \cup A_2)$ and $F_3(A_1, A_2, A_1 \cup A_2)$. Consistency with the original distributions $F_2(A_1, A_2)$, $F_1(A_1)$, and $F_1(A_2)$ is guaranteed by the construction and by the marginal consistency for distributions of disjoint sets. Only the marginal consistency with $F_1(A_1 \cup A_2)$ introduces a new element. Noting that by construction we have

$$F_2(A_1, A_1 \cup A_2; x, y) = \int_0^{\min(x, y)} F_2(A_1, A_2; du, y - u),$$

and letting $x \to \infty$, we see that this requirement reduces precisely to (6.2.6) with $k = 2$. Similarly, for $k > 2$, marginal consistency reduces to checking points covered by the construction, by preceding steps in the induction, by Condition 6.2.V(b) for disjoint sets, or by (6.2.6). $\qquad\square$

EXAMPLE 6.2(a) *Stationary gamma random measure* (continued from Example 6.1(d)). The Laplace transform relation

$$\psi_1(A; s) \equiv \psi(A; s) = (1 + \lambda s)^{-\ell(A)}$$

determines the one-dimensional distributions, while from the independent increments property the joint distributions are given for disjoint sets by the relation

$$\psi_k(A_1, \ldots, A_k; s_1, \ldots, s_k) = \prod_1^k (1 + \lambda s_j)^{-\ell(A_j)}.$$

Consistency of marginals here reduces to the requirement

$$\psi_{k-1}(A_1, \ldots, A_{k-1}; s_1, \ldots, s_{k-1}) = \psi_k(A_1, \ldots, A_k; s_1, \ldots, s_{k-1}, 0),$$

which is trivially satisfied. Also, if $A_n \downarrow \varnothing$, $\ell(A_n) \to 0$ by continuity of Lebesgue measure, and thus

$$\psi_1(A_n; s) = (1 + \lambda s)^{-\ell(A_n)} \to 1,$$

which is equivalent to Condition 6.2.VI(b). Finally, to check (6.2.6) we should verify that

$$\psi_1(A_1 \cup A_2; s) = \psi_2(A_1, A_2; s, s)$$

which is a simple consequence of additivity of Lebesgue measure.

These arguments establish the consistency conditions when the sets occurring in the fidi distributions are disjoint, and it follows from Lemma 6.2.IX that there is a unique consistent extension to arbitrary Borel sets.

Exercises

6.2.1. Given an example of a family of fidi distributions satisfying (6.2.6) for disjoint sets and all other requirements of Theorem 6.2.VII apart from Condition 6.2.VI(a), which is not satisfied. [*Hint*: Let $\mathscr{X}$ be a two-point space, $\{x, y\}$ say, and construct a r.v. Z and a random set function ξ for which Z has the distribution of $\xi(\{x, y\})$ but $Z \neq \xi(\{x\}) + \xi(\{y\})$.]

6.2.2. Given an example of a family of fidi distributions that satisfy (6.2.6) for $k = 2$ but not for some $k \geq 3$, and hence do not satisfy the consistency condition 6.2.V(b). [*Hint*: Modify the previous example.]

6.2.3. Verify that the joint distributions of the Dirichlet process (see Exercise 6.1.4) are consistent.

6.3. Sample-Path Properties and Completely Random Measures

The outstanding feature of the *sample paths* or *realizations* of a random measure is their countable additivity (cf. the last two sections!). Nevertheless, some additional questions remain. When, for example, will the realizations be almost surely purely atomic? or purely nonatomic? or absolutely continuous with respect to some given measure? In this section, we give a partial discussion of questions of this kind, leading to a description of the sample-path properties of a completely random measure.

A technique that runs through our analysis here and later, and has been exploited, for example, by Leadbetter (1968, 1972) and others, makes use of a *dissecting system* $\mathscr{T}$ for the state space $\mathscr{X}$. Here it suffices to recall from Definition A2.1.IV that a dissecting system $\mathscr{T} = \{\mathscr{T}_n: n = 1, 2, \ldots\}$ is a nested sequence of finite partitions $\mathcal{T}_n = \{A_{ni}: i = 1, \ldots, k_n\}$ of Borel sets A_{ni} that ultimately separates points of $\mathcal{X}$; that is, given any two distinct points x and y there exists an n such that x and y are contained in distinct members of $\mathcal{T}_n$ (and hence in distinct members of $\mathcal{T}_{n'}$ for all $n' \geq n$). We note also that for any $A \in \mathcal{B}_{\mathcal{X}}$, $\mathcal{T} \cap A$ is a dissecting system for A.

Proposition A2.1.V asserts that such systems exist for any c.s.m.s. $\mathcal{X}$, while if additionally $\mathcal{X}$ is locally compact (such as when $\mathcal{X}$ is Euclidean), a sufficient condition for a family of nested partitions $\mathcal{T}$ to be dissecting for a bounded Borel set A is that

(6.3.1) $$\max_{1 \leq i \leq k_n} \operatorname{diam}(A_{ni}) \to 0 \qquad (n \to \infty).$$

Returning to sample paths, we start with a consideration of the fixed atoms, abbreviating the notation $\xi(\{x\})$ to $\xi\{x\}$.

Definition 6.3.I. The point x_0 is a *fixed atom* of the random measure ξ if $\mathcal{P}\{\xi\{x_0\} > 0\} > 0$.

It must be remarked that the adjective "fixed" refers to the possible locations of certain atoms of realizations ξ: by contrast, if a realization ξ has $\xi\{x\} > 0$ but $\mathcal{P}\{\xi\{x\} > 0\} = 0$ then such an atom is termed a *random atom*.

Lemma 6.3.II. *The random measure ξ is free of fixed atoms on the bounded Borel set A if and only if for some (and then every) dissecting system $\mathcal{T}$ for A*

(6.3.2) $$\max_{1 \leq i \leq k_n} \mathcal{P}\{\xi(A_{ni}) > \varepsilon\} \to 0 \qquad (n \to \infty)$$

for every fixed $\varepsilon > 0$.

PROOF. We show that (6.3.2) fails if and only if ξ has a fixed atom, so assume that for some dissecting system $\mathcal{T}$ for A, some $\varepsilon > 0$, and some $\eta > 0$,

(6.3.3) $$\mathcal{P}\{\xi(A_{nj}) \geq \varepsilon\} \geq \eta$$

for at least one set A_{nj} in each $\mathcal{T}_n$, $n = 1, 2, \ldots$. Let $\mathcal{J}(n)$ denote all such indices (n, j), and $\mathcal{J} = \mathcal{J}(1) \cup \mathcal{J}(2) \cup \cdots$. Because the partitions $\mathcal{T}_n$ are nested, every $A_{n+1,j} \subseteq A_{n,j'(j)}$ for some $j'(j)$, and because ξ is a measure, $\xi(A_{n+1,j}) \leq \xi(A_{n,j'(j)})$ a.s. Consequently, the infinite set $\mathcal{J}$ is such that every $\mathcal{J}(n)$ contains at least one index (n, j) for which $A_{nj} \supseteq A_{n',j'}$ for infinitely many indices $(n', j') \in \mathcal{J}$. Use this property to construct a sequence $(n, j(n))$ such that $A_{n,j(n)} \supseteq A_{n+1,j(n+1)}$ and $(n, j(n)) \in \mathcal{J}(n)$ for each n. By the separation property of $\mathcal{T}$, $A_\infty \equiv \lim_{n \to \infty} A_{n,j(n)}$ is either the empty set $\varnothing$ or a singleton set, $\{x_0\}$ say. Because A is bounded, so is $A_{1,j(1)}$, and therefore $\infty > \xi(A_{n,j(n)})$. ξ being a random measure, we then have

$$\xi(A_{n,j(n)}) \downarrow \xi(A_\infty) \qquad (n \to \infty),$$

and therefore $\mathcal{P}\{\xi(A_\infty) \geq \varepsilon\} \geq \eta$. Since $\xi(\varnothing) = 0$ a.s. and $\varepsilon > 0$, we must have $A_\infty = \{x_0\}$, and thus ξ has at least one fixed atom.

Conversely, if ξ has a fixed atom $x_0 \in A$, there exists $\varepsilon > 0$ for which $0 < \mathcal{P}\{\xi\{x_0\} > \varepsilon\} \equiv \eta'$. Then, given any dissecting system $\mathcal{T}$ for A, there exists a set $A_{n,\,j(n)}$ in each $\mathcal{T}_n$ such that $x_0 \in A_{n,\,j(n)}$, and

$$\mathcal{P}\{\xi(A_{n,\,j(n)}) > \varepsilon\} \geq \mathcal{P}\{\xi\{x_0\} > \varepsilon\} = \eta' \qquad \text{(all } n\text{)},$$

so (6.3.2) fails for any dissecting system $\mathcal{T}$ for A. $\square$

Once the fixed atoms have been identified, one would anticipate representing the random measure as the superposition of two components, the first containing all fixed atoms and the second free from fixed atoms. It is not absolutely clear, however, that this procedure corresponds to a measurable operation on the original process. To establish this point, we show the following result.

Lemma 6.3.III. *The set D of fixed atoms of a random measure is countably infinite at most.*

PROOF. Suppose on the contrary that D is uncountable. Since $\mathcal{X}$ can be covered by the union of at most countably many bounded Borel sets, there exists a bounded set, A say, containing uncountably many fixed atoms.

Define the subset D_ε of $D \cap A$ by

$$(6.3.4) \qquad\qquad D_\varepsilon = \{x: \mathcal{P}\{\xi\{x\} > \varepsilon\} > \varepsilon\},$$

observing by monotonicity that $D \cap A = \lim_{\varepsilon \downarrow 0} D_\varepsilon$. If D_ε is finite for every $\varepsilon > 0$, then by a familiar construction we can deduce that $D \cap A$ is countable, so for some positive ε (which is fixed for the remainder of the proof), D_ε is infinite.

We can extract from D_ε an infinite sequence of distinct points $\{x_1, x_2, \ldots\}$ for which the events $E_n \equiv \{\xi: \xi\{x_n\} > \varepsilon\}$ have $\mathcal{P}(E_n) > \varepsilon$. Since ξ is boundedly finite,

$$0 = \mathcal{P}\{\xi(A) = \infty\}$$

$$\geq \mathcal{P}\{\xi\{x\} > \varepsilon \text{ for infinitely many } x \in D_\varepsilon\}$$

$$\geq \mathcal{P}\{\text{infinitely many } E_n \text{ occur}\}$$

$$= \mathcal{P}\left\{\bigcap_{n=1}^{\infty} \bigcup_{k=n}^{\infty} E_k\right\} = \lim_{n \to \infty} \mathcal{P}\left\{\bigcup_{k=n}^{\infty} E_k\right\}$$

$$\geq \varepsilon > 0,$$

thereby yielding a contradiction. $\square$

It is convenient to represent the countable set D by $\{x_k\}$ and to write $U_k = \xi\{x_k\}$. Define the *Dirac measure* δ_x by

$$\delta_x(A) = \begin{cases} 1 & x \in \text{Borel set } A, \\ 0 & x \notin A. \end{cases}$$

Then the set function ξ_c defined for bounded Borel sets A by

$$\xi_c(A) = \xi(A) - \sum_{x_k \in D} U_k \delta_{x_k}(A)$$

is positive and countably additive in A, and for every such A it defines a random variable. Thus, it defines a new random measure that is clearly free from fixed atoms, and we have proved the following proposition.

Proposition 6.3.IV. *Every random measure ξ can be written in the form*

$$\xi = \xi_c + \sum_{k=1}^{\infty} U_k \delta_{x_k},$$

where ξ_c is a random measure without fixed atoms, the sequence $\{x_k: k = 1, 2, \dots\}$ constitutes the set D of all fixed atoms of ξ, and $\{U_k: k = 1, 2, \dots\}$ is a sequence of nonnegative random variables.

We turn next to the more general question of finding conditions for the trajectories to be a.s. nonatomic. As before, let A be a bounded Borel set and $\mathscr{T} = \{\mathscr{T}_n: n = 1, 2, \dots\}$ a dissecting system for A. For any given $\varepsilon > 0$, we can "trap" any atoms of ξ with mass ε or greater by the following construction. For each n, set

(6.3.5) $N_\varepsilon^{(n)}(A) = \#\{i: A_{ni} \in \mathscr{T}_n, \xi(A_{ni}) \geq \varepsilon\}.$

Then each $N_\varepsilon^{(n)}(A)$ is a.s. finite, being bounded uniformly in n by $\xi(A)/\varepsilon$. Moreover, as $n \to \infty$, $N_\varepsilon^{(n)}(A)$ converges a.s. to a limit r.v., $N_\varepsilon(A)$ say, which is independent of the particular dissecting system $\mathscr{T}$ and which represents the number of atoms in A with mass ε or greater (see Exercise 6.3.2 for a more formal treatment of these assertions). Consequently, ξ is a.s. nonatomic on A if and only if for each $\varepsilon > 0$, $N_\varepsilon(A) = 0$ a.s. Since $N_\varepsilon^{(n)}(A)$ converges a.s. to $N_\varepsilon(A)$ irrespective of the value of the latter, a necessary and sufficient condition for $N_\varepsilon = 0$ a.s. is that $N_\varepsilon^{(n)} \to 0$ in probability. This leads to the following criterion.

Lemma 6.3.V. *The random measure ξ is a.s. nonatomic on bounded $A \in \mathscr{B}_{\mathscr{X}}$ if and only if for every $\varepsilon > 0$ and for some (and then every) dissecting system $\mathscr{T}$ for A,*

(6.3.6) $\mathscr{P}\{\#\{i: \xi(A_{ni}) \geq \varepsilon\} > 0\} \to 0$ $(n \to \infty).$

Corollary 6.3.VI. *A sufficient condition for ξ to be a.s. nonatomic on bounded $A \in \mathscr{B}_{\mathscr{X}}$ is that for some dissecting system for A and every $\varepsilon > 0$,*

(6.3.7) $\sum_{i=1}^{k_n} \mathscr{P}\{\xi(A_{ni}) \geq \varepsilon\} \to 0$ $(n \to \infty).$

If ξ is a completely random measure then this condition is also necessary.

PROOF. Equation (6.3.7) is sufficient for (6.3.6) to hold because

$$\mathscr{P}\left(\bigcup_{i=1}^{k_n} \{\xi(A_{ni}) \geq \varepsilon\}\right) \leq \sum_{i=1}^{k_n} \mathscr{P}\{\xi(A_{ni}) \geq \varepsilon\}.$$

When ξ is completely random, the r.v.s $\xi(A_{ni})$ are mutually independent and hence

$$(6.3.8) \qquad 1 - \mathscr{P}\left(\bigcup_{i=1}^{k_n} \{\xi(A_{ni}) \geq \varepsilon\}\right) = \mathscr{P}\left(\bigcap_{i=1}^{k_n} \{\xi(A_{ni}) < \varepsilon\}\right)$$

$$= \prod_{i=1}^{k_n} \mathscr{P}\{\xi(A_{ni}) < \varepsilon\}$$

$$= \prod_{i=1}^{k_n} (1 - \mathscr{P}\{\xi(A_{ni}) \geq \varepsilon\}).$$

If now ξ is a.s. nonatomic, then by (6.3.6) the left-hand side of (6.3.8) converges to 1 as $n \to \infty$. Finally, the convergence to 1 of the product on the right-hand side of (6.3.8) implies (6.3.7). □

EXAMPLE 6.3(a) "Quadratic" random measures (continued from Example 6.1(b)). Take A to be the unit interval $(0, 1]$, and for $n = 1, 2, \ldots$ divide this into $k_n \equiv 2^n$ subintervals each of length 2^{-n} to obtain suitable partitions for a dissecting system $\mathscr{T}$. Each $\xi(A_{ni})$ can be represented in the form

$$\xi_{ni} \equiv \xi(A_{ni}) = \int_{i/k_n}^{(i+1)/k_n} Z^2(t)dt \approx (1/k_n)Z^2(i/k_n).$$

Since $Z^2(i/k_n)$ has a χ^2 distribution on one degree of freedom, we deduce (as may be shown by a more careful analysis) that

$$\Pr\{\xi_{ni} > \varepsilon\} = \Pr\{Z^2(i/k_n) > k_n\varepsilon\}(1 + O(1))$$

$$\leq C \exp(-k_n\varepsilon)$$

for some finite constant C. Then

$$\sum_{i=1}^{k_n} \Pr\{\xi_{ni} > \varepsilon\} \leq Ck_n e^{-k_n\varepsilon} \to 0 \qquad (n \to \infty).$$

Thus, ξ being an integral with a.s. continuous integrand its trajectories are a.s. nonatomic.

It appears to be an open question to find simple sufficient conditions, analogous to Corollary 6.3.VI, for the realizations of a random measure to be a.s. absolutely continuous with respect to a given measure (see Example 6.1.1 and Exercises 6.1.4–6.1.6).

As a more extended application of the ideas in this section, let us turn now to a description of the sample-path structure of a general completely random measure on $\mathscr{X}$. A substantial step in the proof of the main representation result,

Equation (6.3.12) in Theorem 6.3.VIII, is the following result, which is of interest in its own right.

Proposition 6.3.VII. *If the completely random measure ξ is a.s. nonatomic, then there is a fixed nonatomic measure v such that*

$$(6.3.9) \qquad\qquad \xi(\cdot) = v(\cdot) \quad a.s.$$

PROOF. We again use a dissecting system $\mathcal{T}$ for any given bounded Borel set A and define the transforms

$$\psi_{ni}(s) = E(\exp[-s\xi(A_{ni})]) \quad (\text{Re}(s) \geq 0).$$

Since ξ is completely random and $\xi(A) = \sum_{i=1}^{k_n} \xi(A_{ni})$, we have

$$\psi_A(s) \equiv E(\exp[-s\xi(A)]) = \prod_{i=1}^{k_n} \psi_{ni}(s).$$

Now

$$1 - \psi_{ni}(s) = E(1 - \exp[-s\xi(A_{ni})])$$
$$= \int_0^\infty se^{-sy}\mathcal{P}\{\xi(A_{ni}) > y\}\,dy,$$

and appealing to Corollary 6.3.VI and the dominated convergence theorem, ξ being a.s. nonatomic implies that

$$\max_{1 \leq i \leq k_n} (1 - \psi_{ni}(s)) \to 0 \qquad (n \to \infty)$$

for every fixed real $s \geq 0$. Using this result in the logarithmic series expansion, it now follows that

$$(6.3.10) \qquad -\log \psi_A(s) = -\sum_{i=1}^{k_n} \log \psi_{ni}(s) = -\lim_{n\to\infty} \sum_{i=1}^{k_n} \log \psi_{ni}(s)$$
$$= \lim_{n\to\infty} \sum_{i=1}^{k_n} (1 - \psi_{ni}(s))$$
$$= \lim_{n\to\infty} \int_0^\infty (1 - e^{-sy})G_n(dy),$$

where $G_n(\cdot)$ is the sum of the k_n individual probability measures of $\xi(A_{ni})$. Again from (6.3.7) we have

$$(6.3.11) \qquad\qquad \int_\varepsilon^\infty G_n(dy) \to 0 \qquad (n \to \infty)$$

for every fixed $\varepsilon > 0$, while from the limit relation (6.3.10) it follows that $\int_0^\varepsilon yG_n(dy)$ remains bounded as $n \to \infty$. Thus, the sequence of measures

$$H_n(dy) \equiv \min(1, y)G_n(dy)$$

is not merely bounded in total mass but, from (6.3.11), is uniformly tight. Again, using (6.3.11), it follows that the only possible limit for $\{H_n\}$ is a degenerate measure with its mass concentrated at the origin. Since uniform tightness implies the existence of convergent subsequences, there must therefore exist a constant $v \equiv v(A)$ and a sequence $\{n_k\}$ for which $H_{n_k} \to v(A)\delta_0$ weakly, and thus

$$-\log \psi_A(s) = \lim_{n_k \to \infty} \int_0^\infty (1 - e^{-sy})G_{n_k}(dy)$$

$$= \lim_{n_k \to \infty} \int_0^\infty \frac{1 - e^{-sy}}{\min(y, 1)} H_{n_k}(dy)$$

$$= sv(A).$$

This result is equivalent to $\xi(A) = v(A)$ a.s. for the given bounded Borel set A. Since such a relation holds for any bounded Borel set A, the family $v(\cdot)$ must be a finitely bounded Borel measure and $\xi = v$ must hold for almost all realizations. Finally, since ξ is a.s. free of fixed atoms the same must also be true of v.   □

The major goal now is the following representation theorem.

Theorem 6.3.VIII. *Any completely random measure ξ on the c.s.m.s. $\mathcal{X}$ can be uniquely represented in the form*

$$(6.3.12) \qquad \xi(A) = \sum_{k=1}^\infty U_k \delta_{x_k}(A) + v(A) + \int_0^\infty yN(A \times dy),$$

where the sequence $\{x_k\}$ enumerates the countable set of fixed atoms of ξ, $\{U_k\}$ is a sequence of mutually independent nonnegative random variables determining (when positive) the masses at these atoms, $v(\cdot)$ is a fixed nonatomic boundedly finite measure on $\mathcal{X}$, and $N(\cdot)$ is a Poisson process on $\mathcal{X} \times (0, \infty)$, independent of $\{U_k\}$, the parameter measure μ of which may be unbounded on sets of the form $A \times (0, \varepsilon)$ but satisfies

$$(6.3.13a) \qquad \int_{y > \varepsilon} \mu(A \times dy) < \infty,$$

$$(6.3.13b) \qquad \int_{0 < y < \varepsilon} y\mu(A \times dy) < \infty$$

for every bounded Borel set A and every $0 < \varepsilon < \infty$, and for all $x \in \mathcal{X}$,

$$(6.3.13c) \qquad \mu(\{x\} \times (0, \infty)) = 0.$$

PROOF. The complete independence property shows that random masses U_k in the first component in (6.3.12), whose identification is assured by Proposition 6.3.IV, are mutually independent and independent also of the sum of the other two terms. So by considering $\xi - \sum U_k \delta_{x_k}$, we may assume that the completely random measure has no fixed atoms. Similar considerations imply (6.3.13c).

The construction of Lemma 6.3.V identifies integer-valued r.v.s $N_a(A)$ associated with the random (i.e., nonfixed) atoms in A of mass a or greater. Define a process by setting

$$\tilde{N}(A \times [a, b)) = N_a(A) - N_b(A)$$

for all bounded Borel sets A and intervals $[a, b)$ with $0 < a < b < \infty$. Then $\tilde{N}(A \times [a, b))$ is a random variable for each such rectangle, is finite a.s. whenever A is bounded, and a, b are finite and bounded away from 0. $\tilde{N}$ may be unbounded on sets $A \times (0, b)$, but by changing the metric on $(0, \infty)$, for example, by setting $\rho(a, b) = |\log b - \log a|$, such sets become unbounded, and then $\tilde{N}$ is boundedly finite in the usual sense for point processes. With this understanding, it follows from Proposition 6.1.III that $\tilde{N}$ defines a random measure on $\mathscr{X} \times (0, \infty)$. Clearly, by construction, $\tilde{N}$ is in fact a point process on $\mathscr{X} \times (0, \infty)$.

To show that $\tilde{N}$ inherits the completely random property, let $V_i = A_i \times [a_i, b_i)$ $(i = 1, 2)$ be any two disjoint product sets of the form described above. If $A_1 \cap A_2 = \varnothing$, it is obvious that $\tilde{N}(V_1)$ and $\tilde{N}(V_2)$ are independent. Consider the other possibility, that $A_1 = A_2 = A$ but $[a_1, b_1)$ and $[a_2, b_2)$ are disjoint. Let $\mathscr{T}$ be a dissecting system for A, and set

$$X_{ni} = \begin{cases} 1 & \text{if } a_1 \le \xi(A_{ni}) < b_1, \\ 0 & \text{otherwise,} \end{cases}$$

$$Y_{ni} = \begin{cases} 1 & \text{if } a_2 \le \xi(A_{ni}) < b_2, \\ 0 & \text{otherwise,} \end{cases}$$

$$p_{ni} = \mathscr{P}\{X_{ni} = 1\}, \qquad q_{ni} = \mathscr{P}\{Y_{ni} = 1\}.$$

Then

$$\tilde{N}(V_1) = \lim_{n \to \infty} \sum_{i=1}^{k_n} X_{ni} \quad \text{a.s.,} \qquad \tilde{N}(V_2) = \lim_{n \to \infty} \sum_{i=1}^{k_n} Y_{ni} \quad \text{a.s.,}$$

and the complete independence property yields for the joint probability generating function [with $|z_i| \le 1$ $(i = 1, 2)$]

$$(6.3.14) \quad E(z_1^{\tilde{N}(V_1)} z_2^{\tilde{N}(V_2)}) = \lim_{n \to \infty} \prod_{i=1}^{k_n} E(z_1^{X_{ni}} z_2^{Y_{ni}})$$

$$= \lim_{n \to \infty} \prod_{i=1}^{k_n} (1 - p_{ni}(1 - z_1) - q_{ni}(1 - z_2)).$$

Similarly,

$$(6.3.15) \quad E(z_1^{\tilde{N}(V_1)}) E(z_2^{\tilde{N}(V_2)}) = \lim_{n \to \infty} \prod_{i=1}^{k_n} (1 - p_{ni}(1 - z_1))(1 - q_{ni}(1 - z_2)).$$

To establish the independence of $\tilde{N}(V_1)$, $\tilde{N}(V_2)$, it is enough to show that (6.3.14) and (6.3.15) are equal for all $0 \leq z_i \leq 1$ ($i = 1, 2$). Taking logarithms, and using the inequalities

(6.3.16)
$$x \leq -\log(1 - x) \leq x/(1 - x),$$

valid for $0 \leq x < 1$, we have for $0 \leq z_i \leq 1$ in (6.3.14), and writing $r_{ni} = p_{ni}(1 - z_1) + q_{ni}(1 - z_2)$,

(6.3.17)
$$0 \leq -\sum_{i=1}^{k_n} \log(1 - r_{ni}) - \sum_{i=1}^{k_n} r_{ni}$$

$$\leq R_n \equiv \sum_{i=1}^{k_n} \frac{r_{ni}^2}{1 - r_{ni}}$$

$$\leq \left(\frac{\max r_{ni}}{1 - \max r_{ni}}\right) \sum_{i=1}^{k_n} r_{ni}.$$

Now from Lemma 6.3.II we must have $\max r_{ni} \to 0$ ($n \to \infty$), while by (6.3.14) and the first inequality at (6.3.17),

$$\sum_{i=1}^{k_n} r_{ni} \leq -\sum_{i=1}^{k_n} \log(1 - r_{ni}) \to -\log E(z_1^{\tilde{N}(V_1)} z_2^{\tilde{N}(V_2)}),$$

which is finite, uniformly in n. So $R_n \to 0$ as $n \to \infty$. Similar estimates apply to the two generating functions at (6.3.15), and since the difference of the leading terms in (6.3.14) and (6.3.15) vanishes, we must have equality of the generating functions as required.

By induction we can demonstrate the independence of any finite family $\{\tilde{N}(V_i): i = 1, \ldots, k\}$ whenever the sets V_i are rectangular and disjoint as considered. Now by Proposition 6.2.III and its corollary, the distribution of $\tilde{N}$ is determined by all the joint distributions $\{\tilde{N}(V_i): i = 1, \ldots, k\}$, and thus $\tilde{N}(\cdot)$ is completely random. Since by construction $\tilde{N}$ is a simple point process, Theorem 2.4.VII implies that $\tilde{N}$ is a Poisson process with parameter measure μ taking finite values on rectangles of the form already considered.

The tighter boundedness properties in (6.3.13) can be established as follows. First, since $N_\varepsilon(A) = \tilde{N}(A \times [\varepsilon, \infty))$ is boundedly finite for fixed $\varepsilon > 0$ and (as just shown) is for fixed A a Poisson process in the range $\infty > \varepsilon > 0$, the finiteness of (6.3.13a) is assured. For (6.3.13b), we observe moreover that for every $\varepsilon > 0$,

(6.3.18)
$$\int_0^\varepsilon y\tilde{N}(A \times dy) \leq \xi(A) < \infty \quad \text{a.s.}$$

since the integral is simply a sum (possibly an infinite series) of the contribution of the random atoms of ξ to its total mass $\xi(A)$ on A. To see that the convergence of the integral at (6.3.18) implies the convergence of its expectation as at (6.3.13b), partition the interval $(0, \varepsilon)$ into the sequence of subintervals $\{[\varepsilon/(r + 1), \varepsilon/r): r = 1, 2, \ldots\}$. Then

$$\int_0^\varepsilon y\mu(A \times dy) \leq \sum_{r=1}^\infty y_r\mu(A_r) \quad \text{where } y_r = \varepsilon/r, \ A_r = A \times [\varepsilon/(r+1), \varepsilon/r).$$

Let $\{\zeta_r\}$ be a sequence of independent Poisson r.v.s with parameters $\mu(A_r)$. Then for the Laplace transform of $\sum y_r\zeta_r$ we have

$$-\log E\left(\exp\left(-s\sum_{r=1}^\infty y_r\zeta_r\right)\right) = \sum_{r=1}^\infty \mu(A_r)(1 - \exp(-sy_r))$$

$$\geq \tfrac{1}{2}s\sum_{r=1}^\infty y_r\mu(A_r)$$

for $0 < s < \varepsilon^{-1}$, since then $0 < sy_r \leq 1$.

Thus, the convergence of $\sum y_r\mu(A_r)$ is implied by the a.s. convergence of $\sum y_r\zeta_r$, concerning which we have

$$\sum y_r\zeta_r = \sum(\varepsilon/r)\zeta_r \geq \int_0^\varepsilon y\tilde{N}(A \times dy) \geq \sum(\varepsilon/(r+1))\zeta_r \geq \tfrac{1}{2}\sum y_r\zeta_r.$$

The asserted finiteness at (6.3.13b) is now established.

Finally, we have that the measure

$$\tilde{v}(A) \equiv \xi(A) - \sum U_k\delta_{x_k}(A) - \int_0^\infty y\tilde{N}(A \times dy)$$

is a.s. nonatomic (by construction) and completely random since ξ is by assumption and the other two terms have been demonstrated to have the property. Then by Proposition 6.3.VII, $\tilde{v} = v$ a.s. for some fixed nonatomic measure v. The theorem is proved on noting that of the three terms in (6.3.12), the first consists of fixed atoms, the second is a constant measure, and the third is purely atomic, so uniqueness is assured. ☐

As a simple corollary we obtain the Lévy-type representation for the Laplace transform of completely random measures.

Proposition 6.3.IX. *In order that the family $\{\psi_A(\cdot), A \in \mathscr{B}_{\mathscr{X}}\}$, denote the Laplace transforms of the one-dimensional distributions of a completely random measure on $\mathscr{X}$, it is necessary and sufficient that $\psi_A(\cdot)$ be representable in the form, for $\mathrm{Re}(s) \geq 0$,*

$$(6.3.19) \quad \psi_A(s) = \exp\left(-\sum_{k=1}^\infty \theta_k(s)\delta_{x_k}(A) - \int_0^\infty (1 - e^{-sy})\mu(A \times dy) - sv(A)\right)$$

where $\{x_k\}$ is a fixed sequence of points, each $\theta_k(\cdot)$ is the logarithm of the Laplace transform of a positive random variable, and the measures v, μ have the same properties as in Theorem 6.3.VIII.

Conversely, given any such family $\{x_k, \theta_k(\cdot), v, \mu\}$, there exists a completely random measure with one-dimensional Laplace transforms given by (6.3.19).

PROOF. The representation (6.3.19) follows immediately on substituting for $\xi(A)$ from (6.3.12) in the expectation $\psi_A(s) = E(e^{-s\xi(A)})$.

To prove the converse it is sufficient to show that the form (6.3.19), together with the definition of joint distributions through the completely random property, yields a consistent family of finite-dimensional distributions. The details of the verifications are left as Exercise 6.3.3.   □

Exercises

6.3.1. Use Lemma 6.3.II to show that a general gamma random measure process (see Exercise 6.1.2) has no fixed atoms if and only if its shape parameter is a nonatomic measure.

6.3.2. An elaboration of the argument leading to Lemma 6.3.V is as follows. Suppose given $\mu \in \mathcal{M}_{\mathcal{X}}$, bounded $A \in \mathcal{B}_{\mathcal{X}}$, a dissecting system $\mathcal{T} = \{\mathcal{T}_n\}$ for A, and $\varepsilon > 0$. Define

$$v_\varepsilon^{(n)}(A) = \#\{i\colon A_{ni} \in \mathcal{T}_n, \mu(A_{ni}) \geq \varepsilon\}.$$

Let $x_1, \ldots, x_k$ be the atoms in A whose masses $u_1, \ldots, u_k$ are at least ε [and, because $\mu(A) < \infty$, k is certainly finite].
(a) Show that $k = 0$ if and only if $v_\varepsilon^{(n)}(A) = 0$ for all sufficiently large n (cf. Lemma 6.3.II).
(b) More generally, show that there exists $n' < \infty$ such that $v_\varepsilon^{(n)}(A) = k$ for all $n \geq n'$.
(c) Since k is independent of $\mathcal{T}$, so is $v_\varepsilon(A) \equiv \lim_{n\to\infty} v_\varepsilon^{(n)}(A)$.
(d) Let A vary over the bounded Borel sets. Show that $v_\varepsilon(\cdot)$ is a measure (in fact, $v_\varepsilon \in \mathcal{N}_{\mathcal{X}}^*$ of Definition 7.1.I).
(e) Given a random measure ξ, so that $\xi(\cdot, \omega) \in \mathcal{N}_{\mathcal{X}}$, denote by $N_\varepsilon(\cdot, \omega)$ the corresponding counting measure. Use Proposition 6.1.III to verify that N_ε is a random measure [indeed, by (d) and Definition 7.1.VII, it is a point process].
(f) Observe that the family of measures defined by $\mu_\varepsilon(A) = \sum_{i=1}^{k} u_i \delta_{x_i}(A)$, indexed by ε, has $\mu_\varepsilon(A) \to \mu(A)$ if and only if μ is purely atomic.

6.3.3. Imitate the discussion of Example 6.2(a) to verify that the fidi distributions of completely random measure, constructed with one-dimensional distributions as at (6.3.19), satisfy the consistency conditions 6.2.V and 6.2.VI.

6.3.4. Let ξ be a stationary completely random measure in $\mathbb{R}$, and let $\psi_t(s)$ denote the Laplace transform of $\xi(0, t]$.
(a) Deduce from Theorem 6.2.VII that

$$\psi_t(s) = \exp\left\{-stv - t\int_{(0,\infty]} (1 - e^{-sy})(1 - e^{-y})^{-1}G(dy)\right\}$$

for some totally finite measure G and some nonnegative finite constant v [$v = v((0, 1])$ in the notation of (6.3.19)]. [This form parallels that given in Kendall (1963); the measure μ of (6.3.13) and (6.3.19) satisfies $\int_{(0,\infty)} (1 - e^{-y})\mu(A \times dy) < \infty$.]
(b) Deduce that $\mathcal{P}\{\xi(0, t] = 0\} > 0$ if and only if both $v = 0$ and $\int_{(0,1)} y^{-1}G(dy) < \infty$. (The condition $v = 0$ precludes any positive linear trend, and the other

condition precludes the possibility of a countable everywhere dense set of atoms.)

6.3.5. For a given random measure ξ let $\mathscr{Y}$ denote the family of measures η satisfying

$$\mathscr{P}\{\xi(A) \geq \eta(A) \text{ (all } A \in \mathscr{B}_{\mathscr{X}})\} = 1.$$

(a) Define

$$v_d(A) = \sup_{\eta \in \mathscr{Y}} \eta(A),$$

check that it is a measure, and confirm that $\xi - v_d$ is a random measure.
(b) Extract from $\xi - v_d$ the random measure ζ_a consisting of all the fixed atoms of $\xi - v_d$, leaving $\xi_r = \xi - v_d - \zeta_a$.
(c) The decomposition

$$\xi = v_d + \zeta_a + \xi_r$$

into a deterministic component v_d, a component of fixed atoms ζ_a, and a random component ξ_r has now been effected. Give an example showing that there may still be bounded $A \in \mathscr{B}_{\mathscr{X}}$ for which $\mathscr{P}\{\xi_r(A) \geq \varepsilon\} = 1$ for some $\varepsilon > 0$. [*Hint*: Let ξ_r give mass 1 to either U or $U + 1$, where U is uniformly distributed on $(0, 1)$.]
(d) Observe that v_d equals v of (6.3.12) if and only if for each k, $\mathscr{P}\{U_k \leq \varepsilon\} > 0$ for every $\varepsilon > 0$.

6.4. Random Integrals, Characteristic Functionals, and Moment Measures

Let f be a Borel measurable function, defined on the same c.s.m.s. space as ξ. No special definitions are needed to introduce the integral

$$(6.4.1) \qquad \xi_f = \int_{\mathscr{X}} f(x)\xi(dx) = \int f \, d\xi$$

for by assumption each realization of ξ is a boundedly finite measure, and the usual theory of the Lebesgue integral applies on a realization by realization basis. In particular, if we introduce the space $BM(\mathscr{X})$ of bounded measurable functions, which vanish outside a bounded set in $\mathscr{X}$, then with probability 1 the integral exists and is finite. It is also a random variable; this can be seen by first taking f to be the indicator function of a bounded Borel set and then applying the usual approximation arguments using linear combinations and monotone limits. Since the class of random variables is closed under both such operations, and $\xi_f = \xi(A)$ is certainly a random variable when $f = I_A$, it follows that ξ_f is a (proper) random variable for any $f \in BM(\mathscr{X})$.

The study of such random integrals, which are evidently linear in f, links the theory of random measure with a whole hierarchy of theories of random linear functionals, of which the theory of random distributions is perhaps the most important, and will be relevant in discussing second-order properties in Chapter 11. We pause, therefore, to give a brief introduction to such general theories.

If we are given any linear space $\mathscr{U}$ on which notions of addition and scalar multiplication are defined, the concept of a linear functional, that is, a mapping γ from $\mathscr{U}$ into the real line satisfying

$$\gamma(\alpha u + \beta v) = \alpha\gamma(u) + \beta\gamma(v)$$

makes sense, and we may consider the space of all such linear functionals on a given $\mathscr{U}$. Furthermore, if $\mathscr{U}$ has a topology conformable with the linear operations (i.e., one making these continuous), we may consider the smaller space of *continuous* linear functionals on $\mathscr{U}$. Many different possibilities arise, depending on the choice of $\mathscr{U}$ and of the topology on $\mathscr{U}$ with respect to which the continuity is defined.

With any such choice there are several ways in which we may associate a random structure with the given space of linear functionals. Of these we distinguish two general classes, which we call *strict sense* and *broad sense* random linear functionals.

A natural σ-algebra in the space $\mathscr{U}^*$ of continuous linear functionals on $\mathscr{U}$ will be the smallest σ-algebra with respect to which the mappings $\gamma \to \gamma(u)$ are measurable with respect to each $u \in \mathscr{U}$. Endowing $\mathscr{U}^*$ with this σ-algebra, we may define a *strict sense* random linear functional on $\mathscr{U}$ as a measurable mapping $\Gamma(\cdot)$ from a probability space into $\mathscr{U}^*$. This ensures, as a minimal property, that $\Gamma(u)$ is a random variable for each $u \in \mathscr{U}$. On the other hand, it is usually difficult to determine conditions on the distributions of a family of random variables $\{\Gamma_u\}$, indexed by the elements $u \in \mathscr{U}$, which will allow us to conclude that the family $\{\Gamma_u\}$ can be identified a.s. with a random functional $\Gamma(u)$ in this strict sense. The same difficulty arises if we attempt to define a random linear functional as a probability distribution on $\mathscr{U}^*$. How can we tell, from the fidi distributions or otherwise, whether such a distribution does indeed correspond to such an object? Even in the random measure case this discussion is not trivial, and in many other situations it remains unresolved.

The alternative, *broad sense*, approach is to accept that a random linear functional cannot be treated as more than a family of random variables indexed by the elements of $\mathscr{U}$ and to impose on this family appropriate linearity and continuity requirements. Thus, we might require

(6.4.2) $$\Gamma_{\alpha u + \beta v} = \alpha\Gamma_u + \beta\Gamma_v \quad \text{(a.s.)}$$

and, if $u_n \to u$ in the given topology on $\mathscr{U}$,

(6.4.3) $$\xi_{u_n} \to \xi_u \quad \text{(a.s.)}$$

or, at (6.4.3), we could merely use convergence in probability or in q.m. If $\Gamma_u = \Gamma(u)$ for all $u \in \mathscr{U}$, where $\Gamma(\cdot)$ is a strict sense random linear functional, then of course both (6.4.2) and (6.4.3) will hold a.s. Dudley (1969) reviews some deeper results pertaining to random linear functionals.

EXAMPLE 6.4(a) *Generalized random Processes or random Schwartz distributions.* Take $\mathscr{X} = \mathbb{R}$, and let $\mathscr{U}$ be the space of all *test functions* on $\mathbb{R}$, that is, all infinitely differentiable functions on $(-\infty, \infty)$ that vanish outside some finite interval. A topology on $\mathscr{U}$ is introduced by setting $u_n \to u$ if and only if the $\{u_n\}$ vanish outside some common finite interval, and for all $k \geq 0$, the kth derivatives $\{u_n^{(k)}\}$ converge uniformly to $u^{(k)}$. Then $\mathscr{U}^*$, the space of all functionals on $\mathscr{U}$ satisfying

(i) $\gamma(\alpha u + \beta v) = \alpha\gamma(u) + \beta\gamma(v)$ (linearity)
(ii) $\gamma(u_n) \to \gamma(u)$ whenever $u_n \to u$ in $\mathscr{U}$,

is identified with the space of generalized functions, or more precisely Schwartz distributions. Any ordinary continuous function g defines such a distribution through the relation

$$\gamma(u) = \int_{-\infty}^{\infty} g(x)u(x)dx,$$

the continuity condition $\gamma(u_n) \to \gamma(u)$ when $u_n \to u$ following from the boundedness of g on the finite interval outside which the u_n vanish, and the uniform convergence of the u_n themselves. Similarly, any bounded finite measure G on $\mathbb{R}$ defines a distribution by the relation

$$\gamma(u) = \int_{\mathbb{R}} u(x)G(dx).$$

However, many further types of Schwartz distribution are possible, relating, for example, to linear operations on the derivatives of u.

The corresponding strict sense theory has been relatively little used, but the broad sense theory plays a central role in the second-order theory of stationary generalized processes, of which the second-order theory of stationary point processes and random measures forms a special case. A similar theory for random generalized fields can be developed by taking test functions on $\mathbb{R}^d$ in place of test functions on $\mathbb{R}$. Gel'fand and Vilenkin (1964) and Yaglom (1961) give systematic treatments of these broad sense theories.

A natural tool for handling any type of random linear functional is the *characteristic functional*, defined by

(6.4.4) $\Phi_\Gamma[g] = E(\exp(i\Gamma_g))$

for $g \in \mathscr{U}$, and Γ_g a random linear functional (strict or wide sense) on $\mathscr{U}$. It can be described as the characteristic function of Γ_g, evaluated at the arbitrary value $s = 1$ and treated as a function of g rather than s.

EXAMPLE 6.4(b) *Gaussian measures on Hilbert space.* Random variables taking their values in a Hilbert space $\mathscr{H}$ can be placed within the general framework of random linear functionals by taking advantage of the fact that the space of continuous linear functionals on a Hilbert space can be identified with the given Hilbert space itself. In this interpretation $\Gamma(u)$ is identified with the inner product $\langle \Gamma, u \rangle$ for $u \in \mathcal{H}$.

If $\mathcal{H}$ is finite dimensional, the characteristic functional reduces to the multivariate characteristic function

$$E(\exp(i\langle \Gamma, u \rangle)) = E\left(\exp\left(i \sum_{k=1}^{n} \Gamma_k u_k\right)\right) = \phi(u_1, \ldots, u_n) = \phi(u),$$

where $\{\Gamma_k\}$ and $\{u_k\}$ are the coordinates of Γ and u. In this case a Gaussian measure is just the ordinary multivariate normal distribution: setting the mean terms equal to zero for simplicity, the characteristic function has the form

$$\phi(u) = \exp(-\tfrac{1}{2} u' A u),$$

where $u'Au$ is the quadratic form associated with the nonnegative definite (positive semidefinite) symmetric matrix A. This suggests the generalization to infinite-dimensional Hilbert space of

(6.4.5) $$\Phi[u] = E(\exp(i\Gamma_u)) = \exp(-\tfrac{1}{2}\langle u, Au \rangle),$$

where A is now a positive definite self-adjoint linear operator. The finite-dimensional distributions of $\Gamma_{u_1}, \ldots, \Gamma_{u_n}$ for arbitrary $u_1, \ldots, u_n$ in $\mathcal{H}$ can be determined by setting $\sum_1^n s_k u_k$ in place of u in (6.4.5): they are of multivariate normal form with $n \times n$ covariance matrix having elements $\langle u_i, Au_j \rangle$. From this representation the consistency conditions are readily checked, as well as the linearity requirement (6.4.2). If $u_n \to u$ (i.e., $\|u_n - u\| \to 0$,) it follows from the boundedness of A that $\langle (u_n - u), A(u_n - u) \rangle \to 0$ and hence that $\Gamma_{u_n} \to \Gamma_u$ in probability and in q.m.

These arguments suffice to show that (6.4.5) defines a broad sense random linear functional on $\mathcal{H}$, but they are not sufficient to imply that (6.4.5) defines a strict sense random linear functional. For this, more stringent requirements are needed, which have their roots in the fact that a probability measure on $\mathcal{H}$ must be *tight*, and hence in a loose sense approximately concentrated on a finite-dimensional subset of $\mathcal{H}$. It is known [e.g., see Parthasarathy (1967, Chap. 8)] that the necessary and sufficient conditions for (6.4.5) to be the characteristic functional of a strict sense random linear functional on $\mathcal{H}$ [so that we can write $\Gamma_u = \Gamma(u) = \langle \Gamma, u \rangle$], or, equivalently, of a probability measure on $\mathcal{H}$ itself, is that the operator A be of Hilbert–Schmidt type. In this case the characteristic functional has the more special form

$$\Phi[u] = \exp(-\tfrac{1}{2}\sum \lambda_k (\langle h_k, u \rangle)^2),$$

where $\{h_k\}$ is a complete set of eigenvectors for A, $\{\lambda_k\}$ is the set of corresponding eigenvalues, and $\sum \lambda_k^2 < \infty$.

Returning to the random measure context, let us first note that random measures can just as easily be characterized by the values of the integrals (6.4.1) as they can by their evaluations on Borel sets; indeed, the latter are just a special case of the former when f is an indicator function. It follows at once that $\mathscr{B}(\mathscr{M}_{\mathscr{X}})$ is the smallest σ-algebra with respect to which the random integrals $\int f\, d\xi$ are measurable for each $f \in BM(\mathscr{X})$, and that a mapping ξ from a probability space into $\mathscr{M}_{\mathscr{X}}$ is a random measure if and only if $\int f\, d\xi$ is a random variable for each $f \in BM(\mathscr{X})$ [a smaller class of functions f suffices: Exercise 3.1 of Kallenberg (1975) indicates a stronger version of this result]. A more useful result is the following analogue of Proposition 6.1.III, the proof of which is left as a further exercise.

Proposition 6.4.I. *Let $\{\xi_f\}$ be a family of random variables, indexed by the elements f of $BM(\mathscr{X})$. Then there exists a random measure ξ such that*

$$\xi_f = \int f\, d\xi \quad \text{a.s.}$$

if and only if

(i) $\xi_{\alpha f + \beta g} = \alpha \xi_f + \beta \xi_g$ *a.s. for all scalars α, β and $f, g \in BM(\mathscr{X})$; and*
(ii) $\xi_{f_n} \to \xi_f$ *a.s. as $n \to \infty$ for all monotonically converging nonnegative sequences $\{f_n\} \subset BM(\mathscr{X})$ (i.e., $f_n \geq 0$ and $f_n \uparrow f$).*

Conditions (i) and (ii) are, of course, nothing but the conditions (6.4.2) and (6.4.3) in a form suitable for random measures; the importance of the proposition is that it implies that the *broad and strict sense approaches are equivalent for random measures*.

From this point it is easy to move to a characterization of the finite-dimensional distributions of the integrals $\int f\, d\xi$ for a random measure; we shall state this in the form of a characterization theorem for characteristic functionals, which we define by

(6.4.6) $\qquad \Phi_\xi[f] = E(\exp(i \int f\, d\xi)), \qquad f \in BM(\mathscr{X})$

as the appropriate special form of (6.4.4).

Theorem 6.4.II. *Let the functional $\Phi[f]$ be real or complex-valued, defined for all $f \in BM(\mathscr{X})$. Then Φ is the characteristic functional of a random measure ξ on $\mathscr{X}$ if and only if*

(i) *for every finite family $f_1, \ldots, f_n$ of functions $f_k \in BM(\mathscr{X})$, the function ϕ_n defined by*

(6.4.7) $\qquad \phi_n(f_1, \ldots, f_n; s_1, \ldots, s_n) = \Phi\left[\sum_1^n s_k f_k\right]$

is the multivariate characteristic function of proper random variables $\xi_{f_1}, \ldots, \xi_{f_n}$, which are nonnegative a.s. when the functions $f_1, \ldots, f_n$ are nonnegative;

(ii) *for every sequence $\{f_n\}$ of functions from $BM(\mathscr{X})$ with $f_n \geq 0$, and $f_n \uparrow f$ pointwise,*

(6.4.8) $\Phi[f_n] \to \Phi[f]$; and

(iii) $\Phi[0] = 1$ where 0 here denotes the zero function in $BM(\mathscr{X})$.

Moreover when the conditions are satisfied, the functional Φ uniquely determines the distribution of ξ.

PROOF. If ξ is a random measure, conditions (i) and (iii) are immediate, and imply that the fidi distributions of ξ, and hence the distribution of ξ itself, are uniquely determined by ξ. If $f_n \to f$ pointwise, and the f_n are either monotonic or bounded by a common element of $BM(\mathscr{X})$, it follows from the Lebesgue convergence theorems that for each realization

$$\xi_{f_n} = \int f_n \, d\xi \to \int f \, d\xi = \xi_f,$$

so that $\xi_{f_n} \to \xi_f$ a.s. Equation (6.4.8) follows from a further application of the dominated convergence theorem, since the random variables $\exp(i \int f_n \, d\xi)$ are uniformly bounded by unity.

Suppose next that conditions (i)–(iii) are satisfied. Condition (i) subsumes both Kolmogorov consistency conditions for the fidi distributions of the random variables ξ_f defined by (6.4.7) for $f \in BM(\mathscr{X})$. For example, in characteristic function terms, the requirement of marginal consistency reduces to the trivial verification that

$$\Phi\left[\sum_1^{n-1} s_i f_i + 0 \cdot f_n\right] = \Phi\left[\sum_1^{n-1} s_i f_i\right].$$

Thus, we may assume the existence of a jointly distributed family of random variables $\{\xi_f, f \in BM(\mathscr{X})\}$.

Condition (i) also implies the linearity property (i) of Proposition 6.4.I, for the condition

$$\xi_{f_3} = \xi_{f_1} + \xi_{f_2} \quad \text{(a.s.)}$$

is equivalent to the identity

$$\Phi[s_1 f_1 + s_2 f_2 + s_3 f_3] = \Phi[(s_1 + s_3)f_1 + (s_2 + s_3)f_2],$$

which will certainly be valid if $f_3 = f_1 + f_2$. A similar argument applies when scalar multiplies α, β are included.

Finally, condition (ii) of the theorem implies that the distribution of ξ_{f-f_n} approaches the distribution degenerate at zero, and hence that ξ_{f-f_n} converges in probability to zero. From the linearity property of the ξ_f we deduce that

(6.4.9) $\xi_{f_n} \to \xi_f$ (in probability).

Since, however, we assume in condition (ii) that the sequence $\{f_n\}$ is monotonic, it follows from condition (i) that the sequence $\{\xi_{f_n}\}$ is a.s. monotonic increasing. Since $\xi_{f_n} \le \xi_f$ a.s. by similar reasoning, ξ_{f_n} converges a.s. to a proper limit random variable X. But then (6.4.9) implies $X = \xi_f$ a.s., so condition (ii) of Proposition 6.4.I is also satisfied. The existence of a random measure with the required properties now follows from Proposition 6.4.I and the part of the theorem already proved.   □

Variants of condition (ii) above are indicated in Exercise 6.4.1.

As with ordinary random variables and characteristic functions, the characteristic functional is closely associated with the moment structure of the random measure, which, as in the point process case studied in Chapter 5, is expressed through a family of *moment measures*. In particular, for any random measure ξ on the c.s.m.s. $\mathscr{X}$ and any Borel set A, consider the expectation

$$(6.4.10) \qquad M(A) = E(\xi(A)) \quad \text{(finite or infinite)}.$$

Clearly, M inherits the property of finite additivity from the underlying random measure ξ. Moreover, if the sequence $\{A_n\}$ of Borel sets is monotonic increasing to A, then by monotone convergence $M(A_n) \uparrow M(A)$. Thus, $M(\cdot)$ is continuous from below and therefore a measure. In general, it need not take finite values, even on bounded sets. When it does so, we say that the *expectation measure of ξ exists* and is given by (6.4.10).

When it does exist, the above argument can readily be extended to the random integrals $\int f\, d\xi$ for $f \in BM(\mathscr{X})$. Thus, if f is the indicator function of the bounded Borel set A, $E(\int f\, d\xi) = M(A)$. Extending in the usual way through linear combinations and monotone limits we find

$$(6.4.11) \qquad E\left(\int f\, d\xi\right) = \int f\, dM \qquad (f \in BM(\mathscr{X})).$$

Equations of the form (6.4.11) have been included under the name *Campbell theorem* (e.g., see MKM, 1978; Matthes, 1972) after early work by Campbell (1909) on the shot noise process in thermionic vacuum tubes [see also Moran (1968, pp. 417–423)]. The expectation measure $M(\cdot)$ may also be called the *first moment measure* of ξ.

Now consider the k-fold product of ξ with itself, that is, the measure defined a.s. for Borel rectangles $A_1 \times \cdots \times A_k$ by

$$(6.4.12) \qquad \xi^{(k)}(A_1 \times \cdots \times A_k) = \prod_1^k \xi(A_i)$$

and extended to a measure, necessarily symmetric, on the product Borel σ-algebra in $\mathscr{X}^{(k)}$. Since the rectangles form a semiring generating this σ-algebra, and since (6.4.12) defines a random variable for every set in this semiring, it follows from Proposition 6.1.III that $\xi^{(k)}$ is a random measure on $\mathscr{X}^{(k)}$.

Definition 6.4.III. The kth-order moment measure $M_k(\cdot)$ of ξ is the expectation measure of $\xi^{(k)}$, whenever this expectation measure exists.

EXAMPLE 6.4(c) *Mixtures of "quadratic" random measures* (continued from Examples 6.1(b) and 6.3(a)). A Gaussian random variable has moments of all orders, from which it follows that the same is true for the stationary quadratic random measure in Example 6.1(b). In particular, its first and second moment measures are defined by the equations

$$M(A) = E(\xi(A)) = E\left(\int_A Z^2(x)dx\right) = \sigma^2 \ell(A),$$

$$M_2(A \times B) = E(\xi(A)\xi(B)) = E\left(\int_A \int_B Z^2(x)Z^2(y)dx\,dy\right)$$

$$= \int_A \int_B (\sigma^4 + 2c^2(x - y))dx\,dy.$$

From these representations it is clear that M and M_2 are both absolutely continuous with respect to Lebesgue measure, with derivatives σ^2 and $\sigma^4 + 2c^2(x - y)$, respectively, where $c(\cdot)$ is the covariance function for Z. Similar representations can be obtained for the higher moments.

Now consider the following modification. Let Λ be a positive random variable, independent of the random measure $\xi(\cdot)$, and set

$$\xi_\Lambda(A) = \Lambda\xi(A).$$

Using independence, the kth-order moment measures $M_\Lambda^{(k)}$ for ξ_Λ are related to those of ξ by the equations

$$M_\Lambda^{(k)}(\cdot) = E(\Lambda^k)M_k(\cdot).$$

Thus, if Λ has infinite moments of order k and higher, the same will be true for the moment measures of ξ_Λ, and conversely if the kth moment of ξ_Λ is finite, the kth-order moment measure of ξ exists.

This particular example is nonergodic [the values of $M(A)$ could not be determined from observations on a single realization of the process], but this is not a necessary feature of examples with infinite moment measures: for example, in place of the r.v. Λ, we could multiply ξ by any continuous ergodic process $\lambda(t)$ with infinite moments and integrate to obtain a random measure with similar moment properties. This procedure of mixing, or randomizing, with respect to a given parameter of a process is a rich source of examples.

EXAMPLE 6.4(d) *Moments of completely random measures.* If $\xi(\cdot)$ is completely random, the first and second moment measures (assuming these are finite) are given by relations of the type

$$M(A) = E(\xi(A)) = \mu(A),$$

$$M_2(A \times B) = E(\xi(A)\xi(B)) = \mu(A)\mu(B) + \text{var}(\xi(A \cap B)).$$

Particular interest here centres on the variance term. It vanishes unless the set $A \times B$ contains some elements of a diagonal set where $x = y$. It therefore represents a measure concentrated along this diagonal. For the stationary gamma process studied in Example 6.1(d),

$$\text{var}(\xi(A)) = \lambda^2 \alpha \ell(A),$$

and so

$$M_2(A \times B) = \lambda^2 \alpha \ell(A \cap B) + \lambda^2 \alpha^2 \ell(A) \ell(B).$$

Thus, M_2 has a constant areal density $\lambda^2 \alpha^2$ off the diagonal and a concentration with linear density $\lambda^2 \alpha$ along it. Such concentrations are associated with the a.s. atomic character of the random measure (cf. Exercise 6.4.5) and should be contrasted with the absolutely continuous moment measures of Example 6.4(c), where the random measure is also absolutely continuous.

The next lemma will be useful in the discussion of characteristic functionals. It summarizes the relation between moment measures and the moments of random integrals.

Lemma 6.4.IV. *Suppose the kth moment measure M_k of the random measure ξ exists. Then for all $f \in BM(\mathcal{X})$, the random integral $\int f\,d\xi$ has finite kth moment given by*

$$(6.4.13) \quad E\left(\left(\int f\,d\xi\right)^k\right) = \int_{\mathcal{X}^{(k)}} f(x_1)\cdots f(x_k) M_k(dx_1 \times \cdots \times dx_k).$$

PROOF. If (6.4.11) is applied to the product measure $\xi^{(k)}$, for which M_k is the expectation measure, we obtain

$$(6.4.14) \quad \int_{\mathcal{X}^k} h(x_1, \ldots, x_k) M_k(dx_1 \times \cdots \times dx_k)$$

$$= E\left(\int_{\mathcal{X}} \cdots \int_{\mathcal{X}} \xi(dx_1)\cdots \xi(dx_k) h(x_1, \ldots, x_k)\right)$$

for all k-dimensional bounded Borel measurable functions $h(x_1, \ldots, x_k)$. Then (6.4.13) is the special case

$$h(x_1, \ldots, x_k) = \prod_{i=1}^{k} f(x_i). \qquad \square$$

We now consider the finite Taylor series expansion of the characteristic functional.

Proposition 6.4.V. *Let Φ be the characteristic functional of the random measure ξ, and suppose that the kth moment measure of ξ exists for some $k \geq 1$. Then for each fixed f in $BM(\mathcal{X})$ and real $s \to 0$,*

$$\Phi[sf] = 1 + \sum_{r=1}^{k} \frac{(is)^r}{r!} \int \cdots \int f(x_1) \cdots f(x_r) M_r(dx_1 \times \cdots \times dx_r) + o(|s|^k).$$

Furthermore, if the $(k + 1)$th moment exists, the remainder term $o(|s|^k)$ is bounded by

(6.4.15)
$$\frac{|s|^{k+1}}{(k + 1)!} C_f^{k+1} M_{k+1}(A_f^{(k+1)}),$$

where C_f is a bound for f, and f vanishes outside the bounded Borel set A_f.

PROOF. Since $\Phi[sf] = \phi_f(s)$, where ϕ_f is the ordinary characteristic function for the random variable $\int f \, d\xi$, both assertions follow from (6.4.13) and the corresponding Taylor series results for ordinary characteristic functions. The bound (6.4.15) is derived from

$$E\left[\left|\int f \, d\xi\right|^{k+1}\right] \leq E\left[\left(\int |f| \, d\xi\right)^{k+1}\right] \leq E([C_f \xi(A_f)]^{k+1}). \qquad \square$$

The analogy with the finite-dimensional situation may be strengthened by noting that the moment measures can be identified with successive Fréchet derivatives of Φ. Specifically, we can write formally

$$M_k(A) = \Phi^{(k)}(I_A).$$

The difficulty with such expressions is that they rarely give much information, either theoretical or computational, concerning the analytic form or other characteristic of the moment measures.

The corresponding expression of the logarithm of the characteristic functional leads to a new family of measures, the *cumulant measures*, associated with ξ. The first cumulant measure coincides with the expectation measure, while the second is the *covariance measure* defined by

$$C_2(A \times B) = M_2(A \times B) - M(A)M(B) = \text{cov}(\xi(A), \xi(B)).$$

In Example 6.4(c), the covariance measure is absolutely continuous with respect to two-dimensional Lebesgue measure, the *covariance density* being given by

$$c_\xi(x, y) = 2c^2(x - y).$$

The covariance density for this random measure is just the ordinary covariance function of the process forming the density of the random measure. Similar relations between the moment and cumulant densities of the random measure, and the moment and cumulant functions of its density, will hold whenever the random measure can be represented as the integral of an underlying process. By contrast, in the second example, the covariance measure is singular, consisting entirely of the concentration along the diagonal $y = x$

with linear density $\lambda^2\alpha$. The relation can be expressed conveniently using the Dirac delta function notation as

$$c_\xi(x, y) = \lambda^2\alpha\delta(x - y).$$

The general relation between the moment measures and the cumulant measures is formally identical to the relation between factorial moment measures and factorial cumulant measures studied in Chapter 5, since both are derived by taking logarithms of an expression of the type (6.4.14).

Finally, we refer to the real variable counterpart of the characteristic functional, the *Laplace functional*, defined for $f \in BM_+(\mathscr{X})$ [i.e., the space of all nonnegative $f \in BM(\mathscr{X})$] by

$$(6.4.16) \qquad L_\xi[f] = E\left(\exp\left(-\int f\, d\xi\right)\right) \qquad (f \in BM_+(\mathscr{X})).$$

An exact counterpart of Theorem 6.4.II holds for Laplace functionals and is set out in Exercise 6.4.2. Observe, in particular, that the theorem implies that the distribution of a random measure is completely determined by the Laplace functional.

In our discussion of mixing properties of cluster processes in Section 10.3, we shall have need of an extension of our definition of $L_\xi[f]$ at (6.4.16). Let f be expressible as the monotone limit of an increasing sequence of functions $\{f_n\} \subset BM_+(\mathscr{X})$; denote the class of such functions by $\overline{BM_+}(\mathscr{X})$. Then by the monotone convergence theorem,

$$\int_{\mathscr{X}} f_n(x)\xi(dx) \uparrow \int_{\mathscr{X}} f(x)\xi(dx) \quad \text{a.s.}$$

whether the limit is finite or infinite, and consequently, by dominated convergence,

$$(6.4.17) \quad L_\xi[f_n] \to L_\xi[f] \equiv E\exp\left(-\int_{\mathscr{X}} f\, d\xi\right) \qquad (f \in \overline{BM_+}(\mathscr{X})),$$

where we use L_ξ (or, more briefly, L) both for the functional as originally defined and for its extension to $\overline{BM_+}(\mathscr{X})$.

This extended Laplace functional has continuity properties as below, but it need not be continuous for monotone sequences $\{f_n\} \subset \overline{BM_+}(\mathscr{X})$ [take $f_\varepsilon(x) = \varepsilon$ (all $x \in \mathscr{X}$), $\xi(\mathscr{X}) = \infty$ a.s.; then for all $\varepsilon > 0$, $L[f_\varepsilon] = 0 \neq L[0] = 1$].

Proposition 6.4.VI. *The extended Laplace functional $L[\cdot]$ satisfies*

$$L[f_n] \to L[f] \qquad (f_n, f \in \overline{BM_+}(\mathscr{X}))$$

whenever either $f_n(x) \uparrow f(x)$ or else $f_n(x) \to f(x)$ and there exists a measurable nonnegative function $\Delta(\cdot)$ such that $\int_{\mathscr{X}} \Delta(x)\xi(dx) < \infty$ a.s. and $|f_n(x) - f(x)| \leq \Delta(x)$ for all sufficiently large n.

PROOF. If $f_n \uparrow f$, then it is easy to construct a monotone sequence of functions $\{f'_n\} \subset BM_+(\mathcal{X})$ with $f'_n(x) \uparrow f(x)$, and (6.4.17) holds by definition.

In the other case, we have for all $n \geq$ some n_0,

$$f_n(x) \leq f(x) + \Delta(x) \leq f_{n_0}(x) + 2\Delta(x),$$

so

$$\int_{\mathcal{X}} f_n(x)\xi(dx) \leq \int_{\mathcal{X}} (f_{n_0}(x) + 2\Delta(x))\xi(dx) \leq \infty \quad \text{a.s.,}$$

and by dominated convergence applied to the sequence $\{f_n(\cdot)\}$,

$$\int_{\mathcal{X}} f_n(x)\xi(dx) \to \int_{\mathcal{X}} f(x)\xi(dx) < \infty \quad \text{a.s.}$$

A second application of the dominated convergence then implies (6.4.17). □

Under the second set of conditions, it follows that $L[\varepsilon f] \to 1 = L[0]$ as $\varepsilon \to 0$, so for such $f_n, f \in BM_+(\mathcal{X})$ the extended Laplace functional has all the properties of the (ordinary) Laplace functional (6.4.16).

Since random measures are inherently nonnegative, the Laplace functional is generally the most appropriate tool to use in handling random measures, just as the Laplace–Stieltjes transform is generally the most useful tool for handling nonnegative random variables. It is only when the r.v. is integer-valued, or, in our context, when the random measure is a point process, that there are advantages in moving to the p.g.f. or its counterpart the p.g.fl.

One of the most important properties of the transforms of r.v.s is the simplification they introduce for handling problems involving sums of independent r.v.s. The summation operator for random measures is defined by

$$(6.4.18) \qquad (\xi_1 + \xi_2)(A) = \xi_1(A) + \xi_2(A) \quad \text{(all } A \in \mathcal{B}_{\mathcal{X}}\text{)},$$

and it is both obvious and important that it extends the notion of *superposition* of point processes. Note that (6.4.18) has the equivalent form

$$(6.4.18') \qquad \int f \, d(\xi_1 + \xi_2) = \int f \, d\xi_1 + \int f \, d\xi_2 \quad \text{(all } f \in BM(\mathcal{X})\text{)}.$$

Now suppose that $\{\xi_i: i = 1, 2, \ldots\}$ is an infinite sequence of random measures, each defined on $(\Omega, \mathcal{E}, \mathcal{P})$, such that

$$(6.4.19) \qquad \zeta(A) \equiv \sum_{i=1}^{\infty} \xi_i(A)$$

is a.s. finite on all bounded $A \in \mathcal{B}_{\mathcal{X}}$. It is well known and easy to check that a countable sum of measures is again a measure. Thus, $\zeta(\cdot)$ is a boundedly finite measure, at least on the ω set where the ξ_i are simultaneously measures, which set has probability 1 by assumption and the fact that only a countable family is involved. Redefining ζ to be zero on the complementary ω set of $\mathcal{P}$-measure zero, and observing that a countable sum of random variables is again a random variable, we obtain a mapping from $(\Omega, \mathscr{E}, \mathscr{P})$ into $(\hat{\mathscr{M}}_{\mathscr{X}})$ satisfying the condition of Corollary 6.1.IV and which is therefore a random measure. Thus, we have the following lemma.

Lemma 6.4.VII. $\zeta(\cdot)$ *defined at* (6.4.19) *is a random measure if and only if the infinite sum at* (6.4.19) *converges for all bounded* $A \in \mathscr{B}_{\mathscr{X}}$.

No new concepts arise in the following definition of independence of two random measures; it extends to the mutual independence of both finite and infinite families of random measures in the usual way.

Definition 6.4.VIII. The random measures ξ_1, ξ_2 are *independent* when they are defined on a common space $(\Omega, \mathscr{E}, \mathscr{P})$ and are such that $\mathscr{P}(\mathscr{F}_1 \cap \mathscr{F}_2) = \mathscr{P}(\mathscr{F}_1)\mathscr{P}(\mathscr{F}_2)$ for all finite families $\mathscr{F}_i$ of events defined on ξ_i ($i = 1, 2$).

Let ξ_i have characteristic functional Φ_i and Laplace functional L_i. By writing $\zeta_n = \xi_1 + \cdots + \xi_n$, the following assertions are simple consequences of the definitions and Lemma 6.4.VII and can be proved by methods exploited already.

Proposition 6.4.IX. *When the random measures* $\xi_1, \xi_2, \ldots$ *are mutually independent, the sum* $\zeta_n = \xi_1 + \cdots + \xi_n$ *has characteristic functional*

$$(6.4.20a) \qquad \Phi_{\zeta_n}[f] = \prod_{i=1}^{n} \Phi_i[f] \quad (\text{all } f \in BM(\mathscr{X}))$$

and Laplace functional

$$(6.4.20b) \qquad L_{\zeta_n}[f] = \prod_{i=1}^{n} L_i[f] \quad (\text{all } f \in BM_+(\mathscr{X})).$$

$L_{\zeta_n}[f]$ *converges to a nonzero limit* L_f *for each* $f \in BM_+(\mathscr{X})$ *if and only if the infinite sum at* (6.4.19) *is finite on bounded* $A \in \mathscr{B}_{\mathscr{X}}$, *and then* L_f *is the Laplace functional of the random measure* ζ *at* (6.4.19).

Exercises

6.4.1. Condition (ii) of Theorem 6.4.II requires the continuity of characteristic functionals

$$(*) \qquad\qquad \Phi[f_n] \to \Phi[f]$$

for $f, f_n \in BM(\mathscr{X})$ when $f_n(x) \to f(x)$ ($x \in \mathscr{X}$) pointwise monotonically from below with f, f_n in fact $\in BM_+(\mathscr{X})$.

   Show that $(*)$ holds without this monotonicity of convergence or nonnegativity of f if either
   (i) $\mathscr{P}\{\xi(\mathscr{X}) < \infty\} = 1$, bounded measurable f and f_n, with

$$(**) \qquad\qquad \sup_{x \in \mathscr{X}} |f(x) - f_n(x)| \to 0 \quad \text{as } n \to \infty; \text{ or}$$

(ii) f and $f_n \in BM(\mathcal{X})$, and the union of their support is a bounded set, with
(**) holding.

Give an example of a random measure ξ and functions f, $f_n \in BM(\mathcal{X})$
satisfying (**) for which (*) fails. [*Hint*: Consider a stationary Poisson process
on $\mathbb{R}_+$ with $f(x) = 0$ (all $x \in \mathbb{R}_+$), $f_n(x) = n^{-1}I_{[0,n]}(x)$.]

6.4.2. *Laplace functional analogues* of various results for characteristic functionals
are available, subject to modifications reflecting the different domain of definition: below, $f \in BM_+(\mathcal{X})$.
(a) (Compare Theorem 6.4.II.) Show that $\{L[f]$: all $f\}$ uniquely determines
the distribution of a random measure ξ.
(b) (Compare Exercise 6.4.1.) For sequences f_n, $L[f_n] \to L[f]$ as $\sup_{x \in \mathcal{X}} |f_n(x) -$
$f(x)| \to 0$ if either ξ is totally bounded, or the pointwise convergence $f_n \to f$
is monotonic, or there is a bounded Borel set containing the support of
every f_n. Give examples to show that, if otherwise, the convergence $L[f_n] \to$
$L[f]$ may fail.
(c) Give an analogue of Proposition 6.4.V [replace $(is)^r$ there by $(-s)^r$, where
now s has $\text{Re}(s) \geq 0$].

6.4.3. Let ξ be a random probability measure on $\mathcal{X}$. Show that for every k, the kth
moment measure exists and defines a probability measure on $\mathcal{X}^{(k)}$. Find these
measures for the Dirichlet process ζ of Exercise 6.1.5, showing in particular
that

$$E\zeta(A) = \frac{\alpha(A)}{\alpha(\mathcal{X})}, \qquad \text{var } \zeta(A) = \frac{\alpha(A)}{\alpha(\mathcal{X})} \frac{1 - \alpha(A)/\alpha(\mathcal{X})}{\alpha(\mathcal{X}) + 1}.$$

6.4.4. For the random measure induced by the limit random d.f. of Exercise 6.1.7,
show that the first moment measure is Lebesgue measure on $[0, 1]$.

6.4.5. Let ξ be a random measure with boundedly finite second moment measure M_2.
Show that ξ is a.s. nonatomic if and only if the diagonal set $\text{diag}(\mathcal{X}^{(2)}) \equiv$
$\{(x, x): x \in \mathcal{X}\}$ has $M_2(\text{diag}(\mathcal{X}^{(2)})) = 0$. [*Hint*: Adapt the argument used below
in the proof of Proposition 7.4.VI.]

6.4.6. Let ξ be a random measure on $\mathcal{X} = \mathbb{R}^d$, and for $g \in BM_+(\mathcal{X})$ define $G(A) =$
$\int_A g(x)\ell(dx)$, where $\ell(dx)$ denotes Lebesgue measure on $\mathbb{R}^d$. Define η on $\mathcal{B}_{\mathcal{X}}$ by

$$\eta(A) = \int_{\mathcal{X}} G(A - x)\xi(dx).$$

(a) Show that $\eta(A)$ is an a.s. finite-valued r.v. for bounded $A \in \mathcal{B}_{\mathcal{X}}$, that it is a.s.
countably additive on $\mathcal{B}_{\mathcal{X}}$, and hence invoke Proposition 6.1.III to conclude that η is a well-defined random measure.
(b) Show that if ξ has moment measures up to order k, so does η, and find
the relation between them. Verify that the kth moment measure of η is
absolutely continuous with respect to Lebesgue measure on $(\mathbb{R}^d)^{(k)}$.
(c) Denoting the characteristic functionals of ξ and η by $\Phi_\xi[\cdot]$ and $\Phi_\eta[\cdot]$, show
that for $f \in BM_+(\mathcal{X})$,

$$h(x) \equiv \int_{\mathcal{X}} f(y)g(y - x)dy$$

is also in $BM_+(\mathscr{X})$, and

$$\Phi_\eta[f] = \Phi_\xi[h].$$

6.4.7. (Continuation) By its very definition, η is a.s. absolutely continuous with respect to Lebesgue measure and its density

$$Y(t) \equiv \int_\mathscr{X} g(t - x)\xi(dx),$$

when ξ is completely random, is called a *linear process*. [The shot noise process noted at (6.4.11) in connection with the original Campbell theorems is an example; for example, see Westcott (1970) for some other references.] Find the characteristic functional of Y when ξ is a stationary gamma random measure. Also, investigate the use of the measure $G(\cdot)$ in Exercise 6.3.4 to give an expression for the Laplace transform $E(e^{-\theta Y(t)})$.

6.4.8. Restate Proposition 6.3.IX in terms of characteristic functionals.

6.4.9. In the context of Proposition 6.4.IX, show that $L_{\zeta_n}[f]$ has a nonzero limit for $f \in BM_+(\mathscr{X})$ if and only if the infinite product $\prod_{i=1}^\infty (1 - \exp[-\xi_i(A)]) > 0$ a.s., that is, when the infinite series at (6.4.19) converges. Hence, complete the proof of the proposition.

6.4.10. For a random measure ξ on the c.s.m.s. $\mathscr{X}$ with Laplace functional $L[\cdot]$, show that for any bounded $A \in \mathscr{B}_\mathscr{X}$, $\mathscr{P}\{\xi(A) = 0\} = \lim_{s \to \infty} L[sI_A]$, while for any A in $\mathscr{B}_\mathscr{X}$, $\mathscr{P}\{\xi(A) < \infty\} = \lim_{s \downarrow 0} \lim_{n \to \infty} L[sI_{A_n}]$, where $\{A_n\}$ is an increasing sequence of bounded sets in $\mathscr{B}_\mathscr{X}$ for which $A = \lim_{n \to \infty} A_n$ (the case $A = \mathscr{X}$ is of obvious interest).

6.4.11. For the random probability distribution on $\mathbb{R}_+$ defined by $F_n(x) = 1 - \exp(-\xi([0, x]))$ as in Exercise 6.1.5, show that ξ is a.s. nonatomic if and only if the second moment measure M_2 of η has $M_2(\text{diag}(\mathbb{R}^{(2)})) = 0$ (cf. also Exercise 6.4.5).

6.4.12. Use an expansion of the exponential function to deduce that if a random measure ξ has a finite kth-order moment measure, then for $\varepsilon > 0$ and f, $g \in BM_+(\mathscr{X})$,

$$L[f + \varepsilon g] = L[f] - \varepsilon E(\xi_g \exp(-\xi_f))$$
$$+ \cdots + ((-\varepsilon)^k/k!)E((\xi_g)^k \exp(-\xi_f)) + o(\varepsilon^k),$$

where ξ_f is as at (6.4.1). [*Hint*: Expand $E(e^{-X-\varepsilon Y})$ for nonnegative r.v.s X and Y.]

CHAPTER 7

Introduction to the General Theory of Point Processes

Although point processes are just integer-valued random measures, their importance justifies a separate treatment, and their special features yield to techniques not readily applicable to general random measures. The first and last parts of the chapter summarize results for point processes, which parallel those for random measures—existence theorems, moment structure, and generating functionals—as well as furnishing illustrative (and important) examples. Many of the results are special cases of the corresponding results in Chapter 6, while others are extensions from the context of finite point processes in Chapter 5. The remaining part of the chapter, on the avoidance functions and intensity measures, deals with properties that are peculiar to point processes and for which the extensions to general random measures are not easily found.

7.1. Definitions and Existence Theorems

In this section we summarize the basic existence results for point processes, emphasizing both the parallels and the points of difference with those of the previous chapter.

Definition 7.1.I. The space $\mathcal{N}_{\mathcal{X}}$ consists of all boundedly finite, integer-valued measures N (called *counting measures* for short) defined on the Borel subsets $\mathcal{B}_{\mathcal{X}}$ of the c.s.m.s. $\mathcal{X}$. The *simple counting measures* are those members of $\mathcal{N}_{\mathcal{X}}$ for which

$$(7.1.1) \qquad N\{x\} \equiv N(\{x\}) = 0 \text{ or } 1 \quad (\text{all } x \in \mathcal{X});$$

they constitute the space $\mathcal{N}_{\mathcal{X}}^{*}$.

There is a fundamental characterization involving a canonical representation for both simple and general counting measures as elements of $\mathcal{N}_{\mathcal{X}}$.

Proposition 7.1.II. *An element of $\mathcal{M}_{\mathcal{X}}$ belongs to $\mathcal{N}_{\mathcal{X}}$ if and only if it is expressible as*

$$(7.1.2) \qquad\qquad N = \sum_i k_i \delta_{x_i},$$

where each k_i is a positive integer and the distinct points $\{x_i\}$ indexing the atoms of the measure (equivalently, the Dirac measures δ.) form a countable set with at most finitely many x_i in any bounded Borel set.

Each N in $\mathcal{N}_{\mathcal{X}}$ defines via (7.1.2) its support counting measure N^* by

$$(7.1.3) \qquad\qquad N^* = \sum_i \delta_{x_i}.$$

N belongs to $\mathcal{N}_{\mathcal{X}}^*$ if and only if at (7.1.2) $k_i = 1$ (all i), or, equivalently, it coincides with its support counting measure.

PROOF. It is clear that any N with the representation (7.1.2) belongs to $\mathcal{N}_{\mathcal{X}}$, and equally clear is the identification of $\mathcal{N}_{\mathcal{X}}^*$ as a subset of $\mathcal{N}_{\mathcal{X}}$.

It remains to show that any counting measure N is expressible in the form (7.1.2). Since N is integer-valued, any atom of N must have positive integral mass; and since N is boundedly finite there can be at most a finite number of such atoms within any bounded set, and at most countably many in all because we can cover $\mathcal{X}$ by a countable number of bounded sets. Hence, to complete the proof it is enough to show that N has no nonatomic component.

Let y be an arbitrary point of $\mathcal{X}$, and $\{\varepsilon_j, j = 1, 2, \ldots\}$ a monotonic sequence of positive reals decreasing to zero, so that the spheres $S(y, \varepsilon_j) \downarrow \{y\}$ as $j \to \infty$. Then by the continuity lemma for measures,

$$N\{y\} = \lim_{j \to \infty} N(S(y, \varepsilon_j)).$$

Each term on the right-hand side is nonnegative integer-valued; the same therefore applies to $N\{y\}$. Thus, if y is not an atom of N, it must be the limit of a sequence of open spheres for which $N(S(y, \varepsilon_j)) = 0$, hence, in particular, the centre of an open sphere with this property. This shows that the support of N (the complement of the largest open set with zero measure) consists exclusively of the atoms of N, or equivalently that N is purely atomic. □

It is worth noting that this proof makes essential use of the topological structure of $\mathcal{X}$; Moyal (1962a) discusses some of the difficulties that arise in extending it to more general contexts.

We now consider the character of $\mathcal{N}_{\mathcal{X}}$ as a subset of $\mathcal{M}_{\mathcal{X}}$. Suppose N_k is a sequence of counting measures converging weakly in $\mathcal{M}_{\mathcal{X}}$ to some limit measure N. As in the previous proof, let y be an arbitrary point of $\mathcal{X}$, and $S(y, \varepsilon_j)$ a sequence of spheres, contracting to y, with the additional property that

$$N(\partial S(y, \varepsilon_j)) = 0 \qquad (j = 1, 2, \ldots)$$

[this is always possible because $N(S(y, \varepsilon))$, as a function of ε, has jumps for at most countably many values of ε, and thus, the complementary set of values of ε being dense, the ε_j can be chosen in the complementary set]. For each such sphere it follows from the properties of $\hat{w}$-convergence (Lemma A2.6.II) that

$$N_k(S(y, \varepsilon_j)) \to N(S(y, \varepsilon_j)).$$

Once again the terms on the left are all positive integers or zero, so the same is true for the term on the right. As in the previous discussion, it then follows that N is purely atomic. This argument shows that $\mathcal{N}_{\mathscr{X}}$ is sequentially closed in $\mathcal{M}_{\mathscr{X}}$, and hence closed, $\mathcal{M}_{\mathscr{X}}$ being separable (Theorem A2.6.III). The same property, stated formally below, is not true for $\mathcal{N}_{\mathscr{X}}^*$ (see Exercise 7.1.1.).

Proposition 7.1.III. *$\mathcal{N}_{\mathscr{X}}$ is a closed subset of $\mathcal{M}_{\mathscr{X}}$, and $\mathcal{N}_{\mathscr{X}}^*$ is a measurable subset of $\mathcal{N}_{\mathscr{X}}$ (and hence of $\mathcal{M}_{\mathscr{X}}$).*

Many properties of $\mathcal{M}_{\mathscr{X}}$ can now be carried over to $\mathcal{N}_{\mathscr{X}}$.

Corollary 7.1.IV. *As a metric space in its own right, with the $\hat{w}$-topology, $\mathcal{N}_{\mathscr{X}}$ is a c.s.m.s.*

PROOF. It is well known that a closed subset of a complete separable metric space is complete in itself and separable.   □

Since a closed set is also a Borel set we have the following corollary.

Corollary 7.1.V. *The Borel sets of $\mathcal{N}_{\mathscr{X}}$, as a metric space in its own right, coincide with the Borel sets of $\mathcal{N}_{\mathscr{X}}$ as a subset of $\mathcal{M}_{\mathscr{X}}$.*

Corollary 7.1.VI. *$\mathscr{B}(\mathcal{N}_{\mathscr{X}})$ is the smallest σ-algebra with respect to which the mappings $N \to N(A)$ are measurable for each $A \in \mathscr{B}_{\mathscr{X}}$.*

We now define a point process formally.

Definition 7.1.VII. A point process N is a measurable mapping from a probability space $(\Omega, \mathscr{E}, \mathscr{P})$ into $(\mathcal{N}_{\mathscr{X}}, \mathscr{B}(\mathcal{N}_{\mathscr{X}}))$. The point process is simple when

(7.1.4) $$\mathscr{P}\{N \in \mathcal{N}_{\mathscr{X}}^*\} = 1.$$

At the beginning of Section 7.2 we treat the formal matter of showing that to each point process N there does indeed correspond a well-defined support point process N^* (cf. Proposition 7.1.II).

It follows from the definition of $\mathcal{N}_{\mathscr{X}}$ that a random measure is a point process if and only if its realizations are a.s. integer-valued. Proposition 6.1.III now implies the following proposition.

Proposition 7.1.VIII. *Let N be a mapping from a probability space into $\mathcal{N}_{\mathscr{X}}$, $\mathscr{A}$ a semiring of bounded Borel sets generating $\mathscr{B}_{\mathscr{X}}$. Then N is a point process if and only if $N(A)$ is a random variable for each $A \in \mathscr{A}$.*

Similarly, from Theorem 6.1.VI, we have the following proposition.

Proposition 7.1.IX. *Let $N_A(\omega)$ be a family of nonnegative, integer-valued random variables indexed by the Borel sets of $\mathscr{X}$. In order that there exist a point process N such that*

$$N(A) = N_A \quad \text{a.s.},$$

it is necessary and sufficient that for all pairs of disjoint, bounded Borel sets A, B

(7.1.5a) $$N(A \cup B) = N(A) + N(B) \quad \text{a.s.}$$

and that for all sequences $\{A_n\}$ of bounded Borel sets, with $A_n \downarrow \varnothing$,

(7.1.5b) $$N(A_n) \to 0 \quad \text{a.s.}$$

The special case of a simple point process on $\mathbb{R}^1$ (or even $\mathbb{R}_+$) recurs so frequently that it deserves special treatment. The object of the next proposition is to formalize the discussion at the end of Section 3.1 concerning the relation between counting and interval properties of a simple point process. Retaining the notation of that section, introduce the space $\mathscr{S}^+$ of all sequences $\{\tau_0, \tau_{+1}, \tau_{+2}, \ldots; x\}$ of positive numbers τ_i with $0 \le x < \tau_0$, $\sum_{i=1}^{\infty} \tau_i = \sum_{i=1}^{\infty} \tau_{-i} = +\infty$, and the mapping $\mathscr{R} \colon \mathscr{N}^* \to \mathscr{S}^+$ defined by

$$\tau_i(N^*) = t_i(N^*) - t_{i-1}(N^*), \qquad x(N^*) = -t_0(N^*),$$

and with the inverse $\mathscr{R}^{-1}$ defined for $s^+ \in \mathscr{S}^+$ by

$$t_0(s^+) = -x(s^+)$$

$$t_i(s^+) = \begin{cases} t_{i-1}(s^+) + \tau_i & (i \ge 1), \\ t_{i+1}(s^+) - \tau_{i+1} & (i < 0). \end{cases}$$

We give $\mathscr{S}^+$ the Borel σ-algebra $\mathscr{B}(\mathscr{S}^+)$ obtained in the usual way as the product of σ-algebras on each copy of $\mathbb{R}_+$.

Proposition 7.1.X. *The mapping $\mathscr{R}$ defined above provides a one-to-one both ways measurable mapping of $\mathscr{N}^*$ into $\mathscr{S}^+$. Hence, in particular,*

(i) *the quantities $\tau_i(N^*)$ and $x(N^*)$ are well-defined random variables when N^* is a simple point process;*

(ii) *there is a one-to-one correspondence between the probability distributions $\mathscr{P}^*$ of simple point processes on $\mathscr{N}^*$ and probability distributions on the space $\mathscr{S}^+$.*

PROOF. The relations (3.1.9) imply that all $t_i(N^*)$ and hence all $\tau_i(N^*)$ are random variables whenever N^* is a simple point process. Appealing to Proposition 7.1.VIII shows, by starting from half-open intervals of the form $(0, t]$, proceeding to general half-open intervals by subtraction, and then to the semiring they generate, that the converse holds.   □

Note, in particular, the intervention of the initial interval $(0, t_1]$, which must be given separately: there is *not* a one-to-one correspondence between intervals and simple counting measures (cf. Exercise 7.1.4).

EXAMPLE 7.1(a) *Finite vectors.* Let $\mathbf{Y} = (y_1, \ldots, y_n)$ be a random vector with components in $\mathscr{X}$, that is, a mapping from a probability space into the n-fold product space $\mathscr{X}^{(n)}$. Does the counting function

$$N(A) = \#\{i: y_i \in A\}$$

define a point process?

The set function $N(A)$ is clearly a.s. integer-valued and finitely additive on Borel sets. Moreover, if $\{A_k\}$ is a decreasing sequence of Borel sets, with $A_k \downarrow \varnothing$, then for $i = 1, \ldots, k$ we have $y_i \notin A_k$ for k sufficiently large, so that

$$N\left(\bigcap_{k=1}^{\infty} A_j\right) = 0 \quad \text{a.s.;}$$

in other words $N(A_k) \to 0$. Thus, $N(\cdot)$ must be a.s. countably as well as finitely additive. This is enough to show that $\mathbf{Y}$ induces a counting measure on $\mathscr{X}$, and so sets up a mapping from its probability space into $\mathscr{N}_{\mathscr{X}}$.

To show that $N(\cdot)$ is a point process, the critical step is to show that this mapping is measurable. From Proposition 7.1.VIII it is enough to show that for each Borel set A, $N(A)$ is a random variable. Define indicator variables $I_i(A)$ by setting

$$(7.1.6) \qquad\qquad I_i(A) = \begin{cases} 1 & y_i \in A, \\ 0 & \text{otherwise.} \end{cases}$$

Since y_i is a random variable with values in $\mathscr{X}$, and A is a Borel subset of $\mathscr{X}$, $I_i(A)$ is a random variable for each $i = 1, \ldots, n$. But then

$$N(A) = \sum_{i=1}^{n} I_i(A),$$

so that $N(A)$ itself is a random variable and $N(\cdot)$ is a point process.

EXAMPLE 7.1(b) *Point processes defined by sequences.* Extend the previous example by taking $Y = \{y_i: i = 0, \pm 1, \ldots\}$ to be a doubly infinite sequence of elements of $\mathscr{X}$, subject to there being with probability 1 only a finite number of the y_i falling within any bounded set. Define $N(\cdot)$ equal to the zero measure on the exceptional set of probability 0 where this condition fails, and for the rest of Ω define

(7.1.7) $\qquad N(A) = \#\{i\colon y_i \in A\} = \sum_{-\infty}^{\infty} I_i(A) \qquad (A \in \mathscr{B}_{\mathscr{X}})$

with $I_i(\cdot)$ as at (7.1.6). Then, as in the previous example, the mapping N from Ω into $\mathscr{N}_{\mathscr{X}}$ is again measurable because $N(A)$ is a random variable for every bounded Borel set A. Thus, $N(\cdot)$ defines a point process.

The main problem with this approach to point processes arises from the need to express, in terms of the distributions of the y_i, the condition that with probability 1 the counting measures are boundedly finite. Suppose, for example, that the y_i are generated as the successive states in a Markov chain with state space $\mathscr{X}$ and that the transition function for the chain satisfies an irreducibility condition sufficient to imply the usual classification into recurrent and transient chains. Then the local finiteness condition is satisfied if and only if the chain is transient.

Questions of similar delicacy arise in more complex situations. More examples are discussed in greater detail in Exercises 7.1.2–7.1.4, together with examples of the converse problem: given a point process $N(\cdot)$ on $\mathscr{X}$, generate from it a sequence of values $\{y_i\}$ (e.g., ordered in terms of increasing distance from some fixed origin in $\mathscr{X}$) and verify that they are well-defined random variables.

We now discuss the fidi distributions of a point process. They are most conveniently specified in the notation of (5.3.9); namely, for bounded Borel sets $A_1, A_2, \ldots$ and nonnegative integers $n_1, n_2, \ldots$,

(7.1.8) $\qquad P_k(A_1, \ldots, A_k; n_1, \ldots, n_k) = \mathscr{P}\{N(A_i) = n_i \ (i = 1, \ldots, k)\}.$

As in Proposition 6.2.III, the distribution of a point process [the measure induced on $(\mathscr{N}_{\mathscr{X}}, \mathscr{B}(\mathscr{N}_{\mathscr{X}}))$] is completely specified by the fidi distribution of $N(A)$ for A in a countable ring generating the Borel sets. The basic existence theorem then takes the following form.

Theorem 7.1.XI. *In order that a family $P_k(A_1, \ldots, A_k; n_1, \ldots, n_k)$ of discrete fidi distributions defined on bounded Borel sets be the fidi distributions of a point process, it is necessary and sufficient that*

(i) *for any permutation $i_1, \ldots, i_k$ of the indices $1, \ldots, k$,*

$\qquad P_k(A_1, \ldots, A_k; n_1, \ldots, n_k) = P_k(A_{i_1}, \ldots, A_{i_k}; n_{i_1}, \ldots, n_{i_k});$

(ii) $\sum_{r=0}^{\infty} P_k(A_1, \ldots, A_{k-1}, A_k; n_1, \ldots, n_{k-1}, r) = P_{k-1}(A_1, \ldots, A_{k-1}; n_1, \ldots, n_{k-1});$

(iii) *for each disjoint pair of bounded Borel sets $A_1, A_2, P_3(A_1, A_2, A_1 \cup A_2; n_1, n_2, n_3)$ has zero mass outside the set where $n_1 + n_2 = n_3$;*

(iv) *for sequences $\{A_n\}$ of bounded Borel sets with $A_n \downarrow \varnothing$, $P_1(A_n; 0) \to 1$.*

The task of checking the conditions in detail here can be lightened by taking advantage of Lemma 6.2.IX, from which it follows that if the consistency conditions (i) and (ii) are satisfied for *disjoint* Borel sets, and if for such disjoint sets the equations

$$(7.1.9) \qquad \sum_{r=0}^{n} P_k(A_1, A_2, A_3, \ldots, A_k; r, n - r, n_3, \ldots, n_k)$$

$$= P_{k-1}(A_1 \cup A_2, A_3, \ldots, A_k; n, n_3, \ldots, n_k)$$

hold, then there is a unique consistent extension to a full set of fidi distributions satisfying (iii).

EXAMPLE 7.1(c) *The Poisson process.* Here the fidi distributions for disjoint Borel sets are readily specified by the generating function relations

$$(7.1.10) \qquad \Pi_k(A_1, \ldots, A_k; z_1, \ldots, z_k) = \prod_{1}^{k} \exp\{-\mu(A_i)(1 - z_i)\},$$

where Π_k is the generating function associated with the distribution P_k. Condition (ii) is readily checked by setting $z_k = 1$; then the term in $1 - z_k$ vanishes and reduces the product to the appropriate form for Π_{k-1}. In generating function terms, Equation (6.2.5) becomes, for $k = 2$,

$$\Pi_2(A_1, A_2; z, z) = \Pi_1(A_1 \cup A_2; z),$$

which expresses the additivity property of the Poisson distribution. Finally, to check condition (iv) we require

$$\Pi_1(A_n; 0) \to 1;$$

that is,

$$\exp\{-\mu(A_n)\} \to 1,$$

which is a corollary of the assumption that μ is a measure, so $\mu(A_n) \to 0$ as $A_n \downarrow \varnothing$.

It should be noted that the form (7.1.10) does *not* hold for arbitrary sets but has to be replaced by such forms as

$$\Pi_2(A_1, A_2; z_1, z_2) = \exp\{-\mu(A_1)(1 - z_1) - \mu(A_2)(1 - z_2)$$

$$+ \mu(A_1 \cap A_2)(1 - z_1)(1 - z_2)\}$$

when the sets overlap. The extension to arbitrary families of nondisjoint sets is unique, but laborious, and need not be pursued in detail.

EXAMPLE 7.1(d) *Finite point processes.* If the distribution of a finite point process is specified in any of the ways described in Proposition 5.3.II, in particular, say, by its Janossy measures, then the fidi distributions are given by (5.3.11); namely,

(5.3.11) $$n_1! \cdots n_k! \, P_k(A_1, \ldots, A_k; n_1, \ldots, n_k)$$

$$= \sum_{r=0}^{\infty} (r!)^{-1} J_{n+r}(A_1^{(n_1)} \times \cdots \times A_k^{(n_k)} \times C^{(r)}),$$

where C is the complement of the union of the disjoint sets $A_1, \ldots, A_k$ and $n = n_1 + \cdots + n_k$.

Although we can infer on other grounds that the point process is well defined, and hence that the fidi distributions must be consistent, it is of interest to check the consistency conditions directly. Since (5.3.11) is restricted to disjoint sets, the appropriate conditions are (i), (ii), and (iv) of Theorem 7.1.X together with (7.1.9).

The permutation condition (i) follows from the symmetry of the Janossy measures. Also, condition (iv) reduces to

$$P_1(A_n; 0) = \sum_{r=0}^{\infty} (r!)^{-1} J_r[(\mathscr{X} \backslash A_n)^{(r)}] \to 1$$

if $A_n \downarrow \varnothing$. But then $\mathscr{X} \backslash A_n \uparrow \mathscr{X}$, and the result follows from dominated convergence, the fact that the $J_r(\cdot)$ are themselves measures, and the normalization condition (5.3.7).

The additivity requirement (7.1.9) follows from identities of the type

$$\sum_{n_1 + \cdots + n_s = n} (n_1! \cdots n_s!)^{-1} J_{n+r}(A_1^{(n_1)} \times \cdots \times A_s^{(n_s)} \times C^{(r)})$$

$$= (n!)^{-1} J_{n+r}((A_1 \cup \cdots \cup A_s)^{(n)} \times C^{(r)}),$$

which are immediate applications of Lemma 5.3.III. Similarly, the marginal condition (ii) reduces to checking the equations

$$\sum_{n_k=0}^{\infty} \sum_{r=0}^{\infty} (n_k! \, r!)^{-1} J_{v+n_k+r}(A_1^{(n_1)} \times \cdots \times A_{k-1}^{(n_{k-1})} \times A_k^{(n_k)} \times C^{(r)})$$

$$= \sum_{s=0}^{\infty} (s!)^{-1} \sum_{t=0}^{s} J_{v+s}(A_1^{(n_1)} \times \cdots \times A_{k-1}^{(n_{k-1})} \times A_k^{(t)} \times C^{(s-t)})$$

$$= \sum_{s=0}^{\infty} (s!)^{-1} J_{v+s}(A_1^{(n_1)} \times \cdots \times A_{k-1}^{(n_{k-1})} \times (A_k \cup C)^{(s)}),$$

where $v = n_1 + \cdots + n_{k-1}$, the first equation is a regrouping of terms, and the second equation is a further application of Lemma 5.3.III.

We conclude this section by formally restating the definitions of marked and multivariate point processes.

Definition 7.1.XII. A *marked point process*, with positions in the c.s.m.s. $\mathscr{X}$ and marks in the c.s.m.s. $\mathscr{K}$, is a point process on $\mathscr{X} \times \mathscr{K}$ with the additional property that the marginal process of locations $\{N(A \times \mathscr{K}): A \in \mathscr{B}_{\mathscr{X}}\}$ is itself a point process. This marginal process may be denoted by $N_{\mathscr{X}}(\cdot)$.

A consequence of this definition is that not all point processes on product spaces are marked point processes. For example, the bivariate Poisson process on $\mathbb{R}^2$ with parameter measure $\mu\,dx\,dy$ cannot be represented as a marked point process on $\mathbb{R} \times \mathbb{R}$, nor in general can we treat the process of jumps and their heights, occurring in the description of completely random measures in Theorem 6.3.VII, as a marked point process on $\mathscr{X} \times (0, \infty)$. However, in the latter example, we can, for every given $\varepsilon > 0$, treat the process of jumps with heights $\geq \varepsilon$ as a marked point process on $\mathscr{X} \times [\varepsilon, \infty)$ with the position of the jump as the location and its height as the mark.

Definition 7.1.XIII. A *multivariate point process* is a point process on the product space $\mathscr{X} \times \{1, \ldots, m\}$ for some finite integer m.

In this definition the finiteness of the mark space immediately implies that each marginal process

$$N_i(\cdot) = N(\cdot \times \{i\})$$

and the sum process

$$N(\cdot) = N(\cdot \times \{1, \ldots, m\}) = \sum_{i=1}^{m} N_i(\cdot)$$

are all well defined [note that when the multivariate point process is regarded as a marked point process this sum process equals $N_{\mathscr{X}}(\cdot)$ only when the sum process is simple; see Section 7.2].

EXAMPLE 7.1(e) *Completely independent marked point processes.* We shall say that a marked point process has the complete independence property when the n random variables of the set

$$\{N(A_i \times B_i): \text{bounded } A_i \in \mathscr{B}_{\mathscr{X}}, B_i \in \mathscr{B}_{\mathscr{X}} \ (i = 1, \ldots, n)\}$$

are mutually independent whenever the A_i are disjoint. This is weaker than requiring them to be independent whenever the product sets $A_i \times B_i$ are disjoint, which property would correspond to N having the complete independence property on the product space $\mathscr{X} \times \mathscr{X}$. It is, however, equivalent to the stronger property whenever the marginal process of locations $N_{\mathscr{X}}$ is simple, or equivalently (see Corollary 6.3.VI)

$$(7.1.11) \qquad \sum_{i=1}^{k_n} \mathscr{P}\{N_{\mathscr{X}}(A_{ni}) > 1\} \to 0 \qquad (n \to \infty)$$

for a dissecting system $\mathscr{T}$ for A. In fact, it is asserted in Exercise 7.1.6 that there is no loss of generality in assuming that the marginal point process of locations of a marked point process is simple; we shall assume henceforth in this example that (7.1.11) is satisfied but shall denote the mark space by $\mathscr{X}'$ as a reminder that it need not be the same mark space $\mathscr{X}$ as for the process N as defined initially.

We can now imitate the proof of Theorem 6.3.VIII to show that for completely independent N, $N(A \times B_1)$ and $N(A \times B_2)$ are independent random variables whenever the mark sets B_1, B_2 are disjoint, and similarly for any finite families of such sets. Thus, if a marked point process is completely random, then it reduces to a simple completely random point process on some product space $\mathscr{X} \times \mathscr{K}'$. We proceed to examine the structure of such a process.

We know from the general results of Chapter 2 that a simple completely random point process reduces to a Poisson process; in the present case the parameter measure μ must satisfy

$$\mu_{\mathscr{X}}(A) \equiv \mu(A \times \mathscr{K}') < \infty$$

for all bounded $A \in \mathscr{B}_{\mathscr{X}}$, since $N_{\mathscr{X}}$ is boundedly finite by assumption. Introduce a family of probability measures $P(B|x)$ on the mark space $(\mathscr{K}', \mathscr{B}(\mathscr{K}'))$ by means of the Radon–Nikodym derivatives

$$(7.1.12) \qquad \mu(A \times B) = \int_A P(B|x)\mu_{\mathscr{X}}(dx).$$

Hence, the absolute continuity condition $\mu(\cdot \times B) \ll \mu_{\mathscr{X}}$ is satisfied, and the property $P(\mathscr{K}'|x) = 1$ (a.s.) follows from the definitions of $\mu_{\mathscr{X}}$. As in the discussions of regular conditional probability (Proposition A1.5.III), we may and shall assume that the family $\{P(B|x): B \in \mathscr{B}(\mathscr{K}'), x \in \mathscr{X}\}$ is so chosen that $P(B|\cdot)$ is measurable in x for each fixed bounded set $B \in \mathscr{B}(\mathscr{K}')$, and $P(\cdot|x)$ is a probability measure on $\mathscr{B}(\mathscr{K}')$ for all $x \in \mathscr{X}$. With this understanding we see that a marked point process with the complete independence property is fully specified by two components:

(i) a Poisson process of locations with parameter measure $\mu_{\mathscr{X}}$;
(ii) a family of probability distributions $P(\cdot|x)$ giving the distribution of the mark in $\mathscr{K}'$ (or, equivalently, a family of marks forming a finite point process on $\mathscr{K}'$), with the property that $P(B|x)$ is measurable in x for each fixed $B \in \mathscr{B}(\mathscr{K}')$. Conversely, given such $\mu_{\mathscr{X}}$ and $P(B|x)$, we can specify a measure on $\mathscr{X} \times \mathscr{K}'$ by means of (7.1.12) and then construct the Poisson process with this measure as its parameter measure; we leave it as an exercise to verify that the resultant process is a marked point process with the complete independence property.

Exercises

7.1.1. The sequence of measures $\{N_k\}$ on $\mathscr{B}_{\mathbb{R}}$ defined by

$$N_k = \delta_0 + \delta_{1/k}$$

converges weakly to the measure $N = 2\delta_0$; $N_k \in \mathscr{N}_{\mathbb{R}}^*$ but the limit measure is not.

7.1.2. Let $\{X_n\}$ be a stationary ergodic real-valued Markov chain whose first absolute moment is finite, and define $Y_n = X_1 + \cdots + X_n$. If $EX_n \neq 0$, then by the ergodic theorem $\{Y_n\}$ obeys the strong law of large numbers and therefore satisfies the conditions of Example 7.1(b).

7.1.3. Let $\{Y_n: n = 0, 1, \ldots\}$ be a random walk in $\mathbb{R}^d$, that is, $Y_0 = 0$ and the $\mathbb{R}^d$-valued r.v.s $X_n \equiv Y_n - Y_{n-1}, n = 1, 2, \ldots$, are i.i.d. Show that the conditions of Example 7.1(b) are satisfied if either $d \geq 3$, or else $d = 1$ or 2 and $E|X_n| < \infty$, $EX_n \neq 0$. [*Hint:* A random walk in $\mathbb{R}^d$ is transient under either of the stated conditions.]

Note that a *renewal process* is the special case $d = 1$ and $X_n \geq 0$ a.s. (and $X_n \neq 0$ a.s.), so that for some d.f. F on $\mathbb{R}_+$ with $0 = F(0-) \leq F(0+) < 1 = \lim_{x \to \infty} F(x)$, and any positive integer r,

$$\mathscr{P}(\{X_i \in (x_i, x_i + dx_i], i = 1, \ldots, r\}) = \prod_{r=1} F((x_i, x_i + dx_i]).$$

7.1.4. Given a nonnull counting measure $N \in \mathscr{N}_{\mathbb{R}}$, define $\{Y_n: n = 0, \pm 1, \pm 2, \ldots\}$ or a subset of this doubly infinite sequence by

$$N(0, Y_n) < n \leq N(0, Y_n] \qquad (n = 1, 2, \ldots),$$

$$N(Y_n, 0] < -n + 1 \leq N[Y_n, 0] \qquad (n = 0, -1, -2, \ldots).$$

Show that if N is a point process then $\{Y_n: -N(-\infty, 0] + 1 \leq n \leq N(0, \infty)\}$ are well-defined r.v.s.

Now let $\mathscr{N}_0$ be the subspace of $\mathscr{N}_{\mathbb{R}}^*$, consisting of simple counting measures on $\mathbb{R}^1$ with a point at the origin, so $N \in \mathscr{N}_0$ is boundedly finite, simple, and $N\{0\} = 1$. Show that if the atoms of such N yield the ordered set $\{\ldots, t_{-1}, 0, t_1, t_2, \ldots\}$ and $\tau_i = t_i - t_{i-1}$ (with $t_0 \equiv 0$), then the mapping $\Theta: \mathscr{N}_0 \to \mathscr{S}_0^+$, which takes the counting measure N into the space $\mathscr{S}_0^+$ of doubly infinite positive sequences $\{\ldots, \tau_{-1}, \tau_0, \tau_1, \ldots\}$, is one-to-one and both ways measurable with respect to the usual σ-fields in $\mathscr{N}_0$ and $\mathscr{S}_0^+$. Hence, probability measures on $\mathscr{N}_0$ and $\mathscr{S}_0^+$ are in one-to-one correspondence.

7.1.5. Verify the assertion that a completely independent marked point process has a simple marginal process of locations $N_{\mathscr{X}}$ if and only if (7.1.11) holds for every dissecting system $\mathscr{T}$ for bounded $A \in \mathscr{B}_{\mathscr{X}}$. Without complete independence (7.1.11) need not hold [cf. (7.2.10) and Proposition 7.2.V].

7.1.6. Show that, except for a set of $\mathscr{P}$-measure zero, a realization of a marked point process can be regarded as a simple point process on the product space $\mathscr{X} \times \mathscr{K}^{\cup}$, where $\mathscr{K}^{\cup} = \mathscr{K}^{(1)} \cup \mathscr{K}^{(2)} \cup \cdots$, each $\mathscr{K}^{(k)}$ consisting of all ordered sets of k-tuples of elements of the k-fold product set of $\mathscr{K}$ with itself, and the measure on each $A \times \mathscr{K}^{(k)}$ is symmetric in the subsets of $\mathscr{K}^{(k)}$. Conclude from this identification that any marked point process is equivalent to another marked point process whose marginal process is simple.

7.1.7. Follow the prescription of Example 7.1(e) and verify that (7.1.12) can be used as described there to construct a marked point process with the complete independence property.

7.2. Simple Point Processes and Orderliness

The study and manipulation of distributions of point processes is much simplified when the point process is simple, or, equivalently, when the point process coincides a.s. with its support point process. This section is largely concerned with analytic techniques allied to simple point processes, although we do give some results for general point processes. We also make use of dissecting systems (Definition A2.1.IV), much as in Section 6.3, in connecting sample-path properties of point processes to analytic properties of their distributions.

We start from the representation (7.1.2) of a counting measure N, writing it in the form

$$(7.2.1) \qquad\qquad N = \sum_{k=1}^{\infty} k N_k^*,$$

where for any $k = 1, 2, \ldots,$

$$(7.2.2) \qquad\qquad N_k^*(A) = \#\{x_i \in A: N\{x_i\} = k\}.$$

Then for the support counting measure N^* of N we have

$$(7.2.3) \qquad\qquad N^* = \sum_{k=1}^{\infty} N_k^*.$$

We would like to regard (7.2.1) and (7.2.3) as statements concerning point processes as well as statements about individual realizations. For this to be valid we need to know that the mappings $N \to N^*$ and $N \to N_k^*$ of $\mathcal{N}_{\mathscr{X}}$ into itself are measurable.

Suppose then that N is a point process, and define the indicator functions

$$(7.2.4) \qquad\qquad Z_k(B) = \begin{cases} 1 & 1 \le N(B) \le k, \\ 0 & \text{otherwise,} \end{cases}$$

which is a r.v. whenever $N(B)$ is a r.v. As in Section 6.3, let $\mathcal{T} = \{\mathcal{T}_n\} = \{\{A_{ni}\}\}$ be a dissecting system for any given bounded $A \in \mathscr{B}_{\mathscr{X}}$, so that

$$\zeta_k^{(n)}(A) = \sum_i Z_k(A_{ni})$$

is also a r.v. whenever the $N(A_{ni})$ are jointly defined r.v.s (the summation is understood to extend over the members of $\mathcal{T}_n$). Each $\mathcal{T}_{n+1}$ contains a partition of each $A_{ni} \in \mathcal{T}_n$, so for fixed k and A,

$$\zeta_k^{(n)}(A) \le \zeta_k^{(n+1)}(A) \le N(A) < \infty \qquad (n = 1, 2, \ldots).$$

Therefore,

$$(7.2.5) \qquad\qquad \zeta_k(A) \equiv \lim_{n \to \infty} \zeta_k^{(n)}(A),$$

being the monotone limit of a bounded sequence, exists and is a r.v. whenever $\{\zeta_k^{(n)}(A)\}$ is a sequence of r.v.s.

In place of the spheres used in the derivation of (7.1.2) we could have used elements of $\mathcal{T}$, thereby showing explicitly that $\zeta_1(A) = N_1^*(A)$ and that $\lim_{k \to \infty} \zeta_k(A)$, which exists because $\zeta_k(A) \le \zeta_{k+1}(A) \le N(A)$ $(k = 1, 2, \ldots)$, equals $N^*(A)$. Similarly,

$$(7.2.6) \qquad\qquad N_k^*(A) = \zeta_k(A) - \zeta_{k-1}(A) \qquad (k = 2, 3, \ldots),$$

so when N is a point process, it follows that $N_k^*(A)$ and $N^*(A)$ are r.v.s, and hence by Proposition 7.1.VIII, as random set functions $N_k^*(\cdot)$ and $N^*(\cdot)$ are in fact point processes. We summarize this discussion in the following proposition.

Proposition 7.2.I. *For any point process N, the construction at (7.1.3) and (7.2.2) applied to the realizations of N define simple point processes N^* and N_k^*, and the relations (7.2.1) and (7.2.3) hold as relations between point processes.*

N is simple if and only if $N_k^* = 0$ $(k = 2, 3, \ldots)$.

Proposition 7.2.II. *The set function*

(7.2.7)
$$\lambda(A) \equiv \sup_{\mathcal{T}_n} \sum_i \mathcal{P}\{N(A_{ni}) \geq 1\}$$

$$= EN^*(A) \equiv M^*(A)$$

defines a measure when it is boundedly finite.

Definition 7.2.III. Whether finite or infinite, λ is called the *intensity measure* of the point process N.

PROOF OF THE PROPOSITION. The indicator function [cf. (7.2.4)]

$$Z(B) = I_{\{N(B) \leq 1\}},$$

being subadditive in its argument, that is, $Z(A \cup B) \leq Z(A) + Z(B)$ for sets A, $B \in \mathcal{B}_{\mathcal{X}}$, has

$$\mathcal{P}\{N(A \cup B) \geq 1\} = EZ(A \cup B) \leq \mathcal{P}\{N(A) \geq 1\} + \mathcal{P}\{N(B) \geq 1\}.$$

Using monotonicity and the interchange of limits that monotone convergence permits,

$$M^*(A) \equiv EN^*(A) = E\left(\lim_{n \to \infty} \zeta^{(n)}(A)\right)$$

$$= \lim_{n \to \infty} E(\zeta^{(n)}(A))$$

$$= \lim_{n \to \infty} \sum_i \mathcal{P}\{N(A_{ni}) \geq 1\}$$

$$= \sup_{\mathcal{T}_n} \sum_i \mathcal{P}\{N(A_{ni}) \geq 1\}.$$

Since $N^*(A \cup B) = N^*(A) + N^*(B)$ for disjoint A, B, the rest of the proposition follows easily. □

The substance of Proposition 7.2.II constitutes a generalization, in the definition of $\lambda(\cdot)$, of what Leadbetter called *Khinchin's existence theorem*.

Two consequences of the equality of $\lambda(\cdot)$ with $M^*(\cdot)$ are that its definition at (7.2.7) is in fact independent of the dissecting system $\mathcal{T}$ used there and that it is a well-defined extended measure [extended meaning that we may have $\lambda(A) = \infty$ for some bounded $A \in \mathcal{B}_{\mathscr{X}}$].

It can also be remarked that the relation (7.2.7) is a particular case of a subadditive set function yielding a measure by addition under refinement (see Exercise 7.2.1.).

In the following result the direct part, which generalizes Proposition 3.3.IV and so may be called *Korolyuk's theorem*, is now trivial: the converse, proved below, may be referred to as *Dobrushin's lemma*, because it is a natural extension of a result first referenced in Volkonski (1960) for stationary point processes.

Proposition 7.2.IV. *For a simple point process N,*

$$(7.2.8) \qquad\qquad \lambda(A) = M(A) \qquad (all\ A \in \mathcal{B}_{\mathscr{X}}).$$

Conversely, if (7.2.8) holds and $\lambda(A) < \infty$ for all bounded A, then N is simple.

PROOF. When N is not simple, there is some bounded $A \in \mathcal{B}_{\mathscr{X}}$ for which $\Delta \equiv \mathcal{P}\{N(A) \neq N^*(A)\} > 0$. Then

$$M(A) = EN(A) \geq \Delta + EN^*(A) = \Delta + \lambda(A)$$

and (7.2.8) cannot hold when $\lambda(A) < \infty$.   □

Proposition 7.2.I asserts that each N_k^* is a simple point process and thus has an intensity measure $\lambda_k^* = EN_k^*$. From (7.2.1) we may therefore deduce the generalized Korolyuk equation

$$(7.2.9) \quad M(A) = EN(A) = \sum_{k=1}^{\infty} k\lambda_k^*(A) = \lambda(A) + \sum_{k=1}^{\infty} (\lambda(A) - \lambda_k(A)),$$

where $\lambda_k = \lambda_1^* + \cdots + \lambda_k^*$ is the intensity measure of the simple point process ζ_k. A version of (7.2.9) applicable to random measures is noted in Exercise 7.2.2.

The converse part of Proposition 7.2.IV gives an analytic condition that is sufficient to imply the a.s. sample-path property of a point process being simple. There are other analytic conditions, involving infinitesimals directly and usually bearing the name orderly or ordinary, the latter deriving from transliteration rather than translation of Khinchin's original terminology. We call N *ordinary* when, given any bounded $A \in \mathcal{B}_{\mathscr{X}}$, there is a dissecting system $\mathscr{T} = \{\mathscr{T}_n\} = \{\{A_{ni}: i = 1, \ldots, k_n\}\}$ for A such that

$$(7.2.10) \qquad\qquad \inf_{\mathscr{T}_n} \sum_{i=1}^{k_n} \mathcal{P}\{N(A_{ni}) \geq 2\} = 0.$$

Then, for an ordinary point process, given $\varepsilon > 0$, there exists a dissecting system for bounded A and some n_ε such that for $n \geq n_\varepsilon$,

$$\varepsilon > \sum_{i=1}^{k_n} \mathcal{P}\{N(A_{ni}) \geq 2\}$$

$$\geq \mathcal{P}\left(\bigcup_{i=1}^{k_n} \{N(A_{ni}) \geq 2\} \right) \equiv \mathcal{P}(B_n).$$

Since the sequence of sets $\{B_n\}$ is monotone decreasing, we have, for any $\varepsilon > 0$,

$$\varepsilon > \mathscr{P}\left(\lim_{n \to \infty} B_n\right) = \mathscr{P}\{N\{x\} \geq 2 \text{ for some } x \in A\},$$

which establishes the direct part of the following result. The proof of the converse is left as Exercise 7.2.3.

Proposition 7.2.V. *An ordinary point process is necessarily simple. Conversely, a simple point process of finite intensity is ordinary, but one of infinite intensity need not be ordinary.*

The following two analytic conditions are of a more local character than the property of being ordinary and hence may be simpler to check in practice. To describe them, take any bounded set A containing a given point x, let $\mathscr{T}$ be a dissecting system for A, and define the set $A_n(x)$, for each $n = 1, 2, \ldots$, to be the member of $\mathscr{T}_n = \{A_{ni}\}$ containing x.

Definition 7.2.VI. (a) A point process on the c.s.m.s. $\mathscr{X}$ is μ-*orderly at* x when μ is a boundedly finite measure and

$$(7.2.11) \qquad f_n(x) \equiv \mathscr{P}\{N(A_n(x)) \geq 2\}/\mu(A_n(x)) \to 0$$

as $n \to \infty$ [here, $f_n(x) = 0$ if $\mathscr{P}\{N(A_n(x)) \geq 2\} = 0 = \mu(A_n(x))$, $= \infty$ if $\mathscr{P}\{N(A_n(x)) \geq 2\} > 0 = \mu(A_n(x))$].
   (b) The process is *Khinchin orderly at* x if

$$(7.2.12) \qquad g_n(x) \equiv \mathscr{P}\{N(A_n(x)) \geq 2 \mid N(A_n(x)) \geq 1\} \to 0$$

as $n \to \infty$ [here, $g_n(x) = 0$ if $\mathscr{P}\{N(A_n(x)) \geq 1\} = 0$].

In many situations the state space $\mathscr{X}$ is a locally compact group with a boundedly finite invariant measure v. If a point process is v-orderly for a dissecting system based on spheres, we speak of the process as being *orderly*. Such usage is consistent with Khinchin's (1955) original use of the term for stationary point processes on $\mathbb{R}$, and a point process on $\mathbb{R}$ uniformly analytically orderly in the terminology of Daley (1974) is orderly in the present sense.

Proposition 7.2.VII. *A point process μ-orderly on bounded $A \in \mathscr{B}_{\mathscr{X}}$ and satisfying*

$$(7.2.13) \qquad \sup_n \sup_{x \in A} f_n(x) < \infty$$

where $f_n(\cdot)$ is defined by (7.2.11), is simple on A.

PROOF. From the definition at (7.2.11),

$$\sum_{i=1}^{k_n} \mathscr{P}\{N(A_{ni}) \geq 2\} = \int_A f_n(x)\mu(dx).$$

Here, $f_n(x) \to 0$ pointwise, and by using (7.2.13) to justify appealing to the dominated convergence theorem, the integral $\to 0$ as $n \to \infty$. The process is thus ordinary, and Proposition 7.2.V completes the proof. $\qquad\square$

The hypotheses here can be weakened slightly by demanding merely that (7.2.11) and (7.2.13) should hold only for μ-a.e. x in A. This observation is the key to obtaining a partial converse to the proposition: we give it in the context of Khinchin orderliness.

Proposition 7.2.VIII. *A point process N with boundedly finite intensity measure $\lambda(\cdot)$ is simple if and only if it is Khinchin orderly for λ-a.e. x on $\mathcal{X}$.*

PROOF. It suffices to restrict attention to a bounded set A. Then since

$$\mathscr{P}\{N(A_{ni}) \geq 1\} \leq \lambda(A_{ni}),$$

we can write

$$\sum_{i=1}^{k_n} \mathscr{P}\{N(A_{ni}) \geq 2\} \leq \int_A g_n(x)\lambda(dx), \quad \to 0 \quad \text{as } n \to \infty$$

because $1 \geq g_n(x) \to 0$ for λ-a.e. x and $\lambda(A) < \infty$.

To prove the necessity, suppose that N is simple: we first show that

$$(7.2.14) \qquad\qquad h_n(x) \equiv \mathscr{P}\{N(A_n(x)) \geq 1\}/\lambda(A_n(x)) \to 1$$

as $n \to \infty$ for λ-a.e. x. We establish this convergence property by making use of a martingale argument much as in the treatment of Radon–Nikodym derivatives [e.g., see Chung (1974, p. 353)]. Construct a sequence of r.v.s $\{X_n\} \equiv \{X_n(\omega)\}$ on a probability space $(A, \mathscr{B}_A, \mathbb{P})$, where $\mathbb{P}(\cdot) = \lambda(\cdot)/\lambda(A)$, by introducing indicator r.v.s $I_{ni}(\omega) = 1$ for $\omega \in A_{ni}$, $= 0$ otherwise, and setting

$$(7.2.15) \qquad\qquad X_n(\omega) = \sum_{i=1}^{k_n} h_n(\omega)I_{ni}(\omega).$$

Let $\mathscr{F}_n'$ denote the σ-field generated by the sets of $\mathscr{T}_1 \cup \cdots \cup \mathscr{T}_n$; since $\{\mathscr{T}_n\}$ is a nested system of partitions, $\mathscr{F}_n'$ has quite a simple structure (!). Then, because $\{\mathscr{F}_n'\}$ is an increasing sequence of σ-fields and

$$E(X_{n+1}|\mathscr{F}_n') = \sum_{j:\, A_{n+1,j} \subseteq A_{ni}} \frac{\mathscr{P}\{N(A_{n+1,j}) \geq 1\}}{\lambda(A_{n+1,j})} \cdot \frac{\lambda(A_{n+1,j})}{\lambda(A_{ni})}$$

$$\geq \mathscr{P}\{N(A_{ni}) \geq 1\}/\lambda(A_{ni}) = X_n \qquad \mathbb{P}\text{-a.s.}$$

(here we have used the subadditivity of $\mathscr{P}\{N(\cdot) \geq 1\}$), $\{X_n\}$ is a submartingale. Now $h_n(x) \leq 1$ (all x), or, equivalently, $X_n(\omega) \leq 1$ (all ω), so we can apply the submartingale convergence theorem [e.g., see Chung (1974, p. 334)] and conclude that $X_n(\omega)$ converges $\mathbb{P}$-a.s. Equivalently, $\lim_{n\to\infty} h_n(x)$ exists λ-a.e. on A, so to complete the proof of (7.2.14) it remains to identify the limit. For this, it is enough to show that $\limsup_{n\to\infty} h_n(x) = 1$ λ-a.e., and this last fact follows from $h_n(x) \leq 1$ (all x) and the chain of relations

$$\lambda(A) = \lim_{n \to \infty} \int_A h_n(x)\lambda(dx)$$

$$\leq \int_A \limsup_{n \to \infty} h_n(x)\lambda(dx) \leq \lambda(A),$$

where we have used the lim sup version of Fatou's lemma.

This same martingale argument can be applied to the functions

$$h_n^{(1)}(x) \equiv \mathscr{P}\{N(A_n(x)) = 1\}/\lambda(A_n(x))$$

$[\equiv 1$ if $\lambda(A_n(x)) = 0]$ because the set function $\mathscr{P}\{N(\cdot) = 1\}$ is again subadditive, and since for a simple point process with boundedly finite λ,

$$\sum_{i=1}^{k_n} \mathscr{P}\{N(A_{ni}) = 1\} \to \lambda_1^*(A) = \lambda(A) \qquad (n \to \infty),$$

it again follows that

(7.2.16) $h_n^{(1)}(x) \to 1 \qquad \lambda\text{-a.e.}$

Combining these results for $h_n(\cdot)$ and $h_n^{(1)}(\cdot)$, we have $g_n(x) = 1 - h_n^{(1)}(x)/h_n(x) \to 0$ λ-a.e. $\square$

Clearly, from (7.2.14) and (7.2.16), the proposition could equally well be phrased in terms of λ-orderliness rather than Khinchin orderliness. In this form the significance of the result is more readily grasped, namely, that for a simple point process with boundedly finite λ, not only are $M(\cdot)$ and $\lambda(\cdot)$ interchangeable but we can also interpret (for suitably "small" sets δA and λ-a.e.)

(7.2.17) $M(\delta A) = \lambda(\delta A) = \mathscr{P}\{N(\delta A) = 1\} (1 + o(1)).$

Note that if $\lambda(\{x\}) > 0$ for any x, then because N is simple, $\lambda(\{x\}) = \mathscr{P}\{N\{x\} = 1\} = \mathscr{P}\{N\{x\} \geq 1\}$. Equation (7.2.17) provides a link between the elementary limits of conditional probability statements in Chapter 3 and those derived by direct appeal to the Radon–Nikodym theorem in Chapter 10. Exercises 7.2.6–7.2.7 show that the λ-a.e. qualification cannot be relaxed.

All the converse parts of the propositions in this section have included the proviso that the intensity measure should be boundedly finite. The assertions may be false without such a qualification (see Exercise 7.2.5 and references there).

Exercises

7.2.1. Let the nonnegative set function ψ defined on the Borel subsets of a space $\mathscr{X}$ be subadditive under refinement. Use a relation like (7.2.7) to define a measure when the quantity so defined is finite on bounded sets.

7.2.2. Let N be a marked point process on $\mathscr{X} \times (0, \infty)$ for which the marginal point process $N_{\mathscr{X}}$ has boundedly finite intensity measure λ. Denote by $\{(x_i, \kappa_i)\}$ the points of a realization of N, and introduce the measure

$$\xi_{\mathscr{X}} = \sum \kappa_i \delta_{x_i},$$

so that $\xi_{\mathscr{X}}$ may be taken as a realization of a random measure. Show that the set function

$$\lambda_x(A) \equiv \sup_{\mathscr{T}} \sum_{i=1}^{k_n} P\{0 < \xi_{\mathscr{X}}(A_{ni}) \leq x\} \quad \text{(bounded } A \in \mathscr{B}_{\mathscr{X}})$$

is a measure for which

$$E\xi_{\mathscr{X}}(A) = \int_0^\infty (\lambda(A) - \lambda_x(A)) dx$$

whether this moment is finite or infinite.

7.2.3. Use Equation (7.2.8) to show that a simple point process with boundedly finite intensity measure is ordinary.

7.2.4. Show that a Poisson process is simple if and only if it is ordinary. [*Hint:* Show that being simple is equivalent to the parameter measure being nonatomic.]

7.2.5. For a stationary mixed Poisson process N on $\mathbb{R}$ with mixing distribution function $F(\cdot)$,

$$\mathscr{P}\{N(0, x] = k\} = \int_0^\infty e^{-\lambda x}(\lambda x)^k (k!)^{-1} dF(\lambda) \quad (0 < x < \infty, k = 0, 1, \ldots).$$

Show that
   (i) N is simple [because $F(\infty-) = 1$];
   (ii) the intensity of N is finite or infinite with $\lim_{y \to \infty} F_1(y)$, where

$$F_1(y) = \int_0^y (1 - F(u)) du;$$

   (iii) irrespective of the intensity being finite or not, the conditional probabilities at (7.2.12) converge to zero when F_1 is of slow variation [i.e., $F_1(2y)/F_1(y) \to 1$ as $y \to \infty$];
   (iv) N is orderly when $y(1 - F(y)) \to 0$ $(y \to \infty)$;
   (v) N is ordinary when $\liminf_{y \to \infty} y(1 - F(y)) = 0$.
   [It follows from results in Daley (1982b) that these results are in fact necessary and sufficient. It is not difficult to find d.f.s F showing that none of the implications (ii) $\Rightarrow$ (iii) $\Rightarrow$ (iv) $\Rightarrow$ (v) $\Rightarrow$ (i) can be reversed; for other examples see MKM (1978, pp. 68, 371)—but note that they use the term orderly for what we have called ordinary—and Daley (1974, 1982a).]

7.2.6. Let the point process N on $\mathbb{R}_+$ have points located at $\{n^2 U : n = 1, 2, \ldots\}$, where the r.v. U is uniformly distributed on $(0, 1)$. Show that for $0 < h < 1$,

$$\mathscr{P}\{N[0, h] \geq k | N[0, h] \geq 1\} = 1/k^2,$$

$$\mathscr{P}\{N[0, h] \geq k\}/\lambda([0, h]) = 6/\pi^2 k^2,$$

and conclude that the λ-a.e. constraint in Proposition 7.2.VIII cannot be relaxed. [See Daley and Vere-Jones (1984) for an extension of this example.]

7.2.7. Suppose that the simple point process N on $\mathscr{X}$ has a boundedly finite intensity measure $\lambda(\cdot)$ that is absolutely continuous with respect to a measure $\mu(\cdot)$ on $\mathscr{X}$, and that there is a version of the Radon–Nikodym derivative $d\lambda/d\mu$ coinciding μ-a.e. with a continuous function. Use the techniques of the proof of Proposition 7.2.VIII to show that, in the notation of (7.2.14),

$$\mathscr{P}\{N(A_n(x)) \geq 1\}/\mu(A_n(x)) \to d\lambda/d\mu \qquad (n \to \infty) \text{ for } \mu\text{-a.e. } x.$$

Deduce in particular that when $\mathscr{X} = \mathbb{R}^d$ and N is stationary (see Chapter 12),

$$\mathscr{P}\{N(A_n(x)) \geq 1\}/\ell(A_n(x)) \to \text{const.} \qquad \ell\text{-a.e. } x,$$

and then use stationarity to eliminate the ℓ-a.e. condition.

7.3. Characterizations via the Avoidance Function

The complement of the probability $\mathscr{P}\{N(A) \geq 1\}$ appearing above [e.g., see (7.2.7)] is the *avoidance function*

$$(7.3.1) \qquad P_0(A) \equiv \mathscr{P}\{N(A) = 0\}.$$

This terminology, used in a more general context by Kendall (1974), reflects the fact that $P_0(A)$ gives the probability of the support of a random set function avoiding a prescribed set A; other possible terms include zero function and avoidance probability function.

At Theorem 2.3.III we quoted Renyi's result that a simple Poisson process on the line is determined by the values of the avoidance function on a suitably rich class $\mathscr{A}$ of Borel sets. We now prove an extension of this result by Mönch (1971), who showed that the Poisson assumption is not needed (see also Kallenberg, 1973, 1975), and give a closely related characterization of the avoidance function due to Kurtz (1974). Unpublished work of Karbe (1973) is presumably the basis of some discussion in MKM (1978, §1.4). Much of this work, though largely couched in algebraic language, had already been developed by McMillan (1953), who in some lectures in Berkeley in 1981 used the term *vacuity function* for $P_0(\cdot)$.

If only the state space $\mathscr{X}$ of the simple point process $N(\cdot)$ were countable, Renyi's result referenced above would be almost trivial, for with i, j, ... denoting distinct points of $\mathscr{X}$, we should have for the first few fidi distributions

$$P_1(\{i\}; 0) = 1 - P_1(\{i\}; 1) = P_0(\{i\});$$

$$P_2(\{i\}, \{j\}; 0, 0) = P_0(\{i, j\});$$

$$P_2(\{i\}, \{j\}; 0, 1) = P_0(\{j\}) - P_0(\{i, j\});$$

$$P_2(\{i\}, \{j\}; 1, 1) = 1 - P_0(\{i\}) - P_0(\{j\}) + P_0(\{i, j\}).$$

Proceeding in this way, all the fidi distributions could be built up through a sequence of differencing operations applied to $P_0(\cdot)$, and it is clear that the avoidance function would thereby determine the fidi distributions uniquely. Our task here is to extend this argument to a general c.s.m.s. $\mathscr{X}$ as state space.

Following Kurtz (1974), the equations

(7.3.2a) $$\Delta(A)\psi(B) = \psi(B) - \psi(A \cup B),$$

(7.3.2b) $$\Delta(A_1, \ldots, A_k, A_{k+1})\psi(B)$$
$$= \Delta(A_{k+1})[\Delta(A_1, \ldots, A_k)\psi(B)] \qquad (k = 1, 2, \ldots)$$

define a difference operator $\Delta(A)$ and its iterates $\Delta(A_1, \ldots, A_k)$ acting on any set function $\psi(\cdot)$ for $A, A_1, A_2, \ldots, B$ in a ring of sets on which $\psi(\cdot)$ is defined. $\Delta(\cdot)$ is tailored to the needs of (7.3.3) in the lemma below: it should be noted that the convention of signs in the definition of Δ at (7.3.2) is opposite to that used by Kurtz and Kallenberg.

Lemma 7.3.I. *For every integer $k \geq 1$ and all Borel sets $A_1, A_2, \ldots, B$,*

(7.3.3) $\quad \Delta(A_1, \ldots, A_k)P_0(B) = \mathscr{P}\{N(A_i) > 0 \ (i = 1, \ldots, k), N(B) = 0\}.$

PROOF. For $k = 1$ we have

$$\mathscr{P}\{N(A_1) > 0, N(B) = 0\} = P_0(B) - P_0(A_1 \cup B) = \Delta(A_1)P_0(B).$$

The general form follows by an induction argument of which we omit details.   □

As a special case of (7.3.3) with B the null set,

(7.3.4) $$\Delta(A_1, \ldots, A_k)P_0(\emptyset) = \mathscr{P}\{N(A_i) > 0 \ (i = 1, \ldots, k)\}.$$

The nonnegativity of (7.3.1) appears later in Theorem 7.3.V in a characterization of the avoidance function. In the meantime, Lemma 7.3.I provides a useful notational convention and serves as a remainder that the probability of the complex event on the right-hand side of (7.3.3) can be expressed immediately in terms of the avoidance function.

The basic idea motivating the introduction of the operator Δ at (7.3.2) is that it leads to a succinct description of the fidi distributions of a point process when, for suitable sets A_i, $N(A_i)$ is "small" in the sense of having

$$\mathscr{P}\{N(A_i) = 0 \text{ or } 1 \text{ (all } i)\} \approx 1.$$

Such an approximation can be realized only if N is simple and the class of sets on which the values of the avoidance function are known contains a dissecting system for $\mathscr{X}$ (see Definition A2.1.IV). Fortunately, on a c.s.m.s. $\mathscr{X}$ the Borel sets $\mathscr{B}_{\mathscr{X}}$ necessarily contain a dissecting system and hence a dissecting ring (Definition A2.1.VI).

Theorem 7.3.II. *The distribution of a simple point process N on a c.s.m.s. $\mathscr{X}$ is determined by the values of the avoidance function P_0 on the bounded sets of a dissecting ring $\mathscr{A}$ for $\mathscr{X}$.*

PROOF. It is enough to show that the fidi distributions of a point process as at (7.1.8), involving only bounded subsets of $\mathscr{X}$, are determined by the avoidance function. Much as at (7.2.4), define indicator r.v.s

$$Z(B) = \begin{cases} 0 & N(B) = 0 \\ 1 & N(B) \geq 1 \end{cases}$$

for any $B \in \mathscr{A}$. Then for a dissecting system $\mathscr{T}$, as there the r.v.s

$$(7.3.5) \qquad \zeta_n(A) \equiv \sum_{i=1}^{k_n} Z(A_{ni}) \qquad (n = 1, 2, \ldots),$$

count the numbers of sets in $\mathscr{T}_n$ containing points of $N(\cdot)$. Since every A_{ni} is the union of elements in $\mathscr{T}_{n+1}$, and the r.v.s $Z(\cdot)$ are subadditive set functions, it is clear that $\{\zeta_n(A)\}$ is a nondecreasing sequence. Moreover, since N is simple and $\{\mathscr{T}_n\}$ is a dissecting system, the limit

$$(7.3.6) \qquad N(A) \equiv \lim_{n \to \infty} \zeta_n(A)$$

exists a.s. Now the joint distribution of the $Z(A_{ni})$, and hence of $\zeta_n(A)$, and (more generally) of $\{\zeta_n(A_i) (i = 1, \ldots, k)\}$, is expressible directly in terms of the avoidance function: for example,

$$(7.3.7) \quad \mathscr{P}\{\zeta_n(A) = r\} = \sum_{\{i_1, \ldots, i_r\}} \Delta(A_{ni_1}, \ldots, A_{ni_r}) P_0\left(A \setminus \left(\bigcup_{j=1}^{r} A_{ni_j}\right)\right),$$

where the sum is taken over all $\binom{k_n}{r}$ distinct combinations of r sets from the $k_n(\geq r)$ sets in the partition $\mathscr{T}_n$ of A. Rather more cumbersome formulae give the joint distributions of $\zeta_n(A_i)$. Because the convergence of $\{\zeta_n\}$ to its limit is monotonic, the sequence of events $\{\zeta_n(A_i) \leq n_i (i = 1, \ldots, k)\}$ is also monotone decreasing in n, and thus $\mathscr{P}\{\zeta_n(A_i) \leq n_i (i = 1, \ldots, k)\} \to \mathscr{P}\{N(A_i) \leq n_i (i = 1, \ldots, k)\}$.

Thus, P_0 determines the fidi distributions as required. $\square$

Corollary 7.3.III. *Let N_1, N_2 be two point processes on $\mathscr{X}$ whose avoidance functions coincide on the bounded sets of a dissecting ring for $\mathscr{X}$. Then their support point processes N_1^* and N_2^* are equivalent.*

Versions of these results, which apply to random measures, can be given (see Exercise 7.3.2): the avoidance functions are replaced by the Laplace transforms $E(e^{-s\xi(A)})$ for fixed $s > 0$.

We turn finally to a characterization problem.

Definition 7.3.IV. *A set function ψ defined on a ring $\mathscr{R}$ of sets is completely monotone on $\mathscr{R}$ if for every sequence $\{A, A_1, A_2, \ldots\}$ of members of $\mathscr{R}$*

$$\Delta(A_1, \ldots, A_n)\psi(A) \geq 0 \quad (\text{every } n = 1, 2, \ldots).$$

We remark that this definition of complete monotonicity differs from the conventional usage by the omission of a factor $(-1)^n$ on the left-hand side of the inequality [cf. also the definition of Δ at (7.3.2)].

By using Definition 7.3.IV, Lemma 7.3.I asserts that the avoidance function of a point process is completely monotone on $\mathscr{B}_{\mathscr{X}}$. Complete monotonicity of a set function is not sufficient on its own to characterize an avoidance function.

Theorem 7.3.V. *Let ψ be a set function defined on the members of a dissecting ring $\mathscr{R}$ covering the c.s.m.s. $\mathscr{X}$. In order that there exist a point process on $\mathscr{X}$ with avoidance function ψ, it is necessary and sufficient that*

(i) *ψ be completely monotone;*
(ii) *$\psi(\varnothing) = 1$;*
(iii) *$\psi(A_n) \to 1$ for any bounded sequence $\{A_n\}$ in $\mathscr{R}$ for which $A_n \to \varnothing$ $(n \to \infty)$; and*
(iv) *for every bounded $A \in \mathscr{R}$,*

$$\lim_{r \to \infty} \lim_{n \to \infty} \left(\psi(A) + \sum_{k=1}^{r} \sum_{\{i_1, \ldots, i_k\}} \Delta(A_{ni_1}, \ldots, A_{ni_k}) \psi\left(A \Big\backslash \left(\bigcup_{j=1}^{k} A_{ni_j} \right) \right) \right) = 1,$$

where $\{\mathscr{T}_n\} = \{\{A_{ni}: i = 1, \ldots, k_n\}\}$ is a dissecting system for A, $\{\mathscr{T}_n\} \subseteq \mathscr{R}$, and the inner summation is over all distinct combinations of k sets from the k_n sets in the partition $\mathscr{T}_n$ for A.

PROOF. The necessity of (i) has been noted in Lemma 7.2.I, condition (ii) is self-evident, while condition (iii) here is the same as (iv) of Theorem 7.1.X. Condition (iv) here follows most readily from (7.3.7) when written in the form

$$\lim_{r \to \infty} \lim_{n \to \infty} \sum_{k=0}^{r} \mathscr{P}\{\zeta_n(A) = k\} = \lim_{r \to \infty} \mathscr{P}\{N(A) \le r\} = 1$$

and expresses the fact that a point process N is boundedly finite.

For the sufficiency, it is clear from (i) and (ii) that we can construct an indicator process Z' on bounded A in $\mathscr{R}$ with finite-dimensional distributions (for any finite number k of disjoint bounded $A_1, \ldots, A_k \in \mathscr{R}$)

(7.3.8a) $\Pr\{Z'(A_1) = 0\} = 1 - \Pr\{Z'(A_1) = 1\} = \psi(A_1) = \Delta(A_1)\psi(\varnothing)$,

(7.3.8b)

$$\begin{cases} \Pr\{Z'(A_i) = 1 \ (i = 1, \ldots, k)\} = \Delta(A_1, \ldots, A_k)\psi(\varnothing), \\ \Pr\{Z'(A_j) = 0, Z'(A_i) = 1 \ (\text{all } i \ne j)\} = \Delta(A_1, \ldots, A_{j-1}, A_{j+1}, \ldots, A_k)\psi(A_j), \\ \Pr\{Z'(A_i) = 0 \ (\text{all } i)\} = \psi(\bigcup_{i=1}^{k} A_i); \end{cases}$$

nonnegativity is ensured by (i), summation to unity by (ii), and marginal consistency reduces to

$$\Delta(A_1, \ldots, A_k, A_{k+1})\psi(B) + \Delta(A_1, \ldots, A_k)\psi(B \cup A_{k+1}) = \Delta(A_1, \ldots, A_k)\psi(B).$$

In other words, we have a family of fidi distributions that, being consistent in the sense of the Kolmogorov existence theorem [e.g., Parthasarathy (1967,

Chap. V)], enable us to assert the existence of a probability space $(\mathcal{Z}, \mathcal{E}, \mathcal{P}')$ on which are jointly defined random variables $\{Z'(A): \text{bounded } A \in \mathcal{R}\}$ that are $\{0, 1\}$-valued and $\mathcal{P}'$ is related to ψ via relations like (7.3.8) (with Pr replaced by $\mathcal{P}'$).

We now introduce random variables $\zeta_n'(A)$ (bounded $A \in \mathcal{R}$) much as at (7.3.5) and observe that the subadditivity of Z' implies that $\zeta_n'(A)$ are a.s. monotone nondecreasing under refinement as before, so

$$(7.3.9) \qquad \lim_{n \to \infty} \zeta_n'(A) \equiv N'(A)$$

exists a.s. and, being the limit of an integer-valued sequence, is itself integer-valued or infinite. From the last relation of (7.3.8b), we have $\mathcal{P}'\{\zeta_n(A) = 0\} = \psi(A)$ for all n, so

$$(7.3.10) \qquad \mathcal{P}'\{N'(A) = 0\} = \psi(A) \quad (\text{all bounded } A \in \mathcal{R}).$$

The a.s. finiteness condition that N' must satisfy on bounded $A \in \mathcal{R}$ is equivalent to demanding that

$$\lim_{k \to \infty} \lim_{n \to \infty} \mathcal{P}'\{\zeta_n'(A) \le k\} = 1,$$

which, expressed in terms of the functions ψ via (7.3.8) and relations like (7.3.7) (with $\mathcal{P}'$ and ψ replacing $\mathcal{P}$ and P_0), reduces to condition (iii).

For bounded disjoint $A, B \in \mathcal{R}$, we find by using a dissecting system for $A \cup B$ containing dissecting systems for A and B separately that

$$N'(A \cup B) = \lim_{n \to \infty} \zeta_n'(A \cup B) = \lim_{n \to \infty} (\zeta_n'(A) + \zeta_n'(B)) = N'(A) + N'(B) \quad \text{a.s.,}$$

and thus N' is finitely additive on $\mathcal{R}$. Let $\{A_i\}$ be any disjoint sequence in $\mathcal{R}$ with bounded union

$$A \equiv \bigcup_{i=1}^{\infty} A_i \in \mathcal{R}:$$

we seek to show that $N'(A) = \sum_{i=1}^{\infty} N'(A_i)$. Let $B_r = \bigcup_{i=r+1}^{\infty} A_i = A \setminus \bigcup_{i=1}^{r} A_i$, so B_r is bounded, $\in \mathcal{R}$, $\downarrow \emptyset$ $(r \to \infty)$, and thus $\mathcal{P}'\{N'(B_r) = 0\} = \psi(B_r) \uparrow 1$; that is, $N'(B_r) \to 0$ a.s. Defining events $C_r \in \mathcal{E}$ by $C_0 = \{N': N'(A) = 0\}$ and $C_r = \{N': N'(B_r) = 0 < N'(B_{r-1})\}$ $(r = 1, 2, \ldots)$, we have $\mathcal{P}'(C_0 \cup C_1 \cup \cdots) = 1$, and

$$N'(A) = \sum_{i=1}^{r} N'(A_i) + N'(B_r) \quad \text{on } C_r.$$

Also, on C_r, it follows from $0 = N'(B_r) = \lim_{n \to \infty} \zeta_n(B_r)$ that $N'(A_i) = 0$ for $i \ge r + 1$ and hence $\sum_{i=r+1}^{\infty} N'(A_i) = 0$ on C_r. Since $\mathcal{P}'(\bigcup_{r=0}^{\infty} C_r) = 1$, it now follows that N' is countably additive on $\mathcal{R}$. Then by the usual extension theorem for measures, N' can be extended a.s. to a countably additive boundedly finite nonnegative integer-valued measure on $\mathcal{B}_{\mathcal{X}}$. This extension, with the appropriate modification on the $\mathcal{P}'$-null set where the extension may fail, provides the required example of a point process with avoidance function $\mathcal{P}'\{N'(A) = 0\} = \psi(A)$ $(A \in \mathcal{R})$ satisfying conditions (i)–(iv). $\qquad\square$

Exercises

7.3.1. Let $A_1, \ldots, A_n$ be disjoint, $A = \bigcup_{i=1}^n A_i$ and $\psi(\varnothing) = 1$. Then the operator Δ at (7.3.2) satisfies

(a) $\quad \Delta(A)\psi(B) = \sum_{k=1}^n \sum_{1 \le i_1 < \cdots < i_k \le n} \Delta(A_{i_1}, \ldots, A_{i_k})\psi\left(B \cup \left(A \setminus \bigcup_{j=1}^k A_{i_j}\right)\right),$

(b) $\quad \sum_{i=1}^n (1 - \psi(A_i)) = \sum_{k=1}^n \sum_{1 \le i_1 < \cdots < i_k \le n} k\Delta(A_{i_1}, \ldots, A_{i_k})\psi\left(A \setminus \bigcup_{j=1}^k A_{i_j}\right).$

(c) Complete the induction proof of (7.3.3).

7.3.2. Let $A_1, A_2, \ldots$ be disjoint, $A = \bigcup_{i=1}^\infty A_i$ and $\psi(\varnothing) = 1$. If

$$1 - \psi(A) = \sum_{k=1}^\infty \sum_{1 \le i_1 < \cdots < i_k < \infty} \Delta(A_{i_1}, \ldots, A_{i_k})\psi\left(A \setminus \bigcup_{j=1}^k A_{i_j}\right),$$

then

$$1 - \psi\left(\bigcup_{i=m}^\infty A_i\right) = \sum_{k=1}^\infty \sum_{m \le i_1 < \cdots < i_k \le \infty} \Delta(A_{i_1}, \ldots, A_{i_k})\psi\left(A \setminus \bigcup_{j=1}^k A_{i_j}\right).$$

7.3.3. Let ξ be a random measure. Show that for each fixed $s > 0$ the transform $\varphi_s(A) \equiv E(e^{-s\xi(A)})$ is completely monotone in the argument A. [*Hint:* $\varphi_s(A)$ is the avoidance function of a doubly stochastic Poisson process with (random) intensity measure $s\xi(\cdot)$.]

7.4. The Probability Generating Functional and Factorial Moment Measures

These quantities were introduced for finite point processes in Sections 5.4 and 5.5. Here we give a general treatment based largely on Westcott (1972) and using a real variable rather than a complex variable approach. (Note that a function $g \in$ Westcott's class V if and only if $1 - g \in \mathscr{V}(\mathscr{X})$ as in the following definition.)

Definition 7.4.I. $\mathscr{V}(\mathscr{X})$ denotes the class of all real-valued Borel functions h defined on the c.s.m.s. $\mathscr{X}$ with $1 - h$ vanishing outside some bounded set and satisfying

$$0 \le h(x) \le 1 \quad \text{(all } x \in \mathscr{X}).$$

Extending Definition 5.5.I, the p.g.fl. of a general point process N on the c.s.m.s. $\mathscr{X}$ is defined for any $h \in \mathscr{V}(\mathscr{X})$ by

(7.4.1) $\qquad G[h] \equiv G_N[h] = E\left[\exp\left(\int_{\mathscr{X}} \log h(x) N(dx)\right)\right].$

Since the process is a.s. finite on the bounded set where $1 - h$ does not vanish, the exponential of the integral at (7.4.1) can legitimately be written in the product form

(7.4.2)
$$G_N[h] = E\left(\prod_i h(x_i)\right),$$

where the product is taken over the points of each realization of N (see Proposition 7.1.I), with the understanding that it takes the value zero if $h(x_i) = 0$ for any x_i, and unity if there are no points of N within the support of $1 - h$. If h is such that $-\log h \in BM_+(\mathcal{X})$, then

$$G[h] = L_N[-\log h]$$

relates the p.g.fl. to the Laplace functional of the point process [cf. (6.4.16)]. Indeed, $-\log h \in BM_+(\mathcal{X})$ implies that the values of h lie within a closed subset of $(0, 1]$, and so, since the distribution of a random measure is determined by all $f \in BM_+(\mathcal{X})$, the distribution of a point process is determined by all $h \in \mathcal{V}_0(\mathcal{X})$, where $\mathcal{V}_0(\mathcal{X})$ denotes the subset of $\mathcal{V}(\mathcal{X})$ consisting of those $(0, 1]$-valued measurable functions h with bounded support and $\inf_{x \in \mathcal{X}} h(x) > 0$. While results for point processes need to be proved only with this more restricted class of functions, it is only in our discussion of mixing properties of cluster processes (see Proposition 10.3.IX) that we need the constraint, so mostly we use $\mathcal{V}(\mathcal{X})$. Note that if $\{h_n\}$ is a pointwise convergent sequence of functions $\in \mathcal{V}_0(\mathcal{X})$ with the support of each $1 - h_n$ contained by some fixed bounded set, then the pointwise limit, h say, has $h \in \mathcal{V}(\mathcal{X})$ but not necessarily $h \in \mathcal{V}_0(\mathcal{X})$. To this extent, $\mathcal{V}(\mathcal{X})$ is a simpler class with which to work.

By putting additional restrictions on the point process, the p.g.fl. can be defined for more general classes of functions h. For example, if the expectation measure M of N exists, and nonnegative h is so chosen that

(7.4.3)
$$\int_{\mathcal{X}} |\log h(x)| M(dx) < \infty,$$

then the integral in (7.4.1) converges a.s. to a finite quantity, and the expectation exists, being finite under the further restriction on h that $h(x) \le 1$ (all $x \in \mathcal{X}$).

The following theorem is a characterization result analogous to Theorem 6.4.II for characteristic functionals of random measures.

Theorem 7.4.II. *Let $G[h]$ be a real-valued functional defined for all $h \in \mathcal{V}(\mathcal{X})$. Then G is the p.g.fl. of a point process N if and only if*

(i) *for every h of the form*

$$1 - h(x) = \sum_{k=1}^{n} (1 - z_k) I_{A_k}(x)$$

where the bounded Borel sets $A_1, \ldots, A_n$ are disjoint, the p.g.fl. $G[h]$ reduces to the joint p.g.f. $P_n(z_1, \ldots, z_n; A_1, \ldots, A_n)$ of an n-dimensional integer-valued random variable;

(ii) *for every sequence of functions* $\{h_n(\cdot)\}$ *with* $h_n \in \mathscr{V}(\mathscr{X})$ *and* $h_n(x) \downarrow h(x)$ *for every* $x \in \mathscr{X}$, $G[h_n] \to G[h]$ *whenever* $1 - h$ *has bounded support; and*

(iii) $G[1] = 1$, *where* **1** *here denotes the function identically equal to unity in* $\mathscr{X}$.

Moreover, when these conditions are satisfied, the functional G uniquely determines the distribution of N.

Since the proof of this result is similar to that of Theorem 6.4.II, we omit the details. Variants on the continuity condition (ii) are possible, but more is needed than just pointwise convergence (see Exercise 7.4.1). Indeed, we shall have a need for the *extended p.g.fl.* $G[\cdot]$ defined by analogy with the extended Laplace functional at (6.4.21) as

$$G[h] \equiv E \exp\left(\int_{\mathscr{X}} \log h(x) N(dx)\right)$$

on the space $\bar{\mathscr{V}}(\mathscr{X})$ of functions h expressible as limits of monotonic sequences $\{h_n\} \subset \mathscr{V}(\mathscr{X})$. Further details are given in Exercise 7.4.2.

We turn next to the finite Taylor series expansion of the p.g.fl. in terms of the factorial moment measures. Suppose that M_k, the kth moment measure of N, is finite. The kth factorial moment measure of N can be defined as at (5.4.2) in the finite case, provided that the sets A_i appearing there are bounded. It is clear that the factorial moment measure $M_{[k]}$ will exist if and only if M_k exists in the sense of both measures being boundedly finite. The relation between them remains as set out in Section 5.4 for the finite case. The advantages of working with the factorial moment measures and associated product densities have also been referred to there and will again be apparent in the discussion and examples below.

Proposition 7.4.III. *Let G be the p.g.fl. of a point process N for which the kth moment measure exists for some positive integer k. Then for $1 - \eta \in \mathscr{V}(\mathscr{X})$ and $0 < \rho < 1$,*

(7.4.4) $G[1 - \rho\eta]$

$$= 1 + \sum_{j=1}^{k} \left(\frac{(-\rho)^k}{k!}\right) \int_{\mathscr{X}} \cdots \int_{\mathscr{X}} \eta(x_1) \cdots \eta(x_j) M_{[j]}(dx_1 \times \cdots \times dx_j)$$

$$+ o(\rho^k).$$

PROOF. Some care is needed in evaluating the difference between $G[1 - \rho\eta]$ and the finite sum on the right-hand side. For fixed η and a given realization $\{y_i\}$ of the point process, consider the expressions

$$S_m(\rho) = 1 + \sum_{j=1}^{m} \left(\frac{(-\rho)^j}{j!}\right) \int_{\mathscr{X}} \cdots \int_{\mathscr{X}} \eta(x_1) \cdots \eta(x_j) N_{[j]}(dx_1 \times \cdots \times dx_j),$$

where $N_{[j]}$ is the modified product counting measure formed by taking all possible ordered j-tuples of different points of the realization of N (with the convention that if $\{y_i\}$ has multiple points these should be treated as different points with the same state space coordinates, that is, as if they represented distinct particles). Each integral then reduces to a sum

$$Q_j = \sum \eta(y_{i_1})\cdots\eta(y_{i_j})$$

over all such j-tuples. Effectively, each sum is a.s. finite, since with probability 1 only a finite number of points of the process will fall within the support of $1 - \eta$. Moreover, the sum will vanish whenever j is larger than the number of points in this support. Since $N_{[j]}$ includes all possible orderings of a given j-tuple, each distinct term in the sum is repeated $j!$ times, so that we can write

$$Q_j = j!\, q_j,$$

where the sum on q_j is extended over all distinct combinations of j points from $\{y_i\}$ (with the same convention as before regarding multiple points). With this notation we can write

$$(7.4.5) \qquad S_m(\rho) = 1 + \sum_{j=1}^{m} (-\rho)^j q_j,$$

and it is not difficult to verify (e.g., by induction) that for all m and η

$$(7.4.6) \qquad S_{2m+1}(\rho) \le \prod_i (1 - \rho\eta(y_i)) \equiv \Pi(\rho) \le S_{2m}(\rho),$$

the product being taken over $\{y_i\}$. [Westcott (1972) gives an interpretation of (7.4.6) in terms of the Bonferroni inequalities; see Exercise 7.4.3.] Taking differences suitably in (7.4.6) and substituting for $|S_k - S_{k-1}|$ from (7.4.5), we find that both

$$(7.4.7) \qquad |S_k(\rho) - \Pi(\rho)| \le q_k \rho^k \quad \text{and} \quad |S_k(\rho) - \Pi(\rho)| \le q_{k+1}\rho^{k+1},$$

the differences within the modulus being alternatively positive and negative according as k is even or odd. Now suppose that M_k, and hence $M_{[k]}$, exists. The former of the above inequalities implies that $(S_k(\rho) - \Pi(\rho))/\rho^k$ is bounded by a random variable with finite expectation

$$E(q_k) = \left(\frac{1}{k!}\right) \int \cdots \int \eta(x_1)\cdots\eta(x_k) M_{[k]}(dx_1 \times \cdots \times dx_k)$$

since $M_{[k]}$ is just the expectation measure of $N_{[k]}$. The second inequality implies that $(S_k(\rho) - \Pi(\rho))/\rho^k \to 0$ as $\rho \to 0$ a.s. The limit behaviour of the remainder term in (7.4.4) now follows by dominated convergence.

Uniqueness follows from the uniqueness of the coefficients in a power series expansion and the fact that, as symmetric measures, the moment measures are uniquely specified by integrals of the type appearing in the expansion (see Exercise 7.4.4).   □

Taking expectations in (7.4.7), we also have the following corollary.

Corollary 7.4.IV. *The remainder term in (7.4.4) is dominated by*

$$\left(\frac{\rho^{k+1}}{(k+1)!}\right) \int \cdots \int \eta(x_1) \cdots \eta(x_{k+1}) M_{[k+1]}(dx_1 \times \cdots \times dx_{k+1})$$

when the measure M_{k+1} exists.

Corollary 7.4.V. *Under the conditions of the theorem, the p.g.fl. can be expressed in terms of the factorial cumulant measures $C_{[j]}$; namely,*

$$(7.4.8) \quad \log G[1 - \rho\eta]$$

$$= \sum_{j=1}^{k} \left(\frac{(-\rho)^j}{j!}\right) \int_{\mathscr{X}} \cdots \int_{\mathscr{X}} \eta(x_1) \cdots \eta(x_j) C_{[j]}(dx_1 \times \cdots \times dx_j)$$

$$+ o(\rho^k) \quad (\rho \to 0).$$

The existence of an expansion of the kind at (7.4.8) follows on taking logarithms of the expression (7.4.4) and using the expansion

$$\log(1 - y) = - \sum_{j=1}^{k} \frac{(-y)^j}{j} + o(y^k) \quad (y \to 0).$$

The expression (7.4.8) serves to define the cumulant measures, which can then be expressed explicitly in terms of the measure $M_{[j]}$ as in Chapter 5. Unfortunately, it does not seem possible to provide a simple bound for the remainder term in (7.4.8) analogous to that of Corollary 7.4.IV.

Note that in all these expansions, the factorial and cumulant measures may be regarded as functional derivatives, of appropriate order, of the generating functional at the function $h(x) = 1$ (all $x \in \mathscr{X}$).

We reiterate here the statement below (5.4.3) that M_k can be regarded as the expectation measure of a point process $N^{(k)}$ on the product space $\mathscr{X}^{(k)}$ (and the same is true for moments of random measures). This remark is illustrated forcefully in the proof below of a result already given at Proposition 5.4.V. Here and in the related exercise 7.4.5,

$$\text{diag } A^{(k)} \equiv \{(x_1, \ldots, x_k) \in \mathscr{X}^{(k)}: x_1 = \cdots = x_k = x \in A\}.$$

Proposition 7.4.VI. *A point process N with boundedly finite second moment measure has $M_2(\text{diag } A^{(2)}) \geq M(A)$ for all bounded $A \in \mathscr{B}_{\mathscr{X}}$; equality holds if and only if N is simple.*

PROOF. Let $\mathscr{T}$ be a dissecting system for A. Because M_2 is a measure that is finite on $A^{(2)}$,

$$M_2(\text{diag } A^{(2)}) = M_2 \left(\lim_{n \to \infty} \bigcup_{i=1}^{k_n} (A_{ni} \times A_{ni}) \right)$$

$$= \lim_{n \to \infty} M_2 \left(\bigcup_{i=1}^{k_n} (A_{ni} \times A_{ni}) \right)$$

$$= \lim_{n\to\infty} E\left(\sum_{i=1}^{k_n} N^2(A_{ni})\right)$$

$$= M(A) + \lim_{n\to\infty} E\left(\sum_{i=1}^{k_n} N(A_{ni})(N(A_{ni}) - 1)\right).$$

Write the last term as EX_n. From the nesting property of $\{\mathcal{T}_n\}$ the r.v.s X_n are a.s. nonincreasing and ≥ 0, so by monotone convergence

$$M_2(\text{diag } A^{(2)}) = M(A) + E\left(\lim_{n\to\infty} X_n\right),$$

and $\lim_{n\to\infty} X_n = 0$ a.s. if and only if $\limsup_{n\to\infty,i} N(A_{ni}) \leq 1$ a.s.; that is, $\mathcal{P}\{N(\{x\}) \leq 1 \text{ for all } x \in A\} = 1$. $\square$

EXAMPLE 7.4(a) *Poisson and compound Poisson processes.* The form of the p.g.fl. for the Poisson process is already implicit in the form of the p.g.f. obtained in Chapter 2 and its multivariate extension

$$(7.4.9) \qquad P_k(A_1, \ldots, A_k: z_1, \ldots, z_k) = \exp\left(-\sum_{j=1}^{k} (1 - z_j)\mu(A_j)\right),$$

where $A_1, \ldots, A_k$ are disjoint and where $\mu(\cdot)$ is the parameter measure of the process. Writing

$$h(x) = 1 - \sum_{j=1}^{k} (1 - z_j)I_{A_j}(x)$$

so that h equals z_j on A_j and unity outside the union of all A_j, (7.4.9) is expressible as

$$(7.4.10) \qquad G[h] = \exp\left(-\int_{\mathcal{X}} (1 - h(x))\mu(dx)\right),$$

which is evidently the required form of the p.g.fl.

The following heuristic derivation of (7.4.10) also throws light on the character of the p.g.fl. Suppose that the support of $1 - h(x)$ is partitioned into small subsets ΔA_i with $x_i \in \Delta A_i$ a "representative point" from each. Then, approximately,

$$\int_{\mathcal{X}} \log h(x)N(dx) \approx \sum_i \log h(x_i)N(\Delta A_i).$$

From the independence assumptions, the random variables $N(\Delta A_i)$ here are independent and so

$$E\left(\exp\left(\int_{\mathcal{X}} \log h(x)N(dx)\right)\right) \approx E\left(\prod_i \exp\{\log h(x_i)^{N(\Delta A_i)}\}\right)$$

$$= \prod_i E(h(x_i)^{N(\Delta A_i)})$$

$$= \prod_i \exp\{-(1 - h(x_i))\mu(\Delta A_i)\}$$

$$\approx \exp\left(-\int_{\mathscr{X}} (1 - h(x))\mu(dx)\right).$$

The corresponding expression for the compound Poisson process (see Section 2.4) is

(7.4.11) $$G[h] = \exp\left(-\int_{\mathscr{X}} (1 - \Pi_{h(x)}(x))\mu(dx)\right)$$

$$= \exp\left(-\int_{\mathscr{X}} \sum_n \pi_n(x)(1 - (h(x))^n)\mu(dx)\right),$$

which yields the form (2.4.5) for the univariate p.g.f. when $h(x) = 1 - (1 - z)I_A(x)$. It is not difficult to check now that G satisfies the conditions of Theorem 7.4.II, and therefore it represents the p.g.fl. of a point process with the complete independence property. A closer analogue with the representation of Proposition 6.3.IX can be obtained by writing $Q(n, dx) = \pi_n(x)\mu(dx)$ so that (7.4.11) becomes

$$G[h] = \exp\left(-\sum_{n=1}^{\infty} \int_{\mathscr{X}} (1 - (h(x))^n)Q(n, dx)\right).$$

Since the p.g.fl. and the Laplace functional are related for $h \in \mathscr{V}_0(\mathscr{X})$ by

$$L[h] = G[e^{-h}],$$

we can use Proposition 6.3.IX to identify the compound Poisson process as a random measure that has the complete independence property, is free of fixed atoms, and has random atoms of positive integral mass. Of course, this is merely a restatement of results obtained directly in Section 2.4.

Expressions for the factorial and cumulant measures of these processes can be read off directly from the p.g.fl. For the Poisson process we have formally, for η with $1 - \eta \in \mathscr{V}$,

$$G[1 + \eta] = 1 + \sum_{k=1}^{\infty} \left(\frac{1}{k!}\right)\left(\int_{\mathscr{X}} \eta(x)\mu(dx)\right)^k$$

$$= 1 + \sum_{k=1}^{\infty} \left(\frac{1}{k!}\right)\int_{\mathscr{X}} \cdots \int_{\mathscr{X}} \eta(x_1)\cdots\eta(x_k)\mu(dx_1)\cdots\mu(dx_k).$$

Thus, *for the Poisson process with parameter measure μ, the k-factorial moment measure $M_{[k]}$ is the k-fold product measure of μ with itself.* The situation with the cumulant measures is even simpler. Here

$$\log G[1 + \eta] = \int_{\mathscr{X}} \eta(x)\mu(dx)$$

so that *for a Poisson process the second and all higher factorial cumulant measures vanish.*

This last result contrasts with the situation for the compound Poisson process for which

$$
\begin{aligned}
\log G[1 + \eta] &= \int_{\mathscr{X}} \sum_n \{(1 + \eta(x))^n - 1\} \pi_n(x)\mu(dx) \\
&= \sum_{k=1}^{\infty} \int_{\mathscr{X}} \left(\frac{(\eta(x))^k}{k!}\right)\left(\sum_{n=k}^{\infty} n^{[k]}\pi_n(x)\right)\mu(dx) \\
&= \sum_k \left(\frac{1}{k!}\right) \int_{\mathscr{X}} \eta(x)^k m_{[k]}(x)\mu(dx),
\end{aligned}
$$

where $m_{[k]}(x)$ is the kth factorial moment of the batch-size distribution $\{\pi_n(x)\}$ at the point x, assuming this moment exists. From this representation we see that $C_{[k]}(\cdot)$ is concentrated on the diagonal set, where $x_1 = \cdots = x_k$, and there it reduces to a measure with density $m_{[k]}(x)$ with respect to $\mu(\cdot)$.

EXAMPLE 7.4(b) *Mixed Poisson process.* Referring to (7.4.9), denote the fidi distributions of a Poisson process by $P_k(\cdot | \mu)$ for short. Then N is a mixed Poisson process when for some r.v. Λ and boundedly finite measure μ its fidi distributions $P_k(\cdot)$ are given by

(7.4.12) $\qquad P_k(\cdot) = E P_k(\cdot | \Lambda\mu),$

the expectation being with respect to Λ. Denote the Laplace–Stieltjes transform of Λ by $L(\cdot)$ so that $L(s) = E(e^{-s\Lambda})$ (Re$(s) \geq 0$). It then follows from (7.4.12) and (7.4.10) that the p.g.fl. of a mixed Poisson process is given by

(7.4.13) $\qquad G[h] = E\left\{\exp\left(-\int_{\mathscr{X}} (1 - h(x))\Lambda\mu(dx)\right)\right\}$

$$
= L\left(\int_{\mathscr{X}} (1 - h(x))\mu(dx)\right).
$$

Supposing that Λ has a finite kth moment, it follows that in a neighbourhood Re$(s) \geq 0$ of $s = 0$,

$$
L(s) = 1 + \sum_{j=1}^{k} \frac{(-s)^j (E\Lambda^j)}{j!} + o(|s|^k).
$$

Then we find for h with $1 - h \in \mathscr{V}$,

$$
\begin{aligned}
G[1 - \rho h] = 1 &+ \sum_{j=1}^{k} \left(\frac{(-\rho)^j (E\Lambda^j)}{j!}\right) \int_{\mathscr{X}} \cdots \int_{\mathscr{X}} h(x_1) \cdots h(x_j)\mu(dx_1) \cdots \mu(dx_j) \\
&+ o(\rho^k)
\end{aligned}
$$

so that the factorial moment measures of the process are given by

(7.4.14) $\quad M_{[j]}(dx_1 \times \cdots \times dx_j) = (E\Lambda^j)\mu(dx_1) \cdots \mu(dx_j) \qquad (j \leq k).$

If, in particular, $\mathscr{X} = \mathbb{R}^d$ and $\mu(\cdot)$ is Lebesgue measure on $\mathbb{R}^d$, $M_{[j]}$ then has a density $m_{[j]}$ with respect to such Lebesgue measure given by

$$m_{[j]}(x_1, \ldots, x_j) = E(\Lambda^j) \qquad (j \le k).$$

Thus, the factorial moment measures for the mixed Poisson process retain the product form of the Poisson case but are multiplied by the scalar factors $E(\Lambda^j)$. McFadden (1965a) and Davidson (1974c) have established the following converse to this result. Let $\{M_{[j]}(\cdot)\}$ be a sequence of product measures of the form (7.4.14) with $\{E(\Lambda^j)\}$ replaced by a sequence $\{\gamma_j\}$. Then the $M_{[j]}(\cdot)$ are the factorial moment measures of a point process if and only if $\{\gamma_j\}$ is the moment sequence of some nonnegative random variable Λ_0. A sufficient condition for the resulting process to be uniquely defined is that $\sum \gamma_j^{-1/j} = \infty$, in which case it is necessarily the mixed Poisson process with parameter measure $\Lambda_0 \mu$, where Λ_0 has a uniquely defined distribution with moments $\{\gamma_j\}$. A weaker version of this result can be deduced from Proposition 5.4.VI (see Exercise 7.4.6).

EXAMPLE 7.4(c) *Negative binomial processes.* In applications in which clustering is the preferred choice after rejection of the Poisson distribution for the one-dimensional distributions, the negative binomial is a common next choice. In the point process context, it is somewhat surprising that the only known examples yielding the negative binomial form for the one-dimensional distributions are both extreme cases, namely, a compound Poisson process that has the complete independence property and in which all the clusters are concentrated at single points, and a mixed Poisson process in which the individual realizations are indistinguishable from those of a Poisson process. The usefulness of the negative binomial distribution in practice stems more from its relative simplicity and tractability than its link to organic physical models, although it will of course be true that for long time intervals, when the time scale of clustering is short compared to the time scale of observation, the compound Poisson model may be an adequate approximation. We describe these two examples; note the useful review article of Diggle and Milne (1984) and the particular discussion in Grégoire (1984).

(i) *Compound Poisson process leading to negative binomial distributions.* For simplicity, suppose given a compound Poisson process in which the cluster size distribution is independent of the location x of the cluster. Then from (7.4.11), when the cluster size has the negative binomial distribution, we may take [cf. Example 5.2(a) above]

$$\pi_n(x) = (\rho^n/n) \log(1/(1 - \rho)).$$

If also the underlying Poisson process has parameter measure $\mu(\cdot)$, the p.g.fl. then has the form, for $h \in \mathscr{V}$,

$$G[h] = \exp\left(\int_{\mathscr{X}} \frac{\log[(1 - \rho h(x))/(1 - \rho)]}{\log(1 - \rho)} \mu(dx)\right).$$

This corresponds to the multivariate p.g.f. for the fidi distributions on disjoint sets $A_1, \ldots, A_k$

$$P_k(A_1, \ldots, A_k; z_1, \ldots, z_k) = \prod_{i=1}^{k} \left(\frac{1 - \rho}{1 - \rho z_i} \right)^{-\mu(A_i)/\log(1-\rho)}.$$

The factorial cumulant measures can be obtained from the expansion

$$\log G[1 + \eta] = \int_{\mathcal{X}} \frac{\log(1 - \rho\eta(x)/(1 - \rho))}{\log(1 - \rho)} \mu(dx)$$

$$= (-\log(1 - \rho))^{-1} \sum_{k=1}^{\infty} \left(\frac{\rho}{1 - \rho} \right)^k k^{-1} \int_{\mathcal{X}} \eta^k(x)\mu(dx),$$

so that $C_{[k]}(\cdot)$ is (for $k \geq 2$) a singular measure with a concentration $c_{[k]}\mu(\cdot)$ on the "diagonal" $x_1 = \cdots = x_k$, where $c_{[k]}$ is the kth factorial moment of the logarithmic distribution, or, equivalently, $c_{[k]}/\log(1/(1 - \rho))$ is the kth factorial cumulant of the negative binomial distribution.

(ii) *Mixed Poisson process leading to negative binomial distributions.* By taking the mixing distribution at (7.4.13) to have the gamma distribution $\Gamma(\alpha, \lambda)$, we have

$$G[h] = L\left(\int_{\mathcal{X}} (1 - h(x))\mu(dx) \right) = \left(1 + \lambda^{-1} \int_{\mathcal{X}} (1 - h(x))\mu(dx) \right)^{-\alpha}$$

so that the multivariate p.g.f. has the form

$$P_k(A_1, \ldots, A_k; z_1, \ldots, z_k) = \left(1 + \lambda^{-1} \sum_{i=1}^{k} (1 - z_i)\mu(A_i) \right)^{-\alpha}.$$

The factorial cumulants can be obtained from the expansion

$$\log G[1 + \eta] = -\alpha \log\left(1 - \lambda^{-1} \int_{\mathcal{X}} \eta(x)\mu(dx) \right)$$

$$= \alpha \sum_{k=1}^{\infty} \lambda^{-k} k^{-1} \left(\int_{\mathcal{X}} \eta(x)\mu(dx) \right)^k,$$

so $C_{[k]}(dx_1 \times \cdots \times dx_k) = \alpha\lambda^{-k}(k - 1)!\,\mu(dx_1)\cdots\mu(dx_k)$, where we can recognize the coefficient of the product measure as the kth cumulant of the negative binomial distribution. Note that Example 5.2(a) corresponds to the special case where the the parameter measure $\mu(\cdot)$ is totally finite; then $\mu(\mathcal{X})/\lambda$ gives the parameter in the earlier example.

The analogue of Proposition 6.4.VII for the p.g.fl. G of the superposition of the independent point processes $N_1, \ldots, N_n$ with p.g.fl.s $G_1, \ldots, G_n$ is easily given (its proof is left as Exercise 7.4.7).

Proposition 7.4.VII. *When the point processes $N_1, N_2, \ldots$ are mutually independent, the superposition $N_1 + \cdots + N_n$ has p.g.fl.*

$$G[h] = \prod_{i=1}^{n} G_i[h] \qquad (h \in \mathcal{V}(\mathcal{X})).$$

The sequence of finite products here converges if and only if the infinite sum

(7.4.15) $$N(A) = \sum_{i=1}^{\infty} N_i(A)$$

is a.s. finite on bounded $A \in \mathcal{B}_{\mathcal{X}}$, *when the infinite product is the p.g.fl. of the point process* N *at* (7.4.15).

Not infrequently our concern with a point process may be with its structure only on some bounded region A of the state space. Within A (assumed to be Borel) N is a.s. finite-valued by assumption, and its probabilistic structure must be expressible in terms of some family of local probability distributions or Janossy measures as in Chapter 5. However, since such point processes are in general a.s. infinite on the whole of $\mathcal{X}$, no such measures exist for the process as a whole. We indicate below how the local characteristics can be described.

We have already referred in Chapter 5 to the global characteristics of the factorial moment and cumulant measures, and the fact that their values are unaffected by whether we look at the process as a whole or restricted to a bounded region. This opens up one possible approach to the definition of local Janossy measures. Denote by $J_n(\cdot | A)$ the Janossy measures localized to A; that is,

$$J_n(dx_1 \times \cdots \times dx_n | A) = \Pr\{\text{exactly } n \text{ points in } A, \text{ at locations } dx_1, \ldots, dx_n\}.$$

Then we can use (5.4.9) to obtain under suitable conditions

(7.4.16) $$J_n(B | A) = \sum_{k=0}^{\infty} (-1)^k M_{[n+k]}(B \times A^{(k)})/k!.$$

Such an approach cannot be used in general because the moment measures appearing in (7.4.16) need not exist, nor need the series converge even when they do exist. The measures $J_n(\cdot | A)$ can, however, be obtained quite simply from the p.g.fl., in principle at least (in practice the computations are often intractable). Let $\mathcal{V}(A)$ denote the space of all measurable functions h on A satisfying $0 \le h \le 1$, and for $h \in \mathcal{V}(A)$ extend h to all $\mathcal{X}$ by putting

$$h^*(x) = \begin{cases} 0 & (x \notin A), \\ h(x) & (x \in A). \end{cases}$$

Then the p.g.fl. $G_A[h]$ of the local process on A is defined in terms of the global p.g.fl. G by the equation

(7.4.17) $$G_A[h] = G[1 - I_A + h^*] \qquad (h \in \mathcal{V}(A)).$$

This representation follows immediately from the interpretation of the p.g.fl. as the expectation

$$G_A[h] = E\left(\prod_{x_i \in A} h(x_i)\right) = E\left(\prod_{x_i \in \mathcal{X}} (1 - I_A(x_i) + h^*(x_i))\right).$$

Thus, the local Janossy measures can be obtained from an expansion of the p.g.fl. about the function $1 - I_A(\cdot)$ rather than about 0. Specifically,

(7.4.18) $G_A[\rho h]$

$$= G[1 - I_A + \rho h^*]$$

$$= p_0(A) + \sum_{n=1}^{\infty} \left(\frac{\rho^n}{n!}\right) \int_{A^{(n)}} \cdots \int h(x_1) \cdots h(x_n) J_n(dx_1 \times \cdots \times dx_n | A).$$

A similar comment applies to the Khinchin measures arising from the expansion of the log p.g.fl. We can introduce local Khinchin measures, $K_n(\cdot | A)$ say, via the expansion [cf. Equation (5.5.10)]

(7.4.19) $\log G_A[\rho h]$

$$= \log G[1 - I_A + \rho h^*]$$

$$= -K_0(A)$$

$$- \sum_{n=1}^{\infty} \left(\frac{\rho^n}{n!}\right) \int_{A^{(n)}} \cdots \int h(x_1) \cdots h(x_n) K_n(dx_1 \times \cdots \times dx_n | A),$$

where $p_0(A) = \exp(-K_0(A))$.

EXAMPLE 7.4(c) (Continued)

The p.g.fl. for the type (i) negative binomial process considered earlier gives us (since the term below involving integration over A^c vanishes)

$$G[1 - I_A + h^*] = \exp\left(\frac{1}{\log(1 - \rho)} \int_A \log\left(\frac{1 - \rho h}{1 - \rho}\right) \mu(dx)\right).$$

Thus, the localized process is still a negative binomial process. The local Janossy measures can be found from the expansion

$$\log\left(\frac{1 - \rho h}{1 - \rho}\right) = -\log(1 - \rho) + \sum_{n=1}^{\infty} \left(\frac{\rho^n}{n}\right) h^{(n)},$$

from which we deduce

$$p_0(A) = \exp(-\mu(A)),$$

$$J_1(dx | A) = \rho p_0(A) \mu(dx),$$

$$J_2(dx_1 \times dx_2 | A) = \rho^2 p_0(A) [\mu(dx_1)\mu(dx_2) + \delta(x_1, x_2)\mu(dx_1)],$$

where the two terms in J_2 represent contributions from two single-point clusters at x_1 and x_2 ($x_1 \neq x_2$) and a two-point cluster at $x_1 = x_2$.

Exercises

7.4.1. Suppose that functions $h_n \in \mathcal{V}(\mathcal{X})$ and that $h_n(x) \to h(x)$ ($n \to \infty$) for every $x \in \mathcal{X}$. In place of the conditions at (ii) of Theorem 7.4.II, show that $G[h_n] \to G[h]$

$(n \to \infty)$ if either (a) N is a.s. totally finite, or (b) N has a finite first moment measure M and

$$\int_{\mathscr{X}} |h_n(x) - h(x)| M(dx) \to 0 \qquad (n \to \infty).$$

Let $h_n(x) = 1 - n^{-1}$ for $|x| < n$, $= 1$ for $|x| \geq n$, so that $h_n(x) \to 1$ (all x) for $n \to \infty$. Show that for a stationary Poisson process at rate λ, $G[h_n] = e^{-2\lambda} \not\to 1 = G[\lim_{n \to \infty} h_n]$ (cf. Exercise 6.4.1).

7.4.2. Let $\{h_n\} \subset \mathscr{V}(\mathscr{X})$ have $h_n(x) \to h(x)$ pointwise as $n \to \infty$. Show that the extended p.g.fl. convergence result $G[h_n] \to G[h]$ holds if any one of the following conditions holds:
(a) h is the monotone limit of functions $h_n \in \mathscr{V}(\mathscr{X})$;
(b) $|\log(h_n(x)/h(x))| \leq \varepsilon(x)$ (all n) and $\int_{\mathscr{X}} \varepsilon(x) N(dx) < \infty$ a.s.;
(c) $\inf_{x \in \mathscr{X}} h_n(x) \geq c$ for some $c > 0$ and sufficiently large n, and

$$\int_{\mathscr{X}} |h_n(x) - h(x)| N(dx) < \infty \quad \text{a.s.}$$

[*Hint*: For part (b), use the method of proof of Proposition 6.4.IX. Part (c) follows from (b). See Daley and Vere-Jones (1987).]

7.4.3. Let $Q_N = \prod_{i=1}^{N} (1 - \alpha_i)$, where $0 < \alpha_i < 1$ for $i = 1, \ldots, N$, and write

$$q_k = \sum_{1 \leq i_1 < \cdots < i_k \leq N} \cdots \sum \alpha_{i_1} \cdots \alpha_{i_k},$$

so that $Q_N = 1 - q_1 + q_2 - \cdots + (-1)^N q_N$. By interpreting $\{\alpha_i\}$ as the set of probabilities of some independent events $A_1, \ldots, A_N$, and using the Bonferroni inequalities (cf. Exercise 5.2.5), show that for all N and positive integers $m \leq N/2$ that

$$S_N^{(2m-1)} \leq Q_N \leq S_N^{(2m)},$$

where

$$S_N^{(k)} = 1 - q_1 + q_2 - \cdots + (-)^k q_k, \qquad k = 1, \ldots, N.$$

Hence, deduce (7.4.6)

7.4.4. Let M_k be a symmetric measure on $(\mathscr{X}^{(k)}, \mathscr{B}^{(k)})$. By starting from indicator functions, show that M_k is uniquely determined by integrals of the form

$$\int \cdots \int \eta(x_1) \cdots \eta(x_k) M_k(dx_1 \times \cdots \times dx_k) \qquad (1 - \eta \in \mathscr{V}(\mathscr{X})).$$

7.4.5. (a) Using the intensity measures λ_k^* of the simple point processes N_k^* in the decomposition at (7.2.1), show that

$$M_2(\text{diag } A^{(2)}) = M(A) + \sum_{k=2}^{\infty} k(k-1)\lambda_k^*(A)$$

$$= M(A) + M_{[2]}(\text{diag } A^{(2)})$$

[cf. (7.2.9) and Proposition 7.4.VI]. More generally,

$$M_r(\text{diag } A^{(r)}) = \sum_{k=1}^{\infty} k^r \lambda_k^*(A).$$

(b) Show that

$$M_{[r]}(\text{diag } A^{(r)}) = 0$$

[assuming that $M_r(A^{(r)}) < \infty$] if and only if $\mathscr{P}\{N(\{x\}) \leq r - 1$ for all $x \in A\} = 1$.

7.4.6. Suppose that measures $M_{[j]}$ are given by (7.4.14) with each $E\Lambda^j$ replaced by some $\gamma_j > 0$ for which $\sum \gamma_j (1 + \varepsilon)^j < \infty$ for some $\varepsilon > 0$. Use (5.4.8) to show that locally the Janossy measures are defined and determine a point process whenever $\{\gamma_j\}$ is a moment sequence.

7.4.7. For an infinite sequence N_1, N_2, ... of independent point processes, show that the necessary and sufficient condition for the infinite superposition $\sum_{i=1}^{\infty} N_i$ to be a well-defined point process is the convergence for every bounded $A \in \mathscr{B}_{\mathscr{X}}$ of the sum $\sum_{i=1}^{\infty} p_i(A)$, where $p_i(A) = \Pr\{N_i(A) > 0\}$. Hence, establish Proposition 7.4.VII.

7.4.8. [Compare Bol'shakov (1969).] Let N be a renewal process with lifetime d.f. F, and denote by $G_{b|a}[h]$ the p.g.fl. of the process on the interval $[a, b]$ conditional on the occurrence of a point of the process at a. Show that this conditional p.g.fl. satisfies the integral equation

$$G_{b|a}[h] = (1 - F(b - a)) + \int_a^b (h(x) + 1)G_{b|x}[h]d_x F(x - a).$$

Similarly, if $\tilde{G}_{a|b}[h]$ denotes the p.g.fl. conditional on a point at b,

$$\tilde{G}_{a|b}[h] = (1 - F(b - a)) + \int_a^b (h(x) + 1)\tilde{G}_{a|x}[h]|d_x F(b - x)|.$$

Find extensions of these equations to the case where the renewal process is replaced by a point process whose intervals form a first-order Markov chain.

CHAPTER 8

Cluster Processes, Infinitely Divisible Processes, and Doubly Stochastic Processes

In this chapter we discuss two of the most widely used classes of point processes in application and associate with the first of them the important theoretical problem of determining the structure of infinitely divisible point processes. Each class contains many special cases that have been the subject of extensive analyses in their own right. A key feature of both classes is that their most important members are derivatives of the Poisson process. They are, indeed, natural extensions of the compound and mixed Poisson processes of the previous chapter: the Poisson cluster process extends the notion of the compound Poisson process and the doubly stochastic Poisson process extends the notion of the mixed Poisson process. Because of this feature, both can be handled compactly by the p.g.fl. techniques introduced in Chapter 7, and we make extensive use of this approach. It should be borne in mind, however, that the main advantage of this approach lies precisely in its compactness: it quickly summarizes information that can still be derived quite readily without it and that in less tractable examples may not be so easily expressible in p.g.fl. form.

The models described in this chapter can be useful both in time series problems and in the study of two- and three-dimensional point patterns. Many of their properties, particularly the moment properties of the counting process, can be obtained explicitly, and they are natural candidates for the second-order analysis of counting properties described in Chapters 10 and 11. Their one major disadvantage is that their likelihood functions are in general exceedingly complex. For this reason, the models lack a systematic theory of inference. Where second-order methods are applied, there is no guarantee (since the processes are non-Gaussian) that they will be optimal, nor is there any easy way of deciding how they should be improved or supplemented.

8.1. Point Processes Defined via Conditioning

Both cluster and doubly stochastic models are defined by a procedure that involves conditioning as an intermediate step. We therefore preface these definitions with a presentation of conditions that justify the conditioning arguments. The relevant measure-theoretic results are in Proposition A1.5.II and can be summarized as follows. Suppose there is given a family of probability distributions on $\mathcal{M}_{\mathcal{Y}}$ for some c.s.m.s. $\mathcal{Y}$ and that the family is indexed by a parameter x from some further c.s.m.s. $\mathcal{X}$. Denote these distributions by $\mathcal{P}(\cdot\,|x)$. Now suppose also that there is an $\mathcal{X}$-valued r.v. $x(\cdot)$ with probability distribution $\Pi(\cdot)$ on $\mathcal{B}_{\mathcal{X}}$. Then Proposition A1.5.II implies that only the measurability of $\mathcal{P}(A|x)$, for each fixed $A \in \mathcal{B}(\mathcal{M}_{\mathcal{Y}})$, is needed to ensure the existence of a process with distribution on $\mathcal{M}_{\mathcal{Y}}$ defined by

$$\mathcal{P}(A) = \int_{\mathcal{X}} \mathcal{P}(A|x)\Pi(dx).$$

As is immediately evident, the r.v. x plays no real role here: it is only its distribution $\Pi(\cdot)$ that is relevant. Note that since $\mathcal{M}_{\mathcal{X}}$ is itself a c.s.m.s., we are at liberty to replace $\mathcal{X}$ by $\mathcal{M}_{\mathcal{X}}$, and so to take the mixing r.v. to be itself a random measure or point process.

It is convenient to use Lemma A1.5.II in conjunction with the p.g.fl. machinery of Chapter 7, leading to the following definition and reformulation of the lemma.

Definition 8.1.I. A family of point processes on the c.s.m.s. $\mathcal{Y}$ with p.g.fl.s $G[h|x]$ ($x \in$ c.s.m.s. $\mathcal{X}$) defined for $h \in \mathcal{V}(\mathcal{Y})$ is a *measurable family* when, for each such h, $G[h|x]$ is a measurable function of x.

Lemma 8.1.II. *Suppose there is given (i) a measurable family of point processes on the c.s.m.s. $\mathcal{Y}$ with p.g.fl.s $G[h|x]$ defined for $h \in \mathcal{V}(\mathcal{Y})$ and $x \in$ c.s.m.s. $\mathcal{X}$, and (ii) a measurable mapping $\mathcal{X}: \Omega \to \mathcal{X}$. Denote by $\Pi(\cdot)$ the probability measure on $\mathcal{B}_{\mathcal{X}}$ induced by $\mathcal{X}$. Then the functional $G[\cdot]$ defined by*

(8.1.1) $$G[h] = \int_{\mathcal{X}} G[h|x]\Pi(dx)$$

is the p.g.fl. of a point process on $\mathcal{Y}$.

PROOF. Denote the probability measure on $\mathcal{N}_{\mathcal{Y}}$ corresponding to $G[h|x]$ by $Q(\cdot\,|x)$. Observe that when $A \in \mathcal{B}(\mathcal{N}_{\mathcal{Y}})$ has the special form of a cylinder set as used in the specification of fidi distributions, $Q(A|x)$ can be obtained from $G[h|x]$ by a suitable choice of h and repeated differentiation, that is, by operations on $G[\cdot\,|x]$ that do not affect the measurability with respect to x of the resultant functions. Denoting by $\mathcal{A}$ the class of subsets A of $\mathcal{N}_{\mathcal{Y}}$ for which

$Q(A|x)$ is a measurable function of x, it follows that $\mathscr{A}$ contains the cylinder sets, and the closure properties of families of measurable functions further imply that $\mathscr{A}$ is closed under monotone limits and therefore contains the σ-field of all subsets of $\mathscr{N}_{\mathscr{Y}}$ generated by the cylinder sets; that is, $\mathscr{A} \supseteq \mathscr{B}(\mathscr{N}_{\mathscr{Y}})$. Consequently,

$$\mathscr{P}(A) = \int_{\mathscr{X}} Q(A|x)\Pi(dx) \qquad (A \in \mathscr{B}(\mathscr{N}_{\mathscr{Y}}))$$

is a probability measure on $\mathscr{B}(\mathscr{N}_{\mathscr{Y}})$, and hence it has the p.g.fl. that, applying Proposition A1.5.II, is given by

$$\begin{aligned} G[h] &= \int_{\mathscr{N}_{\mathscr{Y}}} \exp\left(\int_{\mathscr{Y}} \log h(y)N(dy)\right)\mathscr{P}(dN) \\ &= \int_{\mathscr{X}} \Pi(dx) \int_{\mathscr{N}_{\mathscr{Y}}} \exp\left(\int_{\mathscr{Y}} \log h(y)N(dy)\right)Q(dN|x) \\ &= \int_{\mathscr{X}} G[h|x]\Pi(dx). \end{aligned}$$ $\square$

Special cases of this lemma have been used already, for example, in discussing mixed Poisson and branching processes in Examples 7.4(c) and 5.5(a). What distinguishes the applications in this chapter is that the conditioning element x is itself the realization of some point process or random measure. Problems of existence are reduced to checking that the construction leads to a measurable family of p.g.fl.s.

8.2. The General Cluster Process

The intuitive motivation for a cluster process involves an unseen point process N_c whose generic realization consists of the points $\{x_i\} \subset \mathscr{X}$ and a countable family of point processes $N(\cdot|x_i)$ whose superposition on some common realization space $\mathscr{Y}$ is observed. The centres x_i act as the germs (or ancestors, in the branching process context) for the clusters they generate; it is supposed in general that there are no special features attaching to the points of a given cluster that would allow them to be distinguished from the points in some other cluster. More formally, we have the following definition.

Definition 8.2.I. N is a *cluster process* on the c.s.m.s. $\mathscr{Y}$ with centre process N_c on the c.s.m.s. $\mathscr{X}$ and component processes the measurable family of point processes $\{N(\cdot|x), x \in \mathscr{X}\}$ when for every bounded $A \in \mathscr{B}_{\mathscr{Y}}$,

$$(8.2.1) \qquad N(A) = \int_{\mathscr{X}} N(A|x)N_c(dx) = \sum_i N(A|x_i)$$

is finite almost surely.

The definition requires the superposition of the clusters to be almost surely boundedly finite. There is, however, no requirement in general that the individual clusters must themselves be a.s. finite [i.e., $N(\mathcal{Y}|x) < \infty$ a.s.], although this is a natural constraint in many examples. A general cluster random measure can be introduced in the same way by allowing the component processes to be random measures (see Exercise 8.2.1).

For the remainder of this section we require the component processes to be mutually independent, thereby defining an *independent cluster process*. In this definition it is to be understood that multiple independent copies of $N(\cdot|x)$ are taken when $N_c\{x\} > 1$. If the cluster centre process and the component processes are all defined on the same space $\mathcal{X}$, which admits translations, then the further constraint that the translated components $N(\cdot - x|x)$ are identically distributed may be added; processes with this special character are studied further in Chapter 10.

Let $\{G_m[h|x], x \in \mathcal{X}\}$ denote the p.g.fl.s of the component processes and $G[h|N_c]$ the conditional p.g.fl. of N given N_c, with N as at (8.2.1). Then by Proposition 7.4.VII,

$$(8.2.2) \qquad G[h|N_c] = \prod_i G_m[h|x_i] = \exp\left(\int_{\mathcal{X}} \log G_m[h|x]N_c(dx)\right);$$

because $\{G_m[h|x]\}$ is a measurable function of x, so is $\{\log G_m[h|x]\}$ and thus, when the random integral is regarded as a function of N_c [cf. (6.4.1)], it is measurable (equivalently, $G[h|N_c]: \Omega \to \mathbb{R}$ is a measurable mapping), irrespective of the finiteness of the integral. By Exercise 7.4.6, the convergence of the infinite product at (8.2.2) is equivalent to the finiteness of the infinite superposition at (8.2.1), and hence $G[h|N_c] > 0$ a.s. if and only if

$$(8.2.3) \qquad \sum_i p_A(x_i) = \int_{\mathcal{X}} p_A(x)N_c(dx) < \infty \quad \text{a.s.,}$$

where $p_A(x)$ denotes the probability that a cluster with centre at x contains a point in A; that is, $p_A(x) = \Pr\{N(A|x) > 0\}$.

Assume (8.2.3) holds so that N exists. Then by applying Lemma 8.1.II, N has p.g.fl.

$$(8.2.4) \qquad G[h] = E(G[h|N_c])$$

$$= E\left(\exp\left(\int_{\mathcal{X}} \log G_m[h|x]N_c(dx)\right)\right)$$

$$= G_c[G_m[h|\cdot]],$$

where G_c is the p.g.fl. of the centre process N_c and, as at (5.5.7), $G_m[h|\cdot]$ is to be treated as the argument of G_c. Note that $G[h]$, being a p.g.fl., is well defined for every $h \in \mathcal{V}(\mathcal{Y})$, and therefore so too is $G_c[G_m[h|\cdot]]$ even though in general $G_m[h|x]$ need not be in $\mathcal{V}(\mathcal{X})$.

These results can be summarized as follows.

Proposition 8.2.II. *Let N_c be a point process on the c.s.m.s. $\mathcal{X}$ with probability measure Π_c and p.g.fl. G_c, and let $\mathcal{G}_m \equiv \{G_m[\cdot|x], x \in \mathcal{X}\}$ be the p.g.fl.s of a measurable family of point processes on $\mathcal{Y}$ with generic element $N(\cdot|x)$. Then a cluster process N as at Definition 8.2.I with centre process N_c and component processes $N(\cdot|x)$ exists if and only if the product at (8.2.2) converges Π_c-a.s., or, equivalently, if and only if for any bounded $A \in \mathcal{B}_{\mathcal{Y}}$*

$$(8.2.5) \qquad \int_{\mathcal{X}} p_A(x) N_c(dx) < \infty \qquad \Pi_c\text{-a.s.,}$$

where $p_A(x) = \Pr\{N(A|x) > 0\}$ ($x \in \mathcal{X}$, $A \in \mathcal{B}_{\mathcal{Y}}$).

When (8.2.2) or (8.2.5) converges, the cluster process N has p.g.fl. G as at (8.2.4).

Referring again to Exercise 7.4.6, the condition (8.2.5) can be interpreted as stating that only finitely many of the events

$\quad B_i \equiv \{$component cluster with centre x_i contributes points to some
$\qquad\quad$ bounded $A \in \mathcal{B}_{\mathcal{Y}}\}$

occur with Π_c-measure one.

The usefulness of the conditions (8.2.2) and (8.2.5) is limited by the fact that they appear in a stochastic form that is not easily related to analytic properties of the component processes. It is therefore desirable to give simpler if slightly less general sufficient conditions. In the following corollary, M^c denotes the expectation measure of the cluster process N_c; that is, $M^c(A) = E(N_c(A))$ for bounded $A \in \mathcal{B}_{\mathcal{X}}$.

Corollary 8.2.III. *Given that the component processes form a measurable family, a sufficient condition for the existence of the cluster process is the convergence of the integral*

$$(8.2.6) \qquad \int_{\mathcal{X}} (1 - G_m[h|x]) M^c(dx) \qquad (h \in \mathcal{V}(\mathcal{Y})).$$

If the cluster centre process is a Poisson process, this condition is necessary.

PROOF. When $1 - h = I_A$, the function

$$1 - G_m[h|x] = 1 - G_m[1 - I_A|x] = p_A(x)$$

so the convergence of the integral at (8.2.6) implies (8.2.3) by definition of M^c. If the cluster centre process is a Poisson process with parameter measure $\mu(\cdot)$ then $M^c(dx) = \mu(dx)$ and the expression (8.2.4) takes the special form

$$(8.2.7) \qquad G[h] = \exp\left(-\int_{\mathcal{X}} (1 - G_m[h|x]) \mu(dx)\right)$$

from which the necessity of (8.2.6) is obvious. $\qquad\qquad\qquad\qquad\qquad\square$

Again there is an equivalent statement of the corollary with $p_A(x)$ replacing $1 - G_m[h|x]$ in (8.2.6).

We turn now to a more detailed consideration of moments of the cluster process. We write $M^c_{[k]}$ and $C^c_{[k]}$ for the factorial moment and cumulant measures of the cluster centre process, and $M_{[k]}(\cdot|x)$ for the factorial moment measures of the cluster member process with centre at x. The assumption that these latter measures form a measurable family implies that when they exist the $M_{[k]}(A|x)$ are measurable functions of x for every bounded $A \in \mathscr{B}^{(k)}_{\mathscr{Y}}$ or, equivalently, that the integrals

$$\int_{\mathscr{Y}^{(k)}} h(y_1, \dots, y_k) M_{[k]}(dy_1 \times \cdots \times dy_k|x)$$

are measurable functions of x for every Borel measurable function h vanishing outside a bounded set in $\mathscr{Y}^{(k)}$. The next proposition treats the first and second factorial moments for the cluster process. Expressions for the higher-order moments and cumulants can be obtained similarly.

Proposition 8.2.IV. *Suppose that the cluster member processes form a measurable family and that the expectation measures exist for both cluster member and cluster centre processes. If for all bounded Borel sets A*

$$(8.2.8) \qquad M(A) = \int_{\mathscr{X}} M(A|x) M^c(dx) < \infty,$$

then the cluster process exists, and its expectation measure is given by (8.2.8). Furthermore, if the second moment measures exist, then the second factorial and cumulant measures of the cluster process are given by

$$(8.2.9) \qquad M_{[2]}(A \times B) = \int_{\mathscr{X}} \int_{\mathscr{X}} M(A|x) M(B|w) M^c_{[2]}(dx \times dw)$$

$$+ \int_{\mathscr{X}} M_{[2]}(A \times B|x) M^c(dx),$$

$$(8.2.10) \qquad C_{[2]}(A \times B) = \int_{\mathscr{X}} \int_{\mathscr{X}} M(A|x) M(B|w) C^c_{[2]}(dx \times dw)$$

$$+ \int_{\mathscr{X}} M_{[2]}(A \times B|x) M^c(dx)$$

whenever the integrals in (8.2.9) are finite.

PROOF. For $0 \le z \le 1$, $1 - z^n \le n(1 - z)$ for nonnegative integers n, so on taking expectations,

$$1 - G_m[h|x] \le M(A|x)$$

whenever $h \in \mathscr{V}(\mathscr{Y})$ and $1 - h$ vanishes outside the bounded Borel set A. Thus, (8.2.8) implies (8.2.6) and hence the existence of the cluster process. The relations between the moment measures may be established either by extending the conditioning arguments used to derive the p.g.fl. relation (see Exercise 8.2.3) or by substituting the Taylor series expansions into the relation (8.2.7) as we now illustrate. Substitute

$$G_m[1 + \rho\eta|x] = 1 + \rho\left(\int_{\mathcal{Y}} \eta(y)M(dy|x)\right.$$

$$\left. + \tfrac{1}{2}\rho\int_{\mathcal{Y}}\int_{\mathcal{Y}} \eta(y)\eta(z)M_{[2]}(dy \times dz|x) + o(\rho)\right)$$

into the expansion for the cluster centre p.g.fl.

$$G_c[1 + \sigma v] = 1 + \sigma\int_{\mathcal{X}} v(x)M^c(dx)$$

$$+ \tfrac{1}{2}\sigma^2\int_{\mathcal{X}}\int_{\mathcal{X}} v(x)v(w)M^c_{[2]}(dx \times dw) + o(\sigma^2)$$

(put $\sigma = 1$ and $v = G_m[1 + \rho\eta|\cdot] - 1$) and equate the coefficients of the first and second powers of ρ with those of the cluster process p.g.fl. expansion

$$G[1 + \rho\eta] = 1 + \rho\int_{\mathcal{Y}} \eta(y)M(dy)$$

$$+ \tfrac{1}{2}\rho^2\int_{\mathcal{Y}}\int_{\mathcal{Y}} \eta(y)\eta(z)M_{[2]}(dy \times dz) + o(\rho^2).$$

Equations (8.2.8) and (8.2.9) follow, and a similar expansion of the logarithm gives (8.2.10). The proof is completed by appealing to the uniqueness of the Taylor series expansion.   □

We now consider certain special processes and operations that come under the general umbrella of the cluster process formalism.

EXAMPLE 8.2(a) *Random deletion, or thinning* (Renyi, 1956). Suppose given a measurable function $p(x)$ $(0 \le p(x) \le 1)$ such that $1 - p(x)$ represents the probability of deleting a point located at x. Suppose also that the points are deleted from the original process independently of each other. Each of the points of the original process may be regarded as the centre of a cluster with either zero or one member, being zero if the point is deleted and one otherwise. If the positions of the points retained are not altered, we have

$$G_m[h|x] = p(x)h(x) + 1 - p(x),$$

so that the p.g.fl. G of the thinned process is related to the p.g.fl. G_c of the original process by

$$G[h] = G_c[1 - p + ph].$$

If the original process has factorial moment measure of any given order k, then so does the thinned process, and the two are related for simple point processes by

$$M_{[k]}(dx_1 \times \cdots \times dx_k) = M^c_{[k]}(dx_1 \times \cdots \times dx_k) \prod_{i=1}^{k} p(x_i).$$

In the particular case that the original process is Poisson with parameter measure μ, the thinned process has p.g.fl.

$$G[h] = \exp\left(-\int_{\mathscr{X}} p(x)(1 - h(x))\mu(dx)\right)$$

and is again a Poisson process with parameter measure $p(x)\mu(dx)$. Thus, the property of being a Poisson process is preserved under independent thinning. Of course, this result also follows from the characterization of a Poisson process in terms of complete independence.

EXAMPLE 8.2(b) *Markov shifts, or random translation.* Suppose given a point process on $\mathscr{X}$ and that any particle of this process initially at x is shifted into any $A \in \mathscr{B}_{\mathscr{X}}$ with probability $p(A|x)$, where

$$p(\mathscr{X}|x) = \int_{\mathscr{X}} p(dy|x) \le 1 \quad \text{(all } x),$$

the shortfall $q(x) = 1 - p(\mathscr{X}|x)$ being the probability of deletion of the particle. Arguing as in Example 8.2(a), we find

$$G_m[h|x] = q(x) + \int_{\mathscr{X}} h(y)p(dy|x)$$

$$= 1 - \int_{\mathscr{X}} (1 - h(y))p(dy|x)$$

from which the resultant p.g.fl. can be written down from (8.2.4). The factorial moments for the shifted process are given by

$$M_{[k]}(dy_1 \times \cdots \times dy_k) = \int_{\mathscr{X}} \cdots \int_{\mathscr{X}} p(dy_1|x_1) \cdots p(dy_k|x_k) M^c_{[k]}(dx_1 \times \cdots \times dx_k).$$

Again, for the case where the original process is Poisson with parameter measure μ, the shifted process has p.g.fl.

$$(8.2.11) \qquad G[h] = \exp\left(-\int_{\mathscr{X}} \int_{\mathscr{X}} (1 - h(y))p(dy|x)\mu(dx)\right),$$

and so it is also Poisson, with parameter measure μ_s given by

$$(8.2.12) \qquad \mu_s(A) = \int_{\mathscr{X}} p(A|x)\mu(dx)$$

for bounded Borel sets A. A situation of particular interest arises if $\mu_s = \mu$, that is, if the measure μ is an invariant measure (not necessarily totally finite) for the Markov transition kernel $p(dy|x)$. It then follows from (8.2.11) that a Poisson process with this parameter measure is invariant under the Markov shift operation, a result due to Derman (1955).

Consider finally the case of a pure shift [so that $q(x) = 0$ for all x], and suppose that $\mathcal{X} = \mathbb{R}^d$, $\mu(dx) = \mu\ell(dx)$ [on the right-hand side, μ is a finite positive constant and $\ell(\cdot)$ denotes Lebesgue measure] so that the initial process is stationary, and that $p(dy|x) = F(d(y - x))$, meaning that the shifts are identically distributed about the positions of the original points; that is, we have random translations of the points. Then (8.2.12) is satisfied, and consequently a stationary Poisson process is invariant under a process of i.i.d. shifts.

Both of these examples are degenerate in the sense that the "clusters" consist of at most one point. More general examples can be classified firstly according to the structure of the cluster process and secondly according to the cluster centre process. Two of the most important cluster structures are the i.i.d. and random walk examples introduced in Chapter 5 [Examples 5.3(a), 5.3(b), and 5.5(a)]. To obtain tractable results, however, these generally have to be allied to a very simple cluster centre process, such as a Poisson process or a deterministic process on a lattice. With a Poisson centre process the i.i.d. clusters lead to the Neyman–Scott model and the random walk clusters to the Bartlett–Lewis model: a more detailed discussion is given in Section 8.3.

Exercises

8.2.1. Formulate a definition for a general cluster random measure ζ analogous to Definition 8.2.I by replacing $\{N(\cdot|x)\}$ by a measurable family of random measures $\{\xi(\cdot|x)\}$. When these components are independent and $L_\xi[f|x]$ denotes the Laplace functional of $\xi(\cdot|x)$ [see (6.4.16)] defined over $f \in BM_+(\mathcal{Y})$, the Laplace functional L_ζ of ζ is related to $\{L_\xi[f|x]\}$ and the p.g.fl. G_c of the cluster centre process by

$$L_\zeta = G_c[L_\xi[f|\cdot]]$$

provided ζ is well defined. [This model is elaborated in Le Cam (1961), who was motivated by the problem of modelling precipitation.]

8.2.2. If a measurable family of random measures $\{\xi(\cdot|x)\}$ is mixed by a random measure $\eta(\cdot)$ according to

$$\zeta(A) = \int_{\mathcal{X}} \xi(A|x)\eta(dx),$$

investigate conditions for ζ to be well defined, and relate the Laplace functionals of these random measures. Give analogues of (8.2.8) and [when $\{\xi(\cdot|x)\}$ are independent] of (8.2.9).

8.2.3. *Moment measures for a cluster process.* For a cluster process the r.v. $X_f \equiv \int_{\mathcal{X}} f(y)N(dy)$ can be expressed as the sum $\sum_i Y_f(y_i)$, where the y_i are the cluster centres and $Y_f(y) = \int_{\mathscr{X}} f(x) N_m(dx|y)$ is the potential contribution to X_f from a cluster member with centre at y. Assume that for $f \in BM_+(\mathscr{X})$

$$M_{1,f}(y) \equiv EY_f(y) = \int_{\mathscr{X}} f(u) M_1(du|y) < \infty,$$

$$M_{2,f}(y) \equiv EY_f^2(y) = \int_{\mathscr{X}} \int_{\mathscr{X}} f(u) f(v) M_2(du \times dv|y) < \infty.$$

Use a conditioning argument to obtain the basic relations

$$EX_f = \int_{\mathscr{Y}} EY_f(y) M^c(dy) = \int_{\mathscr{Y}} M_{1,f}(y) M^c(dy)$$

$$= \int_{\mathscr{Y}} \int_{\mathscr{X}} f(u) M_1(du|y) M^c(dy),$$

$$EX_f^2 = \int_{\mathscr{Y}} V_2(y) M^c(dy) + \int_{\mathscr{Y}} \int_{\mathscr{Y}} M_{1,f}(y) M_{1,f}(z) M_2^c(dy \times dz),$$

$$\operatorname{var} X_f = \int_{\mathscr{Y}} V_2(y) M^c(dy) + \int_{\mathscr{Y}} \int_{\mathscr{Y}} M_{1,f}(y) M_{1,f}(z) C_2^c(dy \times dz),$$

where $V_2(y) = M_{2,f}(y) - (M_{1,f}(y))^2 = \operatorname{var} Y_f(y)$. Derive Equations (8.2.8)–(8.2.10) by considering also $\operatorname{cov}(X_f, X_g)$ and setting $f(\cdot) = I_A(\cdot)$, $g(\cdot) = I_B(\cdot)$. (Note that care is needed in passing from ordinary to factorial moments.)

8.3. Poisson Cluster Processes

One class of cluster processes occurs so frequently in applications and is so important in the theory that it warrants special attention. In this class the cluster centres follow a Poisson distribution, and the clusters are independent and finite with probability 1. Whenever the first condition is satisfied, we speak of a *Poisson cluster process*. The basic existence and moment results for Poisson cluster processes are summarized in the proposition below. We continue to assume that the cluster members take their values in the c.s.m.s. $\mathscr{Y}$ and the cluster centres in the c.s.m.s. $\mathscr{X}$.

Proposition 8.3.I. *Suppose that the cluster centre process is Poisson with parameter measure $\mu(\cdot)$ and that the cluster member processes form a measurable family. Then*

(i) *the necessary and sufficient condition for the existence of the resultant process is the convergence for each $h \in \mathscr{V}(\mathscr{Y})$ of the integrals*

(8.3.1) $$\int_{\mathscr{X}} \{1 - G_m[h|x]\} \mu(dx);$$

or, equivalently, the convergence, for each bounded $A \in \mathscr{B}_{\mathscr{Y}}$, of the integrals

(8.3.2)
$$\int_{\mathscr{X}} p_A(x)\mu(dx),$$

where

$$p_A(x) = \Pr\{\text{a cluster with centre at } x \text{ contains a point in } A\};$$

(ii) *when the process exists its p.g.fl. is given by the expression*

(8.3.3)
$$G[h] = \exp\left(\int_{\mathscr{X}} [G_m[h|x] - 1]\mu(dx)\right);$$

(iii) *the first and second factorial moment measures of the resultant process are given by*

(8.3.4) $$M_1(A) = M_{[1]}(A) = \int_{\mathscr{X}} M_{[1]}(A|x)\mu(dx),$$

(8.3.5) $$M_{[2]}(A \times B) = \int_{\mathscr{X}} M_{[2]}(A \times B|x)\mu(dx) + M_1(A)M_1(B),$$

and the second factorial cumulant measure by

(8.3.6) $$C_{[2]}(A \times B) = \int_{\mathscr{X}} M_{[2]}(A \times B|x)\mu(dx)$$

whenever the integrands are defined and the integrals converge.

PROOF. Since $E(N_c(dx)) = \mu(dx)$ for a Poisson cluster process, the condition (8.3.1) implies the a.s. convergence of (8.2.6) and hence the existence of the process. The necessity of (8.3.1) is clear from the form of the p.g.fl. (8.3.3), which, together with the moment measure results, is a special case of the results of the preceding section.   □

The particularly simple form of (8.3.5) and (8.3.6) means that it is generally possible to obtain explicit expressions for the second moments of the counting process in such examples. This feature is exploited in the second-order analysis for stationary processes in Chapter 10. Note also that since the cumulant measure (8.3.6) is everywhere nonnegative the resultant process is generally *overdispersed* relative to a Poisson process with the same first moment measure (i.e., shows greater variance in the number of counts).

Other aspects of the process, such as interval properties, are generally less easy to obtain. Nevertheless, some partial results may be obtained in this direction. The integral in (8.3.2) holds the key to the interval properties. Suppose that $\mathscr{X} = \mathbb{R}$, $\mathscr{Y} = \mathbb{R}$, and we take A to be an interval $(0, t]$. Then the survivor function $S(t)$ [see below (2.1.3)] for the length of the interval from 0 to the first point of the process is given by

(8.3.7)
$$S(t) = \exp\left(-\int_{\mathbb{R}} p(t|x)\mu(dx)\right),$$

where we have written $p(t|x)$ for the probability $p_A(x)$ in this special case. From (8.3.7) we see that

$$
(8.3.8) \qquad -\log S(t) = \int_{\mathbb{R}} p(t|x)\mu(dx),
$$

or, equivalently,

$$
(8.3.8') \qquad r(t) = -\int_{\mathbb{R}} \frac{\partial p(t|x)}{\partial t}\mu(dx),
$$

where $r(t)$ is the hazard function of this first interval. If the process is stationary, a further differentiation will give the hazard function $q(\cdot)$ of the distribution of the interval between two consecutive points of the process, as in Exercise 3.4.2.

In higher dimensions a similar approach may be used for the nearest-neighbour distributions, although explicit expressions here seem hard to come by. Thus, if $\mathcal{X} = \mathbb{R}^2$ say, we may take A as the circle C_r of radius r and centre at the origin. The survivor function for the distance from the origin to the nearest point of the process is then given by

$$
(8.3.9) \qquad S(r) = \exp\left(-\int_{\mathbb{R}^2} p_{C_r}(x)\mu(dx)\right)
$$

from which we can obtain the log survivor function or alternatively the hazard function, the latter being equal to

$$
(8.3.10) \qquad -\int_{\mathbb{R}^2} \frac{\partial p_{C_r}(x)}{\partial r}\mu(dx).
$$

Again there are further extensions where the process is stationary or we are concerned with a higher-dimensional space (see Exercise 8.3.1).

EXAMPLE 8.3(a) *The Neyman–Scott process: Centre-satellite process; process of i.i.d. clusters* (Neyman and Scott, 1958, 1972; Thompson, 1955; Warren, 1962, 1971). Suppose that the individual cluster members are independently and identically distributed; that is, we are dealing with i.i.d. clusters as in Section 5.1 [see also Examples 5.3(a) and 5.5(a)]. Write $F(dy|x)$ for the probability distribution of the cluster members with cluster centre at x, and $Q(z|x)$ for the p.g.f. of the total cluster size (assumed finite). Then the cluster member p.g.fl. is given by (5.5.7), which in the above notation becomes

$$
(8.3.11) \qquad G_m[h|x] = Q\left(\int_{\mathcal{X}} h(y)F(dy|x)\Big|x\right),
$$

while the corresponding factorial measures take the form

$$
(8.3.12) \qquad M_{[k]}(dy_1 \times \cdots \times dy_k|x) = m_{[k]}(x)\prod_{i=1}^{k} F(dy_i|x),
$$

where $m_{[k]}(x)$ is the kth factorial moment for the cluster size distribution when the cluster centre is at x. Note that Example 8.2(b) is the special case when $Q(z|x) \equiv z$, while if F is degenerate at x we recover the compound Poisson process of Example 7.4(a).

In most practical applications with $\mathscr{X} = \mathbb{R}^d$, the cluster centre process is stationary, $Q(z|x)$ is independent of x, and $F(dy|x)$ is a function of the vector distance $y - x$ alone. With these simplifying assumptions the resultant p.g.fl. takes the compact form

$$(8.3.13) \qquad G[h] = \exp\left\{ \mu \int_{\mathbb{R}^d} \left[Q\left(\int_{\mathbb{R}^d} h(x+y)F(dy) \right) - 1 \right] dx \right\},$$

and the density and second factorial cumulant measures for the resultant process are given by

$$m = \mu m_{[1]}$$

and

$$(8.3.14) \qquad \hat{C}_{[2]}(du) = \mu m_{[2]} \int_{\mathbb{R}^d} F(x+du)F(dx),$$

where we have written $\hat{C}_{[2]}(du)$ for the reduced form of the factorial covariance measure $C_{[2]}(\cdot)$ appropriate for the stationary case (see Corollary 10.4.IV).

Also, for the survivor function $S(t)$ of the interval to the first point in the case $d = 1$, we obtain

$$(8.3.15) \qquad -\log S(t) = \mu \int_{\mathbb{R}^d} \{1 - Q(1 - F(x+t) + F(x))\} dx$$

with a pleasing simplification when $F(\cdot)$ is the exponential distribution (see Exercise 8.3.3).

EXAMPLE 8.3(b) *Random walk cluster process: Bartlett–Lewis model; Poisson branching process* (Bartlett, 1963; Lewis, 1964a, b). In this example we take $\mathscr{X} = \mathbb{R}^d$ and suppose that the points in a cluster are the successive end points in a finite random walk, starting from and including the cluster centre. The special case that the random walk has unidirectional steps in $\mathbb{R}^1$, that is, forms a finite renewal process, was studied in depth by Lewis (1964a) as a model for computer failures.

A closed form expression for $G_m[h|x]$ does not appear to exist, although we can write

$$(8.3.16) \quad G_m[h|x] = h(x)\left(q_0 + q_1 \int_{\mathscr{X}} h(x+y_1)F(dy_1) \right.$$

$$\left. + q_2 \int_{\mathscr{X}^{(2)}} h(x+y_1)h(x+y_1+y_2)F(dy_1)F(dy_2) + \cdots \right),$$

where q_j is the probability that the walk terminates after j steps and F is the common step-length distribution, for the special case that both the step lengths and the number of steps are independent of the positions of the cluster centre. Assuming also a constant intensity μ for the Poisson process of cluster centres, the mean density and reduced form for the second factorial cumulant measure are given by

$$(8.3.17a) \qquad m = \mu \sum_{j=0}^{\infty} (j + 1)q_j,$$

$$(8.3.17b) \quad \hat{C}_{[2]}(du) = \mu \sum_{j=1}^{\infty} q_j \sum_{k=1}^{j} (j - k + 1)(F^{k*}(du) + F^{k*}(-du)).$$

Expressions for the nearest point and nearest-neighbour distance can be obtained at least for the case $\mathcal{X} = \mathbb{R}$ and unidirectional $F(\cdot)$. Under these conditions

$$p(t|x) = \begin{cases} 0 & \text{for } x > t, \\ 1 & \text{for } 0 \le x \le t, \\ \sum_{i=0}^{\infty} r_{i+1} \int_{0}^{|x|} dF^{i*}(y)(F(|x| + t - y) - F(|x| - y)) & \text{for } x < 0, \end{cases}$$

where $r_i = \sum_{j=i}^{\infty} q_j$. Substituting in (8.3.8) and simplifying, we obtain

$$(8.3.18) \quad -\log S(t) = \mu t + \mu m_{[1]} \int_{0}^{t} [1 - F(y)]dy = mt - \mu m_{[1]} \int_{0}^{t} F(y)dy,$$

$$(8.3.19) \qquad r(t) = \mu + \mu m_{[1]}(1 - F(t)),$$

where $1 + m_{[1]} = m/\mu$ as at (8.3.17a) (see also Exercise 8.3.4).

EXAMPLE 8.3(c) *The Gauss–Poisson process: Process of correlated pairs* (Bol'shakov, 1969; Newman, 1970; Milne and Westcott, 1972). We now suppose that the clusters contain either one or two points. Let one point be taken as the cluster centre, let $F(dy|x)$ denote the distribution of the second point relative to the first, and let $q_1(x)$, $q_2(x)$ be the probabilities of 1 and 2 points, respectively, when the centre is at x. Then we may regard the process as a special case of the preceding example, with

$$G_m[h|x] = q_1(x)h(x) + q_2(x)h(x) \int_{\mathcal{X}} h(y)F(dy|x),$$

so that for the resultant process

$$(8.3.20) \quad \log G[h] = \int_{\mathcal{X}} (h(x) - 1)q_1(x)\mu(dx)$$

$$+ \int_{\mathcal{X}} \int_{\mathcal{X}} (h(x)h(y) - 1)q_2(x)\mu(dx)F(dy|x).$$

This is not quite in standard form, as the measure $q_2(x)\mu(dx)F(dy|x)$ is not symmetric in general. Since the value of the p.g.fl. is unaltered if we replace this measure by its symmetrized form, say $Q_2(dx \times dy)$, we may write the p.g.fl., without loss of generality, in the form

$$(8.3.21) \qquad \log G[h] = \int_{\mathscr{X}} (h(x) - 1)Q_1(dx)$$

$$+ \int_{\mathscr{X}} \int_{\mathscr{X}} (h(x)h(y) - 1)Q_2(dx \times dy),$$

where Q_1 and Q_2 are boundedly finite and Q_2 is symmetric with boundedly finite marginals.

Conversely, given any two such measures Q_1 and Q_2, any expression of the form (8.3.21) represents the p.g.fl. of a process of correlated points because we can first define a measure μ by

$$\mu(A) = Q_1(A) + Q_2(A \times \mathscr{X}),$$

then appeal to the Radon–Nikodym theorem to assert the existence (a.e. μ) of nonnegative functions $q_1(\cdot)$, $q_2(\cdot)$ with $q_1(x) + q_2(x) = 1$ satisfying

$$Q_1(A) = \int_A q_1(x)\mu(dx), \; Q_2(A \times \mathscr{A}) = \int_A q_2(x)\mu(dx) \quad (\text{all bounded } A \in \mathscr{B}_{\mathscr{X}}),$$

and finally use Proposition A1.5.III concerning regular conditional probabilities to define a family of probability measures $\{F(\cdot|x): x \in \mathscr{X}\}$ by

$$Q_2(A \times B) = \int_A F(B|x)Q_2(dx \times \mathscr{X})$$

$$= \int_A F(B|x)q_2(x)\mu(dx) \quad (B \text{ and bounded } A \in \mathscr{B}_{\mathscr{X}}).$$

This discussion characterizes the p.g.fl. of such two-point cluster processes, but Milne and Westcott (1972) give the following stronger result.

Proposition 8.3.II. *For (8.3.21) to represent the p.g.fl. of a point process, it is necessary and sufficient that*

(i) *Q_1 and Q_2 be nonnegative and boundedly finite;*
(ii) *Q_2 have boundedly finite marginals.*

PROOF. The additional point to be proved is that (8.3.21) fails to be a p.g.fl. if either Q_1 or Q_2 is a signed measure with nontrivial negative part. The details are given in Exercise 8.3.6 [see also Exercise 8.3.11 and Example 8.5(c)]. $\square$

Observe that for the process with p.g.fl. given by (8.3.21), the expectation and second cumulant measures exist and are, given, respectively, by

$$(8.3.22a) \qquad M(dx) = Q_1(dx) + Q_2(dx \times \mathscr{X}) + Q_2(\mathscr{X} \times dx),$$

(8.3.22b) $C_{[2]}(dx \times dy) = Q_2(dx \times dy) + Q_2(dy \times dx),$

the representation holding whether or not Q_2 is given in its symmetric version.

It appears to be an open problem to determine conditions similar to those in Proposition 8.3.II for an expansion such as (8.3.21) with just k terms ($k \geq 3$) to represent the log p.g.fl. of a point process (cf. Milne and Westcott, 1988).

EXAMPLE 8.3(d) *A bivariate Poisson process.* A bivariate process can be represented as a process on the product space $\mathscr{X} \times \{1, 2\}$, where indices (or marks) 1, 2 represent the two component processes. The p.g.fl. expansions are most conveniently written out with the integrals over each component space taken separately. Consider, in particular, a Poisson cluster process in which the clusters may be of three possible types only: a single point in process 1, a single point in process 2, and a pair of points, one from each process. Arguments analogous to those in the preceding example show that the joint p.g.fl. can be written in the form

$$\log G[h_1, h_2] = \int_{\mathscr{X}} (h_1(x) - 1)Q_1(dx) + \int_{\mathscr{X}} (h_2(y) - 1)Q_2(dy)$$

$$+ \int_{\mathscr{X}} \int_{\mathscr{X}} (h_1(x)h_2(y) - 1)Q_3(dx \times dy),$$

where Q_1, Q_2, and Q_3 are boundedly finite and Q_3 has boundedly finite marginals. The marginal p.g.fl. for process 1 can be found by setting $h_2 \equiv 1$ and is therefore a Poisson process with parameter measure

$$\mu_1(dx) = Q_1(dx) + Q_3(dx \times \mathscr{X});$$

similarly, the process with mark 2 is also Poisson with parameter measure

$$\mu_2(dy) = Q_2(dy) + Q_3(\mathscr{X} \times dy).$$

Finally, the superposition of the two processes is of Gauss–Poisson type, with

$$\tilde{Q}_1(dx) = Q_1(dx) + Q_2(dx)$$

and (taking the symmetric form)

$$\tilde{Q}_2(dx \times dy) = [Q_3(dx \times dy) + Q_3(dy \times dx)]/2.$$

Evidently, this is the most general example of a bivariate Poisson cluster process with Poisson marginals, since clusters of any higher order would introduce higher-order clusters in the marginals and hence destroy the Poisson property. It also follows (from Theorem 8.4.V) that it is the most general example of a regular infinitely divisible bivariate Poisson process. The resulting fidi distributions are infinitely divisible bivariate Poisson distributions of the kind studied by Holgate (1964) and Milne (1974); see also Griffiths, Milne, and Wood (1979). The more special bivariate distribution studied by Dwass and Teicher (1957) corresponds to the situation where the pairs must occur for both processes at the same location x. In this case, the resultant process is not only infinitely divisible but also has complete independence.

There are, of course, many examples of bivariate Poisson processes that are not infinitely divisible; one class may be obtained by mixing over the relative proportions of pairs and single points in the above example (see Exercise 8.3.7). A queueing example is given in Daley (1972).

The previous examples illustrate the point that the same process can be represented in several equivalent ways as a Poisson cluster process: the Gauss–Poisson process, for example, can be represented either as a Neyman–Scott or as a Bartlett–Lewis type process with suitable redefinitions of the distributions. This same example also points the way to an intrinsic characterization of Poisson cluster processes. In the following proposition the nonnegative measures $K_k(\cdot)$ are extended versions of the Khinchin measures defined for finite processes by (5.5.10).

Proposition 8.3.III. *The p.g.fl. of every Poisson cluster process with a.s. finite clusters can be uniquely represented in the form*

$$(8.3.23) \quad \log G[h] \sum_{k=1}^{\infty} (k!)^{-1} \int_{\mathcal{Y}^{(k)}} (h(y_1) \cdots h(y_k) - 1) K_k(dy_1 \times \cdots \times dy_k),$$

where the $\{K_k\}$ form a family of symmetric, boundedly finite measures, such that K_k is defined on $\mathcal{B}(\mathcal{Y}^{(k)})$, each $K_k(\cdot)$ has boundedly finite marginals $K_k(\cdot \times \mathcal{Y}^{(k-1)})$, and the sum

$$(8.3.24) \qquad\qquad \sum_{k=1}^{\infty} (k!)^{-1} \sum_{i=1}^{k} \binom{k}{i} K_k(A^{(i)} \times (A^c)^{(k-i)})$$

is finite for bounded $A \in \mathcal{B}_{\mathcal{Y}}$.

Conversely, given any such family of measures $\{K_k: k \geq 1\}$, the p.g.fl. (8.3.23) represents the p.g.fl. of a Poisson cluster process.

PROOF. Suppose there is given a Poisson cluster process with cluster centres defined on the space $\mathcal{X}$ and having parameter measure $\mu(\cdot)$. Suppose also that the clusters are a.s. finite, so that they can be represented in terms of a family of Janossy measures $J_k(\cdot|x)$ (see Section 5.3), conditioned by the location x of the cluster centre. Note that by definition these measures are symmetric. Consequently, we may define measures $K_k(\cdot)$ by setting [for $B \in \mathcal{B}(\mathcal{Y}^{(k)})$]

$$K_k(B) = \int_{\mathcal{X}} J_k(B|x)\mu(dx).$$

From Proposition 8.3.I we know that the integral

$$\int_{\mathcal{X}} p_A(x)\mu(dx)$$

must converge for each bounded set $A \in \mathcal{B}_{\mathcal{Y}}$. Here, $p_A(x)$ is just the sum over

$k \geq 1$ of the probabilities that the cluster has k members of which at least one falls into the set A, so that, referring to (5.3.10),

$$p_A(x) = \sum_{k=1}^{\infty} (k!)^{-1}(J_k(\mathcal{Y}^{(k)}|x) - J_k((A^c)^{(k)}|x))$$

$$= \sum_{k=1}^{\infty} (k!)^{-1} \sum_{i=1}^{k} \binom{k}{i} J_k(A^{(i)} \times (A^c)^{(k-i)}|x).$$

Thus, (8.3.24) is just a restatement of the necessary and sufficient condition that (8.3.2) be finite. We can then obtain the representation (8.3.23) from the standard representation of a Poisson cluster p.g.fl.

$$\log G[h] = \int_{\mathcal{X}} (G[h|x] - 1)\mu(dx) \qquad (h \in \mathcal{V}(\mathcal{Y}))$$

by expressing $G[h|x]$ in terms of the associated Janossy measures as at Equation (5.5.3) and rearranging the integrations. Note that the term with $k = 0$ drops out of the summation. Uniqueness follows from standard results concerning uniqueness of the expression of the p.g.fl. and its logarithm about the origin.

Now suppose conversely that a family of measures K_k satisfying the stated conditions is given. We wish to construct at least one Poisson cluster process that has the p.g.fl. representation (8.3.23). Take $\mathcal{X} = \mathcal{Y}$ and let the measure $\mu_0(\cdot)$ be defined over bounded $A \in \mathcal{B}_{\mathcal{Y}}$ by

(8.3.25) $$\mu_0(A) = \sum_{k=1}^{\infty} K_k(A \times \mathcal{Y}^{(k-1)})/k!$$

as the parameter measure for the cluster centre process. Note that the finiteness condition (8.3.24) entails the finiteness of (8.3.25) because

$$\sum_{i=1}^{k} \binom{k}{i} K_k(A^{(i)} \times (A^c)^{(k-i)})$$

$$= \sum_{i=1}^{k} \frac{k}{i} \binom{k-1}{i-1} K_k(A \times A^{(i-1)} \times (A^c)^{k-i})$$

$$\geq K_k(A \times \mathcal{Y}^{(k-1)}).$$

As in the Gauss–Poisson case, we can define (a.e. μ_0) a probability distribution $\{q_k(x)\}$ on $k = 1, 2, \ldots$ as the Radon–Nikodym derivatives in

$$\int_A q_k(x)\mu_0(dx) = K_k(A \times \mathcal{Y}^{(k-1)})/k!,$$

these probabilities $\{q_k(x)\}$ determining the number of points k in a cluster with centre x. The cluster member structure can be defined by taking one point as the cluster centre and locating the positions of the others relative to it through the distribution $P_{k-1}(B|x)$ defined (a.e. μ_0) over $B \in \mathcal{B}(\mathcal{Y}^{(k-1)})$ by

$$\int_A P_{k-1}(B|x)K_k(dx \times \mathcal{Y}^{(k-1)}) = K_k(A \times B);$$

here again we appeal to the existence of regular conditional probabilities. It can now be checked that the process with these components has the p.g.fl. representation (8.3.23) and that the existence condition (8.3.24) is satisfied. □

Note that there are many other processes that could be constructed from the same ingredients. In particular (cf. below Theorem 2.2.II), we can arbitrarily introduce a probability $\tilde{q}_0(x)$ of empty clusters with $0 \le \tilde{q}_0(x) < 1$ (all x) by redefining, for $k = 1, 2, \dots$,

$$\tilde{q}_k(x) = (1 - \tilde{q}_0(x))q_k(x)$$

and setting

$$\tilde{\mu}(dx) = (1 - \tilde{q}_0(x))^{-1}\mu(dx).$$

The p.g.fl. is unaltered by this transformation, and the resultant processes are equivalent. A practical corollary of this remark is that *the probability of a zero cluster is not an estimable parameter in any Poisson cluster model.*

A similar range of possibilities exists for the way the cluster centre x is defined relative to the joint distributions $P_k(\cdot)$ of the points in the cluster. We have chosen in the above construction to fix the centre at an arbitrary point of the cluster. The measures $J_k(\cdot|x)$ are then related to the $P_k(\cdot|x)$ by $J_1(A) = P_1(A)$ and, for $k \ge 2$, the symmetrization relations

$$J_k(A_1 \times A_2 \times \cdots \times A_k|x) = k^{-1} \sum_{\text{sym}} \delta_x(A_1)P_{k-1}(A_2 \times \cdots \times A_k|x).$$

Alternatively, we might prefer to locate the cluster centre at the multivariate centre of mass of the distribution (assuming this to be defined), or else in some other manner. This can be done without altering the final form of the p.g.fl. If it is necessary to select one particular form of representation for the process, we shall choose that used in the proof above and refer to it as the *regular representation* of the given process. The proposition implies that there is a one-to-one correspondence between measures on $\mathcal{B}(\mathcal{M}_{\mathcal{X}})$ induced by Poisson cluster processes and the elements in their regular representations.

Exercises

8.3.1. Suppose the common d.f. in a Neyman–Scott type process in $\mathbb{R}^2$ is circular normal with density $f(x, y) = (2\pi)^{-1}\exp[-\frac{1}{2}(x^2 + y^2)]$. Show that the probability that a particular point of a given cluster falls in the circle of radius r and centre at the origin, when the cluster centre is at a distance ρ from the origin, is given by

$$P(r|\rho) = e^{-\rho^2/2} \int_0^r ue^{-u^2/2} I_0(u\rho)du,$$

where I_0 is the modified Bessel function of zero order. Then the log survivor function of the distance from the origin to the nearest point of such a Neyman–Scott Poisson cluster process, with cluster p.g.f. $Q(z)$, is given by

$$-\log S(r) = 2\pi\mu \int_0^\infty [1 - Q(1 - P(r|\rho))]\rho \, d\rho.$$

In particular, if the number in each cluster has a Poisson distribution with mean λ,

$$-\log S(r) = 2\pi\mu \int_0^\infty (1 - e^{-\lambda P(r|\rho)})\rho \, d\rho.$$

8.3.2. In $\mathbb{R}^d$, the nearest-neighbour distribution can be derived from quantities similar to the above through the relation

$$\Sigma(r) = \lim_{\delta \to 0} \frac{S(\delta, r) - S(r)}{1 - S(\delta)},$$

where $S(r)$ is the probability that no events occur within a distance r from the origin and $S(\delta, r)$ is the probability that an event occurs within a distance δ from the origin but that no events occur in the annulus (δ, r) (cf. Ambartzumian, 1972; Paloheimo, 1971).

8.3.3. For a Neyman–Scott Poisson cluster process as around (8.3.15) with $\mathcal{Y} = \mathcal{X} = \mathbb{R}$, suppose $F(x)$ has an exponential distribution. Use (8.3.15) to show that the hazard function (8.3.8') for the distance from the origin to the nearest point of the process is given by

$$r(t) = \frac{\mu(1 - Q(e^{-\lambda t}))}{1 - e^{-\lambda t}} \quad \text{(Vere-Jones, 1970)}.$$

8.3.4. Show that the hazard function $r(t)$ for the interval distribution corresponding to (8.3.19) is

$$r(t) = \mu + \mu m_{[1]}(1 - F(t)) - \frac{m_{[1]}f(t)}{1 + m_{[1]}(1 - F(t))},$$

where $f(t)$ is the density corresponding to $F(t)$. Show also that the coefficient of variation of the interval distribution is greater than unity (Lewis, 1964a).

8.3.5. Show that for any stationary Poisson cluster process in $\mathbb{R}$ that is simple (a necessary and sufficient condition for this is that each cluster member process be simple), the d.f. F corresponding to the interval between successive points of the process has coefficient of variation ≥ 1. [*Hint:* Show that $R(t) \equiv -\log S(t)$ at (8.3.8) is a subadditive function in $t > 0$, and hence that $S(t) \geq \exp(-R'(0+)x)$. Use Korolyuk's theorem to identify $1/R'(0+)$ as the first moment of F, and use a hazard function argument (cf. Exercise 3.4.2) to identify the second moment of F with $(2/R'(0+))\int_0^\infty S(x)dx$. The result generalizes part of Exercise 8.3.4.]

8.3.6. Show that $P(z) = \exp\{q_1(z - 1) + q_2(z^2 - 1)\}$ is a univariate p.g.f. if and only if $q_1 \geq 0$, $q_2 \geq 0$. [*Hint:* Being a p.g.f., $P(z)$ has nonnegative coefficients as a power series in z; also, by virtue of its representation, $P(z)$ is an entire function. Hence, show that $\log P(z)$ must be well defined and nondecreasing on the whole positive half-line $z > 0$, and deduce that both q_1 and $q_2 \geq 0$.] Use this result to complete the proof of Proposition 8.3.II.

8.3.7. Let $\mathscr{X} = \mathbb{R}$, and consider two stationary bivariate Poisson processes with identical marginals given structures as follows: in process (1°), the only points are simultaneous pairs, which occur with rate μ in each marginal; in process (2°), each marginal process is independent and Poisson with rate μ. Now form a mixture by taking process (1°) with probability p and process (2°) with probability q. Find the p.g.fl. of the process, and show that it has Poisson marginals but is not a Poisson cluster process and hence is not infinitely divisible.

8.3.8. Frequently, it may be desired specifically to include the cluster centres with the points generated by the cluster member processes with p.g.fl. $G_m[h|x]$. Show that the modified process has p.g.fl. $G_c[h(\cdot)G_m[h|\cdot]]$.

8.3.9. Discuss the structure of marked Neyman–Scott processes, where the mark may depend on the distance from the cluster centre.

8.3.10. The point process N is Gauss–Poisson if and only if the first two Khinchin measures are nonnegative with boundedly finite marginals and all remaining Khinchin measures vanish. [This is a rephrasing of Example 8.3(c) and Proposition 8.3.II.]

8.3.11. Newman (1970) posed the question of characterizing those (possibly signed) measures $\bar{Q}_1(\cdot)$ and $\bar{Q}_2(\cdot \times \cdot)$ for which [cf. (8.3.21)]

$$\int_{\mathscr{X}} (h(x) - 1)\bar{Q}_1(dx) + \frac{1}{2} \int_{\mathscr{X}} \int_{\mathscr{X}} (h(x) - 1)(h(y) - 1)\bar{Q}_2(dx \times dy)$$

equals $\log G[h]$ for the p.g.fl. $G[\cdot]$ for some point processes, proposing the name Gauss–Poisson because the first term is the log p.g.fl. of a Poisson process when $\bar{Q}_1$ is nonnegative, and it is like a Gaussian generating functional in being quadratic in the functional argument [see also Exercise 8.5.8 and Example 8.5(c)]. Show that it is necessary and sufficient that $\bar{Q}_1$ be a nonnegative measure, and that the symmetrized version

$$\bar{Q}_2^s(A \times B) = \tfrac{1}{2}(\bar{Q}_2(A \times B) + \bar{Q}_2(B \times A))$$

be nonnegative and bounded as in

$$\bar{Q}_2^s(A \times B) \leq \min(\bar{Q}_1(A), \bar{Q}_1(B)) \quad \text{(bounded } A, B \in \mathscr{B}_{\mathscr{X}}).$$

8.3.12. In the representation of Proposition 8.3.III for a Poisson cluster process with a.s. finite clusters, realize a cluster of size k and choose one of its points, Y say, at random. Show that

$$\Pr\{Y \in A\} = \frac{K_k(A \times \mathscr{Y}^{(k-1)})}{K_k(\mathscr{Y}^{(k)})},$$

whereas

$$\Pr\{\text{a cluster realization of size } k \text{ has a point in } A\}$$

$$= \sum_{i=1}^{k} \binom{k}{i} \frac{K_k(A^{(i)} \times (A^c)^{(k-i)})}{K_k(\mathscr{Y}^{(k)})}.$$

8.3.13. The factorial cumulant measures $C_{[k]}$ of a Gauss–Poisson process vanish for $k = 3, 4, \ldots$. Show in general that for a Poisson cluster process with clusters of size not exceeding k_0, $C_{[k]}$ vanishes for $k > k_0$. [*Hint*: Use (8.3.23) and write $1 + h$ for h.]

8.4. Infinitely Divisible Point Processes

Our aim in this section is to characterize the class of infinitely divisible point processes, a question we shall find is intimately bound up with characterizations of Poisson cluster processes.

Definition 8.4.I. A point process is said to be *infinitely divisible* if, for every k, it can be represented as the superposition of k independent, identically distributed, point process components.

In symbols, a point process N is infinitely divisible if, for every k, we can write

$$(8.4.1) \qquad N = N_1^{(k)} + \cdots + N_k^{(k)},$$

where the $N_i^{(k)}$ ($i = 1, \ldots, k$) are i.i.d. components. Using p.g.fl.s, the condition takes the form (in an obvious notation)

$$(8.4.2) \qquad G[h] = (G_{1/k}[h])^k \qquad (h \in \mathcal{V}(\mathcal{X})).$$

Since the p.g.fl. is nonnegative for such h, we can restate (8.4.2) as follows: a point process is infinitely divisible if and only if, for every k, the uniquely defined nonnegative kth root of its p.g.fl. is again a p.g.fl. From this we may immediately verify that a Poisson process is infinitely divisible (replace the original parameter measure μ by the measure μ/k for each component), and so more generally are the Poisson cluster processes studied in Section 8.3 (replace the parameter measure μ_c for the cluster centre process by μ_c/k and leave the cluster structure unaltered).

Any fidi distribution has a joint p.g.f. expressible as $G[h_A]$, where $h_A(\cdot)$ is of the form

$$(8.4.3) \qquad h_A(x) = 1 - \sum_{i=1}^{n} (1 - z_i)I_{A_i}(x)$$

for appropriate subsets A_i of the set A. Then from (8.4.2) it follows that the fidi distributions of an infinitely divisible point process are themselves infinitely divisible. Conversely, when a point process has its fidi distributions infinitely divisible, (8.4.2) holds for functions h of the form (8.4.3). Since such functions are dense in $\mathcal{V}(\mathcal{X})$, it follows by continuity as in Theorem 7.4.II that p.g.f.s like $G[h_A]$ and $G_{1/k}[h_A]$ define p.g.fl.s, and we thus see the truth of the following lemma.

Lemma 8.4.II. *A point process is infinitely divisible if and only if its fidi distributions are infinitely divisible.*

We now embark on a systematic exploitation of this remark and the results we have established in earlier sections concerning the representation of infinitely divisible discrete distributions (see, in particular, Exercises 2.2.2 and 2.2.3). We first consider the case that the point process is a.s. finite.

Proposition 8.4.III. *Suppose that the point process N with p.g.fl. $G[\cdot]$ is a.s. finite and infinitely divisible. Then there exists a uniquely defined, a.s. finite point process $\tilde{N}$, such that $\Pr\{\tilde{N}(\mathcal{X}) = 0\} = 0$, and a finite positive number α such that*

$$(8.4.4) \qquad G[h] = \exp(\alpha(G_{\tilde{N}}[h] - 1)) \qquad (h \in \mathcal{V}(\mathcal{X})).$$

Conversely, any functional of the form (8.4.4) represents the p.g.fl. of an a.s. finite point process that is infinitely divisible.

PROOF. It is clear that any functional of the form (8.4.4) is a p.g.fl. and that the point process to which it corresponds is infinitely divisible (replace α by α/k and take kth powers). It is also a.s. finite if $\tilde{N}$ is a.s. finite, since if $G_{\tilde{N}}[\rho I_{\mathcal{X}}] \to 1$ as ρ increases to 1, then also $G[\rho I_{\mathcal{X}}] \to 1$, implying N is a.s. finite (see Exercise 7.4.1).

Suppose conversely that N is infinitely divisible and a.s. finite, and consider its p.g.fl. When h has the special form $\sum_{i=1}^{n} z_i I_{A_i}(\cdot)$, where $A_1, \ldots, A_n$ is a measurable partition of $\mathcal{X}$, we know from Exercise 2.2.3 that $G[h]$, which then reduces to the multivariate p.g.f. $P(z_1, \ldots, z_n)$ of the random variables $N(A_1), \ldots, N(A_n)$, can be represented in the form

$$P(z_1, \ldots, z_n) = \exp\{\alpha(Q(z_1, \ldots, z_n) - 1)\},$$

where Q is itself a p.g.f. with $Q(0, \ldots, 0) = 0$ and α is positive, independent of the choice of the partition and equal to $-\log(\Pr\{N(\mathcal{X}) = 0\})$. Now consider the function

$$\tilde{G}[h] = 1 + \alpha^{-1} \log G[h].$$

When h has the above special form, $\tilde{G}$ reduces to the multivariate p.g.f. Q. Also, $\tilde{G}$ inherits continuity from G. Hence, it is a p.g.fl. by Theorem 7.4.II. To show that the resulting process is a.s. finite consider the behaviour of $G[\rho I_{\mathcal{X}}]$ as ρ increases to 1. Since N itself is a.s. finite, $G[\rho I_{\mathcal{X}}] \to 1$ by Exercise 7.4.1. But then $\log G[\rho I_{\mathcal{X}}] \to 0$ and so $\tilde{G}[\rho I_{\mathcal{X}}] \to 1$, showing that $\tilde{N}$ must be a.s. finite. ☐

The representation (8.4.4) has a dual interpretation. It shows on the one hand that any a.s. finite and infinitely divisible process N can be regarded as the "Poisson randomization" [borrowing a phrase from Milne (1971)] of a certain other point process $\tilde{N}$. In this interpretation, the process N is constructed by first choosing a random integer K according to the Poisson distribution with probabilities

$$p_n = (\alpha^n/n!)e^{-\alpha},$$

and then, given K, taking the superposition of K i.i.d. components each having the same distribution as $\tilde{N}$.

On the other hand, the process N can also be related to the cluster processes of Section 8.3. To see this, first represent the p.g.fl. $G_{\tilde{N}}$ in terms of the Janossy measures for $\tilde{N}$, so that (8.4.4) becomes

$$\log G_N(h) = \alpha\left(\sum_1^\infty (k!)^{-1} \int \cdots \int_{\mathscr{X}^{(k)}} h(x_1)\cdots h(x_k)\tilde{J}_k(dx_1 \times \cdots \times dx_k) - 1\right).$$

This infinite sum can be rewritten as

$$(8.4.5) \quad \log G_N(h) = \sum_1^\infty \int \cdots \int_{\mathscr{X}^{(k)}} [h(x_1)\cdots h(x_k) - 1]Q_k(dx_1 \times \cdots \times dx_k),$$

where $Q_k(\cdot) = (\alpha/k!)\tilde{J}_k(\cdot)$. Observe finally that this last form is the log p.g.fl. of a Poisson cluster process, as in Proposition 8.3.III.

Both interpretations coexist for an a.s. finite process; they represent alternative constructions for the same process.

To investigate the behaviour when the a.s. finite condition is relaxed, we first observe that any infinitely divisible process will remain infinitely divisible but will become a.s. finite if we consider its restriction to any bounded Borel set. Its local representation will therefore continue to have the form (8.4.4). Let us rewrite (8.4.4) for the special case that the bounded set is a sphere $S_n \equiv S(n; x_0)$, and introduce explicitly the distribution, $\tilde{\mathscr{P}}_n$ say, of the process $\tilde{N}$ restricted to $\mathscr{B}(S_n)$. Writing $G_n[\cdot]$ for the corresponding p.g.fl. of N, we have from (8.4.4) that

$$(8.4.6) \quad G_n[h] = \exp\left(\alpha_n \int_{\tilde{N} \in \mathscr{N}(S_n)} \left(\exp\left[\int_{S_n} \log h(x)\tilde{N}(dx)\right] - 1\right)\tilde{\mathscr{P}}_n(d\tilde{N})\right),$$

where we recall the convention that the inner exponential term is to be counted as unity if $\tilde{N}$ has no points in the region where h differs from unity, and as zero if $\tilde{N}$ has any points in the region where h vanishes. Bearing this in mind, we have in particular, from (8.4.6),

$$(8.4.7) \quad \tilde{Q}_n\{\tilde{N}: \tilde{N}(S_n) > 0\} \equiv \alpha_n\tilde{\mathscr{P}}_n\{\tilde{N}: \tilde{N}(S_n) > 0\} = -\log \mathscr{P}\{N(S_n) = 0\},$$

where $\tilde{Q}_n$ is an abbreviation for $\alpha_n\tilde{\mathscr{P}}_n$ and we continue the convention that $\tilde{\mathscr{P}}_n\{\tilde{N}(S_n) = 0\} = 0$, so that $\exp(-\alpha_n)$ is just the probability that the original process has no points in S_n.

Each measure $\tilde{Q}_n$ may be used to induce a similar measure, $\tilde{Q}_n^*$ say, on the class of cylinder sets in the full space $\mathscr{N}_{\mathscr{X}}$ determined by conditions on the behaviour of the counting process on S_n. Specifically, with C a set in $\mathscr{N}(S_n)$ of the form

$$C = \{\tilde{N} \in \mathscr{N}(S_n): \tilde{N}(A_i) = r_i, A_i \subseteq S_n, i = 1, \ldots, k\},$$

where the r_i are nonnegative integers not all zero, we associate the set C^* in $\mathcal{N}_{\mathscr{X}}$ given by

$$C^* = \{\tilde{N} \in \mathcal{N}_{\mathscr{X}}: \tilde{N}(A_i) = r_i, A_i \subseteq S_n, i = 1, \ldots, k\}$$

and put

$$\tilde{Q}_n^*(C^*) = \tilde{Q}_n(C).$$

This construction fails for the set in $\mathcal{N}_{\mathscr{X}}$ for which $\tilde{N}(S_n) = 0$: for this reason we have to define $\tilde{Q}_n^*$ not on the full sub-σ-algebra of cylinder sets with base determined by conditions in S_n, but on the sub-σ-algebra generated by those cylinder sets incorporating the condition $\tilde{N}(S_n) > 0$. Let us denote this sub-σ-algebra by $\mathscr{B}_n$. Then it is clear that the $\mathscr{B}_n$ are monotonic increasing and that

$$\sigma\left(\bigcup_{n=1}^{\infty} \mathscr{B}_n\right) = \mathscr{B}(\hat{\mathcal{N}}_0(\mathscr{X})),$$

where $\hat{\mathcal{N}}_0(\mathscr{X})$ denotes the space $\mathcal{N}_{\mathscr{X}}$ with zero counting measure omitted. On the union $\bigcup_{n=1}^{\infty} \mathscr{B}_n$, we can consistently define a set function $\tilde{Q}^*$, the projective limit of $\{Q_n^*\}$, by setting

$$\tilde{Q}^*(A) = \tilde{Q}_n^*(A)$$

whenever $A \in \mathscr{B}_n$. This is possible because $\tilde{Q}_m^*$ reduces to $\tilde{Q}_n^*$ whenever $m > n$ and we restrict attention to sets in $\mathscr{B}_n$. The set function $\tilde{Q}^*$ is countably additive on each of the $\mathscr{B}_n$ but not obviously so on their union. The situation, however, is similar to that of the Kolmogorov extension theorem for stochastic processes, or to the extension theorem considered in Chapter 6, where countable additivity is ultimately a consequence of the metric assumptions imposed on the space $\mathscr{X}$. The same argument applies here also, but we omit the details (see Exercise 8.4.1). It implies that $\tilde{Q}^*$ has a unique extension to a measure $\tilde{Q}$ on the σ-algebra $\mathscr{B}(\hat{\mathcal{N}}_0(\mathscr{X}))$.

In addition to the fact that it is defined on the sets of $\hat{\mathcal{N}}_0(\mathscr{X})$ rather than $\mathcal{N}_{\mathscr{X}}$, $\tilde{Q}$ enjoys one further special property. We obtain from (8.4.7) that for any bounded set A,

(8.4.8) $\tilde{Q}\{N: N(A) > 0\} < \infty.$

Definition 8.4.IV. A boundedly finite measure $\tilde{Q}$ defined on the Borel sets of $\hat{\mathcal{N}}_0(\mathscr{X}) = \mathcal{N}_{\mathscr{X}} \setminus \{N(\mathscr{X}) = 0\}$, and satisfying the additional property (8.4.8), will be called a *KLM measure*.

The measure is so denoted for basic contributions to the present theory in Kerstan and Matthes (1964) and Lee (1964, 1967).

Theorem 8.4.V. *A point process on the c.s.m.s. $\mathscr{X}$ is infinitely divisible if and only if its p.g.fl. can be represented in the form*

$$(8.4.9) \quad G[h] = \exp\left\{\int_{\mathcal{N}_0(\mathcal{X})}\left[\exp\left(\int_{\mathcal{X}} \log h(x)\tilde{N}(dx)\right) - 1\right]\tilde{Q}(d\tilde{N})\right\}$$

for some KLM measure $\tilde{Q}$. When such a representation exists, it is unique.

PROOF. Suppose that the point process N is infinitely divisible, and let $\tilde{Q}$ be KLM measure constructed as above. When it is equal to unity outside the sphere S_n, the representation (8.4.9) reduces to (8.4.6) from the construction of $\tilde{Q}$, and so the functional G in (8.4.9) must coincide with the p.g.fl. of the original process.

Conversely, suppose a KLM measure $\tilde{Q}$ is given, and consider (8.4.9). If we set

$$\alpha_n = \tilde{Q}\{\tilde{N}: \tilde{N}(S_n) > 0\}$$

(finite by assumption), (8.4.9) can again be reduced to the form (8.4.6) for functions h, which equal unity outside S_n, and therefore, by Proposition 8.4.III, it is the p.g.fl. of a local process defined on S_n. In particular, therefore, (8.4.9) reduces to a joint p.g.f. when h has the form $1 - \sum_{i=1}^{k}(1 - z_i)I_{A_i}$. The continuity condition follows from the remark already made that (8.4.9) defines a local p.g.fl. when we restrict attention to the behaviour of the process on S_n. Thus, (8.4.9) is itself a p.g.fl. Infinite divisibility follows from Lemma 8.4.II and the remarks already made concerning the local behaviour of $G[h]$. Finally, uniqueness follows from the construction and the uniqueness part of Proposition 8.4.III.

EXAMPLE 8.4(a) *Poisson process* (cf. Example 7.4(a)). If (8.4.9) is to reduce to the p.g.fl. (7.4.10) of a Poisson process, each $\tilde{N}$ must be simple and have a single point as its support; that is, we must have $\tilde{Q}\{\tilde{N}(\mathcal{X}) \neq 1\} = 0$, because for given $\tilde{N}$ the integrand for the $\tilde{Q}$ integral at (8.4.9) must reduce to $h(x) - 1$, where $\{x\}$ is the singleton support of $\tilde{N}$. In fact, the KLM measure $\tilde{Q}$ must be related to the parameter measure μ by

$$\tilde{Q}\{\tilde{N}(A) = 1\} = \tilde{Q}\{\tilde{N}: \tilde{N}(\mathcal{X}) = 1 = \tilde{N}(A)\} = \mu(A)$$

for each bounded $A \in \mathcal{B}_{\mathcal{X}}$.

Further insight into the structure of such processes can be obtained from a classification of the properties of their KLM measures. In particular, we make the following definitions.

Definition 8.4.VI. An infinitely divisible point process is *regular* if its KLM measure is carried by the set

$$V_r \equiv \{\tilde{N}: \tilde{N}(\mathcal{X}) < \infty\}$$

and *singular* if its KLM measure is carried by the complementary set

$$V_s \equiv \{\tilde{N}: \tilde{N}(\mathcal{X}) = \infty\}.$$

We then have the following decomposition result.

Proposition 8.4.VII. *Every infinitely divisible point process can be represented as the superposition of a regular infinitely divisible process and a singular infinitely divisible process, the two components being independent.*

PROOF. This follows from the representation (8.4.8) on writing

$$\tilde{Q} = \tilde{Q}_r + \tilde{Q}_s,$$

where for each $A \in \mathcal{B}(\mathcal{N}_0(\mathcal{X}))$,

$$\tilde{Q}_r(A) = \tilde{Q}(A \cap V_r), \qquad \tilde{Q}_s(A) = \tilde{Q}(A \cap V_s).$$

Each of $\tilde{Q}_r(\cdot)$ and $\tilde{Q}_s(\cdot)$ is again a KLM measure, and since the original p.g.fl. appears as the product of the p.g.fl.s of the two components, the corresponding components themselves must be independent and their superposition must give back the original process. $\qquad\square$

The final result in this section characterizes various classes of infinitely divisible processes in terms of their KLM measures; for some refinements in the stationary case see Propositions 10.1.V and VI.

Proposition 8.4.VIII

(i) *An infinitely divisible point process is a.s. finite if and only if it is regular and its KLM measure is totally finite.*

(ii) *An infinitely divisible point process can be represented as a Poisson cluster process, with a.s. finite clusters, if and only if it is regular.*

(iii) *An infinitely divisible point process can be represented as a Poisson randomization if and only if its KLM measure is totally finite.*

PROOF. Part (i) is a restatement of Proposition 8.4.III, regularity coming from the assertion that the process N is a.s. finite, and the total boundedness of the KLM measure from the fact that it can be represented in the form $\alpha\tilde{\mathcal{P}}$, where $0 < \alpha < \infty$ and $\tilde{\mathcal{P}}$ is a probability measure.

Part (ii) follows from the representation in Proposition 8.3.III, taking $\mathcal{X} = \mathcal{Y}$, so that the measures $Q_k(\cdot)$ in that proposition can be combined to give a measure on the space of all finite counting measures, as in Proposition 5.3.II. That this is a KLM measure follows from the absence of any Q_0 term, and the condition (8.3.24), which in the terminology of the present section can be rewritten [cf. (8.3.25)] as

$$\mu(A) = \tilde{Q}\{\tilde{N}: \tilde{N}(A) > 0\} < \infty.$$

Conversely, the KLM measure of any regular infinitely divisible process can be split up into its components on the sets $V_k = \{\tilde{N}: \tilde{N}(\mathcal{X}) = k\}$, in each of which it induces a measure Q_k with the properties described in Proposition 8.3.III.

Finally, part (iii) follows from the observation that here also the KLM measure can be written in the form $\tilde{Q} = \alpha\mathscr{P}$, where α is the parameter of the Poisson randomizing distribution and $\mathscr{P}$ is the distribution of the point process being randomized, which we assume adjusted if necessary so that $\mathscr{P}(\{\tilde{N}: \tilde{N}(\mathscr{X}) = 0\}) = 0$. $\square$

Exercises

8.4.1. *Analogue of the Kolmogorov extension theorem for $\tilde{Q}^*$.* Show that the measure $\tilde{Q}^*$ admits consistent fidi distributions in the sense that

$$\tilde{Q}^*\{N: N(A_i) = k_i, i = 1, \ldots, n\}$$

satisfy the two consistency conditions 6.2.V, namely, marginal consistency and symmetry under permutations. Show also that $\tilde{Q}^*$ is finitely additive and continuous in the sense that for disjoint A_i,

$$\tilde{Q}^*\left\{N: N\left(\bigcup_{i=1}^{n} A_i\right) \neq \sum_{i=1}^{n} N(A_i)\right\} = 0,$$

and

$$\tilde{Q}^*\{N: N(A_n) > 0\} \to 0 \quad \text{when } A_n \downarrow \varnothing.$$

[For the latter, write $V_n = \{N: N(A_n) > 0\}$. Since $N(A_n) \downarrow 0$ for all $N \in \mathcal{N}_{\mathscr{X}}$, $\{V_n\}$ is a monotonic decreasing sequence of sets, say $V_n \downarrow V$. Supposing $N_0 \in V$, then $N_0(A_n) > 0$ for all n giving a contradiction. $\tilde{Q}^*(V_n) \to 0$ follows from the countable additivity of $\tilde{Q}^*(\cdot)$ on S_k, since we may assume the existence of some k for which $A_n \subseteq S_k$ $(n = 1, 2, \ldots)$.] The same arguments as used in the proof of Lemma 6.2.IX now show that there exists a countably additive set function $\tilde{Q}$ defined on $\mathscr{B}(\mathcal{N}_{\mathscr{X}})$ such that $\tilde{Q}(C) = \tilde{Q}^*(C)$ a.s. $\tilde{Q}^*$; that is, $\tilde{Q}^*$ admits a countably additive extension $\tilde{Q}$ as required.

8.4.2. For an infinitely divisible multivariate point process (see Definition 7.1.XII), show that the KLM measure $\tilde{Q}$ is defined on $\mathscr{X} \times \{1, \ldots, m\}$ and satisfies for bounded $A \in \mathscr{B}_{\mathscr{X}}$

$$\tilde{Q}\{\tilde{N} = (\tilde{N}_1, \ldots, \tilde{N}_m): \tilde{N}_1(A) + \cdots + \tilde{N}_m(A) > 0\} < \infty.$$

8.4.3. Find the KLM measure of a Gauss–Poisson process.

8.4.4. Let N be an infinitely divisible marked point process (Definition 7.1.XI) on the space $\mathcal{N}_{\mathscr{X} \times \mathscr{K}}$, with $N(A \times \mathscr{K}) < \infty$ for each bounded $A \in \mathscr{B}_{\mathscr{X}}$. Investigate whether the KLM measure $\tilde{Q}$ has $\tilde{Q}\{\tilde{N}: \tilde{N}(A \times \mathscr{K}) > 0\} < \infty$ for such A.

8.5. Cox Processes (Doubly Stochastic Poisson Processes)

The doubly stochastic Poisson process—or, more briefly, the *Cox process*, so named in recognition of its appearance in a seminal paper of Cox (1955)—is obtained by randomizing the parameter measure in a Poisson process. Specifically, for every realization ξ of some random measure on $\mathscr{X}$, construct the

Poisson process on $\mathscr{X}$ with parameter measure ξ. Since the probabilities in the Poisson process are easily seen to be measurable functions of ξ, we can apply Lemma A1.5.II and take expectations with respect to the distribution of ξ so as to obtain a well-defined "mixed" point process on $\mathscr{X}$.

The algebraic details are easily handled via the p.g.fl. approach outlined in Section 8.1. As a function of the parameter measure ξ, the p.g.fl. of the Poisson process can be written, for $h \in \mathscr{V}(\mathscr{X})$, as

$$(8.5.1) \qquad G[h|\xi] = \exp\left(\int (h(x) - 1)\xi(dx)\right).$$

The properties of random integrals developed in Section 6.4 imply that for each fixed h, (8.5.1) is a measurable function of ξ as an element of $\mathscr{N}_{\mathscr{X}}$. Thus, the family of p.g.fl.s (8.5.1) is a measurable family in the sense of Section 8.1, and therefore, appealing to Lemma 8.1.II, we can indeed construct a point process by taking expectations in (8.5.1) with respect to any probability measure for ξ in $\mathscr{N}_{\mathscr{X}}$. Recalling the definition of the Laplace functional at (6.4.16), we have established the following proposition.

Proposition 8.5.I. *Let ξ be a random measure on the c.s.m.s. $\mathscr{X}$ and L_ξ its Laplace functional. Then*

$$(8.5.2) \qquad G[h] = E_\xi\left[\exp\left(\int (h(x) - 1)\xi(dx)\right)\right] = L_\xi[1 - h]$$

defines the p.g.fl. of a point process on $\mathscr{X}$.

We call the process defined by (8.5.2) the *Cox process directed by the random measure* ξ, and from that representation we deduce immediately the following corollaries.

Corollary 8.5.II. *The fidi distributions of a Cox process are of mixed Poisson type. In particular, the number of points $N(A)$ in the bounded Borel set A has p.g.f.*

$$E(z^{N(A)}) = L_\xi[(1 - z)I_A] = L_A^*(1 - z),$$

where $L_A^*(\theta) = E\{\exp[-\theta\xi(A)]\}$ is the Laplace–Stieltjes transform of the random mass $\xi(A)$.

Corollary 8.5.III. *The Cox process directed by the random measure ξ has moment measures existing up to order n if and only if the same is true for ξ. When they exist the kth factorial moment measure $M_{[k]}$ for the Cox process equals the corresponding ordinary moment measure μ_k for ξ, that is, for bounded $A \in \mathscr{B}_{\mathscr{X}}$,*

$$E(N(A)_{[k]}) = M_{[k]}(A) = \mu_k(A) = E(\xi^k(A)).$$

Similarly, if $C_{[k]}$ and γ_k denote the corresponding factorial and ordinary cumulant *measures,*

$$C_{[k]}(A) = \gamma_k(A) \quad \text{(bounded } A \in \mathcal{B}_{\mathcal{X}}\text{)}.$$

It is to be noted from this last result that the second cumulant measure of a Cox process is nonnegative definite (see Chapter 11), so that for bounded $A \in \mathcal{B}_{\mathcal{X}}$,

$$\begin{aligned}
\text{var } N(A) &= M_{[1]}(A) + C_{[2]}(A \times A) \\
&= M_{[1]}(A) + \text{var}(\xi(A)) \\
&\geq M_{[1]}(A) = EN(A).
\end{aligned}$$

Thus, a Cox process, like a Poisson cluster process, is overdispersed relative to the Poisson.

EXAMPLE 8.5(a) *Shot-noise or trigger process.* In Vere-Jones and Davies (1966) the following model (which occurs elsewhere in the literature) was used to describe earthquake occurrences. The state space $\mathcal{X} = \mathbb{R}$, and it is assumed that with the (unobserved) epochs $\{x_i\}$ of a Poisson process with a constant rate v there are nonnegative random weights $\{Y_i\}$ that combine via some nonnegative integrable function f vanishing on $(-\infty, 0)$ [so that $\int_0^\infty f(u)du = \int_{-\infty}^\infty f(u)du < \infty$] to define the density

$$(8.5.3) \qquad \lambda(t) = \sum_{i: x_i < t} Y_i f(t - x_i)$$

of the observed Poisson process. [In more picturesque language, the epochs $\{x_i\}$ are trigger events with respective sizes (or weights) $\{Y_i\}$ that decay according to the function f. Note that in the definition it is not necessary to assume that f decays monotonically —integrability is sufficient; but see also Exercise 8.5.1.] The observed Poisson process can equally be regarded as having clusters associated with each trigger point x_i, each cluster being an a.s. totally finite inhomogeneous Poisson process with density $Y_i f(t - x_i)$ for the parameter measure.

Since $\lambda(t)$, when finite, is stationary in t and is measurable, it is locally integrable. The random measure

$$\xi(A) \equiv \int_A \lambda(u)du = \sum_i Y_i \int_{A+x_i} f(u)du$$

is therefore well defined and, accordingly, what has been described above as the observed Poisson process does indeed exist. Conditional on the sequence $\{(x_i, Y_i)\}$, we can appeal to (8.5.1) and write

$$(8.5.4) \qquad G[h \mid \{(x_i, Y_i)\}] = \exp\left(\sum_i Y_i \int (h(t) - 1)f(t - x_i)dt\right).$$

Write $\phi(\theta) = E(e^{-\theta Y})$ for the common Laplace–Stieltjes transform of the $\{Y_i\}$. Taking expectations in (8.5.4) first with respect to $\{Y_i\}$, we have for the p.g.fl.

of the process

(8.5.5) $G[h] = E\left(\prod_i \phi\left(\int (1 - h(t))f(t - x_i)dt\right)\right)$

$= \exp\left(\int\left(\phi\left(\int(1 - h(t))f(t - x)dt\right) - 1\right)v\,dx\right).$

By taking logarithms in this expression and expanding, it follows (as indeed is asserted in Corollary 8.5.III) that the point process has factorial cumulant measures existing to as many orders as the r.v.s Y_i have finite moments, and that these moments are absolutely continuous with densities

$$m_1 = v\mu_1 \int_0^\infty f(u)du$$

$$c_{[2]}(t_1, t_2) = c(t_1 - t_2) \equiv c(t_1')$$

$$= v\mu_2 \int_0^\infty f(u)f(t_1' + u)du,$$

$$c_{[k]}(t_1, \ldots, t_k) = c_{[k]}(t_1', \ldots, t_{k-1}')$$

$$= v\mu_k \int_0^\infty f(u)f(t_1' + u)\cdots f(t_{k-1}' + u)du,$$

where $t_j' = t_j - t_k$ $(j = 1, \ldots, k - 1)$ and $\mu_k = EY^k$. These relations are ana-logues of Campbell's formulae in the theory of shot noise, and the first two illustrate Corollary 8.5.III as the right-hand sides represent the ordinary cumulants of the directing shot-noise process.

The representation (8.5.5) shows that the process can also be regarded as a Neyman–Scott Poisson cluster process in which the number of points in a cluster has the distribution of mixed Poisson form with p.g.f.

$$P(z) = E\exp\left((z - 1)Yv\int_0^\infty f(u)du\right)$$

$$= \phi\left((1 - z)v\int_0^\infty f(u)du\right),$$

and the common distribution of the points in a cluster about their cluster centre is the density obtained by normalizing $f(\cdot)$, namely, $f(x)/\int_0^\infty f(u)du$.

The fact that the shot-noise process and the Neyman–Scott process have the same p.g.fl. means that they are identical as point processes: no measure-ments on the point process can distinguish the clustering and doubly stochas-tic (or Cox) mechanisms for these examples. Of course, this ambiguity of interpretation is an extension of the corresponding ambiguity concerning the dual interpretation of contagious distributions alluded to in Exercise 1.2.3. The possibility of such dual interpretations is not restricted to cluster processes: for example, Kingman (1964) has given a nontrivial characterization of the class of those renewal processes that can be represented as Cox processes (see Exercise 8.5.2).

EXAMPLE 8.5(b) *Boson processes* (Macchi, 1971a, 1975). [Compare Example 5.4(b).] In optical problems concerning light beams of low density, the particulate aspects of light are important, and the emission or reception of individual photons (or more generally bosons) can be treated as a point process in time, or space, or both. A standard approach to modelling this situation is to treat the photon process as a Cox process directed by the fluctuating intensity of the light beam, with this latter phenomenon modelled as the squared modulus of a complex Gaussian process. Thus, for the (density of the) random intensity we take the function

$$(8.5.6) \qquad \lambda(t) = \lambda |X(t)|^2 \qquad (\lambda > 0),$$

where $X(\cdot)$ is a complex Gaussian process with zero mean and complex covariance function $C(s, t)$. The process $\lambda(\cdot)$ is similar to the quadratic random measure discussed in Example 6.1(b) with appropriate attention given to the conventions regarding a complex Gaussian process. These require that $X(t) = U(t) + iV(t)$, where $U(\cdot)$ and $V(\cdot)$ are real Gaussian processes such that

$$E(U(s)U(t)) = E(V(s)V(t)) = C_1(s, t),$$

$$E(U(s)V(t)) = -E(U(t)V(s)) = C_2(s, t),$$

$$C(s, t) = E(\bar{X}(s)X(t)) = 2(C_1(s, t) + iC_2(s, t)).$$

Here it is to be understood that C_1 is real, symmetric, and nonnegative definite, while C_2 is antisymmetric [so, in particular, $C_2(s, s) = 0$, and $E(X(s)X(t)) = 0$ for all s, t].

The moments of the process $\lambda(\cdot)$ are given by a classical result concerning the even moments of a complex Gaussian process (e.g., see Goodman and Dubman, 1969)

$$(8.5.7) \qquad E(\bar{X}(s_1)\cdots\bar{X}(s_k)X(t_1)\cdots X(t_k)) = {}^+\begin{vmatrix} C(s_1, t_1) & C(s_1, t_2) \cdots & C(s_1, t_k) \\ & & \vdots \\ C(s_k, t_1) & C(s_k, t_2) \cdots & C(s_k, t_k) \end{vmatrix}^+$$

$$= C^+\begin{pmatrix} s_1, \ldots, s_k \\ t_1, \ldots, t_k \end{pmatrix},$$

where the permanent per $A \equiv {}^+|A|^+$ of a matrix A contains the same terms as the corresponding determinant det A but with constant positive signs for each product of matrix elements in place of the alternating positive and negative signs of the determinant, so, for example,

$${}^+\begin{vmatrix} a & b \\ c & d \end{vmatrix}^+ = ad + bc.$$

It can be shown (see Minc, 1978) that for any nonnegative definite Hermitian matrix A, per $A \geq \det A$.

The results (8.5.6) and (8.5.7), together with Corollary 8.5.III, show that the factorial moment densities for the boson process are given by

$$(8.5.8) \qquad m_{[k]}(t_1, \ldots, t_k) = E(\lambda(t_1) \cdots \lambda(t_k)) = \lambda^k C^+ \begin{pmatrix} t_1, \ldots, t_k \\ t_1, \ldots, t_k \end{pmatrix}.$$

This result paves the way for a discussion that exactly parallels the discussion of the fermion process of Example 5.4(b). In place of the expansion of the Fredholm determinant used there, we have here an analogous expansion of its reciprocal

$$\frac{1}{d(-\lambda)} = 1 + \sum_{k=1}^{\infty} \frac{\lambda^k}{k!} \int \cdots \int_{\Delta^{(k)}} C^+ \begin{pmatrix} u_1, \ldots, u_k \\ u_1, \ldots, u_k \end{pmatrix} du_1 \cdots du_k,$$

where as before the observation region Δ is a closed, bounded set in a general Euclidean space $\mathbb{R}^d$. Corresponding to the expression (5.4.18) for the Fredholm minor is the expression

$$(8.5.9) \quad \lambda^k R_{-\lambda}^+ \begin{pmatrix} x_1, \ldots, x_k \\ y_1, \ldots, y_k \end{pmatrix}$$

$$= d(-\lambda) \left\{ \lambda^k C^+ \begin{pmatrix} x_1, \ldots, x_k \\ y_1, \ldots, y_k \end{pmatrix} \right.$$

$$\left. + \lambda^k \sum_{j=1}^{\infty} (-\lambda)^j \int \cdots \int_{\Delta^{(j)}} C^+ \begin{pmatrix} x_1, \ldots, x_k, u_1, \ldots, u_j \\ y_1, \ldots, y_k, u_1, \ldots, u_j \end{pmatrix} du_1 \cdots du_j \right\}.$$

This shows that the Janossy measures for the photon process have densities

$$(8.5.10) \quad j_k(x_1, \ldots, x_k) = \left(\frac{\lambda^k}{d(-\lambda)} \right) R_{-\lambda}^+ \begin{pmatrix} x_1, \ldots, x_k \\ x_1, \ldots, x_k \end{pmatrix} \qquad (k = 1, 2, \ldots).$$

Macchi (1971a) established (8.5.10) directly by evaluating the expectation

$$j_k(x_1, \ldots, x_k) = E\left(\lambda(x_1) \cdots \lambda(x_k) \exp\left(-\int_{\Delta} \lambda(u) du \right) \right)$$

[see also Grandell (1976) and the exercises for further discussion].

EXAMPLE 8.5(c) *A pseudo-Cox process: The Gauss–Poisson process.* Examine the p.g.fl. (8.3.21) for a Gauss–Poisson process and suppose that the measures Q_1 and Q_2 there are absolutely continuous with respect to Lebesgue measure. Then the p.g.fl. can be written in the form

$$G[h] = \exp\left(\int_{\mathscr{X}} (1 - h(x)) m(x) dx \right.$$

$$\left. - \frac{1}{2} \int_{\mathscr{X}} \int_{\mathscr{X}} (1 - h(x))(1 - h(y)) c(x, y) dx \, dy \right),$$

where, in the notation of (8.3.21), in which $Q_2(\cdot)$ is symmetric,

$$m(x)dx = Q_1(dx) + 2Q_2(dx \times \mathscr{X}),$$

$$c(x, y)dx\,dy = 2Q_2(dx \times dy).$$

This expression for the p.g.fl. is identical with the expression $L^*[1 - h]$ of a Gaussian process, $\{X(t): t \in \mathbb{R}\}$ say, with mean $m(t) = EX(t)$ and covariance $c(t, u) = \text{cov}(X(t), X(u))$, provided only that the function $c(t, u)$ is positive definite. On the other hand, for the expression to be the p.g.fl. of a point process, we must have $m(\cdot)$ and $c(\cdot)$ nonnegative and also

$$m(t) - \int_{\mathscr{X}} c(t, u)du \geq 0 \qquad \ell\text{-a.e.}$$

[cf. Proposition 8.3.II and Macchi (1975)]. However, even when both conditions are satisfied, the process is not an example of the construction described in Proposition 8.5.I because realizations of a Gaussian process take negative values a.s. and thus the notion of a Poisson process with parameter measure with density equal to the realization of such a Gaussian process is void. Nevertheless, it is due to this formal relation that the name "Gauss–Poisson" was introduced.

This example also serves to illustrate that while the conditions of 8.5.I are sufficient for a functional $L^*[1 - h]$ to represent the p.g.fl. of a point process, they are not necessary.

Exercises

8.5.1. [Compare Example 8.5(a).] Denote by $\{x_j\}$ the points of a stationary Poisson process on $\mathbb{R}$ with rate parameter v, and let $\{Y_j: j = 0, \pm 1, \ldots\}$ denote a sequence of i.i.d. r.v.s independent of $\{x_j\}$. Let the function f be as in Example 8.5(a). Investigate conditions under which the formally defined process

$$Y(t) = \sum_{x_j \leq t} Y_j f(t - x_j)$$

is indeed well defined (e.g., by demanding that the series is absolutely convergent a.s.). Show that sufficient conditions are that

(a) $E|Y| < \infty$; or else

(b) $f(\cdot)$ is nonincreasing on $\mathbb{R}_+$ and there is an increasing nonnegative function $g(\cdot)$ with $g(t) \to \infty$ as $t \to \infty$ such that $\int_0^\infty g(t)f(t)dt < \infty$ and whose inverse $g^{-1}(\cdot)$ satisfies $Eg^{-1}(|Y|) < \infty$ [cf. Daley (1981) for a related problem].

8.5.2. Let $\{I_n\} = \{(a_n, b_n]: n = 1, 2, \ldots\}$ be a sequence of random intervals on $\mathbb{R}_+$ of lengths $X_n = b_n - a_n > 0$ a.s. and having gaps $Y_n = a_{n+1} - b_n > 0$ a.s., with $\{X_n\}$ i.i.d. exponential r.v.s, $\{Y_n\}$ i.i.d. r.v.s independent of $\{X_n\}$ and with finite mean, and $a_1 = 0$. Let a Cox process N on $\mathbb{R}_+$ be directed by a random measure ξ, which has density λ on the set $\bigcup_{n=1}^\infty I_n$ and zero elsewhere. Show that $N(\cdot) + \delta_0(\cdot)$ is a renewal process. [The points of the set $\{a_n, b_n: n = 1, 2, \ldots\}$ are those of an alternating renewal process with exponential lifetimes for one of the underlying lifetime distributions. Kingman (1964) showed that any stationary

Cox process that is also a stationary renewal process must effectively be directed by the stationary version of the random measure described.]

8.5.3. Let $C \equiv (c_{ij})$ be a (real or complex) covariance matrix. The discrete counterpart of Example 5.4(b) and its associated exercises is the mixed Poisson process obtained by taking $N(i)$ ($i = 1, \ldots, K$) to be Poisson with random parameter $\lambda |Z_i|^2$, where $Z = (Z_1, \ldots, Z_k)$ has the multivariate normal distribution $N(0, C)$. For $K = 1$ this reduces to a geometric distribution with p.g.f. $P(1 + \eta) = 1/(1 - \lambda c_{11}^2 \eta)$. For $K > 1$ the multivariate p.g.f. has the form

(i) $$P(1 + \eta_1, \ldots, 1 + \eta_K) = \det(I - \lambda D_\eta C)^{-1},$$

where $D_\eta = \mathrm{diag}(\eta_1, \ldots, \eta_K)$.

The factorial moment relations corresponding to (8.5.8) may be written down as follows. For any $k > 0$ let $r_1, \ldots, r_K$ be nonnegative integers such that $r_1 + \cdots + r_K = k$; here, r_j is to be interpreted as the number of repetitions of the index j in defining the factorial moment

$$m_{[k]}(i_1, \ldots, i_k) = E(N(1)^{[r_1]} \cdots N(K)^{[r_K]}),$$

where the set $(i_1, \ldots, i_k)$ consists of the index j repeated r_j times ($j = 1, \ldots, K$). We then have

(ii) $$m_{[k]}(i_1, \ldots, i_k) = \lambda^k C^+ \begin{pmatrix} i_1, \ldots, i_k \\ i_1, \ldots, i_k \end{pmatrix}.$$

8.5.4. The relations (i) and (ii) of Exercise 8.5.3 are together equivalent to the identity for the reciprocal of the characteristic polynomial

$$|\det(I - \lambda D_\eta C) = 1 + \sum_{k=1}^{\infty} \frac{\lambda^k}{k!} \sum_{\mathrm{perm}} C^+ \begin{pmatrix} i_1, \ldots, i_k \\ i_1, \ldots, i_k \end{pmatrix} \eta_{i_1} \cdots \eta_{i_k},$$

where the inner summation extends over all distinct permutations of k indices from the set $i_1, \ldots, i_k$ allowing repetitions [this is related to the master theorem of MacMahon (1915, §§63–66); see also Vere-Jones (1984)].

8.5.5. Using (i) of Exercise 8.5.3, we have also

$$P(z_1, \ldots, z_K) = (d(-\lambda))^{-1} \det(I - \lambda D_z R_{-\lambda}),$$

where $R_{-\lambda} = (I + \lambda C)^{-1}$ and $d(-\lambda) = \det(I + \lambda C)$. From this p.g.f. we obtain the multivariate probabilities in the form (using the notation of preceding exercises)

$$\pi_k(i_1, \ldots, i_k) = \Pr\{N(j) = r_j \ (j = 1, \ldots, K)\}$$

$$= \frac{\lambda^k}{d(-\lambda)} \cdot \frac{R_{-\lambda}^+ \begin{pmatrix} i_1, \ldots, i_k \\ i_1, \ldots, i_k \end{pmatrix}}{r_1! \cdots r_k!}.$$

8.5.6. Derive the results of Example 8.5(b) by a suitable passage to the limit of the last three exercises. [An alternative route to these results uses the expansion of $Z(t)$ in an orthogonal series over Δ: see Macchi (1971a) and Grandell (1976).]

8.5.7. When $C(s, t) = \sigma^2 e^{-\alpha|s-t|}$ in Example 8.5(b), show that

$$\Pr\{N(0, T] = 0\} = e^{\alpha T}(\cosh \beta T + (\alpha + 2\sigma^2)\beta^{-1} \sinh \beta T)^{-1}.$$

CHAPTER 9

Convergence Concepts and Limit Theorems

When random measures and point processes are regarded as probability measures on the appropriate c.s.m.s. $\hat{\mathcal{M}}_{\mathcal{X}}$ or $\mathcal{N}_{\mathcal{X}}$, they may be associated with concepts of both weak and strong convergence of measures on a metric space. In this chapter we examine these concepts more closely, finding necessary and sufficient conditions for weak convergence, relating this concept to other possible definitions of convergence, and applying it to some near-classical questions concerning the convergence of superpositions, thinnings, and translations of point processes.

A common theme in the resulting limit theorems is the emergence of the completely random Poisson process as the limit of repeated applications of some stochastic operation on an initial point process. In a loose sense, each of the operations of superposition, thinning, and random translation is entropy increasing; it is not surprising then that among point processes with fixed mean rate, the limit Poisson process is that with maximum entropy (see Section 13.5). These limit theorems help not only to explain the ubiquitous role of the Poisson process in applications but also to reveal its central place in the structural theory of point processes.

The forms of the limit theorems presented here are not the strongest or most general possible. For example, where we prove weak convergence, some form of strong convergence can often be established, and where we restrict attention to $\mathcal{X} = \mathbb{R}^d$, extensions to more general locally compact groups are usually possible. Many of these extensions are covered in MKM, especially the Russian edition, which systematically extends their earlier work to the context of a general locally compact group.

9.1. Convergence Concepts for Random Measures and Point Processes

In this section we examine different possible modes of convergence for a family of point processes or random measures. We generally suppose that the processes involved are to be thought of as distributions on $\hat{\mathcal{M}}_{\mathscr{X}}$ or $\hat{\mathcal{N}}_{\mathscr{X}}$, where $\mathscr{X}$ as usual is a general c.s.m.s. Then the question is, given a sequence of probability measures $\{\mathscr{P}_n\}$ on $\hat{\mathcal{M}}_{\mathscr{X}}$, in what sense should the statement $\mathscr{P}_n \to \mathscr{P}$ be understood?

Three types of convergence suggest themselves for immediate consideration: strong convergence on $\hat{\mathcal{M}}_{\mathscr{X}}$ (i.e., $\|\mathscr{P}_n - \mathscr{P}\| \to 0$, where $\|\mathscr{P}\|$ is the variation norm as defined in Section A1.3); weak convergence on $\hat{\mathcal{M}}_{\mathscr{X}}$ (i.e., $\mathscr{P}_n \to \mathscr{P}$ in the sense of weak convergence of measures on the metric space $\hat{\mathcal{M}}_{\mathscr{X}}$); and convergence of the finite distributions [i.e., the joint distributions of the random variables $\xi(A_1), \ldots, \xi(A_k)$ under $\mathscr{P}_n$ converge weakly to their limit distribution under $\mathscr{P}$, for all suitable finite families of bounded Borel sets $A_1, \ldots, A_k$]. In the final part of this section we consider some further questions that arise when we try to relate convergence of measures in $\hat{\mathcal{M}}_{\mathscr{X}}$ with convergence of the associated distribution functions in the space $D(-\infty, \infty)$ or its relatives.

In connection with the third of these concepts, we call the Borel set A a *stochastic continuity set* for the measure $\mathscr{P}$ if $\mathscr{P}\{\xi(\partial A) > 0\} = 0$. Without a restriction to sets that are continuity sets for the limit measure, convergence of the fidi distributions would be too strong a concept to be generally useful as the following example shows.

EXAMPLE 9.1(a). Let ξ_n consist of just one point, uniformly distributed over $(k, k + 1/n)$, in each interval $(k, k + 1)$, $k = 0, \pm 1, \pm 2, \ldots$. Then as $n \to \infty$, we would like to say that the sequence converges to the deterministic point process with one point at each integer. However, if $A = (0, 1)$, we have $\mathscr{P}_n\{\xi(0, 1) > 0\} = 1$ while $\mathscr{P}\{\xi(0, 1) > 0\} = 0$. Thus, we can expect difficulties to arise in the definition if the limit random measure has fixed atoms, and these atoms lie on the boundary of the set A considered in the finite-dimensional distribution. Similar but more general examples can readily be constructed.

Granted the need for the restriction it is important to know that there are "sufficiently many" stochastic continuity sets. Given $\mathscr{P}$, let $\mathscr{S}_{\mathscr{P}}$ denote the class of stochastic continuity sets for $\mathscr{P}$. From the elementary properties of set boundaries (see Proposition A1.2.I), it is clear that $\mathscr{S}_{\mathscr{P}}$ is an algebra (see Exercise 9.1.1). The following lemma is then sufficient for most purposes.

Lemma 9.1.I. *Let $\mathscr{X}$ be a c.s.m.s., $\mathscr{P}$ a probability measure on $\mathscr{B}(\hat{\mathcal{M}}_{\mathscr{X}})$, and $\mathscr{S}_{\mathscr{P}}$ the class of stochastic continuity sets for $\mathscr{P}$. Then for all x and, given x, for all but a countable set of values of r, $S(x, r) \in \mathscr{S}_{\mathscr{P}}$.*

PROOF. It is enough to show that for each finite positive ε, δ, and R, the set of values of r satisfying

$$\mathcal{P}\{\xi(\partial S(x, r)) > \delta\} > \varepsilon, \qquad 0 \leq r \leq R,$$

is finite. Suppose the contrary, and let ε, δ, and R be such that for some countable infinite set $\{r_1, r_2, \ldots\}$ of distinct values of r in $0 \leq r \leq R < \infty$, $\mathcal{P}(B_i) > \varepsilon$ for $i = 1, 2, \ldots$, where

$$B_i = \{\xi : \xi(\partial S(x, r_i)) > \delta\}.$$

Then

$$\varepsilon \leq \lim \sup_i \mathcal{P}(B_i) \leq \mathcal{P}(\lim \sup_i B_i) \leq \mathcal{P}\{\xi(\overline{S(x, R)}) = \infty\}$$

since

$$\xi(\overline{S(x, R)}) \geq \sum_{i=1}^{\infty} \xi(\partial S(x, r_i)) = \infty$$

whenever $\xi(\partial S(x, r_i)) \geq \delta > 0$ for an infinite number of values of i. This contradicts the bounded finiteness of ξ. □

Corollary 9.1.II. *The stochastic continuity sets of $\mathcal{P}$ form an algebra that contains both a dissecting ring and a covering ring.*

PROOF. Scrutinizing the constructions of a dissecting system at Proposition A2.1.V and of a covering ring before Corollary A2.3.III reveals that they are not affected if, whenever a sphere $S(d_i, \alpha)$ that is not a stochastic continuity set occurs, it is replaced by a marginally smaller sphere $S(d_i, \alpha')$ that is. Since the remaining stages of the constructions involve only finite unions, intersections, and differences, they do not lead out of the algebra of such continuity sets. □

We can now state the following more formal definitions.

Definition 9.1.III. (a) The sequence of random measures $\{\xi_n\}$ converges *weakly* to a limit ξ if the sequence of probability measures $\{\mathcal{P}_n\}$ induced by $\{\xi_n\}$ on $\mathcal{M}_{\mathcal{X}}$ converges weakly to the probability measure $\mathcal{P}$ induced by ξ.
    (b) The sequence $\{\xi_n\}$ converges in the sense of *convergence of fidi distributions* if for every finite family $\{A_1, \ldots, A_k\}$ of bounded continuity sets $A_i \in \mathcal{B}_{\mathcal{X}}$ the joint distributions of $\{\xi_n(A_1), \ldots, \xi_n(A_k)\}$ converge weakly in $\mathcal{B}(\mathbb{R}^k)$ to the joint distribution of $\xi(A_1), \ldots, \xi(A_k)$.

We may write $\mathcal{P}_n \Rightarrow_w \mathcal{P}$ for weak convergence as in Definition 9.1.III(a).
    Of course, these definitions embody the standard abuse of terminology in that there are no actual requirements for the random measures (as mappings into $\mathcal{M}_{\mathcal{X}}$) themselves to converge; indeed, the same comment applies to all the modes of convergence considered in this chapter.

The mapping that takes a general element ξ of $\mathcal{M}_{\mathscr{X}}$ into $\xi(A)$, where A is a bounded Borel set, is measurable [essentially by definition of the σ-algebra $\mathscr{B}(\mathcal{M}_{\mathscr{X}})$] but not continuous. To see this last point it is enough to consider variants on Example 9.1(a), where the sequence of measures $\{\xi_n\}$ converges on the $\hat{w}$-topology in $\mathcal{M}_{\mathscr{X}}$ to a limit measure ξ that has an atom on the boundary ∂A. However, it is only those measures ξ giving nonzero mass to ∂A that act in this way as discontinuity points of the mapping $\xi \to \xi(A)$. This follows from observing that if $\xi(\partial A) = 0$ and $\xi_n \to \xi$ ($\hat{w}$), then by Theorem A2.3.II, $\xi_n(A) \to \xi(A)$.

Now let $\{\mathscr{P}_n\}$ be a sequence of probability distributions, and suppose that $\mathscr{P}_n \to \mathscr{P}$ weakly and that A is a stochastic continuity set for $\mathscr{P}$. This last is just another way of saying that the set D of discontinuity points for the mapping $f_A: \xi \to \xi(A)$ satisfies the condition $\mathscr{P}(D) = 0$. It then follows from the extended form of the continuous mapping theorem (Proposition A2.3.V) that $\mathscr{P}_n(f_A^{-1}) \to \mathscr{P}f_A^{-1}$, or in other words that the distribution of $\xi(A)$ under $\mathscr{P}_n$ converges to its distribution under $\mathscr{P}$. A similar argument applies to any finite family of bounded Borel sets $\{A_1, \ldots, A_k\}$ satisfying $\mathscr{P}\{\xi(\partial A) = 0\} = 1$ and hence leads to the following lemma.

Lemma 9.1.IV. *Weak convergence implies weak convergence of the finite-dimensional distributions.*

What is more surprising is that the converse of this statement is also true, so that *for random measures and point processes, the concepts of weak convergence and convergence of fidi distributions are equivalent.* The proof of this, which constitutes the main theorem of this section, will be given shortly. Before doing so, we make a few further comments about weak and strong convergence.

For any set $U \in \mathscr{B}(\mathcal{M}_{\mathscr{X}})$, we have in the notation of Section A1.3

$$\|\mathscr{P}_n - \mathscr{P}\| \geq V_{\mathscr{P}_n - \mathscr{P}}(U) \geq |\mathscr{P}_n(U) - \mathscr{P}(U)|,$$

so that strong convergence implies $\mathscr{P}_n(U) \to \mathscr{P}(U)$ for all $U \in \mathscr{B}(\mathcal{M}_{\mathscr{X}})$ and hence implies weak convergence. Here the converse is *not* true; again Example 9.1(a) serves as a counterexample. Indeed, strong convergence implies that any fixed atom for the limit probability must also be a fixed atom for its approximants.

While convergence in variation norm is more difficult to establish, once available it is very convenient to use. This is because in addition to its properties as a norm, it also respects convolution in the sense that

$$\|\mu * \nu\| \leq \|\mu\| \|\nu\|$$

(see Exercise 9.1.4). In practice, it seems convenient to work not so much with the norm on $\mathcal{M}_{\mathscr{X}}$ as such, but rather with the family of norms on each of the spaces of totally finite measures $\mathcal{M}_A$, $A \in \mathscr{B}_{\mathscr{X}}$ and bounded. Yet another approach is to look at norm convergence rather than weak convergence for the fidi distributions.

As mentioned in the introduction to this chapter, we make relatively little use of these stronger concepts in the present text. An illustration of the sort of discussion required is given in the second half of Section 9.3, where some of the preliminary inequalities are derived, which can be used to strengthen the convergence statements in the discussion of thinning. Various other examples are given from time to time in the exercises and elsewhere.

Returning now to the discussion of weak convergence, it is convenient first to set out conditions for the tightness of a family of probability measures on $\mathcal{B}(\hat{\mathcal{M}}_{\mathcal{X}})$ in a form that we can refer to in the sequel.

Proposition 9.1.V. *For a family of probability measures $\{\mathcal{P}_t, t \in \mathcal{T}\}$ on $\mathcal{B}(\hat{\mathcal{M}}_{\mathcal{X}})$ to be uniformly tight, it is necessary and sufficient that, given any closed sphere $\bar{S} \subset \mathcal{X}$ and any $\varepsilon, \delta > 0$, there exists a real number $M < \infty$ and a compact set $C \subseteq \bar{S}$ such that, uniformly for $t \in \mathcal{T}$,*

$$(9.1.1) \qquad\qquad \mathcal{P}_t\{\xi(\bar{S}) > M\} < \varepsilon,$$

$$(9.1.2) \qquad\qquad \mathcal{P}_t\{\xi(\bar{S} - C) > \delta\} < \varepsilon.$$

If $\mathcal{X}$ is locally compact, and in particular if $\mathcal{X} = \mathbb{R}^d$, the second condition is redundant.

PROOF. Uniform tightness means that, for each $\varepsilon > 0$, there exists a compact set $K \in \mathcal{B}(\hat{\mathcal{M}}_{\mathcal{X}})$ such that $\mathcal{P}_t(K) > 1 - \varepsilon$ for all $t \in \mathcal{T}$. From Proposition A2.6.IV and Theorem A2.4.I, K is compact if there exists a sequence of closed spheres $\bar{S}_n \uparrow \mathcal{X}$ such that for each $\delta > 0$ and $n < \infty$ there exist constants M_n and compact sets $C_{n,\delta} \subseteq \bar{S}_n$ such that for all $\xi \in K$,

(a) $\xi(\bar{S}_n) \leq M_n$, and
(b) $\xi(\bar{S}_n - C_{n,\delta}) \leq \delta$.

Effectively, (9.1.1) and (9.1.2) are just reformulations of (a) and (b). Indeed, supposing first that (9.1.1) and (9.1.2) are satisfied, choose any sequence of closed spheres $\bar{S}_n \uparrow \mathcal{X}$ such that each $\bar{S}_n$ is a stochastic continuity set for $\mathcal{P}$. From (9.1.1) we choose M_n' such that

$$\mathcal{P}_t\{\xi(\bar{S}_n) > M_n'\} < \varepsilon/2^{n+1},$$

and from (9.1.2) we choose the compact set $C_{mn}' \subseteq \bar{S}_n$ so that

$$\mathcal{P}_t\{\xi(\bar{S}_n - C_{mn}')\} < \varepsilon/2^{m+n+2}.$$

Define the sets (for $n, m = 1, 2, \ldots$)

$$Q_n = \{\xi: \xi(\bar{S}_n) \leq M_n\},$$

$$Q_{mn} = \{\xi: \xi(\bar{S}_n - C_{mn}') \leq m^{-1}\},$$

$$K = \bigcap_{n=1}^{\infty} \bigcap_{m=1}^{\infty} (Q_n \cap Q_{mn}).$$

By construction, (a) and (b) are satisfied so K is compact, while

$$\mathcal{P}_t(K^c) \le \sum_{n=1}^{\infty} \left[\mathcal{P}_t(Q_n^c) + \sum_{m=1}^{\infty} \mathcal{P}_t(Q_{mn}^c) \right]$$

$$\le \sum_{n=1}^{\infty} \left[\frac{\varepsilon}{2^{n+1}} + \sum_{m=1}^{\infty} \frac{\varepsilon}{2^{m+n+2}} \right] = \varepsilon.$$

Thus, K satisfies all the required conditions.

Suppose conversely that the measures $\mathcal{P}_t$ are uniformly tight. Given ε, choose compact $K \subset \mathcal{M}_{\mathcal{X}}$ and hence deduce the existence of spheres $\bar{S}_n \uparrow \mathcal{X}$ such that there exist constants M_n for which (a) holds, and, given δ, there exist $C_{n,\delta}$ such that (b) holds. Given any $\bar{S}$, choose n so that $\bar{S} \subseteq \bar{S}_n$, set $M = M_n$ so that (9.1.1) is true, and, given δ, set $C = C_{n,\delta} \cap \bar{S}$ so that $\xi(\bar{S} - C) \le \xi(\bar{S}_n - C_{n,\delta})$ and hence (9.1.2) holds.   □

EXAMPLE 9.1(b). Let ξ_n be the degenerate point process in $\mathbb{R}$ in which all the mass is concentrated on the counting measure with a single atom at the point n. Then (9.1.1) holds trivially for all S and ε with $M = 2$. In fact $\xi_n \to \xi_\infty$ weakly, where ξ_∞ has all its mass concentrated on the zero random measure $\varnothing$. Thus, it is important to bear in mind that weak convergence here does not preclude the possibility that the limit point process may be everywhere zero.

Now let $\eta_n = \sum_{k=1}^n \xi_k$. Then for all n we have

$$\eta_n(0, m] \le m$$

so that (9.1.1) still holds with M equal to the radius of the sphere S. In this case $\eta_n \to \eta_\infty$ weakly, where η_∞ is the "deterministic" point process with an atom at each positive integer.

Finally, let $\zeta_n = \sum_{k=1}^n k\xi_{n-k}$. Here condition (9.1.1) fails and no weak limit exists.

Theorem 9.1.VI. *Let $\mathcal{X}$ be a c.s.m.s. and $\{\mathcal{P}_n: n = 1, 2, \ldots\}$, $\mathcal{P}$ distributions on $(\mathcal{M}_{\mathcal{X}}, \mathcal{B}(\mathcal{M}_{\mathcal{X}}))$. Then $\mathcal{P}_n \to \mathcal{P}$ weakly if and only if the fidi distributions of $\mathcal{P}_n$ converge weakly to those of $\mathcal{P}$.*

PROOF. The first part of the theorem has already been proved in Lemma 9.1.IV. Since all the fidi distributions determine a probability measure uniquely, it suffices in order to prove the converse to show that the family $\{\mathcal{P}_n\}$ is uniformly tight (see Theorem A2.4.I), for then every sequence contains a weakly convergent subsequence, and from the convergence of the fidi distributions this must be the limit measure $\mathcal{P}$; thus, all convergent subsequences have the same limit, and so the whole sequence converges.

To complete the proof of the theorem, we use the assumption that the fidi distributions converge for stochastic continuity sets of $\mathcal{P}$ to show that (9.1.1) and (9.1.2) then hold for any given $\bar{S}$, ε, and δ. We start by choosing $\bar{S}' \supseteq \bar{S}$ to be a stochastic continuity set not only for $\mathcal{P}$ but also for each of the $\mathcal{P}_n$, $n = 1$, 2, ... (Since by Lemma 9.1.I only countable sets of exceptional radii are involved, this choice can always be made.) Furthermore, we can choose values

M that are continuity points for the distribution of $\xi(\bar{S}')$ under $\mathscr{P}$ and for which $\mathscr{P}\{\xi(\bar{S}') > M\} < \varepsilon/2$ and $\mathscr{P}_n\{\xi(\bar{S}') > M\} \to \mathscr{P}\{\xi(\bar{S}') > M\}$ as $n \to \infty$. Thus, for $n > n_0$ say, we have

$$\mathscr{P}_n\{\xi(\bar{S}) > M\} < \varepsilon,$$

and by increasing M if necessary we can ensure that this inequality holds for all n. This establishes (9.1.1).

Again working only with spheres that are stochastic continuity sets for $\mathscr{P}$, choose spheres $S(x_i, r_j) \equiv S_{ij}$ centred on the points x_i ($i = 1, 2, \ldots$) of a separability set and with radii $r_j \le 2^{-j}$. Define $C_{ij} = \bar{S}_{ij} \cap \bar{S}'$. Since as $I \to \infty$,

$$\xi\left(\bigcup_{i=1}^{I} C_{ij}\right) \uparrow \xi(\bar{S}'),$$

we can choose I_j so that, with $C_j = \bigcup_{i=1}^{I_j} C_{ij}$,

$$\mathscr{P}\{\xi(\bar{S}' - C_j) \ge \delta_j\} \le \varepsilon/2^{j+1},$$

where $\delta_j \le \delta/2^j$ is chosen to be a continuity point of the distribution of $\xi(\bar{S}' - C_j)$ under $\mathscr{P}$. Again using the weak convergence of the fidi distributions, and increasing the value of I_j if necessary, we can ensure as before that the similar inequality

(9.1.3) $$\mathscr{P}_n\{\xi(\bar{S}' - C_j) \ge \delta_j\} \le \varepsilon/2^j$$

holds for all n. Now define $C = \bigcap_{j=1}^{\infty} C_j$. Then C is closed, and by construction it can be covered by a finite number of ε-spheres for every $\varepsilon > 0$, so by Proposition A2.2.II C is compact. We have moreover from (9.1.3) that, for every n,

$$\mathscr{P}_n\{\xi(\bar{S}') - \xi(C) > \delta\} = \mathscr{P}_n\left\{\xi\left(\bigcup_{j=1}^{\infty} (\bar{S}' - C_j)\right) > \delta\right\}$$

$$\le \sum_{j=1}^{\infty} \mathscr{P}_n\{\xi(\bar{S}' - C_j) > \delta/2^j\}$$

$$\le \sum_{j=1}^{\infty} \mathscr{P}_n\{\xi(\bar{S}' - C_j) > \delta_j\}$$

$$\le \sum_{j=1}^{\infty} \frac{\varepsilon}{2^j} = \varepsilon,$$

thus establishing (9.1.2). Thus, both conditions of Proposition 9.1.V are satisfied, and we conclude that the family $\{\mathscr{P}_n\}$ is tight. $\square$

Several equivalent conditions for weak convergence can be derived essentially as corollaries to the above theorem.

Proposition 9.1.VII. *Each of the following conditions is equivalent to the weak convergence $\mathscr{P}_n \Rightarrow_w \mathscr{P}$:*

(i) *For every bounded continuous function f vanishing outside a bounded set, the distribution of $\int_{\mathscr{X}} f \, d\xi$ under $\mathscr{P}_n$ converges weakly to its distribution under $\mathscr{P}$.*

(ii) *For similar f, the Laplace functionals $L_n[f] \equiv E_{\mathscr{P}_n}(\exp(-\int_{\mathscr{X}} f(x)\xi(dx)))$ converge pointwise to the limit functional $L[f]$.*

(iii) *For point processes, the p.g.fl.s $G_n[h]$ converge to $G[h]$ for each continuous $h \in \mathscr{V}_0$.*

PROOF. For any bounded measurable f vanishing outside a bounded set, we can consider the mapping defined by

$$\Phi_f(\xi) = \int_{\mathscr{X}} f(x)\xi(dx),$$

which is continuous at ξ provided $\xi(Z(f)) = 0$, where $Z(f)$ is the set of discontinuities of f. Hence, in particular, it will be continuous for all ξ whenever f itself is continuous. Thus, the distributions of $\Phi_f(\xi)$ under $\mathscr{P}_n$ converge weakly to its distribution under $\mathscr{P}$.

Now suppose that f is a function of the form $\sum_i c_i I_{A_i}(x)$, where $\sum_i |c_i| < \infty$ and $\{A_i\}$ is a bounded family of bounded Borel sets that are stochastic continuity sets for $\mathscr{P}$. Convergence of the distributions of the integrals $\int_{\mathscr{X}} f \, d\xi$ for all such functions f is equivalent to the joint convergence in distribution of $\xi(A_1), \ldots, \xi(A_k)$ for every finite integer k, that is, to fidi convergence. Since such functions can be approximated by continuous functions, as, for example, in the proof of Theorem A2.3.II, it follows that (i) implies convergence of the fidi distributions and hence weak convergence.

Condition (ii) is equivalent to (i) by well-known results on Laplace transforms.

Finally, if the distributions $\mathscr{P}_n$ correspond to point processes, since $f(x) = -\log h(x)$ is a function as in (i) if and only if h is continuous and $h \in \mathscr{V}_0$, (iii) is then equivalent to (ii).   □

The following sharpened form of the fidi convergence criterion is also useful.

Corollary 9.1.VIII. *For weak convergence as in Definition 9.1.III(b) it is sufficient for the sets $\{A_i\}$ to run through any covering semiring of stochastic continuity sets for the limit measure $\mathscr{P}$.*

PROOF. It is a matter of verifying that the constructions in the proof of Theorem 9.1.VI can be carried through with sets A_i drawn from the covering semiring (or, more generally, from the ring it generates, since it is clear that the convergence carries over to sets taken from this generated ring). Since by definition of a covering ring each open sphere can be approximated by sets in the ring, both constructions in the first part of the proof can be so modified, so the sequence $\{\mathscr{P}_n\}$ is uniformly tight. If $\{\mathscr{P}_{n_k}\}$ is any weakly convergent subsequence from $\{\mathcal{P}_n\}$, with limit $\mathcal{P}'$ say, then $\mathcal{P}$ and $\mathcal{P}'$ must have the same fidi distributions for sets drawn from the covering semiring. Then from Proposition 6.2.III it follows that $\mathcal{P} = \mathcal{P}'$, and hence as before that $\mathcal{P}_n \Rightarrow_w \mathcal{P}$. $\quad\square$

Thus far the results apply equally to random measures or point processes. In the point process case an even more striking sharpened statement is possible when the processes are simple, through the use of the avoidance function (cf. Theorem 7.3.II). In this case the limit measure must correspond to a simple point process if it is to be uniquely characterized by the avoidance function, and condition (ii) below is such an additional requirement about asymptotic orderliness. A number of variants are possible, of which the following is perhaps the simplest.

Proposition 9.1.IX. *Let* $\{\mathcal{P}_n: n = 1, 2, \ldots\}$, $\mathcal{P}$ *be distributions on* $\mathcal{N}_\mathcal{X}$ *with* $\mathcal{P}$ *corresponding to a simple point process, and suppose that* $\mathcal{R} \subseteq \mathcal{S}_\mathcal{P}$ *is a covering dissecting ring. In order that* $\mathcal{P}_n \Rightarrow_w \mathcal{P}$, *it is sufficient that*

(i) $\mathcal{P}_n\{N(A) = 0\} \to \mathcal{P}\{N(A) = 0\}$ *as* $n \to \infty$ *for all bounded* $A \in \mathcal{R}$; *and*
(ii) *for all bounded* $A \in \mathcal{R}$ *and partitions*

$$\mathcal{T}_r = \{A_{ri}: i = 1, \ldots, k_r\}$$

of A by sets of $\mathcal{R}$,

(9.1.4) $$\limsup_{n\to\infty} \sup_{\mathcal{T}_r} \sum_{i=1}^{k_r} \mathcal{P}_n\{N(A_{ri}) \geq 2\} = 0.$$

PROOF. In view of Theorem 7.3.II it is enough to show that under the stated conditions the family $\{\mathcal{P}_n\}$ is uniformly tight and that the limit of any weakly convergent subsequence must be a simple point process.

Let $\bar{S}$ be a closed sphere in $\mathcal{R}$, and in (ii) take $A = \bar{S}$. Observing that $\{N(\bar{S}) > k_r\}$ implies $\{N(A_{ri}) \geq 2$ for at least one $i\}$,

$$\sum_{i=1}^{k_r} \mathcal{P}_n\{N(A_{ri}) \geq 2\} \geq \mathcal{P}_n\{N(\bar{S}) > k_r\}.$$

Given $\varepsilon > 0$, (9.1.4) implies that the sum on the left here is bounded by ε for $n \geq n_0$, hence (by adjusting k_r if necessary) for all n, and thus that the first condition for uniform tightness holds.

Condition (9.1.2) here can be stated in the following form: given $\varepsilon > 0$, there exists a compact set C such that $\mathcal{P}_n\{N(\bar{S} - C) = 0\} > 1 - \varepsilon$ for $n = 1, 2, \ldots$. Choose C so that for the limit distribution we have

$$\mathcal{P}\{N(\bar{S} - C) = 0\} > 1 - \varepsilon/2.$$

From assumption (i) we have $\mathcal{P}_n\{N(\bar{S} - C) = 0\} \to \mathcal{P}\{N(\bar{S} - C) = 0\}$ as $n \to \infty$, from which the required inequality (9.1.2) holds for all sufficiently large n, and hence (by increasing C if necessary) for all n.

Thus, both conditions for uniform tightness of $\{\mathcal{P}_n\}$ are satisfied.

Now let $\{\mathscr{P}_{n_k}\}$ be any weakly convergent subsequence from the family $\{\mathscr{P}_n\}$, with limit $\mathscr{P}'$ say, so that from Theorem 9.1.VI all fidi distributions converge to those of $\mathscr{P}'$; hence, from (i) of the proposition, for $A \in \mathscr{R}$,

$$\mathscr{P}\{N(A) = 0\} = \mathscr{P}'\{N(A) = 0\}.$$

From this result it follows not necessarily that $\mathscr{P} = \mathscr{P}'$ but merely that

$$\mathscr{P}\{N(A) = 0\} = \mathscr{P}'\{N^*(A) = 0\} \quad \text{or} \quad \mathscr{P} = (\mathscr{P}')^*,$$

where N^* is the support point process of N and $(\mathscr{P}')^*$ is its distribution (see Corollary 7.3.III). However, we have

$$\sum_{i=1}^{k_r} \mathscr{P}'\{N(A_{ri}) \geq 2\} = \sum_{i=1}^{k_r} \lim_{k \to \infty} \mathscr{P}_{n_k}\{N(A_{ri}) \geq 2\}$$

so that from (9.1.4)

$$\limsup_{\mathscr{T}_r} \sum_{i=1}^{k_r} \mathscr{P}'\{N(A_{ri}) \geq 2\} \leq \limsup_{k \to \infty} \sum_{\mathscr{T}_r}^{k_r} \mathscr{P}_{n_k}\{N(A_{ri}) \geq 2\} = 0,$$

from which it follows (Proposition 7.2.V) that $\mathscr{P}'$ is simple, and hence that $\mathscr{P}' = (\mathscr{P}')^* = \mathscr{P}$. So all weakly convergent subsequences have limit $\mathscr{P}'$, and thus $\mathscr{P}_n \Rightarrow_w \mathscr{P}$.   □

We conclude this section with a few remarks concerning the relation between weak convergence of random measures with state space $\mathscr{X} = \mathbb{R}_+$ and weak convergence of the associated cumulative processes as elements in $\mathscr{D}(0, \infty)$. Here the cumulative function associated with a measure μ on $\mathbb{R}_+$ is defined by

$$F_\mu(x) = \mu\{(0, x]\} \qquad 0 < x < \infty.$$

Such functions are monotonic increasing, right continuous with left limits, and therefore define a subspace of $\mathscr{D}(0, \infty)$. Since the metrics in $\mathscr{M}(\mathbb{R}_+)$ and $\mathscr{D}(0, \infty)$ are obtained from compounding the analogous metrics over finite intervals, it will be sufficient to compare the behaviour of the two metrics over a common finite interval, which for convenience we take as the interval $(0, 1]$. In both cases we are effectively concerned with the distance between two cumulative functions F, G over $(0, 1)$. Weak convergence of a family of measures on $(0, 1]$ is equivalent to convergence of the cumulative functions with respect to the Lévy metric ρ_L, where $\rho_L(F, G)$ is defined as the infimum of values ε such that for all $x \in (0, 1]$,

$$G(x - \varepsilon) - \varepsilon \leq F(x) \leq G(x + \varepsilon) + \varepsilon$$

[we take $G(-y) = 0$, $G(1 + y) = G(1)$ $(y > 0)$ for the purposes of this definition.] On the other hand convergence of the distribution functions in $\mathscr{D}(0, 1)$ is equivalent to convergence with respect to the Skorohod metric ρ_S, where $\rho_S(F, G)$ is defined as the infimum of values ε such that there exists a continuous mapping λ of $[0, 1]$ onto $[0, 1]$, with $\lambda(0) = 0$, $\lambda(1) = 1$, for which

$$\sup_{0 \le x \le 1} |x - \lambda(x)| < \varepsilon, \qquad \sup_{0 \le x \le 1} |F(\lambda(x)) - G(x)| < \varepsilon.$$

The statements $\rho_L(F, G) < \varepsilon$ and $\rho_S(F, G) < \varepsilon$ both require F and G to be close in the sense that uniformly for $x \in (0, 1]$, the value of $F(x)$ differs from a possibly slightly shifted value of $G(x)$ by less than ε, the shift also not being allowed to exceed ε. In case of the Skorohod metric, the degree of shift is controlled by the function $\lambda(x)$, whereas in the Lévy case it is constrained not to exceed ε but is otherwise not related from one x to any other.

In both cases the statement $\rho(F_n, F) \to 0$ is equivalent to the requirement that $F_n(x) \to F(x)$ at all continuity points of x (see Exercises 9.1.5–9.1.6). Provided therefore that discussion is restricted to the subspace of cumulative processes, the two types of convergence are equivalent. Equivalently, the mapping from $\mathcal{M}(0, 1)$ into $\mathcal{D}(0, 1)$, which takes the measure ξ into its cumulative function F_S, is both ways continuous. The continuous mapping theorem A2.3.V therefore yields the following result.

Lemma 9.1.X. *A sequence of random measures $\{\xi_n\}$ on $\mathcal{M}(\mathbb{R}_+)$ converges weakly to a random measure ξ if and only if the corresponding sequence of cumulative processes F_{ξ_n} converges weakly in $\mathcal{D}(0, \infty)$ to the cumulative process F_ξ.*

Extensions to $\mathbb{R}^d$ can be obtained in terms of the concepts described by Straf (1972).

From the point of view of weak convergence, it is therefore immaterial whether we deal with the random measures directly or the stochastic processes defined by the associated cumulative functions.

Of course, if rescaling is involved, the limits need no longer correspond to random measures, and versions of the functional limit forms of the central limit theorem can be obtained. Here the random measure or point process character of the sample function is essentially irrelevant. As an example we quote the following analogue to Theorem 20.1 of Billingsley (1968). Here the random measure ξ is said to be ψ-mixing if $|\mathscr{P}(U \cap V) - \mathscr{P}(U)\mathscr{P}(V)| \le \psi(u)$ whenever the Borel sets U, V satisfy $U \in \sigma\{\xi(A): A \subseteq (-\infty, t]\}$, $V \in \sigma\{\xi(B), B \subseteq (t + u, \infty)\}$, for some $u > 0$ and $t \in \mathbb{R}$.

Proposition 9.1.XI. *Let the stationary random measure ξ on $\mathscr{X} = \mathbb{R}$ be ψ-mixing for some continuous, monotonic, nonnegative function $\psi(\cdot)$ on $\mathbb{R}_+$ such that $\int_0^\infty [\psi(t)]^{1/2} dt < \infty$ and have boundedly finite first and second moment measures, with mean rate m and reduced covariance measure $C(\cdot)$ satisfying $\sigma^2 = C(\mathbb{R}) > 0$. Then the sequence of random processes $\{Y_n\}$ defined by*

$$Y_n(t) = \{\xi(0, nt] - mnt\}/\sigma n^{1/2} \qquad (0 \le t \le 1)$$

converges weakly in $\mathcal{D}(0, 1)$ to the Wiener process on $(0, 1)$.

Exercises

9.1.1. (a) Let N be a point process on $\mathbb{R}$ and $\mathscr{R}$ the ring generated by half-open intervals like $(a, b]$, so that for $A \in \mathscr{R}$, ∂A consists of the finite set of end points of the constituent intervals of A. Deduce that A is a stochastic continuity set unless any of the end points of its constituent intervals happen to be fixed atoms of the process.
       (b) Deduce that if N on $\mathbb{R}$ is stationary, it has no fixed atoms.
       (c) In general, when $\mathscr{P}$ is a probability measure on $\mathscr{M}_{\mathscr{X}}$, the stochastic continuity sets for $\mathscr{P}$ form an algebra.

9.1.2. When $\mathscr{X} = \mathbb{R}^d$, every sequence of random measures with locally uniformly bounded first moment measures is relatively weakly compact (i.e., contains a weakly convergent subsequence). In particular, any sequence of random measures with uniformly bounded mean densities is weakly compact. [*Hint*: Use Chebyshev's inequality to establish the existence of $C_A < \infty$ such that $\xi_n(A) \leq C_A$ for each bounded Borel set A. Note that it is not asserted that the limit measure is distinct from the degenerate random measure $\varnothing$ which is zero with probability 1.]

9.1.3. *Convergence of moment measures.*
       (a) Let point processes N_n on $\mathbb{R}$ be defined as follows. Choose with probability $1 - n^{-1}$ the lattice point process with points at each integer and with probability n^{-1} the point process with points on the lattice $\{r/n: r = 0, \pm 1, \pm 2, \ldots\}$: randomize the centre of the lattice over the unit interval with a uniform distribution. The resulting sequence $\{N_n\}$ has the properties that (i) it converges weakly to the randomized lattice process obtained by randomizing the initial point on the lattice of integers, and (ii) $E(N_n(A)) = (2 - n^{-1})\ell(A)$ for $n = 1, 2, \ldots$, but $E(N_\infty(A)) = \ell(A)$ for all bounded Borel sets A. Thus, weak convergence and existence and boundedness of the moment measures are not enough to ensure the vague convergence of these measures.
       (b) If $N_n \to N$ weakly, then $E(N(A)) \leq \liminf E(N_n(A))$.
       (c) In general, for the first moment measures $\{M_n(\cdot)\}$ to converge in the $\hat{w}$-topology to the moment measure M of the limit process, it is necessary and sufficient that for a sequence of spheres $\{S_k\}$ with $S_k \uparrow \mathscr{X}$, $E(N_n(S_k)I\{N_n(S_k) \geq a\}) \to 0$ as $a \to \infty$ uniformly in n.

9.1.4. For totally finite signed measures μ, ν on a c.s.m.s. $\mathscr{X}$, show that the variation norm $\|\cdot\|$ (see Section A1.3) has the following properties:
       (a) $\|\alpha\mu\| = |\alpha| \|\mu\|$ for every scalar α.
       (b) $\|\mu + \nu\| \leq \|\mu\| + \|\nu\|$, with equality if the supports of μ and ν are disjoint.
       (c) $\|\mu * \nu\| \leq \|\mu\| \|\nu\|$, with equality if both measures are of constant sign (and thus $\|\mu\| = |\mu(\mathscr{X})|$).

9.1.5. Write $d_0(F, G) \equiv \sup_{x \in \mathbb{R}} |F(x) - G(x)|$ for the sup metric on the space of d.f.s F, G on $\mathbb{R}$, and write μ_F, μ_G for the measures generated by such d.f.s. Then $2d_0(F, G) \leq \|\mu_F - \mu_G\|$.

9.1.6. Let ρ_L, ρ_S refer to the Prohorov and Skorohod metrics, respectively, on the space of finite measures on $(\mathscr{X}, \mathscr{B}_{\mathscr{X}})$ (the Prohorov metric reduces to the Lévy metric on $\mathbb{R}$). Let $\{N_n\}$, N be finite counting measures on $\mathscr{X}$. Prove that $\rho_L(N_n, N) \to 0$ if and only if for all sufficiently large n, N_n has the same number of atoms as N, and the locations of the atoms in N_n converge to their locations under N. Deduce that $\rho_L(N_n, N) \to 0$ implies $\rho_S(N_n, N) \to 0$. [*Hint*: See, for example, Straf (1972).]

9.2. Limit Theorems for Superpositions

The formal setting for studying the sum or superposition of a large number of point processes or random measures is a *triangular array* $\{\xi_{ni}: i = 1, \ldots, m_n; n = 1, 2, \ldots\}$ and its associated row sums

$$\xi_n = \sum_{i=1}^{m_n} \xi_{ni}, \qquad n = 1, 2, \ldots.$$

If for each n the processes $\{\xi_{ni}: i = 1, \ldots, m_n\}$ are mutually independent, we speak of an *independent array*, and when it satisfies the condition that for all $\varepsilon > 0$ and all bounded $A \in \mathcal{B}_{\mathcal{X}}$

$$(9.2.1) \qquad \lim_{n \to \infty} \sup_i \mathscr{P}\{\xi_{ni}(A) > \varepsilon\} = 0,$$

the array is *uniformly asymptotically negligible*, or u.a.n. for short. In the case of a triangular array of point processes, the u.a.n. condition (9.2.1) reduces to the simpler requirement that

$$(9.2.2) \qquad \lim_{n \to \infty} \sup_i \mathscr{P}\{N_{ni}(A) > 0\} = 0.$$

Note that an independent u.a.n. array is called infinitesimal in MKM (1978, §3.4), a null-array in Kallenberg (1975, §6), and holospoudic in Chung (1974, §7.1). The terminology u.a.n. comes from Loève (strictly speaking, Loève used uan); Kallenberg followed Feller (1966) in using null array.

As Kallenberg remarked to us, this formal setting can be extended and the notation simplified throughout this section by taking $m_n = \infty$, from which the finite case is obtained by assuming all but finitely many elements to be zero. This extension is possible because all quantities are nonnegative so there are no convergence difficulties with $m_n = \infty$ other than the finiteness of the sums concerned. We retain the setting with $m_n < \infty$ for the sake of familiarity.

In the present discussion the reader will doubtless observe the very close analogy between the results developed for point processes and the classical theory for sums of i.i.d. random variables in $\mathbb{R}$. This is hardly surprising, for a point process is just a particular type of random measure and a random measure is just a random variable taking its values on the metric Abelian group of boundedly finite signed measures on the state space $\mathcal{X}$. As such it comes under the extension of the classical theory developed, for example, in Parthasarathy (1967, Chap. 4). While we do not follow this approach but develop results for point processes directly, the reader may find it useful to bear the classical theory in mind as a guide; we return to it briefly at the end of the section in reviewing the corresponding results for random measures.

We start with a preliminary result on the convergence of infinitely divisible distributions, continuing with notation from Section 8.4. Let $\{\tilde{Q}_n:$ $n = 1, 2, \ldots\}$ denote a sequence of KLM measures (Definition 8.4.IV) and $\tilde{Q}$ a limit measure. We cannot immediately speak of the weak convergence of $\tilde{Q}_n$ to $\tilde{Q}$, firstly because the KLM measures are only σ-finite in general, and secondly because they are only defined on the Borel subsets of the space $\mathcal{N}_0(\mathcal{X}) \equiv \mathcal{N}_{\mathcal{X}}\backslash\{N(\mathcal{X}) = 0\}$, which is not complete. To define an appropriate modification of weak convergence for the sequence $\{\tilde{Q}_n\}$, recall that for each bounded Borel set A the KLM measure $\tilde{Q}$ induces a totally finite measure $\tilde{Q}^A$ on the space of measures $\mathcal{N}_0(A)$, that is, the nonzero counting measures on A. Extend $\tilde{Q}^A$ to the whole of $\mathcal{N}_A$ by setting $\tilde{Q}^{(A)} = \tilde{Q}^A$ on $\mathcal{N}_0(A)$ and

$$\tilde{Q}^{(A)}\{N: N(A) = 0\} = 0.$$

Definition 9.2.I. The sequence of KLM measures $\{\tilde{Q}_n: n = 1, 2, \ldots\}$ converges *Q-weakly* to the KLM measure $\tilde{Q}$ if for every bounded Borel set A that is a stochastic continuity set for $\tilde{Q}$, the extended measures $\tilde{Q}_n^{(A)}$ converge weakly to $\tilde{Q}^{(A)}$.

This requirement can be spelt out more explicitly in terms of fidi distributions or the convergence of functionals. Thus, it is equivalent to requiring that for every finite family of bounded Borel sets $A_i \in \mathcal{S}_{\tilde{Q}}$

$$(9.2.3) \qquad \tilde{Q}_n\left\{N: N(A_i) = j_i, i = 1, \ldots, k, \sum_{i=1}^{k} j_i > 0\right\}$$

$$\rightarrow \tilde{Q}\{N: N(A_i) = j_i, i = 1, \ldots, k\}.$$

A more convenient form for our purposes is the following: for every continuous function $h \in \mathcal{V}(\mathcal{X})$ equal to one outside some bounded Borel set A, as $n \rightarrow \infty$,

$$(9.2.4) \qquad \int_{\{N(A) > 0\}} \exp\left(\int_{\mathcal{X}} \log h(x) N(dx)\right) \tilde{Q}_n(dN)$$

$$\rightarrow \int_{\{N(A) > 0\}} \exp\left(\int_{\mathcal{X}} \log h(x) N(dx)\right) \tilde{Q}(dN).$$

These restatements are immediate consequences of the conditions for weak convergence developed in Section 9.1 applied to the measures $\tilde{Q}_n^{(A)}$, which, while not probability measures, are totally finite so that the framework for weak convergence remains intact.

Proposition 9.2.II. *The set of infinitely divisible distributions is closed in the topology of weak convergence in $\mathcal{N}_{\mathcal{X}}$. Furthermore, if $\{\mathcal{P}_n: n = 1, 2, \ldots\}$ and $\mathcal{P}$ are infinitely divisible distributions on $\mathcal{N}_{\mathcal{X}}$, and $\{\tilde{Q}_n\}, \tilde{Q}$ the corresponding KLM measures, then $\mathcal{P}_n \Rightarrow_w \mathcal{P}$ if and only if $\tilde{Q}_n \rightarrow \tilde{Q}$ (Q-weakly).*

PROOF. Suppose that $\mathcal{P}_n \Rightarrow_w \mathcal{P}$ and that the $\mathcal{P}_n$ are infinitely divisible. Take any integer k, and observe that if $\mathcal{P}_n$ has p.g.fl. $G_n[\cdot]$, then $(G_n[\cdot])^{1/k}$ is also a p.g.fl. and corresponds to the KLM measure $k^{-1}\tilde{Q}_n(\cdot)$, where $\tilde{Q}_n$ is the KLM measure of $\mathscr{P}_n$. From $G_n[h] \to G[h]$ [all continuous $h \in \mathscr{V}(\mathscr{X})$] it follows that $(G_n[h])^{1/k} \to (G[h])^{1/k}$, so that $(G[h])^{1/k}$ is a p.g.fl. for every integer k, and hence $\mathscr{P}$ is infinitely divisible. Using the p.g.fl. representation (8.4.9), we have for all continuous $h \in \mathscr{V}(\mathscr{X})$,

$$\int_{\mathscr{N}_0(\mathscr{X})} \left[\exp\left(\int_{\mathscr{X}} \log h(x) N(dx) \right) - 1 \right] \tilde{Q}_n(dN)$$

$$\to \int_{\mathscr{N}_0(\mathscr{X})} \left[\exp\left(\int_{\mathscr{X}} \log h(x) N(dx) \right) - 1 \right] \tilde{Q}(dN).$$

Taking A to be a stochastic continuity set for $\tilde{Q}$, we can approximate the step function $h(x) = 0$ $(x \in A)$, $= 1$ (otherwise), arbitrarily closely by $h \in \mathscr{S}_{\tilde{Q}}$ and thus conclude that

$$\tilde{Q}_n\{N: N(A) > 0\} \to \tilde{Q}\{N: N(A) > 0\},$$

as the exponential term above vanishes if $N(A) > 0$. By subtraction we then have that the integrals

$$\int_{\{N(A) > 0\}} \exp\left(\int_{\mathscr{X}} \log h(x) N(dx) \right) \tilde{Q}_n(dN)$$

converge as required at (9.2.4).

Conversely, when $\tilde{Q}_n$ converges Q-weakly to $\tilde{Q}$, the argument can be reversed. □

Given a point process with distribution $\mathscr{P}$ and p.g.fl. $G[\cdot]$, define its *Poisson approximant* (corresponding to the accompanying law in the classical theory) to be the Poisson randomization with distribution $\mathscr{P}^*$ and p.g.fl. $G^*[\cdot]$ given by

(9.2.5) $\qquad G^*[h] = \exp(G[h] - 1)$ $\quad$ (all $h \in \mathscr{V}(\mathscr{X})$).

More generally, given a triangular array $\{N_{ni}\}$, the corresponding Poisson approximants are given by N_{ni}^*, with distributions $\mathscr{P}_{ni}^*$ and p.g.fl.s $G_{ni}^*[\cdot]$; when the N_{ni} are independent assume that the N_{ni}^* are independent. Since

$$\mathscr{P}^*\{N(A) > 0\} = 1 - \exp[-\mathscr{P}\{N(A) > 0\}] \leq \mathscr{P}\{N(A) > 0\},$$

the triangular array $\{N_{ni}^*\}$ is u.a.n. whenever $\{N_{ni}\}$ is a u.a.n. array. The following theorem is basic for point processes.

Theorem 9.2.III. *Let $\{N_{ni}: i = 1, \ldots, m_n; n = 1, 2, \ldots\}$ be an independent u.a.n. array, $\{N_{ni}^*\}$ the corresponding independent array of Poisson approximants, and N an infinitely divisible point process with KLM measure $\tilde{Q}$. Then the following assertions are equivalent:*

(i) $\sum_{i=1}^{m_n} N_{ni} \to N$ *weakly;*

(ii) $\sum_{i=1}^{m_n} N_{ni}^* \to N$ *weakly;*

(iii) $\sum_{i=1}^{m_n} \mathscr{P}_{ni}^{(0)} \to \tilde{Q}$ Q-weakly;

where $\mathscr{P}_{ni}^{(0)}$ is the restriction of $\mathscr{P}_{ni}$, the distribution of N_{ni}, to $\mathcal{N}_0(\mathcal{X})$.

PROOF. Recall the elementary inequalities, valid for $0 \leq 2\alpha_i \leq 1$ $(i = 1, \ldots, m_n)$

(9.2.6)
$$0 \leq -\log\left(\prod_{i=1}^{m_n} (1 - \alpha_i)\right) - \sum_{i=1}^{m_n} \alpha_i$$

$$\leq \sum_{i=1}^{m_n} \alpha_i^2 \leq \left(\sum_{i=1}^{m_n} \alpha_i\right)\left(\max_i \alpha_i\right).$$

We apply these inequalities with $\alpha_i = G_{ni}[h]$, where $h(x) = 1$ for x outside some stochastic continuity set A for $\mathscr{P}$, the distribution of N. From the u.a.n. condition, $1 - G_{ni}[h] \leq \Pr\{N_{ni}(A) > 0\} \leq \frac{1}{2}$ $(i = 1, \ldots, m_n)$ for n sufficiently large, and thus

$$\sum_{i=1}^{m_n} (1 - G_{ni}[h]) \leq \sum_{i=1}^{m_n} \Pr\{N_{ni}(A) > 0\}$$

$$\leq -\log\left(\prod_{i=1}^{m_n} [1 - \Pr\{N_{ni}(A) > 0\}]\right)$$

$$= -\log\left(\Pr\left\{\sum_{i=1}^{m_n} N_{ni}(A) = 0\right\}\right)$$

$$\to -\log(\Pr\{N(A) = 0\}) < \infty,$$

so that the left-hand sum here is uniformly bounded (over subsets of A) for n sufficiently large. It follows from (9.2.6) that if one of

$$\prod_{i=1}^{m_n} G_{ni}[h] \quad \text{and} \quad \exp\left(\sum_{i=1}^{m_n} (1 - G_{ni}[h])\right)$$

converges to a finite nonzero limit, then so does the other, and the limits are equal. This implies the equivalence of (i) and (ii) of the theorem.

The processes N_{ni}^* are infinitely divisible, with KLM measures $\mathscr{P}_{ni}^{(0)}$, so the row sum $\sum N_{ni}^*$ is infinitely divisible, with KLM measure $\sum \mathscr{P}_{ni}^{(0)}$. By appealing to Proposition 9.2.II, the equivalence of (ii) and (iii) follows.   □

The arguments used in the proof lead to an alternative formulation of the result in terms of p.g.fl.s (see Exercise 9.2.3).

The following result is an easy corollary.

Proposition 9.2.IV. *A point process is infinitely divisible if and only if it can be represented as the limit of the row sums of a u.a.n. array.*

The most important application of Theorem 9.2.III is to finding conditions for convergence to a Poisson process.

Theorem 9.2.V. *The triangular u.a.n. array* $\{N_{ni}: i = 1, \ldots, m_n; n = 1, 2, \ldots\}$
converges weakly to a Poisson process with parameter measure μ *if and only if
for all bounded Borel sets* A *with* $\mu(\partial A) = 0$,

(9.2.7)
$$\sum_{i=1}^{m_n} \Pr\{N_{ni}(A) \geq 2\} \to 0 \qquad (n \to \infty)$$

and

(9.2.8)
$$\sum_{i=1}^{m_n} \Pr\{N_{ni}(A) \geq 1\} \to \mu(A) \qquad (n \to \infty).$$

PROOF. Recall from Example 8.4(a) that for a Poisson process the KLM
measure $\tilde{Q}(\cdot)$ is related to the parameter measure $\mu(\cdot)$ by

$$\mu(A) = \tilde{Q}\{N: N(A) > 0\},$$

and that $\tilde{Q}$ itself is concentrated on one-point realizations, so that

$$\tilde{Q}\{N: N(\mathscr{X}) > 1\} = 0.$$

It follows from Theorem 9.2.III that if the array converges to a Poisson
process, then

$$\sum_{i=1}^{m_n} \Pr\{N_{ni}(A) > 0\} \to \tilde{Q}\{N: N(A) > 0\} = \mu(A),$$

and

$$\sum_{i=1}^{m_n} \Pr\{N_{ni}(A) \geq 2\} \to \tilde{Q}\{N: N(A) \geq 2\} = 0,$$

so the conditions (9.2.7) and (9.2.8) are necessary.

Conversely, if (9.2.7) holds for a sequence of sets $A_n \uparrow \mathscr{X}$, we must then have
$\tilde{Q}\{N: N(\mathscr{X}) > 1\} = 0$, so that the limit process must be Poisson, and (9.2.8)
identifies the parameter measure as μ. $\qquad \square$

We remark that as in other applications of weak convergence, it is *sufficient*,
in checking the conditions of the theorem, to let A run through the sets of any
covering semiring of continuity sets of μ (see Corollary 9.1.VII).

The following special case was the first to be studied [e.g., Palm (1943) and
subsequently Khinchin (1955)], and it can be regarded as the prototype limit
theorem for point processes. Its extensions through work of Ososkov (1956),
Franken (1963), and Grigelionis (1963) led ultimately to Theorems 9.2.V and
9.2.III.

Proposition 9.2.VI. *Let* N *be a simple stationary point process on* $\mathscr{X} = \mathbb{R}$ *with
finite intensity* λ, *and let* N_n *denote the point process obtained by superposing* n
independent replicates of N *and dilating the time scale by a factor* n. *Then as*
$n \to \infty$, N_n *converges weakly to a Poisson process with parameter measure* $\lambda \ell(\cdot)$,
where $\ell(\cdot)$ *is Lebesgue measure on* $\mathbb{R}$.

PROOF. Here we can envisage a triangular array situation in which each N_{ni} $(i = 1, \ldots, n)$ has the same distribution as the original process but on a dilated time scale. Hence, using Propositions 3.3.I and 3.3.IV,

$$\Pr\{N_{ni}(0, t] > 0\} = \Pr\{N(0, t/n] > 0\} = (\lambda t/n)(1 + o(1)),$$

and summing on $i = 1, \ldots, n$ leads to (9.2.8) with $\mu(\cdot) = \lambda \ell(\cdot)$. Similarly, from Proposition 3.3.V,

$$\Pr\{N_{ni}(0, t] > 1\} = \Pr\{N(0, t/n] > 1\} = o(1/n),$$

and again summing on i leads to (9.2.7). $\square$

We conclude this section by briefly reviewing some extensions and further developments.

Some of the results that we have handled by generating function arguments can be strengthened to give results concerning bounds in variation norm. In particular, there are elegant bounds that follow via the use of Poisson approximants (see Exercises 9.2.1 and 9.2.2).

Extensions to the multivariate, nonorderly, and marked point process cases can generally be handled by applying the preceding results to the case where $\mathcal{X}$ has the product form $\mathcal{X} \times \mathcal{K}$ for some space $\mathcal{K}$ of marks.

EXAMPLE 9.2(a) *Convergence to a multivariate independent Poisson process.* Suppose there is given a point process in which each point is identifiable as one of a finite set of types $1, \ldots, K$ say. The process can be described by the multivariate processes with component processes $N_{ni}^{(k)}(\cdot)$ $(k = 1, \ldots, K)$. We seek conditions for weak convergence of the superpositions to a limit process in which the different types follow independent Poisson processes with parameter measures μ_k $(k = 1, \ldots, K)$. This last process can thus be regarded as a Poisson process on the space $\mathcal{X} \times \{1, \ldots, K\}$ with overall measure μ such that $\mu_k(\cdot) = \mu(\cdot \times \{k\})$. Similarly, regard the family $\{N_{ni}^{(k)}: k = 1, \ldots, K\}$ as defining a process N_{ni} on $\mathcal{X} \times \{1, \ldots, K\}$. To apply Theorem 9.2.V we have to interpret (9.2.7) and (9.2.8), which apply to the overall processes N_{ni}, in terms of the components. We take A at (9.2.7) and (9.2.8) to be a product set of the form $B \times \{1, \ldots, K\}$ for some bounded Borel set B that is a stochastic continuity set for each $\mu_1, \ldots, \mu_K$; that is,

$$(9.2.9) \qquad\qquad \mu_k(\partial B) = 0 \qquad (k = 1, \ldots, K).$$

Then (9.2.7) becomes

$$(9.2.10) \qquad\qquad \sum_{i=1}^{m_n} \Pr\left\{\sum_{k=1}^{K} N_{ni}^{(k)}(B) \geq 2\right\} \to 0 \qquad (n \to \infty),$$

which incorporates the requirement (crucial if the limit process is to have independent components) that there should be zero limiting probability for two distinct components each to contribute points to the same B.

Similarly, (9.2.8) takes the form, for all $B_1, \ldots, B_K$ for which $\mu_k(\partial B_k) = 0$,

$$\sum_{i=1}^{m_n} \Pr\left\{\sum_{k=1}^{K} N_{ni}^{(k)}(B_k) \geq 1\right\} \to \sum_{k=1}^{K} \mu_k(B_k),$$

which in view of (9.2.10) is satisfied if and only if for each B for which $\mu_k(\partial B) = 0$ $(k = 1, \ldots, K)$,

(9.2.11)
$$\sum_{i=1}^{m_n} \Pr\{N_{ni}^{(k)}(B) \geq 1\} \to \mu_k(B).$$

Note also that the u.a.n. condition here becomes

$$\lim_{n\to\infty} \sup_i \Pr\left\{\sum_{k=1}^{K} N_{ni}^{(k)}(B) > 0\right\} = 0,$$

again apparently incorporating a constraint on the simultaneous occurrence of points of several types. However, since the mark space here consists only of a finite set of types, the u.a.n. condition is equivalent to a componentwise u.a.n. condition; that is,

(9.2.12)
$$\lim_{n\to\infty} \sup_i \Pr\{N_{ni}^{(k)}(B) > 0\} = 0 \qquad (k = 1, \ldots, K).$$

Thus, from Theorem 9.2.V we have the corollary that *for a K-variate independent triangular array satisfying the u.a.n. condition (9.2.12), the necessary and sufficient conditions for convergence to a K-variate Poisson process with independent components are that (9.2.10) and (9.2.11) hold.*

Necessary and sufficient conditions for convergence to other types of infinitely divisible point processes, in particular the Poisson cluster process, can be derived by referring back to the general results of Theorem 9.2.III. The procedure is similar to that outlined in Theorem 9.2.V: first identify the KLM measure for the process of interest, and then use (iii) to obtain necessary and sufficient conditions on the component probabilities to ensure convergence to the appropriate limit. The particular case of convergence to a Gauss–Poisson process is outlined in Exercise 9.2.4.

Finally, we return to the question of convergence of u.a.n. arrays of random measures broached at the beginning of this section. The general structural form of an infinitely divisible random measure is stated in the next result.

Proposition 9.2.VII. *A random measure on the c.s.m.s. $\mathcal{X}$ is infinitely divisible if and only if its Laplace functional can be represented in the form for all $f \in BM_+(\mathcal{X})$*

(9.2.13)
$$L[f] = \exp\left\{-\int_{\mathcal{X}} f(x)\alpha(dx) \right.$$

$$\left. + \int_{\mathcal{M}_0(\mathcal{X})} \left[\exp\left(-\int_{\mathcal{X}} f(x)\xi(dx)\right) - 1\right]\Lambda(d\xi)\right\},$$

where $\alpha \in \mathcal{M}_{\mathcal{X}}$, $\hat{\mathcal{M}}_0(\mathcal{X}) = \mathcal{M}_{\mathcal{X}} - \{\varnothing\}$, and Λ is a σ-finite measure on $\hat{\mathcal{M}}_0(\mathcal{X})$ satisfying, for every bounded Borel set $B \in \mathcal{B}_{\mathcal{X}}$, and distribution $F_1(B; x) \equiv \Lambda\{\xi: \xi(B) \leq x\}$,

(9.2.14)
$$\int_{\mathbb{R}_+} (1 - e^{-x})F_1(B; dx) < \infty.$$

A proof involving the inductive limit of the corresponding representations for the Laplace transforms of the fidi distributions can be given along the same lines as that of Theorem 8.4.V, with (9.2.13) reducing to (8.4.9) when ξ is a point process. The details are omitted [cf. Exercise 9.2.7 or Theorem 6.1 of Kallenberg (1975)].

Following on from Proposition 9.2.VII and analogous to Theorem 9.2.III, conditions for convergence of a u.a.n. array can be stated as follows.

Proposition 9.2.VIII. *Let* $\{\xi_{ni}: i = 1, \ldots, m_n; n = 1, 2, \ldots\}$ *be an independent u.a.n. array of random measures on the c.s.m.s.* $\mathcal{X}$, $\xi_n = \sum_{i=1}^{m_n} \xi_{ni}$, *and* ξ *an infinitely divisible random measure with representation* (9.2.13). *Then necessary and sufficient conditions for* $\xi_n \to \xi$ *(weakly) are*

(i) $\sum_{i=1}^{m_n} \mathcal{P}_{ni}^{(0)} \to \Lambda$ *Q-weakly on* $\hat{\mathcal{M}}_0(\mathcal{X})$;

(ii) *for all bounded* $A \in \mathcal{B}_{\mathcal{X}}$,

$$\lim_{\varepsilon \to 0} \lim_{n \to \infty} \sup \sum_{i=1}^{m_n} E[\xi_{ni}(A)I_{\{x < \varepsilon\}}(\xi_{ni}(A))]$$

$$= \lim_{\varepsilon \to \infty} \lim_{n \to \infty} \inf \sum_{i=1}^{m_n} E[\xi_{ni}(A)I_{\{x < \varepsilon\}}(\xi_{ni}(A))] = \alpha(A);$$

(iii) $\lim_{r \to \infty} \lim_{n \to \infty} \sup \sum_{i=1}^{m_n} \mathcal{P}\{\xi_{ni}(A) > r\} = 0$.

Just as for point processes, the conditions (i)–(iii) of this proposition can be summarized more succinctly into the single requirement that the Laplace functionals should satisfy

(9.2.15) $\sum_{i=1}^{m_n} (1 - L_{ni}[f]) \to \int_{\mathcal{X}} f(x)\alpha(dx)$

$$- \int_{\hat{\mathcal{M}}_{\mathcal{X}}} \left[\exp\left(-\int_{\mathcal{X}} f(x)\xi(dx) \right) - 1 \right] \Lambda(d\xi).$$

For proofs we again refer to the exercises or Kallenberg (1975, Chap. 6).

Exercises

9.2.1. (a) Let $\mathcal{P}$, $\mathcal{P}^*$ be the distributions of a totally finite point process on $\mathcal{X}$ and its Poisson approximant, respectively. Show that

$$\|\mathcal{P} - \mathcal{P}^*\| \leq 2(\mathcal{P}\{N(\mathcal{X}) > 0\})^2.$$

(b) Denoting the convolution of measures $\mathscr{P}_{ni}$ by $*\mathscr{P}_{ni}$, show that

$$\| *\mathscr{P}_{ni} - *\mathscr{P}_{ni}^* \| \leq 2 \sum_i (\mathscr{P}_{ni}\{N(\mathcal{X}) > 0\})^2.$$

(c) Conclude that for independent u.a.n. arrays, Theorem 9.2.III holds with weak convergence replaced by strong convergence.

9.2.2. For finite point processes $\mathscr{P}_1, \mathscr{P}_2$, show that $\| \mathscr{P}_1^* - \mathscr{P}_2^* \| \leq 2\| \mathscr{P}_1 - \mathscr{P}_2 \|$.

9.2.3. (a) Restate Theorem 9.2.III as follows: the necessary and sufficient condition for convergence of an independent u.a.n. array is that

$$\sum_{i=1}^{m_n} (1 - G_{ni}[h]) \rightarrow \int_{\mathscr{N}_0(\mathcal{X})} \left[\exp\left(\int_{\mathcal{X}} \log h(x) N(dx) \right) - 1 \right] Q(dN)$$

for all $h \in \mathcal{V}(\mathcal{X})$, and that the right-hand side then equals $\log G[h]$, where G is the p.g.fl. of the limit point process.
(b) Hence or otherwise deduce that Theorem 9.2.III remains valid in the case $m_n = \infty$ provided only that the resultant superpositions are well defined.

9.2.4. For a Gauss–Poisson process [Example 8.3(c)] the KLM measure $\tilde{Q}$ is the sum of two components, namely, a measure $\tilde{Q}_1$ concentrated on realizations with $N(\mathcal{X}) = 1$, and a measure $\tilde{Q}_2$ concentrated on realizations with $N(\mathcal{X}) = 2$. Deduce that if an independent u.a.n. array converges to a Gauss–Poisson process, then the following hold:
(a) $\sum_i \Pr\{N_{ni}(A) \geq 3\} \rightarrow 0$;
(b) $\sum_i \Pr\{N_{ni}(A) = 1\} \rightarrow \tilde{Q}_1\{N(A) = 1\} + 2\tilde{Q}_2\{N(A) = 1\}$;
(c) $\sum_i \Pr\{N_{ni}(A_1) = 1, N_{ni}(A_2) = 1\} \rightarrow \tilde{Q}_2\{N(A_1) = 1, N(A_2) = 1\}$ for disjoint A_1, A_2.

9.2.5. Express the result of Example 9.2(a) in terms of multivariate p.g.fl.s.

9.2.6. Give an example of a point process that is infinitely divisible as a random measure but not as a point process. [*Hint*: Consider a degenerate process.]

9.2.7. To establish (9.2.13), show the following:
(a) ξ is infinitely divisible if and only if its fidi distributions are infinitely divisible.
(b) Each fidi distribution has a standard representation similar to that of (9.2.13) subject to the constraint (9.2.14).
(c) An inductive limit argument as in Section 8.4 holds.

9.2.8. Compare the statements of Proposition 9.2.VIII and Theorem 9.2.III. To establish the former
(i) introduce Poisson approximants: for a u.a.n. array these converge if the original summands converge;
(ii) prove an analogue of Proposition 9.2.II for convergence of infinitely divisible random measures in terms of convergence of their components α_n and Λ_n;
(iii) apply (ii) to the accompanying law analogues.

9.2.9. (Continuation) Show that the equivalence of (9.2.15) and Proposition 9.2.VIII can be regarded as a continuity theorem for Laplace functionals complicated by the detail of the behaviour near the zero measure.

9.3. Thinned Point Processes

The notion of thinning a point process to construct another point process has been described in Example 4.3(a) for renewal processes and in p.g.fl. terms in Example 8.2(a). The idea underlying the operation is that, in principle, points of a process may occur at any of a very large number of locations, but it is only at a relatively small proportion of such locations that points are observed. The limit theorems described below formulate sufficient conditions for this process of *rarefaction* (or *thinning* or *deletion*) to lead in the limit to a Poisson process.

Let N be a point process on $\mathcal{X} = \mathbb{R}^d$ and $p(\cdot)$ a measurable function on $\mathcal{X}$ with $0 \le p(x) \le 1$ (all x). $N_{p(\cdot)}$ is obtained from N by *independent thinning* according to $p(\cdot)$ when the following holds: in any bounded Borel set A let the realization $N(\cdot, \omega)$ consist of the points $\{x_1, \ldots, x_{N(A)}\}$; construct a subset of these points by taking each x_i in turn, deleting it with probability $1 - p(x_i)$ and retaining it with probability $p(x_i)$, independently for each point; and regard the set of points so retained as defining a realization of the thinned point process $N_{p(\cdot)}(\cdot, \omega)$.

Such a setup is not immediately suited to describing limit theorems: the simplest is the following. Take $p(x) = p$ (all x), and after thinning contract the scale by an amount p, so that the point $x \in \mathcal{X}$ is mapped into px; equivalently, the point process $N_p(\cdot)$ resulting from both thinning and contraction of the scale, will have $N_p(A) = k$ say only if from the original process exactly k of the $N(p^{-1}A)$ points in the set $p^{-1}A$ are retained in the thinning process.

Proposition 9.3.I. *The sequence of point processes $N_p(\cdot)$, obtained by independent thinning and contraction from a point process $N(\cdot)$ on $\mathcal{X} = \mathbb{R}^d$, converges weakly to a stationary Poisson process at rate λ if and only if for every bounded $A \in \mathcal{B}_{\mathcal{X}}$,*

$$(9.3.1) \qquad pN(p^{-1}A) \to_p \lambda \ell(A) \quad as \ p \to 0.$$

PROOF. Using the p.g.fl. results of Example 8.2(a), the p.g.fl. $G_p[h]$ of $N_p(\cdot)$ for $h \in \mathcal{V}(\mathcal{X})$ is given by

$$G_p[h] = E\left(\exp \int_{\mathcal{X}} \log h(x) N_p(dx)\right)$$

$$= E\left[\exp \int_{\mathcal{X}} \log[1 - p(1 - h(x/p))] N(dx)\right]$$

$$= E\left[\exp \int_{\mathcal{X}} \log[1 - p(1 - h(x))] N(dx/p)\right].$$

The logarithmic term here equals $-p(1 - h(x))(1 + O(p))$ for $p \downarrow 0$, so

$$G_p[h] = E\left[\exp\left\{-\int_{\mathcal{X}} (1 - h(x))p(1 + O(p))N(dx/p)\right\}\right]$$

$$\to \exp\left\{-\int_{\mathcal{X}} \lambda(1 - h(x))\ell(dx)\right\}$$

if and only if (9.3.1) holds. □

An equivalent proof in terms of the convergence of one-dimensional distributions and using the characterization result of Theorem 7.3.II is given in Westcott (1976) (see Exercise 9.3.1 and Proposition 9.1.IX).

The construction of $N_p(\cdot) \equiv N_p(\cdot, \omega)$ is dependent on $N(\cdot, \omega)$, so that if instead of (9.3.1) we have

$$(9.3.2) \qquad pN(p^{-1}A, \omega) \to_p \lambda(\omega)\ell(A)$$

for some r.v. $\lambda(\cdot)$ defined on the space $(\Omega, \mathscr{F}, \mathscr{P})$ on which N is defined (and which, implicitly, is assumed to be large enough to embrace the independent thinning process), the conclusion of the proposition is modified as below. This in turn is a special case of Theorem 9.3.III, so the proof is omitted.

Proposition 9.3.II. $N_p(\cdot)$ *converges weakly to a mixed Poisson process if and only if (9.3.2) holds.*

The formulation at (9.3.1) or (9.3.2) specifies a particular form of the measure approximated by $\lambda\ell(A)/p$, namely, $N(p^{-1}A)$. An alternative approach is simply to postulate the existence of a sequence of point processes $\{N_n(\cdot)\}$ such that, given a sequence of thinning probability functions $\{p_n(x)\}$ satisfying

$$(9.3.3a) \qquad 0 \le p_n(x) \le 1 \qquad (x \in \mathcal{X}, n = 1, 2, \ldots)$$

and

$$(9.3.3b) \qquad \sup_{x \in \mathcal{X}} p_n(x) \to 0 \qquad (n \to \infty),$$

the sequence of random measures Λ_n, where $\Lambda_n(A) = \int_A p_n(x)N_n(dx)$, satisfies

$$(9.3.4) \qquad \Lambda_n \to \Lambda \quad \text{(weakly)}$$

for some limit random measure $\Lambda(\cdot)$. Here, we may also allow the functions $p_n(\cdot)$ to be stochastic, subject to the constraints at (9.3.3) and (9.3.4). We let $N_{p_n(\cdot)}(\cdot)$ denote the point process obtained by independent thinning from $N_n(\cdot)$ according to $p_n(\cdot)$.

Theorem 9.3.III. *Let $\{p_n(x), x \in \mathcal{X}, n = 1, 2, \ldots\}$ be a sequence of measurable stochastic processes satisfying (9.3.3), $\{N_n, n = 1, 2, \ldots\}$ a sequence of point processes, and denote by N_{p_n} the process obtained from N_n by thinning according to p_n. Then the sequence $\{N_{p_n}\}$ converges weakly to some point process N if and* *only if* (9.3.4) *holds for some random measure* Λ, *in which case N is the Cox process directed by* Λ.

The statement in this theorem allows for more general limits than Proposition 9.3.II precisely because no construction of the "increasingly dense" processes $N_n(\cdot)$ is specified. In the context of Proposition 9.3.II, it is not possible to have any Cox process other than the mixed Poisson process because when $pN(p^{-1}A, \omega) \to \Lambda(A, \omega)$, say, as $p \to 0$, then also $p_1 p_2 N((p_1 p_2)^{-1}A, \omega) \to p_2\Lambda(p_2^{-1}A, \omega)$ as $p_1 \to 0$, and taking (for example) $\mathcal{X} = \mathbb{R}$ and $A = (0, 1]$, we then have $\Lambda((0, p_2^{-1}], \omega) = p_2^{-1}\Lambda((0, 1], \omega)$ for all $0 < p_2 < 1$, from which it follows that $\Lambda(\cdot, \omega)$ coincides with $\lambda(\omega)\ell(\cdot)$ for some r.v. $\lambda(\cdot)$.

PROOF. We have for the p.g.fl. G_{p_n} of N_{p_n}, with $h \in \mathcal{V}$,

$$G_{p_n}[h] = E\left(\exp \int_{\mathcal{X}} \log[1 - p_n(x)(1 - h(x))]N_n(dx)\right).$$

Under the assumption (9.3.3) we can write

$$-\log[1 - p_n(x)(1 - h(x))] = p_n(x)[1 - h(x)][1 + R_n(x)],$$

where $|R_n(x)| \le \frac{1}{2}p_n(x)$ and as $n \to \infty$

$$\theta_n = \sup_{x \in \mathcal{X}} |R_n(x)| \to 0.$$

We can therefore write

$$-\int_{\mathcal{X}} \log[1 - p_n(x)(1 - h(x))]N_n(dx) = \int_{\mathcal{X}} [1 - h(x)]\Lambda_n(dx)(1 + R_n(x)).$$

If now (9.3.4) holds, then the random variables $\int_{\mathcal{X}} [1 - h(x)]\Lambda_n(dx)$ converge in distribution to $\int_{\mathcal{X}} [1 - h(x)]\Lambda(dx)$, so that their Laplace transforms, and hence also the p.g.fl.s $G_{p_n}[h]$, converge to the Laplace transform of their limit, namely,

(9.3.5) $$G_{p_n}[h] \to E\left(\exp\left[-\int_{\mathcal{X}} [1 - h(x)]\Lambda(dx)\right]\right).$$

The right side here is just the p.g.fl. of the Cox process directed by Λ, which completes the proof that (9.3.4) is sufficient.

Suppose conversely that the point processes N_{p_n} converge. We first establish that the random measures Λ_n are weakly compact. Referring to Proposition 9.1.V, let $\bar{S}$ be a closed sphere in $\mathcal{X}$, and consider the random variables $\Lambda_n(\bar{S})$. Weak convergence of the sequence $\{N_{p_n}\}$ implies $G_{p_n}[h] \to G_\infty[h]$, say, for $h \in \mathcal{V}$, and in particular for $h = h_z$, where $0 \le z \le 1$ and

$$h_z(x) = \begin{cases} z & (x \in \bar{S}) \\ 1 & (x \notin \bar{S}). \end{cases}$$

But this is equivalent [assuming (9.3.3)] to convergence of the Laplace transforms

$$E(\exp[-(1-z)\Lambda_n(\bar{S})])$$

to the limit $G_\infty[h_z]$, which is continuous in z as $z \to 1$. Then the continuity theorem for Laplace transforms implies that the limit is the Laplace transform of a proper distribution, and hence that the distributions of the random variables $\Lambda_n(\bar{S})$ are uniformly tight. Thus, given $\varepsilon > 0$ we can find $M < \infty$ such that for all n,

$$\mathscr{P}\{\xi_n(\bar{S}) > M\} < \varepsilon;$$

that is, (9.1.1) holds.

As for (9.1.2), if the N_{p_n} converge weakly then, given $\eta > 0$, there exists a compact C such that for $n = 1, 2, \ldots$

$$\mathscr{P}\{N_{p_n}(\bar{S} - C) > 0\} < \eta$$

[i.e., we use the necessity of (9.1.2) for the point processes]. Now set $h(x) = 0$ ($x \in \bar{S} - C$), $h(x) = 1$ ($x \notin \bar{S} - C$) and deduce as above that from (9.3.3), as $n \to \infty$,

$$1 - \mathscr{P}\{N_{p_n}(\bar{S} - C) > 0\} - E[\exp(-\Lambda_n(\bar{S} - C))] \to 0.$$

Thus, for sufficiently large n,

(9.3.6) $E(1 - \exp[-\Lambda_n(\bar{S} - C)]) \le \mathscr{P}\{N_{p_n}(\bar{S} - C) > 0\} + \eta$

$$\le 2\eta.$$

But by Chebyshev's inequality

$$\mathscr{P}\{\Lambda_n(\bar{S} - C) > \delta\} \le E[1 - e^{-\Lambda_n(\bar{S}-C)}]/(1 - e^{-\delta})$$

$$\le 2\eta/(1 - e^{-\delta}).$$

Thus, no matter how small δ and ε, we may find C such that $\mathscr{P}\{\Lambda_n(\bar{S} - C) > \delta\} < \varepsilon$ for all sufficiently large n, and hence (by modifying C if necessary) for all $n > 0$.

Thus, both conditions (9.1.1) and (9.1.2) hold for the sequence Λ_n. It is now a simple matter to deduce from the convergence of the G_{p_n} that any limit random measure Λ must satisfy

$$E\left[\exp - \int_{\mathscr{X}} (1 - h(x))\Lambda(dx)\right] = G_\infty[h].$$

It follows that the limit Λ must be unique and that the Laplace functionals of the Λ_n converge to that of Λ, so that (9.3.4) holds.   □

One of the most important applications of point process methods, and of the concept of thinning in particular, is to the study of high-level crossings of a continuous stochastic process. The special questions that arise here lie beyond the scope of the present text to treat in detail; they are explained at length in Leadbetter, Lindgren, and Rootzen (1983), as well as in the earlier text by Cramér and Leadbetter (1967). One possible approach to level crossing problems may be indicated briefly, however. Suppose we consider a non-negative, discrete time process $\{X_n\}$ and associate with each n the point (n, X_n) of a marked point process in $\mathbb{R} \times \mathbb{R}_+$, where $\mathbb{R}_+$ plays the role of the mark space $\mathcal{K}$ in Definition 7.1.XII. The underlying process of time points in $\mathbb{R}$ can then be thinned by rejecting all pairs (n, X_n), for which (say) $X_n \leq M$, and then rescaling the time axis. One could then ask for conditions under which the rescaled process converges to a limit as $M \to \infty$. In general, the thinnings here will not be independent and the resulting process may exhibit substantial clustering properties. With suitable precautions, however, and assuming some asymptotic independent or mixing conditions, we may anticipate convergence to a Poisson limit. (An alternative approach to dependent thinnings, where the probability of thinning is allowed to depend on the previous history, is outlined in Proposition 13.4.VI.)

A richer theory might be expected to result if one could retain the values of the marks accepted, albeit themselves rescaled in an appropriate manner. We consider below an example of this kind, in the especially simple case where the marks $\{X_n\}$ are i.i.d.

EXAMPLE 9.3(a) *Thinning by the tails of a regularly varying distribution.* With the setup just described, suppose that the initial points $\{t_i\}$ form a stationary, ergodic process N_0 with finite mean rate m and that the marks X_i are i.i.d. with regularly varying tails [e.g., see Feller (1971, Chap. VIII, §8)], so that as $x \to \infty$, for some $\alpha > 0$,

$$1 - F(x) = L(x)x^{-\alpha},$$

where $L(x)$ is *slowly varying* at infinity; that is, $L(cx)/L(x) \to 1$ for all $c > 0$.

We now consider a sequence of point processes on the space $\mathbb{R} \times \mathbb{R}_+$ obtained in the following manner. For each $n = 1, 2, \ldots$, we set

$$N_n((t_1, t_2] \times (u, v]) = \#\{(t_i, x_i): nt_1 < t_i \leq nt_2 \text{ and } a_n u < x_i \leq a_n v\},$$

where the sequence of constants $\{a_n: n = 1, 2, \ldots\}$ is defined by

$$1 - F(a_n) = 1/n, \quad \text{that is,} \quad a_n = F^{-1}(1 - 1/n),$$

and we assume for convenience that the distribution of F is continuous so the inverse F^{-1} is well defined.

Since the marks are independent, the p.g.fl. of the marked process on $\mathbb{R} \times \mathbb{R}_+$ can be written in the form

$$G[h] = E\left(\exp \int_{\mathbb{R}} \left\{\log\left[\int_{\mathbb{R}_+} h(t, y)dF(y)\right]\right\} N_0(dt)\right).$$

The limit of the rescaled process defined above is boundedly finite only in y intervals bounded away from the origin. Strictly speaking, this means that we should work with a modified metric that places the origin on the y axis at ∞. The permissible functions h we consider here should thus be equal to unity in a neighbourhood of the origin: with this proviso the earlier theory carries through without change.

For the rescaled process, we have to consider

$$\int_{\mathbb{R}_+} h(t/n, y/a_n)dF(y) = \int_{\mathbb{R}_+} h(t/n, y)dF(a_n y)$$

$$= 1 - \int_0^\infty (1 - h(t/n, y))dF(a_n y).$$

The assumption of regular variation of F is equivalent to the weak convergence of the measures $nF(a_n\cdot)$ to the measure v defined by $v(y, \infty) = y^{-\alpha}$, because for any interval $(u, v]$ with $0 < u < v < \infty$,

$$n\int_u^v dF(a_n y) = n\{(1 - F(a_n u)) - (1 - F(a_n v))\}$$

$$= n\left\{\frac{1 - F(a_n u)}{1 - F(a_n)} - \frac{1 - F(a_n v)}{1 - F(a_n)}\right\}$$

$$= [L(a_n u)/L(a_n)]u^{-\alpha} - [L(a_n v)/L(a_n)]v^{-\alpha}$$

$$\to u^{-\alpha} - v^{-\alpha}.$$

Consequently, the innermost integral in the expression for $G[h]$ is expressible

$$\int_0^\infty h(t/n, y/a_n)dF(y) = 1 - n^{-1}(1 + o(1))\int_0^\infty (1 - h(t/n, y))dv(y);$$

thus, the p.g.fl. of the rescaled process, G_n say, is given by

$$G_n[h] = E \exp\left(\int_{\mathbb{R}} \left\{\log\left[\int_{\mathbb{R}_+} h(t/n, y/a_n)F(dy)\right]\right\}N_0(dt)\right)$$

$$= E \exp\left(\int_{\mathbb{R}} n^{-1}(1 + o(1))\int_{\mathbb{R}_+} (1 - h(t/n, y))v(dy)N_0(dt)\right)$$

$$\to E \exp\left(\int_{\mathbb{R}}\int_{\mathbb{R}_+} (1 - h(u, y))v(dy)m\,du\right) \quad \text{as } n \to \infty,$$

using the ergodicity of N_0. The limit process is thus a Poisson process on $\mathbb{R} \times \mathbb{R}_+$ with intensity measure $m\ell(\cdot) \times v$. Equivalently, we can regard the limit process as a marked point process where conditionally on a mark, exceeding c say, the marks are distributed on (c, ∞) according to the distribution with d.f. $F_c(x) = 1 - (x/c)^{-\alpha}$.

For further details and applications see Resnick (1987).

We now indicate how the results of Theorem 9.3.III can be strengthened. Implicit in the assertion of the theorem is the weak convergence of the fidi distributions: we prove the stronger property of convergence in variation norm, and at the same time provide a bound on the rate of convergence. For probability measures $\mathcal{P}_1$, $\mathcal{P}_2$ on the measurable space $(\Omega, \mathcal{E})$ define the *variation metric d* by

$$d(\mathcal{P}_1, \mathcal{P}_2) = \sup_B |\mathcal{P}_1(B) - \mathcal{P}_2(B)|.$$

This metric has the probabilistic interpretation that

$$d(\mathcal{P}_1, \mathcal{P}_2) = \inf \Pr\{\omega: X(\omega) \neq Y(\omega)\},$$

where the infimum is taken over all pairs of measurable functions X, Y on $(\Omega, \mathcal{E}, \Pr)$ inducing the measures $\mathcal{P}_1$, $\mathcal{P}_2$, respectively. A pair (X, Y) for which equality holds constitutes a maximal coupling for the probability measures $\mathcal{P}_1$, $\mathcal{P}_2$. The metric d differs by a factor of 2 from the variation norm $\|\cdot\|$, which for the totally bounded signed measure $(\mathcal{P}_1 - \mathcal{P}_2)(\cdot)$ on the space $(\Omega, \mathcal{E})$ is defined as in Section A1.3 by

$$\|\mathcal{P}_1 - \mathcal{P}_2\| = \int_\Omega |\mathcal{P}_1(d\omega) - \mathcal{P}_2(d\omega)| = 2d(\mathcal{P}_1, \mathcal{P}_2).$$

The notation $\|\cdot\|$ agrees with that of MKM (1978), who also use $\mathrm{Var}(\cdot) = \|\cdot\|$.

Since the limiting r.v. in Theorem 9.3.III is Poisson, our concern is with $d(\mathcal{P}_n, \mathcal{P}_\infty)$, where the limit probability measure $\mathcal{P}_\infty$ is Poisson and nonatomic. The Renyi–Mönch result (cf. Theorem 7.3.II) asserts that such measures are characterized by their one-dimensional distributions, and by Proposition 9.1.IX it is then enough here to consider the quantity

$$d(N_n(A), N(A)) \equiv d(\Pr\{N_n(A) \in \cdot\}, \Pr\{N(A) \in \cdot\})$$

for any bounded Borel set A. Note the abuse of notation in replacing the distributions of r.v.s in $d(\cdot, \cdot)$ by the r.v.s themselves. Furthermore, for nonnegative integer-valued r.v.s, X, Y say, with distributions $\{p_k\}$, $\{q_k\}$ say, we have

$$d(X, Y) = d(\{p_k\}, \{q_k\}) = \sup_{A \subset \mathbb{Z}_+} \left| \sum_{k \in A} (p_k - q_k) \right|$$

$$= \frac{1}{2} \sum_{k=0}^{\infty} |p_k - q_k| = \sum_{k=0}^{\infty} (p_k - q_k)_+.$$

Proposition 9.3.IV. *With the notation of Theorem 9.3.III, for bounded $A \in \mathcal{B}_{\mathscr{X}}$,*

$$d(N_{p_n}(A), N(A)) \leq E\left(\sup_{x \in A} |p_n(x)| + \{1 - \exp[-|\Lambda_n(A) - \Lambda(A)|]\} \right).$$

PROOF. Observe that it is enough to prove the result in the context that the functions p_n and measures Λ_n, Λ are deterministic, for if otherwise, describe these entities as functions of ω' with distribution $\mu(\cdot)$. Then

$$d(N_{p_n}(A), N(A)) = \sup_B |\mathscr{P}_1(B) - \mathscr{P}_2(B)|$$

$$= \sup_B \left| \int_\Omega (\mathscr{P}_1(B; \omega') - \mathscr{P}_2(B; \omega'))\mu(d\omega') \right|$$

$$\leq \int_\Omega \sup_B |\mathscr{P}_1(B; \omega') - \mathscr{P}_2(B; \omega')|\mu(d\omega')$$

$$= \int_\Omega d(N_{p_n}(A), N(A)|\omega')\mu(d\omega').$$

The first term in the bound comes from Lemma 9.3.V below, while the second follows from the fact that if X, Y are Poisson r.v.s with means λ, μ then $d(X, Y) \leq d(0, Z) = 1 - \exp(-|\lambda - \mu|)$, where Z is Poisson with mean $|\lambda - \mu|$.   □

The second term in the bound can be tightened: see Exercise 9.3.5.

Lemma 9.3.V. *Let* $X_1, \ldots, X_n$ *be independent Bernoulli r.v.s with* $\Pr\{X_j = 1\} = p_j = 1 - \Pr\{X_j = 0\}$, *and* Y *a Poisson r.v. with mean* $\lambda = \sum_{j=1}^n p_j$. *Then the variation metric between the distributions of* $S = X_1 + \cdots + X_n$ *and* Y *is bounded as in*

(9.3.7) $$d(S, Y) \leq C \sum_{j=1}^n p_j^2 \Big/ \sum_{j=1}^n p_j \leq C \max_j \{p_j\},$$

where $C \leq 0.71$ *when* $\max_j\{p_j\} \leq 0.25$. *Always,* $C \leq 1$.

Remarks. The method of proof below, which draws in part on work of Samuels (1965) and Kerstan (1964), shows that the value of the constant C depends on the value of max $\{p_j\}$ and can be reduced further by supposing that the maximum is smaller than 0.25. Its smallest value, when the maximum → 0, is equal (by the method below) to 0.409, which is tighter than that quoted by Romanowska (1978) for the more restricted case of a simple binomial approximated by a Poisson. The general result that $C \leq 1$ follows from work of Barbour and Hall (1984) and is not discussed here.

PROOF. The sum S has a Poisson binomial distribution, $\{b_k\}$ say, for which the generating function is

$$\sum_{k=0}^n b_k z^k = \prod_{j=1}^n (1 - p_j + p_j z) \qquad (|z| \leq 1).$$

An inequality of Newton used in Samuels (1965) implies that $c_k \equiv b_k/\binom{n}{k}$ is a log concave sequence; that is, $c_k^2 \geq c_{k-1}c_{k+1}$ for $k = 0, 1, \ldots, n$; equivalently,

$$b_k^2 \geq (1 + (n - k)^{-1})(1 + k^{-1})b_{k-1}b_{k+1}$$

for $k = 1, \ldots, n - 1$. Write $\pi_k = \pi_k(\lambda) = e^{-\lambda}\lambda^k/k!$. Then

$$d(S, Y) = \sum_{k=0}^{n} (b_k - \pi_k)_+ = \sum_{k=0}^{n} \pi_k(b_k/\pi_k - 1)_+,$$

and this summation will involve nonzero terms on a single interval of integers, $\{k_0 + 1, \ldots, k_1\}$ say, if the sequence of ratios $\{b_k/\pi_k\}$ is unimodal. For this it suffices that the ratio of ratios $(b_k/\pi_k)/(b_{k-1}/\pi_{k-1})$, which equals $kb_k/\lambda b_{k-1}$, be monotonic in k, and this is implied by the corollary to the Newton inequality. Consequently, the supremum norm

$$d_0(S, Y) \equiv \sup_k |\Pr\{S \le k\} - \Pr\{Y \le k\}|$$

$$= \max\left(\sum_{k=0}^{k_0} (\pi_k - b_k), \sum_{k=k_1+1}^{n} (\pi_k - b_k)\right).$$

By addition, we thus have $2d_0(S, Y) \ge d(S, Y) \ge d_0(S, Y)$. In order to bound the variation metric, it suffices to bound the supremum metric, which we now do.

The Fourier inversion relation gives

$$d_0(S, Y) = \sup_k \left|(2\pi i)^{-1} \int_{-\pi}^{\pi} e^{-i\theta k}[E(e^{i\theta S}) - E(e^{i\theta Y})](1 - e^{i\theta})^{-1} d\theta\right|$$

$$\le \frac{1}{2\pi} \int_{-\pi}^{\pi} |E(e^{i\theta S}) - E(e^{i\theta Y})| \, |2 \sin \tfrac{1}{2}\theta|^{-1} d\theta.$$

The characteristic functions here are $E(e^{i\theta Y}) = \exp[-\lambda(1 - e^{i\theta})]$ and

$$E(e^{i\theta S}) = \prod_{j=1}^{n} (1 - p_j(1 - e^{i\theta}))$$

$$= E(e^{i\theta Y}) \prod_{j=1}^{n} \exp[p_j(1 - e^{i\theta})][1 - p_j(1 - e^{i\theta})].$$

Each term in the product here is of the form

$$[1 - p(1 - e^{i\theta})]\exp[p(1 - e^{i\theta})] = 1 - \sum_{k=2}^{\infty} \frac{[p(1 - e^{i\theta})]^k(k - 1)}{k!}$$

$$\equiv 1 - p^2(1 - e^{i\theta})^2 f(p; \theta),$$

so that

$$|E(e^{i\theta S}) - E(e^{i\theta Y})|$$

$$= |E(e^{i\theta Y})|\left|\prod_{j=1}^{n} [1 - p_j^2(1 - e^{i\theta})^2 f(p_j; \theta)] - 1\right|$$

$$= e^{-\lambda(1-\cos\theta)}\left|\sum_{r=1}^{n} [-(1 - e^{i\theta})^2]^r\left[\sum_{j_1 < \cdots < j_r} (p_{j_k}^2 f(p_{j_k}; \theta))\right]\right|$$

$$\le e^{-\lambda(1-\cos\theta)}\left(\prod_{j=1}^{n} (1 + 2(1 - \cos\theta)p_j^2|f(p_j; \theta)|) - 1\right)$$

$$\le e^{-\lambda(1-\cos\theta)}(\exp[\lambda\xi(\theta)(1 - \cos\theta)] - 1),$$

where

$$\xi(\theta) = 2 \sum_{j=1}^{n} p_j^2 |f(p_j; \theta)| \Big/ \sum_{j=1}^{n} p_j,$$

and with $\psi = |2p \sin \frac{1}{2}\theta|$,

$$|f(p; \theta)| \leq \sum_{k=2}^{\infty} |2p \sin \frac{1}{2}\theta|^{k-2}(k-1)/k! = (1 - (1 - \psi)e^{\psi})/\psi^2.$$

This bound is a maximum for $|\theta| \leq \pi$ at $\theta = \pi$ where it equals $(1 - (1 - 2p)e^{2p})/4p^2$, which increases monotonically with p in $p > 0$. Write $\xi = \xi(\pi)$. Then using $d \leq 2d_0$ and the bounds above gives

$$(9.3.8) \qquad d(S, Y) \leq \frac{1}{\pi} \int_0^{\pi} e^{-\lambda(1-\cos\theta)} [e^{\lambda\xi(1-\cos\theta)} - 1](\sin \tfrac{1}{2}\theta)^{-1} d\theta$$

$$= \frac{2\lambda}{\pi} \int_0^{\pi} \sin \tfrac{1}{2}\theta \, d\theta \int_0^{\xi} \exp[-2\lambda(1-y)\sin^2 \tfrac{1}{2}\theta] dy$$

$$= \frac{4\lambda}{\pi} \int_0^1 du \int_0^{\xi} \exp[-2\lambda(1-y)(1-u^2)] dy$$

$$\leq \frac{4\lambda}{\pi} \int_0^{\xi} dy \int_0^1 \exp[-2\lambda(1-y)(1-u)] du$$

$$\leq \frac{1}{2\pi} \int_0^{\xi} (1-y)^{-1} dy = -2\pi^{-1} \log(1 - \xi),$$

uniformly in λ. For $\max_j\{p_j\} \leq 0.25$, $\xi \leq 0.3513$, and thus $d(S, Y) \leq [(2\pi^{-1} \log(1/0.6487))/0.25]\varpi = 1.102\varpi$, where we follow Le Cam (1960) in writing $\varpi = \sum_{j=1}^n p_j^2 / \sum_{j=1}^n p_j$. Alternatively, the inequality (9.3.8) can be replaced by the tighter bound based on

$$\sup_{\alpha > 0} \int_0^1 \alpha \exp[-\alpha(1 - u^2)] du = c = 0.642374$$

(this supremum is attained at $\alpha = 2.255$), leading to

$$d(S, Y) \leq 2c\pi^{-1} \int_0^{\xi} (1-y)^{-1} dy = -2c\pi^{-1} \log(1 - \xi).$$

For $\max_j\{p_j\} \leq 0.25$, this yields $d(S, Y) \leq 0.70789\varpi$, and as this maximum $\downarrow 0$, $d(S, Y) \leq 2c/\pi = 0.40895$. $\qquad\qquad\square$

The coefficient of ϖ in the bounds for positive $\max\{p_j\}$ can be tightened further by retaining ξ as a function of θ and integrating numerically. It leads, for example, to 0.61 in place of 0.70789 above.

Exercises

9.3.1. Apply Proposition 9.1.IX to furnish an alternative proof of Proposition 9.3.I.

9.3.2. Give a direct proof of Proposition 9.3.II either via p.g.fl.s or by extension of the previous exercise.

9.3.3. (a) Let $b_k(n; p) = \binom{n}{k} p^k (1-p)^{n-k}$, $k = 0, 1, \ldots, n$, $0 < p < 1$, denote binomial probabilities, and write $\pi_k(\lambda)$ for Poisson probabilities as in the proof of Lemma 9.3.V. Show directly that $\{b_k(n; p)/\pi_k(\lambda)\}$ is a unimodal sequence in k by virtue of the monotonicity of $(k+1)b_{k+1}/b_k$.
   (b) Now let $\{b_k\} = \{b_k(n; p_1, \ldots, p_n)\}$ denote the Poisson binomial distribution of S of the lemma. Show by induction on n that $\{(k+1)b_{k+1}/b_k\}$ is monotonic in k.
   (c) Deduce that $d(S, Y) \leq \max_k \{b_k/\pi_k\} - 1$.

9.3.4. Use Theorem 9.3.III to show that a distribution $\mathscr{P}$ on $\mathscr{N}_{\mathscr{X}}$ is a Cox distribution if and only if for each c in $0 < c < 1$ there exists a distribution $\mathscr{P}_c$, which under independent random thinning with constant probability c yields $\mathscr{P}$ (see Mecke, 1968).

9.3.5. (a) Show that $a_k \equiv \sup_{\lambda > 0} \pi_k(\lambda)\sqrt{\lambda}$ occurs for $\lambda = k + \frac{1}{2}$ and that the sequence of ratios $\{a_{k+1}/a_k\}$ is monotonic. Deduce that $a_0 > a_1 > \cdots$ with $a_0 = 1/\sqrt{2e}$ and that $\pi_k(\lambda) \leq 1/\sqrt{2e\lambda}$ for every $\lambda > 0$ and $k = 0, 1, \ldots$.
   (b) Express $d(\{\pi_k(\lambda)\}, \{\pi_k(\mu)\})$ as an integral with density $\pi_j(\cdot)$ for some j, and hence deduce that this variation metric is bounded above by $\sqrt{2/e}|\sqrt{\lambda} - \sqrt{\mu}|$. Thus, except for small Λ_n, Λ, the last term in Proposition 9.3.IV can be tightened (see Daley, 1987).

9.4. Random Translations and Cluster Iterates

The remaining class of stochastic operations that we consider has as its prototype *random translations*: each point x_i in the realization of some initial point process N_0 is shifted independently of its neighbours through a random vector Y_i, the Y_i forming a sequence of i.i.d. random variables. Generalizations occur if the translations are replaced by more general clustering mechanisms in which the mean number of points per cluster is held equal to one.

One possible approach to such problems is to view the resultant process as the superposition of its individual clusters, one from each point of the initial realization, and to seek to apply the results of Section 9.2 on triangular arrays. Here the nth row in the array relates to the process derived from n stages of clustering (translation); although the number of terms N_{ni} in the nth row is infinite, this does not affect the validity of the criteria provided their superpositions are well defined (see Exercise 9.2.3), as they must be in this case for the resultant processes themselves to be well defined.

In the case of random translations in $\mathbb{R}^d$ this leads us to a result of the following kind. Let $v(\cdot)$ denote the common distribution on $\mathscr{B}(\mathbb{R}^d)$ for the translations Y_i, and $v_n(\cdot)$ the n-fold convolution of v, corresponding therefore to the effect of n successive random translations. Each process N_{ni} contains just one point, and the u.a.n. condition (9.2.2) reduces to the requirement

(9.4.1) $$\sup_i v_n(A + x_i) \to 0 \qquad (n \to \infty).$$

For convergence to a Poisson limit, condition (9.2.6) is here trivial $(\mathscr{P}\{N_{ni}(A) \geq 2\} \equiv 0)$, while (9.2.7) translates into

(9.4.2) $$\int_{\mathscr{X}} v_n(A + x)N_0(dx) = \sum_i v_n(A + x_i) \to \mu(A) \qquad (n \to \infty).$$

The problem then is to find conditions on the initial process N_0 and the distribution v that will ensure the truth of (9.4.1) and (9.4.2). The former of these is closely related to the concept of the *concentration function* $Q_A(F)$ of a distribution F on $\mathscr{B}(\mathbb{R}^d)$ defined for bounded Borel sets A by

$$Q_A(F) = \sup_{x \in \mathbb{R}^d} F(x + A).$$

The expression in (9.4.1) is clearly bounded above by $Q_A(v_n)$, and thus the u.a.n. statement there is a direct consequence of the following result [for a non-Fourier analytic proof see Ibragimov and Linnik (1970, Chap. 15, §2)].

Lemma 9.4.I. *Let F be a distribution on $\mathscr{B}(\mathbb{R}^d)$ and F^{n*} its nth convolution power. Then $Q_A(F^{n*}) \to 0$ as $n \to \infty$ if and only if the support of F contains at least two distinct points.*

PROOF. If F is degenerate, then $Q_A(F) = Q_A(F^{n*}) = 1$ for every n for every nonempty A. Otherwise, we shall in fact show that

(9.4.3) $$Q_A(F^{n*}) \leq c(F, A)/n^{1/2}$$

for some constant $c(F, A)$, observing that it is enough to prove this in the case $d = 1$ as, in the general case, since $Q_A(F)$ increases for monotonic increasing A, we can embed A in a set corresponding to a marginal distribution.

Write $\tilde{H}(y) = (\sin \frac{1}{2}y/\frac{1}{2}y)^2$ for the c.f. of the probability measure $H(\cdot)$ with triangular density function $H'(x) = (1 - |x|)_+$. Then the Parseval relation (A2.8.8) yields for any d.f. G, positive a, and real γ,

(9.4.4) $$\int_{-\infty}^{\infty} \tilde{H}(a(x - \gamma))G(dx) = a^{-1} \int_{-\infty}^{\infty} \tilde{G}(\omega)e^{-i\omega\gamma}(1 - |\omega|/a)_+ d\omega.$$

Substitute $G = F^{n*}$, so that recognizing that the integral on the right here is over the interval $(-a, a)$, and since the left-hand side is real, an upper bound that is uniform in γ is given by

$$a^{-1} \int_{-a}^{a} |\tilde{F}(\omega)|^n d\omega \leq a^{-1} \int_{-a}^{a} \exp(-n(1 - |\tilde{F}(\omega)|^2)/2)d\omega,$$

using $x = 1 + (x - 1) < e^{x-1}$ in this inequality. Now $|\tilde{F}|^2$ is the c.f. of the d.f. F_S of the symmetrized r.v. $X' - X''$, where X' and X'' are i.i.d. like X with d.f. F. Thus,

$$1 - |\tilde{F}(\omega)|^2 = 1 - E(\exp[i\omega(X' - X'')]) = 1 - E(\cos \omega(X' - X''))$$
$$= 2E(\sin^2 \omega(X' - X'')/2)$$
$$\geq 2 \int_{|y| > b} \sin^2(\omega y/2) F_S(dy)$$

for some positive b, which, since F is nondegenerate, can and is so chosen that

$$\int_{|y| > b} F_S(dy) = \Pr\{|X' - X''| > b\} \equiv \eta > 0.$$

Use Jensen's inequality in the form $\exp[Ef(Y)] \leq E(\exp[f(Y)])$ to write

$$a^{-1} \int_{-a}^{a} |\tilde{F}(\omega)|^n d\omega \leq a^{-1} \int_{-a}^{a} d\omega \int_{|y| > b} \exp[-n\eta \sin^2(\omega y/2)]\eta^{-1} F_S(dy)$$

$$= a^{-1} \int_{|y| > b} \eta^{-1} F_S(dy)|y|^{-1}$$

$$\times \int_{|z| < a|y|} \exp[-n\eta \sin^2(z/2)] dz$$

$$\leq (\text{constant}) \int_{|z| < ab} \exp[-n\eta \sin^2(z/2)] dz$$

$$\leq (\text{constant})/(n\eta)^{1/2},$$

where the constant is independent of n but may depend on a and b (and hence on A and F).

Refer back to (9.4.4) and observe that $\tilde{H}(y) \geq (2/\pi)^2$ for $|y| < \pi$, so the left-hand side there is bounded below by $4\pi^{-2}[G(\gamma + \pi/a) - G(\gamma - \pi/a - 0)]$. Therefore, for any bounded set $A \subseteq [-\pi/a, \pi/a]$,

$$Q_A(F^{n*}) \leq (\pi^2/4)(\text{constant})/(n\eta)^{1/2}.$$

Fix $a = \pi/\rho b$ for any $\rho > 1$, so that then for any $A \subseteq [-\rho b, \rho b]$ (9.4.3) holds. Since b is positive and we can choose ρ arbitrarily large, the lemma is proved.
□

Condition (9.4.2) is more difficult to realize, although it is certainly satisfied when the initial realization is sufficiently regular. Suppose, as an extreme example, that $d = 1$ and that N_0 consists of the lattice process with a point at every integer. We can then proceed via an application of the Poisson summation formula (see Exercise 11.1.4), which yields for sufficiently smooth functions g

$$\sum_k (v_n * g)(k) = \sum_j \tilde{v}_n(2\pi j)\tilde{g}(2\pi j),$$

where $\tilde{v}_n(\omega) = \tilde{v}(\omega)^n$ is the Fourier–Stieltjes transform of v^{n*}, $\tilde{g}$ is the ordinary Fourier transform of the continuous integrable function g, and we assume g chosen so that $\tilde{g}$ is integrable and $\sum |\tilde{g}(2\pi j)|$ is convergent.

Recall that a distribution in $\mathbb{R}^1$ is *nonlattice* if its distribution is not concentrated on a lattice (shifted multiple of the set of integers) in $\mathbb{R}^1$, and that such a distribution satisfies

$$|\tilde{v}(\omega)| < 1 \qquad (\omega \neq 0).$$

Letting $n \to \infty$ in (9.4.3) we obtain by dominated convergence

$$\sum_k (v_n * g)(k) \to \tilde{v}_n(0)\tilde{g}(0) = \int_{\mathbb{R}} g(x)dx.$$

To show that this implies (9.4.2) for intervals it is enough to sandwich the indicator function of an interval A between two functions g_1, g_2 with the properties required above, that is, in such a way that for given $\varepsilon > 0$

$$\sup_x |g_2(x) - g_1(x)| < \varepsilon, \qquad g_1(x) \leq I_A(x) \leq g_2(x).$$

[This can be achieved, for example, by taking for g_2 the function $I_{A^{\varepsilon/2}} * t_{\varepsilon/2}$ and for g_1 the function $I_{A^{-\varepsilon/2}} * t_{\varepsilon/2}$, where t_α is the triangular distribution on base $(-\alpha, \alpha)$.] Thus, (9.4.2) holds whenever v is nonlattice and A is an interval. Since it is enough in the convergence Theorem 9.2.V to let A run through intervals, we can conclude from that theorem that *if the initial process has a point on every integer and the distribution v is nonlattice, then the processes N_n, obtained by successive random translations according to v, converge weakly to the stationary Poisson process with unit rate.*

Obviously, the condition that the initial points lie on a lattice can be relaxed, but, unfortunately, it cannot be relaxed far enough to apply with probability 1 to the realizations of a typical stationary point process. Indeed, it follows from a theorem of Stone (1968) that the essential requirement on the initial process, if this is regarded as fixed, is that

$$(9.4.5) \qquad N_0(x + A_n)/\ell(A_n) \to \text{constant uniformly in } x,$$

where A_n is the sequence of hypercubes $\mathbb{U}_n^d$ of side n in $\mathbb{R}^d$ or, more generally, a convex averaging sequence in the sense of Section 10.2. Such a condition is not satisfied with probability 1 even by the realizations of a stationary Poisson process. On the other hand, averaged forms of (9.4.5), that is, with convergence in L_1 or L_2, follow directly from the ergodic theorems of Section 10.2, and in these the uniformity is trivial when the initial process is stationary. We therefore seek an alternative approach that will bypass the probability 1 requirements on the initial configuration.

For this purpose we return to a direct study of the p.g.fl. of the processes N_n, which we recall from Example 8.2(b) can be written in the form, for $h \in \mathcal{V}$ and $\mathcal{X} = \mathbb{R}^d$,

$$G_n[h] = G_0\left[\int_{\mathcal{X}} h(\cdot + y)v_n(dy)\right]$$

$$= E\left\{\exp\left[\int_{\mathcal{X}} \log\left(\int_{\mathcal{X}} h(x + y)v_n(dy)\right) N_0(dx)\right]\right\}.$$

To establish weak convergence of the translated versions N_n to a Poisson limit with rate m, it will be enough to show that for $h \in \mathcal{V}$,

$$\int_{\mathcal{X}} \log\left[\int_{\mathcal{X}} h(x + y)v_n(dy)\right] N_0(dx) \to_p m \int_{\mathcal{X}} [h(x) - 1]dx,$$

since this implies convergence of the Laplace transforms of the random variables on the left side, and hence of the p.g.fl.s.

To ease the notation write $u(x) = 1 - h(x)$, so that u vanishes outside a bounded set and satisfies $0 \le u \le 1$. Then the above requirement becomes

(9.4.6) $$-\int_{\mathcal{X}} \log\left[1 - \int_{\mathcal{X}} u(x + y)v_n(dy)\right] N_0(dx) \to_p m \int_{\mathcal{X}} u(x)dx.$$

From Lemma 9.4.I, if v has at least two points in its support, we can easily deduce that as $n \to \infty$

$$\theta_n \equiv \sup_x \int_{\mathcal{X}} u(x + y)v_n(dy) \to 0.$$

We can therefore approximate the logarithm by its leading term, with remainder, for sufficiently large n, bounded by

$$\left|\int_{\mathcal{X}} u(x + y)v_n(dy) + \log\left[1 - \int_{\mathcal{X}} u(x + y)v_n(dy)\right]\right| \le \theta_n \int_{\mathcal{X}} u(x + y)v_n(dy).$$

Suppose now that N_0 is stationary with finite mean rate m. Then (9.4.6) is implied by the corresponding L_1 convergence, which leads us to estimate the expected difference by

$$E\left|m \int_{\mathcal{X}} u(x)dx + \int_{\mathcal{X}} \log\left[1 - \int_{\mathcal{X}} u(x + y)v_n(dy)\right] N_0(dx)\right|$$

$$\le E\left|m \int_{\mathcal{X}} u(x)dx - \int_{\mathcal{X}}\int_{\mathcal{X}} u(x + y)v_n(dy)N_0(dx)\right|$$

$$+ E\left|\int_{\mathcal{X}}\left\{\int_{\mathcal{X}} u(x + y)v_n(dy) + \int_{\mathcal{X}} \log[1 - u(x + y)]v_n(dy)\right\} N_0(dx)\right|,$$

where the second expectation is bounded by

$$\theta_n E\left[\int_{\mathcal{X}}\int_{\mathcal{X}} u(x + y)v_n(dy)N_0(dx)\right] = m\theta_n \int_{\mathcal{X}} u(x)dx,$$

which tends to zero by Lemma 9.4.I. Thus, for weak convergence to the Poisson limit it is enough to show that for measurable u with bounded support and $0 \le u \le 1$

(9.4.7) $$E\left|m \int_{\mathcal{X}} u(x)dx - \int_{\mathcal{X}}\int_{\mathcal{X}} u(x + y)v_n(dy)N_0(dx)\right| \to 0.$$

A complication arises here if the stationary distribution N_0 is nonergodic, for the ergodic theorems then assert convergence not to the constant m but to the random variable (asymptotic density of N_0)

$$(9.4.8) \qquad\qquad Y = E[N_0(\mathbb{U}^d) | \mathscr{I}],$$

where $\mathbb{U}^d$ is the unit cube in $\mathbb{R}^d$, $\mathscr{I}$ is the invariant σ-algebra, and $E(Y) = m$ (see Theorem 10.2.IV). In this case (9.4.7) should be replaced by the more general requirement (justified by a completely analogous argument)

$$(9.4.9) \qquad E\left| Y \int_{\mathscr{X}} u(x)dx - \int_{\mathscr{X}} \int_{\mathscr{X}} u(x + y)v_n(dy)N_0(dx) \right| \to 0.$$

Note that (9.4.7) and (9.4.9) may be regarded as L_1 versions of (9.4.2).

A full discussion of (9.4.9) involves further delicate analysis of the convolution powers of v; we content ourselves here with the much easier L_2 version, assuming the initial point process has boundedly finite second moment measure. This leads us to the following theorem.

Theorem 9.4.II. *Let N_0 be a second-order stationary point process on $\mathscr{X} = \mathbb{R}^d$ and v a distribution on $\mathbb{R}^d$ that is nonlattice. Then the sequence of point processes $\{N_n\}$, derived from N_0 by successive random translations according to v, converges weakly to the stationary mixed Poisson process with p.g.fl.*

$$(9.4.10) \qquad G[h] = E\left[\exp\left\{ -Y \int_{\mathscr{X}} [1 - h(x)]dx \right\} \right],$$

where Y is given by (9.4.8).

PROOF. We again use a Fourier argument, observing that in the ergodic case

$$(9.4.11) \qquad E\left| m \int_{\mathscr{X}} u(x)dx - \int_{\mathscr{X}} \int_{\mathscr{X}} u(x + y)v_n(dy)N_0(dx) \right|^2$$

$$= \mathrm{var}\left[\int_{\mathscr{X}} \int_{\mathscr{X}} u(x + y)v_n(dy)N_0(dx) \right]$$

$$= \int_{\mathscr{X}} \Gamma(d\omega)|\tilde{u}(\omega)|^2 |\tilde{v}(\omega)|^{2n},$$

where $\Gamma(\cdot)$ is the Bartlett spectrum introduced in Definition 11.2.II. The validity of the above relation follows from the Parseval relation (11.1.10) and Lemma 11.1.V, which ensures the Γ-integrability of $|\tilde{u}(\omega)|^2$ and hence of $|\tilde{v}(\omega)|^{2n}|\tilde{u}(\omega)|^2$.

As in the earlier example, $|\tilde{v}(\omega)| < 1$ for $\omega \neq 0$ (this holds for nonlattice distributions in $\mathbb{R}^d$ for arbitrary $d \geq 1$), so the right side of the identity above converges to $\Gamma\{0\}$, which vanishes for an ergodic process.

In the general case we have to replace Γ by a modified measure Γ^*

introduced as the Fourier transform of the modified covariance measure

$$C^*(A \times B) = E[(N_0(A) - Y\ell(A))(N_0(B) - Y\ell(B))],$$

where Y is defined by (9.4.8). Then Γ^* differs from Γ precisely by the absence of the atom at zero, which is given by

$$\Gamma\{0\} = \text{var}(Y)$$

(see also Exercise 11.2.10). Now, arguing as in the ergodic case, we can deduce that

$$E \left| \int_{\mathscr{X}} \int_{\mathscr{X}} u(x + y) v_n(dy) N_0(dx) - Y \int_{\mathscr{X}} u(x) dx \right|^2 \to \Gamma^*\{0\} = 0.$$

This result implies (9.4.9) and so completes the proof. ☐

It was pointed out in Example 8.2(b) that the stationary Poisson process [and by immediate extension also the mixed Poisson process (9.4.10)] is invariant under the operation of random translation. As a corollary to the theorem we obtain now the following converse.

Corollary 9.4.III. *Suppose that N is a stationary, second-order point process that is invariant under the operation of random translation according to a nonlattice distribution v. Then N is a stationary mixed Poisson process.*

PROOF. Take N as the initial distribution in the theorem, and observe that if N is invariant the weak limit of the N_n must coincide with N. ☐

A second case of interest arises when the random translations v_n are derived from the movements over time n of particles with fixed but random and independently chosen velocities. If these velocities have a common distribution v, we can then write

$$v_n(dx) = v(n^{-1}dx)$$

and observe that from (d) of Exercise 9.4.3

$$Q_A(v_n) = Q_{A/n}(v) \to 0.$$

Moreover, the integral at (9.4.11) becomes

$$\int \Gamma(d\omega) |\tilde{u}(\omega)|^2 |\tilde{v}(n\omega)|^2.$$

Now if v is absolutely continuous, $|\tilde{v}(n\omega)| \to 0$ as $n \to \infty$ for every $\omega \neq 0$ by the Riemann–Lebesgue lemma, so that the proof of (9.4.7) and its extension (9.4.9) to the ergodic case can be completed as in the previous discussion. The restriction to integer values n is here immaterial and we therefore obtain the following further result.

Theorem 9.4.IV. *Let N_0 be as in Theorem 9.4.II, and for all $t \geq 0$ let the point processes N_t be derived from N_0 by random translations through time t by fixed but random velocities with common distribution v. If v is absolutely continuous with respect to Lebesgue measure on $\mathbb{R}^d$, the processes N_t converge weakly to a mixed Poisson process as in (9.4.10).*

Corollary 9.4.V. *Let the point process N_t represent the position at time t of a system of particles moving in $\mathbb{R}^d$ with fixed velocities independently and randomly chosen according to a distribution v that is absolutely continuous with respect to Lebesgue measure in $\mathbb{R}^d$. If the distribution of N_t is independent of t, spatially homogeneous, and of second order, then N_t is a mixed Poisson process as in (9.4.10).*

Before leaving this topic we make a few remarks concerning the L_1 theory referred to briefly before Theorem 9.4.II. A key step here is to show that in both situations considered, the distributions v_n satisfy the condition, for all bounded Borel sets $A \in \mathbb{R}^d$,

$$(9.4.12) \qquad \int_{\mathbb{R}^d} |v_n(y + A) - v_n(x + y + A)| \, dy \to 0 \quad \text{(uniformly in x)}.$$

This condition, or the apparently stronger but in fact equivalent condition

$$(9.4.13) \qquad \|v_n * \gamma_1 - v_n * \gamma_2\| \to 0$$

for all pairs γ_1, γ_2 of distributions a.c. with respect to Lebesgue measure in $\mathbb{R}^d$, is referred to in MKM as *weak asymptotic uniformity* of the sequence $\{v_n\}$. A particular example of such a sequence is the sequence of uniform distributions on the sets $\{A_n\}$ of a convex averaging sequence. The major technical difficulty is then to show that the standard form of conclusion of the mean ergodic theorem, which can be written as

$$E \left| \int_{\mathbb{R}^d} H_n(x + A) N_0(dx) - Y\ell(A) \right| \to 0,$$

where H_n is this special case of a weakly asymptotically uniform sequence, can be extended to the general case and therefore implies (9.4.9) in each of the two situations under consideration.

The definitive treatment of the L_1 case was given by Stone (1968), after earlier work by Dobrushin (1956) and Maruyama (1955) in the context of iterated random translation, and by Breiman (1963) and Thedeen (1964) for the random velocities scheme. Further extensions and generalizations occur in a series of papers by Matthes and co-workers; for details we refer to MKM (see in particular Chapter 11) and the further references contained therein. An algebraic treatment of (9.4.12) and related properties, when v_n are convolution powers, is contained in the papers by Stam (1967a, b). The second-order treatment developed above is an extension of the discussion in Vere-Jones

(1968). Some partial results concerning (9.4.12) and related topics are covered in Exercises 9.4.2 and 9.4.3.

We turn next to the operation of iterated cluster formation, considering clusters with mean size unity but excluding the case $\mathscr{P}\{N(\mathscr{X}|x) = 1\} = 1$ (all x) since this is the case of random translations already considered.

In every other case it is well known from standard results on branching processes [e.g., see Harris (1963, Chap. 1)] that for critical branching processes (mean cluster size $m = 1$) the offspring from a given ancestor eventually become extinct, or in other words the iterated clusters eventually collapse to the zero measures. In such circumstances it may seem surprising that stable limit behaviour can occur. The explanation is to be found in the infinite character of the initial distribution, which allows local depletion to be perpetually replenished by immigration from more successful clusters in distant parts of the state space. The higher the dimension of the space, the greater the opportunities for such replenishment become, so that stable behaviour is the norm for $d \geq 3$, whereas it is the exception for $d = 1$ or even $d = 2$.

The nature of the limiting behaviour is most easily understood by studying first the situation where the initial process is Poisson, with mean density equal to unity say. Any limit, though no longer Poisson, is still infinitely divisible, so the discussion can be phrased in terms of the convergence of the associated KLM measures to their limit (Proposition 9.2.II). Since the successive Poisson cluster processes formed by iterating the clustering operation are also stationary, the discussions can be further reduced to the study of the Palm measures associated with these KLM measures. (For the concept of Palm measure, refer to Chapter 12 and, in particular, Exercise 12.2.4.) The essential question can now be phrased in terms of the Palm measures $\{Q_0^{(n)}\}$ formed from the KLM measures $\{\tilde{Q}_n\}$ corresponding to the sequence $\{N_n\}$ of cluster processes formed from an initial Poisson process of unit rate according to successive clusterings with some given cluster mechanism: *find conditions on the cluster mechanism such that $Q_0^{(n)}$ converges to some boundedly finite limit measure $Q_0^{(\infty)}$ say.*

The cluster mechanism itself can be conveniently specified in terms of

(9.4.14a) a distribution $\{\pi_k: k \geq 0\}$ for the size of the cluster (note the assumptions $E\{N(\mathscr{X}|x)\} = 1$, $\mathscr{P}\{N(\mathscr{X}|x) = 1\} < 1$ imply $\pi_0 > 0$);

(9.4.14b) a family of symmetric distribution functions $P_k(dx_1 \times \cdots \times dx_k)$, $k \geq 1$, specifying the locations of the cluster members relative to the cluster centre at the origin. [Note that by assumption the cluster mechanisms are homogeneous in space, so that the locations relative to a cluster centre not at 0 will be specified by the appropriately shifted versions of the $P_k(\cdot)$.]

The assumption that the mean cluster size $m = 1$ implies

$$1 = \sum_{k=0}^{\infty} \pi_k = \sum_{k=0}^{\infty} k\pi_k.$$

The KLM measure corresponding to the Poisson cluster process formed at the first stage of clustering is concentrated on the set of totally finite counting measures and allocates mass π_k to those trajectories containing just k points. Since $m = 1$, it may be considered as a probability distribution on $\mathcal{N}_0(\mathcal{X})$ in its own right. The associated Palm measure is then formed, loosely speaking, by selecting at random an arbitrary point of an arbitrary cluster, placing it at the origin, and studying the locations of its "siblings", that is, the remaining points belonging to the same cluster. More precisely, it can be defined in terms of a modified cluster structure, in which the cluster size is distributed according to

$$\{\pi_k'\} = \{k\pi_k : k \geq 0\} \quad \text{(note } \pi_0' = 0),$$

and the locations of the cluster members are specified by placing one cluster member at the origin and distributing the remaining $k - 1$ points about it according to the symmetrized measures

$$\tilde{P}_{k-1}(A_2 \times \cdots \times A_k) = \int_{\mathcal{X}} P_k(dy \times (y + A_2) \times \cdots \times (y + A_k)).$$

Note that these latter are also the distributions that arise in the regular representation of the cluster process (see Proposition 10.1.VI). Thus, the Palm clusters considered here differ from the clusters arising in the regular representation only through the relative weightings given to the different cluster sizes. Note also that the intensity measure for the underlying cluster process, given by

$$(9.4.15) \qquad \rho(dx) = \sum_{k=1}^{\infty} k\pi_k \int_{\mathcal{X}^{(k-1)}} P_k(dx \times dy_2 \times \cdots \times dy_k),$$

is here a probability measure on $\mathcal{X}$, while the intensity measure for the Palm cluster process is given by

$$\tilde{\rho}(dx) = \delta_0(dx) + \sum_{k=2}^{\infty} k(k-1)\pi_k \int_{\mathcal{X}^{(k-1)}} P_k((y_2 + dx) \times dy_2 \times \cdots \times dy_k).$$

Now consider the Palm cluster resulting from two stages of clustering. To ease the notation only, we use here density notation, with corresponding lowercase symbols. First note that the quantity

$$(9.4.16) \qquad k\pi_k p_k(y, x_2 + y, \ldots, x_k + y)$$

can be interpreted as the joint density of locating the parent (cluster centre) at $-y$ and $k - 1$ siblings at $x_2, \ldots, x_k$, given one point of the cluster at the origin (cf. Exercise 1.2.5). The marginal density for the parent, given a point at the origin, is thus

$$g(y) = \sum_{k=1}^{\infty} k\pi_k \int \cdots \int p_k(y, x_2 + y, \ldots, x_k + y) = \rho(y),$$

where we here write $\rho(y)$ for the density of the intensity measure (9.4.15). The members of the two-stage Palm cluster can now be classified into three groups: first, the point located at the origin; second, its immediate siblings, jointly located with the cluster centre according to (9.4.16); and third, its "cousins," found by locating a grandparent and a set of "uncles" by (9.4.16), but given the parent at $-y$ rather than at the origin, and then superposing the clusters generated by each of the uncles. In symbols, we may write briefly

$$\tilde{N}_2 = \delta_0 + N_1 + N_2.$$

Evidently, this process, introduced by Kallenberg (1977) and called by him the "method of backward trees," can be continued. At each stage we move one generation further back, taking the location of what was previously the oldest ancestor as origin, locating the ancestor of next order and the siblings of the previously oldest ancestor by (9.4.16), then moving forward to add in to the current generation the superposition of clusters of appropriate order deriving from the siblings of the previously oldest ancestor.

The processes $\tilde{N}_n$ developed in this way have a monotonic character, because we can imagine them as defined on a common probability space and imbedded into an indefinitely continued process of superposition of this kind. Whether the Palm measures $Q_0^{(n)}$ converge to some limit $Q_0^{(\infty)}$ thus reduces to the question of whether this process of superposition produces in the limit an a.s. boundedly finite limit measure. Since each stage is formed from its predecessor by an independent operation representing a shift of locations and corresponding augmentation of the number of branches by the distribution (9.4.16), it follows from the Hewitt–Savage zero–one law that the limit will be boundedly finite either with probability 1 or with probability 0.

This dichotomy allows us to make the following definition.

Definition 9.4.VI. The cluster mechanism described by (9.4.14a, b) is *stable* or *unstable* according as the sequence of processes $\tilde{N}_n$ described above converges a.s. to a boundedly finite limit or diverges a.s.

In complete generality, the problem of determining conditions that are necessary and sufficient for the stability of a given cluster mechanism is still open. It is known, however, that the conditions are closely linked to the behaviour of the random walk with step-length distribution governed by the symmetrized form

(9.4.17) $\sigma = \rho * \rho_-$

[where $\rho_-(A) = \rho(-A)$] of the intensity measure for the clusters.

To see how this measure arises, suppose that the mean square cluster size is finite ($\sum_{k=1}^{\infty} k^2 \pi_k < \infty$); this ensures that the Palm clusters also have finite intensity, which we write in the form

$$\tilde{\rho} = \delta_0 + \hat{\rho},$$

where

$$\hat{\rho}(A) = \sum_{k=2}^{\infty} (k-1)\mathscr{P}_{k-1}(A \times \mathscr{X} \times \cdots \times \mathscr{X}),$$

and we note

$$\hat{\rho}(\mathscr{X}) = \sum_{k=2}^{\infty} k(k-1)\pi_k.$$

Consider now the differences $\tilde{N}_{n+1} - \tilde{N}_n$ between the Palm clusters at the $(n+1)$th and nth stages of clustering. To obtain the intensity measure of this increment, we should start from ρ_-^{n*}, representing the n steps taken to the left (i.e., according to ρ_-) to locate the position of the nth generation ancestor, convolve this with $\hat{\rho}$ to obtain the locations of that ancestor's siblings, and finally convolve again with ρ_+^{n*} to obtain the intensity measure of the superposition of the nth stage clusters generated by those siblings. Thus, if $\tilde{\rho}_n$ denotes the intensity measure for $\tilde{N}_n$, we have

$$\tilde{\rho}_{n+1} = \tilde{\rho}_n + \rho_-^{n*} * \hat{\rho} * \rho_+^{n*} = \tilde{\rho}_n + \sigma^{n*} * \hat{\rho};$$

hence,

$$\tilde{\rho}_n = \delta_0 + \hat{\rho} * (\delta_0 + \sigma + \sigma^{2*} + \cdots + \sigma^{(n-1)*}).$$

The series on the right converges toward the renewal measure (boundedly finite or infinite) of the random walk with step-length distributions σ. It is boundedly finite if and only if the random walk is transient (see Exercise 7.1.3). On the other hand, it follows from the monotonic character of the $\tilde{N}_n$ that they converge to a boundedly finite limit with boundedly finite first moment measure if and only if the sequence $\tilde{\rho}_n$ so converges. We are thus led to the following result (see Liemant, 1969, 1975).

Proposition 9.4.VII. *A critical cluster member process with finite mean square cluster size is stable if and only if the random walk generated by the symmetrized intensity measure (9.4.17) is transient.*

Since random walks in three or more dimensions are necessarily transient, it follows that a properly three-dimensional cluster process with finite mean square cluster size is always stable; in one or two dimensions, however, a random walk is not necessarily transient: it is if the step distribution has nonzero mean ($d = 1$ or 2) or infinite variance ($d = 2$), so it is only under rather special conditions that the associated cluster process can be stable.

Further results concerning stability are given by Kallenberg (1977), who shows, in particular, that for a process of Neyman–Scott type, transience of the random walk alone is necessary and sufficient for stability, while in full generality necessary and sufficient conditions for stability cannot be formulated solely in terms of conditions on the cluster size distribution and the cluster intensity measure.

Granted that the cluster mechanism is stable, convergence to a limiting process can be established by arguments similar to those used in discussing random translations. As above, write $Q_0^{(n)}$ for the Palm measure corresponding to the Poisson cluster process formed after n stages of clustering from a Poisson process with unit rate, and suppose the clusters are stable, so that by hypothesis

$$Q_0^{(n)} \to Q_0^{(\infty)} \quad \text{(weakly in } \mathcal{N}_0\text{)}$$

for some limit distribution $Q_0^{(\infty)}$. This convergence implies the corresponding assertion for the associated KLM measures (see Exercise 12.2.7), say

(9.4.18) $\tilde{Q}_n \to \tilde{Q}_\infty$.

Unlike $Q_0^{(n)}$, $Q_0^{(\infty)}$ (and hence also $\tilde{Q}_\infty$) allots zero mass to the totally finite counting measures. To see this, observe that the successive increments $\tilde{N}_{n+1} - \tilde{N}_n$ are independent and nonnegative, and that for positive constants c, c',

$$\mathcal{P}\{\tilde{N}_{n+1} - \tilde{N}_n \geq 1\} \geq c\mathcal{P}\{Z_n > 0\} \geq c'/n,$$

where $\{Z_n\}$ is a Galton–Watson branching process governed by the cluster size distribution $\{\pi_k\}$ [see Harris (1963, Chap. 1)]. Since the sum of these terms diverges, it follows from the Borel–Cantelli lemmas that an infinite number of the events on the left occur, with probability 1. Thus, $\lim_{n \to \infty} \tilde{N}_n(\mathcal{X})$ is infinite a.s., which is equivalent to the assertion that $Q_0^{(\infty)}$ allots zero mass to the counting measures with finite total mass.

Since the various Poisson cluster processes formed from the initial Poisson process all have unit rate, their distributions on $\mathcal{N}_{\mathcal{X}}$ are weakly relatively compact, while from (9.4.18) above and Proposition 9.2.II it follows that the limit of any weakly converging subsequence must be infinitely divisible with KLM measure $\tilde{Q}_\infty$. This limit process must therefore be the overall weak limit. Recalling that an infinitely divisible point process is singular if its KLM measure is supported by the counting measure with infinite total mass, we can assert the following result.

Lemma 9.4.VIII. *In the stable case, the Poisson cluster processes derived from an initial Poisson process of unit rate converge weakly to a limit point process that is stationary, singular infinitely divisible, and has KLM measure $\tilde{Q}_\infty$.*

It can be shown further that the limit process is actually mixing and therefore weakly singular (Fleischmann, 1978). Also, if we start from an initial Poisson process of rate λ, the Poisson cluster processes converge to a limit point process that is infinitely divisible with KLM measure $\lambda\tilde{Q}_\infty$.

Granted the Palm versions of the cluster iterates converge to the limit $\tilde{Q}_\infty$, we may raise more generally the question of convergence of the processes formed by successive clusterings from a general initial distribution. Since stability implies that the intensity measure $\rho(\cdot)$ of the cluster member process has at least two points in its support, we first obtain the following estimate for the p.g.fl. $G_n[h]$ for the nth cluster iterate with cluster centre at the origin: for $h \in \mathcal{V}$,

$$\sup_x |G_n[T_x h] - 1| \le \theta_n \equiv \sup_x \int_{\mathscr{X}} \rho^{n*}(x + dy)(1 - h(y)) \to 0,$$

the last assertion following from Lemma 9.4.I.

Making use of this estimate, we can start the discussion along much the same lines as that of Theorem 9.4.II. As in that proof, the above estimate implies

$$E\left(\left| -\int_{\mathscr{X}} \log G_n[T_x h] N_0(dx) - \int_{\mathscr{X}} (1 - G_n[T_x h]) N_0(dx) \right|\right) \to 0.$$

If now Y is given by (9.4.8) and we write $G_\infty[h]$ for the putative limit of the terms in the exponent, namely,

$$G_\infty[h] = \int_{\mathscr{N}_0(\mathscr{X})} \left\{ \exp\left[\int_{\mathscr{X}} \log h(x) \tilde{N}(dx) \right] - 1 \right\} \tilde{Q}_\infty(d\tilde{N}),$$

then to complete the proof along the lines of Theorem 9.4.II we need to show that

$$E\left\{ \left| \int_{\mathscr{X}} (1 - G_n[T_x h]) N_0(dx) - Y G_\infty[h] \right|^2 \right\} \to 0.$$

Since we have already established that the KLM measures of the Poisson cluster processes converge to $\tilde{Q}_\infty$, we have further that

$$\int_{\mathscr{X}} (1 - G_n[T_x h]) dx \to G_\infty[h],$$

so that in fact it is sufficient to show that

$$(9.4.19) \quad E\left\{ \left| \int_{\mathscr{X}} (1 - G_n[T_x h]) N_0(dx) - Y \int_{\mathscr{X}} (1 - G_n[T_x h]) dx \right|^2 \right\} \to 0.$$

At this point we meet a difficulty, because we do not have the detailed information concerning the asymptotic behaviour of the cluster p.g.fl.s $1 - G_n[T_x h]$, in x and n, which would correspond to the information concerning the convolution powers $1 - \int_{\mathscr{X}} \rho^{n*}(x + dy)h(y)$ used to complete the proof of Theorem 9.4.II.

Such information can in fact be obtained by the "method of reduced trees" introduced by Fleischmann and Prehn (1974, 1975). The underlying idea here is that if the clustering survives a large number of generations, the offspring in the current generation come with high probability from a single line in the family tree, other lines having become extinct. In other words, the current offspring have a single common ancestor a few generations back, so that for all generations preceding that it is enough to track the positions of this single ancestor and its forbears. Each backward step in this reduced part of the tree corresponds to a step in a random walk governed by the distribution $\rho(\cdot)$, as discussed below (9.4.16). Hence, we may approximate the p.g.fl.s $G_n[T_x h]$ in

(9.4.18) by the corresponding p.g.fl.s $\int_{\mathscr{X}} \rho^{n*}(x + dy)h(y)$ for the random translations process governed by the distribution ρ. Then we may refer to the proof of Theorem 9.4.II again to deduce that for this process, assuming ρ is nonlattice, the terms corresponding to those in (9.4.19) are asymptotically equal.

Such considerations lead to the limit result set out in Theorem 9.4.IX below, representing an extension of Theorem 9.4.II. For details of the above argument, as well as extensions and strengthenings of the theorem and analogous results for subcritical branching mechanisms, see Chapter 12 of MKM and more especially the corresponding but extended and updated version (Chap. 10) of the Russian edition.

Theorem 9.4.IX. *Let N_0 be a second-order stationary point process on $\mathscr{X} = \mathbb{R}^d$, and let $\{\pi_k, P_k\}$ be a stable cluster mechanism in the sense of Definition 9.4.VI. Furthermore, let $\tilde{Q}_\infty$ denote the limiting KLM measure (9.4.18) associated with the iterates of the cluster mechanism and $\{N_n\}$ the sequence of point processes derived from N_0 by successive independent clusterings according to $\{\pi_k, P_k\}$. If the intensity measure ρ for $\{\pi_k, P_k\}$ is nonlattice, then the sequence $\{N_n\}$ converges weakly to the limit point process with p.g.fl.*

$$G[h] \equiv E\left[\exp\left(Y \int_{\mathscr{N}_0(\mathscr{X})} \left(\exp\left[\int_{\mathscr{X}} \log h(x)\tilde{N}(dx)\right] - 1\right) \tilde{Q}_\infty(d\tilde{N})\right)\right],$$

where Y is given by (9.4.8).

Exercises

9.4.1. The binomial distribution $\{b_k(n; p)\} = \{\binom{n}{k}p^k(1 - p)^{n-k}\}$ with $0 < p < 1$ is the n-fold convolution of the simplest nondegenerate d.f. F that can arise with Lemma 9.4.I. The order of the bound at (9.4.3) cannot be tightened because

$$\frac{1}{(2\pi(n + 1)p(1 - p))^{1/2}} \le Q_{\{0\}}(\{b_k(n; p)\}) \le \frac{1}{(4(n + 1)p(1 - p))^{1/2}}$$

[e.g., see MKM (1978, pp. 476–477), or else Daley (1987)].

9.4.2. For a given distribution F on $\mathbb{R}^d$, let $\mathscr{S}$ denote the set of points a in $\mathbb{R}^d$ such that for all intervals A,

(*) $\sup_x |F^{n*}(x + a + A) - F^{n*}(x + A)| \to 0$ as $n \to \infty$.

Show that
(a) $\mathscr{S}$ is an algebra;
(b) if $a \in \text{supp}(F)$, then $a \in \mathscr{S}$;
(c) if $\text{supp}(F)$ is contained in no proper subalgebra of $\mathbb{R}^d$, then $\mathscr{S} = \mathbb{R}^d$.

9.4.3. (Continuation) A sequence of measures $\{v_n\}$ is *weakly asymptotically uniformly distributed* if for all absolutely continuous distributions σ on $\mathscr{B}(\mathbb{R}^d)$ and all $x \in \mathbb{R}^d$,

(**) $\|\sigma * v_n * \delta_x - \sigma * v_n\| \to 0$ as $n \to \infty$.

(a) Show that $(*)$ implies $(**)$ in the special case that σ is the uniform distribution on the interval A and $\{v_n\} = \{F^{n*}\}$.

(b) By extending this result, deduce that if F is nonlattice, the sequence of convolution powers of F is weakly asymptotically uniformly distributed.

(c) Prove that $(**)$ is equivalent to

$$\|v_n * \sigma_1 - v_n * \sigma_2\| \to 0 \quad \text{as } n \to \infty$$

for all pairs of absolutely continuous distributions σ_1 and σ_2.

(d) If $(**)$ holds then $Q_A(v_n) \to 0$ (cf. Lemma 9.4.I, a result for the sequence of convolution powers).

[*Remark*: For further details and applications see MKM (1978, Chap. 11).]

9.4.4. Find the class of point processes invariant under the cluster operation of Theorem 9.4.IX (i.e., find an analogue of Corollary 9.4.III to Theorem 9.4.II for Theorem 9.4.IX).

9.4.5. Let the critical branching mechanism $\{\pi_k, P_k\}$ be neither stable nor a random translation. Show that the cluster iterates $\{N_n\}$ starting from a stationary second-order point process N_0 converge weakly to the zero point process. [*Hint*: Consider first the case where N_0 is a stationary Poisson process.]

9.4.6. Let $P(x, A)$ denote a stochastic or substochastic kernel defined for all $x \in \mathbb{R}^d$ and $A \in \mathscr{B}(\mathbb{R}^d)$ such that it has an infinite invariant measure v. Consider the operation of random translation according to the kernel P [i.e., a point initially at x is translated to a new point y according to the distribution $P(x, \cdot)$].

(a) The Poisson process with intensity measure v is invariant under this operation [cf. Example 8.2(b)].

(b) If P is continuous, then the initial process N_0 is invariant under this operation if and only if it is a Cox process directed by Yv, where Y is a nonnegative random variable.

(c) Investigate conditions under which the sequence of point processes $\{N_n\}$ obtained from an initial process N_0 by successive iteration of this operation will converge to a limit of the form described in (b).

[*Hint*: See Kerstan and Debes (1969) and Debes, Kerstan, Liemant, and Matthes (1971). Part (a) goes back to Derman (1955). The case where v is totally finite is discussed in MKM (1978, §4.8).]

CHAPTER 10

Stationary Point Processes and Random Measures

Stationary point processes play an exceptionally important role in applications and lead also to a rich theory. In this chapter we develop the basic properties of stationary point processes and indicate some of their applications. Some parts of the theory are minor variants of the corresponding theory of stationary continuous processes, others can be treated as special cases of more general theories such as concern processes with stationary increments or stationary random distributions, while still other aspects are peculiar to point processes and random measures.

The first three sections contain basic concepts and examples, and a discussion of ergodic and mixing properties. The fourth section is concerned with the moment structure of stationary random measures and point processes, particularly second-order properties, leading in Chapter 11 to a parallel development in the frequency domain, that is, the spectral theory of point processes.

The final two sections provide an introduction to some examples in stochastic geometry, where stationary processes of random lines and other geometrical objects are treated as point processes in some suitable state space in which they are invariant under the transformations in that space corresponding to stationarity of the original process in $\mathbb{R}^d$. Here it is important to mention that while the paradigm situation is stationarity with respect to translations of the real line (i.e., the time axis), there are natural extensions to translations in $\mathbb{R}^d$ and to other group operations such as rotations and changes of scale. Such applications make it natural to seek a general theory that encompasses a general group of transformations on some general state space. Almost all the results in this chapter could be developed in such generality, but for the most part we choose to place the main emphasis on results for translations in $\mathbb{R}^d$, with more general results indicated by way of additional examples and comments. Some notation and terminology from the theory of measures on topological groups, needed for the more general approach, are summarized in Appendix A2.7.

10.1. Basic Concepts

We consider first $\mathscr{X} = \mathbb{R}^d$ and invariance properties with respect to translations (or shifts). For arbitrary $u, x \in \mathscr{X}$, and $A \in \mathscr{B}_{\mathscr{X}}$, write

$$(10.1.1) \qquad T_u x = x + u, \qquad T_u A = A + u = \{x + u \colon x \in A\}.$$

Then T_u induces a transformation S_u of $\mathscr{M}_{\mathscr{X}}$ (and also on $\mathscr{N}_{\mathscr{X}}$) through the equation[‡]

$$(10.1.2) \qquad\qquad (S_u \mu)(A) = \mu(T_u A), \qquad \mu \in \mathscr{M}_{\mathscr{X}}, A \in \mathscr{B}_{\mathscr{X}}.$$

It is clear that $S_u \mu \in \mathscr{M}_{\mathscr{X}}$ whenever $\mu \in \mathscr{M}_{\mathscr{X}}$; that is, S_u maps $\mathscr{M}_{\mathscr{X}}$ into (indeed, onto) itself. Moreover, S_u is continuous: to see this, let $\{\mu_n\}$ be a sequence of measures on $\mathscr{B}_{\mathscr{X}}$ converging in the $\hat{w}$-topology to a limit μ, and let f be a bounded continuous function vanishing outside a bounded set. Then its translate $f(x - u)$ has similar properties, so from Lemma A2.6.II

$$\int_{\mathscr{X}} f(x)(S_u \mu_n)(dx) = \int_{\mathscr{X}} f(x - u)\mu_n(dx)$$

$$\to \int_{\mathscr{X}} f(x - u)\mu(dx) = \int_{\mathscr{X}} f(x)(S_u \mu)(dx).$$

An application of the sufficiency half of Lemma A2.6.II shows that $S_u \mu_n \to_{\hat{w}} S_u \mu$, and hence that S_u is continuous. Since a shifted counting measure is again a counting measure, while $\mathscr{N}_{\mathscr{X}}$ is closed in $\mathscr{M}_{\mathscr{X}}$, the same conclusion holds for the effects of shifts T_u on counting measures. This establishes the following simple but important result.

Lemma 10.1.I. *For $\mathscr{X} = \mathbb{R}^d$ and $u \in \mathbb{R}^d$, both the mappings $S_u \colon \mathscr{M}_{\mathscr{X}} \to \mathscr{M}_{\mathscr{X}}$ and $S_u \colon \mathscr{N}_{\mathscr{X}} \to \mathscr{N}_{\mathscr{X}}$ defined via the shift operator T_u at (10.1.2) are continuous (and hence measurable) and one-to-one.*

[‡] With the operators $T_{.}$ and $S_{.}$ as defined, the Dirac measure $\delta(\cdot)$ has the property that $(S_u \delta_x)(\cdot) = \delta_{x-u}(\cdot)$ and

$$\int f(x)(S_u \mu)(dx) = \int f(x)\mu(d(x + u)) = \int f(x - u)\mu(dx).$$

Sometimes, an operator S_u' for which $S_u' = S_{-u}$ is used instead. Then the $+$ and $-$ signs in the equations above are interchanged. The operator S_u we use is the same as T_u in MKM (1978, p. 258) and as T_{-u} in Kallenberg (1975, Ex. 10.10).

It now follows that if ξ is a random measure or point process, then so is $S_u\xi$ for every $u \in \mathbb{R}^d$ because $S_u\xi$ is then the composition of two measurable mappings. This remark enables us to make the following definition.

Definition 10.1.II. A random measure or point process ξ with state space $\mathcal{X} = \mathbb{R}^d$ is *stationary* if, for all $u \in \mathbb{R}^d$, the fidi distributions of the random measures ξ and $S_u\xi$ coincide.

If extra emphasis is needed, we shall call such random measures *strictly stationary* or *stationary as a whole* to distinguish them from random measures that are stationary in weaker senses to be defined in the sequel. It is also appropriate to remark that this definition is the natural extension to $\mathbb{R}^d$ and to $\mathcal{M}_{\mathcal{X}}$ of Definition 3.2.I.

Definition 10.1.II can be stated in a compact form by defining a transformation $\hat{S}_u$ that operates at a third level of abstraction, on measures $\mathcal{P}$ on the Borel sets of $\mathcal{M}_{\mathcal{X}}$. For $B \in \mathcal{B}(\mathcal{M}_{\mathcal{X}})$ set

(10.1.3) $\hat{S}_u\mathcal{P}(B) = \mathcal{P}(S_uB),$

where $S_uB = \{S_u\mu : \mu \in B\}$. The remark just prior to Definition 10.1.II implies that $\hat{S}_u$ maps $\mathcal{M}_{\mathcal{X}}$ (or $\mathcal{N}_{\mathcal{X}}$) into itself, while an argument similar to that establishing Lemma 10.1.I shows that the mapping is even continuous (see Exercise 10.1.1). Then Definition 10.1.II is equivalent to stating that *a random measure on $\mathbb{R}^d$ is* stationary *if its distribution on $\mathcal{M}_{\mathcal{X}}$ is invariant under shifts $\hat{S}_u$.*

The results of Chapter 6 imply that the distribution of a random measure is completely determined either by its fidi distributions or by its Laplace functional (see Propositions 6.2.III and 6.4.II). Similarly, the distribution of a point process is completely determined by its fidi distributions or its p.g.fl. (Theorem 7.4.II) or, if the point process is simple, by its avoidance function (Theorem 7.3.II). Applying these criteria to the definition of stationarity, we deduce that a random measure is stationary if and only if its fidi distributions are stationary, or, equivalently, if and only if its Laplace functional is stationary. Similarly, a point process is stationary if and only if its p.g.fl. is stationary, or, if it is simple, if and only if its avoidance function is stationary. Spelling out the detail of these remarks yields the following theorem.

Theorem 10.1.III. *Let ξ be a random measure with state space $\mathcal{X} = \mathbb{R}^d$. Each of the following conditions is necessary and sufficient for ξ to be stationary:*

(i) *For each $u \in \mathbb{R}^d$ and $k = 1, 2, \ldots$, the fidi distributions satisfy*

(10.1.4) $F_k(A_1, \ldots, A_k; x_1, \ldots, x_k) = F_k(A_1 + u, \ldots, A_k + u; x_1, \ldots, x_k).$

(ii) *For each $u \in \mathbb{R}^d$ and $f \in BM(\mathbb{R}^d)$ the characteristic functional satisfies*

(10.1.5) $\Phi[f(\cdot)] = \Phi[f(\cdot - u)].$

If ξ is a point process these conditions are also equivalent to the following.

(iii) *For each $u \in \mathbb{R}^d$ and $h \in \mathcal{V}(\mathbb{R}^d)$, the p.g.fl. G satisfies*

(10.1.6) $$G[h(\cdot)] = G[h(\cdot - u)].$$

If, moreover, ξ is a simple point process, the conditions are equivalent to the following.

(iv) *For each $u \in \mathbb{R}^d$ and all bounded Borel sets $A \in \mathcal{B}(\mathbb{R}^d)$, the avoidance function $P_0(\cdot)$ of ξ satisfies*

(10.1.7) $$P_0(A) = P_0(A + u).$$

Furthermore, in (i) and (iv) it is sufficient for the results to hold for disjoint sets A_i and A from a dissecting semiring generating $\mathcal{B}(\mathbb{R}^d)$.

The final statement of the theorem implies that is enough in (i) and (iv) to have the statements holding for disjoint sets, which can be represented as finite unions of half-open rectangles. It is not possible to relax this condition significantly: in $\mathbb{R}^1$ the counterexample of Lee quoted in Exercise 2.3.1 exhibits two processes with the same distributions for $N(I)$ whenever I is an interval, one of these processes being stationary (indeed, a stationary Poisson process) and the other not. See also Exercise 10.1.2.

The examples below illustrate some applications of Theorem 10.1.III.

EXAMPLE 10.1(a) *The Poisson process* (continued from Example 7.4(a)). From the representation of the p.g.fl. at (7.4.10) we have, for $\mathcal{X} = \mathbb{R}^d$,

$$\log G[h(\cdot - u)] = \int_{\mathcal{X}} (h(x - u) - 1)\mu(dx) = \int_{\mathcal{X}} (h(y) - 1)(S_u\mu)(dy),$$

which under the assumption of stationarity at (10.1.6) is to be equal to

$$\int_{\mathcal{X}} (h(y) - 1)\mu(dy).$$

Since the measure μ is completely determined by its integrals of functions of the form $h(y) - 1$ for $h \in \mathcal{V}(\mathbb{R}^d)$, it follows that a Poisson process is stationary if and only if its parameter measure is invariant under translation. Since the only measure on $\mathbb{R}^d$ invariant under translations is Lebesgue measure, $\mu(\cdot)$ must be a multiple of Lebesgue measure on $\mathbb{R}^d$; that is, for some $\mu \geq 0$,

$$\mu(\cdot) = \mu\ell(\cdot).$$

Alternatively, we may first observe that a stationary random measure can have no fixed atoms, then use the fact (Theorem 2.4.II) that a Poisson process has no fixed atoms if and only if its parameter measure is nonatomic, in which case the process is simple, and finally appeal to (10.1.7), which yields

$$e^{-\mu(A)} = e^{-\mu(A+u)},$$

implying the same result even more directly.

EXAMPLE 10.1(b) *Random thinnings and translations* (continued from Examples 8.2(a) and 8.2(b)). Let N be a stationary point process and assume that each point x_i of a realization of N is independently and randomly shifted through a random distance X_i, where the $\{X_i\}$ are identically distributed with common d.f. $F(\cdot)$, which may be defective: set $q = 1 - F(\mathbb{R}^d)$. Then from Example 8.2(b) the p.g.fl.s G and G_c of the shifted process and N, respectively, are related by

$$G[h(\cdot)] = G_c\left[q + \int_x h(y)F(dy - \cdot)\right].$$

Now, much as in the previous example, if G_c is itself stationary, we have $G_c[h(\cdot)] = G_c[h(\cdot - u)]$ for all $u \in \mathbb{R}^d$ and $h \in \mathcal{V}(\mathbb{R}^d)$. Then the right-hand side of the expression for $G[\cdot]$ equals

$$G_c\left[q + \int_x h(y - u)F(dy - \cdot)\right] = G[h(\cdot - u)],$$

and thus by (iii) the transformed process is again stationary. Random deletions result when F is concentrated at 0 and pure translations when $q = 0$.

The stationarity of Cox processes and some cluster processes can be verified by similar techniques (see Exercises 10.1.3–10.1.6). The use of (i) or (iv) rather than (ii) or (iii) of Theorem 10.1.III is indicated in the next example.

EXAMPLE 10.1(c) *Stationary renewal process and regenerative measure* (cf. the direct treatment in Section 4.2 and the formal discussion in Example 7.1(b) and Exercises 7.1.3 and 7.1.4). The following definition is more general than is needed to discuss stationary renewal processes, but it will be used later to exhibit an example of a weakly singular infinitely divisible point process.

Let μ be a measure defined on the space of sequences $\{Y_n : n = 0, 1, \ldots\}$ satisfying $Y_0 = 0 \le Y_1 \le \cdots \le Y_n \to \infty$ $(n \to \infty)$, and put $X_n = Y_n - Y_{n-1}$ $(n = 1, 2, \ldots)$. We call μ *regenerative* when for any positive integer r and $x_i \in \mathbb{R}_+$ $(i = 1, \ldots, r)$,

$$\mu(\{X_i \in (x_i, x_i + dx_i], i = 1, \ldots, r\}) = \mu_1(x_1, x_1 + dx_1] \prod_{i=2}^{r} F((x_i, x_i + dx_i]),$$

where μ_1 is a boundedly finite measure on $\mathbb{R}_+$ and F is a d.f. as in Exercise 7.1.3. Then it follows that μ defines a measure on $\mathcal{B}(\mathcal{N}_x)$.

Our first aim is to show that when

$$\mu_1(x_1, x_1 + dx_1] = [1 - F(x_1)]dx_1,$$

the measure μ is invariant under shifts S_u for $u > 0$, much as in Definition 10.1.II in the case of a probability measure. When the boundedly finite counting measure $N(\cdot)$ on $\mathbb{R}_+$ consists of a succession of unit atoms at Y_1, $Y_2, \ldots$, with $N[0, Y_r] = r$ for $r = 1, 2, \ldots$, as in Exercise 7.1.4, the successive atoms $\{Y_n'\}$ for the counting measure $N(T_u \cdot)$ for $u > 0$ are given by

$$Y_n' = Y_{n+v} - u,$$

where the index $v = 0$ if $Y_1 > u$, $= \sup\{n: Y_n \le u\}$ otherwise. Consequently, the measure $S_u \mu$ on $\{Y_n'\}$ is related to μ, writing $X_n' = Y_n' - Y_{n-1}'$ ($Y_0' \equiv 0$), by

$$(S_u \mu)(\{X_i' \in (x_i, x_i + dx_i], i = 1, \ldots, r\})$$

$$= (\{X_1 \in (u + x_1, u + x_1 + dx_1], X_i \in (x_i, x_i + dx_i], i = 2, \ldots, r\})$$

$$+ \sum_{j=1}^{\infty} \mu(\{X_1 + \cdots + X_j \le u, X_1 + \cdots + X_{j+1} \in (u + x_1, u + x_1 + dx_1],$$

$$X_{j+i} \in (x_i, x_i + dx_i], i = 2, \ldots, r\})$$

$$= \left[\mu(\{X_1 \in (u + x_1, u + x_1 + dx_1]\}) + \sum_{j=1}^{\infty} \mu(\{X_1 + \cdots + X_j \le u,$$

$$X_1 + \cdots + X_{j+1} \in (u + x_1, u + x_1 + dx_1]\}) \right] \times \prod_{i=2}^{r} F((x_i, x_i + dx_i]).$$

For convenience, integrate x_1 over $(0, y]$ say, so that on the right-hand side, when $\mu_1(0, y] = \int_0^y [1 - F(x_1)] dx_1$, the coefficient of the product of $F(\cdot)$ values equals

$$\int_u^{u+y} [1 - F(x_1)] dx_1 + \sum_{j=1}^{\infty} \int \cdots \int [1 - F(x_1)] dx_1 F(dx_2) \cdots F(dx_{j+1}),$$

where the multiple integral is over the set $\{x_1 + \cdots + x_j \le u, u < x_1 + \cdots + x_{j+1} \le u + y\}$. Writing $U_1(x) = \sum_{j=1}^{\infty} F^{j*}(x)$ so that U_1 satisfies the renewal equation

$$U_1(x) = F(x) + \int_0^x F(x - y) U_1(dy),$$

the multiple integral can be expressed as

$$\int_0^u [1 - F(x_1)] dx_1 \int_{u-x_1}^{u-x_1+y} F(dx_2) + \int_0^u U_1(dv) \int_0^{u-v} [1 - F(x_1)] dx_1$$

$$\times \int_{u-x_1-v}^{u-x_1-v+y} F(dx_2) = \int_0^u [1 - F(u - x)] dx \int_x^{x+y} F(dz)$$

$$+ \int_0^u U_1(dv) \int_0^{u-v} [1 - F(u - v - x)] dx \int_x^{x+y} F(dz).$$

The second term equals

$$\int_0^u dx \int_0^{u-x} [1 - F(u - x - v)] U_1(dv) \int_x^{x+y} F(dz)$$

$$= \int_0^u F(u - x) dx \int_x^{x+y} F(dz),$$

so the coefficient of the product of $F(\cdot)$ values equals

$$\int_u^{u+y} [1 - F(x)]dx + \int_0^u [F(y + x) - F(x)]dx = \int_0^y [1 - F(x)]dx,$$

showing that μ is invariant as required.

When $\int_0^\infty [1 - F(x)]dx \equiv \lambda^{-1} < \infty$, $\lambda\mu(\cdot)$ is a probability measure, and we can then describe the counting measures $N(\cdot)$ with such a stationary distribution as a *stationary renewal process*.

The following proposition will be used in discussing stationary infinitely divisible point processes; the result is of wider importance (e.g., see Section 3.4 and the discussion of parallel lines in a stationary line process preceding Proposition 10.6.V).

Proposition 10.1.IV. *For a stationary random measure ξ on $\mathscr{X} = \mathbb{R}^d$,*

$$\mathscr{P}\{\xi(\mathscr{X}) = 0 \text{ or } \infty\} = 1.$$

PROOF. The assertion is equivalent to showing that $\mathscr{P}\{0 < \xi(\mathscr{X}) < \infty\} = 0$. Supposing the contrary, it necessarily follows that there exists some positive constants a and γ such that for the hypercube $\mathbb{U}_\gamma^d$ with vertices $(\pm\gamma/2, \ldots, \pm\gamma/2)$ and its complement $(\mathbb{U}_\gamma^d)^c$,

$$\mathscr{P}\{\xi(\mathbb{U}_\gamma^d) > a, \xi((\mathbb{U}_\gamma^d)^c) < a\} = \alpha > 0.$$

Now write $T_{\gamma r}\mathbb{U}_\gamma^d$ for the shift of $\mathbb{U}_\gamma^d$ through the vector $\gamma r = (\gamma r_1, \ldots, \gamma r_d)$, where r has integer-valued components, and consider the events

$$V_r = \{\xi: \xi(T_{\gamma r}\mathbb{U}_\gamma^d) > a, \xi(T_{\gamma r}(\mathbb{U}_\gamma^d)^c) < a\}.$$

By stationarity,

$$\mathscr{P}(V_r) = \mathscr{P}(V_0) = \alpha$$

for all r, and since the events V_r are disjoint for distinct r,

$$\mathscr{P}\left(\bigcup_r V_r\right) = \sum_r \mathscr{P}(V_r) = \infty \cdot \alpha,$$

which is impossible when $\mathscr{P}$ is a probability measure unless $\alpha = 0$. □

We now consider the implications of demanding that an infinitely divisible point process be stationary. In the notation of Section 8.4, let $\tilde{Q}$ denote the KLM measure of such a process so that from (8.4.9)

$$(10.1.8) \quad \log G[h(\cdot - u)] = \int_{\mathscr{N}_0(\mathscr{X})} \left(\exp\left[\int_{\mathscr{X}} \log h(x - u)\tilde{N}(dx)\right] - 1\right)\tilde{Q}(d\tilde{N})$$

$$= \int_{\mathscr{N}_0(\mathscr{X})} \left(\exp\left[\int_{\mathscr{X}} \log h(y)\tilde{N}(dy)\right] - 1\right)\tilde{Q}(S_u d\tilde{N}),$$

which must coincide with the original form of (8.4.9),

$$\log G[h] = \int_{\mathcal{N}_0(\mathcal{X})} \left(\exp\left[\int_{\mathcal{X}} \log h(y) \tilde{N}(dy) \right] - 1 \right) \tilde{Q}(d\tilde{N})$$

if the random measure is to be stationary. As in (10.1.3) we can define a new measure $\hat{S}_u \tilde{Q}$ through

$$\hat{S}_u \tilde{Q}(B) = \tilde{Q}\{\tilde{N} : S_u \tilde{N} \in B\}$$

so that (10.1.8) could equally well be written in the form (8.4.9) with $\hat{S}_u \tilde{Q}$ in place of $\tilde{Q}$. But by Theorem 8.4.V the KLM measure is unique, so $\tilde{Q}$ and $\hat{S}_u \tilde{Q}$ must coincide, and we have established the following result (see also Exercise 10.1.7).

Proposition 10.1.V. *An infinitely divisible point process on $\mathbb{R}^d$ is stationary if and only if its KLM measure is stationary (i.e., invariant under the shifts $\hat{S}_u$).*

Consider a stationary infinitely divisible point process whose KLM measure $\tilde{Q}$ is totally finite, so that $\mathcal{P}(\cdot) \equiv \tilde{Q}(\cdot)/\tilde{Q}(\mathcal{N}_0(\mathcal{X}))$ is the probability measure of a stationary point process $\tilde{N}$ for which $\mathcal{P}\{\tilde{N}(\mathcal{X}) = 0\} = 0$, and so by Proposition 10.1.IV we must have $\mathcal{P}\{\tilde{N}(\mathcal{X}) = \infty\} = 1$. This is enough to prove (i) of the following result, which can be used to strengthen (iii) of Proposition 8.4.VIII in the stationary case.

Proposition 10.1.VI. *Let N be a stationary infinitely divisible point process on $\mathbb{R}^d$.*

(i) *If N has a representation as a Poisson randomization then it is singular.*

(ii) *N is regular if and only if it can be represented as a Poisson cluster process with a stationary Poisson process of cluster centres and a cluster structure that depends only on the relative locations of the points in a cluster and not on the location of the cluster itself.*

PROOF. From the decomposition result at Proposition 8.4.VII of the regular and singular parts of an infinitely divisible point process, and from the fact that $\hat{S}_u$ maps $\{\tilde{N} \in \mathcal{N}_0(\mathcal{X}) : \tilde{N}(\mathcal{X}) = \infty\}$ into itself, it follows that we may discuss the effects of stationarity separately for each type of process. Now from the discussion in Sections 8.3 and 8.4 we know that a regular infinitely divisible point process has a representation as a cluster process. With $\mathcal{Y} = \mathcal{X} = \mathbb{R}^d$, each of the measures $K_k(\cdot \times \mathcal{Y}^{(k-1)})$ in Proposition 8.3.III must be invariant under shifts and so reduce to a multiple of Lebesgue measure on $\mathbb{R}^d$; the same then applies to the parameter measure μ of the Poisson process of the cluster centres [see (8.3.25)]. More generally, the measures $K_k(\cdot)$ must be invariant under the diagonal shifts of product sets $A_1 \times \cdots \times A_k$ as in the equation

$$K_k(T_u A_1 \times \cdots \times T_u A_k) = K_k(A_1 \times \cdots \times A_k).$$

Applying this property to the Radon–Nikodym derivatives $P_{k-1}(\cdot \mid x)$ defining the cluster structure, we deduce that, for fixed u and all x,

$$P_{k-1}(T_u A_2 \times \cdots \times T_u A_k | x + u) \quad \text{and} \quad P_{k-1}(A_2 \times \cdots \times A_k | x)$$

are versions of the same density and hence equal a.e. in x. It then follows (though the details are not quite trivial: see Exercise 10.1.9) that there exists a unique measure $\tilde{P}_{k-1}$ on $\mathcal{B}(\mathcal{X}^{(k-1)})$ such that

(10.1.9) $P_{k-1}(T_u A_2 \times \cdots \times T_u A_k | u) = \tilde{P}_{k-1}(A_2 \times \cdots \times A_k).$

The interpretation of $\tilde{P}_{k-1}$ is that it describes the location of cluster members relative to a given cluster member as centre, that is, taking that given member as the origin; then (10.1.9) asserts that these relative distributions are invariant under changes of the location of the cluster. This establishes the necessity part of the assertion in (ii).

The sufficiency part is outlined in Exercises 10.1.8 and 10.1.9.

An alternative proof uses Lemma A2.7.II.   □

Observe that, from (i) of this proposition, the singular infinitely divisible distributions can be classified into those with totally finite KLM measures, namely, the Poisson randomizations, and those with unbounded KLM measure. An alternative and more interesting classification can be based on the $\tilde{Q}$-measures of the sets of trajectories with zero or strictly positive asymptotic densities; however, we defer further discussion until after the treatment of ergodic theorems in Section 10.2.

EXAMPLE 10.1(d) *The regular representation of a stationary Neyman–Scott process.* In the Neyman–Scott model the cluster members have a common distribution $F(\cdot)$ about the cluster centre. To obtain the regular representation we should refer the distribution of the cluster members to an arbitrarily chosen member of the cluster itself as origin. For clusters with just one element we have evidently

$$\tilde{P}_0(A) = \delta_0(A);$$

that is, the cluster is necessarily centred at its sole representative. For $k = 2$ we obtain

$$\tilde{P}_1(A) = \Pr\{Y - X \in A\} = \int_{\mathcal{X}} F(dx)F(x + A),$$

where X, Y are independent random variables with the distribution F.

Similarly, for general k

$$\tilde{P}_{k-1}(A_2 \times \cdots \times A_k) = \int_{\mathcal{X}} F(dx)F(x + A_2) \cdots F(x + A_k).$$

In the branching process interpretation of the cluster members, $\tilde{P}_{k-1}$ gives the distribution of the locations of the other siblings given that the arbitrarily chosen member comes from a family of size k.

Note that this illustrates that the regular representation need not be the most convenient for computational or interpretative purposes.

The discussion so far has centred on invariance with respect to shifts in $\mathbb{R}^d$, but the ideas can be carried over with only nominal changes to processes invariant under other types of transformation, such as rotations, permutations of coordinates, or changes of scale. In the context of Appendix A2.7 we consider a group of transformations $\{T_g: g \in \mathscr{G}\}$ acting continuously on $\mathscr{X}$, for some c.s.m.s. $\mathscr{X}$ and taking bounded sets into bounded sets, and where $\mathscr{G}$ is a σ-group (a metric group that is a c.s.m.s. and has closed bounded sets compact). These assumptions imply that each T_g induces a mapping S_g, as at (10.1.3), which is, as there, a continuous mapping of $\mathscr{M}_{\mathscr{X}}$ (or $\mathscr{N}_{\mathscr{X}}$) into itself. We can then define a process that is invariant under the mappings $\{T_g\}$ as in Definition 10.1.II and invoke the same criteria for uniquely specifying the distribution of a process as were used to obtain the statements in Theorem 10.1.III. Thus, by making appropriate changes of notation and terminology, the results of that theorem apply to this more general context.

The main difficulties in applying these results relate to the fact that, in general, the group of transformations split the space into equivalence classes that may have quite a complex structure. By contrast, the shifts act transitively on the whole space (any point can be transformed by a member of $\mathscr{G}$ into any other point) so here the equivalence classes are trivial.

EXAMPLE 10.1(e) *Scale invariant Poisson processes.* We call a process on $\mathscr{X} = \mathbb{R}^d$ *scale invariant* if it is invariant under the group of scale changes $\{T_\alpha: 0 < \alpha < \infty\}$, where

$$(10.1.10) \qquad\qquad T_\alpha x = \alpha x, \qquad x \in \mathbb{R}^d.$$

For $d = 1$ there are three equivalence classes, $(-\infty, 0)$, $\{0\}$, and $(0, \infty)$, the first and third of which we may identify with the two-point group $\mathscr{T}_2 = \{-1, 1\}$ under multiplication. A measure on $\mathbb{R}^1$ can then be considered as a point mass at zero and a measure on the product space $\mathscr{T}_2 \times \mathbb{R}_+$. $\mathbb{R}_+$ is a group under multiplication and it has the unique invariant measure $h(dx) = dx/x$. It is now obvious, but it also follows from Lemma A2.7.II, that any measure on $\mathbb{R}^1 \backslash \{0\}$, which is invariant under scale changes, can be represented as a direct product of a two-point mass on $\mathscr{T}_2$ and the measure $h(\cdot)$ on $\mathbb{R}_+$. In general, therefore, a measure on $\mathbb{R}^1$ that is invariant under scale changes can be represented as the sum of three components: a point mass at zero, a nonnegative multiple $m_1 \, dx/x$ on $(0, \infty)$, and a nonnegative multiple $m_2 \, dx/|x|$ on $(-\infty, 0)$.

Now consider a Poisson process invariant under scale changes. As in Example 10.1(a) we deduce that the parameter measure must be invariant under scale changes and must therefore have the structure described above. In particular, it follows from this discussion that *a Poisson process cannot be simultaneously invariant under both scale changes and translations.* A similar argument can be applied to the first moment measure of a point process, whenever it exists, so that we can deduce more generally that *no stationary random measure with finite expectation measure can be scale invariant.*

Next, consider the situation in the plane. The mapping $(r, \theta) \to (r \cos \theta,$ $r \sin \theta)$ provides a representation of $\mathbb{R}^2 \backslash \{0\}$ as the product set $\mathbb{R}_+ \times \mathbb{S}$, where $\mathbb{S}$ is the circle group. We deduce from Lemma A2.7.II that a scale invariant measure on $\mathbb{R}^2$ can be represented as the sum of a point mass at the origin and a measure $\kappa(d\theta)dr/r$ on $\mathbb{R}^2 \backslash \{0\}$, where $\kappa(\cdot)$ is an arbitrary totally finite measure on $\mathbb{S}$. An analogous representation holds for the intensity measure of a scale invariant Poisson process on $\mathbb{R}^2$ and, indeed, for Poisson processes on $\mathbb{R}^d$ for all finite integers $d \geq 2$.

Considerable interest has focused recently (Mandelbrot, 1975; Taqqu, 1978; Sinai, 1976) on processes that are scale invariant in a weaker sense than that used above. We call a random measure *self-similar*, with similarity parameter H, a finite positive constant, if its distribution is invariant under the group of transformations $\{R_\alpha^{(H)}: \alpha \in \mathbb{R}_+\}$ defined by

$$(10.1.11) \qquad\qquad R_\alpha^{(H)} \mu(A) = \alpha^{-H} \mu(\alpha A) \qquad (A \in \mathscr{B}_{\mathscr{X}}).$$

Here, change in mass compensates for the scale change. The transformations $R_\alpha^{(H)}$ do not result simply from transformations of the phase space $\mathscr{X}$ but do still define a group, the *renormalization group*, of bounded continuous transformations of $\mathscr{M}(\mathbb{R}^d)$ into itself. Because of the change in mass, the group does not map $\mathscr{N}(\mathbb{R}^d)$ into itself, so that a self-similar point process cannot exist. Self-similar processes typically exhibit long-term dependence and have been studied principally for Gaussian processes and their functionals. Stable processes can also exhibit self-similarity as in the next example.

EXAMPLE 10.1(f) *Self-similar completely random measures.* We start from the representation for completely random measures given in Theorem 6.3.VIII. From (6.3.12) we have (in differential notation)

$$R_\alpha^{(H)} \xi(dx) = \alpha^{-H} \nu(\alpha\, dx) + \int_0^\infty y\alpha^{-H} N(\alpha\, dx \times dy) + \sum U_k \alpha^{-H} \delta_{x_k/\alpha}(dx)$$

$$= \alpha^{-H} \nu(\alpha\, dx) + \int_0^\infty yN(\alpha\, dx \times \alpha^H\, dy) + \sum U_k \alpha^{-H} \delta_{x_k/\alpha}(dx),$$

which, from the uniqueness of the representation, shows that the transformed random measure again has the completely random property, with the measure ν transformed by $R_\alpha^{(H)}$ as at (10.1.11), the bivariate Poisson process N subjected to the transformation on $\mathscr{X} \times \mathbb{R}_+$ given by

$$(10.1.12) \qquad\qquad D_\alpha^{(H)}(x, y) = (\alpha x, \alpha^H y),$$

and the fixed atoms transformed both in mass and in location.

   If the distribution of the completely random measure is to remain invariant under all transformations $R_\alpha^{(H)}$ ($\alpha > 0$), then it is clear that there can be no fixed atoms, that the (deterministic) measure ν must be invariant under the transformations $R_\alpha^{(H)}$, and that the parameter measure μ of the bivariate

Poisson process N must be invariant under the transformations $D_\alpha^{(H)}$. Thus, we have reduced the problem of characterizing the class of self-similar completely random measures to the problem of characterizing the classes of measures invariant under these two groups of transformations.

For simplicity we consider only the case $\mathscr{X} = \mathbb{R}^1$; the details for the case $\mathscr{X} = \mathbb{R}^d$ are similar (see Exercise 10.1.8 for the case $d = 2$).

As in Example 10.1(e), it is necessary to consider separately the action of the transformations on $\mathbb{R}_+$, $\{0\}$, and $\mathbb{R}_-$. Since the processes have no fixed atoms, $v\{0\} = 0$ and μ, the parameter measure of N, has $\mu(\{0\} \times \mathbb{R}_+) = 0$. Thus, we may consider the effect of $R_\alpha^{(H)}$ and $D_\alpha^{(H)}$ on $\mathbb{R}_+$ and $\mathbb{R}_+ \times \mathbb{R}_+$, respectively, with similar results following for these effects on $\mathbb{R}_-$ and $\mathbb{R}_- \times \mathbb{R}_+$.

Write $r(x) = v(0, x)$, so that invariance of v under $R_\alpha^{(H)}$ implies

$$\alpha^{-H} r(\alpha x) = r(x) \qquad (\alpha > 0, x > 0);$$

hence, setting $x = 1$, $r(\alpha) = \alpha^H r(1) = c_1 \alpha^H$ for some nonnegative constant c_1. Thus v on $\mathbb{R}_+$ is expressible there in terms of Lebesgue measure ℓ as $v(dx) = c_1 x^{H-1} \ell(dx)$ $(0 < x < \infty)$. Similarly, on $\mathbb{R}_-$, we have $v(dx) = c_2 |x|^{H-1} \ell(dx)$ $(-\infty < x < 0)$.

Next, consider the representation of the parameter measure μ on the quadrant $\mathbb{R}_+ \times \mathbb{R}_+$. Invariance of the distribution of N under (10.1.12) implies that μ is invariant under shifts along the curves $x^H/y = \text{constant}$. This suggests writing

$$u = \log x, \qquad v = H \log x - \log y,$$

so that in the (u, v) plane the transformations (10.1.12) reduce to

$$(u, v) \to (u + \log \alpha, v).$$

We now deduce from Lemma A2.7.II that $\tilde{\mu}$, the image of μ under this mapping, reduces to a product of Lebesgue measure along the u axis and an arbitrary measure $\tilde{\rho}$ along the v axis. Thus, integration with respect to μ can be represented in the form

$$(10.1.13) \qquad \int_0^\infty \int_0^\infty f(x, y)\mu(dx \times dy) = \int_{-\infty}^\infty \int_{-\infty}^\infty f(e^u, e^{Hu-v})du\,\tilde{\rho}(dv).$$

If, in particular, $\tilde{\rho}$ is absolutely continuous with respect to Lebesgue measure so that $\tilde{\rho}(dv) = \tilde{\rho}_1(v)dv$, then on $\mathbb{R}_+ \times \mathbb{R}_+$,

$$\mu(dx \times dy) = \tilde{\rho}_1(\log(x^H/y))x^{-1}y^{-1}\,dx\,dy \equiv \rho_1(x^H/y)x^{-1}y^{-1}\,dx\,dy.$$

Similar considerations may be applied on $\mathbb{R}_- \times \mathbb{R}_+$. With such absolutely continuous measures $\tilde{\rho}$, the Laplace functional $L[f]$ for the random measure ξ takes the form

$$(10.1.14a) \qquad L[f] = \exp\{L_1[f] + L_2[f]\} \qquad (f \in BM_+(\mathbb{R})),$$

where

(10.1.14b) $L_1[f] = -c_1 \int_0^\infty x^{H-1} f(x) dx$

$$+ \int_0^\infty \int_0^\infty (e^{yf(x)} - 1) \rho_1(x^H/y) x^{-1} \, dx \, y^{-1} \, dy$$

and a similar expression holds for L_2 with c_1 replaced by c_2, $\rho_1(x^H/y)$ by $\rho_2(|x|^H/y)$, and integration of x is over $(-\infty, 0)$; furthermore, ρ_1 and ρ_2 must be chosen so as to satisfy the constraints (6.3.13), which when expressed in the form

$$\int_0^\infty (1 - e^{-y}) \mu(A \times dy) < \infty \quad \text{(bounded } A \in \mathcal{B}(\mathbb{R}))$$

lead after some manipulation to the requirements for $i = 1, 2$,

(10.1.15a) $\int_0^1 (1 + \log |z|) z^{-1} \rho_i(z) dz < \infty$,

(10.1.15b) $\int_1^\infty z^{-2} \rho_i(z) dz < \infty$.

We thus have a complete answer to the representation problem. For applications we generally require the random measure to be stationary as well as self-similar, in which case the representation must also be invariant under shifts along the x axis. In this case, the first term must vanish unless $H = 1$ when it reduces to a constant multiple of Lebesgue measure along the full real axis, while for the second term we must have $\rho_1(v) = \rho v^{1/H}$ and the constraints at (10.1.15) require $H < \infty$ and $H > 1$, respectively. Hence, it follows that the class of completely random measures that are both stationary and self-similar reduces, for $H = 1$, to the trivial example of a constant multiple of Lebesgue measure and, for $1 < H < \infty$, to the stable processes with index $\alpha = 1/H$ and Laplace functional of the form [see Example VIII.7(c) of Feller (1966)]

$$-\log L[f] = \rho \int_{-\infty}^\infty dx \int_0^\infty (1 - e^{-yf(x)}) y^{-1-1/H} \, dy$$

$$= \rho H \Gamma(1 - 1/H) \int_{-\infty}^\infty (f(x))^{1/H} \, dx.$$

Exercises

10.1.1. Show that $\hat{S}_u$ defined at (10.1.3) is a continuous and hence measurable mapping of the space $\mathcal{M}(\mathcal{M}_{\mathcal{X}})$ of boundedly finite measures on $\mathcal{M}_{\mathcal{X}}$ into itself. Show also that $\hat{S}_u$ preserves measure and hence maps the set of all probability measures on $\mathcal{M}_{\mathcal{X}}$ into itself. Verify that $\hat{S}_u$ acts on the space $\mathcal{M}(\mathcal{N}_{\mathcal{X}})$ of all boundedly finite measures on $\mathcal{N}_{\mathcal{X}}$ in a similar way. [*Hint*: $\hat{S}_u$ inherits the properties of S_u in the same kind of way that S_u inherits properties of T_u.]

10.1.2. Find counterexamples to the following statements: (a) a point process is stationary if its avoidance function is stationary and (b) a point process is stationary if its one-dimensional distributions are stationary. [*Hint*: For integer-valued r.v.s X, Y, and $X + Y$, with X, $Y \geq 0$ a.s., find a bivariate distribution for dependent X and Y with the same marginal distribution for $X + Y$ as though X, Y are independent. Take $\mathcal{X}$ = the integers $\{0, \pm 1, \ldots\}$, and define the fidi distributions of a point process by using the dependent and independent bivariate distributions for alternate pairs of integers (cf. Ripley, 1976).]

10.1.3. Show that a Cox process on $\mathbb{R}^d$ directed by the random measure ξ is stationary if and only if ξ is stationary.

10.1.4. Show that a cluster process on $\mathbb{R}^d$ is stationary if its cluster centre process is stationary and the cluster member process is homogeneous on $\mathbb{R}^d$, in the sense that the fidi distributions of the cluster member process depend only on the positions relative to the cluster centre. [*Hint*: Using the notation of Proposition 8.2.II, the last condition implies that for every x, $G_m[h(\cdot)|x] = G_m[h(\cdot + x)|0]$.]

10.1.5. The following two examples show that a stationary cluster process can be realized from nonstationary components (cf. Exercise 10.1.4).
   (a) In Example 8.2(a), a random thinning with deletion probability $|x|/(1 + |x|)$ at $x \in \mathbb{R}^1$ of an inhomogeneous Poisson process at rate $\mu(dx) = (1 + |x|)dx$ yields a stationary Poisson process.
   (b) Take a simple point process with points at $\{2n + U: n = 0, \pm 1, \ldots\}$, where the r.v. U is uniformly distributed on $(0, 1)$, to be a (nonstationary) cluster centre process. Let clusters be independent, and let them consist of precisely two points at distances X_1 and $1 + X_2$ from the cluster centre, where for each cluster X_1 and X_2 are i.i.d. r.v.s. Then the cluster process so constructed is the same as in Example 8.2(b) with stationary deterministic cluster centre process.

10.1.6. Let the r.v. Y be uniformly distributed over the unit cube $\mathbb{U}^d$ in $\mathbb{R}^d$, and let $\mathbb{Z}^d$ denote the set of all integer-valued lattice points in $\mathbb{R}^d$. Show that the point process N with sample realizations $\{n + Y: n \in \mathbb{Z}^d\}$ is stationary. (We call N the *stationary deterministic process* at unit rate in $\mathbb{R}^d$.)

10.1.7. Show that if an infinitely divisible point process on the c.s.m.s. $\mathcal{X}$ is invariant under a σ-group $\{T_g: g \in \mathcal{G}\}$ of transformations as in Proposition 10.1.IV, then its KLM measure is also invariant under the transformations $\hat{S}_g$ induced by $\{T_g\}$.

10.1.8. (a) Let $f(\cdot)$ be a nonnegative measurable function on $\mathbb{R}^1$ satisfying for each fixed $u \in \mathbb{R}^1$

$$(*) \qquad\qquad f(x + u) = f(x) \quad \text{(a.e. } x\text{)}.$$

Show that there exists a finite constant α such that $f(x) = \alpha$ (a.e. x). [*Hint*: Consider $F(y) = \int_0^y f(x)dx$ and show that $F(x + y) = F(x) + F(y)$.]
   (b) Extend the result of (a) to $\mathbb{R}^d$ [*Hint*: Apply (a) in a coordinate-wise manner to deduce, at the first step, for example, that in place of the constant α is a measurable function $\alpha(x_{d-1})$ $(x_{d-1} \in \mathbb{R}^{d-1})$ that satisfies $(*)$.]

10.1.9. (a) Show that the function $P_{k-1}(T_u A_2 \times \cdots \times T_u A_k | u)$ as around (10.1.9) is a measurable function of u for fixed $A_2, \ldots, A_k$, implying by part

(b) of the last exercise that $P_{k-1}(\cdot|\cdot)$ reduces a.e. u to a constant $P_{k-1}(A_2 \times \cdots \times A_k)$. [*Hint:* For fixed u, the Radon–Nikodym theorem shows that $P_{k-1}(T_u A_2 \times \cdots \times T_u A_k|x + u) = P_{k-1}(A_2 \times \cdots \times A_k|x) Q_k^1$-a.e. x. Integrate $Q_k(T_u A_1 \times \cdots \times T_u A_k)$ over u to establish, via application of the Radon–Nikodym and Fubini theorems, the joint measurability of $P_{k-1}(T_u A_2 \times \cdots \times T_u A_k|x + u)$, and hence, by putting $x = 0$, that $P_{k-1}(T_u A_2 \times \cdots \times T_u A_k|u)$ is a measurable function of u equal to $P_{k-1}(A_2 \times \cdots \times A_k|0)$ a.e. u.]

(b) Finally, take a countable semiring $\mathscr{A}$ generating $\mathscr{B}(\mathbb{R}^d)$ and show that $\tilde{P}_{k-1}$ is countably additive on product sets of the form $A_2 \times \cdots \times A_k$ for $A_i \in A$ and so can be extended uniquely to a measure $\tilde{P}$ on $\mathscr{B}(\mathbb{R}^{(k-1)d})$ such that

$$P_{k-1}(T_u A_2 \times \cdots \times T_u A_k|x) = \tilde{P}(A_2 \times \cdots \times A_k) \quad \text{(a.e. } x)$$

for all product sets with $A_i \in \mathscr{B}(\mathbb{R}^d)$.

10.1.10. For $n = 1, 2, \ldots$ let N_n be independent stationary infinitely divisible point processes on $\mathbb{R}$ that are Poisson randomizations (with mean number $= 1$) of Poisson processes at rate λ_n, where $\sum_1^\infty \lambda_n < \infty$. Verify that $N^* = \sum_1^\infty N_n$ is a well-defined stationary point process that is singular infinitely divisible with infinite KLM measure.

10.1.11. Find the representation of self-similar completely random measures in $\mathbb{R}^2$ analogous to (10.1.14), and investigate the effects of imposing the further conditions of (a) stationarity, or (b) isotropy, or (c) both.

10.2. Ergodic Theorems

In this section we review some basic results of ergodic theory and apply them to random measures.

Let $(\Omega, \mathscr{E}, \mu)$ be a measure space and S a measure-preserving operator on this space; that is, $\mu(S^{-1}E) = \mu(E)$ for $E \in \mathscr{E}$. The classical ergodic theorems assert the convergence, in some sense, of the averages $n^{-1}\sum_{r=1}^n f(S^r\omega)$ to a limit function $\bar{f}(\omega)$, which is invariant under the action of S [i.e., $\bar{f}(S\omega) = \bar{f}(\omega)$] for a measurable function f. When f is μ-integrable, the limit function $\bar{f}$ is also μ-integrable and the *individual ergodic theorem* asserts convergence μ-a.e. When $f \in L_p(\mu)$ for some $1 \le p < \infty$, $\bar{f} \in L_p(\mu)$ also and the *statistical ergodic theorem* asserts convergence in the L_p norm. In the case that μ is a probability measure, the limit function $\bar{f}(\omega)$ is a random variable that can be identified with the conditional expectation of f with respect to the σ-algebra $\mathscr{I}$ of *invariant events* under S, that is, of those sets $E \in \mathscr{E}$ for which $\mu(S^{-1}E \triangle E) = 0$. Writing X for $f(\omega)$, X_n for $X(S^n\omega)$, and $Y_X = E(X|\mathscr{I})$ for $\bar{f}$, the individual ergodic theorem in the probability case can be written more graphically in the form

$$(10.2.1) \qquad n^{-1} \sum_{r=1}^n X_r \to E(X|\mathscr{I}) \equiv Y_X \quad \text{(a.s.)}.$$

An important special case arises when the probability measure is such that the events in $\mathscr{I}$ all have probability measure either 0 or 1. In this case the transformation S is said to be *metrically transitive* with respect to the measure μ. In such circumstances the only invariant functions are constants, the conditional expectation in (10.2.1) reduces to the ordinary expectation, and (10.2.1) takes the familiar form

$$n^{-1} \sum_{r=1}^{n} X_r \to m \equiv EX.$$

For a fuller discussion of these results with proofs and references, see, for example, Billingsley (1965).

One other prefatory remark is in order. Given a stationary process $\{X(t): t \in \mathbb{R}\}$, the two σ-fields $\mathcal{I}_1$ and $\mathcal{I}$ invariant under the shift transformations $\{S_n: n = 0, \pm 1, \ldots\}$ and $\{S_t: t \in \mathbb{R}\}$, respectively, are in general different, with $\mathcal{I} \subset \mathcal{I}_1$. Of course, if $\mathcal{I}_1$ is trivial, then so is $\mathcal{I}$. This and the consequences of the sandwich argument below cover our main concerns.

We consider first the implications of these results for stationary random measures on $\mathbb{R}$. Here we take $\Omega = \mathcal{M}_{\mathbb{R}}$ and S as the shift through the unit distance. The measure-preserving character of S is then a corollary of stationarity. The simplest choice for X is the random variable

$$X = \int_0^1 \xi(dx),$$

which has finite expectation whenever ξ has finite mean intensity. Then

$$X_n = \int_0^1 \xi(n + dx) = \int_n^{n+1} \xi(dx)$$

and the assertion in (10.2.1) becomes

(10.2.2) $$n^{-1}\xi(0, n] \to E\left(\int_0^1 \xi(dx)|\mathcal{I}\right) \quad \text{(a.e.)}.$$

If, in particular, ξ is ergodic then

(10.2.3) $$n^{-1}\xi(0, n] \to m \quad \text{(a.e.)}.$$

The results (10.2.2) and (10.2.3) seem simple, but they can be applied to many more general situations of which the simplest is to a continuous time process. Observe first that the simple sandwich argument

$$\frac{[T]}{T} \cdot \frac{\xi(0, [T]]}{[T]} \leq \frac{\xi(0, T]}{T} \leq \frac{[T + 1]}{T} \cdot \frac{\xi(0, [T + 1]]}{[T + 1]}$$

extends (10.2.2) to arbitrary intervals, so that

(10.2.4) $$T^{-1}\xi(0, T] \to E\left(\int_0^1 \xi(dx)|\mathcal{I}\right) \quad \text{(a.s.)}.$$

Because the limit is invariant under all shifts $\{S_t: t \in \mathbb{R}\}$, it is $\mathcal{I}$-measurable rather than just $\mathcal{I}_1$-measurable, so that the conditional expectation can and will be taken with respect to $\mathcal{I}$. When $X(\cdot)$ is a stationary measurable stochastic process, on $\mathbb{R}$ say, and $f(\cdot)$ a nonnegative measurable function on

$\mathbb{R}$ such that $Ef(X(t)) < \infty$, we can define a random measure ξ with finite mean intensity by setting

$$\xi(A) = \int_A f(X(t))dt.$$

Applying (10.2.4) to such ξ yields the result

$$\frac{1}{T} \int_0^T f(X(t))dt \to E(f(X(t))|\mathscr{I}) \quad \text{(a.s.)}.$$

The only restricting feature is the limitation to nonnegative functions f: this is in fact not inherent in the ergodic problem but arises from our concern with random measures rather than random signed measures.

A similar situation obtains in higher-dimensional spaces and in the more general context considered at the end of Section 10.1. The main point of difficulty concerns the choice of averaging sets to replace the intervals $(0, n]$ in (10.2.2). Even in the plane it is not difficult to find sequences $\{A_n\}$ with $A_n \subset A_{n+1}$ and $\ell(A_n) \to \infty$ such that the analogue of (10.2.2) fails in some cases (see Exercise 10.2.1). To consider this question further, let $(\Omega, \mathscr{E}, \mu)$ be a measure space acted on measurably [i.e., so that $(g, \omega) \to S_g\omega$ is jointly measurable] by the group of measurable transformations $\{S_g: g \in \mathscr{G}\}$, where $\mathscr{G}$ is a σ-group with unique right invariant Haar measure χ. Note the most important fact that averaging in ergodic theorems takes place over sets in $\mathscr{G}$ and not the state space $\mathscr{X}$. For example, the individual ergodic theorem takes the form that, for suitable sequences $\{A_n\}$,

$$(10.2.5) \qquad \frac{1}{\chi(A_n)} \int_{A_n} f(S_g\omega)\chi(dg) \to \overline{f}(\omega) \quad (\mu\text{-a.e.}),$$

where, in the probability case, $\overline{f}(\omega)$ is the conditional expectation $E(f|\mathscr{I})$ with respect to the σ-algebra of events invariant under the whole family $\{S_g: g \in \mathscr{G}\}$.

A thorough discussion of extensions of the classical ergodic theorems to this context is given by Tempel'man (1972), who sets out a range of conditions on the sequence $\{A_n\}$—some necessary, others sufficient—for the validity both of (10.2.5) and of corresponding statistical ergodic theorems. For the present discussion we adopt only the simplest of the conditions he describes.

Definition 10.2.I. Let $\mathscr{X} = \mathbb{R}^d$. The sequence $\{A_n\}$ of bounded Borel sets in $\mathbb{R}^d$ is a *convex averaging sequence* if

(i) each A_n is convex,
(ii) $A_n \subseteq A_{n+1}$ for $n = 1, 2, \ldots$, and
(iii) $r(A_n) \to \infty$ as $n \to \infty$, where $r(A) = \sup\{r: A \text{ contains a ball of radius } r\}$.

Using this terminology, we set out versions of the individual and statistical ergodic theorems, referring to Tempel'man (1972) for proofs and further extensions.

Proposition 10.2.II (a) (Individual ergodic theorem for d-dimensional shifts). *Let $(\Omega, \mathscr{E}, \mathscr{P})$ be a probability space, $\{S_x: x \in \mathbb{R}^d\}$ a group of measure-preserving transformations acting measurably on $(\Omega, \mathscr{E}, \mathscr{P})$ and indexed by the points of $\mathbb{R}^d$, $\{A_n: n = 1, 2, \ldots\}$ a convex averaging sequence in $\mathbb{R}^d$, and $\mathscr{I}$ the σ-algebra of events in $\mathscr{E}$ that are invariant under the transformations $\{S_x\}$. Then for all measurable functions (random variables) f on $(\Omega, \mathscr{E}, \mathscr{P})$ with $E|f| < \infty$,*

$$(10.2.6) \qquad \frac{1}{\ell(A_n)} \int_{A_n} f(S_x \omega) dx \to E(f|\mathscr{I}) \quad \text{(a.s.)}.$$

(b) (*Statistical ergodic theorems for d-dimensional shifts*). *Under the conditions as in (a) and $p \geq 1$,*

$$(10.2.7) \qquad E \left| \frac{1}{\ell(A_n)} \int_{A_n} f(S_x \omega) dx - E(f|\mathscr{I}) \right|^p \to 0$$

for all $f \in L_p(\mathscr{P})$.

We remark that in general the statistical ergodic theorem holds under weaker conditions on the sequence $\{A_n\}$ than the individual ergodic theorem. Versions of the theorem remain true when the probability measure $\mathscr{P}$ is replaced by a σ-finite measure μ, subject of course to the condition that $\int |f(\omega)| \mu(d\omega) < \infty$; we shall need such a version in discussing the KLM measure of stationary infinitely divisible processes.

Our task is to apply these theorems to stationary random measures on the c.s.m.s. $\mathscr{X}$: we consider two cases, $\mathscr{X} = \mathbb{R}^d$ and $\mathscr{X} = \mathbb{R}^d \times \mathscr{K}$, where the c.s.m.s. $\mathscr{K}$ may be considered a space of marks (cf. Definition 7.1.XII). With $\mathscr{X} = \mathbb{R}^d$, we identify $(\Omega, \mathscr{E})$ with the space $(\hat{\mathscr{M}}_{\mathscr{X}}, \mathscr{B}(\hat{\mathscr{M}}_{\mathscr{X}}))$ of boundedly finite measures ξ defined on $\mathscr{B}_{\mathscr{X}}$, and S_x with the shift taking $\xi(\cdot)$ into $\xi(\cdot + x)$. If ξ has finite first moment measure, stationarity requires that this should reduce to a constant multiple $m\ell(\cdot)$ of Lebesgue measure on $\mathbb{R}^d$. More generally, if $\mathscr{X} = \mathbb{R}^d \times \mathscr{K}$, we still take $(\Omega, \mathscr{E}) = (\hat{\mathscr{M}}_{\mathscr{X}}, \mathscr{B}(\hat{\mathscr{M}}_{\mathscr{X}}))$ but identify $\{S_x\}$ with shifts in the first coordinate only. In this case the factorization lemma A2.7.II implies that the first moment measure has the product form $\ell \times v$, where v is a boundedly finite measure on $\mathscr{K}$. We proceed to an extension of these remarks to the conditional expectation of ξ with respect to the appropriate invariant σ-algebra $\mathscr{I}$.

Lemma 10.2.III. *Let ξ be a random measure on the product space $\mathscr{X} = \mathbb{R}^d \times \mathscr{K}$, $\mathscr{I}$ the σ-algebra of invariant events with respect to the shifts S_x in $\mathbb{R}^d$, and suppose that ξ is stationary with respect to these shifts and that its expectation measure exists. Then there exists an $\mathscr{I}$-measurable random measure $\psi(\cdot)$ on $\mathscr{K}$ such that for all nonnegative measurable functions f on $\mathscr{X}$,*

$$(10.2.8) \quad E\left(\int_{\mathbb{R}^d \times \mathscr{K}} f(x, k) \xi(dx \times dk) \Big| \mathscr{I} \right) = \int_{\mathscr{K}} \psi(dk) \int_{\mathbb{R}^d} f(x, k) \ell(dx) \quad (\mathscr{P}\text{-a.s.}).$$

In particular, for $B \in \mathscr{B}(\mathbb{R}^d)$ and $K \in \mathscr{B}_{\mathscr{K}}$,

$$(10.2.9) \qquad E(\xi(B \times K)|\mathscr{I}) = \ell(B) \psi(K) \quad (\mathscr{P}\text{-a.s.}).$$

PROOF. Let X be any r.v. on $(\Omega, \mathscr{E}, \mathscr{P})$ with finite expectation and $G \in \mathscr{I}$ be an invariant set, so that $\mathscr{P}(G \triangle S_x G) = 0$. Then

$$\int_G X(\omega)\mathscr{P}(d\omega) = \int_{S_x G} X(\omega)\mathscr{P}(d\omega) = \int_G X(S_{-x}\omega)\mathscr{P}(d(S_{-x}\omega))$$

$$= \int_G X(S_{-x}\omega)\mathscr{P}(d\omega).$$

Thus, for all $x \in \mathbb{R}^d$, we have

$$(10.2.10) \qquad\qquad E(X|\mathscr{I}) = E(S_x X|\mathscr{I}) \quad (\mathscr{P}\text{-a.s.}).$$

Take $X = \xi(A)$, and recall from Proposition 6.1.VII that there is a version of the conditional expectation, $E(\xi(\cdot)|\mathscr{I}) \equiv \eta(\cdot)$ say, which is again a random measure. Then (10.2.10) asserts that

$$\eta(S_x A) = \eta(A) \quad (\mathscr{P}\text{-a.s.}).$$

Take A of the form $B \times K$ as at (10.2.9), and let B and K run through the members of countable rings generating $\mathscr{B}(\mathbb{R}^d)$ and $\mathscr{B}_\mathscr{K}$, respectively, and x through a countable dense set in $\mathbb{R}^d$. Since only a countable family of null sets is involved, we can assume that (10.2.10) holds simultaneously for all such B, K, x, and for ω outside a single set V with $\mathscr{P}(V) = 0$. For $\omega \notin V$ it now follows from Lemma A2.7.II that

$$\eta(B \times K, \omega) = \ell(B)\psi(K, \omega)$$

for some kernel ψ on $\mathscr{K} \times \Omega$. But $\eta(\cdot)$ was chosen to be an $\mathscr{I}$-measurable random measure, so for each K the left-hand side is an $\mathscr{I}$-measurable r.v. (more precisely, it can be extended to all $\omega \in \Omega$, in such a way as to form such a r.v.). Also, for a fixed $\omega \notin V$, $\psi(K, \omega)$ is countably additive and its extension to V can be constructed so as to retain this property. Thus, $\psi(\cdot)$ is a random measure on $\mathscr{K}$, from Proposition 6.1.III. This establishes (10.2.9), and (10.2.8) follows by standard extension arguments. $\qquad\square$

In the special case that $\mathscr{X} = \mathbb{R}^d$, $\mathscr{K}$ reduces to a single point, and thus the random measure ψ is then an $\mathscr{I}$-measurable random variable

$$Y = E(\xi(\mathbb{U}^d)|\mathscr{I}),$$

where $\mathbb{U}^d$ is the unit cube in $\mathbb{R}^d$. Then (10.2.10) becomes the more familiar assertion that

$$(10.2.10') \qquad\qquad E(\xi(A)|\mathscr{I}) = Y\ell(A) \quad (\mathscr{P}\text{-a.s.}).$$

We can now state our first theorem, which is for the case $\mathscr{X} = \mathbb{R}^d$ and combines simple versions of both the individual and the statistical ergodic theorems. For more extensive results see MKM (1978, §6.2) and Nguyen and Zessin (1979).

Theorem 10.2.IV. *Let ξ be a stationary random measure on $\mathscr{X} = \mathbb{R}^d$ with finite mean density m, and $\{A_n\}$ a convex averaging sequence of Borel sets in $\mathbb{R}^d$. Then as $n \to \infty$,*

$$(10.2.11) \qquad \xi(A_n)/\ell(A_n) \to Y = E(\xi(\mathbb{U}^d)|\mathscr{I})$$

almost surely and in L_1 mean. If also the second moment measure of ξ exists, then convergence in (10.2.11) occurs also in mean square.

PROOF. For some fixed $\varepsilon > 0$, let g_ε be a continuous function in $\mathbb{R}^d$ with the following properties:

(i) $g_\varepsilon(x) \geq 0$, $\int_{\mathbb{R}^d} g_\varepsilon(x)dx = 1$.

(ii) The support of $g_\varepsilon(\cdot) \subseteq S(0, \varepsilon)$, the ball in $\mathbb{R}^d$ with centre at 0 and radius ε.

A function f on $\mathscr{M}_{\mathscr{X}}$ can now be defined by

$$f(\xi) = \int_{\mathbb{R}^d} g_\varepsilon(y)\xi(dy).$$

It is clear that f is measurable and, since ξ has finite expectation measure, is a $\mathscr{P}$-integrable function with

$$E(f) = m \int_{\mathbb{R}^d} g_\varepsilon(x)dx = m.$$

Observe that when $\{A_n\}$ is a convex averaging sequence, so are the related sequences with elements

$$A_n^\varepsilon = \bigcup_{x \in A_n} S(x, \varepsilon),$$

$$A_n^{-\varepsilon} = \{x: S(x, \varepsilon) \subseteq A_n\}.$$

Also,

$$f(S_x\xi) = \int_{\mathbb{R}^d} g_\varepsilon(y)\xi(x + dy) = \int_{\mathbb{R}^d} g_\varepsilon(u - x)\xi(du).$$

Thus,

$$\int_{A_n^\varepsilon} f(S_x\xi)dx = \int_{\mathbb{R}^d} \xi(du) \int_{A_n^\varepsilon} g_\varepsilon(u - x)dx$$

$$\geq \xi(A_n)$$

$$\geq \int_{\mathbb{R}^d} \xi(du) \int_{A_n^{-\varepsilon}} g_\varepsilon(u - x)dx = \int_{A_n^{-\varepsilon}} f(S_x\xi)dx,$$

where the inequalities are consequences of properties (i) and (ii) of $g_\varepsilon(\cdot)$, which in turn imply that

$$\int_{A_n^\varepsilon} g_\varepsilon(u - x)dx = 1 \qquad (u \in A_n),$$

$$\int_{A_n^{-\varepsilon}} g_\varepsilon(u - x)dx = 0 \qquad (u \notin A_n).$$

Invoking Proposition 10.2.II(a), we obtain, $\mathscr{P}$-a.s.,

$$Y \limsup \ell(A_n^\varepsilon)/\ell(A_n) \geq \limsup \xi(A_n)/\ell(A_n)$$

$$\geq \liminf \xi(A_n)/\ell(A_n) \geq Y \liminf \ell(A_n^{-\varepsilon})/\ell(A_n).$$

Since $r(A_n) \to \infty$ and A_n is convex, $\ell(A_n^\varepsilon)/\ell(A_n) \to 1$ and $\ell(A_n^{-\varepsilon})/\ell(A_n) \to 1$ as $n \to \infty$. This establishes the a.s. assertion of the theorem.

Also from Proposition 10.2.II(b), with $p = 1$, we have, with f as defined above,

$$E\left| \frac{1}{\ell(A_n^\varepsilon)} \int_{A_n^\varepsilon} f(S_x\xi)dx - Y \right| \to 0 \qquad (n \to \infty),$$

$$E\left| \frac{1}{\ell(A_n^{-\varepsilon})} \int_{A_n^{-\varepsilon}} f(S_x\xi)dx - Y \right| \to 0 \qquad (n \to \infty).$$

Denoting the first terms in these differences by U_n, L_n, respectively, these equations imply that $E|U_n - L_n| \to 0$ as $n \to \infty$, and hence from

$$(\ell(A_n^\varepsilon)/\ell(A_n))U_n \geq \xi(A_n)/\ell(A_n) \geq (\ell(A_n^{-\varepsilon})/\ell(A_n))L_n$$

and the convergence to 1 of $\ell(A_n^\varepsilon)/\ell(A_n)$ and $\ell(A_n^{-\varepsilon})/\ell(A_n)$ that $E|\xi(A_n)/\ell(A_n) - Y| \to 0$ as $n \to \infty$. This establishes the L_1 convergence.

When the second moment measure exists, a similar argument with the L_2 norm replacing the L_1 norm establishes the L_2 convergence.   □

Corollary 10.2.V. *If ξ is stationary and metrically transitive with finite mean density m, then*

(10.2.12) $$\xi(A_n)/\ell(A_n) \to m \quad (a.s. \text{ and in } L_1 \text{ norm}).$$

For a version of the L_2 norm result requiring only second-order stationarity, see Exercise 10.2.7.

Numerous other special cases and corollaries follow from the theorem. For example, as in Lemma 10.2.III, the convergence at (10.2.11) can be extended to the statement

(10.2.13)

$$(\ell(A_n))^{-1} \int_{\mathbb{R}^d} h(y)\xi(A_n + y)dy = (\ell(A_n))^{-1} \int_{A_n} \xi(dx) \int_{\mathbb{R}^d} h(u - x)dx$$

$$\to Y \int_{\mathbb{R}^d} h(y)dy \quad (a.s. \text{ and in } L_1 \text{ norm})$$

for any measurable integrable function $h(\cdot)$ on $\mathbb{R}^d$.

In all of these results, the convex averaging sequence $\{A_n\}$ can of course be specialized to sequences of balls about the origin or nested hyper-rectangles whose smallest dimension $\rightarrow \infty$.

Important applications of the ergodic theorems arise in establishing the consistency of nonparametric estimates of the moment densities, and in discussing the frequency of occurrence of specialized configurations of points. Indeed, this latter procedure is one way of approaching the definition of Palm probabilities (see Chapter 12) and is used later in Proposition 12.2.VI to establish a kth-order version of Theorem 10.2.IV. Such results can often be reduced to an application of Theorem 10.2.IV itself by introducing a suitable auxiliary measure. We illustrate the procedure in a simple case where the expectation in the limit can be evaluated explicitly.

EXAMPLE 10.2(a) *Configurations in a Poisson process.* Let N be a stationary Poisson process in $\mathbb{R}^d$ at rate μ. Consider first the configuration consisting of a single point of the process with no neighbours within a distance a. The general (estimation) procedure is to take a convex region A, which we suppose to be a member of a convex averaging sequence, and count the number of points in A satisfying the required condition. Write this as the sum

$$Y(A) = \sum_{i:x_i \in A} I_B(S_{x_i} N),$$

where $B = \{N: N(\{0\}) = 1 = N(S(0; a))\}$. Evidently, the sum can also be written as the counting process integral

$$Y(A) = \int_A I_B(S_x N) N(dx)$$

and can be regarded as the value of a further point process $Y(\cdot)$ if A is allowed to range more generally over bounded sets of $\mathcal{B}(\mathbb{R}^d)$. In fact, Y here is just a "thinned" version of the original process.

Applying Theorem 10.2.IV to $Y(\cdot)$ yields the result

$$(10.2.14) \qquad \frac{Y(A)}{\ell(A)} \rightarrow E\left[\int_{\mathsf{U}^d} I_B(S_x N) N(dx)\right] = \mu p_B,$$

where p_B may be regarded as the probability that a given point will be retained in the thinning process. (Later, we shall see that p_B can be interpreted as the Palm probability of the event B.) In the special case considered here, we can evaluate the expectation by a simple approximation argument using the independence properties of the Poisson process as follows. The probability that there is a point in the small region $(x, x + \delta x)$ and none in the remainder of a ball $S(x; a)$ centred at x is $\mu\ell(\delta x)\exp\{-\mu[\ell(S(x; a)) - \ell(\delta x)]\}$, and since the process is simple this is also the expected number of such configurations associated with the element $(x, x + \delta x)$. Integration over U^d gives the limit as $\mu e^{-\mu V(a)}$, where $V(a) = \ell(S(x; a))$ is the volume of a sphere of radius a.

Theorem 10.2.IV here asserts that the average density of points in A, which have no neighbours closer than a, approaches this value as a limit when $\ell(A) \to \infty$ through a convex averaging sequence.

Similarly, the average density of points in A that have at least k neighbours within a distance a approaches the limit

$$\mu[1 - e^{-\mu V(a)}(1 + \mu V(a) + \cdots + (\mu V(a))^{k-1}/(k-1)!)].$$

Finally, consider the numbers of *pairs* of points that lie within a distance a of one another. Taking one point of any such pair as a reference origin, at x say, the number of such pairs to which it belongs is just $N(S(x; a)) - 1$. Summing over all points in A leads to the integral

$$Y_2(A) = \frac{1}{2} \int_A [N(S(x; a)) - 1] N(dx),$$

the factor $\frac{1}{2}$ arising (asymptotically when the edge effects from points near the boundary of A become negligible) from the fact that each point of each pair is counted twice. Dividing by $\ell(A)$ and noting that $Y_2(\cdot)$ again defines a random measure to which the theorems can be applied, we obtain for the limiting value of such an average density of pairs the quantity $EY_2(\mathbb{U}^d)$, which again can be evaluated by an approximation argument that uses the independence properties of the Poisson process as

$$EY_2(\mathbb{U}^d) = \frac{1}{2} \int_{\mathbb{U}^d} E[(N(S(x; a)\setminus \delta x) N(dx)]$$

$$= \frac{1}{2} \int_{\mathbb{U}^d} \mu(V(a) - \ell(dx))\mu \, dx = \frac{1}{2}\mu^2 V(a).$$

Of course, the expected numbers of pairs is related to the second factorial moment measure of the process, and the general version of the above argument leads to a higher-order ergodic theorem in which the reduced factorial moment measures appear as ergodic limits.

We turn next to the extension of these results to product spaces $\mathscr{X} = \mathbb{R}^d \times \mathscr{K}$. Again we identify the transformations S_x with shifts on the $\mathbb{R}^d$ component of $\mathscr{X}$. Define a function f on $\mathscr{M}_{\mathscr{X}}$ by

$$f(\xi) = \int_{\mathbb{R}^d \times \mathscr{K}} g_\varepsilon(y) h(k) \xi(dy \times dk)$$

and observe that $f(S_x \xi)$ is the same integral with $g_\varepsilon(y)$ replaced by $g_\varepsilon(y - x)$. Then form the integrals

$$\int_{A_n^\varepsilon} f(S_x \xi) dx, \qquad \int_{A_n^{-\varepsilon}} f(S_x \xi) dx,$$

and invoke the general form of Lemma 10.2.III to assert that

$$(\ell(A_n^\varepsilon))^{-1} \int_{A_n^\varepsilon} f(S_x \xi) dx \to \int_{\mathscr{K}} h(k) \psi(dk),$$

where $\psi(\cdot)$ is the invariant random measure defined by the lemma. Essentially, the same inequalities and argument apply as indicated for the proof of Theorem 10.2.IV, yielding the following extension.

Proposition 10.2.VI. *Let the random measure ξ on $\mathscr{X} = \mathbb{R}^d \times \mathscr{K}$ for some c.s.m.s. $\mathscr{K}$ be stationary with respect to shifts on $\mathbb{R}^d$ and have boundedly finite expectation measure $\ell \times \nu$. Let ψ be the invariant random measure defined as in Lemma 10.2.III. Then for any convex averaging sequence $\{A_n\}$ on $\mathbb{R}^d$ and any ν-integrable function h on $\mathscr{K}$.*

$$(10.2.15) \qquad \frac{1}{\ell(A_n)} \int_{\mathscr{K}} h(k)\xi(A_n \times dk) \to \int_{\mathscr{K}} h(k)\psi(dk)$$

a.s. and in L_1 norm. If the second moment measure exists and

$$E\left[\left(\int_{\mathscr{K}} h(k)\xi(\mathbb{U}^d \times dk) \right)^2 \right] < \infty,$$

then convergence at (10.2.15) also holds in mean square.

Corollary 10.2.VII. *If $\{(x_i, z_i)\}$ is the realization of a stationary ergodic marked point process on $\mathbb{R}^d \times \mathscr{K}$, then with ν as above,*

$$(10.2.16) \qquad \frac{1}{\ell(A_n)} \sum_{i: x_i \in A_n} h(z_i) \to \int_{\mathscr{K}} h(z)\nu(dz) \quad (a.s.).$$

We conclude with a brief discussion of further ergodic theorems amenable to a similar approach.

Proposition 10.2.VIII (Weighted Averages). *Let $\{a_n(\cdot)\}$ be a monotonic increasing sequence of nonnegative functions, convex upward, $\{A_n\}$ a convex averaging sequence in $\mathbb{R}^d$, and ξ a stationary random measure on $\mathbb{R}^d$ with finite intensity m. Then as $n \to \infty$, and a.s.,*

$$(10.2.17) \qquad \left[\int_{A_n} a_n(x)dx \right]^{-1} \int_{A_n} a_n(x)\xi(dx) \to Z \equiv E(\xi(\mathbb{U}^d)|\mathscr{I}).$$

PROOF. Define an associated random measure ξ' on $\mathbb{R}^d \times \mathbb{R}$ by $\xi'(A \times B) = \xi(A)\ell(B)$. Then ξ' is a stationary random measure in $\mathbb{R}^{d+1}$, and the sets

$$A'_n = \{(x, u): x \in A_n, 0 \le u \le a_n(x)\}$$

are those of a convex averaging sequence in $\mathbb{R}^{d+1}$. Equation (10.2.17) follows by applying Theorem 10.2.IV to ξ'. $\qquad \square$

Some other classes of weighting functions can be handled by using the more general averaging sequences considered by Tempel'man (1972). In particular, this includes the class $a_n(x) = a(x/t_n)$, where the nonnegative measurable function $a(\cdot)$ has bounded support (e.g., the unit cube) and $\{t_n\}$ is a sequence of nonnegative reals $\to \infty$; $a(\cdot)$ need not be convex upward. Also, the assumptions of the last proposition can be trivially extended to the case where there exist positive constants b_n such that $a_n(x) \le b_n a_{n+1}(x)$.

Exercises

10.2.1. Let $Z \in \mathbb{R}^2$ be uniformly distributed on the rectangle $(0, 1] \times (0, 2]$, and let sample realizations of the point process $N(\cdot)$ consist of the points $\{Z + (n_1, 2n_2): n_1, n_2 = 0, \pm 1, \ldots\}$. Contrast the a.s. limits of $N(A_n)/\ell(A_n)$ for the two sequences (a) $A_n = (0, n] \times (0, 1]$ and (b) $A_n = \bigcup_{j=1}^{n} (j - 1, j] \times (j - 1, j]$.

10.2.2. Show formally that (a) if ξ has a trivial invariant σ-field, then the only invariant functions are the constant functions; and (b) metric transitivity implies ergodicity [i.e., (10.2.12) holds].

10.2.3. Show that Theorem 10.2.IV, which in the text is deduced from Proposition 10.2.II, implies the latter in the sense that, if ξ is a stationary random measure on $\mathbb{R}^d$ satisfying the assumptions of Theorem 10.2.IV and (10.2.11) holds, then (10.2.6) holds also. [*Hint*: For such ξ and $f(\xi(\cdot))$ a functional with finite expectation, define a new random measure ξ_f on bounded $A \in \mathcal{B}(\mathbb{R}^d)$ by

$$\xi_f(A) = \int_A f(S_x \xi(\cdot)) dx.$$

Apply Theorem 10.2.IV to ξ_f to deduce Proposition 10.2.II(a) as applied to the original random measure ξ.]

10.2.4. Let $\mathscr{F}$ be a σ-algebra in $\mathcal{B}(\mathcal{M}_{\mathcal{X}})$ and $\xi(\cdot)$ a random measure on $\mathcal{X}$ with finite expectation measure.
  (a) Show that there exists a random measure ψ such that for bounded $A \in \mathcal{B}_{\mathcal{X}}$,

$$\psi(A) = E(\xi(A)|\mathscr{F}) \quad \text{(a.s.)}.$$

  [*Hint*: Use Theorem 6.1.VI.]
  (b) Show that if $\mathscr{F}$ is chosen to be the σ-algebra of events invariant under shifts S_x, then $\psi(\cdot)$ is invariant in the sense that

$$S_x \psi(A) = \psi(A) \quad \text{a.s.} \quad \text{(bounded } A \in \mathcal{B}_{\mathcal{X}}).$$

  [*Hint*: Show first that the indicator function of any event in $\mathscr{F}$ is invariant and hence that any $\mathscr{F}$-measurable r.v. is invariant.]

10.2.5. Interpret the strong law result at Exercise 4.1.1 in the setting of Theorem 10.2.IV.

10.2.6. Establish statistical ergodic theorem versions of the individual ergodic theorems at Theorem 10.2.IV, Corollary 10.2.V, and Propositions 10.2.VI and 10.2.VIII. [*Hint*: Use Proposition 10.2.II(b).]

10.2.7. Let the simple point process N on $\mathbb{R}$ have stationary second-order distributions and finite second-order moment. Then the expectation function $U(\cdot)$ of (3.5.2) satisfies $U(x)/x \to \lambda'$ for some $\lambda' \ge \lambda$ [cf. Lemma 9 in Daley (1971)]. Examine the implications for an L_2 norm result.

10.3. Mixing Properties

In practice, the useful applications of the ergodic theorem are to those situations where the ergodic limit is constant or, in other words, where the process is metrically transitive. It is therefore important to characterize as broadly as possible the various classes of processes that have this property. Now the absence of nontrivial invariant events is closely related to the absence of long-term dependence, and thus, checking for metric transitivity is generally accomplished by verifying that some kind of asymptotic independence or *mixing* condition is satisfied. This section contains a review of such conditions and their application to some particular classes of point processes is demonstrated.

As in the previous section we suppose that $\mathscr{X} = \mathbb{R}^d$ and write S_x for the shift operator on $\mathscr{M}_{\mathscr{X}}$ defined by $S_x \xi(\cdot) = \xi(\cdot + x)$. We also write $\mathbb{U}_{2a}^d$ for the hypercube in $\mathbb{R}^d$ with sides of length $2a$ and vertices $(\pm a, \ldots, \pm a)$, and $\mathscr{P}$ for the probability measure of a random measure on $\mathscr{M}_{\mathscr{X}}$ or a point process on $\mathscr{N}_{\mathscr{X}}$.

Definition 10.3.I. The stationary random measure (or point process), with state space $\mathbb{R}^d$, is

(i) *mixing* if for all V, W in $\mathscr{B}(\mathscr{M}_{\mathscr{X}})$ [or $\mathscr{B}(\mathscr{N}_{\mathscr{X}})$]

(10.3.1) $\mathscr{P}(S_x V \cap W) - \mathscr{P}(V)\mathscr{P}(W) \to 0$ as $\|x\| \to \infty$;

(ii) *weakly mixing* if for all such V, W,

(10.3.2) $\dfrac{1}{\ell(\mathbb{U}_a^d)} \displaystyle\int_{\mathbb{U}_a^d} |\mathscr{P}(S_x V \cap W) - \mathscr{P}(V)\mathscr{P}(W)| \, dx \to 0$ as $a \to \infty$;

(iii) *ergodic* if for all such V, W,

(10.3.3) $\dfrac{1}{\ell(\mathbb{U}_a^d)} \displaystyle\int_{\mathbb{U}_a^d} (\mathscr{P}(S_x V \cap W) - \mathscr{P}(V)\mathscr{P}(W)) \, dx \to 0$ as $a \to \infty$.

It is clear that mixing implies weak mixing, which in turn implies ergodicity. Furthermore, any completely random measure, such as the Poisson process, clearly satisfies (10.3.1) and hence all three conditions. Before examining the conditions in more detail and considering their application to wider classes of processes, we show that in general it is enough to check the properties on any semiring generating the Borel sets in $\mathscr{M}_{\mathscr{X}}$: replacing $\mathscr{M}_{\mathscr{X}}$ by $\mathscr{N}_{\mathscr{X}}$ throughout leads to the same statement for point processes.

Lemma 10.3.II. *For a stationary random measure the limits in* (10.3.1)–(10.3.3) *hold for all* $V, W \in \mathscr{B}(\mathscr{M}_{\mathscr{X}})$ *if and only if they hold for* V, W *in a semiring* S *generating* $\mathscr{B}(\mathscr{M}_{\mathscr{X}})$.

PROOF. We establish the truth of the assertion for (10.3.1); the other cases are proved similarly.

Let $\mathscr{F} \subseteq \mathscr{B}(\hat{\mathscr{M}}_x)$ denote the class of sets for which (10.3.1) holds. It is clear that if (10.3.1) holds for finite families of disjoint sets $V_1, \ldots, V_j$ and $W_1, \ldots, W_k$ then it holds also for $V = \bigcup_{i=1}^{j} V_i$ and $W = \bigcup_{i=1}^{k} W_i$. Thus, if (10.3.1) holds for sets in a semiring $\mathscr{S}$ it holds for sets in the ring $\mathscr{R}$ generated by $\mathscr{S}$.

Suppose that $W \in \mathscr{F}$ and $V_n \in \mathscr{F}$ for $n = 1, 2, \ldots$ with $V_n \uparrow V$. Now

$$|\mathscr{P}(S_x V \cap W) - \mathscr{P}(V)\mathscr{P}(W)| \leq |\mathscr{P}(S_x V \cap W) - \mathscr{P}(S_x V_n \cap W)|$$
$$+ |\mathscr{P}(S_x V_n \cap W) - \mathscr{P}(V_n)\mathscr{P}(W)|$$
$$+ |\mathscr{P}(V_n)\mathscr{P}(W) - \mathscr{P}(V)\mathscr{P}(W)|,$$

in which the first term on the right-hand side is bounded above by

$$\mathscr{P}(S_x(V \bigtriangleup V_n) \cap W) < \mathscr{P}(S_x(V \bigtriangleup V_n)) = \mathscr{P}(V \bigtriangleup V_n),$$

and the last term equals $|\mathscr{P}(V_n) - \mathscr{P}(V)|\mathscr{P}(W)$. By the continuity of $\mathscr{P}(\cdot)$, both these terms $\to 0$ as $n \to \infty$, so, given $\varepsilon > 0$, we can fix n large enough such that each term $< \varepsilon$, uniformly in x. For the middle term, having fixed n, (10.3.1) holds for the pair V_n, W, and thus the term $< \varepsilon$ for $\|x\| >$ some x_0. Thus,

$$|\mathscr{P}(S_x V \cap W) - \mathscr{P}(V)\mathscr{P}(W)| < 3\varepsilon \quad (\text{all } \|x\| > x_0).$$

Similarly, we may also replace W by a sequence $\{W_n\} \subseteq \mathscr{R}$ with $W_n \to W$, showing that $\mathscr{F}$ is closed under monotone limits.

Thus, $\mathscr{F}$ is a monotone class that, since it includes $\mathscr{R}$, includes $\sigma\{\mathscr{R}\} = \mathscr{B}(\hat{\mathscr{M}}_x)$. $\qquad\square$

Our first results exhibit links with the theorems of the previous section.

Proposition 10.3.III. *A stationary random measure (or point process) is ergodic if and only if it is metrically transitive; that is, the invariant σ-algebra $\mathscr{I}$ is trivial.*

PROOF. Let ξ be ergodic as at (10.3.3) above and let A be an invariant event. Putting $V = W = A$ in (10.3.3), observe from invariance that $\mathscr{P}(S_x A \cap A) = \mathscr{P}(A)$ and hence that

$$\frac{1}{\ell(\bigcup_a^d)} \int_{\bigcup_a^d} [\mathscr{P}(A) - (\mathscr{P}(A))^2] dx \to 0$$

as $a \to \infty$; therefore, $\mathscr{P}(A) = 0$ or 1.

Conversely, suppose that $\mathscr{I}$ is trivial, so that (10.2.6) takes the form (and using the notation as there)

(10.3.4) $$\frac{1}{\ell(A_n)} \int_{A_n} f(S_x \xi) dx \to Ef(\xi) \quad (\text{a.s.}).$$

Let V, W be as in Definition 10.3.1 and take $f(\xi) = I_V(\xi)$, so that $Ef(\xi) = \mathscr{P}(V)$ and (10.3.4) yields

$$\frac{1}{\ell(A_n)} \int_{A_n} I_V(S_x\xi)\,dx \to \mathscr{P}(V) \quad \text{(a.s.)}.$$

Writing $g_n(\xi)$ for the left-hand side of this equation, observe that $0 \le g_n(\xi) \le 1$ and that $g_n(\xi)$ is a measurable function of ξ in $(\mathscr{M}_{\mathscr{X}}, \mathscr{B}(\mathscr{M}_{\mathscr{X}}))$. Integrating over W and using dominated convergence and Fubini's theorem, we obtain

$$\frac{1}{\ell(A_n)} \int_{A_n} \int_W I_V(S_x\xi)\,dx\, \mathscr{P}(d\xi) \to \mathscr{P}(V)\mathscr{P}(W),$$

which reduces to (10.3.3) in the special case $A_n = \mathsf{U}_n^d$. $\qquad\square$

Just as ergodicity is related to the invariant σ-algebra $\mathscr{I}$ being trivial, so mixing is related to the (in general) larger σ-algebra of "tail events" defined on the process ξ being trivial. To define these events, denote by $\mathscr{T}_a$, for each $a > 0$, the σ-algebra of events defined by the behaviour of ξ outside U_a^d; that is, $\mathscr{T}_a$ is the smallest σ-algebra in $\mathscr{B}(\mathscr{M}_{\mathscr{X}})$ with respect to which the $\xi(A)$ are measurable for $A \in \mathscr{B}(\mathscr{X} \setminus \mathsf{U}_a^d)$.

Definition 10.3.IV. The tail σ-algebra of the process ξ is the intersection $\mathscr{T}_\infty \equiv \bigcap_{a>0} \mathscr{T}_a = \bigcap_{n=1}^\infty \mathscr{T}_n$. An element of $\mathscr{T}_\infty$ is a *tail event*.

Thus, $\mathscr{T}_\infty$ defines the class of events that are determined by the behaviour of ξ outside any bounded subset of $\mathscr{X}$. It is not difficult to show that, modulo sets of $\mathscr{P}$-measure zero, any invariant event is in the tail σ-algebra (see Exercise 10.3.2). The converse is not true, however: periodic processes provide typical examples of processes that are ergodic but for which the tail σ-algebra is non-trivial (see Exercise 10.3.1). The triviality result referred to above is as follows.

Proposition 10.3.V. *If the tail σ-algebra is trivial, then the random measure ξ is mixing.*

PROOF. Let V be any set in $\mathscr{B}(\mathscr{M}_{\mathscr{X}})$. Since $\mathscr{T}_n \downarrow \mathscr{T}_\infty$, we have for any random variable with expectation, and hence in particular for the indicator function $I_V(\cdot)$,

$$E(I_V | \mathscr{T}_n) \to E(I_V | \mathscr{T}_\infty) \quad \text{(a.s.)}$$

[this is a standard result for backward martingales, as, for example, Theorem 9.4.7 of Chung (1974)].

When $\mathscr{T}_\infty$ is trivial, the right-hand side here reduces to $E(I_V) = \mathscr{P}(V)$ a.s. Consequently, given $\varepsilon > 0$, we can choose n_0 such that for $n \ge n_0$,

(10.3.5) $$|E(I_V | \mathscr{T}_n) - \mathscr{P}(V)| < \varepsilon \quad \text{(a.s.)}.$$

Now let W be a cylinder set belonging to the σ-algebra generated by the family $\{\xi(A): A \in \mathscr{B}(\mathsf{U}_a^d)\}$. For $\|x\|$ sufficiently large (to be precise, $\|x\| > d^{1/2}n$), $T_x\mathsf{U}_n^d$ lies in the complement of U_n^d and hence $S_x W \in \mathscr{T}_n$. For fixed n and $\|x\|$ large enough, the indicator function $I_{S_x W}$ is therefore $\mathscr{T}_n$-measurable and so satisfies

$$E(I_{S_x W} I_V | \mathscr{T}_n) = I_{S_x W} E(I_V | \mathscr{T}_n) \quad \text{(a.s.)}.$$

Taking expectations and using (10.3.5), we obtain

$$\mathscr{P}(S_x W \cap V) = \mathscr{P}(S_x W)\mathscr{P}(V) + E(I_{S_x W} Y),$$

where the r.v. Y has $|Y| < \varepsilon$ a.s. This establishes the mixing property for arbitrary V and any cylinder set W. Since the cylinder sets generate $\mathscr{B}(\mathscr{M}_{\mathscr{X}})$, the proposition follows from Lemma 10.3.II. $\square$

Mixing is also closely related to the conditions for convergence to equilibrium as indicated in Exercise 10.3.5 and discussed further in Section 12.4.

We already observed in the proof of the last proposition that it is enough to verify the mixing or weak mixing or ergodicity conditions for cylinder sets, that is, for sets of the type that occur in the definition of the fidi distributions. While this may sometimes be convenient, it is generally easier to check the conditions in a form that relates to the generating functionals rather than directly to the fidi distributions. The next proposition provides such conditions: the discussion here, as in the applications that follow, is based on Westcott (1972). In the proposition below we define the shift operator for functions by writing

$$(T_x h)(y) = h(y + x).$$

Proposition 10.3.VI. (a) *Let ξ be a random measure, $L[\cdot]$ its Laplace functional, and h_1, h_2 functions in $BM_+(\mathscr{X})$. Then ξ is*

(i) *mixing if and only if for all such h_1, h_2, as $\|x\| \to \infty$,*

(10.3.6) $$L[h_1 + T_x h_2] \to L[h_1]L[h_2];$$

(ii) *weakly mixing if and only if for all such h_1, h_2, as $n \to \infty$,*

(10.3.7) $$\frac{1}{\ell(\mathsf{U}_n^d)} \int_{\mathsf{U}_n^d} |L[h_1 + T_x h_2] - L[h_1]L[h_2]| dx \to 0;$$

(iii) *ergodic if and only if for all such h_1, h_2, as $n \to \infty$*

(10.3.8) $$\frac{1}{\ell(\mathsf{U}_n^d)} \int_{\mathsf{U}_n^d} (L[h_1 + T_x h_2] - L[h_1]L[h_2]) dx \to 0.$$

(b) *Let N be a point process, $G[\cdot]$ its p.g.fl., and h_1, h_2 functions in $\mathscr{V}(\mathscr{X})$. Then N is*

(i) *mixing if and only if for all such h_1, h_2, as $\|x\| \to \infty$,*

(10.3.9) $$G[h_1 T_x h_2] \to G[h_1]G[h_2];$$

(ii) *weakly mixing if and only if for all such h_1, h_2, as $n \to \infty$,*

(10.3.10) $$\frac{1}{\ell(\mathsf{U}_n^d)} \int_{\mathsf{U}_n^d} |G[h_1 T_x h_2] - G[h_1]G[h_2]| dx \to 0;$$

(iii) *ergodic if and only if for all such h_1, h_2, as $n \to \infty$.*

$$(10.3.11) \qquad \frac{1}{\ell(\mathbb{U}_n^d)} \int_{\mathbb{U}_n^d} (G[h_1 T_x h_2] - G[h_1]G[h_2])dx \to 0.$$

PROOF. (a) Let $A_1, \ldots, A_J, B_1, \ldots, B_K$ be bounded on $\mathcal{X}$, and consider the family of random variables $\{\xi(A_1), \ldots, \xi(A_J), \xi(T_x B_1), \ldots, \xi(T_x B_K)\}$. If ξ is mixing then (10.3.1) implies that the joint distribution of this family converges to the product of the two joint distributions of the families $\{\xi(A_1), \ldots, \xi(A_J)\}$ and $\{\xi(B_1), \ldots, \xi(B_K)\}$ and $\{\xi(B_1), \ldots, \xi(B_K)\}$. It follows that the multivariate Laplace transforms of these joint distributions satisfy for real nonnegative α_j and β_k

$$E\left(\exp\left(-\sum_{j=1}^{J} \alpha_j \xi(A_j) - \sum_{k=1}^{K} \beta_k \xi(T_x B_k)\right)\right)$$
$$\to E\left(\exp\left(-\sum_{j=1}^{J} \alpha_j \xi(A_J)\right)\right) E\left(\exp\left(-\sum_{k=1}^{K} \beta_k \xi(B_k)\right)\right).$$

But this is just the statement (10.3.6) for the special case that the h_i are the simple functions

$$(10.3.12) \qquad h_1(x) = \sum_{j=1}^{J} \alpha_j I_{A_j}(x), \qquad h_2(x) = \sum_{k=1}^{K} \beta_k I_{B_k}(x).$$

Since any $h \in BM_+(\mathcal{X})$ can be monotonically and uniformly approximated by simple functions of this form, an argument similar to that of Lemma 10.3.II shows that (10.3.6) holds as stated.

Conversely, when (10.3.6) holds, take h_1, h_2 to be simple functions as at (10.3.12). Then it follows from the continuity theorem for Laplace transforms that the joint distributions of $\xi(A_1), \ldots, \xi(A_J)$ and $\xi(T_x B_1), \ldots, \xi(T_x B_K)$ converge for all families $A_1, \ldots, A_J$ and $B_1, \ldots, B_K$, and hence that (10.3.1) holds for the corresponding cylinder sets, that is, a semiring generating $\mathscr{B}(\mathcal{M}_{\mathcal{X}})$. Then by Lemma 10.3.II, (10.3.1) holds generally and so ξ is mixing. Analogous statements hold in the other cases and we omit the details. $\square$

It is important for the proof of Proposition 10.3.IX to observe that the convergence properties in Equations (10.3.6)–(10.3.11) hold for wider classes of functions than those with bounded support. For example, when each h_i is the monotone limit of a sequence $\{h_{in}\} \subset BM_+(\mathcal{X})$, (10.3.6) holds provided we interpret the functionals as extended Laplace functionals [cf. (6.4.21)]. To see this, recall that any function in $BM_+(\mathcal{X})$ is the monotone limit of simple functions, and first assume that the functions h_1 and $\{h_{2n}\}$ are simple functions. By the argument leading to (10.3.12) we then have, when ξ is stationary and mixing,

$$L[h_1 + T_x h_{2n}] \to L[h_1]L[h_{2n}] \quad \text{as } \|x\| \to \infty.$$

Thus,

$$0 \le |L[h_1]L[h_2] - L[h_1 + T_x h_2]|$$

$$\le |L[h_1](L[h_2] - L[h_{2n}])| + |L[h_1]L[h_{2n}] - L[h_1 + T_x h_{2n}]|$$

$$+ |L[h_1 + T_x h_{2n}] - L[h_1 + T_x h_2]|$$

$$\equiv \delta_{1n} + \delta_{2n}(x) + \delta_{3n}(x), \text{ say.}$$

Now

$$\delta_{3n}(x) = \left| E\left\{ \exp\left(-\int h_1 \, d\xi \right) \right\} \left\{ \exp\left(-\int T_x h_{2n} \, d\xi \right) - \exp\left(-\int T_x h_2 \, d\xi \right) \right\} \right|$$

$$\le |L[T_x h_{2n}] - L[T_x h_2]| \quad \text{by nonnegativity and monotonicity,}$$

$$= |L[h_{2n}] - L[h_2]| \quad \text{by stationarity.}$$

and by monotone convergence, $L[h_{2n}] \downarrow L[h_2]$ as $n \to \infty$. Similarly, $\delta_{1n} \le |L[h_{2n}] - L[h_2]|$ and so, given $\varepsilon > 0$, we can make both $\delta_{1n} < \varepsilon$ and $\delta_{3n}(x) < \varepsilon$, uniformly in x, by choosing n sufficiently large. Fixing such n, (10.3.12) now implies that we can make $\delta_{2n}(x) < \varepsilon$ by taking $\|x\|$ sufficiently large. Thus, (10.3.6) holds for simple $h_1 \in BM_+(\mathcal{X})$ and $h_2 \in BM_+(\mathcal{X})$, and a similar argument establishes it for $h_1 \in \overline{BM}_+(\mathcal{X})$ as well.

Extensions of (10.3.7)–(10.3.11) are established in a similar manner.

It is also pertinent to note that in part (b), it is enough to restrict the functions h_i to the subspace $\mathcal{V}_0(\mathcal{X}) \subset \mathcal{V}(\mathcal{X})$. This follows directly from part (a) and the remark following (7.4.2).

Using these results, we can investigate the mixing and ergodicity properties of some classes of point processes as below and in Exercises 10.3.1 and 10.3.3. We start by considering Cox processes (cf. Section 8.5).

Proposition 10.3.VII. *A stationary Cox process N on $\mathcal{X} = \mathbb{R}^d$ is mixing, weakly mixing, or ergodic if and only if the random measure Λ directing N has the same property.*

PROOF. Recall from Proposition 8.5.I that the p.g.fl. $G[\cdot]$ of a Cox process N is related to the Laplace functional $L[\cdot]$ of the random measure Λ directing N by $G[h] = L[1 - h]$ for $h \in \mathcal{V}(\mathcal{X})$. To verify the mixing property, for example, we start from the relation

$$G[h_1 T_x h_2] = L[1 - h_1 T_x h_2]$$

$$= L[1 - h_1 + T_x(1 - h_2) - (1 - h_1)T_x(1 - h_2)].$$

Since each $1 - h_i$ ($i = 1, 2$) has bounded support, the last term vanishes for sufficiently large $\|x\|$, and for such x, appealing to (10.3.6) for $\|x\| \to \infty$,

$$G[h_1 T_x h_2] = L[(1 - h_1) + T_x(1 - h_2)]$$

$$\to L[1 - h_1]L[1 - h_2] = G[h_1]G[h_2].$$

This argument is reversible and proves the result concerning the mixing property. The proofs for the weakly mixing and ergodicity properties are similar. $\qquad\Box$

Corollary 10.3.VIII. *A stationary mixed Poisson process N is mixing if and only if it is a simple Poisson process.*

PROOF. From Example 7.4(b) and Exercise 10.1.6, the directing measure ξ must be a random multiple of Lebesgue measure, $\Lambda\ell(\cdot)$ say, so that with $\phi_\Lambda(\cdot)$ denoting the Laplace–Stieltjes transform of Λ, the p.g.fl. $G[h]$ of N for $h \in \mathcal{V}(\mathbb{R}^d)$ is given by

$$G[h] = \phi_\Lambda\left(\int_{\mathbb{R}^d} (1 - h(x))dx\right).$$

Now as $\|x\| \to \infty$,

$$L[(1 - h_1) + T_x(1 - h_2)] \to \phi_\Lambda\left[\int_{\mathbb{R}^d} (1 - h_1(x))dx + \int_{\mathbb{R}^d} (1 - h_2(x))dx\right],$$

which can equal the product of the $\phi_\Lambda[\int_{\mathbb{R}^d} (1 - h_i(x))dx]$ for all $h_i \in \mathcal{V}(\mathbb{R}^d)$ if and only if ϕ_Λ is an exponential function, and hence the distribution of Λ is concentrated at a single point. $\qquad\Box$

In speaking of a stationary cluster process N on $\mathbb{R}^d$, we mean a process as in Exercise 10.1.3; that is, the cluster centre process N_c is defined on $\mathbb{R}^d$ and stationary, and the generic cluster member process $N_m(\cdot|x)$ on $\mathbb{R}^d$ with centre at x has fidi distributions that, relative to x, are independent of x. Using G_c and $G_m[\cdot|x]$ to denote the p.g.fl.s of N_c and $N_m(\cdot|x)$, it then follows from the discussion in Section 8.2 (see, in particular, Proposition 8.2.II and the corollary following it) that a stationary cluster process N on $\mathbb{R}^d$ is well defined if and only if

$$(10.3.13) \qquad \int_{\mathbb{R}^d} (1 - G_m[h|u])N_c(du) < \infty \quad \text{(a.s.)}.$$

Proposition 10.3.IX. *A stationary cluster process as above is mixing, weakly mixing, or ergodic, whenever the cluster centre process has the same property.*

PROOF. We give details for the mixing case only, since the other cases can be treated in a similar fashion. Also, while we generally follow the p.g.fl. proof of Westcott (1971) [for an alternative proof see Proposition 11.1.4 of MKM (1978)], some further argument is needed as in Daley and Vere-Jones (1987). In particular, we use the idea of extended p.g.fl.s and use Proposition 10.3.VI(b) with functions $h_i \in \mathcal{V}_0(\mathcal{X})$ (see the last remark following that proposition). Then in view of (8.2.4) and (10.3.9) with $h_i \in \mathcal{V}_0(\mathcal{X})$, it is enough to deduce from $G_c[h_1 T_x h_2] \to G_c[h_1]G_c[h_2]$ as $\|x\| \to \infty$ that

$$(10.3.14) \qquad G_c[G_m[h_1 T_x h_2|\cdot]] \to G_c[G_m[h_1|\cdot]]G_c[G_m[h_2|\cdot]].$$

Formally, the mixing property implies that the right-hand side here is the limit at $\|x\| \to \infty$ of

$$G_c[G_m[h_1|\cdot]\,T_x G_m[h_2|\cdot]] \equiv G_c[\tilde{h}_1\,T_x\tilde{h}_2],$$

where $\tilde{h}_i(y) = G_m[h_i|y]$; so, formally, it is enough to show that as $\|x\| \to \infty$,

(10.3.15) $G_c(\tilde{h}_1\,T_x\tilde{h}_2) - G_c[G_m[h_1\,T_x h_2|\cdot]] \to 0.$

We have said "formally" because, while $h_i \in \mathscr{V}_0(\mathbb{R}^d)$, the same need not necessarily by true of $\tilde{h}_i$. However, by replacing the generic cluster $N_m(\cdot|0)$ by $N_{mn}(\cdot|0) \equiv N_m(\cdot \cap \mathbb{U}_n^d|0)$ and letting $n \to \infty$, each $\tilde{h}_i$ is expressed as the limit of the monotonic sequence $\{\tilde{h}_{in}\}$ for which $\tilde{h}_{in} \in \mathscr{V}_0(\mathbb{R}^d)$. Consequently, appealing to the convergence properties of extended p.g.fl.s established in Exercise 7.4.2(b) and the extended form of the mixing property (10.3.9) noted below Proposition 10.3.VI, it follows that when $N_c(\cdot)$ is mixing, $G_c[\tilde{h}_1\,T_x\tilde{h}_2] \to G_c[\tilde{h}_1]G_c[\tilde{h}_2]$ as $\|x\| \to \infty$.

To complete the proof, define

$$\Delta_x(u) = G_m[h_1\,T_x h_2|u] - G_m[h_1|u]\,T_x G_m[h_2|u].$$

As upper bounds on $\Delta_x(u)$ we have

$$\Delta_x(u) \le G_m[T_x h_2|u](1 - G_m[h_1|u]) \le 1 - G_m[h_1|u],$$

$$\Delta_x(u) \le G_m[h_1|u](1 - G_m[T_x h_2|u]) \le 1 - G_m[T_x h_2|u];$$

as lower bounds we have

$$\Delta_x(u) \ge G_m[h_1\,T_x h_2|u] - G_m[T_x h_2|u]$$

$$= -E\left[\left\{\exp\int_{\mathscr{X}}\log[T_x h_2(y)]N_m(dy|u)\right\}\right.$$

$$\left.\times\left\{1 - \exp\int_{\mathscr{X}}\log h_1(y)N_m(dy|u)\right\}\right]$$

$$\ge -(1 - G_m[h_1|u])$$

and, similarly, $\Delta_x(u) \ge -(1 - G_m[T_x h_2|u])$. Because $h_2 \in \mathscr{V}_0(\mathbb{R}^d)$ and $N_m(\mathbb{R}^d|u) < \infty$ a.s., $G_m[T_x h_2|u] \to 1$ as $\|x\| \to \infty$ and thus $\Delta_x(u) \to 0$ as $\|x\| \to \infty$. Also, since the cluster process exists, (10.3.13) holds, and therefore the bounding function in

$$|\Delta_x(u)| \le 1 - G_m[h_1|u]$$

is N_c-integrable a.s. Indeed, again since $h_1 \in \mathscr{V}_0(\mathbb{R}^d)$ and $N_m(\mathbb{R}^d|u) < \infty$ a.s., it also holds that $1 \ge G_m[h_1|u] \ge c_1$, uniformly in u, for some positive constant c_1, and similarly for $G_m[T_x h_2|u]$. Thus,

$$\chi_x(u) \equiv G_m[h_1|u]\,T_x G_m[h_2|u] \ge c > 0$$

for some constant c, uniformly in x and u. Now

$$|G_c[G_m[h_1\,T_x h_2|\cdot]] - G_c[G_m[h_1|\cdot]\,T_x G_m[h_2|\cdot]]|$$

$$= |G_c[\chi_x + \Delta_x] - G_c[\chi_x]|$$

$$= \left| E \left\{ \exp \int_{\mathbb{R}^d} \log[\chi_x(u) + \Delta_x(u)] N_c(du) - \exp \int_{\mathbb{R}^d} \log \chi_x(u) N_c(du) \right\} \right|$$

$$\leq 1 - E \exp \left\{ - \int_{\mathbb{R}^d} \log[1 + |\Delta_x(u)| / \chi_x(u)] N_c(du) \right\}.$$

This expression $\to 0$ as $\|x\| \to \infty$ because $1 \geq \chi_x(u) \geq c > 0$ (all x and u), $\Delta_x(u) \to 0$ pointwise, and $\Delta_x(u)$, and hence $c^{-1} \Delta_x(u)$ also, is N_c-integrable a.s. uniformly in x (cf. Exercise 7.4.2). Thus, (10.3.14) is proved. $\qquad \square$

We now resume from Section 10.1 our discussion of stationary infinitely divisible point processes. The last example, coupled with part (ii) of Proposition 8.4.VIII, shows that every regular stationary infinitely divisible point process is mixing and hence ergodic, so it remains to discuss the singular case, following essentially Kerstan and Matthes (1967) and MKM (1978, Chap. 6). We first give a general simple result.

Lemma 10.3.X. *If the stationary random measure ξ on $\mathcal{X} = \mathbb{R}^d$ is ergodic, it cannot be represented as a mixture of two distinct stationary processes.*

PROOF. Suppose the contrary, so that $\mathscr{P} = \alpha \mathscr{P}_1 + (1 - \alpha) \mathscr{P}_2$ say, where $0 < \alpha < 1$ and the other three terms are stationary probability measures on $\mathcal{M}_{\mathcal{X}}$. Evidently, $\mathscr{P}_1 \ll \mathscr{P}$ and the Radon–Nikodym derivative $d\mathscr{P}_1/d\mathscr{P}$ is invariant under shifts S_x. When $\mathscr{P}$ is ergodic the only invariant functions are constants a.s., so $\mathscr{P}_1 = c\mathscr{P}$; hence, $c = 1$ because both $\mathscr{P}$ and $\mathscr{P}_1$ are probability measures. Thus, $\mathscr{P}_1 = \mathscr{P}$, and similarly $\mathscr{P}_2 = \mathscr{P}$, showing that the decomposition is trivial. $\qquad \square$

Proposition 10.3.XI. *No stationary Poisson randomization, nor more generally any process that can be represented as the superposition of a stationary process and a Poisson randomization, is ergodic.*

PROOF. By definition, a Poisson randomization is a nontrivial discrete mixture of distinct components, and thus the criterion of Lemma 10.3.X is violated. More generally, supposing that $\mathscr{P} = \mathscr{P}_1 * \mathscr{P}_2$ (with $*$ denoting convolution), with $\mathscr{P}_2$ expressible as $\alpha \mathscr{P}_2' + (1 - \alpha) \mathscr{P}_2''$, we then have $\mathscr{P} = \mathscr{P}_1 * (\alpha \mathscr{P}_2' + (1 - \alpha) \mathscr{P}_2'') = \alpha(\mathscr{P}_1 * \mathscr{P}_2') + (1 - \alpha)(\mathscr{P}_1 * \mathscr{P}_2'')$, and the criterion is again violated. $\qquad \square$

From this result it may seem plausible that no singular stationary infinitely divisible process could be ergodic. Such is not the case: the next result, due to Kerstan and Matthes (1967), spells out in terms of the KLM measure those properties that lead to ergodicity or mixing, and we show that such properties include examples of singular infinitely divisible processes.

Proposition 10.3.XII. *Let N be a stationary infinitely divisible point process on $\mathbb{R}^d$ with KLM measure $\tilde{Q}$. Then*

(i) N *is mixing if and only if for all* $\|x\| \to \infty$ *and all bounded* $A, B \in \mathcal{B}_{\mathscr{X}}$

(10.3.16) $\tilde{Q}\{\tilde{N}: \tilde{N}(T_x A) > 0 \text{ and } \tilde{N}(B) > 0\} \to 0;$

(ii) N *is ergodic if and only if for such* $A, B,$

(10.3.17) $\dfrac{1}{\ell(\mathsf{U}_n^d)} \displaystyle\int_{\mathsf{U}_n^d} \tilde{Q}\{\tilde{N}: \tilde{N}(T_x A) > 0 \text{ and } \tilde{N}(B) > 0\} dx \to 0 \quad (n \to \infty),$

in which case N *is also weakly mixing.*

PROOF. We use the p.g.fl. formulation of the mixing condition and, for $h \in \mathcal{V}(\mathbb{R}^d)$, we write

$$\tilde{G}[h] = \log G[h] = \int_{\mathcal{N}_{\mathscr{X}}} \left[\exp\left(\int_{\mathscr{X}} \log h(x) \tilde{N}(dx) \right) - 1 \right] \tilde{Q}(d\tilde{N}).$$

Then the mixing condition (10.3.9) is expressible as

(10.3.18) $\tilde{G}[h_1 T_x h_2] \to \tilde{G}[h_1] + \tilde{G}[h_2] \qquad (\|x\| \to \infty).$

To show that this condition is the same as (10.3.16), take $h_1 = 1 - I_B$, $h_2 = 1 - I_A$, and consider the difference

(10.3.19)

$$\tilde{G}[h_1 T_x h_2] - \tilde{G}[h_1] - \tilde{G}[h_2] = \int_{\mathcal{N}_{\mathscr{X}}} \left(\prod_i a_i b_i - \prod_i a_i - \prod_i b_i + 1 \right) \tilde{Q}(d\tilde{N}),$$

where $a_i = h_1(x_i)$, $b_i = h_2(x_i - x)$, and the x_i are the points of the particular realization $\tilde{N}$. For the particular h_1, h_2, the integrand on the right vanishes except for realizations of $\tilde{N}$ for which both $\tilde{N}(B) > 0$ and $\tilde{N}(T_x A) > 0$, when it reduces to unity. Thus, the left-hand side of (10.3.19) coincides with the expression at (10.3.16) for such h_1, h_2, and thus (10.3.18) implies (10.3.16).

Conversely, when (10.3.16) holds, (10.3.18) holds whenever $1 - h_i$ are indicator functions as above. For more general $h_i \in \mathcal{V}(\mathbb{R}^d)$, the difference at (10.3.19) is dominated by the corresponding difference when h_1 and h_2 are replaced by $1 - I_B$ and $1 - I_A$, where B and A are the supports of $1 - h_1$ and $1 - h_2$. Thus, (10.3.16) also implies (10.3.18) for these more general h_i, and part (i) is established.

To prove part (ii) we need to develop some auxiliary results. Since $\tilde{Q}$ is stationary, though perhaps only σ-finite, an extension of the ergodic theorem (see comment following Proposition 10.2.II) can be applied to deduce the limit, for any convex averaging sequence $\{A_n\}$,

(10.3.20) $\displaystyle\lim_{n \to \infty} \dfrac{1}{\ell(A_n)} \int_{A_n} f(S_x \tilde{N}) dx = \bar{f}(\tilde{N}) \quad \text{(a.e. } \tilde{Q})$

whenever the $\mathcal{B}(\mathcal{N}_{\mathscr{X}})$-measurable function f satisfies $\int_{\mathcal{N}_{\mathscr{X}}} f(\tilde{N}) \tilde{Q}(d\tilde{N}) < \infty$.

Let I_V be the indicator function of the set $V = \{\tilde{N}: \tilde{N}(A) > 0\}$ for bounded $A \in \mathcal{B}(\mathbb{R}^d)$. Then $\tilde{Q}(V) < \infty$ by (8.4.8), so the limit in (10.3.20), $\bar{I}_V(\tilde{N})$ say, exists a.e. $\tilde{Q}$. We assert that if the infinitely divisible process is ergodic, then this limit must be zero a.e. $\tilde{Q}$. To see this, consider for any fixed positive c the set $J_c = \{\tilde{N}: \bar{I}_V(\tilde{N}) > c > 0\}$, which is measurable and invariant because $\bar{I}_V(.)$ is. Furthermore,

$$c\tilde{Q}(J_c) \le \int_{J_c} \bar{I}_V(\tilde{N})\tilde{Q}(d\tilde{N}) \le \int_{\mathcal{N}_{\mathcal{X}}} \bar{I}_V(\tilde{N})\tilde{Q}(d\tilde{N})$$

$$\le \limsup_{n\to\infty} \frac{1}{\ell(A_n)} \int_{A_n} \int_{\mathcal{N}_{\mathcal{X}}} I_V(S_x\tilde{N})\tilde{Q}(d\tilde{N})dx$$

$$= \tilde{Q}(V) < \infty.$$

Consequently, J_c has finite $\tilde{Q}$ measure and is invariant. If in fact $\tilde{Q}(J_c) > 0$, we can construct a stationary probability measure $\mathcal{P}_V$ on $\mathcal{N}_{\mathcal{X}}$ by setting

$$\mathcal{P}_V(\cdot) = \tilde{Q}(J_c \cap \cdot)/\tilde{Q}(J_c),$$

and it then follows that the original process has the Poisson randomization of $\mathcal{P}_V$ as a convolution factor. But for an ergodic process this is impossible by Proposition 10.3.XI, so $\tilde{Q}(J_c) = 0$ for every $c > 0$, and $\bar{I}_V(\tilde{N}) = 0$ a.e. $\tilde{Q}$ as asserted.

Now let B be any bounded set in $\mathcal{B}(\mathbb{R}^d)$, write $W = \{\tilde{N}: \tilde{N}(B) > 0\}$, and consider the sequence

$$\frac{1}{\ell(A_n)} \int_{A_n} \tilde{Q}\{\tilde{N}: \tilde{N}(A) > 0 \text{ and } \tilde{N}(B + x) > 0\}dx$$

$$= \frac{1}{\ell(A_n)} \int_{A_n} \int_{\mathcal{N}_{\mathcal{X}}} I_V(\tilde{N})I_{S_xW}(\tilde{N})\tilde{Q}(d\tilde{N})dx$$

$$= \int_{\mathcal{N}_{\mathcal{X}}} I_V(\tilde{N})\left(\frac{1}{\ell(A_n)} \int_{A_n} I_{S_xW}(\tilde{N})dx\right)\tilde{Q}(d\tilde{N}).$$

We have just shown that the inner integral here $\to 0$ as $n \to \infty$ a.e. $\tilde{Q}$, and since this integral ≤ 1 and $\tilde{Q}(V) < \infty$, we can apply the dominated convergence theorem and conclude that the entire expression $\to 0$ as $n \to \infty$; that is, (10.3.17) holds.

The converse implication depends on the inequality [see under (10.3.19)]

$$0 \le \tilde{G}[h_1 T_x h_2] - \tilde{G}[h_1] - \tilde{G}[h_2]$$

$$\le \tilde{Q}\{\tilde{N}: \tilde{N}(A) > 0 \text{ and } \tilde{N}(T_x B) > 0\} = q(x) \quad \text{say,}$$

where A, B are the supports of $1 - h_1$ and $1 - h_2$. Using the elementary inequality $e^\alpha - 1 \le \alpha e^\alpha$ $(\alpha > 0)$ and taking exponentials, we obtain

(10.3.21) $0 \le G[h_1 T_x h_2] - G[h_1]G[h_2] \le G[h_1]G[h_2]q(x)e^{q(x)}.$

Since $q(x) < \tilde{Q}\{\tilde{N}: \tilde{N}(A) > 0\} < \infty$ uniformly in x, it follows that the difference in (10.3.21) is bounded by $Kq(x)$ for some finite positive constant K. Then the integral at (10.3.11) is bounded by

$$\frac{K}{\ell(\mathbb{U}_n^d)} \int_{\mathbb{U}_n^d} q(x)dx,$$

which $\to 0$ as $n \to \infty$ when (10.3.17) holds. Part (b) (iii) of Proposition 10.3.VI now shows that the process must be ergodic, and since the difference at (10.3.21) is already nonnegative, we have the stronger convergence statement at (10.3.10) holding, and the process is in fact weakly mixing as asserted.   □

The arguments used in the course of this proof can be taken further. Here, we consider in particular the invariant function $\bar{I}_V(\cdot)$ introduced below (10.3.20), fixing A as $A = \mathbb{U}^d$ say for definiteness. The trajectories $\tilde{N}$ can be classified a.e. $\tilde{Q}$ by defining

$$\mathscr{S}_w = \{\tilde{N}: \bar{I}_V(\tilde{N}) = 0\}, \qquad \mathscr{S}_s = \{\tilde{N}: I_V(\tilde{N}) > 0\}.$$

Both these subsets of $\mathscr{N}_{\mathscr{X}}$ are measurable, and their complement has zero $\tilde{Q}$ measure, so $\tilde{Q}$ can be decomposed as $\tilde{Q} = \tilde{Q}_w + \tilde{Q}_s$, where

$$\tilde{Q}_w(\cdot) = \tilde{Q}(\mathscr{S}_w \cap \cdot), \qquad \tilde{Q}_s = \tilde{Q}(\mathscr{S}_s \cap \cdot).$$

The notation here comes from the definition of a singular stationary infinitely divisible point process as *weakly singular* if $\tilde{Q}_s$ vanishes and *strongly singular* if $\tilde{Q}_w$ vanishes. Just as a general infinitely divisible point process can be represented as the superposition of regular and singular components, so in the stationary case the singular component can be further represented as the superposition of weakly singular and strongly singular components. Evidently, a Poisson randomization is strongly singular, and any stationary singular process that is ergodic must be weakly singular (in fact, the condition is necessary and sufficient: see Exercises 10.3.8 and 10.3.9). Examples of weakly singular processes are not easy to construct: one such construction that uses a modified randomization procedure starting from a renewal process with infinite mean interval length is indicated in Exercise 10.3.10. Other examples arise from the stable cluster processes described in Section 9.4. See also Example 12.3(b).

For additional results see MKM (1978, §§6.3, 9.6), and MKM (1982, §6.2).

Exercises

10.3.1. Prove that a stationary renewal process can exist if and only if the lifetime distribution has a finite mean and that such a process is ergodic but need not be mixing. Show that if the lifetime distribution is nonlattice then the process is mixing. [*Hint:* Use the renewal theorem in different forms. A periodic renewal process can be made into a stationary process by suitably distributing the initial point (e.g., see the stationary deterministic process at Exercise 10.1.6), but such a process is not mixing because, for example, the events $V = \{N(0, \frac{1}{2}] > 0\}$ and $W = \{N(\frac{1}{2}, 1] > 0\}$ do not satisfy the mixing property (10.3.1) when x is an integer and the process has period 1.]

10.3.2. Show that any event in $\mathscr{I}$ is equal (modulo sets of measure zero) to an event in $\mathscr{T}_\infty$, but not conversely. [*Hint:* See Exercise 10.3.1 for the converse. For $W \in \mathscr{I}$, consider $W = \bigcap_{n=1}^\infty S_{x_n} V$, where $\|x_n\| \to \infty$ as $n \to \infty$.]

10.3.3. As an example of a cluster process that is mixing but for which the cluster centre process is not mixing, take the cluster centre process to be a mixture of two Neyman–Scott cluster processes with member distributions F_1 and F_2 about the centre, and the cluster member process again of Neyman–Scott type with distribution F_3 such that $F_1 * F_3 = F_2 * F_3$.

10.3.4. Say that a process ξ has *short-range correlation* if for $W \in \mathscr{B}(\hat{\mathscr{M}}_{\mathscr{X}})$ with $\mathscr{P}(W) > 0$, and arbitrary $\varepsilon > 0$, there exists a bounded set $A \in \mathscr{B}_{\mathscr{X}}$ such that on the sub-σ-algebra of $\mathscr{B}(\hat{\mathscr{M}}_{\mathscr{X}})$ determined by $\{\xi(B): B \in \mathscr{X} \setminus A\}$, the variation norm of the difference as below satisfies

$$\|\mathscr{P}_{\mathscr{X} \setminus A}(\cdot \mid W) - \mathscr{P}_{\mathscr{X} \setminus A}(\cdot)\| < \varepsilon.$$

(a) Show that ξ has short-range correlation if and only if the tail σ-algebra $\mathscr{T}_\infty$ is trivial. [*Hint:* Consider the sequence of Radon–Nikodym derivatives $p_n(\cdot) \equiv d\mathscr{P}_{\mathscr{X} \setminus A_n}(\cdot \mid W)/d\mathscr{P}_{\mathscr{X} \setminus A_n}(\cdot)$ for $A_n = \bigcup_n^d$ (for example). Show that these functions $\{p_n(\cdot)\}$ constitute a martingale that converges to a limit $p_\infty(\cdot)$, which is $\mathscr{T}_\infty$-measurable, and that $h_\infty \neq$ constant a.s. if $\|\mathscr{P}_{\mathscr{X} \setminus A}(\cdot \mid W) - \mathscr{P}_{\mathscr{X} \setminus A}(\cdot)\| > c > 0$ for some real c and every bounded $A \in \mathscr{B}_{\mathscr{X}}$. See Theorem 1.10.1 of the Russian edition of MKM (1982), where the result is attributed to Lanford and Ruelle (1969).]

(b) $\mathscr{T}_\infty$ is trivial for every regular infinitely divisible distribution. [*Hint:* Use the short-range correlation inequality above and equation (10.3.21) to show that for some positive c,

$$|\mathscr{P}(V \cap W) - \mathscr{P}(V)\mathscr{P}(W)| \leq c\tilde{Q}\{\tilde{N}(B)\} > 0 \text{ and } \tilde{N}(\mathscr{X} \setminus A) > 0,$$

where for bounded A, $B \in \mathscr{B}_{\mathscr{X}}$, V and W are in the sub-σ-algebras determined by

$$\{\xi(B'): B' \in \mathscr{B}_{\mathscr{X}}, B' \subseteq B\} \quad \text{and} \quad \{\xi(A'): A' \in \mathscr{B}_{\mathscr{X}}, A' \in \mathscr{X} \setminus A\}.$$

Now use the regularity of ξ to show that the right-hand side $\to 0$ as $A \uparrow \mathscr{X}$, and hence that events in $\mathscr{T}_\infty$ have probability 0 or 1. See MKM (1982, p. 97), in which the result is attributed to K. Hermann.]

10.3.5. (a) Let r.v.s $X(\xi)$, $Y(\xi)$ be defined on the stationary random measure ξ and have finite expectations. Show that ξ is mixing if and only if

$$\int_{\mathscr{M}_{\mathscr{X}}} X(S_x \xi) Y(\xi) \mathscr{P}(d\xi) \to EX EY \quad \text{as } \|x\| \to \infty$$

for all such r.v.s X, Y.

(b) Suppose $\mathscr{P}$, $\mathscr{P}_0$ are measures on $\hat{\mathscr{M}}_{\mathscr{X}}$ with $\mathscr{P}_0 \ll \mathscr{P}$. Show that if $\mathscr{P}$ is mixing then $\mathscr{P}_x$ converges weakly to $\mathscr{P}$ as $\|x\| \to \infty$, where, for $V \in \mathscr{B}(\hat{\mathscr{M}}_{\mathscr{X}})$,

$$\mathscr{P}_x(V) = \int_{\mathscr{M}_{\mathscr{X}}} I_V(S_x \xi) \mathscr{P}_0(d\xi).$$

[*Hint:* Let $p(\xi)$ be a measurable version of the Radon–Nikodym derivative; apply part (a).]

10.3.6. A process is *mixing of order k* if for all $V_0, \ldots, V_{k-1} \in \mathscr{B}(\mathscr{M}_{\mathscr{X}})$,

$$\mathscr{P}(V_0 \cap S_{x_1} V_1 \cap \cdots \cap S_{x_{k-1}} V_{k-1}) \to \mathscr{P}(V_0)\mathscr{P}(V_1) \cdots \mathscr{P}(V_{k-1})$$

as $\|x_i\| \to \infty$ $(i = 1, \ldots, k-1)$ in such a way that $\|x_i - x_j\| \to \infty$ also for all $i \neq j$.

(a) Show that if an infinitely divisible process is mixing then it is mixing of all orders.

(b) More generally, show that when $\mathscr{T}_\infty$ is trivial the process is mixing of all orders. [*Hint*: Use the method of proof of Proposition 10.3.V. See also Theorem 6.3.6 of MKM (1978) and Theorem 6.2.9 of MKM (1982).]

10.3.7. Verify the assertions of Proposition 10.3.IX concerning weakly mixing and ergodicity conditions.

10.3.8. Show that a singular infinitely divisible process is strongly singular if and only if it can be represented as a countable superposition of Poisson randomizations. [*Hint*: Consider the restriction $\tilde{Q}_n$ of $\tilde{Q}$ to the set

$$J_n = \{\tilde{N}: \bar{I}_V(\tilde{N}) \in ((n+1)^{-1}, n^{-1}]\},$$

where $V = \{\tilde{N}: \tilde{N}(A) > 0\}$ for some bounded $A \in \mathscr{B}(\mathbb{R}^d)$, much as in the proof of Proposition 10.3.XII. Then $\tilde{Q}_n$ is totally finite and so can be regarded as the KLM measure of a Poisson randomization. The original process is equivalent to the convolution of these randomizations.]

10.3.9. Show the equivalence of the following conditions for a singular infinitely divisible point process:

(a) the process is weakly singular;

(b) the process is ergodic;

(c) if $V \in \mathscr{I}$ then $\tilde{Q}(V) = 0$ or ∞.

[*Hint*: To show (a) ⇔ (b), use the characterization of weak singularity in terms of $\bar{I}_V$ together with relevant parts of the proof of Proposition 10.3.XII. That (a) ⇔ (c) comes from a modification of the argument of Exercise 10.3.8.]

10.3.10. Let a stationary infinitely divisible point process on $\mathbb{R}_+$ have as its (stationary) KLM measure a finite positive multiple $\alpha\mu$ of the shift-invariant regenerative measure of Example 10.1(c), so that (using the notation from there)

$$\tilde{Q}(\{\tilde{N}(0, y] > 0\}) = \alpha \int_0^y [1 - F(u)]\,du,$$

which has a finite or infinite limit according as the d.f. $F(\cdot)$ has finite or infinite mean. Show that for $x > y > 0$ and $z > 0$,

$$\tilde{Q}(\{\tilde{N}(0, y] > 0\}, \{\tilde{N}(x, x+z] > 0\})$$

$$= \alpha \int_0^y [1 - F(u)]\,du \int_{x-u}^{x-u+z} [1 - F(x - u + z - v)] U_1(dv),$$

and that this quantity has limit zero when F has infinite mean. Hence, conclude that the point process is then weakly singular. [For some other details, see MKM (1978, §9.6).]

10.4. Moment Stationarity

In this section we examine the effects of stationarity on the moment structure
of a point process or random measure. The essential feature, which in fact is
a particular application of the general factorization result at Lemma A2.7.II,
is a "diagonal factorization" whereby each moment measure is represented as
a product of Lebesgue measure along the main diagonal and a "reduced
measure" in a complementary subspace. These reduced measures determine
the moment structure of the process and are the quantities most important to
estimate in applications. Their Fourier transforms provide the various spectra
of the random measure and are discussed in Chapter 11.

   The importance of the factorization theorem in the present context emerged
in the work of Brillinger (1972) and Vere-Jones (1971), being subsumed by
the more general results on the disintegration of moment measures developed
in Krickeberg (1974b).

   We start with some definitions, supposing again that $\mathscr{X} = \mathbb{R}^d$, and writing
T_x for the shift operator as at (10.1.1).

Definition 10.4.I. A random measure or point process is kth-order stationary
if its kth moment measure exists, and for each $j = 1, \ldots, k$, bounded Borel
sets $A_1, \ldots, A_j$, and $x \in \mathbb{R}^d$,

$$(10.4.1) \qquad M_j(T_x A_1 \times \cdots \times T_x A_j) = M_j(A_1 \times \cdots \times A_j).$$

   If ξ is a stationary random measure, the joint distributions of $\{\xi(T_x A_1, \ldots, \xi(T_x A_j)\}$ coincide with those of $\{\xi(A_1), \ldots, \xi(A_j)\}$ (see around Definition
10.1.II), so that *a stationary random measure for which the kth-order moment
measure exists is kth-order stationary*. The converse implication is not true in
general (see Exercise 10.4.1), but in particular parametric models, moment
stationarity, even of relatively low order, generally requires stationarity of the
process as a whole. A Poisson process, for example, is stationary if and only
if it is first-order stationary.

   The imposition of conditions on M_j for $j < k$ in Definition 10.4.I is
certainly redundant in the case of a simple point process, for the lower-
order moment measures appear as diagonal concentrations and are thereby
identified uniquely (cf. Proposition 7.4.VI and Exercise 7.4.4). It may be
redundant more generally, but the question appears to be open. It is relatively
easy, however, to find a process for which the second cumulant measure is
stationary while the expectation measure is not (see Exercise 10.4.2).

   The case $k = 1$ of the condition (10.4.1) simply asserts that the expectation
measure $M_1(\cdot)$ is invariant under shifts. It must therefore reduce to a multiple
of the unique measure on $\mathbb{R}^d$ with this property, namely, Lebesgue measure.
We thus have the following proposition.

Proposition 10.4.II. *A random measure on $\mathbb{R}^d$ is first-order stationary if and only if its expectation measure is a finite positive multiple of Lebesgue measure $\ell(\cdot)$ on $\mathbb{R}^d$.*

The proportionality constant referred to in this proposition is usually denoted by m and called the *mean density* or, more briefly, the density of the process.

For $k > 1$, the conditions at (10.4.1) imply, via the generating properties of rectangle sets, that the whole measure M_k is invariant under the group of *diagonal shifts* $D_x^{(k)}$ defined for $x \in \mathbb{R}^d$, $y = (y_1, \ldots, y_k)$ with $y_i \in \mathbb{R}^d$ for $i = 1, \ldots, k$, by

$$(10.4.2) \qquad D_x^{(k)}(y_1, \ldots, y_k) = (x + y_1, \ldots, x + y_k).$$

The cosets under this group of transformations are images of the main diagonal $y_1 = \cdots = y_k$. Along any such coset, the action of $D_x^{(k)}$ reduces to an ordinary shift through the vector x. Thus, we should anticipate that any measure invariant under the diagonal shifts should reduce to a multiple of Lebesgue measure along each such coset. The next lemma makes this idea precise: by the *diagonal subspace* we mean the space $\{(y_1, \ldots, y_k); y_1 = \cdots = y_k \in \mathbb{R}^d\}$.

Lemma 10.4.III. *Let μ be a boundedly finite Borel measure on $\mathscr{X}^{(k)}$ with $\mathscr{X} = \mathbb{R}^d$. Then μ is invariant under the diagonal shifts $D_x^{(k)}$ if and only if it can be represented as a product of Lebesgue measure on the diagonal subspace and a reduced measure $\hat{\mu}$ on $\mathscr{X}^{(k-1)}$ such that, for any function $f \in BM(\mathscr{X}^{(k)})$*

$$(10.4.3) \qquad \int_{\mathscr{X}^{(k)}} f(x_1, \ldots, x_k)\mu(dx_1 \times \cdots \times dx_k)$$

$$= \int_{\mathscr{X}} dx \int_{\mathscr{X}^{(k-1)}} f(x, x + y_1, \ldots, x + y_{k-1})\hat{\mu}(dy_1 \times \cdots \times dy_{k-1}).$$

PROOF. Consider the mapping from $\mathscr{X} \times \mathscr{X}^{(k-1)}$ into $\mathscr{X}^{(k)}$ defined by

$$(10.4.4) \qquad (x, (y_1, \ldots, y_{k-1})) \to (x, x + y_1, \ldots, x + y_{k-1}).$$

Given any $(x_1, \ldots, x_k) \in \mathscr{X}^{(k)}$, we have uniquely $x = x_1$ and $y_i = x_{i+1} - x_1$ $(i = 1, \ldots, k-1)$, so the mapping is one-to-one and onto; it is clearly continuous and hence measurable. Under the mapping, the action of the diagonal shifts $D_x^{(k)}$ on $\mathscr{X}^{(k)}$ is reduced to the ordinary shift T_x on the $\mathscr{X}$ component of the product $\mathscr{X} \times \mathscr{X}^{(k-1)}$. We therefore have a representation of the original space $\mathscr{X}^{(k)}$ to which we can apply Lemma A2.7.II. The lemma asserts that the image, μ^* say, of μ induced by the mapping (10.4.4) reduces to a product of d-dimensional Lebesgue measure along $\mathscr{X}$ and some measure $\hat{\mu}$ on the other factor space $\mathscr{X}^{(k-1)}$; that is, $\mu^* = \ell \times \hat{\mu}$. Then $\hat{\mu}$ and μ are related as at (10.4.3). $\qquad\qquad \square$

The remarks preceding this lemma imply that it can be applied to the kth moment measure of any kth-order stationary random measure, and indeed to the factorial moment and cumulant measures as well. We therefore have the following corollary.

Corollary 10.4.IV. *For any kth-order stationary random measure or point process on $\mathbb{R}^d$, there exist reduced measures $\hat{M}_k$, $\hat{M}_{[k]}$, $\hat{C}_k$, and $\hat{C}_{[k]}$ related to the corresponding kth-order measures M_k, $M_{[k]}$, C_k, and $C_{[k]}$ through (10.4.3).*

We call $\hat{M}_k$, $\hat{M}_{[k]}$, $\hat{C}_k$, and $\hat{C}_{[k]}$ the *reduced kth-order moment measure*, the *reduced kth-order factorial moment measure*, the *reduced kth-order cumulant measure*, and the *reduced kth-order factorial cumulant measure*, respectively. For $k = 1$ these reduced measures all coincide and equal the mean density $m = M_1(\mathbb{U}^d)$. For $k = 2$ we mostly use $\hat{C}_2$, which may also be called the *reduced covariance measure*; it is defined on $\mathscr{B}_{\mathscr{X}}$.

Note that the disintegration furnished by (10.4.3) is of the form

$$M_k^* = \ell \times \hat{M}_k,$$

where ℓ is the standard Lebesgue measure on $\mathbb{R}^d$, so that any scale factors remain in the reduced measure. The same disintegration result can also be obtained via an argument involving Radon–Nikodym derivatives with respect to the first moment measure (see Exercises 10.4.3 and 10.4.4 for an outline). This alternative approach leads to a decomposition of the form

$$M_k^* = M_1 \times (m^{-1} \hat{M}_k)$$

with $M_1 = m\ell$, which has led some authors to adopt $m^{-1} \hat{M}_k$ as the definition of the reduced measure. We have preferred not to adopt this convention, mainly because of its incompatibility with the usual definition of the stationary form of the covariance function when the measure is absolutely continuous.

These reduced moment measures are the key quantities in any discussion of the moment structure of a stationary random measure. They appear as ergodic limits in the appropriate forms of the ergodic theorem, and they appear again in Chapter 12 as moment measures of the Palm measure of the process. Some of the more accessible properties of the reduced moment measures are given in the next proposition; analogous statements for factorial moment and cumulant measures are found in Exercise 10.4.5.

Proposition 10.4.V. *Let $\hat{M}_k$ be the kth-order reduced moment measure for the kth-order stationary random measure ξ on $\mathscr{X} = \mathbb{R}^d$. Then*

(i) *$\hat{M}_k(\cdot)$ is a symmetric measure on $\mathscr{X}^{(k-1)}$ (invariant under permutations of the arguments in the product space) and is invariant also under the "shift reflection" transformation mapping $(u_1, u_2, \ldots, u_{k-1})$ into $(-u_1, u_2 - u_1, \ldots, u_{k-1} - u_1)$;*

(ii) *if M_k is absolutely continuous with density m_k, then $\hat{M}_k$ is also absolutely* *continuous, and its density $\hat{m}_k$ is related to m_k by*

$$m_k(x_1, x_2, \ldots, x_k) = \hat{m}_k(x_2 - x_1, \ldots, x_k - x_1);$$

(iii) *for all bounded Borel sets $A_1, \ldots, A_{k-1} \in \mathscr{X}$,*

$$(10.4.5) \quad \hat{M}_k(A_1 \times \cdots \times A_{k-1}) = E\left(\int_{U^d} \xi(x + A_1) \cdots \xi(x + A_{k-1})\xi(dx)\right).$$

PROOF. In (10.4.3) set

$$f(x_1, \ldots, x_k) = g(x_1)h(x_2 - x_1, \ldots, x_k - x_1),$$

where $g(\cdot)$ and $h(\cdot)$ are bounded Borel functions of bounded support on $\mathscr{X}$ and $\mathscr{X}^{(k-1)}$, respectively, so that

$$(10.4.6) \quad \int_{\mathscr{X}^{(k)}} g(x_1)h(x_2 - x_1, \ldots, x_k - x_1)M_k(dx_1 \times \cdots \times dx_k)$$

$$= \int_{\mathscr{X}} g(x)dx \int_{\mathscr{X}^{(k-1)}} h(y_1, \ldots, y_{k-1})\hat{M}_k(dy_1 \times \cdots \times dy_{k-1}).$$

Now let the variables $x_2, \ldots, x_k$ in the argument of $h(\cdot)$ on the left-hand side be permuted. Because of the symmetry properties of $M_k(\cdot)$, this leaves the integral unaltered. Observe also that it corresponds to permuting the variables $y_1, \ldots, y_{k-1}$ in the argument of $h(\cdot)$ on the right-hand side of (10.4.6). Equivalently, it corresponds to leaving the variables in $h(\cdot)$ unaltered and permuting the variables in $\hat{M}_k$. Since a measure on $\mathscr{X}^{(k-1)}$ is uniquely determined by the integrals of all such functions $h(\cdot)$, it follows that $\hat{M}_k$ must be invariant under permutations of its arguments; that is, it is symmetric.

Alternatively, if we interchange x_1 and x_2 on the left-hand side of (10.4.6), the integral is unaltered, while from (10.4.3) the right-hand side becomes

$$\int_{\mathscr{X}} dx \int_{\mathscr{X}^{(k-1)}} g(x + y_1)h(-y_1, y_2 - y_1, \ldots, y_{k-1} - y_1)\hat{M}_k(dy_1 \times \cdots \times dy_{k-1}).$$

Since $\int_{\mathscr{X}} g(x + y_1)dx = \int_{\mathscr{X}} g(x)dx$, we conclude that

$$\int_{\mathscr{X}^{(k-1)}} h(y_1, \ldots, y_{k-1})\hat{M}_k(dy_1 \times \cdots \times dy_{k-1})$$

$$= \int_{\mathscr{X}^{(k-1)}} h(-y_1, y_2 - y_1, \ldots, y_{k-1} - y_1)\hat{M}_k(dy_1 \times \cdots \times dy_{k-1}),$$

hence follows the shift reflection invariance assertion in (i).

If M_k has density m_k (meaning density with respect to Lebesgue measure on $\mathbb{R}^{dk}$), invariance of M_k implies that $m_k(x, x + y_1, \ldots, x + y_{k-1})$ is independent of x, so on cancelling the factor $\int_{\mathscr{X}} g(x)dx$ in (10.4.6) we obtain

$$\int_{\mathcal{X}^{(k-1)}} h(y_1, \ldots, y_{k-1}) \hat{M}_k(dy_1 \times \cdots \times dy_{k-1})$$

$$= \int_{\mathcal{X}^{(k-1)}} h(y_1, \ldots, y_{k-1}) m_k(x, x + y_1, \ldots, x + y_{k-1}) dy_1 \cdots dy_{k-1}.$$

Thus, $\hat{M}_k$ is absolutely continuous with density $m_k(x, x + y_1, \ldots, x + y_{k-1})$, which is equivalent to the assertion (ii).

Finally, in (10.4.6) set $g(x) = I_{\cup^d}(x)$ and $h(y_1, \ldots, y_{k-1}) = \prod_{j=1}^{k-1} I_{A_j}(y_j)$. Then since $\int_{\mathcal{X}} g(x) dx = \ell(\cup^d) = 1$, (10.4.5) follows directly. $\square$

The identification at (10.4.5) of $\hat{M}_k(\cdot)$ as an expectation suggests the existence of higher-order ergodic theorems in which the reduced moment measures appear as the ergodic limits. To identify the limits in the nonergodic situation, we use the following corollary to Lemma 10.2.III.

Lemma 10.4.VI. Let ξ be a strictly stationary random measure with finite kth moment measure. Then there exists a symmetric $\mathcal{I}$-measurable random measure $\hat{\psi}_k$ on $\mathcal{X}^{(k-1)}$, invariant also under the shift reflections of Proposition 10.4.V, such that for bounded Borel functions f of bounded support on $\mathcal{X}^{(k)}$,

$$(10.4.7) \quad E\left(\int_{\mathcal{X}^{(k)}} f(x_1, \ldots, x_k) \xi(dx_1) \cdots \xi(dx_k) | \mathcal{I}\right)$$

$$= \int_{\mathcal{X}} dx \int_{\mathcal{X}^{(k-1)}} f(x, x + y_1, \ldots, x + y_{k-1}) \hat{\psi}_k(dy_1 \times \cdots \times dy_{k-1}).$$

In particular, for bounded $A_1, \ldots, A_{k-1} \in \mathcal{B}_{\mathcal{X}}$,

$$(10.4.8) \quad \hat{\psi}_k(A_1 \times \cdots \times A_{k-1}) = E\left(\int_{\cup^d} \xi(x + A_1) \cdots \xi(x + A_{k-1}) \xi(dx) | \mathcal{I}\right).$$

PROOF. Represent $\mathcal{X}^{(k)}$ in the product form $\mathcal{X} \times \mathcal{X}^{(k-1)}$ via the mapping (10.4.4). On the space $\mathcal{X}^{(k)}$, ξ induces a new random measure, namely, the k-fold product $\xi^{(k)}$ of ξ with itself, and $\xi^{(k)}$ is stationary with respect to diagonal shifts. Its image under (10.4.4) is therefore stationary with respect to shifts in the first component. We now have a situation to which the general result in Lemma 10.2.III applies. On the product space $\mathcal{X} \times \mathcal{X}^{(k-1)}$ there exists a σ-algebra of sets invariant under shifts in the first component, and the image of $\xi^{(k)}$ under (10.4.4) has a conditional expectation with respect to this σ-algebra, which factorizes into a product of Lebesgue measure on $\mathcal{X}$ and an $\mathcal{I}$-measurable random measure $\hat{\psi}_k$ on $\mathcal{X}^{(k-1)}$, which is readily checked as having the properties described in the lemma. $\square$

We can now generalize the ergodic theorem at 10.2.IV (cf. Nguyen and Zessin, 1976).

Theorem 10.4.VII. *Let ξ be a strictly stationary random measure for which the kth moment measure exists, $\hat{\psi}_k$ the invariant random measure defined by (10.4.8), and $B_1, \ldots, B_{k-1}$ a family of bounded Borel sets in $\mathbb{R}^d$. Then, for any convex averaging sequence $\{A_n\}$ in $\mathbb{R}^d$, as $n \to \infty$,*

$$(10.4.9) \qquad \frac{1}{\ell(A_n)} \int_{A_n} \xi(x + B_1) \cdots \xi(x + B_{k-1}) \xi(dx)$$

$$\to \hat{\psi}_k(B_1 \times \cdots \times B_{k-1}) \quad \text{(a.s.)}.$$

In particular, if ξ is ergodic,

$$(10.4.10) \qquad \frac{1}{\ell(A_n)} \int_{A_n} \xi(x + B_1) \cdots \xi(x + B_{k-1}) \xi(dx)$$

$$\to \hat{M}_k(B_1 \times \cdots \times B_{k-1}) \quad \text{(a.s.)}.$$

PROOF. Given a bounded Borel function g of bounded support on $\mathscr{X}^{(k)}$, consider the random function

$$f(\xi) \equiv \int_{\mathscr{X}^{(k)}} g(x_1, \ldots, x_k) \xi(dx_1) \cdots \xi(dx_k),$$

noting that, by assumption, we must have $Ef(\xi) < \infty$.

Appealing to Proposition 10.2.II(a) and evaluating the limit in (10.2.6) from (10.4.7), we obtain, for $n \to \infty$,

$$(10.4.11) \quad \frac{1}{\ell(A_n)} \int_{A_n} f(S_x \xi) dx$$

$$= \frac{1}{\ell(A_n)} \int_{A_n} dx \int_{\mathscr{X}^{(k)}} g(u_1 - x, \ldots, u_k - x) \xi(du_1) \cdots \xi(du_k)$$

$$\to \int_{\mathscr{X}} dx \int_{\mathscr{X}^{(k-1)}} g(x, x + y_1, \ldots, x + y_{k-1})$$

$$\times \hat{\psi}_k(dy_1 \times \cdots \times dy_{k-1}) \quad \text{(a.s.)}.$$

In particular, by taking $g(x_1, \ldots, x_k) = g_\varepsilon(x_1) h(x_2 - x_1, \ldots, x_k - x_1)$, where $g_\varepsilon(\cdot)$ has the same properties as in the proof of Theorem 10.2.IV, it follows, for example, that

$$\int_{A_n^\varepsilon} f(S_x \xi) dx$$

$$= \int_{A_n^\varepsilon} g_\varepsilon(u_1 - x) dx \int_{\mathscr{X}^{(k)}} h(u_2 - u_1, \ldots, u_k - u_1) \xi(du_1) \cdots \xi(du_k)$$

$$= \int_{A_n^\varepsilon} g_\varepsilon(u_1 - x) dx \int_{\mathscr{X}^{(k)}} h(v_1, \ldots, v_{k-1}) \xi(du_1) \xi(u_1 + dv_1) \cdots \xi(u_1 + dv_{k-1})$$

$$\geq \int_{A_n} \xi(du_1) \int_{\mathscr{X}^{(k-1)}} h(v_1, \ldots, v_{k-1}) \xi(u_1 + dv_1) \cdots \xi(u_1 + dv_{k-1}).$$

Thus, we can use the approximation argument exploited in Theorem 10.2.IV to deduce that for nonnegative bounded functions h of bounded support in $\mathscr{X}^{(k-1)}$, as $n \to \infty$,

$$(10.4.12) \quad \frac{1}{\ell(A_n)} \int_{A_n} \xi(du) \int_{\mathscr{X}^{(k-1)}} h(v_1, \ldots, v_{k-1}) \xi(u + dv_1) \cdots \xi(u + dv_{k-1})$$

$$\to \int_{\mathscr{X}^{(k-1)}} h(v_1, \ldots, v_{k-1}) \hat{\psi}_k(dv_1 \times \cdots \times dv_{k-1}) \quad \text{(a.s.)}.$$

Equations (10.4.9) and (10.4.10) are now easily derived as special cases of (10.4.12). $\qquad\square$

It is, of course, a corollary of (10.4.8) that

$$E(\hat{\psi}_k(B_1 \times \cdots \times B_{k-1})) = \hat{M}_k(B_1 \times \cdots \times B_{k-1}).$$

The next example, even if somewhat artificial in character, illustrates some of the types of behaviour that can occur.

EXAMPLE 10.4(a) *Poisson cluster process with dependent clusters.* Suppose that $\mathscr{X} = \mathbb{R}$ and that cluster centres occur at rate λ. Set up a common pattern for the clusters from a realization $\{y_1, \ldots, y_Z\}$ of a finite Poisson process on $\mathbb{R}$ with a nonatomic parameter measure $\mu(\cdot)$, so that Z is a Poisson r.v. with mean $EZ = \mu(\mathbb{R}) \equiv v$ and, conditional on Z, the r.v.s $y_1, \ldots, y_Z$ are i.i.d. r.v.s with distribution $\mu(\cdot)/v$. Then, given a realization $\{x_i\}$ of the cluster centre process, we associate with the cluster centre x_i the cluster $\{x_i + y_j: j = 1, \ldots, Z\}$, so that the whole process has as its realization the points $\{x_i + y_j: i = 0, \pm 1, \ldots; j = 1, \ldots, Z\}$. The r.v.s $\{Z, y_1, \ldots, y_Z\}$ define a σ-algebra of events, which, in fact, coincides with the invariant σ-algebra $\mathscr{I}$ for the whole process. We can then compute characteristics of the process as follows:

(i) The conditional intensity given the invariant σ-algebra $\mathscr{I}$, that is, the r.v. Y of Theorem 10.2.IV, here equals λZ, while the density of the whole process equals

$$m = E(\lambda Z) = \lambda \mu(\mathbb{R}) = \lambda v.$$

(ii) The random measure ψ_2 of Lemma 10.4.VI, before reduction, has three components: a multiple $\lambda^2 Z^2$ of Lebesgue measure in the plane; a line concentration with density λZ along the main diagonal $x = y$; and line concentrations of density λ along each of the $Z(Z-1)$ lines $y = x + y_i - y_j$, where $i \neq j$ but both orderings are permitted. Then the reduced moment measure $\hat{\psi}_2(\cdot)$ on $\mathscr{B}_{\mathbb{R}}$ can be written

$$\hat{\psi}_2(du) = \lambda^2 Z^2 \, du + \lambda Z \delta(u) du + \lambda \sum_{i \neq j} \delta(u - y_i + y_j) du,$$

where the δ-function terms represent atoms at the origin and the points

$\pm |y_i - y_j|$ $(i \neq j)$. Taking expectations leads to the reduced second moment measure:

$$\hat{M}_2(du) = \lambda^2 v(v + 1)du + \lambda v \delta(u)du + \lambda \int_{\mathbb{R}} \mu(x + du)\mu(dx).$$

(iii) Third- and higher-order moments can be built up in a similar way from a consideration of the possible locations of all triples of points $\{y_i\}$ and so on.

Observe that $\hat{\psi}_2$ is just the form that the reduced moment measure would take if the cluster structure were fixed for all realizations: the process would then be infinitely divisible and ergodic.

A variant of this Poisson cluster process, but having conditionally independent clusters, can be obtained by treating the clusters as a Cox process directed by some a.s. finite random measure ξ replacing the fixed measure $\mu(\cdot)$ above: regard ξ as fixed for any given realization with the points in each cluster now being determined mutually independently according to a Poisson process with parameter measure $\xi(\cdot)$. Then $\hat{M}_2$ as above equals the random measure $\hat{\psi}_2$ of this process and the new $\hat{M}_2$ is obtained by a further averaging over the realizations of ξ.

Further variants of the model are possible.

The representations (10.4.9) and (10.4.10) suggest a natural class of estimates for the reduced moment measures. When as often happens we are concerned with estimates from a finite part of a single realization of an ergodic process, (10.4.10) is the relevant form. Consider, in particular, estimates for the reduced second moment measure for a point process. If B denotes a suitable test set, such as an interval on the line or a rectangle or disc in the plane, and A is a (larger) observation region, the left-hand side of (10.4.10) is expressible in the form

$$(10.4.13) \qquad \hat{M}_2(B; A) = \frac{1}{\ell(A)} \sum_{i:x_i \in A} N(x_i + B).$$

In other words, taking each point x_i in A in turn as origin, count the number of points in sets $x_i + B$ having a common relative position to x_i, and then average by dividing by the Lebesgue measure of the counting region. If B is small, and we further divide by the measure of B, the resulting ratio can be regarded as an estimate of the corresponding density at a representative point of B. The relation at (10.4.8) and the assumed ergodicity of the process imply that this estimate (10.4.13) is unbiased, while (10.4.10) asserts that it is consistent. In practice, some technical difficulties arise with edge effects, since information on $N(x_i + B)$ may not be available if x_i lies near the boundary of A. The bias arising from this cause may be corrected in a variety of ways, either by introducing an explicit correction factor, or by weighting the averages appropriately, or by taking observations over a slightly larger region than is needed for the set A itself. One commonly used correction replaces (10.4.13) by the form

$$\hat{M}_2(B; A) = \left[\frac{N(A)\ell(B)}{\ell(A)}\right]\left[\sum_{x_i \in A} N(A \cap T_{x_i}B)\Big/ \sum_{x_i \in A} \ell(A \cap T_{x_i}B)\right]$$

so that each observation count $N(x_i + B)$ is weighted by that fraction of $\ell(T_{x_i}B)$ that remains inside A. In estimating the corresponding density, averaged over the test region B, the multiplying factor $\ell(B)$ would be omitted.

Estimates of the corresponding factorial moment and cumulant measures can be made in a similar way, except that we take only *distinct* pairs in counting the points in the test region; that is, we replace the measure N in the summation at (10.4.13) by $N^*(x + B) = N(x + B) - \delta_0(B)$, so that $N(x + B)$ is reduced by one when B contains the origin. Then (10.4.13) takes the form

$$(10.4.14) \qquad \hat{M}_{[2]}(B; A) = \frac{1}{\ell(A)} \sum_{i:x_i \in A} N^*(x_i + B),$$

and (10.4.13) can be interpreted as an estimate of the average density of *pairs* of points so related that if the first is taken as origin, the second lies within B, while (10.4.14) has a similar interpretation with the proviso that identical pairs (x_i, x_i) are omitted.

Note that in the case of a process with multiple points, the points at each x_i should be labelled $x_i^{(1)}, \ldots, x_i^{(n_i)}$, and the definition of N^* implies that we omit pairs $(x_i^{(j)}, x_i^{(j)})$ but not any pair $(x_i^{(j)}, x_i^{(k)})$ with $j \neq k$.

Estimates of the reduced covariance measures can be obtained by subtracting appropriate multiples of $\ell(B)$, as indicated by (10.4.19) and (10.4.20). Estimates of the mean square and variance functions can be treated in a similar manner. For example, using (10.4.11) with $g(x, y) = I_B(x)I_B(y)$ yields the estimate for $E(N(B))^2$,

$$(10.4.15) \qquad M_2(B \times B; A) = \frac{1}{\ell(A)} \int_A (N(x + B))^2 \, dx,$$

from which a corresponding estimate of the variance function can be obtained by subtracting the square of the estimate of $m\ell(B)$. Observe that (10.4.15) suggests estimating the mean square by a family of continuously overlapping test values x; more commonly, $(N(x + B))^2$ will be estimated for the points x in a lattice and the divisor replaced by the number of such lattice points in the observation region A. Again, (10.4.8) and (10.4.10) can be used to establish that such estimates are consistent and asymptotically unbiased.

These comments are included to suggest a basis for the systematic treatment of moment estimation for point processes; Krickeberg (1980) and Jolivet (1978) discuss some further issues and special problems, while applications are discussed by Ripley (1976, 1981), Diggle (1983), Vere-Jones (1978), and many others.

In applications to point processes, the factorial moment and cumulant measures are often to be preferred because for simple point processes (though not in general) they are free of the complications of diagonal concentrations. In this case also, $M_{[k]}(A)$ has the important interpretation as the expected number of distinct k-tuples of the process lying in the set A from the product space $\mathscr{X}^{(k)}$. On the other hand, the cumulant measures are generally more revealing of structural features than the corresponding moment measures. This suggests that an important form for interpreting data or identifying models is often the reduced second factorial cumulant measure $\hat{C}_{[2]}$; we call this the *reduced factorial covariance measure* and refer to its density, when it exists, as the *reduced factorial covariance density* $\hat{c}_{[2]}$, or the *covariance density* for short.

The variety of different names and modifications of the definitions and their estimates, which have been introduced, often independently, in different contexts, gives the impression of a topic of greater complexity than is really the case. Here we consider briefly some of the possible forms and their connections. The factorial form $\hat{C}_{[2]}$ of the reduced covariance measure differs from the ordinary form $\hat{C}_2$ by an atom at the origin, corresponding to a line concentration in the unreduced form along the diagonal $x = y$: for bounded Borel sets A

$$(10.4.16) \qquad \hat{C}_2(A) = m\delta_0(A) + \hat{C}_{[2]}(A).$$

Even when $\hat{C}_{[2]}(\cdot)$ is absolutely continuous, $\hat{C}_2(\cdot)$ has an atom at the origin, a feature that led Bartlett (1963) to define a *complete covariance density* (using δ-function notation)

$$(10.4.17) \qquad \hat{c}_2(x) = m\delta(x) + \hat{c}_{[2]}(x).$$

For nonsimple point processes, both $\hat{c}_2$ and $\hat{c}_{[2]}$ have δ-function terms at the origin. In general, the presence of such atoms in both moment and cumulant measures reflects a lack of absolute continuity of the realizations: for example, a sufficient condition for an absolutely continuous covariance measure is the mean square continuity of the derivative process $d\xi(x)/dx$ (see Exercise 10.4.8).

The reduced second-order factorial and ordinary moment measures are related to the covariance measure $\hat{C}_{[2]}$ by the equations

$$(10.4.18) \qquad \hat{M}_{[2]}(A) = \hat{C}_{[2]}(A) + m^2 \ell(A),$$

$$(10.4.19) \qquad \hat{M}_2(A) = \hat{C}_{[2]}(A) + m^2 \ell(A) + m\delta_0(A),$$

which follow directly from the relations between the unreduced forms of these measures, stationarity, and the disintegration relation (10.4.3).

Again, $\hat{M}_{[2]}$ may be absolutely continuous for simple processes, in which case its density is related to the covariance density by

$$(10.4.20) \qquad \hat{m}_{[2]}(x) = \hat{c}_{[2]}(x) + m^2.$$

When this density exists, the ratio $\hat{m}_{[2]}(x)/m$ has been called the intensity of the process [e.g., see Cox and Lewis (1966, p. 69)] and the conditional intensity function [e.g., see Cox and Isham (1980, §2.5)]. We call it the *second-order intensity* and denote it by $\hat{h}_2(\cdot)$, so that

$$\hat{h}_2(x) = \hat{m}_{[2]}(x)/m = m + \hat{c}_{[2]}(x)/m.$$

The interpretation of $\hat{h}_2$ as the intensity at x of the process conditional on a point at the origin [hence the terminology noted above: the notation reflects the identification of $\hat{h}_2(\cdot)$ as the renewal density of a simple renewal process] is taken up in the discussion of Palm measures in Chapter 12. Vere-Jones (1978) called the ratio

(10.4.21) $$r_2(x) \equiv \hat{h}_2(x)/m = \hat{m}_{[2]}(x)/m^2$$

the relative conditional intensity (for consistency with the terminology above we should call it the relative second-order intensity). It is equal to unity for a stationary Poisson process, while for other stationary processes it provides a useful indication of the strength and character of second-order dependence effects between pairs of points at varying relative distances and directions. When $r_2(x) > 1$, clustering or contagion is indicated at separations equal to x, while $r_2(x) < 1$ indicates a tendency for points to be spaced out (and separations equal to x are less likely than other values). For isotropic processes in $\mathbb{R}^2$ the quantity $r_2(x) - 1$ becomes a function of $|x|$; it has been referred to as the *radial correlation function* (e.g., see Glass and Tobler, 1971) and is discussed further in Section 10.5.

The variance function

(10.4.22) $$V(A) \equiv \mathrm{var}(N(A)) = \int_{\mathscr{X}^{(2)}} I_A(x) I_A(y) C_2(dx \times dy)$$

$$= m\ell(A) + \int_A \hat{C}_{[2]}(x - A)dx$$

is also widely used in applications, often in the form of the ratio to the expected value $M(A)$,

(10.4.23) $$\frac{V(A)}{M(A)} = 1 + \frac{1}{m\ell(A)} \int_A \hat{C}_{[2]}(x - A)dx.$$

Like $r_2(\cdot)$, this ratio equals 1 for a Poisson process, while values in excess of 1 indicate clustering and values below 1 indicate repulsion or some tendency to regular spacing. For suitably small sets, so that $\ell(A) \to 0$, $V(A)/M(A) \to 1$; that is, locally the process is like a Poisson process in having the variance-to-mean ratio ≈ 1 (see Exercise 10.4.10). As $\ell(A) \to \infty$, various possibilities for the behaviour of $V(A)/M(A)$ exist and are realizable (see Exercise 10.4.11), but most commonly, the covariance measure is totally finite, in which case

$$V(A)/M(A) \to 1 + m^{-1}\hat{C}_{[2]}(\mathscr{X})$$

as A expands to $\mathscr{X}$. For a stationary Poisson cluster process, the cluster member process satisfies

$$M_{[2]}(A_n \times A_n | x) \to E(Z(Z - 1))$$

as $\ell(A_n) \to \infty$ through a convex averaging sequence $\{A_n\}$, where $Z \equiv N_m(\mathscr{X} | 0)$ denotes a generic r.v. for the total number of points in a cluster. Then, from (8.3.6), we have $C_{[2]}(\mathscr{X}) = E(Z(Z-1))$, and thus

$$(10.4.24) \qquad V(A)/M(A) \to 1 + E(Z(Z-1))/EZ = EZ^2/EZ.$$

Characteristically, therefore, the variance-to-mean ratio for a Poisson cluster process increases from a value approximately equal to 1 for very small sets to a limiting value equal to the ratio of the mean square cluster size to the mean cluster size for very large sets (cf. the formula for the compound Poisson process in Exercise 2.1.8). The region of rapid growth of the ratio occurs as A passes through sets with dimensions comparable to those of (the spread of) individual clusters.

   These comments provide the background to diagnostic procedures such as plotting the ratio $V(A)/M(A)$ against $M(A)$ or $\ell(A)$ as $\ell(A) \to \infty$, and the Greig-Smith method of nested quadrats, which uses a components-of-variance analysis to determine the characteristic dimensions at which clustering effects or local inhomogeneities begin to influence the variance [for further discussion see Greig-Smith (1964)].

   In $\mathbb{R}$, (10.4.22) can be written in the alternative forms

$$V(x) = \mathrm{var}(N(0, x]) = mx + \int_{-x}^{x} (x - |u|) \hat{C}_{[2]}(du)$$

$$= 2 \int_{0-}^{x} F_c(u)\,du,$$

where

$$F_c(x) = (m + \hat{C}_{[2]}\{0\})/2 + \hat{C}_{[2]}(0, x] = \hat{C}_2\{0\}/2 + \hat{C}_2(0, x] = \hat{C}_2[-x, x]/2$$

is a symmetrized form of the distribution function corresponding to the reduced covariance measure. Properties of $V(x)$ can be read off rather simply from this last representation: for example, it is absolutely continuous with a density function of which there exists a version that is continuous except perhaps at up to a countable number of finite discontinuities [see Daley (1971) and Exercise 10.4.12]. Observe that, when it exists, the covariance density is a second derivative in $(0, \infty)$ of $V(x)$.

EXAMPLE 10.4(b) *A model for underdispersion* (Matérn, 1960). Given a realization $\{x_n'\}$ of a stationary Poisson process N' on the line with mean rate λ, identify the subset $\{x_n''\}$ of those points of the realization that are within a distance R of another such point; that is,

$$\{x_n''\} = \{x \in \{x_n'\}: |x - y| < R \text{ for some } y \neq x, y \in \{x_n'\}\}.$$

Let $\{x_n'\}\backslash\{x_n''\} \equiv \{x_n\}$ constitute a realization of a new point process N. The probability that any given point x of N' will be absent from N is then the probability, $1 - e^{-2\lambda R}$, that at least one further point of N' is within a distance R of x. While these probabilities are of events that are not mutually independent, they have the same probability, and so the mean rate m for the modified process equals

$$m = \lambda e^{-2\lambda R}.$$

To find the second-order properties of N, consider the probability $q(v)$ that for a given pair of points distance v apart in N', they are both also in N. Then

$$q(v) = \begin{cases} 0 & (0 < v \le R) \\ \exp[-\lambda(2R + \min(v, 2R))] & (v > R). \end{cases}$$

The factorial moment density of N is thus $\hat{m}_{[2]}(x) = \lambda^2 q(x)$, and the relative conditional intensity is given by

$$r_2(x) = \begin{cases} 0 & (0 < x \le R), \\ e^{\lambda(2R-x)_+} & (R < x). \end{cases}$$

Thus, the process shows complete inhibition up to distance R and then a region of overdispersion for distances between R and $2R$, before settling down to Poisson-type behaviour for distances beyond $2R$.

The process is in fact of renewal type: the results above and others can be deduced from the renewal function for the process (see Exercise 10.4.14 for further details).

The model can readily be extended to point processes in the plane or space, but the analogues of the explicit expressions above become more cumbersome as the expression for the area or volume of the common intersection of circles or spheres becomes more complex (see Exercise 10.4.15).

EXAMPLE 10.4(c) *The Hawkes process—self-exciting process, infectivity model.* In introducing this model Hawkes (1971a, b, 1972) stressed the linear representation aspect to which the term self-exciting refers. Here it is introduced through the alternative representation as a cluster process (Hawkes and Oakes, 1974) because this leads directly to a generalization to $\mathbb{R}^d$.

Suppose we are given a stationary Poisson process of rate λ for the cluster centres. Assume that the clusters form independent realizations of a finite branching process with structure as in Exercise 5.5.5; that is, a parent at x generates offspring according to a finite Poisson process with parameter measure $\mu(\cdot \,|\, x) = \mu(\cdot - x)$, where $\mu(\mathcal{X}) = v < 1$. The cluster centres may be regarded as "infected immigrants" from outside the system and the clusters they generate as the process of new infections they produce. Thus, $\mu(du)$ is a measure of the infectivity at the point u due to an infected individual at the origin.

From the general results for Poisson cluster processes, and specifically from the relations at (8.3.4) and (8.3.6), the mean rate and covariance measure for the resultant cluster process are given by

(10.4.25) $m = \lambda M_1(\mathscr{X}|0)$ and $\hat{C}_{[2]}(A) = \lambda \int_{\mathscr{X}} M_{[2]}(dy, y + A|0),$

where $M_1(\cdot\,|0)$ and $M_{[2]}(\cdot,\ \cdot|0)$ refer to the first and second factorial moment measures for a cluster with centre at the origin. From Exercise 5.5.6 we have, for bounded $A \in \mathscr{B}_{\mathscr{X}}$,

$$M_1(A|0) = \delta_0(A) + \int_{\mathscr{X}} M_1(A|x)\mu(dx);$$

so

$$M_1(\mathscr{X}|0) = (1 - v)^{-1},$$

$$\int_{\mathscr{X}} M_{[2]}(dy, y + A|0) = \int_{\mathscr{X}} M_1(y + A|0)M_1(dy|0) - \delta_0(A)$$

$$+ \int_{\mathscr{X}} M_{[2]}(du, u + A|0) \int_{\mathscr{X}} \mu(dv),$$

and hence

(10.4.26) $\hat{C}_{[2]}(A) = \dfrac{\lambda}{1 - v}\left[\int_{\mathscr{X}} M_1(y + A|0)M_1(dy|0) - \delta_0(A)\right].$

An important feature of these formulae is that they lead to simple Fourier transforms, and we exploit this fact later in illustrating the spectral theory in Example 11.2(e).

For a parametric example, with $\mathscr{X} = \mathbb{R}$ and $\mu(\cdot)$ with support in $\mathbb{R}_+$, suppose that for some $\alpha > 0$ and $0 < v < 1$

$$\mu(dx) = v\alpha e^{-\alpha x}\, dx \qquad (x \geq 0)$$

and $\mu(\cdot)$ zero otherwise. Then $M_1(\cdot)$ is absolutely continuous apart from an atom at the origin; for its density $m_1(\cdot)$ we find on $x \geq 0$ that

$$m_1(x) = \delta(x) + v\alpha e^{-\alpha(1-v)x}.$$

Then $\hat{C}_{[2]}(\cdot)$ is absolutely continuous also, and by substituting in (10.4.25) and (10.4.26) we find that the covariance density is given by

$$c_{[2]}(y) = \lambda\alpha v(1 - v)^{-1} e^{-\alpha(1-v)|y|}.$$

EXAMPLE 10.4(d) *Interacting point processes.* A number of important applications, especially in neurophysiology, concern situations where the points from one point process either inhibit or stimulate the occurrence of points in another process. Numerous examples of this type can be found, for example, in Lawrance (1971) or Sampath and Srinivasan (1977), which can be consulted for detail and references: here we give one example.

Suppose we are given a pair of stationary simple point processes N_0, N_1, which proceed independently of one another except that each successive point t_i of the process N_1 is followed by a "dead time" Z_i, during which any point of the process N_0 is deleted. Suppose that $Z_i = \min(Y_i, t_{i+1} - t_i)$, where $\{Y_i\}$ is a sequence of i.i.d. nonnegative r.v.s independent of both N_0 and N_1. We observe N_1 and the thinned process N_2 consisting of those points of N_0 that are not deleted. Our aim here is to describe the first and second moment measures of the output (N_1, N_2), particularly as they relate to the same measures for N_0.

Consider the $\{0, 1\}$-valued process $J(t)$ equal to 1 in the intervals $(t_i + Z_i, t_{i+1}]$ between the dead periods. Since the marked point process $\{t_i, (Y_i, t_{i+1} - t_i)\}$ on $\mathbb{R} \times \mathbb{R}_+^2$ is stationary whenever N_1 (with realizations the points $\{t_i\}$) is stationary, it follows that then $J(\cdot)$ is itself a stationary process, with first and second moments

$$\alpha = EJ(t) \quad \text{(all } t\text{)}, \qquad \beta(u) = E(J(t)J(t + u)) \quad \text{(all } t, u\text{)}.$$

Furthermore, we then have $N_2(dx) = J(x)N_0(dx)$. Since J and N_0 are independent, it follows that the mean densities m_k of N_k ($k = 0, 1, 2$) are related in the first instance by $m_2 = \alpha m_0$ because, for any bounded measurable h of bounded support,

$$m_2 \int_{\mathbb{R}} h(x)dx = E \int_{\mathbb{R}} h(x)N_2(dx) = E \int_{\mathbb{R}} h(x)J(x)N_0(dx)$$

$$= E\left\{E\left(\int_{\mathbb{R}} h(x)J(x)N_0(dx)|N_1\right)\right\}$$

$$= E\left\{m_0 \int_{\mathbb{R}} h(x)J(x)dx\right\} = \alpha m_0 \int_{\mathbb{R}} h(x)dx.$$

In addition, for bounded measurable h of bounded support in $\mathbb{R}^2$, and writing $D = \{(x, y): x = y\}$ for the diagonal of $\mathbb{R}^2$, the second factorial measure $M_{[2]}^{(2)}(\cdot)$ of N_2 satisfies

$$\int_{\mathbb{R}^2 \backslash D} h(x, y)M_{[2]}^{(2)}(dx \times dy) = E \int_{\mathbb{R}^2 \backslash D} h(x, y)N_2(dx)N_2(dy)$$

$$= E \int_{\mathbb{R}^2 \backslash D} h(x, y)J(x)J(y)N_0(dx)N_0(dy),$$

which, assuming the existence of a reduced factorial moment density $\hat{m}_{[2]}(\cdot)$ for N_0, leads to

$$E \int_{\mathbb{R}^2 \backslash D} h(x, y)J(x)J(y)\hat{m}_{[2]}(x - y)dx\, dy$$

$$= \int_{\mathbb{R}^2 \backslash D} h(x, y)\beta(x - y)\hat{m}_{[2]}(x - y)dx\, dy.$$

Consequently, $M_{[2]}^{(2)}(\cdot)$ then has a reduced measure with density $\hat{m}_{[2]}^{(2)}(\cdot)$ given by

$$\hat{m}_{[2]}^{(2)}(u) = \beta(u)\hat{m}_{[2]}(u).$$

Finally, for the cross-intensity we find similarly (using differential notation for brevity) that

$$E(N_1(dx)N_2(dy)) = m_0\gamma(y - x)dx\, dy,$$

where $\gamma(u)dx = E(J(x + u)N_1(dx))$. Here, $\gamma(u)$ can be interpreted as the rate of occurrence of points t_i of N_1 such that $t_i + u$ lies outside any dead time interval.

Evaluation of the characteristics α, $\beta(\cdot)$, and $\gamma(\cdot)$ of the process N_1 and the associated dead time mechanism requires more detail than is embodied in these moment functions. If the process N_1 is ergodic, then it can be shown that

$$\alpha = m_1 \int_0^\infty G(v)(1 - F(v))dv,$$

where G is the common d.f. of the Y_i and F is the d.f. of $t_{i+1} - t_i$ (all i), being given by

$$F(x) = \lim_{h\downarrow 0} \Pr\{N_1(0, x] \geq 1 | N_1(-h, 0] \geq 1\}$$

(cf. Chapters 3 and 12). The functions β and γ are necessarily more complex, involving joint distributions, as we now illustrate in the case that N_1 is a stationary renewal process with life time d.f. F as just given. Writing

$$\pi(t) = \Pr\{J(t) = 0 | N_1 \text{ has a point at the origin}\}$$

for the conditional dead time probability function, the regenerative properties of N_1 imply that $\pi(\cdot)$ satisfies the renewal equation

$$\pi(t) = (1 - G(t))(1 - F(t)) + \int_0^t \pi(t - v)dF(v)$$

$$= \int_0^t (1 - G(t - v))(1 - F(t - v))dU(v),$$

where $U(\cdot)$ is the renewal function generated by the d.f. F [see (4.1.7)]. When F is such that the nonlattice form of the renewal theorem 4.4.I holds, (4.4.2) yields

$$\pi(t) \to \int_0^\infty (1 - G(v))(1 - F(v))m_1\, dv \qquad (t \to \infty).$$

Thus, writing B for a stationary backward recurrence time r.v. (see Section 4.2), we can also write

$$\lim_{t\to\infty} \pi(t) = \Pr\{Z > B\} = 1 - \alpha.$$

For general t, we have $\gamma(t) = m_1(1 - \pi(t))$, so it remains only to identify $\beta(\cdot)$. When N_1 is stationary, write B_t and T_t for the backward and forward recurrence time r.v.s at time t, noting that stationarity implies from (4.2.7) and

(4.4.2) that their joint distribution has

$$\Pr\{B_t > x, T_t > y\} = m_1 \int_{x+y}^{\infty} (1 - F(v))dv.$$

For $u > 0$ we have

$$\beta(u) = E(J(t)J(t + u))$$

$$= \Pr\{B_t > Z, T_t > u\} + \int_0^u \Pr\{B_t > Z, T_t \in (v, v + dv)\}(1 - \pi(u - v))$$

$$= \alpha - m_1 \int_0^{\infty} dG(z) \int_0^u \pi(u - v)(1 - F(z + v))dv,$$

$$\to \alpha^2 \text{ as } u \to \infty \text{ when } \pi(t) \to 1 - \alpha \text{ as } t \to \infty.$$

While the properties of $\beta(u)$ and $\gamma(u)$ noted for large u reflect asymptotic independence, it is primarily the local properties, for u closer to zero, that are of interest in practice, since it is these that reflect any causal relation between the two processes N_0 and N_1. Parametric models are then called for but take us even further from the theme of this section.

Exercises

10.4.1. Consider a nonstationary Poisson cluster process on $\mathbb{R}$ with cluster centres having intensity $\mu(t)$ and a cluster with centre t having either a single point at t with probability $p_1(t)$, or two points, one at t and the other at $t + X$, where the r.v. X has d.f. F. Show that $p_1(\cdot)$ and $\mu(\cdot)$ can be chosen so that the process is first-order stationary but not second-order stationary.

10.4.2. Construct an example of a point process that has stationary covariance measure but nonstationary expectation measure. [*Hint:* Such a process is necessarily not simple: consider a compound Poisson process in which the rate of occurrence of groups and mean square group size are adjusted suitably.]

10.4.3. Establish the following "disintegration" of the kth moment measure of any random measure (not necessarily stationary) for which $M_k(\cdot)$ and $M(\cdot)$ are both boundedly finite: show that there exists a Radon–Nikodym family $\hat{M}_k(B|x)$ with the following properties:
(a) For each bounded $B \in \mathcal{B}^{(k-1)}(\mathcal{X})$, $\hat{M}_k(B|x)$ is a measurable function of x that is integrable with respect to M on bounded sets.
(b) For M-almost all x, $\hat{M}_k(\cdot|x)$ is a boundedly finite measure on $\mathcal{B}^{(k-1)}(\mathcal{X})$.
(c) For $A \in \mathcal{B}(\mathcal{X})$, $B \in \mathcal{B}^{(k-1)}(\mathcal{X})$,

$$M_k(A \times B) = \int_A \hat{M}_k(B|x)M(dx).$$

[*Hint:* $M_k(A \times B)$ is absolutely continuous with respect to M for each fixed $B \in \mathcal{B}^{(k-1)}(\mathcal{X})$.]

10.4.4. (Continuation) Deduce that if $\mathscr{X} = \mathbb{R}^d$ and the process is kth-order stationary, then there exists a version of $\hat{M}_k(\cdot\,|x)$ that is invariant under simultaneous translations; that is, $\hat{M}_k(D_y^{(k-1)}B|x + y) = \hat{M}_k(B|x)$. Hence, give an alternative proof of Lemma 10.4.III.

10.4.5. Give analogous statements to those of Proposition 10.4.V for the reduced factorial moment measure and for the reduced ordinary and factorial cumulant measures. Investigate the analogue of (10.4.6) when M_k is replaced by $M_{[k]}$ and g and h are indicator functions as in the proof of (10.4.5). Relate the case $k = 2$ to the ergodicity result underlying (10.4.14).

10.4.6. Find the reduced moment and cumulant measures for a stationary renewal process. In particular, show that if the renewal function has a density $h(\cdot)$, then reduced kth factorial moment measures exist for all $k = 2, 3, \ldots$ and have densities

$$\hat{m}_{[k]}(x_1, \ldots, x_{k-1}) = \lambda h(x_1')h(x_2' - x_1') \cdots h(x_{k-1}' - x_{k-2}'),$$

where $\{x_1', \ldots, x_{k-1}'\}$ is the set $\{x_1, \ldots, x_{k-1}\}$ arranged in ascending order. [Hint: See Example 5.4(a).]

10.4.7. (a) Show that when the reduced kth factorial cumulant measure of a kth-order stationary point process is finite, the kth cumulant of $N(A)$ is asymptotically proportional to $\ell(A)$ as $A \uparrow \mathscr{X}$ through a convex averaging sequence.
   (b) Show that a stationary Poisson cluster process for which the cluster size distribution has finite kth moment, satisfies the conditions of (a).
   (c) Show that the conditions of (a) are not satisfied for $k \geq 2$ by (i) any nontrivial mixture of Poisson processes and (ii) a stationary renewal process whose lifetime distribution has finite first moment but infinite second moment. [Hint: Compare Exercises 4.1.1 and 4.1.2.]

10.4.8. Suppose that the stationary random measure $\xi(\cdot)$ has the representation

$$\xi(A) = \int_A \eta(u)\,du$$

for some mean square continuous nonnegative random function $\eta(\cdot)$. Prove that the covariance measure C_2 of $\xi(\cdot)$ is free of any atom at the origin. When $\eta(\cdot)$ is stationary and $\mathrm{cov}(\eta(x), \eta(y)) = \sigma^2 \rho(|x - y|)$, show that for $x > 0$,

$$V((0, x]) = 2\sigma^2 \int_0^x (x - y)\rho(y)\,dy.$$

10.4.9. Establish (10.4.19) from (10.4.5).

10.4.10. (a) If $\{I_n\}$ is a nested decreasing sequence of intervals with $\ell(I_n) \to 0$ as $n \to \infty$, show that for any second-order stationary simple point process on $\mathbb{R}$, $V(I_n)/M(I_n) \to 1$.
   (b) Show that replacing $\{I_n\}$ by more general nested sets $\{A_n\}$ may lead to $V(A_n)/M(A_n) \not\to 1$. [Hint: Consider a stationary deterministic process at unit rate, and for some fixed integer $j \geq 2$, let $A_n = \bigcup_{i=1}^j (i, i + 1/n]$.]
   (c) Let $\{A_n\}$ be a nested decreasing sequence of sets in $\mathbb{R}^d$ with $\mathrm{diam}(A_n) \to 0$ as $n \to \infty$. Show that $V(A_n)/M(A_n) \to 1$ as $n \to \infty$ for second-order stationary simple point processes on $\mathbb{R}^d$.

10.4.11. Prove the following statements:
(a) For a Poisson process, $V(x)/\lambda x = 1$ (all $x > 0$).
(b) For a cluster process with stationary deterministic process as the cluster centre process and i.i.d. clusters with finite second moment, $V(x)/x \to 0$ as $x \to \infty$.

10.4.12. Let $V(x) \equiv V((0, x])$ denote the variance function of a second-order stationary point process on the line, and write $M_2(x) = V(x) + (mx)^2$, where $m = EN(0, 1]$.
(a) Show that $M_2(x)$ is superadditive in $x > 0$, and hence that $V'(0+) \equiv \lim_{x \downarrow 0} V(x)/x$ exists, with $V'(0+) \geq m$.
(b) Show that $(M_2(x))^{1/2}$ is subadditive, and hence that $\lim_{x \to \infty} V(x)/x^2$ exists finite.
(c) When $N(\cdot)$ is crudely stationary (cf. Section 3.2), show that $V'(0+) = m$ if and only if the process is simple.
(d) Construct an example of a second-order stationary point process for which the set of discontinuities of the left and right derivatives of $V(\cdot)$ is countably dense in $(0, \infty)$.
(e) Writing $M_2(x) = \lambda \int_0^x (1 + 2U(y))dy$, where λ is the intensity of $N(\cdot)$, show that $\lim_{x \to \infty} U(x)/\lambda x$ exists and is ≥ 1.
(f) Show that $\sup_{x > 0}(U(x + y) - U(x)) \leq 2U(y) + m/\lambda$. [See Daley (1971) and, for part (f), see Berbée (1983).]

10.4.13. Show that for the Neyman–Scott process of Example 8.3(a), the function $r_2(x)$ at (10.4.21) is given by

$$r_2(x) = 1 + \frac{m_{[2]}}{m} \int_{\mathcal{X}} f(x + u)f(u)du$$

when the distribution of cluster points from the cluster centre has density function $f(\cdot)$ and $m, m_{[2]}$ are the first two factorial moments of the cluster size distribution.

10.4.14. [Compare Example 10.4(b).] Let $\{t'_n: n = 1, 2, \ldots\}$ be the successive epochs in $(1, \infty)$ of a Poisson process on $\mathbb{R}_+$ at rate λ, and attach marks $I(t'_n) = 0$ or 1 successively as follows, starting with t'_1 initially unmarked. If t'_n is unmarked, then $I(t'_n) = 0$ if $t'_{n+1} < t'_n + 1$, in which case $I(t'_{n+1}) = 0$ also, or else $t'_{n+1} > t'_n + 1$, $I(t'_n) = 1$ and t'_{n+1} is initially unmarked. If $I(t'_n) = 0$, then $I(t'_{n+1}) = 0$ if $t'_{n+1} < t'_n + 1$, or else $t'_{n+1} > t'_n + 1$ and t'_{n+1} is initially unmarked. Show that $\{t_n: n = 0, 1, \ldots\}$, defined by $t_0 = 0$ and $t_{n+1} = \{\inf t'_j > t_n: I(t'_j) = 1\}$ $(n = 0, 1, \ldots)$, are the epochs of a renewal process and that it has renewal density function $h(\cdot)$ give by

$$h(x)dx = \begin{cases} 0 & (0 < x \leq 1), \\ \lambda e^{-\lambda x} & (1 < x \leq 2), \\ \lambda e^{-2\lambda} & (2 < x). \end{cases}$$

Show also that Example 10.4(b) is a version of the corresponding stationary renewal process.

10.4.15. Construct a point process in $\mathbb{R}^d$ analogous to the process in $\mathbb{R}$ of Example 10.4(b). Using $v(R, a)$ to denote the volume of the intersection of hyperspheres of radius R with centres a distance a apart, show that this $\mathbb{R}^d$ analogue has

$$M(A) = \lambda e^{-\lambda v(R,0)} \ell(A),$$

$$\hat{h}_2(x) = \begin{cases} 0 & (0 < |x| \le R), \\ \lambda e^{-\lambda[v(R,0)-v(R,|x|)]} & (R < |x| \le 2R), \\ \lambda e^{-\lambda v(R,0)} & (2R < |x|). \end{cases}$$

[For details when $d = 2$, see Exercise 6.3 of Cox and Isham (1980).]

10.4.16. Find formulae for estimates of the reduced covariance measures on the line and the plane that incorporate correction factors for edge effects [e.g., see Miles (1974) and Vere-Jones (1978, p. 80)].

10.4.17. Suppose that the process N_0 in Example 10.4(d) is Poisson with rate parameter λ_0. Then the output process N_2 has covariance density

$$\lambda_0^2 c(u) = \lambda_0^2 \operatorname{cov}(J(0), J(u)) = \lambda_0^2(\beta(u) - \alpha^2).$$

Show that when N_1 is a Poisson process at rate λ_1 and the Y_i are exponentially distributed with mean $1/\mu$, then

$$\alpha = \mu/(\lambda_1 + \mu),$$

$$\pi(t) = (\lambda_1 + \mu e^{-(\lambda_1+\mu)t})/(\lambda_1 + \mu),$$

$$\beta(u) = \mu(\lambda_1 e^{-(\lambda_1+\mu)u} + \mu)/(\lambda_1 + \mu)^2,$$

$$\gamma(u) = \lambda_1(1 - \pi(u)) = \lambda_1\mu(1 - e^{-(\lambda_1+\mu)t})/(\lambda_1 + \mu).$$

10.4.18. Replace the inhibitory mechanism of Example 10.4(d) defined via the i.i.d. sequence $\{Y_i\}$ by $Z_i = \min(T_{t_i}, t_{i+1} - t_i)$, where T_t is the forward recurrence time r.v. of the process N_0. Show that when N_0 and N_1 are independent stationary simple point processes with intensity λ_0, the output process has intensity

$$\lambda_2 = \lambda_0 \int_0^\infty G(t)\,dF(t),$$

where G is now the d.f. of a lifetime r.v. Y for the process N_0 and F is the d.f. of the backward recurrence time r.v. of the process N_1.

10.5. Marked and Planar Point Processes

In the next two sections we examine the moment structure of some further examples drawn from the area of stochastic geometry, which, for present purposes, we take to mean the study of families of geometric objects randomly located in one-, two-, or three-dimensional Euclidean space. To qualify as an "object" all we demand is that the entity can be specified by a finite (or perhaps countably infinite) set of real parameters that describe aspects such as location, size, and shape, though in fact we hardly proceed beyond the study of points and lines. To each such object there corresponds a point in a Euclidean parameter space of suitably high dimension, and random families of such objects can be defined as point processes on the parameter space as state space. We are mainly concerned with the first- and second-order properties of processes defined in this way.

A characteristic feature of geometric objects is their invariance under rigid motions such as translation, rotation, and reflection, so it is natural to study first the properties of families that are stochastically stationary with respect to these motions, or, more precisely, with respect to the groups of transformations that these motions induce in the relevant parameter space. A key question is thus the implication of such invariance properties on the first and second moment properties of the process. The examples considered below show no fundamental differences from those discussed earlier: essentially these properties are still applications of the factorization lemma A2.7.II or equivalent disintegration results, but as the motions become more varied, so also do the applications become more varied and more intricate.

Some basic principles of stochastic geometry, in the sense indicated above, are outlined in the introductory article by D. G. Kendall in Harding and Kendall (1974). Our discussion leans heavily on the first half dozen sections of that book. The monograph by Stoyan and Mecke (1983) has appeared in a substantially revised version in English jointly with W. S. Kendall (Stoyan, Kendall, and Mecke, 1987); it presents a comprehensive introduction with numerous illustrative examples and an extensive bibliography.

We start by considering stationary marked point processes.

For simplicity we treat only the case $\mathscr{X} = \mathbb{R} \times \mathscr{K}$ for some c.s.m.s. $\mathscr{K}$, so that the process consists of pairs (t_i, K_i), where $t_i \in \mathbb{R}$ and $K_i \in \mathscr{K}$. We assume stationarity along the time axis $\mathbb{R}$, and suppose that the first and second moment measures exist as boundedly finite measures in $\mathbb{R} \times \mathscr{K}$.

Proposition 10.5.I. *Let $N(\cdot)$ on $\mathbb{R} \times \mathscr{K}$ be a simple stationary marked point process for which the first and second moment measures exist. Then the first and second factorial moment measures have respective factorizations*

(10.5.1) $$M_1(dt \times dk) = \Gamma(dk)dt,$$

(10.5.2) $$M_{[2]}(dt_1 \times dt_2 \times dk_1 \times dk_2) = \hat{M}_{[2]}(du \times dk_1 \times dk_2)dt_1$$
$$(u \equiv t_2 - t_1),$$

corresponding, respectively, to the following integral relations, valid for bounded measurable h with bounded support:

(10.5.3) $$\int_{\mathbb{R} \times \mathscr{K}} h(t, k)M_1(dt \times dk) = \int_{\mathbb{R}} dt \int_{\mathscr{K}} h(t, k)\Gamma(dk),$$

(10.5.4) $$\int_{(\mathbb{R} \times \mathscr{K})^{(2)}} h(t_1, t_2, k_1, k_2)M_{[2]}(dt_1 \times dt_2 \times dk_1 \times dk_2)$$
$$= \int_{\mathbb{R}} dt \int_{\mathbb{R} \times \mathscr{K} \times \mathscr{K}} h(t, t + u, k_1, k_2)\hat{M}_{[2]}(du \times dk_1 \times dk_2).$$

PROOF. Both statements are straightforward applications of Lemma A2.7.II, the second after taking coordinates in the space $\mathscr{X}^{(2)}$ so that

$$(t_1, t_2, k_1, k_2) \to (t_1, t_1 + u, k_1, k_2).$$ □

If the process has overall a finite mean rate m in the sense that

$$E[N((0, 1] \times \mathscr{X})] = m < \infty,$$

then the measure Γ is totally finite with $\Gamma(\mathscr{X}) = m$, and we can thus introduce a probability measure Π on $(\mathscr{X}, \mathscr{B}(\mathscr{X}))$ by setting

(10.5.5) $$\Pi(A) = \Gamma(A)/\Gamma(\mathscr{X})   (A \in \mathscr{B}(\mathscr{X})).$$

$\Pi(A)$ can then be interpreted as the stationary distribution of marks, or the distribution of the mark associated with an arbitrary time point (event) t_i of the process. It is also an ergodic probability in the sense that (from Proposition 10.2.VI)

$$T^{-1} \# \{(t_i, k_i): 0 < t_i < T, k_i \in A\}$$
$$= T^{-1} N((0, T] \times A) \to \Pi(A)   \text{a.s. as } T \to \infty.$$

The reduced second moment measure $\hat{M}_{[2]}(du \times dk_1 \times dk_2)$ can be interpreted, for $u \neq 0$, as the rate of occurrence of pairs of points u time units apart, with one having its mark in $(k_1, k_1 + dk_1)$ and the other at the (signed) distance u from the first having its mark in $(k_2, k_2 + dk_2)$. If $\hat{M}_{[2]}$ possesses a density with respect to u, its Radon–Nikodym derivative

$$\hat{m}_{[2]}(u, k_1, A) = \hat{M}_{[2]}(du \times dk_1 \times A)/du \, \Gamma(dk_1)$$

can be interpreted as a *cross-intensity*: it represents the rate of occurrence of points with marks in A conditional on the occurrence of a point with mark k_1 at a time origin u time units previously. Again, there is an interpretation as an ergodic limit, as, for example,

$$T^{-1} \# \{\text{pairs}(t_i, k_i), (t_j, k_j): 0 < t_i < T, 0 < t_j - t_i < u, k_i \in A, k_j \in B\}$$
$$\to \hat{M}_{[2]}((0, u] \times A \times B)   \text{a.s. as } T \to \infty.$$

Note that the order of marks can be distinguished; when the density $\hat{m}_{[2]}$ exists, we have

$$\hat{m}_{[2]}(u, k_1, k_2) = \hat{m}_{[2]}(-u, k_2, k_1),$$
$$\neq \hat{m}_{[2]}(u, k_2, k_1)   \text{in general}.$$

The densities $\hat{m}_{[2]}(u, k_1, k_2)$ or the corresponding factorial covariance densities $\hat{c}_{[2]}(u, k_1, k_2)$ are usually the principal objects of investigation in a second-order analysis of a marked or multivariate point process.

EXAMPLE 10.5(a) *Process of independent marks.* Let the simple point process have mean rate m and suppose the marks are allocated independently according to the probability distribution $\Pi(\cdot)$. Then $\Pi(\cdot)$ coincides with the stationary mark distribution at (10.5.5) while the reduced factorial moment measure $\hat{M}_{[2]}$ takes the form

$$\hat{M}_{[2]}(du \times dk_1 \times dk_2) = \hat{M}_{[2]}^{(1)}(du) \times \Pi(dk_1) \times \Pi(dk_2)$$

and

$$\hat{C}_{[2]}(du \times dk_1 \times dk_2) = \hat{C}_{[2]}^{(1)}(du) \times \Pi(dk_1) \times \Pi(dk_2),$$

where $\hat{M}_{[2]}^{(1)}$ and $\hat{C}_{[2]}^{(1)}$ are the reduced factorial moment and cumulant measures of the process of time points.

Such a simple model may be useful as a null hypothesis in testing for more complex interactions, as, for example, in the discussion of earthquake magnitudes in Vere-Jones (1970). Note that a process of overall infinite mean rate can be obtained by supposing the mean rates $m_1, m_2, \ldots$ of marks within each of a successive family of disjoint mark sets $K_1, K_2, \ldots$ are all finite but have an infinite sum.

From a theoretical viewpoint, the most interesting application of stationary marked point processes has been to situations where the marks are not merely statistically dependent on the past evolution of the process but are in fact functionally dependent on it. In an extreme cases, the mark at time t can be taken as the whole past history of a point process up to time t. This idea lies behind one approach to the Palm theory of Chapter 12: the following elementary example gives some insight into this application.

EXAMPLE 10.5(b) *Forward recurrence times.* Assume we are given a simple stationary point process on $\mathbb{R}$, and associate with any point t_i of the process the length $L_i = \inf\{u: N(t_i - u, t_i) \geq 1\}$ of the previous interval. Then the marked point process consisting of the pairs (t_i, L_i) is stationary. Assuming a finite mean occurrence rate m, it follows from Proposition 10.5.I and (10.5.5) that a stationary probability distribution $\Pi_L(\cdot)$ exists for the interoccurrence times. The integral relation (10.5.3) then leads to important relations involving $\Pi_L(\cdot)$. Thus, by taking $h(t, k) = g(t)$ if $0 \leq t \leq k$, $= 0$ otherwise, and defining $t_1' = \inf\{t_i: t_i > 0\}$, $= t_{i'}$ say, so that $0 < t_{i'} < L_{i'}$, (10.5.3) reduces to

$$E(g(t_1')) = m \int_0^\infty \int_0^k g(u)du\, \Pi_L(dk)$$

$$= m \int_0^\infty (1 - F_L(u))g(u)du,$$

where $F_L(t) = \int_0^t \Pi_L(du)$ is the distribution function for the interval length. Since g is an arbitrary function, this identifies the distribution for the point t_1' immediately following the origin (i.e., the distribution for the *forward recurrence time*) with the distribution having density

$$f_1(t) = m(1 - F_L(t)) = (1 - F_L(t))/\mu_L,$$

where μ_L is the mean interval length. This simple derivation of a Palm–Khinchin relation uses an argument similar to Palm's original derivation (Palm, 1943).

EXAMPLE 10.5(c) *Vehicles on a road.* We consider a spatially stationary distribution of cars along a long straight road, the car at x_i having a (constant) velocity v_i, with $v_i \neq v_j$ in general. Our aim is to determine the evolution in time, if any, of characteristics of the process.

The family of transformations that concerns us is that for which, for real t,

$$(x_i, v_i) \rightarrow (x_i + tv_i, v_i).$$

Denote by m_t, $\Pi_t(\cdot)$, and $c_2(u, v_1, v_2)$ the mean rate, the stationary (in space) velocity distribution, and the spatial covariance density at time t. From (10.5.3) we have for the space–velocity mean density at time t, say $M_t(dx \times dv)$,

$$\int h(x, v) M_t(dx \times dv) = \int h(x + tv, v) m_0 \, dx \, \Pi_0(dv)$$

$$= \int h(y, v) m_0 \, dy \, \Pi_0(dv),$$

so that the mean vehicle density and velocity distribution remain constant in time, whatever their initial forms.

Applying a similar argument to the second-order integrals implies that, if the covariance densities $c_t(u, v_1, v_2)$ exist for $t = 0$, they exist for all $t > 0$ and are given by

$$c_t(u, v_1, v_2) = c_0(u + t(v_2 - v_1), v_1, v_2).$$

The asymptotic covariance properties of $c_t(\cdot)$ at $t \rightarrow \infty$ thus depend on the behaviour of $c_0(u, v_1, v_2)$ for large u. In most practical cases, a mixing condition holds and implies that $c_0(u, v_1, v_2) \rightarrow 0$ as $|u| \rightarrow \infty$ for all v_1, v_2. Under these conditions, any correlation structure tends to die out, this being an illustration of the "Poisson tendency" of vehicular traffic (Thedeen, 1964).

This example can also be treated as a line process and extended in various ways (e.g., see Bartlett, 1967; Solomon and Wang, 1972).

We turn now to planar point processes.

Consider first a point process whose probability structure is invariant under rotations about a fixed point in the plane. Such a process may represent, for example, the distribution of seedlings about a parent plant or of animals or other organisms about a nest or point of release (Byth, 1981). It is natural in such a case to take the fixed point as origin and to represent the points on the plane in terms of polar coordinates (r, θ), with $0 \leq r < \infty$ and $0 < \theta \leq 2\pi$. By omitting the origin, which plays a special role, it can be represented as a product $\mathbb{R}_+ \times \mathbb{S}$, where $\mathbb{R}_+ = (0, \infty)$ and $\mathbb{S}$ denotes both the circle group and its representation as $(0, 2\pi]$.

Isotropy implies invariance under the group of rotations. Assuming that with probability 1 there are no points at the origin (and, we hasten to add, there is little difficulty in incorporating the contribution of an atom at the origin if so desired), we have a process with the same kind of structure as described earlier in this section, with the distance from the origin constituting the mark and the angular distance θ from a fixed reference axis corresponding to the time coordinate. The factorization lemma applies in a similar fashion and leads to the following representation of the first and second moment measures.

Proposition 10.5.II. *Let $N(\cdot)$ be a point process in the plane $\mathbb{R}^2$, invariant under rotations about the origin with $N(\{0\}) = 0$ a.s., and having boundedly finite first and second moment measures. Then the first and second factorial moment measures have the respective factorizations*

$$M_1(dr \times d\theta) = K_1(dr)d\theta/2\pi,$$

$$M_{[2]}(dr_1 \times dr_2 \times d\theta_1 \times d\theta_2) = \hat{M}_{[2]}(dr_1 \times dr_2 \times d\phi)d\theta_1/2\pi,$$

where $\phi \equiv \theta_2 - \theta_1$ (mod 2π), corresponding to the integral relations, valid for bounded measurable $h(\cdot)$ with bounded support

$$E \int_{\mathbb{R}_+ \times \mathbb{S}} h(r, \theta)N(dr \times d\theta) = \int_0^{2\pi} \frac{1}{2\pi} d\theta \int_0^\infty h(r, \theta)K_1(dr),$$

$$\int_{(\mathbb{R}_+ \times \mathbb{S})^{(2)}} h(r_1, r_2, \theta_1, \theta_2)M_{[2]}(dr_1 \times dr_2 \times d\theta_1 \times d\theta_2)$$

$$= \int_0^{2\pi} \frac{1}{2\pi} d\theta \int_{\mathbb{R}_+^{(2)} \times \mathbb{S}} h(r_1, r_2, \theta, \theta + \phi)\hat{M}_{[2]}(dr_1 \times dr_2 \times d\phi).$$

PROOF. See Exercise 10.5.3. □

Even without isotropy, for such a "centred" process it is frequently convenient to use polar coordinates and hence to represent the first moment measure (assuming it is boundedly finite) in the form $M_1(dr \times d\theta)$. Writing

$$K_1(r) = EN(S(0; r)) = \int_0^r \int_0^{2\pi} M_1(dr \times d\theta)$$

for the expected number of points within a distance r of the origin, we can then define a *directional rose* as the Radon–Nikodym derivative

(10.5.6) $$\Gamma(d\theta|r) = M_1(dr \times d\theta)/K_1(dr).$$

Observe that Γ, in contrast to K_1, is necessarily a probability distribution. In these terms, isotropy embodies two features: first, the directional rose is independent of the radius r, and second, it is uniform over all angles (and equal to $1/2\pi$).

When densities exist, we may wish to express $M_1(\cdot)$ in terms of a density with respect to Lebesgue measure in the original plane $\mathbb{R}^2$, rather than in the representation space $\mathbb{R}_+ \times \mathbb{S}$. This leads to a density of the form

(10.5.7) $m(x, y) = r^{-1}k_1(r)\gamma(\theta|r)$,

where $r = (x^2 + y^2)^{1/2}$, $\theta = \text{artan}(y/x)$, $k_1(r) = dK_1(r)/dr$, and $\gamma(\theta|r) = d\Gamma(\theta|r)/d\theta$. In the isotropic case, $\gamma(\theta|r) = 1/2\pi$.

For the second-order analysis also, we can introduce a factorial moment measure for the counting process on centred spheres $N(S(0; r))$ by setting

$$K_{[2]}(dr_1 \times dr_2) = \int_{\mathbb{S}^{(2)}} M_{[2]}(dr_1 \times dr_2 \times d\theta_1 \times d\theta_2).$$

In the isotropic case we can then introduce a second-order directional rose $\Gamma_2(d\phi|r_1, r_2)$ as the Radon–Nikodym derivative

$$\Gamma_2(d\phi|r_1, r_2) = \hat{M}_{[2]}(dr_1 \times dr_2 \times d\phi)/K_{[2]}(dr_1 \times dr_2).$$

$K_{[2]}(dr_1 \times dr_2)$ represents the expected numbers of pairs of points located with one point at distance $(r_1, r_1 + dr_1)$ from the origin and the other at distance $(r_2, r_2 + dr_2)$, while $\Gamma_2(d\phi|r_1, r_2)$ gives the conditional probability distribution of the angular separation ϕ between the points. The symmetry properties of the second-order moments again lead to

$$\Gamma_2(d\phi|r_1, r_2) = \Gamma_2(2\pi - d\phi|r_2, r_1),$$

$$\neq \Gamma_2(d\phi|r_2, r_1) \quad \text{in general.}$$

EXAMPLE 10.5(d) *Isotropic centred Poisson process.* Let $N(\cdot)$ be a Poisson process in the plane with rate parameter having density $\mu(x, y) = \mu(r)$ for $r = (x^2 + y^2)^{1/2}$. Then

$$k_1(r) = 2\pi r\mu(r),$$

$$\gamma(\theta|r) = 1/2\pi,$$

$$k_{[2]}(r_1, r_2) = 4\pi^2 r_1 r_2 \mu(r_1)\mu(r_2),$$

$$\gamma_2(\phi|r_1, r_2) = 1/2\pi.$$

Here, isotropy entails that the angular separation between pairs of points is also uniformly distributed. It is also easy to verify that the counting process on centred spheres is a Poisson process on $\mathbb{R}_+$ with density $2\pi r\mu(r)$.

EXAMPLE 10.5(e) *Isotropic centred Gauss–Poisson process.* Define a Gauss–Poisson process by supposing that parent points are located around the origin according to a Poisson process with density $\mu(\cdot)$, as in Example 10.5(d), and that with each such parent point there is associated an offspring or secondary point whose location relative to a parent point on the circle of radius r_1 is governed by the probability distribution with density function $f(r_2, \phi|r_1)$, where r_2 is the distance of the secondary point from the origin and ϕ its angular separation from the parent point (for isotropy, we suppose that this angular separation is independent of the θ coordinate of the parent). The overall intensity $k_1(r)$ at distance r from the origin is then the sum of two components, an intensity $2\pi r\mu(r)$ of parent points and an intensity of secondary points obtained by averaging over all locations of parent points:

$$k_1(r) = 2\pi r\mu(r) + \int_0^\infty 2\pi s\mu(s)ds \int_0^{2\pi} f(r, \phi|s)d\phi.$$

Similarly, for the second-order radial moment measure density we find

$$k_{[2]}(r_1, r_2) = k_1(r_1)k_1(r_2)$$
$$+ \int_0^{2\pi} [2\pi r_1\mu(r_1)f(r_2, \phi|r_1) + 2\pi r_2\mu(r_2)f(r_1, 2\pi - \phi|r_2)]d\phi.$$

The first-order directional rose is of course uniform, but the second-order rose is not and in general depends on the form of the density function $f(r_2, \phi|r_1)$. If it so happens that it factorizes in the form $f(r_2, \phi|r_1) = f(r_2|r_1)g(\phi)$, then

$$k_{[2]}(r_1, r_2) = k_1(r_1)k_1(r_2) + 2\pi[r_1\mu(r_1)f(r_2|r_1) + r_2\mu(r_2)f(r_1|r_2)],$$
$$\gamma_2(\phi|r_1, r_2) = p(r_1, r_2)/2\pi + q(r_1, r_2)g(\phi),$$

where $p(r_1, r_2) = k_1(r_1)k_2(r_2)/k_{[2]}(r_1, r_2)$ and $q(r_1, r_2) = 1 - p(r_1, r_2)$. Thus, the second-order directional rose is a mixture of two components, depending on the relative proportions of pairs of points with radii r_1, r_2 coming from independent point pairs and parent–offspring point pairs, respectively.

Note that if given any parent point at distance r_1 from the origin there is only probability $p(r_1)$ of there being an offspring point, then it is enough to change $f(r_2, \phi|r_1)$ into a subprobability density function with

$$\int_{\mathbb{R}_+ \times \mathbb{S}} f(r_2, \phi|r_1)dr_2\,d\phi = p(r_1).$$

We turn now to consider those planar point processes, which are stationary as well as isotropic, that is, they are invariant under the group of rigid body motions in $\mathbb{R}^2$. By Proposition 10.4.II the first moment measure is a multiple of Lebesgue measure in $\mathbb{R}^2$ by virtue of stationarity alone, so the effect of isotropy shows up first on the second moment measure, that is, on pairs of points. Since the only property of a pair of points that is invariant under rigid body motions is the distance between them, the natural coordinate transformation of $\mathbb{R}^2 \times \mathbb{R}^2$ to consider is of the form

$$(x_1, y_1, x_2, y_2) \to (x_1, y_1, x_1 + r\cos\theta, y_1 + r\sin\theta),$$

where $0 \le r < \infty$ and $0 < \theta \le 2\pi$, with r the distance between the two points and θ the angle between the directed line joining them and a fixed reference axis. Assuming the point process to be simple and considering just the factorial and cumulant measures, $\{r = 0\}$ has zero probability and so the second factorial cumulant measure can be represented as a measure on the space $\mathbb{R}^2 \times \mathbb{R}_+ \times \mathbb{S}$, corresponding to the coordinates x, y, r, θ just introduced. Stationarity implies invariance with respect to shifts in the first two co-ordinates and so yields the usual representation in terms of a reduced factorial measure, which we write in the form $\hat{M}_{[2]}(dr \times d\theta)$.

Without yet assuming isotropy, introduce a radial measure $\hat{K}_2(dr)$ and a second-order directional rose $\Gamma_2(d\theta|r)$ via

$$\hat{K}_2(dr) = \int_0^{2\pi} \hat{M}_{[2]}(dr \times d\theta),$$

$$\Gamma_2(d\theta|r) = \hat{M}_{[2]}(dr \times d\theta)/\hat{K}_2(dr).$$

The function

$$\hat{K}_2(r) = \int_0^r \hat{K}_2(ds)$$

can now be interpreted as the expected number of pairs of points separated by a distance r or less and for which the first point of the pair lies within a region of unit area. The directional rose $\Gamma_2(d\theta|r)$ then represents the probability that, given the separation is r, the directed line joining the first point to the second makes an angle with the fixed reference axis falling in the interval $(\theta, \theta + d\theta)$. An alternative interpretation of $\hat{K}_2(\cdot)$ is as a Palm measure, namely, the product of the mean density m and the expected number of points in a circle of radius r about the origin given a point at the origin.

Consider now the implication of isotropy. A rotation through α transforms the angle θ to a new angle θ' that depends in general on x, y as well as α. Given any θ and θ', we can find x, y, and α such that θ is transformed into θ'. Rotational invariance implies therefore that $\Gamma_2(d\theta|r)$ must be invariant under arbitrary shifts $\theta \to \theta'$ and so reduces to the uniform distribution on $\mathbb{S}$. We summarize all this as follows.

Proposition 10.5.III. *Let $\hat{M}_{[2]}(\cdot)$ denote the reduced second factorial moment measure of a simple stationary point process in the plane. Then $\hat{M}_2(\cdot)$ can be expressed as*

(10.5.8) $\hat{M}_{[2]}(dr \times d\theta) = \hat{K}_2(dr)\Gamma_2(d\theta|r),$

corresponding to the integral representation of the second factorial moment measure $M_2(\cdot)$ (for bounded measurable h with bounded support)

$$\int_{\mathbb{R}^2 \times \mathbb{R}^2} h(x_1, y_1, x_2, y_2)M_{[2]}(dx_1 \times dy_1 \times dx_2 \times dy_2)$$

$$= \int_{\mathbb{R}^2} dx\, dy \int_{\mathbb{R}_+ \times \mathbb{S}} h(x, y, x + r \cos\theta, y + r \sin\theta)\hat{K}_2(dr)\Gamma_2(d\theta|r),$$

where $\hat{K}_2(\cdot)$ is a boundedly finite measure on $\mathbb{R}_+$ and for each $r > 0$, $\Gamma_2(\cdot|r)$ is a probability measure on $\mathbb{S}$. If the process is also isotropic then for all θ and r

$$\Gamma_2(d\theta|r) = d\theta/2\pi.$$

Ripley (1976, 1977) introduced the function $\hat{K}_2(\cdot)$, advocating its use because it determines the second-order behaviour and it can be estimated consistently from data. Diggle (1983) divided $\hat{K}_2$ by m^2 so that in the Poisson case his $K_2(r) = \pi r^2$, independent of the underlying rate. In the isotropic case, $\hat{K}_2(r)$ provides a complete characterization of the second-order behaviour, as does its density when the latter exists. Indeed, the function

$$\rho(r) = \hat{K}_2(dr)/(2\pi m^2 r\, dr) - 1,$$

known as the *radial correlation function* in the statistical physics literature (though it need not be a correlation!), was suggested earlier by Glass and Tobler (1971) as a suitable basis for statistical estimation. The usual methods of estimating $\hat{K}_2(\cdot)$ incorporate edge corrections and are of the form

$$\hat{K}_2(r) = \pi r^2 \sum_{x_i \in A} N(S(x_i; r)) \Bigg/ \sum_{x_i \in A} \ell(S(x_i; r) \cap A),$$

where A is the observation region and $\ell(S(x_i; r) \cap A)/\pi r^2$ is the proportion of the area of the circle of radius r, centred on the point x_i of the process, lying within the observation region. The density $\hat{K}_2(dr)/dr$ is related to the conditional intensity $\hat{m}_{[2]}(x, y)$ by

$$\hat{m}_{[2]}(x, y)/m = (\hat{K}_2(dr)/dr)/2\pi m r.$$

Examples of the use of $\hat{M}_{[2]}(\cdot)$ in the nonisotropic case are given in Vere-Jones (1978) and in more detail in Chong (1980); a more recent discussion can be found in Ohser and Stoyan (1981).

The symmetry properties of $\hat{M}_{[2]}(\cdot)$ here in the stationary case imply that

$$\Gamma_2(d\theta|r) = \Gamma_2(\pi + d\theta|r),$$

which is the analogue for the representation being used here of the property noted for $\Gamma_2(\cdot|r_1, r_2)$ in the representation being used earlier (but in the case of an isotropic process).

EXAMPLE 10.5(f) *A two-dimensional Neyman–Scott process.* By using the general result at (8.3.14), the reduced second factorial cumulant measure is given by

$$\hat{C}_{[2]}(dx \times dy) = \mu m_{[2]} \int_{\mathbb{R}^2} F(u + dx, v + dy)F(dx, dy)$$

$$= \mu m_{[2]} G(dx \times dy),$$

where G is the distribution function of the difference $(x_1 - x_2, y_1 - y_2)$ of the pair (x_1, y_1) and (x_2, y_2) of independent random vectors with common d.f. F, which determines the location about a cluster centre of a cluster member, μ is the Poisson density of cluster centres, and $m_{[2]}$ is the second factorial moment of the number of cluster members. For the function $\hat{K}_2$ we find

$$\hat{K}_2(r) = m^2 \pi r^2 + m_{[2]} G_1(r),$$

where $m = \mu m_1$ is the mean rate of the process and $G_1(r)$ is the distribution function for the distance between two "offspring" from the same "parent."

The directional rose is more easily presented for the covariance measure than the second factorial moment measure, amounting simply to the conditional distribution of the angle between the line joining two "offspring" [as for $G_1(\cdot)$ above] and a fixed reference axis, given the distance between the "offspring."

Some particular results for the case where F is a bivariate normal distribution are given in Exercise 10.5.5.

Exercises

10.5.1. Suppose the *bivariate simple Poisson process* model of Example 8.3(d) is stationary, so that it can be described in terms of three rate functions μ_1, μ_2, μ_3 and a distribution function $H(\cdot)$ of the signed distance between a pair of related points, taking a type 1 point as the initial point. Show that in terms of these quantities,

$$m_1 = \mu_1 + \mu_3, \qquad m_2 = \mu_2 + u_3,$$

$$\hat{C}_{[2]}(du; 1, 2) = \mu_3 H(du) = \hat{C}_{[2]}(-du; 2, 1).$$

Use the p.g.fl. or otherwise to show that when $\mathcal{X} = \mathbb{R}$, the joint distribution of the distances T_1, T_2 from an arbitrary origin to the nearest points of types 1, 2, respectively, is given by

$$\log \Pr\{T_1 > x, T_2 > y\}$$

$$= -2m_1 x - 2m_2 y + \mu_3 \int_{-x-y}^{x+y} (\min(x, y - v) - \max(-x, -y - v)) H(dv),$$

while the joint distribution of the forward recurrence times T_1^+, T_2^+ from the origin to the nearest points in the positive direction is given by

$$\log \Pr\{T_1^+ > x, T_2^+ > y\}$$

$$= -m_1 x - m_2 y + \mu_3 \int_{-x}^{y} (\min(x, y - v) - \max(0, -v)) H(dv).$$

Consider extensions to the case $\mathcal{X} = \mathbb{R}^d$.

10.5.2. Extend the argument of Example 10.5(b) to the case of a bivariate process, taking the mark at a point t_i of the process to be of the form $(j_i; L_{1i}, L_{2i})$, where j_i is the type of the point and L_{1i}, L_{2i} are the times back to the last occurring points of types 1, 2, respectively. Obtain a bivariate extension of the Palm–Khinchin equations, and compare these with the extensions to nonorderly point processes discussed in (3.4.14). Hence or otherwise, obtain expressions for the joint distributions of the intervals between an arbitrary point of type i

($i = 1, 2$) and the next occurring points of types 1, 2 in Exercise 10.5.1 (cf. also Daley and Milne, 1975).

10.5.3. Prove explicitly the mappings needed to apply the factorization lemma to the proof of Proposition 10.5.II.

10.5.4. (a) Consider a point process with state space the surface of a cone with semiangle α. Parameterize the points by the distance from the apex of the cone and the angle subtended at the centre by a plane through the point and the axis of the cone and a fixed plane through the axis (i.e., the "longitude" of a point on the cone). Describe the first and second moment structure of a process invariant under rotations of the cone.

(b) For an alternative parameterization, cut the cone down a straight line from the apex and "unwrap" it onto a plane, so that it fills the plane apart from a sector of angle $2\pi - \theta$, where $\theta = 2\pi \sin \alpha$. Rotations of the cone correspond to rotations in the plane modulo θ, where the two edges of the missing sector are identified. Rephrase the results in (a) in terms of this parameterization. [See Byth (1981) who uses the term θ-stationary process.]

10.5.5. In Example 10.5(f) suppose that the d.f. F is the bivariate normal distribution with zero mean and covariance matrix

$$\Sigma = \begin{bmatrix} \sigma_1^2 & \rho\sigma_1\sigma_2 \\ \rho\sigma_1\sigma_2 & \sigma_2^2 \end{bmatrix}.$$

Then the symmetrized d.f. G for the vector distance between two offspring from the same parent is bivariate normal also with zero mean vector and covariance matrix 2Σ.

When $\sigma_1^2 = \sigma_2^2 = \sigma^2$ say and $\rho = 0$, the process is isotropic and

$$\hat{K}_2(r) = \pi r^2 \mu^2 m_1^2 + \mu m_{[2]}(1 - e^{-r^2/4\sigma^2}).$$

In the nonisotropic case, the directional rose has a density $\gamma_2(\theta|r)$ proportional to

$$2\pi m_1 + (m_{[2]}/4\pi\sigma_1\sigma_2(1 - \rho^2)^{1/2})\exp\{-r^2 g(\theta, \Sigma)/4(1 - \rho^2)\},$$

where $g(\theta, \Sigma) = \sigma_1^{-2}\cos^2\theta - 2\rho\sigma_1^{-1}\sigma_2^{-1}\cos\theta\sin\theta + \sigma_2^{-2}\sin^2\theta$; that is, $\gamma_2(\theta|r) = p(r)/2\pi + q(r)\exp\{\cdots\}$, where $p(r)$, $q(r)$ are nonnegative functions, involving a Bessel function arising from the normalizing condition $\int_0^\infty \gamma_2(\theta|r)d\theta = 1$, and $p(r) \to 1$ as $r \to \infty$.

10.5.6. Let N be a marked point process on $\mathbb{R}^d \times \mathcal{K}$, stationary as in Lemma 10.2.III. Extend Proposition 10.1.IV to the statement that for each $K \in \mathcal{B}(\mathcal{K})$,

$$P\{N(\mathbb{R}^d \times \mathcal{K}) = \infty\} + P\{N(\mathbb{R}^d \times \mathcal{K}) = 0\} = 1.$$

10.6. Stationary Line Processes in the Plane

Stationary line processes constitute the paradigm for many of the recent developments in stochastic geometry. In particular, Davidson's conjecture that all stationary isotropic line processes are doubly stochastic and his imaginative early investigations of this question inspired important further studies by Krickeberg, Papangelou, Kallenberg, and others, and these in turn laid the foundation for recent work on the relations between conditional intensities and Gibbs potentials in the models of statistical physics. Here we give a brief introduction to the properties of line processes, based largely on the early sections of Harding and Kendall (1974) and the work of Roger Miles. The same circle of ideas is introduced in Stoyan and Mecke (1983, Chap. 7).

It is convenient to characterize a line in the plane by its (p, θ) coordinates, where p is the (signed) perpendicular distance from the line to a fixed origin, and θ is the angle between this directed perpendicular line and a fixed reference direction. Mostly, we consider the case of directed lines, in which case a *random line process* can be *defined* as a *point process on the cylinder* $\mathbb{R} \times \mathbb{S}$, each (random) point on the cylinder being equivalent to the (random) line in $\mathbb{R}^2$. We always assume this point process (and hence the line process) to be simple. A process of undirected lines can be treated as either a point process on $\mathbb{R}_+ \times \mathbb{S}$ or a process on $\mathbb{R} \times (0, \pi]$: the latter fits more easily into our discussion and follows, for example, Stoyan and Mecke (1983) (see also Exercise 10.6.1).

As in Section 10.5, the principal questions we study relate to the effects of stationarity or isotropy on the moment structure of the process. By these conditions we mean of course invariance of the process of lines under translations and rotations in the plane, so our first task is to examine the effect of these motions on the (p, θ) coordinates of a line. Rotation through an angle α about the fixed origin corresponds to rotation of the cylinder through the same angle. A translation of the plane a distance d in a direction making an angle ϕ with the fixed reference axis induces the transformation

$$(10.6.1) \quad (p, \theta) \to (p + d\cos(\theta - \phi), \theta) \qquad (-\infty < d < \infty, 0 < \phi \le \pi)$$

on the cylinder, corresponding to a shear whereby points on the cylinder are displaced parallel to its axis through a distance varying (when $d = 1$) from -1 at $\theta = \phi + \pi$ through 0 at $\theta = \phi \pm \pi/2$ to $+1$ at $\theta = \phi$ (here, addition of angles is taken modulo 2π).

We start by showing that any Borel measure on the cylinder that is invariant under the action of the shears (but not necessarily under rotations) has the product form $\ell(dp)G(d\theta)$, where $\ell(\cdot)$ denotes Lebesgue measure on $\mathbb{R}$. This is the first occasion where we encounter an invariance result that cannot be handled via the factorization lemma A2.7.II: this is so because shears do not generate translations of the cylinder along its axis. Nevertheless, the result we require is still a simple corollary of the more general theorems about the decomposition of invariant measures, which can be established via the general theory of the disintegration of measures [see, in particular, Theorem 2 of Krickeberg (1974b)]. For the sake of completeness we sketch a simplified version of the theorem as it applies here.

Lemma 10.6.I. *Let $M(dp \times d\theta)$ be a boundedly finite Borel measure on the cylinder $\mathbb{R} \times \mathbb{S}$, and let $M(\cdot)$ be invariant with respect to the action of the shears* *as at (10.5.9). Then there exists a totally finite Borel measure G on $\mathbb{S}$ such that*

(10.6.2) $M(dp \times d\theta) = \ell(dp)G(d\theta),$

where $\ell(\cdot)$ denotes Lebesgue measure on $\mathbb{R}$.

PROOF. In outline, we find a factorization of M of the form $K(dp|\theta)G_1(d\theta)$, and then show that $K(dp|\theta)$ factorizes as $\lambda(\theta)\ell(dp)$. To start with, there exists a function $f(p)$ such that $f(p) > 0$ (all p) and $\int_{-\infty}^{\infty} f(p)\int_0^{2\pi} M(dp \times d\theta) < \infty$. For example, the function

$$f(p) = e^{-|n|}/\max(1, M_n)   (n < p \le n + 1, n = 0, \pm 1, \ldots),$$

where $M_n = \int_n^{n+1}\int_0^{2\pi} M(dp \times d\theta)$ will do. Introduce the measure

$$G_1(d\theta) = \int_{-\infty}^{\infty} f(p)M(dp \times d\theta).$$

For all Borel sets A, $M(A \times d\theta) \ll G_1(d\theta)$, so by appealing to the usual arguments leading to the existence of regular conditional probabilities, we deduce the existence of a kernel $K(dp|\theta)$ such that $K(A|\theta)$ is a measureable function of θ for each bounded Borel set A, $K(\cdot|\theta)$ is a Borel measure on $\mathbb{R}$ for G_1-almost all θ, and $M(dp \times d\theta) = K(dp|\theta)G_1(d\theta)$.

Invariance under the action of a given shear (10.6.1), with parameters (d, ϕ) say, implies that for any bounded measurable $h(\cdot)$ of bounded support,

$$\int_{\mathbb{R} \times \mathbb{S}} h(p, \theta)M(dp \times d\theta) = \int_{\mathbb{R} \times \mathbb{S}} h(p, \theta)K(dp|\theta)G_1(d\theta)$$

$$= \int_{\mathbb{R} \times \mathbb{S}} h(p + d\cos(\theta - \phi), \theta)K(dp|\theta)G_1(d\theta)$$

$$= \int_{\mathbb{R} \times \mathbb{S}} h(p, \theta)K(dp - d\cos(\theta - \phi)|\theta)G_1(d\theta).$$

Since this is true for all such h, it must be that, for G_1-almost all θ, the measure $K(\cdot|\theta)$ coincides with its shifted version $K(\cdot - d\cos(\theta - \phi)|\theta)$. By choosing two appropriate values of d and ϕ, we infer that, for such θ, the measure $K(\cdot|\theta)$ is invariant under the action of two incommensurate shifts. This is enough to ensure that $K(\cdot|\theta)$ is a multiple, $\lambda(\theta)\ell(\cdot)$ say, of Lebesgue measure (see Exercise 10.6.2 for details). Since then $K(A|\theta) = \ell(A)\lambda(\theta)$, and the left-hand side is a measurable function of θ, it follows that there is a measurable version $\lambda^*(\theta)$ of $\lambda(\theta)$ such that $\lambda^*(\theta) = \lambda(\theta)$, for G_1-almost all θ. Setting $G(d\theta) = \lambda^*(\theta)G_1(d\theta)$ proves the lemma.   □

Corollary 10.6.II. *Let a stationary line process have first moment measure M on $\mathbb{R} \times \mathbb{S}$. Then M factorizes in the form (10.6.2).*

Since the measure G is totally finite, it can be normalized to give a first-order directional rose $\Pi(\cdot)$ on $\mathbb{S}$

$$\Pi(d\theta) = \frac{G(d\theta)}{\int_{\mathbb{S}} G(d\theta)} = \frac{G(d\theta)}{G(\mathbb{S})}.$$

$\Pi(d\theta)$ may be interpreted as the probability that an arbitrary line has orientation θ, while the total measure $m \equiv G(\mathbb{S})$ has an interpretation as the *mean density of the line measure* induced by the process. To explain this idea, observe that for any line W and any closed bounded convex set $A \subset \mathbb{R}^2$, there exists a well-defined length $\ell(W \cap A)$. Given any configuration $\{W_i\}$ of lines on the plane, we can introduce a corresponding line measure

$$Z(A) = \sum_i \ell(W_i \cap A).$$

This set function $Z(\cdot)$ is clearly countably additive and extends to a measure on arbitrary Borel sets in the plane. Furthermore, if W_i has coordinates (p_i, θ_i) in the cylinder $\mathbb{R} \times \mathbb{S}$, then the mapping $(p_i, \theta_i) \to \ell(W_i \cap A)$ is measurable, so that if the $\{W_i\}$ constitute a realization of a stochastic line process, each $Z(A)$ is a random variable. From Proposition 6.1.III it follows that $Z(\cdot)$ is a random measure, which we call the *line measure* associated with the original line process.

Proposition 10.6.III. *Let Z be the line measure associated with a stationary line process W in $\mathbb{R}^2$. Then Z is a stationary random measure on $\mathbb{R}^2$, and if W has finite first moment measure $M(\cdot)$, Z has mean density*

(10.6.3) $$m = G(\mathbb{S}) = \int_0^1 \int_{\mathbb{S}} M(dp \times d\theta).$$

PROOF. Writing $\ell_A(p, \theta) = \ell(W(p, \theta) \cap A)$ for a line with coordinates (p, θ) and any bounded Borel set $A \subset \mathbb{R}^2$, we can express

$$Z(A) = \int_{\mathbb{R} \times \mathbb{S}} \ell_A(p, \theta) N(dp \times d\theta)$$

in terms of the point process N on the cylinder. Since $\ell_A \geq 0$, we have

$$EZ(A) = \int_{\mathbb{R} \times \mathbb{S}} \ell_A(p, \theta) M(dp \times d\theta)$$

$$= \int_{\mathbb{S}} G(d\theta) \int_{\mathbb{R}} \ell_A(p, \theta) \ell(dp).$$

For fixed θ, the integral over $\mathbb{R}$ is simply the area of A evaluated as the integral of its cross-sections perpendicular to the direction θ. Writing ℓ_2 for Lebesgue measure in $\mathbb{R}^2$, we have

$$EZ(A) = \int_{\mathbb{S}} G(d\theta) \ell_2(A) = m \ell_2(A),$$

establishing (10.6.3). Stationary of $Z(\cdot)$ follows from the stationarity of the line process defining $Z(\cdot)$.   □

Given a configuration $\{W_i\}$, an alternative to the line measure $Z(A)$ is the number of lines hitting A. This set function is subadditive but not in general additive over sets, and thus not a measure, although for each convex set A it defines a random variable whose distribution and moments can be investigated. If, however, A is itself a line, we do obtain a random measure, namely, the point process on the line formed by its intersections with the lines W_i.

Proposition 10.6.IV. *Let a stationary line process in $\mathbb{R}^2$ be given with mean density m and directional rose $\Pi(\cdot)$.*

(i) *Let V be a fixed line in $\mathbb{R}^2$ with coordinates (p_V, α), and let $N_V(\cdot)$ be the point process on V generated by its intersections with the line process. Then N_V is a stationary point process on V with mean density m_V given by*

(10.6.4) $$m_V = m \int_{\mathsf{S}} |\cos(\theta - \alpha)| \, \Pi(d\theta).$$

If the line process is isotropic, m_V is independent of V with

(10.6.4') $$m_V = 2m/\pi \quad \text{(all } V\text{)}.$$

(ii) *Let A be a closed bounded convex set in $\mathbb{R}^2$, and let $Y(A)$ be the number of distinct lines of the line process intersecting A. If the line process is isotropic then*

(10.6.5) $$EY(A) = mL(A)/\pi,$$

where $L(A)$ is the length of the perimeter of A.

PROOF. For any bounded measurable function h of bounded support in $\mathbb{R}$, we have

$$\int_{\mathbb{R}} h(x) N_V(dx) = \int_{\mathbb{R} \times \mathsf{S}} h(x(p, \theta)) N(dp \times d\theta),$$

where $x = x(p, \theta)$ denotes the distance from a fixed origin on V to a point of intersection of a line with coordinates (p, θ), and $N(\cdot)$ refers to the point process on the cylinder equivalent to the given line process. Because of stationarity, there is no loss of generality in taking the fixed origin on V as the origin for the cylindrical (p, θ) coordinates. Then $x(p, \theta) = p \sec(\theta - \alpha)$, and on taking expectations, we obtain

(10.6.6) $$E \int_{\mathbb{R}} h(x) N_V(dx) = \int_{\mathbb{R} \times \mathsf{S}} h(p \sec(\theta - \alpha)) \ell(dp) m \Pi(d\theta).$$

Substituting $u = p \sec(\theta - \alpha)$, $\ell(dp) = |\cos(\theta - \alpha)| \ell(du)$, from which (10.6.4) follows because N_V, being stationary, has $EN_V(dx) = m_V \ell(dx)$.

In the isotropic case, $\Pi(d\theta) = d\theta/2\pi$ and integration at (10.6.4) leads to $2m/\pi$ as asserted.

To prove (ii), suppose first that A is a convex polygon. Apply the result of

(i) to each side of the polygon in turn, so that adding over all sides shows that the expected number of intersections of lines from the line process with the perimeter of A equals $2mL(A)/\pi$. Convexity implies that each line intersecting the polygon does so exactly twice (except possibly for a set of lines of zero probability), so the factor 2 cancels and (10.5.5) is established for convex polygons. A limiting argument extends the result to any closed bounded convex set A. □

Propositions 10.6.III and 10.6.IV can be extended to processes of random hyperplanes and more generally random "flats" in $\mathbb{R}^d$: see Exercises 10.6.3 and 10.6.4 for some preliminary results and the extensive series of papers by Miles (1969, 1971, 1974). Krickeberg (1974b) sets out a general form of the required theory of moment measures.

When further distributional aspects are specified, the results can be sharpened as in the basic example below. For extensions to higher dimensions see Exercise 10.6.5 and the cited papers by Miles.

EXAMPLE 10.6(a) We define a *stationary Poisson process of lines* in terms of the associated point process $N(\cdot)$ on the cylinder $\mathbb{R} \times \mathbb{S}$. For the line process to be stationary in $\mathbb{R}^2$, the point process $N(\cdot)$ must be invariant under shears of the cylinder, and its first moment measure must decompose as at (10.6.2). Since the first moment measure of a Poisson process coincides with its parameter measure $\mu(\cdot)$, we must have

$$\mu(dp \times d\theta) = \mu\ell(dp)\Pi(d\theta)$$

for some density μ and probability distribution (here, the directional rose of the line process) $\Pi(\cdot)$. We can therefore write for the p.g.fl. of the point process $N(\cdot)$, with suitable functions $h(\cdot)$,

$$G[h] = E\left[\exp\left\{\int_{\mathbb{R}\times\mathbb{S}} \log h(p, \theta)N(dp \times d\theta)\right\}\right]$$

$$= \exp\left\{\mu \int_{\mathbb{R}} \ell(dp) \int_{\mathbb{S}} (h(p, \theta) - 1)\Pi(d\theta)\right\}.$$

Thus, for example, the second factorial moment measure is given by

$$M_{[2]}(dp \times dp' \times d\theta \times d\theta') = \mu^2\ell(dp)\ell(dp')\Pi(d\theta)\Pi(d\theta')$$

$$= M(dp \times d\theta)M(dp' \times d\theta'),$$

which is of course of the product form expected for a Poisson process.

The p.g.fl. for the point process N_V of intersections of the line process on a fixed line V follows from an extension of the reasoning leading to (10.6.6). In the notation used there,

$$G_{N_V}[h] = E\left[\exp\left\{\int_{\mathbb{R}} \log h(x)N_V(dx)\right\}\right]$$

$$= E\left[\exp\left\{\int_{\mathbb{R}\times\mathbb{S}} \log h(p \sec(\theta - \alpha))N(dp \times d\theta)\right\}\right]$$

$$= \exp\left\{\mu \int_{\mathbb{R} \times \mathbb{S}} [h(p \sec(\theta - \alpha)) - 1]\ell(dp)\Pi(d\theta)\right\}$$

$$= \exp\left\{\mu \int_{\mathbb{S}} |\cos(\theta - \alpha)|\,\Pi(d\theta) \int_{-\infty}^{\infty} (h(u) - 1)du\right\},$$

which we recognize as the p.g.fl. of a stationary Poisson process on V with density m_V as at (10.6.4). In particular, for a stationary isotropic Poisson line process, the density $m_V = 2\mu/\pi$ is independent of the orientation α of V, and the number of lines crossing a closed convex set A has a Poisson distribution with parameter $\mu L(A)/\pi$ with μ equal to the mean line density.

In turning now to the discussion of second-order properties of line processes, we confine our attention to stationary isotropic processes. Since it is clear that one invariant of a pair of lines, under both translations and rotations on the plane, is the angle ϕ between them (where we take $0 < \phi \le 2\pi$ to allow for directed lines), we take coordinates in the form

$$(p, \theta, p', \theta') \to (p, \theta, p', \theta + \phi).$$

Invariance under rotations then implies that the second factorial moment measure $M_{[2]}$ of the point process N representing the stationary isotropic line process in $\mathbb{R}^2$ factorizes into a product

$$M_{[2]}(dp \times dp' \times d\theta \times d\theta') = \hat{M}_{[2]}(dp \times dp' \times d\phi)d\theta/2\pi.$$

To handle the term $\hat{M}_{[2]}$ we proceed much as in Propositions 10.5.II and 10.5.III, deducing first that we can write

$$\hat{M}_{[2]}(dp \times dp' \times d\phi) = K_{[2]}(dp \times dp'|\phi)G_{[2]}(d\phi).$$

Invariance of N under shears implies that for almost all ϕ and at least for (say) rational r and $\psi = \theta - \alpha$,

$$K_{[2]}(dp \times dp'|\phi) = K_{[2]}((dp - r\cos\psi) \times (dp - r\cos(\psi + \phi))|\phi).$$

Provided $\phi \ne 0$ or π, the equations $r\cos\psi = u$ and $r\cos(\psi + \phi) = v$ have unique solutions for all real u, v, and therefore $K_{[2]}(dp \times dp'|\phi)$ is invariant under at least a countable dense family of translations $(p, p') \to (p + u, p' + v)$, including incommensurate pairs $(u, v), (u', v')$. For such values of ϕ then, $K_{[2]}(dp \times dp'|\phi)$ reduces to a multiple of Lebesgue measure in $\mathbb{R}^2$, $\lambda(\phi)\ell_2(dp \times dp')$ say, where as earlier we can take $\lambda(\phi)$ to be a measurable function of ϕ.

The exceptional cases $\phi = 0$ and π correspond to the occurrence of pairs of parallel and antiparallel lines, respectively. In both cases, the signed distance y between the lines is a further invariant of the motion. In the first case, invariance under translation implies that

$$K_{[2]}(dp \times dp'|0) = K_{[2]}((dp + r\cos(\theta - \alpha)) \times (dp' + r\cos(\theta - \alpha))|0),$$

so that setting $p' = p + y$, the measure factorizes into the form

$$K_{[2]}(dp \times dp'|0) = \tilde{K}_{+}(dy)\ell(dp)$$

for some boundedly finite measure $\tilde{K}_+$ on $\mathbb{R}$. Similarly, for $\phi = \pi$, the measure $K_{[2]}(dp \times dp' | \pi)$ is invariant under the transformations

$$(p, p') \rightarrow (p + r\cos(\theta - \alpha), p' - r\cos(\theta - \alpha))$$

so that setting now $p' = y - p$, where y is the distance between parallel lines oriented in opposite senses,

$$K_{[2]}(dp \times dp' | \pi) = \tilde{K}_-(dy)\ell(dp)$$

for boundedly finite $\tilde{K}_-$. Finally, since $M_{[2]}$ is symmetric under the transformation

$$(p, p', \theta, \theta') \rightarrow (p', p, \theta', \theta),$$

all three of $G_{[2]}$, $\tilde{K}_+$, and $\tilde{K}_-$ are symmetric under reflection in their respective origins. We have proved the following result (Davidson, 1974a; Krickeberg, 1974a,b).

Proposition 10.6.V. *Let $M_{[2]}$ be the second factorial moment measure of a stationary isotropic line process in $\mathbb{R}^2$. Then $M_{[2]}$ admits a representation in terms of the factors:*

  (i) *a totally finite symmetric measure $G_{[2]}(d\phi)$ on $(0, \pi) \cup (\pi, 2\pi)$ governing the intensity of pairs of lines intersecting at an angle ϕ;*
 (ii) *a boundedly finite symmetric measure $\tilde{K}_+(dy)$ on $\mathbb{R}$ governing the intensity of pairs of parallel lines distance y apart;*
(iii) *a similar measure $\tilde{K}_-(dy)$ governing the intensity of pairs of antiparallel lines a distance y apart.*

The representation is realized by the integral relation, valid for bounded measurable nonnegative functions h of bounded support on $\mathbb{R} \times \mathbb{R} \times \mathbb{S} \times \mathbb{S} = \mathbb{R}^2 \times \mathbb{S}^2$,

$$(10.6.7) \quad \int_{\mathbb{R}^2 \times \mathbb{S}^2} h(p, p', \theta, \theta') M_{[2]}(dp \times dp' \times d\theta \times d\theta')$$

$$= \int_{(0,\pi)\cup(\pi,2\pi)} G_{[2]}(d\phi) \int_{\mathbb{R}^2 \times \mathbb{S}} h(p, p', \theta, \theta + \phi) dp\, dp'\, d\theta$$

$$+ \int_{\mathbb{R}} \tilde{K}_+(dy) \int_{\mathbb{R} \times \mathbb{S}} h(p, p + y, \theta, \theta) dp\, d\theta$$

$$+ \int_{\mathbb{R}} \tilde{K}_-(dy) \int_{\mathbb{R} \times \mathbb{S}} h(p, y - p, \theta, \theta + \pi) dp\, d\theta.$$

A similar representation holds for the factorial covariance measure.

As Rollo Davidson observed, many remarkable corollaries follow from the representation (10.6.7).

Corollary 10.6.VI. *With probability 1, a stationary isotropic line process in $\mathbb{R}^2$ either has no pairs of parallel or antiparallel lines, or has infinitely many pairs of parallel lines, or has infinitely many pairs of antiparallel lines, according as $\tilde{K}_+(\mathbb{R}) = \tilde{K}_-(\mathbb{R}) = 0$, or $\tilde{K}_+(\mathbb{R}) > 0$, or $\tilde{K}_-(\mathbb{R}) > 0$, respectively.*

PROOF. Let A be a bounded Borel set in $\mathbb{R}$ and V a fixed line in the plane. Then by the preceding discussion and (10.6.4') we can interpret $2\tilde{K}_+(A)/\pi$ as the mean density of the stationary point process on V generated by its intersections with lines of the process, which have other lines of the process parallel to them and at separation $y \in A$. If $\tilde{K}_+(\mathbb{R}) = 0$, any such process of interaction has zero mean density and is therefore a.s. empty. Letting $A \uparrow \mathbb{R}$, we deduce that with probability 1 no line of the process has another line of the process parallel to it. Conversely, if $\tilde{K}_+(\mathbb{R}) > 0$, we can find a bounded Borel set A with $\tilde{K}_+(A) > 0$ and a line V such that the process of associated points on V is stationary with positive mean density and therefore has an infinite number of points (see Proposition 10.1.IV).

The argument concerning antiparallel lines is similar.   □

Corollary 10.6.VII. *$M_{[2]}$ is invariant under reflections if and only if the process has a.s. no pairs of antiparallel lines, in which case it is also invariant under translations $p \to p + y$ of the cylinder parallel to its axis.*

PROOF. If $\tilde{K}_-(\mathbb{R}) = 0$, then it follows from (10.6.7) that $M_{[2]}$ is invariant under the transformation

$$(p, p', \theta, \theta') \to (p, p', -\theta, -\theta')$$

on account of the symmetry properties of $G_{[2]}$. This mapping corresponds to reflection in the reference axis. Hence, by isotropy and stationarity, it is invariant under any other reflection. A similar conclusion holds for the transformation

$$(p, p', \theta, \theta') \to (p + y, p' + y, \theta, \theta').$$

Conversely, if $\tilde{K}_-(\mathbb{R}) > 0$, we can choose $h(\cdot)$ in (10.6.7) so that a contradiction arises if we assume that $M_{[2]}$ is invariant under either of these transformations.   □

Provided that $T^{-1}\tilde{K}_+((0, T])$ and $T^{-1}\tilde{K}_-((0, T])$ both vanish in the limit as $T \to \infty$, we can show that the measure $G_{[2]}$ of Proposition 10.6.V is positive-definite: we proceed under the more restrictive assumption that $\tilde{K}_+(\mathbb{R}) = \tilde{K}_-(\mathbb{R}) = 0$, that is, that there are a.s. no parallel or antiparallel pairs of lines.

Let $a(\theta)$ be a bounded measurable function on $(0, 2\pi)$ and in (10.6.7) set

$$h(p, p', \theta, \theta') = I_{0T}(p)I_{0T}(p')a(\theta)a(\theta') \equiv h(p, \theta)h(p', \theta'),$$

where $I_{0T}(\cdot)$ is the indicator function of the interval $(0, T]$. In place of $M_{[2]}$, consider the ordinary second moment measure M_2 for which

$$M_2(A \times B) = M_{[2]}(A \times B) + M_1(A \cap B).$$

$$0 \le E\left[\left(\int_{\mathbb{R} \times \mathbb{S}} h(p, \theta) N(dp, d\theta)\right)^2\right]$$

$$= \int_{(\mathbb{R} \times \mathbb{S})^{(2)}} h(p, \theta) h(p', \theta') M_{[2]}(dp \times dp' \times d\theta \times d\theta')$$

$$+ \int_{\mathbb{R} \times \mathbb{S}} h^2(p, \theta) M_1(dp \times d\theta)$$

$$= T^2 \int_{\mathbb{S}} \int_{\mathbb{S}} a(\theta) a(\theta + \phi) G_{[2]}(d\phi) d\theta + \int_{\mathbb{S}} \frac{a^2(\theta) m T \, d\theta}{2\pi}.$$

Division by T^2 and rearrangement yield

$$\int_{\mathbb{S}} \int_{\mathbb{S}} a(\theta) a(\theta + \phi) G_{[2]}(d\phi) d\theta \ge - \int_{\mathbb{S}} \frac{a^2(\theta) m \, d\theta}{2\pi T} \to 0 \qquad (T \to \infty);$$

that is, the measure $G_{[2]}(\cdot)$ is positive definite (equivalently, in the terminology of Definition 11.1.I, it is a p.p.d. measure).

This result immediately suggests asking whether $G_{[2]}(\cdot)$ can be interpreted as a covariance measure: accordingly, we look for some random measure Y on $\mathbb{S}$ with which $G_{[2]}(\cdot)$ may be associated. The appropriate candidate (as we now show) is the ergodic limit of the original point process on $\mathbb{R} \times \mathbb{S}$ with respect to translations of the cylinder parallel to its axis, or, equivalently, the conditional expectation $E(N(\cdot)|\mathscr{I}_\mathbb{S})$ of the original process with respect to the invariant σ-algebra $\mathscr{I}_\mathbb{S}$ generated by these translations. That such ergodic limits exist follows directly from Proposition 10.2.VI, and we then have, for $A, B \in \mathscr{B}(\mathbb{S})$,

$$E(Y(A) Y(B)) = \lim_{T \to \infty} T^{-2} \int_{(\mathbb{R} \times \mathbb{S})^{(2)}} M_{[2]}(dp \times dp' \times d\theta \times d\theta')$$

$$\times I_{0T}(p) I_{0T}(p') I_A(\theta) I_B(\theta') dp \, dp' d\theta \, d\theta'$$

$$= \int_{\mathbb{S}^2} I_A(\theta) I_B(\theta + \phi) G_{[2]}(d\phi) d\theta.$$

An even more surprising corollary is the following. Consider the Cox process N^* on the cylinder $\mathbb{R} \times \mathbb{S}$ directed by the random measure $\ell \times Y$. It is readily checked that N^* is invariant under rotations and translations of the cylinder and that for $A, B \in \mathscr{B}(\mathscr{S})$ and $\mathbb{U}$ the unit interval

$$EN^*(\mathbb{U} \times A) = m\ell(A)/2\pi = EY(A),$$

$$M_{[2]}^*(\mathbb{U} \times \mathbb{U} \times A \times B) = E(Y(A) Y(B)).$$

Thus, N and N^* have the same first and second moment measure. We summarize this as follows.

Proposition 10.6.VIII. *If a stationary isotropic line process has boundedly finite second moment measure and has a.s. no parallel or antiparallel lines, then the reduced moment measure $G_{[2]}(\cdot)$ of Proposition 10.6.V is positive definite and can be identified with the second moment measure of the random measure on $\mathbb{S}$*

$$Y(A) = E(N(\mathbb{U} \times A)|\mathscr{I}) =_{\text{a.s.}} \lim_{T \to \infty} \frac{1}{T} \int_0^T N(dp \times A),$$

where $\mathscr{I}$ is the invariant σ-algebra associated with shifts of the cylinder parallel to its axis. Furthermore, N has the same second moment measure as the Cox process N^* directed by $\ell \times Y$.

This proposition, coupled with his failure to find counterexamples, led Davidson to formulate his celebrated conjecture ["the big problem" of Davidson (1974b, p. 70)] that any stationary isotropic line process with a.s. no parallel or antiparallel lines and boundedly finite second moment measure must be a Cox process. Davidson showed that no counterexample could be constructed by taking a point process on a line and putting lines through its points [cf. Proposition 10.6.IV(i)), nor by taking a stationary point process in $\mathbb{R}^2$ and putting lines through its points, nor seemingly "by tinkering with a Poisson line process." The structure of stationary isotropic line processes, as well as of the more general stationary hyperplane processes in spaces $\mathbb{R}^{2d}$, differs radically from those of stationary point processes in $\mathbb{R}^1$. That Davidson's conjecture is false was shown by Kallenberg (1977) whose main idea was to construct a process from a lattice configuration in a parameterization with respect to a fixed line (see also Mecke, 1979). The following is an attempted simple modification of Kallenberg's construction.

EXAMPLE 10.6(b) *Kallenberg's randomized lattice.* For some positive integer k start with lattice points $\{(i, 2\pi j/k): i = 0, \pm 1, \ldots, j = 0, 1, \ldots, k - 1\}$ on the cylinder $\mathbb{R} \times \mathbb{S}$, and randomize the location of the lattice by rotating the cylinder through an angle θ uniformly distributed on $[0, 2\pi)$ and then shifting it parallel to its axis through a distance Y uniformly distributed on $[0, 1)$.

The essential idea of Kallenberg is that there be two further randomizations. First, "twist" the cylinder according to a transformation of the form

$$(p, \theta) \to (p, \theta + p\alpha),$$

where α is again uniformly distributed over $[0, 2\pi)$. Then, with probability 1, the corresponding line process no longer has any pairs of parallel or antiparallel lines. The process is also invariant under rotations and vertical translations of the cylinder but not at this stage under shears. To secure this last property, consider a sequence of further randomizations of the form

$$(p, \theta) \to (p + X_n|\cos \theta|, \theta);$$

here, X_n is uniformly distributed over $(-n, n)$, and as $n \to \infty$ we have a sequence of point processes on the cylinder more and more nearly invariant under shifts.

Observe that this sequence of point processes is tight, as follows from the fact that the processes all have the same mean density (see Exercise 9.1.2). Thus, there exists at least one weakly convergent subsequence. In fact, not only are the densities constant, but the number of points in any "band" of the cylinder, say $-1 < p \leq 1$, can only change marginally, as, for example,

$$k \leq N((-1, 1] \times \mathbb{S}) \leq 3k.$$

This implies that the limit of any weakly convergent subsequence from the sequence is nonempty, and furthermore that the expected number within the band converges (i.e., a uniform integrability condition holds as in Exercise 9.1.3) and converges to the expected number of the limit. Thus, the limit of any subsequence is nondegenerate and has constant mean density. The limit is not a Poisson process because it still has an a.s. lattice character, but it is from the construction invariant under both rotations and shears. Finally, its second factorial moment measure exists, and a further analysis shows that $\tilde{K}_+(\mathbb{R}) = \tilde{K}_-(\mathbb{R}) = 0$, while $G_{[2]}(\cdot)$ is uniformly distributed on $\mathbb{S}$. This is the same second moment structure as for the simple Poisson process itself. Since it is not the Poisson process, it cannot be a Cox process either.

The corresponding line process is thus invariant under translations and rotations of the plane, has finite first and second moment measures, has a.s. no parallel or antiparallel lines, and is not a Cox process. It therefore refutes Davidson's conjecture.

Exercises

10.6.1. A *process of undirected lines* can be parameterized in either of the ways indicated below. For each of them, describe a line process that is homogeneous and isotropic.
   (a) Either (i) take the distance $p > 0$ from the origin to the line as one parameter and the angle made by the line and a fixed reference axis as the other, or (ii) allow the distance to be signed but restrict the angle to the range $(0, \pi]$. The line process is represented as a point process on $\mathbb{R}_+ \times \mathbb{S}$ in (i) and on $\mathbb{R} \times (0, \pi]$ in (ii).
   (b) Describe a line by its intercepts on the x and y axes as parameters. Then a line process is represented as a point process in the plane.

10.6.2. Let μ be a measure on $\mathbb{R}$ invariant under shifts T_a and T_b for incommensurate a and b. Set $F(x) = \mu((0, x])$ for $x > 0$, $= -\mu((x, 0])$ for $x \leq 0$, and let U be the set of points $u \in \mathbb{R}$ such that μ is invariant under shifts T_u. Show that $u \in U$ implies $-u \in U$, and that for $u, v \in U$, $F(u + v) = F(u) + F(v)$, so that U is an additive group and thus contains all points of the form $ja + kb$ for positive or negative integers j, k. Deduce that $F(x) = \alpha x$ for all x and some $\alpha \geq 0$. [This result, like Exercise 10.1.8, is a variant on the Hamel equation at (3.6.3).]

10.6.3. (Compare references in text.) A hyperplane is a $(d - d')$-dimensional linear subspace of $\mathbb{R}^d$ shifted through some vector $x \in \mathbb{R}^d$ for some positive integer $d' < d$.

(a) Show that a directed hyperplane is uniquely specified by a pair (p, θ), where θ lies on the d-dimensional unit ball S^d, $p \in \mathbb{R}$, and the sense of the hyperplane (whether the normal to the origin is directed toward or away from the hyperplane) is determined by the sign of p.

(b) A process of random $d - d'$ hyperplanes can be represented as a point process in $S^d \times \mathbb{R}$. Rotation of the original plane corresponds to rotation by an element of S^d, while a translation of the original plane corresponds to the transformation $(p, \theta) \to (p + \langle x, \theta \rangle, \theta)$, where $\langle x, \theta \rangle$ is the inner product in $\mathbb{R}^d$.

(c) Such a process is homogeneous and isotropic if and only if the point process is invariant under both rotations and generalized shears as defined above, and its first moment measure, if it exists, is then a multiple of Lebesgue measure on $S^d \times \mathbb{R}$, $m\ell_d(\cdot)$ say.

(d) Define a random measure $\xi(A)$ for bounded Borel A in $\mathbb{R}^d$ as the sum of the hypervolumes $A \cap S_i$, where the particular hyperplanes of the process are denoted by $\{S_i\}$. Then $m\ell_d(\cdot)$ is the mean density of this random meausre.

(e) If L is an arbitrary fixed line in $\mathbb{R}^d$, then the points of intersection of L with $\{S_i\}$ form a stationary point process with mean density $m\Gamma(\tfrac{1}{2}d)/2\pi^{1/2}$.

10.6.4. The special case of *random lines in* $\mathbb{R}^3$ uses the representation of such lines as points in $S^2 \times \mathbb{R}^2$, where the component in S^2 determines the direction of the line and the point in $\mathbb{R}^2$ its point of intersection with the orthogonal plane passing through the origin. Find analogues to (d) and (e) of Exercise 10.6.3 for the "line density" of the process (a random measure in $\mathbb{R}^3$) and the point process generated by the points of intersection of the lines with an arbitrary plane in $\mathbb{R}^3$.

10.6.5. Extend the result of Example 10.6(a) to the context of Exercises 10.6.3(e) and 10.6.4 (i.e., show that if the original process is Poisson so are the induced processes on the line and plane, respectively).

10.6.6. Given a homogeneous isotropic Poisson directed line process in $\mathbb{R}^2$, form a "clustered" line process with pairs of lines in each cluster in one of the following three ways.

(a) *Railway line process (i)*: To each line (p_i, θ_i) of the process, add the line $(p_i + d, \theta_i)$ for some fixed positive d. In the notation of Proposition 10.6.V, $G_{[2]}$ and K_- are null while K_+ has an atom at d. The process is invariant under translation, rotation, and reflection.

(b) *Davidson's railway line process (ii)*: To each line (p_i, θ_i) add the antiparallel line $(-p_i - d, \pi + \theta_i)$. Then $G_{[2]}$ and K_+ are null, K_- has an atom at d, and because of the built-in handedness, this process is not invariant under reflections of the plane.

(c) To each line (p_i, θ_i) add the line $(p_i, \theta_i + \alpha)$ for some fixed α in $0 < \alpha < \pi$. The resulting line process is no longer translation invariant.

[Each of these processes is a possible analogue of the Poisson process of deterministic cluster pairs as in Bartlett. (1963, p. 266) or Daley (1971, Example 5).]

10.6.7. (a) Show that two distinct lines (p, θ) and (p', θ') intersect in a point inside the unit circle if and only if $|p| < 1$, $|p'| < 1$, and

$$p^2 + p'^2 - 2pp' \cos(\theta - \theta') < \sin^2(\theta - \theta').$$

The expected number of line pairs intersecting within the circle is thus found by integrating the second factorial moment measure over the region defined by these inequalities.

(b) More generally, the first moment measure M of the process of intersections is found from integrals of the form

$$\int_{\mathbb{R}^2} h(x, y) M(dx \times dy) = \int_{\mathbb{R}^2 \times S^2} h(x(\mathbf{p}), y(\mathbf{p})) M_{[2]}(dp \times dp' \times d\theta \times d\theta'),$$

where $\mathbf{p}$ denotes the vector of coordinates p, p', θ, θ' and the two lines (p, θ) and (p', θ') intersect in the point $(x(\mathbf{p}), y(\mathbf{p}))$, and $h(\cdot)$ is a bounded measurable function of bounded support.

(c) When the line process is homogeneous and isotropic, $M_{[2]}$ reduces to the form described in Proposition 10.6.V. Assuming there are a.s. no parallel or antiparallel lines, use the representation of (b) to show that the intersection process is stationary and has mean density given by

$$4\pi \int_{(0, \pi)} \sin \phi \, G_{[2]}(d\phi).$$

10.6.8. Show that if a stationary isotropic line process has a.s. no parallel or antiparallel lines, then it cannot be a Poisson cluster process. [*Hint*: Consider the form of the second factorial moment measure; a Poisson cluster process with nontrivial cluster distribution cannot factorize in the form of Proposition 10.6.V.]

CHAPTER 11

Spectral Theory

The spectral theory of point processes and random measures is concerned with frequency (i.e., Fourier) representations of various kinds and degrees of generality. In this chapter we look first at the frequency representation of the reduced second-order measures introduced in Chapter 10 and then at frequency representations and related questions for the process itself. Such representations have less value in the present context than in the continuous (especially, Gaussian) context, for reasons already touched on in previous chapters: the mean square representations rarely preserve the character of the original trajectories of the process, and the linear predictors to which they give rise can often be improved upon by quite simple nonlinear predictors (cf Chapter 13).

Nevertheless, the spectral theory approach to point processes and random measures has an established place both in the theory and in practical applications. The theory is essentially a development of the theory of Fourier transforms of unbounded measures (e.g., see Argabright and de Lamadrid, 1974). As such it requires an extension, which is not quite trivial, of the classical Bochner theorem and related results used in standard time series analysis. On the practical side, the point process periodogram, introduced by Bartlett (1963), plays an essential role in any investigation of periodic effects and is valuable also as a general descriptive tool (see Cox and Lewis, 1966; Brillinger, 1972). Most of the point process applications are in the one-dimensional context, but the spectral analysis of spatial processes is also important (e.g., see Bartlett, 1964; Ripley, 1981), and more general contexts can be considered (Ripley, 1976). A survey contrasting selected continuous and point process aspects is given in Brillinger (1978), reprinted in Brillinger (1981).

It should be noted that we shall be concerned in this chapter only with the "count spectrum" in the terminology of Cox and Lewis (1966). The spectrum of intervals is an important descriptive feature of a one-dimensional point process, but it does not generalize readily beyond this one-dimensional context and does not require any special theory.

11.1. Positive Positive-Definite Measures

In this section and the next we develop the properties of the Fourier transforms of the reduced second moment measures described in Section 10.4, following mainly the work of Daley (1971), Vere-Jones (1974), and Thornett (1979). Since neither the reduced moment measures nor their Fourier transforms are totally finite in general, we must first define what is meant by a Fourier transform in this context. No significant complications arise in developing the theory for $\mathbb{R}^d$ rather than for the line, so we follow our earlier treatment by discussing the theory for $\mathbb{R}^d$ from the outset. However, most of the examples are taken from the one-dimensional context. Further aspects of spectral analysis in $\mathbb{R}^d$ ($d \geq 2$), such as the effect of isotropy, are touched on in Section 11.5.

As in the theory of generalized functions (e.g., see Schwarz, 1951), we make extensive use of Parseval identities

$$(11.1.1) \qquad \int_{\mathbb{R}^d} \psi(x)\nu(dx) = \int_{\mathbb{R}^d} \tilde{\psi}(\omega)\mu(d\omega)$$

to identify the measure ν as the Fourier transform of the measure μ: in (11.1.1),

$$\tilde{\psi}(\omega) = \int_{\mathbb{R}^d} e^{ix \cdot \omega}\psi(x)dx$$

is the ordinary (d-dimensional) Fourier transform of $\psi(\cdot)$, but such functions must be suitably restricted. A convenient domain for ψ is the space $\mathscr{S}$ of real or complex functions of *rapid decay*, that is, of infinitely differentiable functions that, together with their derivatives, satisfy inequalities of the form

$$\left| \frac{\partial^k \psi(x)}{\partial x_1^{k_1} \cdots \partial x_d^{k_d}} \right| \leq \frac{C(k, r)}{(1 + |x|)^r}$$

for some constants $C(k, r) < \infty$, all positive integers r, and all finite families of nonnegative integers $(k_1, \ldots, k_d)$ with $k_1 + \cdots + k_d = k$.

The space $\mathscr{S}$ has certain relevant properties, proofs of which are sketched in Exercise 11.1.1:

(i) It remains invariant under the Fourier transformation taking ψ into $\tilde{\psi}$.
(ii) It remains invariant under multiplication or convolution by real- or complex-valued integrable functions g on $\mathbb{R}^d$ such that both g and $\tilde{g}$ are zero free.
(iii) Integrals with respect to all functions $\psi \in \mathscr{S}$ uniquely determine any boundedly finite measure on $\mathbb{R}^d$.

The following definitions collect together some properties of boundedly finite measures that are important in the sequel. We use the notation

$$(\psi * \phi)(x) = \int_{\mathbb{R}^d} \psi(y)\overline{\phi(x-y)}dy, \qquad \psi^*(x) = \overline{\psi(-x)},$$

so that

$$(\psi * \psi^*)(x) = \int_{\mathbb{R}^d} \psi(y)\psi(y-x)dy.$$

Definition 11.1.I. A boundedly finite signed measure $\mu(\cdot)$ on $\mathbb{R}^d$ is

(i) *translation bounded* if for all $h > 0$ and $x \in \mathbb{R}^d$ there exists a finite constant K_h such that

(11.1.2) $$|\mu(S(x; h))| \leq K_h;$$

(ii) *positive-definite* if for all bounded measurable functions ψ of bounded support,

(11.1.3) $$\int_{\mathbb{R}^d} (\psi * \psi^*)(x)\mu(dx) \geq 0;$$

(iii) *transformable* if there exists a boundedly finite measure v on $\mathbb{R}^d$ such that (11.1.1) holds for all $\psi \in \mathscr{S}$;

(iv) a *p.p.d. measure* if it is nonnegative (i.e., a measure rather than a signed measure) and positive definite.

A few comments on these definitions are in order. The concept of translation boundedness appears naturally in this context and is discussed further by Lin (1965), Argabright and de Lamadrid (1974), Thornett (1979), and Robertson and Thornett (1984). If μ is nonnegative, then it is clear that if (11.1.2) holds for some $h > 0$ it holds for all such h. The notion of positive definiteness in (11.1.3) is a direct extension of the same notion for continuous functions; indeed, if μ is absolutely continuous, then it is positive definite in the sense of (11.1.3) if and only if its density is a positive definite function in the usual sense. Concerning the Parseval relation at (11.1.1) it is important to note that if the measure μ is transformable, then v is uniquely determined by μ, and conversely. Equation (11.1.1) generalises the relation

$$c(x) = \int_{\mathbb{R}^d} e^{i\omega \cdot x}F(d\omega)$$

for the covariance density in terms of the spectral measure F of a mean square continuous process, to which it reduces (with the appropriate identifications) when the random measure and associated covariance measure are absolutely continuous.

Our main interest is in the class of p.p.d. measures on $\mathbb{R}^d$, denoted below by $\mathscr{P}^+$. Some examples may help to indicate the scope and character of $\mathscr{P}^+$.

EXAMPLE 11.1(a) *Simple examples of p.p.d. measures.*

(i) The measure on $\mathbb{R}^d$ with unit mass at each of the two points ± 1 is *not* a p.p.d. measure, because its Fourier transform $2 \cos \omega$ can take negative values and it thus fails to be positive definite. On the other hand, the convolution of this measure with itself (i.e., the measure with unit mass at ± 2 and mass of two units at 0) *is* a p.p.d. measure, and its Fourier transform is the boundedly finite (but not totally bounded) measure with density $4 \cos^2 \omega$.

(ii) Every nonnegative positive definite function defines the density of an absolutely continuous p.p.d. measure.

(iii) Let μ have unit mass at every $2\pi j$ for $j = 0, \pm 1, \ldots$. Then for $\psi \in \mathscr{S}$, (11.1.1) reduces to the Poisson summation formula (see Exercise 11.1.4 for details)

$$\sum_{n=-\infty}^{\infty} \psi(n) = \sum_{j=-\infty}^{\infty} \tilde{\psi}(2\pi j);$$

that is, μ has as its Fourier transform the measure ν with unit mass at each of the integers $n = 0, \pm 1, \ldots$. It also shows that ν, and thus μ as well, is positive definite (take for ψ a function of the form $\phi * \phi^*$ so that the right-hand side becomes $\sum |\tilde{\phi}(2\pi j)|^2 \geq 0$).

(iv) Let $\mu_1, \ldots, \mu_d$ be p.p.d. measures on $\mathbb{R}$ with Fourier transforms $\tilde{\mu}_1, \ldots, \tilde{\mu}_d$. Then the product measure $\mu_1 \times \cdots \times \mu_d$ is a p.p.d. measure on $\mathbb{R}^d$ with Fourier transform $\tilde{\mu}_1 \times \cdots \times \tilde{\mu}_d$.

A simple and elegant theory for measures in $\mathscr{P}^+$ can be developed by the standard device of approximating μ by a smoothed version obtained by convoluting μ with a suitable smoothing function such as the symmetric probability densities

$$t(x) = (1 - |x|)_+ \quad \text{(triangular density)},$$

$$e_\lambda(x) = (\lambda/2)e^{-\lambda|x|} \quad \text{(two-sided exponential density)},$$

and their multivariate extensions

(11.1.4a)
$$t(x) = \prod_{i=1}^{d} (1 - |x_i|)_+,$$

(11.1.4b)
$$e_\lambda(x) = \left(\frac{\lambda}{2}\right)^d \exp\left(-\lambda \sum_{i=1}^{d} |x_i|\right).$$

Observe that

(11.1.4a')
$$t(x) = \int_{\mathbb{R}^d} I_{\mathsf{U}^d}(x - y)I_{\mathsf{U}^d}(-y)dy.$$

Lemma 11.1.II. (i) *$\mathscr{P}^+$ is a closed positive cone in $\mathscr{M}(\mathbb{R}^d)$.*
(ii) *Every p.p.d. measure is symmetric and translation bounded.*

PROOF. In (i) we mean by "a positive cone" a set closed under the formation of positive linear combinations. Then (i) is just the statement that if a sequence of boundedly finite measures in $\mathbb{R}^d$ converges vaguely to a limit, and if each measure in the sequence is positive-definite, then so is the limit. This follows directly from the definition of vague convergence and the defining relation (11.1.3).

Now let μ be a p.p.d. measure on $\mathbb{R}^d$, and convolve it with $t(\cdot)$ as at (11.1.4a) so that the convolution is well defined. The resultant function

$$(11.1.5) \qquad c(x) \equiv \int_{\mathbb{R}^d} t(x-y)\mu(dy)$$

is real-valued, continuous, and for all bounded measurable ψ of bounded support it satisfies [in view of (11.1.4a$'$)]

$$\int_{\mathbb{R}^d} c(u)(\psi * \psi^*)(u)du = \int_{\mathbb{R}^d} ((\psi * I_{\mathbb{U}^d}) * (\psi * I_{\mathbb{U}^d})^*)(y)\mu(dy) \geq 0;$$

note that (11.1.3) applies because $\psi * I_{\mathbb{U}^d}$ is measurable and bounded with bounded support whenever ψ is. In other words, the function $c(\cdot)$ is real-valued and positive-definite, and hence, from standard properties of such functions, also symmetric and bounded. Since $t(\cdot)$ is symmetric, it is clear that $c(\cdot)$ is symmetric if and only if μ is symmetric, which must therefore hold. Finally, it follows from the positivity of μ and the inequality $t(x) \geq 2^{-d}$ for $\|x\| \leq \frac{1}{4}$, that if K is a bound for $c(\cdot)$,

$$\mu(S(x, \tfrac{1}{4})) \leq 2^d \int_{S(x, 1/4)} c(y)dy \leq 2^d K < \infty.$$

Inequality (11.1.2) is thus established for the case $h = \frac{1}{4}$, and since μ is nonnegative, its validity for any other value of h is now apparent. $\qquad \square$

The Fourier transform properties can be established by similar arguments, though it is now more convenient to work with the double exponential function $e_\lambda(\cdot)$ because its Fourier transform

$$\tilde{e}_\lambda(\omega) = \prod_{i=1}^{d} \frac{\lambda^2}{\lambda^2 + \omega_i^2}$$

has no real zeros. The existence of the convolution $\mu * e_\lambda$ follows from the translation boundedness just established. The relation

$$d_\lambda(x) = \int_{\mathbb{R}^d} e_\lambda(x-y)\mu(dy)$$

again defines a continuous positive-definite function. By Bochner's theorem in $\mathbb{R}^d$, it can therefore be represented as the Fourier transform

$$d_\lambda(x) = \int_{\mathbb{R}^d} e^{i\omega \cdot x} G_\lambda(d\omega)$$

for some totally finite measure $G_\lambda(\cdot)$.

Now let $\psi(\omega)$ be an arbitrary element of $\mathscr{S}$, and consider the function $\tilde{\kappa}(\omega)$ defined by

$$\tilde{\kappa}(\omega) = (1 + \omega^2)\psi(-\omega)/(2\pi)^d.$$

Then $\tilde{\kappa} \in \mathscr{S}$ also, and hence $\tilde{\kappa}$ is the Fourier transform of some integrable function κ satisfying

$$\tilde{\psi}(y) = (\kappa * e_1)(y).$$

From the Fourier representation of d_1 we have

$$\int_{\mathbb{R}^d} \kappa(x)d_1(x)dx = \int_{\mathbb{R}^d} \tilde{\kappa}(\omega)G_1(d\omega)$$

for all integrable κ, and hence in particular for the function κ just constructed. Substituting for κ we obtain, for all $\psi \in \mathscr{S}$,

$$\int_{\mathbb{R}^d} \tilde{\psi}(y)\mu(dy) = \int_{\mathbb{R}^d} (\kappa * e_1)(y)\mu(dy)$$

$$= \int_{\mathbb{R}^d} \kappa(x)d_1(x)dx = \int_{\mathbb{R}^d} \tilde{\kappa}(\omega)G_1(d\omega)$$

$$= \frac{1}{(2\pi)^d} \int_{\mathbb{R}^d} \psi(\omega)(1 + \omega^2)G_1(-d\omega).$$

We now *define* the measure v by

$$v(d\omega) = (2\pi)^{-d}(1 + \omega^2)G_1(-d\omega),$$

and observe that v is boundedly finite and satisfies the equation (11.1.1), which represents v as the Fourier transform of μ. Thus, we have shown that any p.p.d. measure μ is transformable.

Recall that $\mathscr{S}$ is preserved under the mapping $\psi \to \tilde{\psi}$. Then interchanging the roles of ψ and $\tilde{\psi}$ in (11.1.1) shows that every p.p.d. measure is itself a transform, and hence that v is positive definite as well as positive; that is, it is itself a p.p.d. measure. Since the determining properties of $\mathscr{S}$ imply that each of the two measures in (11.1.1) is uniquely determined by the other, we have established the principal result of the following theorem.

Theorem 11.1.III. *Every p.p.d. measure $\mu(\cdot)$ is transformable, and the Parseval equation (11.1.1) establishes a one-to-one mapping of $\mathscr{P}^+$ onto itself. This mapping can also be represented by the inversion formulae: for bounded v-continuity sets A,*

(11.1.6) $$v(A) = \lim_{\lambda \to \infty} \int_{\mathbb{R}^d} \tilde{I}_A(\omega)\tilde{e}_\lambda(\omega)\mu(d\omega);$$

for bounded μ-continuity sets B,

(11.1.7) $$\mu(B) = \lim_{\lambda \to \infty} \frac{1}{(2\pi)^d} \int_{\mathbb{R}^d} \tilde{I}_B(-x)\tilde{e}_\lambda(-x)v(dx);$$

$$(11.1.8) \qquad v(\{a\}) = \lim_{T \to \infty} \frac{1}{T^d} \int_{U_T^d} e^{-i\omega \cdot a} \mu(d\omega);$$

$$(11.1.9) \qquad \mu(\{b\}) = \lim_{T \to \infty} \frac{1}{(2\pi T)^d} \int_{U_T^d} e^{ix \cdot b} v(dx).$$

For all Lebesgue integrable ϕ for which $\tilde{\phi}$ is μ-integrable, there holds the extended Parseval relation

$$(11.1.10) \qquad \int_{\mathbb{R}^d} \phi(x + y) v(dy) = \int_{\mathbb{R}^d} e^{i\omega \cdot x} \tilde{\phi}(\omega) \mu(d\omega) \quad \text{(a.e. } x).$$

PROOF. It remains to establish the formulae (11.1.6)–(11.1.10), all of which are effectively corollaries of the basic identity (11.1.1). Suppose first that A is a bounded continuity set for $v(\cdot)$, and hence a fortiori for the smoothed version $v * e_\lambda$. Then for all finite λ it is a consequence of the Parseval theorem that

$$(v * e_\lambda)(A) = \int_{\mathbb{R}^d} \tilde{I}_A(\omega) \tilde{e}_\lambda(\omega) \mu(d\omega).$$

Now letting $\lambda \to \infty$, the left-hand side $\to v(A)$ by standard properties of weak convergence, since it is clear that $v * e_\lambda \to v$ weakly on the closure $\bar{A}$ of A. This proves (11.1.6), and a dual argument gives (11.1.7).

To establish (11.1.8) we return to a consideration of the convolution with the triangular density $t(\cdot)$. By changing the base of the triangle from $(-1, 1)$ to $(-h, h)$, we can ensure that the Fourier transform $\tilde{t}(\omega)$ does not vanish at $\omega = a$ for any given a. Using the Parseval identity, we can check that the totally finite spectral measure corresponding to the continuous function $c(x)$ in (11.1.5) can be identified with $\tilde{t}(\omega) v(d\omega)$. From standard properties of continuous positive-definite functions, we then have

$$(11.1.11) \qquad \tilde{t}(a) v(\{a\}) = \lim_{T \to \infty} \frac{1}{(4\pi T)^d} \int_{U_{2T}^d} e^{-ia \cdot x} c(x) dx.$$

Consider the difference

$$D_T \equiv \tilde{t}(a) \int_{U_{2T}^d} e^{-ia \cdot x} \mu(dx) - \int_{U_{2T}^d} e^{-ia \cdot x} c(x) dx,$$

which on using the definition of $c(\cdot)$ as the convolution $t * \mu$ yields

$$D_T = \int_{\mathbb{R}^d} e^{-ia \cdot x} \mu(dx) \left\{ \tilde{t}(a) I_{U_{2T}^d}(x) - \int_{-T-x_1}^{T-x_1} \cdots \int_{-T-x_d}^{T-x_d} e^{-ia \cdot y} t(y) dy \right\}.$$

The expression inside the braces vanishes inside the hypercube with vertices $(\pm(T - h), \ldots, \pm(T - h))$ since the second integral then reduces to $\tilde{t}(a)$, and also outside the hypercube with vertices $(\pm(T + h), \ldots, \pm(T + h))$ since both terms are then zero. Because μ is translation bounded, there is an upper bound, K_h say, on the mass it allots to any hypercube with edge of length $2h$. The number of such hypercubes needed to cover the region where the integrand is nonzero is certainly bounded by $2d(2 + T/h)^{d-1}$, within which region the integrand is bounded by M say. Thus,

$$(4\pi T)^{-d}|D_T| \leq (4\pi)^{-d}2d(h^{-1} + 2T^{-1})^{d-1}MK_h/T \to 0 \qquad (T \to \infty).$$

Equation (11.1.8) now follows from (11.1.11), and (11.1.9) follows by a dual argument with the roles of μ and ν interchanged.

It is already evident by analogy with the argument used in constructing $\nu(\cdot)$ that the Parseval relation (11.1.1) holds not only for $\psi \in \mathcal{S}$ but also for any function of the form $(\phi * e_\lambda)(x)$, where ϕ is integrable. In particular, any function of the form

$$\theta(x) = \int_{\mathbb{R}^d} \phi(y)\overline{\psi(x - y)}dy = (\phi * \psi)(x)$$

has this form for $\psi \in \mathcal{S}$ and ϕ integrable. Hence, for all $\psi \in \mathcal{S}$

$$\int_{\mathbb{R}^d} \psi(x)dx \int_{\mathbb{R}^d} \phi(x + y)\nu(dy) = \int_{\mathbb{R}^d} \tilde{\phi}(\omega)\overline{\tilde{\psi}(\omega)}\mu(d\omega).$$

If, furthermore, $\tilde{\phi}$ is μ-integrable, we can rewrite the right-hand side of this equation in the form

$$\int_{\mathbb{R}^d} \psi(x)dx \int_{\mathbb{R}^d} e^{i\omega \cdot x}\tilde{\phi}(\omega)\mu(d\omega).$$

Since equality holds for all $\psi \in \mathcal{S}$, the coefficients of $\psi(x)$ in the two integrals must be a.e. equal, which gives (11.1.10).   □

Many variants on the inversion results given above are possible: the essential point is that μ and ν determine each other uniquely through the Parseval relation (11.1.1). A number of further extensions of this relation can be deduced from (11.1.10), including the following important result.

Proposition 11.1.IV. *For all p.p.d. measures μ with Fourier transform ν as at (11.1.1), and for all bounded functions f of bounded support,*

$$(11.1.12) \qquad \int_{\mathbb{R}^d} (f * f^*)(x)\nu(dx) = \int_{\mathbb{R}^d} |\tilde{f}(\omega)|^2 \mu(d\omega).$$

PROOF. Examining (11.1.10), we see that the assumed integrability condition implies that the right-hand side there is continuous in x and consequently that the two sides are equal for any value of x at which the left-hand side is also continuous (note that the a.e. condition cannot be dropped in general because altering ϕ at a single point will alter the left-hand side whenever ν has atoms while the right-hand side will remain unchanged). Thus, to check (11.1.12) it is enough to establish the continuity of the left-hand side and the integrability of $|\tilde{f}(\omega)|^2$ with respect to μ on the right-hand side. Appealing to the dominated convergence theorem shows first that $\int_{\mathbb{R}^d} f(u)f(x + u)du$ is a continuous function of x, and second, since this function vanishes outside a bounded set within which $v(\cdot)$ is finite, that the integral

$$\int_{\mathbb{R}^d} (f * f^*)(x + y)v(dy)$$

also defines a continuous function of x. To establish that $|\tilde{f}(\omega)|^2$ is μ-integrable, we use the following lemma (Lin, 1965), which is of interest in its own right.

Lemma 11.1.V. *Let A be a bounded set in $\mathbb{R}^d$, h a positive constant, and $\theta(x)$ a square integrable function with respect to Lebesgue measure on A. For $k = (k_1, \ldots, k_d)$ let B_k be the half-open cube $\{k_i h < x_i \leq k_i h + h; i = 1, \ldots, d\}$, and set*

$$b_k = \sup_{\omega \in B_k} |\tilde{\theta}(\omega)|^2.$$

Then for all such $\theta(\cdot)$ there exists a finite constant $K(h, A)$ independent of $\theta(\cdot)$ and such that

(11.1.13) $$\sum_k b_k \leq K(h, A) \int_A |\theta(x)|^2 \, dx,$$

where summation extends over all integers $k_1, \ldots, k_d = 0, \pm 1, \ldots$.

PROOF. For simplicity we sketch the proof for $d = 1$, $h = 1$, $A = [-1, 1]$, leaving it to the reader to supply the details needed to extend the result to the general case. Write

$$\alpha_k = \frac{1}{2} \int_{-1}^{1} e^{i\pi k x} \theta(x) dx$$

for the kth Fourier coefficient of θ as a function on the interval $(-1, 1)$. Then from standard properties of Fourier series we have

(11.1.14) $$\sum_{j=-\infty}^{\infty} |\alpha_j|^2 = \int_{-1}^{1} |\theta(x)|^2 \, dx < \infty.$$

Now let ω_k be any point in $B_k = (k, k + 1]$, and consider the Taylor series expansion of $\tilde{\theta}(\omega)$ at ω_k. Since A is bounded, $\tilde{\theta}$ is an entire function, and hence the Taylor series about the point k converges throughout B_k, and we can write

$$\sum_{k=-\infty}^{\infty} |\tilde{\theta}(\omega_k)|^2 = \sum_{k=-\infty}^{\infty} \left| \sum_{n=0}^{\infty} \frac{(\omega_k - k)^n}{n!} \tilde{\theta}^{(n)}(k) \right|^2$$

$$\leq \sum_{k=-\infty}^{\infty} \left\{ \left(\sum_{n=0}^{\infty} \frac{|\omega_k - k|^{2n}}{n!} \right) \left(\sum_{n=0}^{\infty} \frac{|\tilde{\theta}^{(n)}(k)|^2}{n!} \right) \right\}$$

from the Cauchy inequality. The first series is dominated by $\sum_{n=0}^{\infty} 1/n! = e$ for all choices of ω_k; hence, by analogy with (11.1.14), we obtain

$$\sum_{k=-\infty}^{\infty} |\tilde{\theta}(\omega_k)|^2 \le e \sum_{n=0}^{\infty} \frac{1}{n!} \left(\sum_{k=-\infty}^{\infty} |\tilde{\theta}^{(n)}(k)|^2 \right)$$

$$= e \sum_{n=0}^{\infty} \frac{1}{n!} \int_{-1}^{1} |x^n \theta(x)|^2 \, dx$$

$$\le e^2 \int_{-1}^{1} |\theta(x)|^2 \, dx.$$

In particular, choosing ω_k in B_k to maximize $|\tilde{\theta}(\omega_k)|^2$ and so give b_k, (11.1.13) now follows. $\qquad\qquad\square$

Returning to the right-hand side of (11.1.12), express the integral there as a sum of integrals over regions B_k as in the lemma. For each term we then have

$$\int_{B_k} |\tilde{f}(\omega)|^2 \mu(d\omega) \le b_k \mu(B_k) \le K b_k$$

for some finite constant K, using the translation boundedness property. Finiteness of the integral follows on summing over k and using (11.1.13).

Another integrability result is noted in Exercise 11.1.8.

EXAMPLE 11.1(b). As a simple illustration of (11.1.12), let $f(x)$ be the indicator function of the hyper-rectangle $(0, T_1] \times \cdots \times (0, T_d]$. It then follows that

$$\int_{\mathbb{R}^d} \prod_{i=1}^{d} (T_i - |x_i|)_+ \, v(dx) = \int_{\mathbb{R}^d} \prod_{i=1}^{d} \left(\frac{\sin(\omega_i T_i/2)}{\omega_i/2} \right)^2 \mu(d\omega).$$

Exercises

11.1.1. *The space $\mathscr{S}$.*
   (a) Show that if $\mathscr{X} = \mathbb{R}$ and $\psi \colon \mathbb{R} \to \mathbb{R}$ has an integrable kth derivative then $|\omega^k \tilde{\psi}(\omega)| \to 0$ as $|\omega| \to \infty$, and that, conversely, if $\int_{-\infty}^{\infty} |x|^k |\psi(x)| \, dx < \infty$ then $\tilde{\psi}(\omega)$ is k-times differentiable. Deduce that $\mathscr{S}$ is invariant under the Fourier mapping taking ψ into $\tilde{\psi}$. Extend the result to $\mathbb{R}^d$.
   (b) Let $g \colon \mathbb{R}^d \to \mathbb{R}$ be an integrable function with Fourier transform $\tilde{g}$ such that both g and $\tilde{g}$ are zero free on $\mathbb{R}^d$. Show that both the mappings $\psi \to \psi * g$ and $\tilde{\psi} \to \tilde{\psi} g$ are one-to-one mappings of $\mathscr{S}$ onto itself. In particular, deduce that this result holds when $\psi(\cdot)$ has the double exponential form $e_\lambda(\cdot)$ of (11.1.4b).
   (c) Show that if μ, v are boundedly finite measures on $\mathbb{R}$ such that $\int_{\mathbb{R}} \psi \, d\mu = \int_{\mathbb{R}} \psi \, dv$ for all $\psi \in \mathscr{S}$, then $\mu = v$. [*Hint:* Consider $\psi \in \mathscr{S}$ of bounded support, and approximate indicator functions.] Extend to $\mathbb{R}^d$.

11.1.2. Let $\{c_n \colon n = 0, \pm 1, \ldots\}$ denote a doubly infinite sequence of reals. Say that $\{c_n\}$ is
   (i) *transformable* if there exists a measure v on $[0, 2\pi]$ such that $c_n = \int_0^{2\pi} e^{i\omega n} v(d\omega)$;

(ii) *positive-definite* if for all finite families $\{\alpha_1, \ldots, \alpha_k\}$ of complex numbers,

$$\sum_{i=1}^{k} \sum_{j=1}^{k} \alpha_i \bar{\alpha}_j c_{i-j} \geq 0.$$

Let $\mathscr{P}^+(\mathbb{Z})$ denote the class of all p.p.d. sequences and $\mathscr{P}^+(0, 2\pi]$ the class of all p.p.d. measures on $(0, 2\pi]$. Show that every $\{c_n\} \in \mathscr{P}^+(\mathbb{Z})$ is bounded, transformable, and symmetric [i.e., $c_n = c_{-n}$ (all n)], and that a one-to-one mapping between $\mathscr{P}^+(\mathbb{Z})$ and $\mathscr{P}^+(0, 2\pi]$ is defined by requiring the Parseval relation

$$\sum_{j=1}^{k} a_j c_j = \int_0^{2\pi} \tilde{a}(\omega) v(d\omega)$$

to hold for all $\tilde{a}(\omega) = \sum_{j=1}^{k} a_j e^{i\omega j}$, where $a_1, \ldots, a_k$ is any finite sequence of reals.

11.1.3. Show that not all translation bounded sequences are transformable. [*Hint*: Let $\mathscr{X} = \mathbb{R}$, and exhibit a sequence that is bounded but for which $T^{-1} \sum_{j=-T}^{T} c_j$ does not converge to a limit as $T \to \infty$. Use this to define an atomic measure on $\mathbb{R}$ that is not transformable.]

11.1.4. *Poisson summation formula.* Show that if both ψ and $\tilde{\psi}$ are integrable on $\mathbb{R}$, then

$$\sum_{k=-\infty}^{\infty} \tilde{\psi}(2\pi k + x) = \sum_{j=-\infty}^{\infty} \psi(j) e^{-ijx}$$

whenever the left-hand side defines a continuous function of x. [*Hint*: Under the stated conditions, the left-hand side, $a(x)$ say, is a bounded continuous function of x. Denote by $a_n = (2\pi)^{-1} \int_0^{2\pi} e^{inx} a(x) dx$ its nth Fourier coefficient, and show by rearrangement that $a_n = \psi(-n)$. Then the relation is just the representation of $a(\cdot)$ in terms of its Fourier series. Observe that the conditions hold for $\psi \in \mathscr{S}$, and that the formula in Example 11.1(a) (iii) is the special case $x = 0$.]

11.1.5. Show that any p.p.d. measure on $\mathbb{R}$ integrates $(1 + \omega^2)^{-\alpha}$ for $\alpha > \frac{1}{2}$, and hence conclude that any p.p.d. measure is a *tempered measure* in the language of generalised functions.

11.1.6. (a) Let $c(x) = |x|^{-1/2}$ $(|x| \leq 1)$, $= 0$ elsewhere, and set $g(\omega) = 4 - \int_{-\infty}^{\infty} e^{i\omega x} c(x) dx$. Show that the measure G with density g is nonnegative and translation bounded but cannot be made into a p.p.d. measure by adding an atom at the origin.

(b) Show that the measure defined on bounded $A \in \mathscr{B}$ by

$$v(A) = \int_A (2 - \sin|x|)^{-1} dx$$

is a spectral measure but is not a transform (Thornett, 1979).

11.1.7. Show that for $1 < \gamma < 2$ the following functions are densities of p.p.d. measures in $\mathbb{R}^2$, and find their spectral measures:

(a) $c_1(x, y) = \{\sin(\gamma\pi/2)\Gamma(\gamma + 1)/2\pi\}^2 |xy|^{1-\gamma}$;

(b) $c_2(x, y) = 2^{2(\gamma-2)}\pi^{\gamma-3}(\Gamma(2 - \gamma))^{-1} |x^2 + y^2|^{1-\gamma}$.

[*Hint*: Both spectral measures are absolutely continuous with densities $g_1(\omega_1, \omega_2) = [\gamma(\gamma - 1)/2]^2 |\omega_1 \omega_2|^{\gamma-2}$ and $g_2(\omega_1, \omega_2) = \pi^{\gamma-2}(\Gamma(\gamma - 1))^{-1} |\omega_1^2 +$

$\omega_2^2|^{-2}$, respectively. See Thornett (1979) who gives formulae for similar p.p.d. measures in $\mathbb{R}^d$.]

11.1.8. A nonnegative Borel measure μ on $\mathscr{B}(\mathbb{R}^d)$ satisfies

$$\int_{\mathbb{R}^d} |\tilde{I}_A(\omega)|^2 \mu(d\omega) < \infty \quad \text{(all bounded } A \in \mathscr{B}(\mathbb{R}^d))$$

if and only if the measure μ is translation bounded. [*Hint*: Establish a converse to Lemma 11.1.V of the form

$$\int |\tilde{f}(\omega)|^2 \mu(d\omega) \le K^2 \sup_{x \in A} |f(x)|^2,$$

where f, with Fourier transform $\tilde{f}$, is any bounded measurable function vanishing outside the bounded Borel set A and K is an absolute constant that may depend only on μ. See Robertson and Thornett (1984) for further detail. Other results and references for such measures, but on locally compact Abelian groups, are given in Bloom (1984).]

11.2. The Bartlett Spectrum

Now suppose that ξ is a second-order stationary random measure on $\mathbb{R}^d$. Its reduced second moment measure $\hat{M}_2(\cdot)$ is clearly nonnegative, and the fact that $\hat{M}_2(\cdot)$ is also positive definite is an immediate consequence of the inequalities, valid for all measurable ϕ,

$$\int_{\mathbb{R}^d} \hat{M}_2(dx) \int_{\mathbb{R}^d} \phi(u)\overline{\phi(x+u)}\,du = E\left|\int_{\mathbb{R}^d} \phi(u)\xi(du)\right|^2 \ge 0.$$

From this it follows that $\hat{M}_2$ is a p.p.d. measure, and the results of the preceding section apply; by convention we identify $\hat{M}_2$ with v. The reduced covariance measure is also positive definite—just replace the expectation above by the variance of $\int_{\mathbb{R}^d} \phi(u)\xi(du)$—but it need not be positive. However, since it is derived from the reduced second moment measure by subtracting the multiple $m^2 l(\cdot)$ of Lebesgue measure, where m is the density, it is just the difference of two p.p.d. measures, and all the results for such measures given in Section 11.1, including the different versions of the Parseval relation and the inversion theorem, continue to apply. A similar remark applies to the reduced second factorial moment measure and the corresponding factorial cumulant measure, where it is a matter of subtracting an atom at the origin. These results can be summed up as below.

Proposition 11.2.I. *Let ξ be a second-order stationary random measure on $\mathbb{R}^d$. Then*

(i) *the reduced second moment and covariance measures, and (in the point process case) the reduced second factorial moment and cumulant measures, are symmetric and translation bounded; and*

(ii) *each such measure can be represented as the Fourier transform [in the sense of (11.1.1)] of a spectral measure, which is also symmetric and translation bounded, and the relations (11.1.6)–(11.1.10) and (11.1.12) hold (with μ identified as the spectral measure and v as the reduced measure).*

Any one of these four measures could be taken as the basis for further development of the spectral theory. It is convenient, and consistent with the standard time-series convention, to choose as the spectrum of the process ξ the inverse Fourier transform of the (ordinary) covariance measure.

Definition 11.2.II. The *Bartlett spectrum* of a second-order stationary point process or random measure is the boundedly finite measure, $\Gamma(\cdot)$ say, associated with the reduced covariance measure $\hat{C}_2$ by the Parseval relation

$$(11.2.1) \qquad \int_{\mathbb{R}^d} \psi(x)\hat{C}_2(dx) = \int_{\mathbb{R}^d} \tilde{\psi}(\omega)\Gamma(d\omega) \qquad (\psi \in \mathcal{S}).$$

It follows from Proposition 11.2.I that Γ is symmetric, translation bounded, and (see Corollary 11.1.IV) satisfies the relation

$$(11.2.2) \qquad \int_{\mathbb{R}^d} |\tilde{\psi}(\omega)|^2 \Gamma(d\omega) = \operatorname{var}\left(\int_{\mathbb{R}^d} \psi(x)\xi(dx)\right) \geq 0$$

both for $\psi \in \mathcal{S}$ and also for bounded measurable ψ with bounded support. It is clear from (11.2.2), since $|\tilde{\psi}|^2 \geq 0$, that Γ is a positive measure. It is not in general a p.p.d. measure, but since the reduced second moment measure $\hat{M}_2$ is a positive measure and is the Fourier transform of the positive measure $\Gamma(\cdot) + (m^2/(2\pi)^d)\delta_0(\cdot)$, $\Gamma(\cdot)$ can be made into a p.p.d. measure by the addition of a sufficiently large atom at the origin.

Equation (11.2.2) is generally the most convenient result to use in establishing the form of the Bartlett spectrum for a given process. We note in particular the special case for $\mathcal{X} = \mathbb{R}$ and ϕ the indicator function for $(0, t]$,

$$(11.2.3) \qquad \operatorname{var} \xi(0, t] = \int_{\mathbb{R}} \left(\frac{\sin \frac{1}{2}\omega t}{\frac{1}{2}\omega}\right)^2 \Gamma(d\omega),$$

which is essentially Daley's (1971) representation for the variance function of a point process or random measure. In the point process case, the reduced covariance measure has an atom at the origin of mass equal to the mean square batch size times the intensity (see Proposition 3.3.IX for $d = 1$ and Exercise 7.4.4 for the more general result). This atom transforms into a multiple of Lebesgue measure, and consequently the Bartlett spectrum of a point process is never totally finite. For simple point processes, the atom has mass m, and so the reduced factorial (as distinct from ordinary) covariance measure then has no atom at the origin. Moreover, in many applications the factorial covariance measure is both absolutely continuous and totally finite. In these circumstances $\Gamma(\cdot)$ is absolutely continuous with a density $\gamma(\cdot)$, which can be written (for the case $d = 1$)

(11.2.4)
$$2\pi\gamma(\omega) = m + \int_{-\infty}^{\infty} e^{-i\omega x} c_{[2]}(x)dx$$

$$= m + \tilde{c}_{[2]}(-\omega) = m + \tilde{c}_{[2]}(\omega).$$

It was in this form that the spectral measure was originally introduced by Bartlett (1963).

EXAMPLE 11.2(a) *Poisson process with constant intensity.* Here $\hat{C}_2$ consists only of the atom $m\delta_0(\cdot)$ so Γ is absolutely continuous with density $m/(2\pi)^d$. This "white noise" spectrum is consistent with the completely random character of the process. Note that the Parseval equations (11.2.1) and (11.2.2) take, respectively, the special forms

$$m\psi(0) = \frac{m}{(2\pi)^d} \int_{\mathbb{R}^d} \tilde{\psi}(\omega)d\omega$$

and

$$m \int_{\mathbb{R}^d} |\phi(x)|^2 \, dx = \frac{m}{(2\pi)^d} \int_{\mathbb{R}^d} |\tilde{\phi}(\omega)|^2 \, d\omega.$$

EXAMPLE 11.2(b) *Stationary renewal process.* If the renewal density $h(t)$ exists and the difference $h(t) - \mu^{-1}$ is integrable on $(0, \infty)$, (11.2.4) yields for $\omega \neq 0$

(11.2.5) $\gamma(\omega) = (2\pi\mu)^{-1}\{1 + \tilde{F}(\omega)(1 - \tilde{F}(\omega))^{-1} + \tilde{F}(-\omega)(1 - \tilde{F}(-\omega))^{-1}\}$

$$= (2\pi\mu)^{-1}\{(1 - \tilde{F}(\omega))^{-1} + (1 - \tilde{F}(-\omega))^{-1} - 1\},$$

where $\tilde{F}(\omega) = \int_0^\infty e^{i\omega x} \, dF(x)$ is the characteristic function of the lifetime distribution. For $\omega = 0$ we obtain

$$\gamma(0) = \frac{1}{2\pi\mu}\left(1 + \frac{\sigma^2 + \mu^2}{\mu^2}\right) = \frac{1}{2\pi\mu}\left(1 + \int_0^\infty \left(h(u) - \frac{1}{\mu}\right)du\right).$$

Since a stationary renewal process has moment measures of all orders whenever it exists, the Bartlett spectrum exists for all such processes but may not be absolutely continuous or (even if it is) $\gamma(0)$ need not be finite as above. The following extreme case is worth particular mention.

EXAMPLE 11.2(c) *Stationary deterministic process.* Here points occur on a regular lattice of span a, the whole lattice being randomly shifted so that the first point to the right of the origin is uniformly distributed on $(0, a]$. The measure $\hat{M}_2(\cdot)$ has the infinite sum form of Example 11.1(a)(iii), with mass $1/a$ at each of the points ka ($k = 0, \pm1, \ldots$). Its Fourier transform has mass a^{-2} at each of the points $2\pi j/a$ ($j = 0, \pm1, \ldots$). Moving to the Fourier transform of the covariance measure deletes the atom at $j = 0$, so that $\Gamma(\cdot)$ can be written in terms of Dirac measures as

(11.2.6) $$\Gamma(A) = a^{-2} \sum_{j=1}^{\infty} \{\delta_{2\pi j/a}(A) + \delta_{-2\pi j/a}(A)\}.$$

EXAMPLE 11.2(d) *Cluster processes.* For a general cluster process in $\mathbb{R}^d$, the variance of an integral $\int_{\mathbb{R}^d} \phi(x)N(dx)$ can be written in the form (see Exercise 8.2.3)

$$(11.2.7) \quad \text{var}\left(\int_{\mathbb{R}^d} \phi(x)N(dx)\right) = \int_{\mathbb{R}^d} V_2(u)M^c(du)$$
$$+ \int_{\mathbb{R}^d} \int_{\mathbb{R}^d} m(u)m(v)C_2^c(du \times dv),$$

where

$$m(u) = \int_{\mathbb{R}^d} \phi(x)M_1(dx|u), \qquad V_2(u) = \int_{\mathbb{R}^d} \int_{\mathbb{R}^d} \phi(s)\phi(t)C_2(ds \times dt|u)$$

and we use the notation of Section 8.2. In the stationary case, $M^c(du) = m^c\, du$, where m^c is the mean density of the cluster centre process, while C_2^c has a reduced form that can be written in terms of the Bartlett spectrum Γ^c of the cluster centre process. Since also $C_2(ds \times dt|y)$ depends only on the differences $s - y$ and $t - y$, the first term in (11.2.7) can be written in terms of the measure B defined by

$$\int_{\mathbb{R}^d} h(y)B(dy) = \int_{\mathbb{R}^d} \int_{\mathbb{R}^d} h(s - t)C_2(ds \times dt|0).$$

Here the measure B is both positive definite and totally finite (since the mean square cluster size is necessarily finite); it has therefore an ordinary Fourier transform $\tilde{B}(\omega) = (2\pi)^{-d}\int_{\mathbb{R}^d} e^{-i\omega \cdot x}B(dx)$, which can be written in the symmetric form

$$\tilde{B}(\omega) = \text{var}\left(\int_{\mathbb{R}^d} e^{-i\omega \cdot x}N_m(dx|0)\right),$$

where, it should be recalled, var $Z = E|Z|^2 - |EZ|^2$ for a complex-valued r.v. Z. Thus, writing

$$\tilde{M}_1(\omega|0) = \int_{\mathbb{R}^d} e^{-i\omega \cdot x}M_1(dx|0) = E \int_{\mathbb{R}^d} e^{-i\omega \cdot x}N_m(dx|0),$$

we obtain from (11.2.7)

$$\text{var}\left(\int_{\mathbb{R}^d} \phi(x)N(dx)\right) = \int_{\mathbb{R}^d} |\tilde{\phi}(\omega)|^2[\tilde{B}(\omega)m^c(2\pi)^{-d}\, d\omega + |\tilde{M}_1(\omega|0)|^2\Gamma^c(d\omega)].$$

This relation shows that the Bartlett spectrum of the cluster process N can be identified with the measure

$$(11.2.8) \qquad \Gamma(d\omega) = \tilde{B}(\omega)m^c(2\pi)^{-d}\, d\omega + |\tilde{M}_1(\omega|0)|^2\Gamma^c(d\omega).$$

This first term can be regarded as the contribution to the spectrum from the internal cluster structure; the second term is a filtered version of the spectrum of the cluster centre process with the filtering reflecting the mean distribution of the cluster.

For a Poisson cluster process further simplification occurs; Γ then has a density γ, which has the simple alternative forms

$$(11.2.9) \quad \gamma(\omega) = \frac{m^c}{(2\pi)^d}\left[\int_{\mathbb{R}^d} M_1(dx|0) + \int_{\mathbb{R}^d}\int_{\mathbb{R}^d} e^{-iy\cdot\omega} M_{[2]}(dx \times dy|0)\right]$$

$$= \frac{m^c}{(2\pi)^d} E\left|\int_{\mathbb{R}^d} e^{ix\cdot\omega} N_m(dx|0)\right|^2,$$

which is easily recognized as the transformed version of (8.3.6). Specific results for the Neyman–Scott and Bartlett–Lewis processes follow readily from these equations (see Exercises 11.2.6 and 11.2.7).

By suitable specifications of the components, both renewal and cluster processes can give rise to spectral measures with rational spectral densities. For example, it is clear from (11.2.5) that this will occur whenever the interval distribution of a renewal process has a rational Laplace transform, that is, whenever the distribution is expressible as a finite convolution or mixture of exponentials. Several types of cluster processes, as well as Cox processes, have rational spectral densities, in particular the Neyman–Scott process with an exponential or Erlang distribution for the distances of the cluster elements from the cluster centre [see also Exercise 11.2.6(b)]. The wide choice of such examples shows not only the richness of the class, but also the relative lack of discrimination in the spectrum as a means of distinguishing between processes whose characters in other respects may be quite dissimilar.

Another difficulty is that there is no obvious candidate to act as the canonical family of point processes with rational spectral density to be used in graduating point process spectra in the way that autoregressive and moving average (ARMA) processes can be used to graduate the spectra of standard time series. One possible contender for such a family is the Hawkes (self-exciting) process with a suitable choice of the infectivity function $\mu(\cdot)$. The possibility of using the Hawkes process in this way was explored by Hawkes (1971b), Hawkes and Adamopoulos (1973), and, more deliberately, by Ogata and Akaike (1982), with an application in Ogata et al. (1982). In Hawkes and Adamopoulos a method of parameter estimation based on the sample periodogram is used, while in Ozaki (1979) and Ogata and Akaike a maximum likelihood approach is advocated. The latter procedure is more flexible and more likely to be successful in modelling the process as a whole, but even so a Hawkes process is useful as a model only in those relatively limited circumstances where a suitable kind of clustering is present.

EXAMPLE 11.2(e) *Hawkes process with rational spectral density* (continued from Example 10.4(c)). We have (cf. also Exercise 5.5.6)

$$\tilde{M}_1(\omega|0) = [1 - \tilde{\mu}(\omega)]^{-1}, \quad \text{where} \quad \tilde{\mu}(\omega) = \int_0^\infty e^{i\omega x}\mu(dx)$$

is the Fourier–Stieltjes transform of the infectivity measure. Similarly, from

(10.4.24) and (11.2.8) we find the spectral density for the process as

(11.2.10) $$\gamma(\omega) = (\lambda/2\pi)(1 - v)^{-1}|1 - \tilde{\mu}(\omega)|^{-2}.$$

Ogata and Akaike (1982) suggest taking for μ a measure on $[0, \infty)$ with density (for some suitably chosen r)

$$e^{-\beta x} \sum_{j=0}^{r} \alpha_j x^j,$$

where β and $\alpha_0, \ldots, \alpha_r$ are fitted either directly from this form or after representation through Laguerre polynomials. There are various examples in the papers cited and in Vere-Jones and Ozaki (1982). In principle, the parameters should be constrained so as to ensure that the density is nonnegative; for stationarity they must yield total mass < 1.

The form of (11.2.10) is that of an autoregression in continuous time, and this has led some authors to suggest that the Hawkes model might have a role to play similar to that of autoregressive models in the context of mean square continuous processes. Unfortunately, this hope is frustrated by the special probabilistic structure of the Hawkes model, which requires that $\mu(\cdot) \geq 0$. If this condition is violated, it is not clear that there exists any point process with the spectral form (11.2.10), and if such a process does exist it certainly will not have the Poisson branching structure of a Hawkes process. Within this somewhat restricted range, however, the Hawkes model is one of the most flexible models available in that it allows both the calculation of the form of the spectrum and the investigation of probabilistic aspects of the process.

We conclude this section with a brief review of some open problems and further extensions of the work outlined above.

An outstanding open problem is the determination of the class of measures that can appear as the Bartlett spectrum either of a random measure or of a point process. More specifically, we do not know whether every p.p.d. measure can arise as the second moment measure of some random measure, nor, when it does, how to construct a process yielding the given measure as its second moment measure. The standard construction using Gaussian processes or measures is not available here, as such processes do not have nonnegative trajectories [cf. Example 10.4(c)!]. Davidson (1974b) provided a construction for random measures on the circle (see Exercise 11.1.2 and Proposition 11.5.I below), but it relies on the finiteness of the invariant measure on a circle, and it is not obvious how it might be extended to either point processes or random measures on the line.

Only partial results are available for the extension of the above theory to random signed measures. Thornett (1979) developed a wide-sense second-order theory in which a second-order random measure is defined as a family of random variables $\{W(A)\}$ with finite first and second moments, indexed by the Borel sets, satisfying the additivity and continuity requirements (6.1.7) and (6.1.8), and second-order stationary. The resulting theory may be regarded as a natural generalization to $\mathbb{R}^d$ of the theory of random interval functions developed by Bochner (1955) and extended and applied to a statistical context by Brillinger (1972). Similarly, only partial analogues of the results presented in Section 11.1 can be carried over to the general wide-sense context. Their main usefulness is in connection with spectral representations for the process, and we therefore postpone a more detailed discussion to Section 11.3. Some results for multivariate and marked point processes are given in Section 11.5.

Exercises

11.2.1. *Superposition.*
(a) Show that if ξ_1, ξ_2 are independent second-order stationary random measures with Bartlett spectra Γ_1, Γ_2, respectively, then $\xi_1 + \xi_2$ has spectrum $\Gamma_1 + \Gamma_2$.
(b) More generally, if ξ_1, ξ_2, ... are independent second-order stationary random measures such that the L_2 limit

$$\xi = \xi_1 + \xi_2 + \cdots$$

exists, then ξ has Bartlett spectrum $\Gamma_1 + \Gamma_2 + \cdots$.

11.2.2. *Cox process.* Let ξ be a second-order stationary random measure on $\mathbb{R}^d$ with Bartlett spectrum Γ and mean density m. Show that the Cox process directed by ξ has Bartlett spectrum $\Gamma(\cdot) + m(2\pi)^{-d}\ell(\cdot)$, where $\ell(\cdot)$ denotes Lebesgue measure on $\mathbb{R}^d$.

11.2.3. *Quadratic random measure.* [Compare Examples 6.1(b) and 6.4(c).]
(a) Let $Z_i(t)$ $(i = 1, 2)$ be independent mean square continuous second-order stationary random processes on $\mathbb{R}$ with respective spectral d.f.s F_i and zero mean. Show that the product $Z_1 Z_2$ is a mean square continuous second-order stationary process with spectral measure $F_1 * F_2$.
(b) If Z is a mean square continuous stationary Gaussian process with spectral d.f. F and zero mean, then the quadratic random measure whose sample paths have density $Z^2(\cdot)$ has covariance density $2|c(\cdot)|^2$ and Bartlett spectrum $2F * F$, where $c(x) = \text{cov}(Z(0), Z(x))$.
(c) Investigate what changes are needed in (a) and (b) when the zero mean assumption is omitted.

11.2.4. *Random translations.* Let the point process N be second-order stationary with Bartlett spectrum Γ and mean density m. If the points of N are subjected to independent random translation with common d.f. F, show that the resultant point process N_T has Bartlett spectrum

$$\Gamma_T(d\omega) = |\tilde{F}(\omega)|^2\Gamma(d\omega) + m(2\pi)^{-d}(1 - |\tilde{F}(\omega)|^2)\ell(d\omega).$$

11.2.5. *Iterated random translations.* Let the independent translation of points of N as in Exercise 11.2.4 be iterated n times. Show that the Bartlett spectrum Γ_n of the resulting process satisfies

$$\Gamma_n(d\omega) = |\tilde{F}(\omega)|^2\Gamma_{n-1}(d\omega) + m(2\pi)^{-d}(1 - |\tilde{F}(\omega)|^2)\ell(d\omega)$$

$$= |\tilde{F}(\omega)|^{2n}\Gamma(d\omega) + m(2\pi)^{-d}(1 - |\tilde{F}(\omega)|^{2n})\ell(d\omega),$$

and hence give conditions for $\Gamma_n(\cdot)$ to converge weakly to $m(2\pi)^{-d}\ell(\cdot)$. (cf. Section 9.4).

11.2.6. *Neyman–Scott process* [continued from Example 8.3(a)].

(a) Show that the Bartlett spectrum for a Neyman–Scott process on $\mathbb{R}$, with (Poisson) cluster centre process at rate μ, $m_{[1]}$ and $m_{[2]}$ for the first two factorial moments of the cluster size distribution, and common d.f. F for the distances of the points of a cluster from their centre, has density $\gamma_{NS}(\omega)$ given by

$$\gamma_{NS}(\omega) = (\mu/2\pi)[m_{[1]} + m_{[2]}|\tilde{F}(\omega)|^2],$$

where $\tilde{F}(\omega) = \int_{-\infty}^{\infty} e^{ix\omega} F(dx)$.

(b) In the particular case that $F(x) = 1 - e^{-\alpha x}$ ($x \geq 0$), deduce that $\gamma_{NS}(\cdot)$ is the rational function

$$\gamma_{NS}(\omega) = (\mu m_{[1]}/2\pi)[1 + (\alpha^2 m_{[2]}/m_{[1]})(\alpha^2 + \omega^2)^{-1}].$$

(c) When the Neyman–Scott process is as above on $\mathbb{R}^d$, show that

$$\gamma_{NS}(\omega) = (\mu m_{[1]}/(2\pi)^d)[1 + (m_{[2]}/m_{[1]})|\tilde{F}(\omega)|^2]$$

with $\tilde{F}(\omega) = \int_{\mathbb{R}^d} e^{ix\cdot\omega} F(dx)$. Deduce that when $d = 2$ and $F(\cdot)$ is a bivariate normal d.f. with zero mean and the usual second moment parameters σ_1^2, σ_2^2, and $\rho\sigma_1\sigma_2$, the spectrum has density

$$\gamma_{NS}(\omega_1, \omega_2) = \frac{\mu m_{[1]}}{4\pi^2}\left[1 + \frac{m_{[2]}}{m_{[1]}}\exp(-\sigma_1^2\omega_1^2 - 2\rho\sigma_1\sigma_2\omega_1\omega_2 - \rho_2^2\omega_2^2)\right].$$

(d) Show that if in (a) the cluster structure is modified so as to include the cluster centre, then

$$\gamma_{NS}(\omega) = (\mu/2\pi)[1 + m_{[1]}(1 + \tilde{F}(\omega) + \tilde{F}(-\omega)) + m_{[2]}|\tilde{F}(\omega)|^2].$$

(e) Show that if in (a) the cluster center process is a general stationary point process with mean intensity μ and Bartlett spectrum $\Gamma(\cdot)$, then the Bartlett spectrum $\Gamma_{NS}(\cdot)$ of the cluster process is given by

$$\Gamma_{NS}(d\omega) = |m_{[1]}\tilde{F}(\omega)|^2\Gamma(d\omega) + (\mu/2\pi)[m_{[1]} + (m_{[2]} - m_{[1]}^2)|\tilde{F}(\omega)|^2]\ell(d\omega).$$

[*Hint*: Except for (d), the results can be derived, first by compounding, and then by using random translations as in Exercise 11.2.4.]

11.2.7. *Bartlett–Lewis model* [continued from Example 8.3(b)].

(a) Use (8.3.17) to show that the Bartlett spectrum has density $\gamma_{BL}(\cdot)$ given by

$$\gamma_{BL}(\omega) = \left(\frac{\mu}{2\pi}\right)\left\{\sum_{j=0}^{\infty}(j + 1)q_j + \sum_{j=1}^{\infty}\sum_{k=j}^{\infty}(k + 1 - j)q_k(\tilde{F}^j(\omega) + \tilde{F}^j(-\omega))\right\}.$$

Observe that $\gamma_{BL}(\omega) = \gamma_{NS}(\omega)$ as in (d) of Exercise 11.2.6 in the cases $q_1 = 1$ and $m_{[1]} = 1$, $m_{[2]} = 0$, respectively.

(b) Show that when $q_j = (1 - \alpha)\alpha^j$ ($j = 0, 1, \ldots$) with $0 < \alpha < 1$, so that each cluster is a transient renewal process,

$$\gamma_{BL}(\omega) = (\mu(1 - \alpha)^{-1}/2\pi)\{(1 - \alpha\tilde{F}(\omega))^{-1} + (1 - \alpha\tilde{F}(-\omega))^{-1} - 1\},$$

while when $q_0 = 0$, $q_j = (1 - \alpha)\alpha^{j-1}$ $(j = 1, 2, \ldots)$,

$$\gamma_{\mathrm{BL}}(\omega) = (\mu\alpha^{-1}(1 - \alpha)^{-1}/2\pi)\{(1 - \alpha\tilde{F}(\omega))^{-1} + (1 - \alpha\tilde{F}(-\omega))^{-1}$$
$$- 1 - (1 - \alpha)^2\}.$$

(c) The formulae in parts (a) and (b) assume that the cluster centre is included in the cluster process. Show that the omission of the cluster centres leads to

$$\gamma_{\mathrm{BL}}(\omega) = \frac{\mu}{2\pi}\left\{\sum_{j=1}^{\infty} jq_j + \sum_{j=1}^{\infty}\sum_{k=j+1}^{\infty} (k - j)q_k(\tilde{F}^j(\omega) + \tilde{F}^j(-\omega))\right\}$$
$$= \frac{\mu}{2\pi}\left\{\sum_{j=1}^{\infty} jq_j + \sum_{j=2}^{\infty} q_j\sum_{k=1}^{j-1} (j - k)(\tilde{F}^k(\omega) + \tilde{F}^k(-\omega))\right\}.$$

11.2.8. Let M_2 be a p.p.d. measure on $\mathscr{B}_{\mathbb{R}}$ with density m_2. Show that if $0 < a \leq m_2(x) \leq b < \infty$ (all x) then there exists a zero-mean Gaussian process $X(t)$ such that $m_2(x) = E[X^2(t)X^2(t + x)]$, and hence that M_2 is the reduced second moment measure of the process $\xi(A) = \int_A X^2(t)dt$ $(A \in \mathscr{B}_{\mathbb{R}})$. Deduce that any p.p.d. function $c_2(\cdot)$ can be a reduced covariance density, with $m_2(x) = a + c_2(x)$ for some $a > 0$.

11.2.9. Let F be any totally bounded symmetric measure $\mathbb{R}^d$. Show that F can be a covariance measure. [*Hint*: Construct a Gauss–Poisson process, and compare with Proposition 8.3.II. See Milne and Westcott (1972) for further details.]

11.2.10. Use Theorem 10.2.IV, the inversion result at (11.1.8), and the identification of the Bartlett spectrum as in Definition 11.2.II to show that for a nonergodic second-order stationary random measure ξ on $\mathbb{R}^d$,

$$\Gamma(\{0\}) = \mathrm{var}(Y),$$

where $Y = E(\xi(\mathbb{U}^d)|\mathscr{I})$ as at (10.2.11).

11.3. The Spectral Representation

A Cramér-type spectral representation for the process can be established by straightforward extensions of the arguments used in Section 11.2. In $\mathbb{R}$ this representation is essentially a corollary of the spectral representation for processes with stationary increments given by Doob (1949) and for stationary interval functions given by Brillinger (1972). Minor variations arise as a result of the additional properties available for p.p.d. measures. We give a brief but essentially self-contained account of the representation theory for random measures in $\mathbb{R}^d$ following the general lines of the approach in Vere-Jones (1974). The relation to spectral representations for stationary generalized processes is discussed in Daley (1971) and Jowett and Vere-Jones (1972).

So as to be consistent with the representation theory for continuous time processes, we work throughout with the process

$$\xi^0(dx) = \xi(dx) - m\,dx$$

with zero mean, where ξ is a second-order stationary random measure with mean density m. Thus, we are concerned with properties of the Bartlett spectrum rather than the Fourier transform of the reduced second moment measure, although the properties of the latter, as a p.p.d. measure, are what give the theory its special features. An equivalent and perhaps slightly more direct theory could be built up from the properties of $\xi(\cdot)$ and the second moment measure: the differences are outlined in Exercise 11.3.1.

The essence of the Cramér representation is an isomorphism between two Hilbert spaces, one of random variables defined on a probability space and the other of functions on the state space $\mathscr{X} = \mathbb{R}^d$. In the present context we use the notation $L_2(\xi^0)$ to denote the Hilbert space of (equivalence classes of) random variables formed from linear combinations of the second-order random variables $\xi^0(A)$ (bounded $A \in \mathscr{B}_{\mathscr{X}}$) and their mean square limits, while $L_2(\Gamma)$ denotes the Hilbert space of (equivalence classes of) measurable functions square integrable with respect to Γ. Since Γ is not in general totally finite, we cannot apply directly the theory for mean square continuous processes. Rather, there are two possible routes to the required representations: we can exploit the results already available for continuous processes by means of the smoothing techniques used in Sections 11.1 and 11.2, or we can develop the theory from first principles, using appropriate modifications of the classical proofs where necessary. The latter approach seems more illuminating although we only sketch the arguments where they directly mimic the standard theory.

A convenient starting point is the following lemma in which, as in Section 11.1, $\mathscr{S}$ denotes the space of all infinitely differentiable functions of rapid decay in $\mathbb{R}^d$.

Lemma 11.3.I. *Given any boundedly finite measure Γ in $\mathbb{R}^d$, the space $\mathscr{S}$ is dense in $L_2(\Gamma)$.*

PROOF. The result is a minor modification of standard results [e.g., see Kingman and Taylor (1966, p. 131) and Exercise 11.3.2]. $\qquad\square$

The key step in establishing the isomorphism is the equivalence of norms asserted in Corollary 11.1.IV, which, with the notation

$$(11.3.1) \qquad \zeta_f = \int_{\mathbb{R}^d} f(x)\xi^0(dx),$$

where f is a bounded Borel function of bounded support, can be stated in the form

$$(11.3.2) \quad \|\tilde{f}\|_{L_2(\Gamma)} = \int_{\mathbb{R}^d} |\tilde{f}(w)|^2 \Gamma(dw)$$

$$= \int_{\mathbb{R}^d} \hat{C}_2(dx) \int_{\mathbb{R}^d} f(x)f(x+u)\,du = \mathrm{var}(\zeta_f) = \|\zeta_f\|_{L_2(\xi^0)}.$$

A first corollary of this equality of norms is the following counterpart of Lemma 11.3.I.

Lemma 11.3.II. *For $\psi \in \mathscr{S}$, the random integrals ζ_ψ as at (11.3.1) are dense in $L_2(\xi^0)$.*

PROOF. It is enough to show that for any given bounded $A \in \mathscr{B}(\mathbb{R}^d)$, $\xi^0(A)$ can be approximated in mean square by elements ζ_{ψ_n} with $\psi_n \in \mathscr{S}$. Working from the Fourier transform side, it follows from Proposition 11.1.IV that $\tilde{I}_A \in L_2(\Gamma)$, and thus by Lemma 11.3.I that $\tilde{I}_A$ can be approximated by a sequence of functions in $\mathscr{S}$. Now $\mathscr{S}$ is invariant under the Fourier transform map, so this sequence can be written as $\tilde{\psi}_n$ with $\psi_n \in \mathscr{S}$. Applying (11.3.2) with $\psi = I_A - \psi_n$, leads to

$$\|\tilde{I}_A - \tilde{\psi}_n\|_{L_2(\Gamma)} = \|\xi^0(A) - \zeta_{\psi_n}\|_{L_2(\xi^0)}.$$

By construction, the left-hand side $\to 0$ as $n \to \infty$, and hence also the right-hand side $\to 0$, which in view of our opening remark is all that is required.   □

Lemmas 11.3.I and 11.3.II show that for $\psi \in \mathscr{S}$ there is a correspondence $\tilde{\psi} \leftrightarrow \mathscr{Z}_\psi$ between elements $\tilde{\psi}$ of a set dense in $L_2(\Gamma)$ and elements ζ_ψ of a set dense in $L_2(\xi^0)$. The correspondence is one-to-one between equivalence classes of functions and norm preserving. From this last fact it follows that the correspondence can be extended to an isometric isomorphism between the full Hilbert spaces $L_2(\Gamma)$ and $L_2(\xi^0)$ (for details see Exercise 11.3.3), thus establishing the following proposition.

Proposition 11.3.III. *There is an isometric isomorphism between $L_2(\Gamma)$ and $L_2(\xi^0)$ in which, for $\psi \in \mathscr{S}$, the integral ζ_ψ at $(11.3.1) \in L_2(\xi^0)$ and the Fourier transform $\tilde{\psi} \in L_2(\Gamma)$ are corresponding elements.*

The main weakness of this proposition is that it does not give an explicit Fourier representation of the random measure and associated integrals ζ_ψ.

To overcome this deficiency we adopt the standard procedure of introducing a mean square integral with respect to a certain wide-sense random signed measure with uncorrelated values on disjoint sets: for any bounded $A \in \mathscr{B}(\mathbb{R}^d)$, let $Z(A)$ denote the random element in $L_2(\xi^0)$, corresponding to $\tilde{\psi}(\omega) \equiv I_A(\omega)$ in $L_2(\Gamma)$. For disjoint sets A_1, A_2, it follows from the polarized form of (11.3.2) (i.e., expressing inner products in terms of norms) that

$$E(Z(A_1)\overline{Z(A_2)}) = \int_{\mathbb{R}^d} I_{A_1}(\omega)I_{A_2}(\omega)\Gamma(d\omega) = 0,$$

so that the $Z(\cdot)$ are indeed uncorrelated on disjoint sets (or, in $\mathbb{R}$ terminology, have orthogonal increments). The definition of a mean square integral with respect to such a family is a standard procedure (e.g., see Doob, 1953; Cramér and Leadbetter, 1967) and leads to the conclusion that for every $g \in L_2(\Gamma)$ the integral

$$\int_{\mathbb{R}^d} g(\omega)Z(d\omega)$$

can be defined uniquely as a mean square limit of integrals of simple functions and can be identified with the unique random variable associated with g in the isomorphism theorem described by Proposition 11.3.III. In particular, for $g = \tilde{\psi} \in \mathscr{S}$, the integral below can be identified with the random element ζ_ψ; that is,

$$\int_{\mathbb{R}^d} \tilde{\psi}(\omega)Z(d\omega) = \int_{\mathbb{R}^d} \psi(x)\xi^0(dx).$$

More generally, it follows from Proposition 11.1.IV and (11.3.2) that the same conclusion holds for any bounded ψ of bounded support. Thus, we have the following result, which is a slight strengthening, as well as an extension to $\mathbb{R}^d$, of the corresponding result in Vere-Jones (1974).

Theorem 11.3.IV. *Let ξ be a second-order stationary random measure or point process in $\mathbb{R}^d$, with Bartlett spectrum Γ. Then there exists a second-order wide-sense random measure $Z(\cdot)$ defined on bounded $A \in \mathscr{B}(\mathbb{R}^d)$ for which*

(11.3.3) (i) *$EZ(A) = 0 = E(Z(A)\overline{Z(B)})$ for bounded disjoint $A, B \in \mathscr{B}(\mathbb{R}^d)$,*
(11.3.4) (ii) *$\text{var } Z(A) = E|Z(A)|^2 = \Gamma(A)$,*
          (iii) *for all $g \in L_2(\Gamma)$, the random variable ζ corresponding to g in the isomorphism of Proposition 11.3.III is expressible as*

$$\zeta = \int_{\mathbb{R}^d} g(\omega)Z(d\omega),$$

          (iv) *for all $\psi \in \mathscr{S}$ and all bounded measurable ψ of bounded support,*

(11.3.5) $$\zeta_\psi \equiv \int_{\mathbb{R}^d} \psi(x)\xi^0(dx) = \int_{\mathbb{R}^d} \tilde{\psi}(\omega)Z(d\omega) \quad \text{a.s.}$$

We remark in connection with (iv) that the left-hand side of (11.3.5) represents the usual random integral defined on a realization by realization basis, whereas the right-hand side is a mean square integral that does not have a meaning in this sense. The two most important classes of functions ψ are covered by the theorem, while a slight extension is indicated in Exercise 11.3.5.

An alternative approach to the substance of part (iv) of this theorem is simply to *define* the integral on the left-hand side of (11.3.5) to be equal to the right-hand side there for all $\tilde{\psi} \in L_2(\Gamma)$, but this begs the question as to when this definition coincides with the a.s. definition of the integral used until now.

More explicit representation theorems can be obtained as corollaries to (11.3.5). In particular, taking $\psi(x) = I_A(x)$ we have the following corollaries.

Corollary 11.3.V. *For all bounded $A \in \mathscr{B}(\mathbb{R}^d)$,*

(11.3.6) $$\xi^0(A) = \int_{\mathbb{R}^d} \tilde{I}_A(\omega)Z(d\omega) \quad \text{a.s.}$$

We cannot immediately obtain an inversion theorem for $Z(\cdot)$ in this form, since the corresponding integral $(2\pi)^{-d}\int_{\mathbb{R}^d}\tilde{I}_B(-x)\xi^0(dx)$ need not exist. The finite integral over $\mathbb{U}_T^d$ presents no difficulties however, and leads to the following corollary.

Corollary 11.3.VI. *For all bounded $A \in \mathbb{R}^d$ that are Γ-continuity sets,*

$$(11.3.7) \qquad Z(A) = \text{l.i.m.} \frac{1}{T\to\infty} \frac{1}{(2\pi)^d} \int_{\mathbb{U}_T^d} \tilde{I}_A(-x)\xi^0(dx).$$

PROOF. From the theorem, the finite integral in (11.3.7) can be transformed into the expression

$$\int_{\mathbb{R}^d} Z(d\omega) \int_A \left[\prod_{i=1}^d \left(\frac{\sin T(\omega_i - \theta_i)}{\omega_i - \theta_i}\right)\right] d\theta.$$

Provided A is a continuity set for Γ, the integrand convolved with $I_A(\omega)$ converges in $L_2(\Gamma)$ to $I_A(\omega)$ as $T \to \infty$ (see Exercise 11.3.4: the proof is straightforward for intervals A but not so direct for general bounded A), and hence the integral converges in mean square to $Z(A)$. $\square$

The Parseval relation (11.3.5) can be extended to somewhat wider classes of functions, and in particular it is shown in Exercise 11.3.5 that (11.3.5) continues to hold, whenever ψ is Lebesgue integrable and $\tilde{\psi} \in L_2(\Gamma)$. This establishes a conjecture in Vere-Jones (1974).

The examples that follow, all discussed for the case $d = 1$ but capable of extension, are intended to illustrate both uses and limitations of this second-order theory.

EXAMPLE 11.3(a) *Linear filters.* One of the most valuable uses of spectral representation theory of continuous time processes is to obtain the spectral characteristics of processes acted on by a linear filter. This use carries over formally unchanged to the present context. Let $\xi(\cdot)$ be a (second-order stationary) random measure, $\psi \in L_1$ a smoothing function, and consider the smoothed process defined by

$$(11.3.8) \qquad X(t) = \int_{-\infty}^{\infty} \psi(t-u)\xi(du).$$

Substituting from the Parseval relation (11.3.5), and recalling that the Fourier transform of the shifted function $\psi(t-u)$ is $\tilde{\psi}(-\omega)e^{i\omega t}$, we find

$$(11.3.9) \qquad X(t) = \int_{-\infty}^{\infty} e^{i\omega t}\tilde{\psi}(-\omega)Z(d\omega).$$

The spectrum $\Gamma_X(\cdot)$ of the transformed process is

$$(11.3.10) \qquad \Gamma_X(d\omega) = |\tilde{\psi}(-\omega)|^2\Gamma(d\omega),$$

which will be totally finite [implying that $X(\cdot)$ is a mean square continuous process] provided $\tilde{\psi} \in L_2(\Gamma)$. The relation (11.3.8) can be interpreted even more broadly; for example, if $A(\cdot)$ is a totally finite measure, the convolution $A * \xi$ still defines a.s. a random measure and (11.3.9) and (11.3.10) continue to hold.

EXAMPLE 11.3(b) *Binning*. A special case of practical importance arises when the measure ξ is "binned," that is, integrated over intervals of constant length, say Δ. Considering first the continuous time process $X(t) \equiv \xi(t - \Delta/2, t + \Delta/2]$, (11.3.9) yields

$$X(t) = \int_{-\infty}^{\infty} e^{i\omega t} \left(\frac{\sin(\omega\Delta/2)}{\omega/2} \right) Z(d\omega),$$

so that

$$\Gamma_X(d\omega) = \left(\frac{\sin(\omega\Delta/2)}{\omega/2} \right)^2 \Gamma(d\omega).$$

It is commonly the case that the binned process is sampled only at the lattice points $\{n\Delta: n = 0, \pm 1, \ldots\}$. The sampled process can then be represented in the aliased form

$$Y(n) \equiv X(n\Delta) = \int_0^{2\pi/\Delta} e^{in\theta} \left(\sum_{k=-\infty}^{\infty} Z_X(2k\pi/\Delta + d\theta) \right).$$

If we take Δ as the unit of time, then we can see from this representation that the discrete time process $\{Y(n)\}$ has spectral measure $G_Y(\cdot)$ on $(0, 2\pi]$ given by

$$G_Y(d\theta) = \sin^2\theta \sum_{k=-\infty}^{\infty} \frac{\Gamma(2k\pi + d\theta)}{(\theta + 2k\pi)^2}.$$

In the simplest case of a Poisson process, $\Gamma(d\omega) = (\mu/2\pi)d\omega$ so that

$$G_Y(d\theta) = \sin^2\theta \sum_{k=-\infty}^{\infty} \frac{(\mu/2\pi)d\theta}{(\theta + 2k\pi)^2} = \left(\frac{\mu}{2\pi} \right) d\theta,$$

since the infinite series is just an expansion of $\mathrm{cosec}^2\, \theta$. This reduction reflects the fact that the random variables $Y(n)$ are then independent with common variance μ.

For applications of these results to earthquake data see Vere-Jones and Davies (1966) and Vere-Jones (1970).

EXAMPLE 11.3(c) *The Fourier transform of the Poisson process*. In very simple cases we can use Corollary 11.3.VI to calculate directly the process $Z(\cdot)$ having orthogonal increments. For example, with $d = 1$ and ξ a Poisson process with parameter λ, it follows from (11.3.7) that

$$Z((a, b]) = \underset{T \to \infty}{\mathrm{l.i.m.}} \frac{1}{2\pi i} \int_{-T}^{T} \frac{e^{-ixa} - e^{-ixb}}{x} (N(dx) - \lambda\, dx).$$

Consider in particular the process

$$U_a(\omega) \equiv Z(\omega + a) - Z(\omega - a) = \underset{T \to \infty}{\text{l.i.m.}} \frac{1}{\pi} \int_{-T}^{T} \frac{e^{-i\omega x} \sin ax}{x} (N(dx) - \lambda\, dx).$$

Using standard results for the characteristic functional of the Poisson process [e.g., see (7.4.10)] we find

(11.3.11) $\Phi(\omega, s)$

$$\equiv E \exp(isU_a(\omega))$$

$$= \exp\left\{ \lambda \int_{-\infty}^{\infty} \left[\exp\left(\frac{ise^{-i\omega x} \sin ax}{x} \right) - 1 - \frac{ise^{-i\omega x} \sin ax}{x} \right] dx \right\}$$

$$= \exp\left\{ \lambda \int_{-\infty}^{\infty} \left[-\frac{1}{2} s^2 \cos \omega x \left(\frac{\sin ax}{x} \right)^2 + O(s^3) \left(\frac{\sin ax}{x} \right)^3 \right] dx \right\}$$

$$= \exp\{ -\tfrac{1}{2}\pi\lambda a s^2 + O(s^3) \}$$

uniformly in ω [for evaluation of the integral see Copson (1935, p. 153)]. It follows that the variance of $U_a(\omega)$ is proportional to the length of the interval and independence of location, corresponding to the presumption that $Z(\cdot)$ in this case must be a process with orthogonal and second-order stationary increments.

On the other hand, it is clear that $Z(\cdot)$ does not have stationary increments, for the characteristic function depends nontrivially on ω. Similarly, it can be checked from the joint characteristic function that Z does not have independent increments. Indeed, as follows from inspecting its characteristic function, $U_a(\omega)$ has an infinitely divisible distribution of pure jump type, with a rather subtle dependence of the jump distribution on a and ω that produces the requisite characteristics of the second-order properties.

This example illustrates the potential dangers of using the second-order representation for anything other than second-order properties.

We conclude this section with a brief account of the wide-sense second-order theory referred to at the end of Section 11.2.

Definition 11.3.VII. A *wide-sense second-order stationary random measure* on $\mathscr{X} = \mathbb{R}^d$ is a jointly distributed family of real or complex valued random variables $\{\xi(A): A \in \mathscr{B}_{\mathscr{X}}\}$ satisfying the conditions, for bounded A, $\{A_n\}$, $B \in \mathscr{B}_{\mathscr{X}}$,

(i) $E\xi(A) = m\ell(A)$, var $\xi(A) < \infty$;
(ii) $\text{var}((S_x\xi)(A)) = \text{var } \xi(T_xA) = \text{var } \xi(A)$;
(iii) $\xi(A \cup B) = \xi(A) + \xi(B)$ a.s. for disjoint A, B;
(iv) $\xi(A_n) \to 0$ in mean square when $A_n \downarrow \varnothing$ $(n \to \infty)$.

If the random variables $\xi(\cdot)$ here are nonnegative, then (iii) reduces to (6.1.7) and implies that in (iv) the random variables $\xi(A_n)$ decrease monotonically a.s.; that is, $\xi(A_{n+1}) \leq \xi(A_n)$ a.s., so that (iv) can be strengthened to $\xi(A_n) \to 0$ a.s. when $A_n \downarrow \varnothing$ as $n \to \infty$. We then know from Theorem 6.1.VI that there exists a strict-sense random measure that can be taken as a version of $\xi(\cdot)$ so that nothing new is obtained. Thus, the essence of the extension in Definition 11.3.VII is to random signed measures.

For the sequel we work only with the mean corrected version, taking $m = 0$ in the definition. Given such a family then, we can always find a Gaussian family with the same first and second moment properties: the construction is standard and needs no detailed explanation (see Doob, 1953; Thornett, 1979). For example, the Poisson process, corrected to have zero mean, has var $\xi(A) = \lambda \ell(A)$, where λ is the intensity, and we have already noted that this is the same as the variance function for the Wiener chaos process in Example 6.1(e).

While the definition refers only to variances, covariances are defined by implication from the relation, valid for $\xi(\cdot)$ real-valued and disjoint A and B,

$$2 \operatorname{cov}(\xi(A), \xi(B)) = \operatorname{var} \xi(A \cup B) - \operatorname{var} \xi(A) - \operatorname{var} \xi(B).$$

For general A, B, we then have

$$\operatorname{cov}(\xi(A), \xi(B)) = \operatorname{cov}(\xi(A \cap B) + \xi(A \backslash B), \xi(A \cap B) + \xi(B \backslash A))$$

$$= \operatorname{var} \xi(A \cap B) + \operatorname{cov}(\xi(A \cap B), \xi(A \triangle B))$$

$$+ \operatorname{cov}(\xi(A \backslash B), \xi(B \backslash A)).$$

Although we can obtain in this way a covariance function $C(A \times B)$ defined on products of bounded $A, B \in \mathcal{B}_{\mathcal{X}}$, it is not obvious that it can be extended to a signed measure on $\mathcal{B}(\mathcal{X}^{(2)})$. Consequently, it is not clear whether or not a covariance measure exists for such a family. When it does, the further theory can be developed much as in Sections 10.1 and 10.3. Irrespective of such existence, it is still possible to define both a spectrum for the process and an associated spectral representation. Thus, for any bounded Borel set A, consider the process

$$X_A(x) \equiv \xi(T_x A).$$

Mean square continuity follows from condition (iv), so $X_A(\cdot)$ has a spectral measure $\Gamma_A(\cdot)$, and we can define

$$\Gamma(d\omega) = |\tilde{I}_A(\omega)|^{-2} \Gamma_A(d\omega)$$

for all ω such that $|\tilde{I}_A(\omega)| \neq 0$. Since we cannot ensure that $|\tilde{I}_A(\omega)| \neq 0$ for all ω, some care is needed in showing that the resultant measure $\Gamma(\cdot)$ can in fact be consistently defined for a sufficiently rich class of sets A [one approach is outlined by Thornett (1979) and given as Exercise 11.3.6]. Just as before, the measure Γ is translation bounded and hence integrates $(1 + \omega^2)^{-1}$, for example. On the other hand, it is not positive definite in general and not all the explicit inversion theorems can be carried over. Nevertheless, for all bounded $A \in \mathcal{B}_{\mathscr{X}}$, we certainly have

$$(11.3.12) \qquad\qquad \text{var } \xi(A) = \int |\tilde{I}_A(\omega)|^2 \Gamma(d\omega)$$

and its covariance extension

$$(11.3.13) \qquad\qquad \text{cov}(\xi(A), \xi(B)) = \int \tilde{I}_A(\omega)\overline{\tilde{I}_B(\omega)}\Gamma(d\omega).$$

Since the indicator functions are dense in $L_2(\Gamma)$, more general integrals of the form $\int \phi(x)\xi(dx)$ can be defined as mean square limits of linear combinations of the random variables $\xi(A)$, at least when $\tilde{\phi} \in L_2(\Gamma)$. For such integrals the more general formulae

$$\text{var}\left(\int \phi(x)\xi(dx)\right) = \int |\tilde{\phi}(\omega)|^2 \Gamma(d\omega)$$

and

$$\text{cov}\left(\int \phi(x)\xi(dx), \int \psi(x)\xi(dx)\right) = \int \tilde{\phi}(\omega)\tilde{\psi}(\omega)\Gamma(d\omega)$$

are available, but it is not clear whether the integrals make sense other than in this mean square sense. As noted earlier, it is also an open question as to whether Γ is necessarily the Fourier transform of some measure, which we could then interpret as a reduced covariance measure.

The isomorphism result at Proposition 11.3.III can be extended to this wider context with only minor changes in the argument: it asserts the isomorphism between $L_2(X)$ and $L_2(\Gamma)$ and provides a spectral representation, for bounded $A \in \mathcal{B}_{\mathscr{X}}$,

$$(11.3.14) \qquad\qquad \xi(A) = \int \tilde{I}_A(\omega)Z(d\omega) \quad \text{a.s.}$$

just as in the previous discussion.

To summarize, we have the following theorem of which further details of proof are left to the reader.

Theorem 11.3.VIII. *Let $\{\xi(\cdot)\}$ be a wide-sense second-order stationary random measure as in Definition 11.3.VII. Then there exists a spectral measure $\Gamma(\cdot)$ and a process $Z(\cdot)$ of orthogonal increments with var $Z(d\omega) = \Gamma(d\omega)$, such that (11.3.12)–(11.3.14) hold.*

EXAMPLE 11.3(d) *Random sampling of random process.* A situation of some practical importance arises when a stationary continuous time stochastic process $X(t)$ is sampled at the epochs $\{t_i\}$ of a stationary point process. The resultant process can be considered in two ways, either as a discrete time process $Y_i = X(t_i)$, or as a random measure with jump increments

$$\xi(dt) = X(t)N(dt).$$

Neither operation is linear, but the second equation is just a multiplication of the two processes and leads to the more tractable results. $N(\cdot)$ is not a process with zero mean; to express it as a process with zero mean we write

$$\xi(dt) = X(t)N^0(dt) + mX(t)dt,$$

where $N^0(dt) = N(dt) - m\,dt$ and $m = EN(0, 1]$. Proceeding formally leads to

$$\int_{\mathbb{R}} \phi(t)\xi(dt) = \int_{\mathbb{R}} \int_{\mathbb{R}} \tilde{\phi}(u - v)Z_X(du)N(dv) + m \int_{\mathbb{R}} \tilde{\phi}(u)Z_X(du)$$

corresponding to a representation of the measure Z_ξ as a convolution of Z_X and Z_N with an additional term for the mean. Leaving aside the general case, suppose that the processes $X(\cdot)$ and $N(\cdot)$ are independent. Then we find

$$\text{var}\left(\int_{\mathbb{R}} \phi(t)\xi(dt) \right) = \int_{\mathbb{R}} \int_{\mathbb{R}} |\tilde{\phi}(u - v)|^2 \gamma_X(du)\gamma_N(dv) + m^2 \int_{\mathbb{R}} |\tilde{\phi}(u)|^2 \gamma_N(du),$$

from which we deduce

$$\gamma_\xi(d\omega) = \int \gamma_X(d\omega - u)\gamma_N(du) + m^2\gamma_X(d\omega).$$

Hence, for the covariance measures we have

$$\hat{C}_\xi(du) = \hat{c}_X(u)(m^2\,du + \hat{C}_N(du)) = \hat{c}_X(u)\hat{M}_2(du).$$

Of course, the last result can easily be derived directly from a consideration of

$$E(X(t)N(t, t + dt]X(t + u)N(t + u, t + u + du]).$$

In practice, one generally must estimate the spectrum $\gamma_X(\cdot)$ given a (finite portion of a) realization of $\xi(\cdot)$. When N is a Poisson process at rate m,

$$\gamma_\xi(d\omega) = (m/2\pi)(\text{var } X)d\omega + m^2\gamma_X(d\omega),$$

so γ_X can be obtained quite easily from γ_ξ. In general, however, a deconvolution procedure may be needed, and the problem is complicated further by the fact that the spectral measures concerned are not totally finite. Consequently, numerical Fourier transform routines cannot be applied without some further manipulations [for further details see Brillinger (1972)].

Exercises

11.3.1. *Representation in terms of the second moment measure.* Show that the effect of working with the Fourier transform of the second moment rather than the Bartlett spectrum would be to set up an isomorphism between the spaces $L_2(\xi)$ generated by all linear combinations of the r.v.s $\xi(A)$ and $L_2(v)$, where v is the inverse Fourier transform of M_2. Show that the representation

$$\int_{\mathbb{R}^d} \phi(x)\xi(dx) = \int_{\mathbb{R}^d} \tilde{\phi}(\omega)Z_1(d\omega)$$

holds for functions ϕ in a suitably restricted class, where $Z_1(A) = m\delta_0(A) + Z(A)$, and Z and Z_1 differ only by an atom at $\omega = 0$.

11.3.2. Given a nontrivial boundedly finite measure Γ, show the following:

(a) Simple functions of the form $\sum a_k I_{A_k}$ (bounded $A_k \in \mathcal{B}(\mathbb{R}^d)$) are dense in $L_2(\Gamma)$.

(b) For bounded $A \in \mathcal{B}(\mathbb{R}^d)$, there exist open sets $U_n \in \mathcal{B}(\mathbb{R}^d)$ with $U_n \supseteq A$, $\Gamma(U_n) \downarrow \Gamma(A)$.

(c) Any such U_n is the countable union of hyper-rectangles of the form $\{\alpha_i < x_i \leq \beta_i, i = 1, \ldots, d\}$.

(d) Indicator functions on such hyper-rectangles can be approximated by sequences of infinitely differentiable functions of bounded support. Now complete the proof of Lemma 11.3.I.

11.3.3. Given $\tilde{\psi} \in L_2(\Gamma)$, choose $\tilde{\psi}_n \in \mathcal{S}$ such that $\|\tilde{\psi} - \psi\|_{L_2(\Gamma)} \to 0$ ($n \to \infty$), and deduce that $\{Z_{\psi_n}\}$ is a Cauchy sequence in $L_2(\xi^0)$. Show that there is a unique r.v. $\zeta \in L_2(\xi^0)$ such that $Z_{\psi_n} \to \zeta$ in mean square. Interchange the roles of $L_2(\Gamma)$ and $L_2(\xi^0)$ and deduce the assertion of Proposition 11.3.III.

11.3.4. Consider the function $h_T(\omega) \equiv \omega^{-1} \sin \omega T$. Show the following:

(a) $\int_{-\infty}^{\infty} h_T(\omega) = \pi$.

(b) For any continuous function ϕ with bounded support,

$$\phi_T(\omega) \equiv \int_{-\infty}^{\infty} \phi(\omega - u)h_T(u)du \to \phi(\omega) \quad \text{pointwise as } T \to \infty.$$

[This is an application of "Fourier's single integral" (cf. Zygmund (1968), §16.1)). The essential conditions are that $\phi \in L_1(\mathbb{R})$ and that ϕ be of bounded variation in any closed interval contained in its support.]

(c) $\phi_T(\omega) \to \phi(\omega)$ in $L_2(\Gamma)$ for any p.p.d. measure (or for any Bartlett spectrum) Γ. [*Hint*: $|\phi_T(\omega)| \leq \text{constant}/|\omega|$ for large $|\omega|$ while $\sup_\omega |\phi_T(\omega)| < \infty$; these properties are enough to ensure that $|\phi_T(\omega)|^2 \leq g(\omega)$ for some Γ-integrable function g.]

(d) Interpret the convergence in (c) as

$$\int_{\mathbb{R}} |\phi_T(\omega)|^2 \Gamma(d\omega) = \int_{\mathbb{R}} \int_{\mathbb{R}} h_T(\omega - u)\phi(u)du \int_{\mathbb{R}} \overline{h_T(\omega - v)\phi(v)}dv \, \Gamma(d\omega)$$

$$= \int_{\mathbb{R}} \int_{\mathbb{R}} \phi(u)\overline{\phi(v)}du \, dv \int_{\mathbb{R}} h_T(\omega - u)\overline{h_T(\omega - v)}\Gamma(d\omega)$$

$$= \int_{\mathbb{R}^2} \phi(u)\overline{\phi(v)}\Gamma_T^*(du \times dv)$$

$$\to \int_{\mathbb{R}^2} \phi(u)\overline{\phi(v)}\Gamma^*(du \times dv)$$

$$= \int_{\mathbb{R}} |\phi(\omega)|^2 \Gamma(d\omega),$$

where $\Gamma_T^*(du \times dv)$ is the measure in $\mathcal{B}(\mathbb{R}^2)$ with density

$\int_{\mathbb{R}} h_T(\omega - u)\overline{h_T(\omega - v)}\Gamma(d\omega)$ and Γ^* is the measure on $\mathscr{B}(\mathbb{R}^2)$, which reduces to Γ along the diagonal $u = v$.

These results are enough to establish that $\Gamma_T^* \to \Gamma^*$ vaguely in $\mathbb{R}^2$, and hence
that a similar result holds when $\phi(\cdot)$ is replaced by the indicator function of a
bounded Borel set in $\mathbb{R}^1$ that is a continuity set for Γ.

11.3.5. Show that (11.3.5) can be extended to all L_1 functions ϕ such that $\tilde{\phi} \in L_2(\Gamma)$.
[*Hint*: The left-hand side can be represented as an a.s. limit of integrals of
bounded functions of bounded support, while the right-hand side can be
represented as a mean square limit. When both limits exist they must be equal
a.s.]

11.3.6. (a) Show that for Γ to be the spectral measure of a wide-sense second-order
stationary random measure, it is necessary and sufficient that Γ integrate
all functions $|\tilde{I}_A(\omega)|^2$ for bounded Borel sets A. [*Hint*: Use a Gaussian
construction for the sufficiency.]

(b) Hence, show that any translation bounded measure can be a spectral
measure. [*Hint*: Use Lin's lemma. See also Thornett (1979).]

11.3.7. (a) Show that if a wide-sense second-order stationary process has a reduced
covariance measure $\hat{C}(\cdot)$, then

$$\hat{C}(\{0\}) = \lim_{T \to \infty} \Gamma((-T, T])/2T$$

continues to hold (cf. Theorem 11.1.III).

(b) Use Exercise 11.2.3 to show that not all spectral measures are transforms;
that is, not all wide-sense processes have an associated reduced covariance
measure (cf. also Exercise 11.1.3).

11.4. Linear Prediction

By a *linear predictor* we mean a predictor of the form $\int_{-\infty}^{t} f(t - u)\xi(du)$, that
is, a linear functional of the past, with the quantity to be predicted a similar
linear functional of the future. We consider one-dimensional univariate processes: extensions to multivariate and marked processes are possible.

Even in the point process case, the problem commonly reduces to predicting, as a linear functional of the past, the mean intensity at some point in
the future. When the process has a mean square continuous density (cf.
Exercise 6.1.1), this corresponds exactly to the classical problem of predicting
a future value of the process as a linear functional of its past. Thus, our task
is essentially to check when the classical procedures can be carried over to
random measures and to write out the forms that they take in random measure
terms.

Other types of prediction, for example, of the time to the next event in a
point process, do not lend themselves as naturally to extensions of the classical
linear theory. Such quantities are inherently nonlinear in character, and it is
frequently possible to find simple nonlinear predictors that are more effective
than even the optimal linear predictor. The conditional intensity function

holds the key to such general prediction problems, which are considered in Chapter 13.

The Wold decomposition theorem plays an important role in the linear prediction problem for mean square continuous processes, and we start with an extension of this theorem for random measures. As in Section 11.3, we use ξ and ξ^0 to denote a second-order stationary random measure and its zero mean form, respectively, with the additional understanding that $\mathcal{X} = \mathbb{R}$. Since the results to be developed depend only on the spectral representation theorems, ξ can be either a strict-sense or a wide-sense random measure. We continue to use $L_2(\xi^0)$ to denote the Hilbert space of equivalence classes of random variables formed from linear combinations of $\xi^0(A)$ for bounded $A \in \mathcal{B}$ and their mean square limits. Similarly, $L_2(\xi^0; t)$ denotes the Hilbert space formed from $\xi^0(A)$ with the further constraint that $A \subset (-\infty, t]$.

Definition 11.4.I. The second-order strict- or wide-sense stationary random measure ξ is *deterministic* if $\bigcap_{t \in \mathbb{R}} L_2(\xi^0; t) = L_2(\xi^0)$, and *purely nondeterministic* if $\bigcap_{t \in \mathbb{R}} L_2(\xi^0; t) = \{0\}$.

Then the following extension of Wold's theorem holds (Vere-Jones, 1974).

Theorem 11.4.II. *For any second-order stationary random measure ξ, the zero mean process ξ^0 can be written uniquely in the form*

$$\xi^0 = \xi_1^0 + \xi_2^0,$$

where ξ_1^0 and ξ_2^0 are mutually orthogonal, stationary, wide-sense zero-mean random measures, and ξ_1^0 is deterministic and ξ_2^0 purely nondeterministic.

PROOF. Again we start from the known theorems for mean square continuous processes [e.g., see Cramér and Leadbetter (1967), especially Chaps. 5–7] and use smoothing arguments similar to those of Section 11.1 to extend them to the random measure context. To this end, set

$$(11.4.1) \qquad X(t) = \int_{-\infty}^{t} e^{-(t-u)} \xi^0(du),$$

where the integral can be understood, whether ξ^0 is a strict- or wide-sense random measure, as a mean square limit of linear combinations of indicator functions. These indicator functions can all be taken of sets $\subseteq (-\infty, t]$, so we have $X(t) \in L_2(\xi^0; t)$, and more generally, $X(s) \in L_2(\xi^0; t)$ for any $s \le t$, so $L_2(X; t) \subseteq L_2(\xi^0; t)$. To show that we have equality here, we write

$$X(t+h) - e^{-h}X(t) - \xi^0(t, t+h] = \int_{t}^{t+h} [e^{-(t+h-u)} - 1]\xi^0(du),$$

$$= \int_{-\infty}^{\infty} e^{i\omega t}\left(\frac{e^{i\omega h} - e^{-h}}{1 + i\omega} - \frac{e^{i\omega h} - 1}{i\omega}\right) Z(d\omega)$$

on using the representation at (11.3.6). Subdividing any finite interval $(a, a + \Delta]$ into n subintervals of length $h = \Delta/n$, we obtain

$$\sum_{k=1}^{n} [X(a + kh) - e^{-h}X(a + (k + 1)h)] - \xi^0(a, a + \Delta]$$

$$= \int_{-\infty}^{\infty} \left(\sum_{k=1}^{n} e^{i\omega(a+kh)}\right) \left(\frac{e^{i\omega h} - e^{-h}}{1 + i\omega} - \frac{e^{i\omega h} - 1}{i\omega}\right) Z(d\omega).$$

The variance of the left-hand side therefore equals

$$\int_{-\infty}^{\infty} \left\{\frac{\sin(\omega\Delta/2)}{\sin(\omega h/2)}\right\}^2 \left|1 - e^{-h} - \frac{e^{i\omega} - 1}{i\omega}\right|^2 \frac{\Gamma(d\omega)}{1 + \omega^2}.$$

The measure $(1 + \omega^2)^{-1}\Gamma(d\omega)$ is totally finite (see Exercise 11.1.5), the term $|\cdot|^2$ is uniformly bounded in ω by $4h^2$ and for fixed ω it is $o(h^2)$ as $h \to 0$, and the term in braces is bounded by $(\Delta/h)^2$ and for fixed ω equals constant $\times$ $h^{-2}(1 + o(1))$ as $h \to 0$. The dominated convergence theorem can therefore be applied to conclude that this variance $\to 0$ as $h \to 0$, and hence that $\xi^0(a, b]$ can be approximated in mean square by linear combinations of $\{X(t): t \le b\}$. This shows that $L_2(\xi^0; t) \subseteq L_2(X; t)$, and thus we must have $L_2(\xi^0; t) = L_2(X; t)$.

The Wold decomposition for $X(t)$ takes the form

$$X(t) = X_1(t) + X_2(t),$$

where $X_1(\cdot)$ is deterministic and $X_2(\cdot)$ purely nondeterministic. The decomposition reflects an orthogonal decomposition of $L_2(X)$ [and hence of $L_2(\xi^0)$] into two orthogonal subspaces such that $X_1(t)$ is the projection of $X(t)$ onto one and $X_2(t)$ the projection onto the other. Then $\xi_1^0(A)$ and $\xi_2^0(A)$ may be defined as the projections of $\xi^0(A)$ onto these same subspaces. Furthermore, $\xi_1^0(a, b]$ and $\xi_2^0(a, b]$ can be expressed as mean square limits of linear combinations of $X_1(t)$ and $X_2(t)$ in exactly the same way as $\xi^0(a, b]$ is expressed above in terms of $X(t)$. The deterministic and purely nondeterministic properties of $X_1(\cdot)$ and $X_2(\cdot)$, respectively, carry over to $\xi_1^0(\cdot)$ and $\xi_2^0(\cdot)$. Uniqueness is a consequence of the uniqueness of any orthogonal decomposition. To verify the additivity property of $\xi_1^0(\cdot)$ and $\xi_1^0(\cdot)$, take a sequence $\{A_n\}$ of disjoint bounded Borel sets with bounded union. From the a.s. countable additivity of ξ^0, which is equivalent to property (iv) of Definition 11.3.VII, we have

$$\xi^0\left(\bigcup_{n=1}^{\infty} A_n\right) = \sum_{n=1}^{\infty} \xi^0(A_n);$$

hence,

$$\xi_1^0\left(\bigcup_{n=1}^{\infty} A_n\right) - \sum_{n=1}^{\infty} \xi_1^0(A_n) = \xi_2^0\left(\bigcup_{n=1}^{\infty} A_n\right) - \sum_{n=1}^{\infty} \xi_2^0(A_n) \quad \text{a.s.}$$

Since the expressions on the two sides of this equation belong to orthogonal subspaces, both must reduce a.s. to the zero random variable. Properties (i)–(iii) of Definition 11.3.VII are readily checked, and it thus follows that both $\xi_1^0(\cdot)$ and $\xi_2^0(\cdot)$ are wide-sense second-order stationary random measures. (Note, however, that even when ξ^0 is known to be a strict-sense random measure the above argument shows only that ξ_1^0 and ξ_1^0 are wide-sense random measures.) ☐

The classical results that relate the presence of a deterministic component to properties of the spectral measure can also be carried over from $X(\cdot)$ to the random measure $\xi(\cdot)$. They are set out in the following theorem.

Theorem 11.4.III. *Let $\xi(\cdot)$ be a strict- or wide-sense second-order stationary random measure with Bartlett spectrum Γ. Then $\xi(\cdot)$ is purely nondeterministic if and only if Γ is absolutely continuous and its density γ satisfies the condition*

$$(11.4.2) \qquad \int_{-\infty}^{\infty} \frac{\log \gamma(\omega)d\omega}{1 + \omega^2} > -\infty.$$

This condition is equivalent to the existence of a factorization

$$(11.4.3) \qquad \gamma(\omega) = |\tilde{g}(\omega)|^2$$

where $\tilde{g}(\cdot)$ is the Fourier transform of a (real) generalized function with support on $[0, \infty)$ and can be written in the form $\tilde{g}(\omega) = (1 - i\omega)\tilde{g}_1(\omega)$, where $\tilde{g}_1(\cdot)$ is the Fourier transform of an $L_2(\mathbb{R})$ function with its support in $\mathbb{R}_+$. The function $\tilde{g}(\cdot)$ can be characterized uniquely among all possible factorizations by the requirement that it have an analytic continuation into the upper half-plane $\text{Im}(\omega) > 0$, where it is zero free and satisfies the normalization condition

$$(11.4.4) \qquad \tilde{g}(i) = \exp\left(\frac{1}{2\pi} \int_{-\infty}^{\infty} \frac{\log \gamma(\omega)d\omega}{1 + \omega^2}\right).$$

PROOF. Since ξ is purely nondeterministic if and only if X defined at (11.4.1) is purely nondeterministic, the results follow from those for the continuous time process $X(\cdot)$ as set out, for example, in Chapter III, Section 4 of Hannan (1970). From Sections 11.1 and 11.3 it follows that the spectral measure Γ_X of $X(\cdot)$ is related to the Bartlett spectrum Γ by $\Gamma_X(d\omega) = (1 + \omega^2)^{-1}\Gamma(d\omega)$, so Γ_X has a density γ_X if and only if Γ has a density, and the density γ satisfies (11.4.2) if and only if γ_X does because the discrepancy $\int_{-\infty}^{\infty} (1 + \omega^2)^{-1} \log(1 + \omega^2)d\omega$ is finite.

Similarly, if $\gamma_X(\omega) = |\tilde{g}_X(\omega)|^2$, where $\tilde{g}_X(\cdot)$ is the Fourier transform of an $L_2(\mathbb{R})$ function with support in $\mathbb{R}_+$, we can set $g_1 = g_X$ and (11.4.3) and the related assertions hold.

Finally, (11.4.4) follows from the corresponding relation for g_1 since

$$\tilde{g}(i) = 2\tilde{g}_1(i) = 2 \exp\left(\frac{1}{2\pi} \int_{-\infty}^{\infty} \frac{\log \gamma_X(\omega)d\omega}{1 + \omega^2}\right),$$

$$= \exp\left(\frac{1}{2\pi} \int_{-\infty}^{\infty} \frac{\log \gamma(\omega)d\omega}{1 + \omega^2}\right)$$

on using the identity

$$\int_{-\infty}^{\infty} (1 + \omega^2)^{-1} \log(1 + \omega^2) d\omega = 2\pi \log 2. \qquad \square$$

These extensions, from Γ_X to Γ, are to be expected because the criteria are analytic and relate to the factorization of a function γ rather than to its behaviour as $\omega \to \pm\infty$. We illustrate the results by two examples.

EXAMPLE 11.4(a) *Two-point Poisson cluster process.* Suppose that clusters occur at the instants of a Poisson process with parameter μ and that each cluster contains exactly two members, one at the cluster centre and the other at a fixed time h after the first. Then the reduced covariance measure has just three atoms, one of mass 2μ at 0 and the others at $\pm h$ each of mass μ. The Bartlett spectrum is therefore absolutely continuous with density

$$\gamma(\omega) = \mu\pi^{-1}(1 + \cos \omega h) = 2\mu\pi^{-1} \cos^2(\omega h/2).$$

In seeking a factorization of the form (11.4.3), it is natural to try $(2\mu/\pi)^{1/2} \cos(\omega h/2)$ as a candidate, but checking the normalization condition (11.4.4) reveals a discrepancy: using the relation

$$\int_{-\infty}^{\infty} (1 + \omega^2) \log(\cos^2(\omega h/2)) d\omega = 2\pi \log((1 + e^{-h})/2),$$

leads to $(2\mu/\pi)^{1/2}(1 + e^{-h})/2$ for the right-hand side of (11.4.4), while the candidate gives $\tilde{g}(i) = (2\mu/\pi)^{1/2} \cosh(\omega h/2)$. It is not difficult to see that the correct factorization is

$$\tilde{g}(\omega) = (2\mu/\pi)^{1/2}(1 + e^{i\omega h})/2 = (2\mu/\pi)^{1/2} e^{i\omega h/2} \cos(\omega h/2).$$

In this form we can recognize $\tilde{g}(\cdot)$ as the Fourier transform of a measure with atoms $(\mu/2\pi)^{1/2}$ at $t = 0$ and $t = h$, whereas the unsuccessful candidate function is the transform of a measure with atoms of the same mass but at $t = \pm h/2$; that is, the support is not contained in $[0, \infty)$.

EXAMPLE 11.4(b) *Random measures with rational spectral density.* When the spectral density is expressible as a rational function, and hence of the form

$$\left(\prod_{j=1}^{m} (\omega^2 + \alpha_j^2)\right) \bigg/ \left(\prod_{j=1}^{n} (\omega^2 + \beta_j^2)\right)$$

for nonnegative integers m, n with $m \leq n$, and real α_j, β_j, the identification of the canonical factorization is much simpler because it is uniquely determined (up to a constant of unit modulus) by the requirements that $\tilde{g}(\omega)$ be analytic and zero free in the upper half-plane. Two situations commonly occur, according to whether $m < n$ or $m = n$. In the former case the process has a mean square continuous density $x(\cdot)$ and $\Gamma(\cdot)$ is a totally finite measure. The problem reduces to the classical one of identifying the canonical factorization of the spectrum for the density of the process. For point processes, however, the δ-function in the covariance measure produces a term that does not converge to zero as $|\omega| \to \infty$, implying that $m = n$; the same situation obtains whenever the random measure has a purely atomic component. For example, in Section 11.2 we examined several point process models leading to spectral densities of the form

$$\gamma(\omega) = A^2(\alpha^2 + \omega^2)/(\beta^2 + \omega^2).$$

The canonical factorization here takes the form (with A, α, and β real and positive)

$$\tilde{g}(\omega) = A(\alpha - i\omega)/(\beta - i\omega) = A[1 + (\alpha - \beta)/(\beta - i\omega)],$$

corresponding to the time-domain representation

$$g(t) = A[\delta_0(t) + (\alpha - \beta)I_{[0,\infty)}(t)e^{-\beta t}].$$

Similar forms occur in more general cases, with the exponential replaced by a combination of exponential polynomials.

The main thrust of these factorization results is that they lead to a time-domain representation that can be used to develop explicit prediction formulae. The fact that the canonical factor $\tilde{g}(\omega)$ is in general the transform not of a function but only of a generalized function leads to some specific difficulties. However, much of the argument is not affected by this fact, as we now indicate.

Let $Z(\cdot)$ be the process of orthogonal increments arising in the spectral representation of ξ^0, and $\tilde{g}(\cdot)$ the canonical factor described in Theorem 11.4.III. Introduce a further process $U(\cdot)$ with orthogonal increments by scaling the $Z(\cdot)$ process to have stationary increments as in

$$(11.4.5) \qquad\qquad Z(d\omega) = \overline{\tilde{g}(\omega)}U(d\omega),$$

where the invertibility of $\tilde{g}$ implies that for all real ω

$$E|U(d\omega)|^2 = |\tilde{g}(\omega)|^{-2}E|Z(d\omega)|^2 = d\omega.$$

Note that the use of the complex conjugate of $\tilde{g}$ in (11.4.5) is purely conventional: it simplifies the resulting moving average representation in the time domain.

Corresponding to U in the frequency domain we may, in the usual way, define a new process V in the time domain through the Parseval relations, so

$$(11.4.6) \qquad\qquad \int_{-\infty}^{\infty} \phi(t)V(dt) = \int_{-\infty}^{\infty} \tilde{\phi}(\omega)U(d\omega),$$

which in this case can be extended to all functions $\phi \in L_2(\mathbb{R})$. It can be verified that $V(\cdot)$ also has orthogonal and stationary increments, with

$$E|V(dt)|^2 = 2\pi\, dt,$$

corresponding to the more complete statement

$$\text{var}\left(\int_{-\infty}^{\infty} \phi(t)V(dt)\right) = 2\pi \int_{-\infty}^{\infty} |\phi(t)|^2 \, dt$$

$$= \int_{-\infty}^{\infty} |\tilde{\phi}(\omega)|^2 \, d\omega = \text{var}\left(\int_{-\infty}^{\infty} \tilde{\phi}(\omega)U(d\omega)\right).$$

On the other hand, from the Parseval relation for the ξ^0 process, we have for integrable ϕ, for which $\tilde{\phi} \in L_2(\Gamma)$,

$$(11.4.7) \quad \int_{-\infty}^{\infty} \phi(t)\xi^0(dt) = \int_{-\infty}^{\infty} \tilde{\phi}(\omega)Z(d\omega) = \int_{-\infty}^{\infty} \tilde{\phi}(\omega)\overline{\tilde{g}(\omega)}U(d\omega).$$

Thus, if we can identify $\tilde{\phi}\overline{\tilde{g}}$ with the Fourier transform of some function $\phi * g^*$ in the time domain, it is possible to write

$$(11.4.8) \quad \int_{-\infty}^{\infty} \phi(t)\xi^0(dt) = \int_{-\infty}^{\infty} (\phi * g^*)(s)V(ds)$$

$$= \int_{-\infty}^{\infty} \phi(t)dt \int_{-\infty}^{t} g(t-s)V(ds),$$

corresponding to the moving average representation

$$(11.4.9) \quad \xi^0(dt) = \int_{-\infty}^{t} g(t-s)V(ds)dt.$$

Because $g(\cdot)$ is not, in general, a function, these last steps have a purely formal character. They are valid in the case of a process ξ^0 having a mean square continuous density, but in general we need to impose further conditions before obtaining any meaningful results. In most point process examples, the generalized function $g(\cdot)$ can be represented as a measure, but it is an open question as to whether this is true for all second-order random measures. We proceed by imposing conditions that, although restrictive, are at least general enough to cover the case of a point process with rational spectral density. They correspond to assuming that the reduced factorial cumulant measure $\hat{C}_{[2]}$ is totally finite, so that the spectral density can be written in the form

$$\gamma(\omega) = (2\pi)^{-1}(m + \tilde{c}_{[2]}(\omega)).$$

Specifically, assume that

$$(11.4.10) \quad \tilde{g}(\omega) = A(1 + \tilde{c}(\omega))$$

for some positive constant A and function $\tilde{c} \in L_2(\mathbb{R})$. Then the generalized function aspect of $g(\cdot)$ is limited to a δ-function at the origin, and there exists an $L_2(\mathbb{R})$ function $c(\cdot)$ such that

$$(11.4.11) \quad g(t) = \begin{cases} A(\delta_0(t) + c(t)) & (t \geq 0), \\ 0 & (t < 0). \end{cases}$$

Under the same conditions the reciprocal $1/\tilde{g}(\omega)$ can be written

(11.4.12) $$1/\tilde{g}(\omega) = A^{-1}(1 - \tilde{d}(\omega)),$$

where $\tilde{d}(\omega) = \tilde{c}(\omega)/(1 + \tilde{c}(\omega))$, and from

$$\int_{-\infty}^{\infty} |\tilde{d}(\omega)|^2 \gamma(\omega) d\omega = A^2 \int_{-\infty}^{\infty} |\tilde{c}(\omega)|^2 \, d\omega < \infty$$

it follows that $\tilde{d} \in L_2(\gamma)$. In most cases we have $L_2(\gamma) \subseteq L_2(\mathbb{R})$ and thus $\tilde{d} \in L_2(\mathbb{R})$, implying the existence of a representation of a Fourier inverse of $1/\tilde{g}(\omega)$ as

(11.4.13) $$\begin{cases} A^{-1}(\delta_0(t) - d(t)) & (t \geq 0) \\ 0 & (t < 0) \end{cases}$$

for some function $d \in L_2(\mathbb{R})$.

Proposition 11.4.IV. *Suppose* (11.4.10) *holds for some* $\tilde{c} \in L_2(\mathbb{R})$. *Then using the notation of* (11.4.10)–(11.4.13), *the zero-mean process* $\xi^0(\cdot)$ *can be written, for* $\phi \in L_1(\mathbb{R})$ *such that* $\tilde{\phi} \in L_2(\mathbb{R})$, *in the form*

(11.4.14) $$\int_{\mathbb{R}} \phi(t)\xi^0(dt) = \int_{\mathbb{R}} \tilde{\phi}(t)V(dt) + \int_{\mathbb{R}} \tilde{\phi}(t)X(t)dt,$$

where $V(\cdot)$ *is a zero-mean process with stationary orthogonal increments such that*

(11.4.15) $$E|V(dt)|^2 = 2\pi A^2 \, dt$$

and $X(\cdot)$ *is a mean square continuous process that can be written in the moving average form*

(11.4.16) $$X(t) = \int_{-\infty}^{t} c(t - u)V(du),$$

or, if furthermore $\tilde{d} \in L_2(\mathbb{R})$, *in the autoregressive form*

(11.4.17) $$X(t) = -\int_{-\infty}^{t} d(t - u)\xi^0(du).$$

PROOF. Under the stated assumptions it follows from (11.4.7) that

(11.4.18) $$\int_{\mathbb{R}} \phi(t)\xi^0(dt) = A \int_{\mathbb{R}} \tilde{\phi}(\omega)U(d\omega) + A \int_{\mathbb{R}} \tilde{\phi}(\omega)\tilde{c}(\omega)U(d\omega).$$

Consider now the process $X(\cdot)$ defined by (11.4.16). It is mean square integrable with the spectral representation, say

(11.4.19) $$X(t) = \int_{\mathbb{R}} e^{it\omega}\tilde{c}(\omega)U(d\omega) = \int_{\mathbb{R}} e^{it\omega}Z_X(d\omega),$$

where Z_X corresponds to the spectral density $\gamma_X(\omega) = |\tilde{c}(\omega)|^2 \, d\omega$. Applying the discussion of Section 11.3 to the $X(\cdot)$ process, it follows that $\int_{\mathbb{R}} X(t)\phi(t)dt$ can be validly interpreted as a mean square integral provided $\tilde{\phi} \in L_2(\gamma_X)$, that is, provided

$$\int_{\mathbb{R}} |\tilde{\phi}(\omega)|^2 |\tilde{c}(\omega)|^2 \, d\omega < \infty.$$

But $\phi \in L_1(\mathbb{R})$ implies that $|\tilde{\phi}(\omega)|$ is bounded for $\omega \in \mathbb{R}$, and the finiteness is then a consequence of the assumption that $\tilde{c} \in L_2(\mathbb{R})$.

The terms on the right-hand side of (11.4.18) can now be replaced by their corresponding time-domain versions. Thus, we have

$$A \int_{\mathbb{R}} \tilde{\phi}(\omega) U(d\omega) = \int_{\mathbb{R}} \phi(t) V(dt),$$

absorbing the constant A into the definition of V as at (11.4.6). Also, the discussion above implies that the last term in (11.4.18) can be replaced by the last term in (11.4.14) with $X(t)$ defined as at (11.4.16).

To establish the autoregressive form at (11.4.17) consider first

$$Y(t) \equiv \int_{\mathbb{R}} e^{it\omega} \tilde{d}(\omega) Z(d\omega) = A \int_{\mathbb{R}} e^{it\omega} \tilde{d}(\omega)(1 + \tilde{c}(\omega)) U(d\omega)$$

$$= A \int_{\mathbb{R}} e^{it\omega} \tilde{c}(\omega) U(d\omega) = X(t),$$

the integrals being well defined and equal a.s. from the assumption that $\tilde{c} \in L_2(\mathbb{R})$, from which it follows that $\tilde{d} \in L_2(\Gamma)$. If ξ^0 is a strict-sense random measure then the time-domain integral (11.4.17) is well defined for $\phi \in L_1(\mathbb{R})$ and we know from Section 10.3 that it can be identified a.s. with its frequency-domain version $Y(t)$ above. If ξ^0 is merely a wide-sense process, then (11.4.17) can be defined only as a mean square limit, which will exist whenever $\tilde{d} \in L_2(\Gamma)$. In either case, therefore, $X(t) = Y(t)$ a.s. □

Note that Equations (11.4.14)–(11.4.16) can be expressed in the abbreviated but suggestive forms

(11.4.20) $$\xi^0(dt) = V(dt) + \int_{-\infty}^{t-} c(t - u) V(du) dt,$$

(11.4.21) $$\xi^0(dt) = V(dt) - \int_{-\infty}^{t-} d(t - u) \xi^0(du) dt.$$

Finally, we can examine the form of the linear predictors themselves when the assumptions of Proposition 11.4.IV hold: we consider the problem of predicting the integral

(11.4.22) $$Q \equiv \int_{\mathbb{R}} \phi(s) \xi^0(ds)$$

from observations on $\xi^0(\cdot)$ up to time t. The best linear predictor, in the mean square sense, is just the projection of ϕ onto the Hilbert space $L_2(\xi^0; t)$, and it can be written as

$$(11.4.23) \qquad \hat{Q}_t = \int_{-\infty}^t \phi(s)\xi^0(ds) + \int_t^\infty \phi(s)\hat{X}_t(s)ds,$$

where for $s > t$,

$$(11.4.24) \qquad \hat{X}_t(s) = \int_{-\infty}^t c(s - u)V(du).$$

The truncated function

$$c_t(u) = \begin{cases} c(u) & (u > s - t) \\ 0 & (u \le s - t) \end{cases}$$

is in $L_2(\mathbb{R})$ when c is, and the same is true of its Fourier transform. Consequently, the random integrals in the definitions of $\hat{X}_t(s)$ and $\hat{Q}_t$ are well defined by virtue of the same argument as used in proving Proposition 11.4.IV. This already gives an explicit form for the predictor, but since it involves $V(\cdot)$ it is not convenient in practice. Here it is more convenient to use the autoregressive representation of $\hat{X}_t(s)$, which [cf. (11.4.21)] takes the form

$$(11.4.25) \quad \hat{X}_t(s) = \int_{-\infty}^t \left\{ c(s - u) - \int_0^{t-u} c(s - u - v)d(v)dv \right\} \xi^0(du).$$

The integrand has as its Fourier transform $\tilde{c}_t(\omega)(1 - \tilde{d}(\omega))$, where $\tilde{c}_t(\omega)$ is the Fourier transform of the truncated version of $c(\cdot)$. This is in $L_2(\Gamma)$ since

$$\int_{\mathbb{R}} |\tilde{c}_t(\omega)|^2 |1 - \tilde{d}(\omega)|^2 \gamma(d\omega) = \int_{\mathbb{R}} |\tilde{c}_t(\omega)|^2 \, d\omega \le \int_{\mathbb{R}} |\tilde{c}(\omega)|^2 \, d\omega.$$

The integral is therefore well defined in the mean square sense, and also in the a.s. sense if $d \in L_1(\mathbb{R})$, since the integrand can also be written in the form

$$-d(s - u) + \int_{t-u}^{s-u} c(s - u - v)d(v)dv,$$

that is, as the difference of two $L_1(\mathbb{R})$ functions.

These arguments are enough to establish the validity of the autoregressive form (11.4.25) as an alternative to (11.4.24). It is important to note that $\hat{X}_t(s)$ is to be interpreted as the predictor of the intensity of the ξ^0 process at time $s > t$, or in abbreviated notation,

$$(11.4.26) \qquad \xi^0(ds|\mathcal{H}_t) = \hat{X}_t(s)ds.$$

Thus, our assumptions imply that the intensity is predicted forward as a mean square continuous function of the past. In contrast to the case of a mean square continuous process, where the predictors may involve differentiations, here they are always smoothing operators. Our discussion can be summarized as follows.

Proposition 11.4.V. *Under the conditions of Proposition* 11.4.IV *the best linear predictor of the functional* Q *at* (11.4.22), *given the history* $\mathcal{H}_t$ *of the* ξ^0 *process on* $(-\infty, t]$, *is as at* (11.4.23) *in which the mean square continuous process* $\hat{X}_t(s)$ *may be regarded as the best linear predictor of the "intensity"* $\xi^0(ds)/ds$ *for* $s > t$ *and has the moving average representation* (11.4.24) *and the autoregressive representation*

$$\hat{X}_t(s) = \int_{-\infty}^{t} h_t(s - u)\xi^0(du),$$

where

$$(11.4.27) \qquad h_t(s - u) = c(s - u) - \int_0^{t-u} c(s - u - v)d(v)dv$$

$$= -d(s - u) + \int_{t-u}^{s-u} c(s - u - w)d(w)dw.$$

Returning to the original random measure ξ (as distinct from ξ^0), we obtain the following straightforward corollary, stated in the abbreviated form analogous to (11.4.26).

Corollary 11.4.VI. *The random measure* ξ *can be predicted forward with predicted intensity at* $s > t$ *given by*

$$\tilde{\xi}(ds|\mathcal{H}_t) = (m + \hat{X}_t(s))ds.$$

EXAMPLE 11.4(c) *Point process with rational spectral density* (continued from Example 11.4(b)). Consider the simple case where $\gamma(\omega) = A^2(\alpha^2 + \omega^2)/(\beta^2 + \omega^2)$. From the form of $\tilde{g}(\omega)$ as earlier, it follows that

$$\tilde{c}(\omega) = (\alpha - \beta)/(\beta - i\omega),$$
$$c(t) = (\alpha - \beta)e^{-\beta t} \qquad (t \geq 0),$$
$$\tilde{d}(\omega) = (\alpha - \beta)/(\alpha - i\omega),$$
$$d(t) = (\alpha - \beta)e^{-\alpha t} \qquad (t \geq 0).$$

Substituting into (11.4.27) we find

$$h_t(s - u) = (\alpha - \beta)e^{-\beta(s-u)} - (\alpha - \beta)^2 e^{-\beta(s-u)} \int_0^{t-u} e^{-(\alpha-\beta)v} \, dv$$

$$= (\alpha - \beta)e^{-\beta(s-t)}e^{-\alpha(t-u)}$$

so that

$$\hat{X}_t(s) = (\alpha - \beta)e^{-\beta(s-t)} \int_{-\infty}^{t} e^{-\alpha(t-u)}\xi^0(du).$$

Thus, the predictor here is a form of exponential smoothing of the past.

EXAMPLE 11.4(d) *Two-point Poisson cluster process* (continued from Example 11.4(a)). This example does *not* satisfy the assumptions of the preceding discussion but is nonetheless simple enough to handle directly. From the expression for $\tilde{g}(\omega)$ given earlier, the moving average representation can be written in the form

$$\zeta^0(dt) = (\mu/2\pi)^{1/2}\{V(dt) + V(dt - h)\}.$$

The reciprocal has the form

$$1/\tilde{g}(\omega) = (2\pi/\mu)^{1/2}(1 + e^{i\omega h})^{-1},$$

which, if we proceed formally, can be regarded as being the sum of an infinite series corresponding to the time-domain representation

$$V(dt) = (2\pi/\mu)^{1/2}(\zeta^0(dt) - \zeta^0(dt - h) + \zeta^0(dt - 2h) - \cdots).$$

In fact, the sum is a.s. finite and has the effect of retaining in V only those atoms in ζ^0 that are not preceded by a further atom h time units previously, that is, of retaining the atoms at cluster centres but rejecting their cluster companions. From this it is clear that the process $V(\cdot)$ is just a scaled version of the zero-mean version of the original Poisson process of cluster centres, and the moving average representation is simply a statement of how the clusters are formed. It is now easy to form linear predictors: we have

$$\hat{\zeta}^0(ds\,|\,\mathscr{H}_t) = \begin{cases} 0 & (s - t > h), \\ (\mu/2\pi)^{1/2}V(ds - h) & (0 \le h \le s - t), \end{cases}$$

and on $0 \le h \le s - t$ we also have

$$\hat{\zeta}^0(ds\,|\,\mathscr{H}_t) = \sum_{j=1}^{\infty} (-1)^j \zeta^0(ds - jh).$$

The effect of the last formula is to scan the past to see if there is an atom at $s - h$ not preceded by a further atom at $s - 2h$: the predictor predicts an atom at s when this is the case, and zero otherwise.

11.5. Applications to Multivariate and Other Point Processes

As in Chapter 10, we conclude this chapter also with a series of examples that illustrate further applications and extensions of the ideas behind the theory developed in Sections 11.1–11.4. We consider multivariate point processes, then point processes on the circle, and finally stationary isotropic point processes in $\mathbb{R}^2$.

The spectral theory of random measures and point processes extends easily to multivariate processes on $\mathbb{R}$. Each second-order moment or covariance measure is replaced by a matrix of auto- and cross-moment (or covariance) measures with elements, say

$$M_{ij}(A \times B) = E(\xi_i(A)\xi_j(B)) \qquad (i, j = 1, \ldots, k)$$
$$C_{ij}(A \times B) = M_{ij}(A \times B) - M_i(A)M_j(B),$$

where $M_i(\cdot)$, $M_j(\cdot)$ are the corresponding first moment measures of the k-variate random measure. Under stationarity, every linear combination $\sum_{i=1}^{k} \alpha_i \xi_i(A)$ is again stationary, so that the corresponding quadratic functions $\sum_{i=1}^{k} \sum_{j=1}^{k} \alpha_i \alpha_j M_{ij}(\cdot)$ are stationary under diagonal shifts and therefore possess a diagonal factorization. From this there follows the existence of reduced forms, $\hat{M}_{ij}$, $\hat{C}_{ij}$ say, for each of the components. In the point process case the off-diagonal components $\hat{C}_{ij}$ ($i \neq j$) no longer necessarily have the atom at the origin characteristic of the diagonal components $\hat{C}_{ii}$ unless there is positive probability of pairs of points occurring simultaneously in both the i and j streams. In all cases the matrix $\hat{M} = (\hat{M}_{ij})$ has a matrix version of the p.p.d. properties; namely,

(i) $\hat{M}_{ij}(\cdot) \geq 0$, and
(ii) for all finite sequences $\{f_i\}$ of bounded measurable complex functions of bounded support,

$$(11.5.1) \qquad \sum_{i=1}^{k} \sum_{j=1}^{k} \int_{\mathbb{R}} f_i(x) \overline{f_j(x + u)} \hat{M}_{ij}(du) \geq 0.$$

These properties are preserved by the Fourier transform map implying that the moment measures can be represented by a matrix of spectral measures, which has the matrix p.p.d. property (see Exercise 11.5.1).

For practical purposes, the multivariate extensions of the Bartlett spectrum (Definition 11.2.II) are of potential importance. We can again form the matrix Γ of auto- and cross-spectral measures ($\Gamma_{ij}(\cdot)$) in which the diagonal elements $\Gamma_{ii}(\cdot)$ have the properties described in Section 11.2 and the matrix as a whole has the positive definiteness property at (11.5.1). Indeed, (11.5.1) can be regarded as being derived from the filtered form

$$(11.5.2) \qquad X(t) = \sum_{i=1}^{k} \int_{-\infty}^{\infty} f_i(t - u)\xi_i(du),$$

of which (11.3.10) is the spectral form with the right-hand side replaced by the sum

$$(11.5.3) \qquad \sum_{i=1}^{k} \sum_{j=1}^{k} \tilde{f}_i(\omega)\tilde{f}_j^*(\omega)\Gamma_{ij}(d\omega).$$

The components ξ_i at (11.5.2) may be point processes or random measures, which, if they have densities, imply that the appropriate components of the matrix Γ are just the ordinary spectra and cross-spectra of the stationary processes formed by their densities. In this way the theory embraces both point and continuous processes, as well as mixed versions. If the continuous process has varying sign, as occurs with a Gaussian process, or is given in the weak sense only, then the appropriate framework is the matrix extension of the setting and results summarized in Theorem 11.3.VIII. From the practical viewpoint, these remarks mean that the interaction of point process systems, or mixtures of point process and continuous systems, can be studied in the frequency domain very much as if they were all continuous systems. The essential difference to note is that each point process component leads to a δ-function component in the diagonal terms $\hat{C}_{ii}(\cdot)$ to which there is then a corresponding nonzero constant contribution in the spectral measure $\Gamma_{ii}(\cdot)$. Bearing this in mind, all the standard concepts of multivariate spectral theory, in particular, coherence and phase, real and quadratic spectra, can be carried over to this more general context and provide valuable tools for the descriptive analysis of multivariate point processes and mixed systems.

In terms of models also, there is a rich variety of possibilities, arising largely as multivariate generalizations of the principal of univariate models described earlier. The next three examples illustrate simple special cases of such extensions.

EXAMPLE 11.5(a) *A bivariate Poisson process* (continued from Example 8.3(d)). The stationary bivariate point process described earlier is determined by three parameters: rates μ_1 and μ_2 for the occurrence of single points in processes 1 and 2, respectively, and boundedly finite measure $\hat{Q}_3(du)$ representing the rate of occurrence of pairs of points, the first in process 1 and the second from process 2 separated by a distance lying in $(u, u + du)$, where u is signed. Since the overall rate of occurrence must remain finite, $\hat{Q}_3$ must in fact be totally finite, and thus $\hat{Q}_3(du) = \mu_3 G(du)$ for some distribution G referring to the (signed) separation distance of a pair of points and some rate parameter μ_3 giving the overall rate of occurrence of pairs.

Since the two component processes are both Poisson, the only nonzero second-order factorial cumulant measure is in the cross-covariance term, with

$$\hat{C}_{12}(A) = \mu_3 G(A) = \hat{C}_{21}(-A).$$

The corresponding Bartlett spectra are all absolutely continuous, the densities $\gamma_{ij}(\cdot)$ of the matrix being given by

(11.5.4)
$$\gamma_{11}(\omega) = (\mu_1 + \mu_3)/2\pi, \qquad \gamma_{22}(\omega) = (\mu_2 + \mu_3)/2\pi,$$

$$\gamma_{12}(\omega) = \gamma_{21}(-\omega) = (\mu_3/2\pi)\tilde{G}(\omega) \equiv \frac{\mu_3}{2\pi}\int_{\mathbb{R}} e^{iu\omega}G(du).$$

The *coherence* of the two processes, at frequency ω, is the ratio

$$\rho_{12}(\omega) = \mu_3|\tilde{G}(\omega)|/\{(\mu_1 + \mu_3)(\mu_2 + \mu_3)\}^{1/2},$$

while their *phase* at the same frequency is

$$\theta_{12}(\omega) = \text{artan}\left(\frac{\text{Im}(\tilde{G}(\omega))}{\text{Re}(\tilde{G}(\omega))}\right).$$

EXAMPLE 11.5(b) *System identification: A special case.* In the previous example the spectral densities completely determine the parameters of the process. This leads to the more general problem of determining the characteristics of a point process *system,* meaning some mechanism for producing a point process output from a point process input. Deletions (or thinnings), delays (or translations), and triggering of clusters can all be regarded as examples of point process systems. The problem of system identification then consists of determining the mechanism, or at least its main features, from measurements on its input and output. The two components of the previous example can be regarded as the input and output of a system specified as follows: a proportion $\pi_1 = \mu_1/(\mu_1 + \mu_3)$ of the input points are randomly deleted while each of the points in the remaining proportion $\pi_2 = 1 - \pi_1$ are transmitted after independent delays with d.f. G [such a specification requires $G(\cdot)$ to be concentrated on a half-line], with this transmitted output being contaminated with "noise" consisting of the points of a Poisson process at rate μ_2. It is evident from the spectral representation at (11.5.4) that the three parameters π_1, G, and μ_2 of the system can be identified by using a Poisson input process and finding the joint first- and second-order properties of the input and output. It is equally evident that this identification is impossible on the basis of separate observation of the input and output.

Suppose now that the Poisson input process is replaced by any simple stationary input process with spectral density $\gamma(\cdot)$ [instead of $(\mu_1 + \mu_3)/2\pi$] and mean density m. Then in place of the matrix with components at (11.5.4) we would have the matrix

$$(11.5.5) \quad \begin{bmatrix} \gamma(\omega) & \gamma(\omega)\tilde{G}(\omega) \\ \overline{\gamma(\omega)\tilde{G}(\omega)} & (\mu_2 + \pi_2 m)/2\pi + \pi_1^2 |\tilde{G}(\omega)|^2 (\gamma(\omega) - m/2\pi) \end{bmatrix}$$

Once more it is evident that in principle the parameters π_1, G, and μ can be identified from this matrix of spectral densities.

EXAMPLE 11.5(c) *Mutually exciting point processes.* Hawkes (1971b, 1972) generalized the model described in Examples 10.4(c) and 11.2(e) to both the multivariate and marked point process cases. We give here the multivariate model but via a cluster process representation, where the branching process now consists of points of K different types and for each $i, j = 1, \ldots, K$ there is a Poisson process of offspring of type j generated by an ancestor of type i at time t governed by the parameter measure $\mu_{ij}(\cdot \,|t)$, all these processes being independent and each new offspring generating its own Poisson process. Assume homogeneity of such offspring processes by setting $\mu_{ij}(\cdot \,|t) = \mu_{ij}(\cdot - t)$ (all t) as earlier in Example 10.4(c), and in order to ensure that there are a.s. only finitely many descendants to any given individual, assume that the largest eigenvalue of the matrix $(\mu_{ij}(\mathbb{R}))$, which by Perron–Frobenius theory is necessarily positive, is smaller than 1. Finally, suppose that type i points enter the system from outside as ancestors in a Poisson process at rate λ_i $(i = 1, \ldots, K)$.

For notational simplicity, confine attention to the case where densities exist. Then results from branching processes in Section 5.5 (e.g., see Exercise 5.5.6) yield

$$(11.5.6) \quad m_{ki}(x) = \delta_{ik}\delta_0(x) + \sum_{l=1}^{K} \int_{\mathbb{R}} \mu_{kl}(v)m_{li}(x - v)dv,$$

$$(11.5.7) \quad m_{k,ij}(x, y) = m_{ki}(x)m_{kj}(y) + \sum_{l=1}^{K} \int_{\mathbb{R}} \mu_{kl}(v)m_{l,ij}(x - v, y - v)dv,$$

where the first and second moment densities, which incorporate an appropriate δ-function, can also be interpreted as

$$m_{ki}(x)dx = \text{Pr}\{\text{ancestor of type } k \text{ born at 0 has type } i \text{ descendant born in } (x, x + dx)\},$$

$$m_{k,ij}(x, y)dx\,dy = \text{Pr}\{\text{ancestor of type } k \text{ born at 0 has type } i \text{ and } j \text{ descendants born in } (x, x + dx) \text{ and } (y, y + dy), \text{ respectively}\}$$

and we have written $\mu_{kl}(v)dv = \mu_{kl}(dv)$. Thus, the mean density of type i points, assuming stationarity, is given by

$$(11.5.8) \qquad\qquad m_i \equiv \sum_{k} \int_{\mathbb{R}} m_{ki}(x)\lambda_k\,dx.$$

The integral here can be found by solving (11.5.6) after integration, but for later use it is better now to introduce the Fourier transforms

$$\tilde{m}_{ki}(\omega) = \int_{\mathbb{R}} e^{ix\omega}m_{ki}(x)dx, \qquad \tilde{\mu}_{ki}(\omega) = \int_{\mathbb{R}} e^{ix\omega}\mu_{ki}(x)dx,$$

so that $\tilde{m}(\omega) \equiv (\tilde{m}_{ij}(\omega))$ and $\tilde{\mu}(\omega) \equiv (\mu_{ij}(\omega))$ are related by

$$(11.5.9) \qquad\qquad \tilde{m}(\omega) = (I - \tilde{\mu}(\omega))^{-1}.$$

Then the column vector $(m_1, \ldots, m_K)^T = \tilde{m}(0)(\lambda_1, \ldots, \lambda_k)^T$.

Similar, lengthier analysis starting from (11.5.7) and using the relation for the reduced covariance density

$$c_{ij}(u) = \sum_{k=1}^{K} \lambda_k \int_{\mathbb{R}} m_{k,ij}(x, x + u)dx$$

leads ultimately to the matrix of spectral densities as

$$(11.5.10) \quad (\gamma_{ij}(\omega)) = \left((2\pi)^{-1} \int_{\mathbb{R}} e^{iu\omega}c_{ij}(u)du\right)$$

$$= (2\pi)^{-1}\tilde{m}^T(-\omega)\,\text{diag}(m_1, \ldots, m_K)\tilde{m}(\omega)$$

$$= (2\pi)^{-1}(I - \tilde{\mu}^T(-\omega))^{-1}\,\text{diag}(m_1, \ldots, m_K)(I - \tilde{\mu}(\omega))^{-1},$$

which generalizes (11.2.10).

Hawkes (1971b) derived (11.5.10) via the linear intensity structure and a

Wiener–Hopf argument, which is not needed here because the existence of $(I - \tilde{\mu}(0))^{-1}$ ensures that of $(I - \tilde{\mu}(\omega))^{-1}$ (all real ω).

As a variant on this theme, consider a more general cluster process in which the cluster centres form a simple stationary point process with mean density λ and Bartlett spectrum having the density $\gamma_{11}(\cdot)$, while the clusters have the Hawkes branching structure. For simplicity, assume that densities exist and consider only the univariate case. The resultant process may be considered as the output of a system with the cluster centre process the input and the clustering structure describing a kind of positive feedback with linear structure (since the clusters of a Hawkes process have such an interpretation). Arguing from the general relations for the second-order properties of a cluster process, the output process here has the form

$$\gamma_{22}(\omega) = \{(\lambda/2\pi)((1 - v)^{-1} - 1) + \gamma_{11}(\omega)\}/|1 - \tilde{\mu}(\omega)|^2,$$

where $v = \tilde{\mu}(0)$, which is a different generalization of (11.2.10) to (11.5.10). The only contributions to the cross-covariance terms are from the cluster centre to cluster members, leading to $c_{12}(u) = \lambda m_1(u|0)$ (cf. the notation in Exercise 5.5.6), and thus

$$\gamma_{12}(\omega) = (\lambda/2\pi)/(1 - \tilde{\mu}(\omega))^{-1} = \gamma_{21}(-\omega).$$

By specializing $\gamma_{11}(\cdot)$, more specific examples of input/output systems are obtained. For example, the input may be a Cox process directed by a continuous nonnegative process $X(\cdot)$, in which case we have a continuous input process $X(\cdot)$ causally affecting an output point process. If, moreover, $X(\cdot)$ is itself a shot-noise process generated by some primary point process, we recover a somewhat more general case of mutually exciting point processes.

In all these examples, the spectral approach provides insight into the structure of the causal mechanism and allows important characteristics of the system components to be estimated. It is straightforward to apply and is based on extensions of known procedures for continuous processes. However, it is not necessarily the most powerful approach, as the nonlinear filtering procedures based on the conditional intensity are usually available for these Hawkes-type models (cf. Chapter 13) and these then bring into play the power of likelihood techniques.

We now consider a random measure ξ on the circle $\mathbb{S}$, supposing that ξ is second-order stationary under rotations of $\mathbb{S}$. This implies that its second moment measure $M_2(d\theta \times d\phi)$ is invariant under diagonal shifts [i.e., $(\theta, \phi) \to (\theta + \alpha, \phi + \alpha)$, where addition on $\mathbb{S}$ is always understood to be modulo 2π] and leads therefore to a reduced moment measure $\hat{M}_2$ such that

(11.5.11) $M_2(d\theta \times d\phi) = (d\theta/2\pi)\hat{M}_2(d\psi) = E(\xi(d\theta)\xi(\theta - d\phi)),$

where $\psi = \theta - \phi$. Observe that $\hat{M}_2$ is defined here via the normalized invariant measure $d\theta/2\pi$ on $\mathbb{S}$.

$\hat{M}_2(\cdot)$ is a p.p.d. measure on $\mathbb{S}$, and its Fourier transform is a p.p.d.

sequence $\{\gamma_n\}$ of Fourier coefficients

$$\gamma_n = (2\pi)^{-1} \int_{\mathbb{S}} e^{i\psi n} \hat{M}_2(d\psi), \qquad n = 0, \pm 1, \ldots$$

(cf. Exercise 11.1.2 where the dual situation is described; i.e., starting from a stationary random measure on the integers, form its reduced second moment measures and Fourier transform, this last being a p.p.d. measure on the circle).

Integrating (11.5.11) over $A \times \mathbb{S}$ for $A \in \mathcal{B}(\mathbb{S})$ yields the important representation

$$(11.5.12) \qquad \hat{M}_2(A) = E\left(\int_{\mathbb{S}} \xi(\theta - A)\xi(d\theta)\right)$$

(cf. Proposition 10.4.V, Lemma 10.4.VI, and Theorem 10.4.VII). Indeed, a representation like (11.5.12) holds whenever the state space, here $\mathbb{S}$, forms a compact group so that its Haar measure is totally finite.

Equation (11.5.12) can be taken as underlying a statement in Davidson (1974b) (his Theorem 4), which, in the present context, would be equivalent to asserting that a measure v on $(\mathbb{S}, \mathcal{B}(\mathbb{S}))$ is the reduced second moment measure of a stationary random measure on $\mathbb{S}$ if and only if it belongs to the closed positive cone in $\mathcal{M}(\mathbb{S})$ generated by squared measures of the form $\eta = \zeta * \zeta^*$; that is,

$$(11.5.13) \qquad v = v(\mathbb{S}) \int_{\mathscr{L}} \eta \Pi(d\eta)$$

for some probability distribution $\Pi(\cdot)$ on $(\mathcal{M}_1(\mathbb{S}), \mathcal{B}(\mathcal{M}_1(\mathbb{S})))$ and

$$\mathscr{L} = \left\{\eta \in \mathcal{M}_1(\mathbb{S}): \eta(A) = \int_{\mathbb{S}} \zeta(\theta - A)\zeta(d\theta) \text{ for some } \zeta \in \mathcal{M}_1(\mathbb{S})\right\},$$

with $\mathcal{M}_1(\mathbb{S})$ the space of probability measures on $\mathbb{S}$. In one direction, this statement is obvious as a paraphrase of (11.5.12), but the converse is more troublesome. Starting from a representation as at (11.5.13), how can the *existence* of a well-defined random measure be ensured?

Given $\eta \in \mathscr{L}$, so that $\eta = \zeta * \zeta^*$ for some measure ζ on $\mathbb{S}$, construct a random measure ξ on $\mathbb{S}$ via

$$\xi(A, \omega) = \zeta(A + U(\omega)) \qquad (A \in \mathcal{B}(\mathbb{S})),$$

where $U(\omega)$ is a r.v. uniformly distributed on $\mathbb{S}$. Then for bounded measurable $h(\theta, \phi)$ $(\theta, \phi \in \mathbb{S})$ we have

$$(11.5.14) \quad E\left(\int_{\mathbb{S}} \int_{\mathbb{S}} h(\theta, \phi)\xi(d\theta)\xi(d\phi)\right)$$

$$= (2\pi)^{-1} \int_{\mathbb{S}} du \int_{\mathbb{S}} \int_{\mathbb{S}} h(\theta, \phi)\zeta(u + d\theta)\zeta(u + d\phi)$$

$$= (2\pi)^{-1} \int_\mathbb{S} du \int_\mathbb{S} \int_\mathbb{S} h(\theta, \theta + \psi) \zeta(u + d\theta) \zeta(u + \theta - d\psi)$$

$$\text{(putting } \psi = \theta - \phi)$$

$$= (2\pi)^{-1} \int_\mathbb{S} du \int_\mathbb{S} \int_\mathbb{S} h(v - u, v - u + \psi) \zeta(dv) \zeta(v - d\psi)$$

$$\text{(putting } v = \theta + u)$$

$$= (2\pi)^{-1} \int_\mathbb{S} d\theta \int_\mathbb{S} \int_\mathbb{S} h(\theta, \theta + \psi) \zeta(dv) \zeta(v - d\psi)$$

$$\text{(putting } \theta = v - u)$$

$$= \int_\mathbb{S} \int_\mathbb{S} h(\theta, \theta + \psi) \eta(d\psi) d\theta / 2\pi \qquad \text{(by definition of } \eta),$$

thereby exhibiting η as the reduced second moment measure of the random measure ξ.

More generally, supposing that v has a representation as at (11.5.13), we use $\Pi(\cdot)$ to choose $\eta \in \mathscr{L}$, and then for such η we use some ζ for which $\eta = \zeta * \zeta^*$ and proceed as above so that now the random measure is represented as a probabilistic mixture. It is easy to check (11.5.13) via

$$E\left(\int_\mathbb{S} \int_\mathbb{S} h(\theta, \phi) \xi(d\theta) \xi(d\phi) \right)$$

$$= \int_\mathscr{L} \Pi(d\eta) \int_\mathbb{S} (2\pi)^{-1} du \int_\mathbb{S} \int_\mathbb{S} h(\theta, \phi) \zeta(u + d\theta) \zeta(u + d\phi)$$

$$= \int_\mathscr{L} \Pi(d\eta) \int_\mathbb{S} \int_\mathbb{S} h(\theta, \theta + \psi) \eta(d\psi) d\theta / 2\pi$$

$$= \int_\mathbb{S} \int_\mathbb{S} h(\theta, \theta + \psi) v(d\psi) d\theta / 2\pi.$$

Since the reduced second moment measures of the random measures ξ and $a\xi$ are just v say, and then $a^2 v$, the constant $v(\mathbb{S})$ in (11.5.13), is easily accommodated.

The argument above *assumes* that a measurable mapping $\eta \to \mathscr{L}$ is given. Finding such a mapping in order to legitimize the argument is a more difficult problem, and the absence of such a step from Davidson's proof seems to us to leave his assertion not fully established. A related question is whether the class of p.p.d. measures coincides with the class of reduced second moment measures (and hence if the extension of Davidson's assertion indicated above is true, with convex combinations of "squared" measures). The next example demonstrates an affirmative answer in a fairly simple case.

EXAMPLE 11.5(d) *A cyclic point process on four points.* A point process on a cyclic group of order four can be represented as a point process on the four compass points, N, E, S, W, with group operation represented by rotation through a right angle. Stationarity is thus invariance under such rotations.

Any simple point process on NESW has a realization consisting of at most four points whose relative configuration is one of the six possibilities, which we write (in an obvious NESW shorthand) 0000, 1000, 1100, 1010, 1110, and 1111. Let the probabilities of these relative configurations be p_0, p_1, p_{21}, p_{22}, p_3, and p_4, respectively, so that the mean density at each location is

$$m = p_1/4 + (p_{21} + p_{22})/2 + 3p_3/4 + p_4.$$

The reduced second moment measure is proportional to $(a \quad b \quad c \quad d)$, where

$$a = m,$$

$$b = p_{21}/4 + p_3/2 + p_4 = d,$$

$$c = p_{22}/2 + p_3/2 + p_4.$$

This is a p.p.d. measure, with Fourier transform proportional to $(a + c + 2b, a - c, a + c - 2b, a - c)$. Thus,

(11.5.15) $a \geq c, \qquad a + c \geq 2b.$

We now ask what p.p.d. measures $(a \quad b \quad c \quad b)$ can arise as the reduced moment measures of stationary simple point processes on NESW. This means that we are seeking nonnegative $p_0, \ldots, p_4$ with sum 1 and equal to a, b, c as above. Clearly, each of a, b, c must lie in $(0, 1]$, and satisfy (11.5.15), but not every such p.p.d. measure can come from a probability distribution, for if $a = 1 - \varepsilon$ for some positive $\varepsilon < \frac{1}{4}$, then $p_4 \geq 1 - 4\varepsilon$ and thus b and c must also be $\geq 1 - 4\varepsilon$. The most general situation we can thus hope for is that, given a p.p.d. measure $(\alpha \quad \beta \quad \gamma \quad \beta)$ on NESW, there may necessarily exist a distribution $p_0, \ldots, p_4$ and a positive constant λ such that, in the notation as above, $a = \lambda\alpha$, $b = \lambda\beta$, $c = \lambda\gamma$. The first point to observe in solving such a system is that if λ yields a solution, so does $\pi\lambda$ for every $0 < \pi < 1$, and since $a \leq 1$, this implies that there is a largest value of λ for given α, β, γ, such that $p_0 = 0$. Some elementary algebra shows that we can find a nonnegative solution, namely, $p_3 = 0$, $p_1 = 4\lambda(\alpha + \gamma - 2 \max(\beta, \gamma))$, $p_{21} = 2\lambda(\beta - \gamma)_+$, $p_{22} = 2\lambda(\gamma - \beta)_+$, and $p_4 = \lambda \min(\beta, \gamma)$; finally, positive λ is determined from the normalizing condition. This can be viewed another way, namely, that every p.p.d. measure of the form $(1 \quad \beta \quad \gamma \quad \beta)$ can be represented as the convex sum of the basic p.p.d. measures coming from 1000, 1010, 1100, and 1111, with

$$m(1 \quad \beta \quad \gamma \quad \beta) = \tfrac{1}{4}p_1(1 \quad 0 \quad 0 \quad 0) + \tfrac{1}{2}p_{21}(1 \quad \tfrac{1}{2} \quad 0 \quad \tfrac{1}{2})$$
$$+ \tfrac{1}{2}p_{22}(1 \quad 0 \quad 1 \quad 0) + p_4(1 \quad 1 \quad 1 \quad 1).$$

Since $p_3 = 0$, this relation (noting the definition of m) exhibits $(1 \quad \beta \quad \gamma \quad \beta)$ in the form at (11.5.13).

We resume our discussion from Section 10.5 of stationary isotropic simple point processes in $\mathbb{R}^2$, this time looking at the Fourier transform. Recall from Proposition 10.5.III that such a point process is fully described by its mean density m and reduced radial measure $\hat{K}_2(\cdot)$. The question studied here is what additional constraint on the Bartlett spectrum in $\mathbb{R}^2$ is implied by this isotropy condition; we then show how it is expressed through $\hat{K}_2(\cdot)$.

Consider first the effect of the double Fourier transform on a function $h: \mathbb{R}^2 \to \mathbb{R}$, which, in addition to being bounded, measurable, and of bounded support, is circularly symmetric; that is,

$$h(x, y) = h(r \cos \theta, r \sin \theta) = g(r) \quad (\text{all } \theta \in \mathbb{S})$$

for some function g. The transform is given by

$$\tilde{h}(\omega, \phi) \equiv \int_{\mathbb{R}^2} e^{i(\omega x + \phi y)} h(x, y) dx\, dy$$

$$= \int_0^\infty rg(r) dr \int_0^{2\pi} e^{ir(\omega \cos \theta + \phi \sin \theta)}\, d\theta$$

$$= \int_0^\infty rg(r) dr \int_0^{2\pi} e^{ir\rho \cos(\theta - \psi)}\, d\theta,$$

using (ρ, ψ) as polar coordinates in the (ω, ϕ) plane. Now the integral over θ is simply a Bessel function

$$J_0(u) = (2\pi)^{-1} \int_0^{2\pi} e^{iu \cos \theta}\, d\theta,$$

so

$$(11.5.16) \quad \tilde{h}(\omega, \phi) = 2\pi \int_0^\infty rJ_0(r\rho)g(r) dr \equiv \tilde{g}^B(\rho) \quad \text{where } \rho = (\omega^2 + \phi^2)^{1/2}.$$

Consequently, $\tilde{h}(\omega, \phi)$ is again circularly symmetric, reducing to the function $\tilde{g}^B(\cdot)$, which we call the *Bessel transform* of $g(\cdot)$ (we have included the factor 2π, which is a departure from the usual definition) and which is also called a Hankel transform—for example, see Copson (1935, p. 342). By arguing analogously from the inverse Fourier transform

$$h(x, y) = (2\pi)^{-2} \int_{\mathbb{R}^2} e^{-i(\omega x + \phi y)} \tilde{h}(\omega, \phi) d\omega\, d\phi,$$

it follows that the Bessel transform is inverted as in

$$(11.5.17) \qquad g(r) = (2\pi)^{-1} \int_0^\infty \rho \tilde{g}^B(\rho) J_0(r\rho) d\rho.$$

From this discussion we should expect the Bartlett spectral density of a stationary isotropic process to be circularly symmetric in frequency space and to be related to the inverse Bessel transform of the density of $\hat{K}_2(\cdot)$. To cover the situation where densities may not exist, the Bessel transform relation needs to be put into the form of a Parseval equation so that it can be extended to measures, as follows.

Proposition 11.5.I. Let $\Gamma(\cdot)$ be the Bartlett spectrum on $\mathbb{R}^2$ associated with a simple stationary isotropic point process in $\mathbb{R}^2$. Then $\Gamma(\cdot)$ is circularly symmetric and is expressible via $(\omega_1, \omega_2) = (\rho \cos \psi, \rho \sin \psi)$ as

$$(11.5.18) \quad \Gamma(d\rho \times d\psi) = (m\rho \, d\rho/2\pi + \kappa(d\rho) + 2\pi m^2 \delta_0(d\rho))d\psi/2\pi,$$

where κ is related to the radial measure $\hat{K}_2(\cdot)$ of Proposition 10.5.III by the Parseval–Bessel equation

$$(11.5.19) \qquad \int_0^\infty \tilde{g}^B(\rho)\kappa(d\rho) = \int_0^\infty g(r)\hat{K}_2(dr)$$

for all bounded measurable g of finite support on $\mathbb{R}_+$ and $\tilde{g}^B$ defined by (11.5.16).

PROOF. Recall that the Bartlett spectrum is the Fourier transform in $\mathbb{R}^2$ of the complete covariance measure $\hat{C}_2$, here taking the form (using mixed notation)

$$\hat{C}_2(dx \times dy) = m\delta_0(dx \times dy) - m^2 \, dx \, dy + \hat{K}_2(dr)d\theta/2\pi.$$

The first term here arises from the diagonal concentration associated with a simple point process; the second is the term involving the square of the mean, which must be subtracted from the second moment to yield the covariance; and the third term is the form of the reduced second factorial moment measure derived in Proposition 10.5.III. The first and second terms have the following inverse Fourier transforms, respectively:

$$(2\pi)^{-2} m \, d\omega_1 \, d\omega_2 = (2\pi)^{-2} m\rho \, d\rho \, d\psi = (m\rho \, d\rho/2\pi)(d\psi/2\pi),$$

$$(2\pi)^{-2}4\pi^2 m^2 \delta_0(d\omega_1 \times d\omega_2) = 2\pi m^2 \delta_0(d\rho)(d\psi/2\pi).$$

Denoting the double Fourier transform of the measure $\hat{K}(dr)d\theta/2\pi$ by $L(d\omega_1 \times d\omega_2)$, the Parseval relation for such transforms implies that, with h and $\tilde{h}$ as earlier,

$$\int_{\mathbb{R}^2} \tilde{h}(\omega_1, \omega_2)L(d\omega_1 \times d\omega_2) = \int_0^\infty \hat{K}(dr) \int_0^{2\pi} h(r \cos \theta, r \sin \theta)d\theta/2\pi.$$

Now

$$\int_0^{2\pi} h(r \cos \theta, r \sin \theta)d\theta/2\pi$$

$$= (2\pi)^{-2} \int_0^{2\pi} d\theta \int_0^\infty d\rho \int_0^{2\pi} e^{-i\rho r \cos(\theta - \psi)}\rho\tilde{h}(\rho \cos \psi, \rho \sin \psi)d\psi$$

$$= (2\pi)^{-1} \int_0^\infty d\rho \int_0^{2\pi} \rho J_0(\rho r)\tilde{h}(\rho \cos \psi, \rho \sin \psi)d\psi,$$

where as before the invariance of integrating θ over any interval of length 2π has been used. If, in particular, we take $\tilde{h}(\omega_1, \omega_2)$ to have the product form $\tilde{g}^B(\rho)f(\psi)$, we obtain from this relation and the Bessel transform equation (11.5.17) that

$$\int_0^\infty \int_0^{2\pi} \tilde{g}^B(\rho)f(\psi)L(d\rho \times d\psi) = \int_0^{2\pi} f(\psi)\left(\frac{d\psi}{2\pi}\right)\int_0^\infty g(r)\hat{K}_2(dr).$$

Since the integral here depends on f only through its integral over $(0, 2\pi)$, a uniqueness argument implies that $L(\cdot)$ has a disintegration of the form $L(d\rho \times d\psi) = \kappa(d\rho)(d\psi/2\pi)$, where $\kappa(\cdot)$ satisfies (11.5.19). $\qquad\square$

Note that (11.5.19) defines $\hat{K}_2(dr)/r\,dr$ (and not $\hat{K}_2$), in the sense of generalized functions, as the Bessel transform of $\kappa(d\rho)/\rho\,d\rho$.

EXAMPLE 11.5(e) *An isotropic Neyman–Scott process* (continued from Example 10.5(f)). Consider the circularly symmetric case from 10.5(f) and Exercise 10.5.5, for which we have

$$\hat{K}_2(dr) = 2\pi r\mu^2 m_1^2\,dr + \mu m_{[2]}re^{-r^2/4\sigma^2}\,dr/2\sigma^2.$$

The mean rate here is μm_1, and the first term can be recognized as the square of the mean [indeed, it is easy to check from (11.5.19) that the measure $2\pi r\,dr$ on $\mathbb{R}_+$ is the Parseval–Bessel transform of the measure consisting of a unit atom at the origin]. The second term is a density, which can be derived (via the Fourier transform in $\mathbb{R}^2$ or otherwise) as the Parseval–Bessel transform of the density

$$\kappa(\rho) = (\mu m_{[2]}/2\pi)\rho e^{-\sigma^2\rho^2}.$$

Consequently, for this isotropic Neyman–Scott model, the Bartlett spectrum is absolutely continuous with spectral density

$$\gamma(\omega, \phi) = \mu m_1/4\pi^2 + (\mu m_{[2]}/2\pi)e^{-\sigma^2(\omega^2 + \phi^2)}$$

or, in polar form, $\beta(\rho)d\rho\,d\psi/2\pi$, where

$$\beta(\rho) = \mu m_1\rho/2\pi + \mu m_{[2]}\rho e^{-\sigma^2\rho^2}.$$

Exercise

11.5.1. Let the matrix $(\hat{M}_{ij}(\cdot))$ of nonnegative measures be positive definite as at (11.5.1). Show that the matrix of Fourier transforms $(\Gamma_{ij}(\cdot))$ consists of nonnegative measures with the same positive-definite property.

CHAPTER 12

Palm Theory

In Section 3.4 we gave a brief introduction to the Palm–Khinchin equations and noted that, for a stationary point process on the line, they provide a partial link between counting and interval properties. In this chapter we study this link both in more detail and in a more general setting. It is a topic that has continued to be a focus of work over three decades, with recent theoretical study of its relation with ergodic theory and in applications to queueing theory and other fields.

Early contributions by Palm (1943) and Khinchin (1955) have already been noted. Subsequently, the general theme was taken up by Kaplan (1955), who was influenced by Doob's (1948) work on renewal processes, Ryll-Nardzewski (1961), and Slivnyak (1962, 1966). Slivnyak extended the subadditivity arguments of Section 3.4 to a wider class of events and, using this extension, was able to demonstrate a one-to-one relation between the probability measures of stationary counting processes on $\mathbb{R}$ and stationary sequences of intervals. The approach of Ryll-Nardzewski, followed by Papangelou (1972a, 1974a) and others, used a Radon–Nikodym argument after assuming the existence of first moments.

Kummer and Matthes (1970) introduced the important notion that they called Campbell measure, in essence a notion that underlies the Radon–Nikodym approach, and applied it in particular to studying the properties of infinitely divisible point processes. The later evolution of their work can be traced through the three editions of Matthes, Kerstan, and Mecke (1974, 1978, 1982). The relation with ergodic theory (the theory of flows and of flows under a function) has been studied by Neveu (1968, 1976), Papangelou (1970), and Delasnerie (1977), among others. A systematic account of the applications to queueing theory is given in Franken et al. (1981), following earlier work by König and Matthes (1963), König, Matthes, and Nawrotzki (1967), Franken

(1975), and Rolski (1981), among others. Closely related applications in stochastic geometry are sketched or referenced in Stoyan and Mecke (1983). An introduction to more recent developments is given in Chapter 14 below.

Of these approaches ours follows most closely that of Matthes et al. (1978), referenced in this book as MKM. The main emphasis is on the stationary case, and the main results are derived by a factorization of the Campbell measure, which parallels the factorization of the moment measures derived in Section 10.4; indeed, the reduced moment measures reappear in this chapter as multiples of the moment measures of the Palm distribution.

The definition of Campbell measure and a brief account of the Radon–Nikodym approach is given in Section 12.1. The main results for stationary processes are set out in Section 12.2, and their specializations to point processes are developed in Section 12.3, where, in particular, the interpretation of the Palm distribution as the distribution "conditional on a point at the origin" is recovered in the setting of point processes in $\mathbb{R}^d$. Section 12.4 is concerned with the closely related questions of convergence to equilibrium and the consequences of various concepts of mixing.

12.1. Campbell Measures and Palm Distributions

For any random measure ξ, including possibly a point process, on the c.s.m.s. $\mathscr{X}$, a measure on the product space $\mathscr{W} \equiv \mathscr{X} \times \mathscr{M}_\mathscr{X}$ can be introduced by setting, for $A \in \mathscr{B}_\mathscr{X}$, $U \in \mathscr{B}(\mathscr{M}_\mathscr{X})$, and $\mathscr{P}$ the distribution on $\mathscr{M}_\mathscr{X}$ associated with the given random measure,

$$(12.1.1) \qquad C_\mathscr{P}(A \times U) = E(\xi(A)I_U(\xi)) = \int_U \int_A \xi(dx)\mathscr{P}(d\xi).$$

Write $\mathscr{B}_\mathscr{W}$ for the product Borel σ-field $\mathscr{B}_\mathscr{X} \otimes \mathscr{B}(\mathscr{M}_\mathscr{X})$ [i.e., $\mathscr{B}_\mathscr{W}$ is generated by all $A \times U \in \mathscr{W}$ with $A \in \mathscr{B}_\mathscr{X}$ and $U \in \mathscr{B}(\mathscr{M}_\mathscr{X})$.] The set function $C_\mathscr{P}(\cdot)$ is clearly countably additive on such product sets but is totally finite if and only if the first moment measure exists and is totally finite. To see that $C_\mathscr{P}(\cdot)$ is always σ-finite, let $\{A_m\}$ $(m = 1, 2, \ldots)$ be a sequence of bounded Borel sets covering $\mathscr{X}$, and define

$$U_{mn} = \{\xi: \xi(A_m) \le n\} \qquad (n = 1, 2, \ldots).$$

Then the inequalities

$$C_\mathscr{P}(A_m \times U_{mn}) = \int_{A_m} \int_{U_{mn}} \xi(dx)\mathscr{P}(d\xi) \le n\mathscr{P}(U_{mn}) \le n$$

imply that $C_\mathscr{P}$ is certainly finite on each set $A_m \times U_{mn}$. These sets cover $\mathscr{W}$, because for any given $(x, \xi) \in \mathscr{W}$, we can select $A_m \ni x$ and then, because any $\xi \in \mathscr{M}_\mathscr{X}$ is boundedly finite, we can find U_{mn} for which $\xi(A_m) \le n$, so

$(x, \xi) \in A_m \times U_{mn}$. It then follows that the set function $C_{\mathcal{P}}$ extends uniquely to a σ-finite measure on $\mathcal{B}_{\mathcal{W}}$. We continue to use $C_{\mathcal{P}}$ for this extension.

Definition 12.1.I. The *Campbell measure* $C_{\mathcal{P}}$ associated with the random measure ξ on the c.s.m.s. $\mathcal{X}$, having distribution $\mathcal{P}$ on $\mathcal{M}_{\mathcal{X}}$, is the unique extension of the set function defined at (12.1.1) to a σ-finite measure on $\mathcal{B}_{\mathcal{W}}$.

By following the usual route from indicator functions to simple functions and limits of simple functions, this definition starting from (12.1.1) extends to the following integral form.

Lemma 12.1.II. *For $\mathcal{B}_{\mathcal{W}}$-measurable functions $g(x, \xi)$ that are either nonnegative or $C_{\mathcal{P}}$-integrable,*

$$(12.1.2) \qquad \int_{\mathcal{W}} g(x, \xi) C_{\mathcal{P}}(dx \times d\xi) = E\left(\int_{\mathcal{X}} g(x, \xi) \xi(dx) \right)$$

$$= \int_{\mathcal{M}_{\mathcal{X}}} \int_{\mathcal{X}} g(x, \xi) \xi(dx) \mathcal{P}(d\xi).$$

Two comments must be made concerning this definition. First, the construction is not restricted to probability measures $\mathcal{P}$ on $\mathcal{M}_{\mathcal{X}}$ but can be carried through for any σ-finite measure, Q say, for which we can identify a suitable family, $\{V_{mn}\}$ say, on which Q takes finite values. In particular, the construction is possible for the KLM measures $\tilde{Q}$ associated with an infinitely divisible random measure (see Exercise 12.1.1) and is also used in Chapters 13 and 14. Second, while it is clear from the construction that Q determines C_Q uniquely, the converse is true only with the reservation that C_Q always gives zero mass to sets of the form $A \times \{\varnothing\}$ in $\mathcal{W}$, where $\varnothing$ denotes the zero measure. The value of $Q(\{\varnothing\})$ cannot be determined directly from the Campbell measure; some additional information is necessary.

Lemma 12.1.III. *C_Q determines Q uniquely on $\mathcal{M}_{\mathcal{X}} \setminus \{\varnothing\}$ and, in particular, determines Q uniquely if either Q is a probability measure or $Q(\{\varnothing\}) = 0$.*

PROOF. Let $\{A_m\}$, $\{U_{mn}\}$ be as in the discussion following (12.1.1), and

$$F(x) = Q\{\xi: \xi(A_m) \leq x\}$$

[thus, $F(\cdot)$ is a d.f. when Q is a probability measure]. Then, say

$$C_{\mathcal{P}}(A_m \times U_{mn}) = \int_0^y x \, dF(x) = G(y),$$

so the Campbell measure determines a kind of weighted d.f. $G(\cdot)$. It follows that, apart from the value of $F(0+)$, $F(\cdot)$ is recovered via the relation

$$dF(x) = x^{-1} \, dG(x).$$

Analogous arguments apply to the multivariate fidi distributions [recall that the basic sample functions $\xi(\cdot)$ are random measures] and show that the Campbell measure determines all the fidi distributions of Q, and hence Q itself, up to the value of $Q(\{\varnothing\})$. This last is clearly determined if $Q(\mathcal{M}_{\mathcal{X}}) = 1$. □

There is an obvious close connection between the Campbell measure and the first moment measure, for by setting $U = \mathcal{M}_{\mathcal{X}}$ in (12.1.1), we see that

$$C_{\mathcal{P}}(A \times \mathcal{M}_{\mathcal{X}}) = E(\xi(A)) = M(A)$$

whenever the first moment measure $M(\cdot)$ exists. The link with Campbell's theorem noted around (6.4.11) follows most easily from (12.1.2), which yields, when $M(\cdot)$ exists as a boundedly finite measure,

$$E\left(\int_{\mathcal{X}} g(x)\xi(dx) \right) = \int_{\mathcal{X}} g(x) \int_{\mathcal{M}_{\mathcal{X}}} \xi(dx)\mathcal{P}(d\xi) = \int_{\mathcal{X}} g(x)M(dx),$$

that is, precisely (6.4.11), of which Campbell's (1909) original result is the special case for a stationary Poisson process.

It was this link with (6.4.11) that no doubt Kummer and Matthes (1970) had in mind in coining the term "Campbell measure" for the measure $C_{\mathcal{P}}$, because the latter is essentially a refinement of the moment measure M, just as Lemma 12.1.II can be regarded as a refinement (or extension) of (6.4.11).

As Kallenberg (1975, p. 69; 1983a, p. 103) remarks, refinements of higher-order moment measures can be defined in a similar way. For example, a second-order Campbell measure $C_{\mathcal{P}}^{(2)}$ can be defined on $\mathcal{X}^{(2)} \times \mathcal{M}_{\mathcal{X}}$ by setting

(12.1.3) $$C_{\mathcal{P}}^{(2)}(A \times B \times U) = E(\xi(A)\xi(B)I_U(\xi))$$

for $A, B \in \mathcal{B}_{\mathcal{X}}$, $U \in \mathcal{B}(\mathcal{M}_{\mathcal{X}})$. It is obvious that the second moment measure $M_2(A \times B)$, when it exists, appears as the marginal distribution on integrating out $\mathcal{P}$ (see Exercise 12.1.2).

The relation between $C_{\mathcal{P}}$ and the first moment measure is also the key to the Radon–Nikodym approach to the Palm theory, because if $M(\cdot)$ exists, then for each fixed $U \in \mathcal{B}(\mathcal{M}_{\mathcal{X}})$, $C_{\mathcal{P}}(\cdot \times U)$ is absolutely continuous with respect to $M(\cdot)$. We can thus introduce the Radon–Nikodym derivative as a $\mathcal{B}_{\mathcal{X}}$-measurable function $\mathcal{P}_0(x, U)$ satisfying, for each $A \in \mathcal{B}_{\mathcal{X}}$,

(12.1.4) $$\int_A \mathcal{P}_0(x, U)M(dx) = C_{\mathcal{P}}(A \times U).$$

$\mathcal{P}_0(x, U)$ is then defined uniquely up to values on sets of M-measure zero. Furthermore, just as in the discussion of regular conditional probabilities (see Proposition A1.5.III) the family $\{\mathcal{P}_0(x, U)\}$ can be chosen so that

(12.1.5a)　for each fixed $U \in \mathcal{B}(\mathcal{M}_{\mathcal{X}})$, $\mathcal{P}_0(x, U)$ is a measurable function of x, M-integrable on bounded subsets of $\mathcal{X}$; and

(12.1.5b)　for each fixed $x \in \mathcal{X}$, $\mathcal{P}_0(x, U)$ is a probability measure on $U \in \mathcal{B}(\mathcal{M}_{\mathcal{X}})$.

Each such measure $\mathscr{P}_0(x, \cdot)$ may be called a *local Palm distribution,* and a family of such measures satisfying (12.1.5a,b) a *Palm kernel* associated with the random measure. Then the discussion above implies the following result, in which (12.1.6) follows from (12.1.4) by the usual extension arguments.

Proposition 12.1.IV. *Let ξ be a random measure for which the first moment measure M exists. Then ξ admits a regular family of local Palm distributions $\mathscr{P}_0(\cdot)$, which are defined uniquely up to values on M-null sets and satisfy for all $\mathscr{B}_\mathscr{M}$-measurable functions g that are either nonnegative or $C_\mathscr{P}$-integrable*

$$(12.1.6) \qquad E\left(\int_\mathscr{X} g(x, \xi)\xi(dx)\right) = \int_{\mathscr{X} \times \mathscr{M}_\mathscr{X}} g(x, \xi)C_\mathscr{P}(dx \times d\xi)$$

$$= \int_\mathscr{X} M(dx)E_0^{(x)}(g(x, \xi)),$$

where

$$E_0^{(x)}(g(x, \xi)) = \int_{\mathscr{M}_\mathscr{X}} g(x, \xi)\mathscr{P}_0(x, d\xi).$$

Note that this proposition holds equally for random measures and point processes and does not require the process to be stationary. However, it is chiefly in the stationary case that the use of Palm distributions provides a simplification from the structural point of view (see Section 12.2), and only for point processes that it seems a natural object of study (see Section 12.3).

The nature of the Palm distribution when the random measure has a density is somewhat clarified by the following example.

EXAMPLE 12.1(a) *Palm distributions for a random measure with density.* Suppose that the random measure ξ on $\mathbb{R}$ has trajectories with a.s. continuous locally bounded derivatives $d\xi/dx$ and that the first moment measure $M(\cdot)$ has a continuous locally bounded density $M'(x) = m(x) = E(d\xi/dx)$. In (12.1.6) let $g(\cdot)$ run through a sequence of functions of the form $g_n(x, \xi) = h_n(x)I_U(\xi)$, where $\{h_n(x)\}$ is a δ-function sequence converging to δ_{x_0} for some $x_0 \in \mathbb{R}$ and $U \in \mathscr{B}(\mathscr{M}_\mathscr{X})$ is fixed. From (12.1.6) we obtain

$$\int_U \mathscr{P}(d\xi)\int_\mathscr{X} h_n(x)\frac{d\xi}{dx}\,dx = \int_\mathscr{X} m(x)h_n(x)\mathscr{P}_0(x, U)dx.$$

Using the a.s. continuity and local boundedness, the left-hand side converges as $n \to \infty$ to

$$\int_U \frac{d\xi}{dx}\bigg|_{x_0}\mathscr{P}(d\xi),$$

while the right-hand side converges to $m(x_0)\mathscr{P}_0(x_0, U)$ provided these kernel functions are continuous in x, so

$$\mathscr{P}_0(x_0, U) = (m(x_0))^{-1} \int_U \frac{d\xi}{dx}\bigg|_{x_0} \mathscr{P}(d\xi).$$

Thus, the measure $\mathscr{P}_0(x_0, \cdot)$ appears as a weighted average of the masses allocated to the realizations in U, the weights being proportional to the value of the densities $d\xi/dx$ at the chosen point x_0.

A condition such as the assumed continuity in x at x_0 of $\mathscr{P}_0(x, U)$ is essential, as can be shown by counterexamples where the right and left limits at x_0 of $\mathscr{P}_0(x, U)$ exist but are different [see Leadbetter (1972) for the point process context].

When the random measure is stationary, the local Palm distributions become translated versions of a single basic distribution, so that

(12.1.7) $\qquad\qquad \mathscr{P}_0(x, S_x U) = \tilde{\mathscr{P}}_0(U) \quad \text{for } \ell\text{-a.e. } x.$

A direct proof of this result can be given by arguing as in Exercise 10.1.9 (cf. Exercise 12.1.3); it is discussed in Sections 12.2 and 12.3, where a diagonal reduction argument is used and there is no requirement for the existence of first moments.

We conclude this section with a characterization of Palm distributions via Laplace functionals and some of the results that can be deduced via this characterization. Much as at (6.4.16), write $L[f]$, where $f \in BM_+(\mathscr{X})$, for the Laplace functional of a random measure with distribution $\mathscr{P}$, and $\{L[f; x]\}$ for the family of Laplace functionals derived from the Palm kernel at (12.1.5), so that

(12.1.8) $\quad L[f; x] = \int_{\mathscr{M}_{\mathscr{X}}} \exp\left(-\int_{\mathscr{X}} f(y)\xi(dy)\right) \mathscr{P}_0(x, d\xi) \quad (x \in \mathscr{X}, f \in BM_+).$

Proposition 12.1.V. *Let ξ be a random measure with finite first moment measure M and $L[f]$, $L[f; x]$ the Laplace functionals associated with the original random measure and its Palm kernel, respectively. Then the functionals $L[f]$ and $L[f; x]$ satisfy the relation, for $f, g \in BM_+(\mathscr{X})$,*

(12.1.9) $\qquad \lim_{\varepsilon \downarrow 0} \varepsilon^{-1}(L[f] - L[f + \varepsilon g]) = \int_{\mathscr{X}} g(x)L[f; x]M(dx).$

Conversely, if a family $\{L[f; x]\}$ satisfies (12.1.9) for all $f, g \in BM_+(\mathscr{X})$ and some random measure ξ with Laplace functional $L[\cdot]$ and first moment measure $M(\cdot)$, then the functionals $\{L[f; x]\}$ coincide M-a.e. with the Laplace functionals of the Palm kernel associated with ξ.

PROOF. Since the first moment measure exists, a finite Taylor expansion (see Exercise 6.4.12) for $\varepsilon > 0$ and $f, g \in BM_+(\mathscr{X})$ yields

(12.1.10)

$$L[f + \varepsilon g] = L[f] - \varepsilon E\left(\int_{\mathscr{X}} g(x) \exp\left(-\int_{\mathscr{X}} f(y)\xi(dy)\right)\xi(dx)\right) + o(\varepsilon).$$

From (12.1.6),

$$E\left(\int_{\mathscr{X}} g(x) \exp\left(- \int_{\mathscr{X}} f(y)\xi(dy) \right) \xi(dx) \right)$$

$$= \int_{\mathscr{X}} g(x)M(dx) \int_{\mathscr{M}_{\mathscr{X}}} \exp\left(- \int_{\mathscr{X}} f(y)\xi(dy) \right) \mathscr{P}_0(x, d\xi)$$

$$= \int_{\mathscr{X}} g(x)L[f; x]M(dx),$$

which on substitution into (12.1.10) followed by rearrangement leads to (12.1.9).

For the converse, suppose that (12.1.9) holds for some functions $\{\tilde{L}[f; x]\}$. Since it holds for all $g \in BM_+(\mathscr{X})$, the measures $L[f; x]M(dx)$ and $\tilde{L}[f; x]M(dx)$ coincide; hence, L and $\tilde{L}$ agree for M-a.e. x.   □

The relation at (12.1.9) is useful in identifying the form of the Palm kernel in some simple cases.

EXAMPLE 12.1(b) *The Palm kernel for a Poisson process.* For a Poisson process with parameter measure $\mu(\cdot)$,

$$L[f] = \exp\left(- \int_{\mathscr{X}} (1 - e^{-f(x)})\mu(dx) \right).$$

It follows therefore that

$$\frac{dL[f + \varepsilon g]}{d\varepsilon} = -L[f + \varepsilon g]\frac{d}{d\varepsilon}\left(\int_{\mathscr{X}} (1 - e^{-f(x)-\varepsilon g(x)})\mu(dx) \right)$$

$$= -L[f + \varepsilon g] \int_{\mathscr{X}} g(x)e^{-f(x)-\varepsilon g(x)}\mu(dx)$$

$$\to -L[f] \int_{\mathscr{X}} g(x)e^{-f(x)}\mu(dx) \qquad (\varepsilon \to 0).$$

This can be put in the form of (12.1.9) by making the identification $M(\cdot) = \mu(\cdot)$ and

(12.1.11) $$L[f; x] = e^{-f(x)}L[f] = L_{\delta_x}[f]L[f],$$

where $L_{\delta_x}[\cdot]$ is the Laplace functional of the degenerate random measure with an atom of unit mass at x and no other mass.

The interpretation is that the local Palm distribution $\mathscr{P}_0(x, \cdot)$ coincides with the distribution of the original process except for the addition of an extra point at x itself to each trajectory. If we interpret the local Palm distribution as being conditional on a point at x, then the independence properties of the Poisson process imply that, apart from the given point at x, the probability structure of the conditional process is identical with that of the original process.

The relation embodied in (12.1.11) can also be written in the form

(12.1.12) $$\mathscr{P}_x = \mathscr{P} * \delta_x$$

and as such is the subject of a characterization of the Poisson process in Slivnyak (1962).

Proposition 12.1.VI. *The distribution of a random measure with finite first moment measure satisfies the functional relation* (12.1.12) *if and only if the random measure is a Poisson process.*

PROOF. [Compare Mecke (1967b).] The necessity of (12.1.12) has been shown above. For the converse, supposing that $\mathscr{P}_x$ satisfies (12.1.12); then from (12.1.6) we obtain

$$\frac{dL[\varepsilon f]}{d\varepsilon} = -L[\varepsilon f] \int_{\mathscr{X}} f(x)e^{-\varepsilon f(x)}M(dx),$$

where M is the first moment measure, assumed to exist. Hence, using $\log L[0] = \log 1 = 0$,

$$-\log L[f] = \int_{\mathscr{X}} \int_0^1 f(x)e^{-\varepsilon f(x)} \, d\varepsilon \, M(dx)$$

$$= \int_{\mathscr{X}} (1 - e^{-f(x)})M(dx),$$

so that $L[f]$ is the Laplace functional of a Poisson process with parameter measure equal to $M(\cdot)$. $\qquad\square$

Exercises

12.1.1. Use the analogue of (12.1.1) to define the Campbell measure $C_{\tilde{Q}}(\cdot)$ of the KLM measure $\tilde{Q}$, using (8.4.8) to establish the σ-finiteness property of $C_{\tilde{Q}}(\cdot)$ on appropriate subsets of $\mathscr{X} \times \mathscr{N}_{\mathscr{X}}$. Appeal to Lemma 12.1.III to establish that $C_{\tilde{Q}}(\cdot)$ determines $\tilde{Q}$ uniquely.

12.1.2. Show that the set function $C_{\mathscr{P}}^{(2)}(\cdot)$ defined at (12.1.3) has a unique extension to a σ-finite measure on $\mathscr{X} \times \mathscr{X} \times \mathscr{M}_{\mathscr{X}}$. When the second moment measure exists, define a second-order family of Palm distributions $\mathscr{P}_0^{(2)}(x, y, U)$ satisfying

$$\int_{A \times B} \mathscr{P}_0^{(2)}(x, y, U)M_2(dx \times dy) = C_{\mathscr{P}}^{(2)}(A \times B \times U).$$

12.1.3. When the first moment measure exists and the process is stationary, use $\{\mathscr{P}_0(x, S_x U)\}$ and (12.1.4) to show that (12.1.7) holds. What can be said about $\mathscr{P}_0^{(2)}(\cdot)$ when the process is stationary? [*Hint*: See Exercise 10.1.9.]

12.1.4. Let C denote the mapping $(x, \mu) \to S_x\mu$: $\mathscr{W} \to \mathscr{M}_{\mathscr{X}}$. Then C is continuous and hence measurable. [*Hint*: Suppose $x_n \to_w 0$, $\mu_n \to_w \mu$. Let K be a closed sphere, which is also a continuity set for μ, and suppose $\varepsilon > 0$ is given. Then

$$\liminf \mu_n(K^{-\varepsilon}) \leq \liminf \mu_n(T_{x_n}K) \leq \limsup \mu_n(T_{x_n}K) \leq \limsup \mu(\overline{K^\varepsilon})$$

(see Theorem A2.3.II). Deduce that $S_{x_n}\mu_{x_n} \to_{\hat{w}} \mu$.]

12.1.5. Let ξ be a random measure having the integers $\{0, \pm 1, \ldots\}$ as state space and with finite first moment measure. Describe its Palm and Campbell measures [cf. (12.1.4)]. When ξ is a simple point process, reinterpret the Palm measure as a conditional distribution.

12.1.6. The measure $C(\cdot)$ on $\mathscr{X} \times \hat{\mathscr{M}}_{\mathscr{X}}$ is the Campbell measure $C_{\mathscr{P}}$ of some random measure ξ with σ-finite first moment measure if and only if the following three conditions hold:
   (i) $C(A \times \hat{\mathscr{M}}_{\mathscr{X}}) < \infty$ for bounded $A \in B_{\mathscr{X}}$;
   (ii) $\int_{\mathscr{X} \times \hat{\mathscr{M}}_{\mathscr{X}}} g(x, \eta) C(dx \times d\eta) = 0$ whenever $\int_{\mathscr{X}} g(x, \eta)\eta(dx) = 0$ for each $\eta \in \hat{\mathscr{M}}_{\mathscr{X}}$;
   (iii) $1 - \phi_A \equiv \int_{A \times \{\eta : \eta(A) > 0\}} (\eta(A))^{-1} C(dx \times d\eta) \leq 1$ for bounded $A \in \mathscr{B}_{\mathscr{X}}$.
   When the conditions hold, $\inf_A \phi_A = \mathscr{P}\{\xi = \varnothing\}$. [*Hint*: For the converse, define a measure $\mathscr{P}$ on $\hat{\mathscr{M}}_{\mathscr{X}}$ by

$$\int_{\hat{\mathscr{M}}_{\mathscr{X}}} f(\eta)\mathscr{P}(d\eta) = \int_{\mathscr{X}} \int_{\hat{\mathscr{M}}_{\mathscr{X}}} k(x, S_{-x}\eta)f(S_{-x}\eta)C(dx \times d\eta),$$

where $k(\cdot)$ satisfies (12.2.5); then verify that C and $C_{\mathscr{P}}$ coincide. See Wegmann (1977) for details.]

12.1.7. Proposition 12.1.IV fails when $C_{\mathscr{P}}(A \times \hat{\mathscr{M}}_{\mathscr{X}}) = M(A) = \infty$ for some bounded $A \in \mathscr{B}_{\mathscr{X}}$. In that case, use a nonnegative function $h(\cdot)$ for which

$$\int_{A \times \hat{\mathscr{M}}_{\mathscr{X}}} h(x, \xi) C_{\mathscr{P}}(dx \times d\xi) < \infty \quad \text{(bounded } A \in \mathscr{B}_{\mathscr{X}}\text{)}$$

to define a new measure $H(dx \times d\xi) = h(x, \xi)C_{\mathscr{P}}(dx \times d\xi)$ and apply Radon–Nikodym theorem arguments to $H(\cdot)$. [For example, set $h(x, \xi) = I_B(x)/(1 + \xi(B))$ for some fixed bounded $B \in \mathscr{B}_{\mathscr{X}}$.] What can be deduced concerning the decomposition of the original measure?

12.2. Palm Theory for Stationary Random Measures

Throughout this section we suppose that $\mathscr{X} = \mathbb{R}^d$ and that the random measure ξ is stationary (Definition 10.1.II), or, equivalently, that its distribution $\mathscr{P}$ is invariant under the transformation $\xi \to S_u\xi$ (all $u \in \mathscr{X}$). Recall also the notation $\hat{S}_u\mathscr{P}$ for the transformation of the distribution induced by S_u:

$$(\hat{S}_u\mathscr{P})(B) = \mathscr{P}(S_uB) \quad (B \in \mathscr{B}(\hat{\mathscr{M}}_{\mathscr{X}})).$$

Actually, the only properties of $\mathbb{R}^d$ that are critical for the discussion are the existence and uniqueness of the invariant measure, various standard results such as that any measure $\mu \in \hat{\mathscr{M}}_{\mathscr{X}}$ is determined by its integrals $\int_{\mathscr{X}} f(x)\mu(dx)$ for bounded nonnegative measurable functions f, and the reduction Lemma A2.7.II. Thus, the results hold equally when $\mathscr{X}$ is the circle group $\mathbb{S}$, or more generally whenever $\mathscr{X}$ is an Abelian σ-group as defined in Section A2.7.

First, we investigate the effect of stationarity on the Campbell measure (cf. also Exercise 12.2.1).

Proposition 12.2.I. *Let ξ be a random measure on $\mathcal{X} = \mathbb{R}^d$ with distribution $\mathcal{P}$ and $C_{\mathcal{P}}$ the associated Campbell measure. Then ξ is stationary if and only if $C_{\mathcal{P}}$ is invariant under the group of transformations $\theta_u \colon \mathcal{W} \to \mathcal{W}$ defined for each $u \in \mathcal{X}$ by*

$$(12.2.1) \qquad \theta_u(x, \xi) = (x - u, S_u\xi).$$

Note that by writing $\hat{\theta}_u$ for the mapping on measures on $\mathcal{W}$ induced by θ_u, the assertion of the proposition is expressed more succinctly as

$$\mathcal{P} = \hat{S}_u\mathcal{P} \quad \text{(all u)} \quad \text{if and only if} \quad C_{\mathcal{P}} = \hat{\theta}_u C_{\mathcal{P}} \quad \text{(all u)}.$$

PROOF. When $C_{\mathcal{P}}$ is the Campbell measure associated with $\mathcal{P}$, the Campbell measure associated with $\hat{S}_u\mathcal{P}$ yields

$$\int_{\mathcal{X}} \int_{\mathcal{M}_{\mathcal{X}}} g(x, \xi)\xi(dx)\mathcal{P}(S_u d\xi) = \int_{\mathcal{X}} \int_{\mathcal{M}_{\mathcal{X}}} g(x, \xi)S_u\xi(dx - u)\mathcal{P}(S_u d\xi)$$

$$= \int_{\mathcal{X}} \int_{\mathcal{M}_{\mathcal{X}}} g(x, \xi)C_{\mathcal{P}}(\theta_u(dx \times d\xi))$$

$$= \int_{\mathcal{X}} \int_{\mathcal{M}_{\mathcal{X}}} g(x, \xi)\hat{\theta}_u C_{\mathcal{P}}(dx \times d\xi)$$

and is thus equal to $\hat{\theta}_u C_{\mathcal{P}}$. Consequently, if $\mathcal{P}$ and $\hat{S}_u\mathcal{P}$ coincide, so do $C_{\mathcal{P}}$ and $\hat{\theta}_u C_{\mathcal{P}}$.

Conversely, if $C_{\mathcal{P}}$ and $\hat{\theta}_u C_{\mathcal{P}}$ coincide, then from Lemma 12.1.III it follows that the probabilities $\mathcal{P}$ and $\hat{S}_u\mathcal{P}$ from which they are derived coincide. $\square$

We now look for a product representation of the space $\mathcal{X} \times \mathcal{M}_{\mathcal{X}}$, on which the transformations $\{\theta_u\}$ act, such that Lemma A2.7.II may be applicable. Consider the transformation $D \colon \mathcal{X} \times \mathcal{M}_{\mathcal{X}} \to \mathcal{W}$ for which $D(x, \psi) = (x, S_{-x}\psi)$ for $(x, \psi) \in \mathcal{X} \times \mathcal{M}_{\mathcal{X}}$. Much as in Exercise 10.1.1, this transformation is continuous and hence measurable. It is also one-to-one and onto, since the inverse mapping D^{-1} has $D^{-1}(x, \xi) = (x, S_x\xi)$. We now observe that

$$(12.2.2) \qquad \theta_u(D(x, \psi)) = \theta_u(x, S_{-x}\psi) = (x - u, S_{u-x}\psi)$$

$$= D(x - u, \psi),$$

so that D provides a representation of $\mathcal{W}$ under the actions of the group θ_u. Hence, with $\tilde{C}_{\mathcal{P}}$ denoting the image of $C_{\mathcal{P}}$ under D, $\tilde{C}_{\mathcal{P}}$ is invariant under shifts in its first argument. While it may appear that Lemma A2.7.II should now be applicable and thereby yield the required decomposition of $\tilde{C}_{\mathcal{P}}$, there is a technical difficulty: it is not obvious in general (and may not be true if the first moments are infinite) that $\tilde{C}_{\mathcal{P}}$ takes finite values on products of bounded subsets of $\mathcal{X} \times \mathcal{M}_{\mathcal{X}}$.

To overcome this difficulty, use the σ-finiteness of $\tilde{C}_{\mathscr{P}}$ to construct a modified measure, with the same invariance properties, to which Proposition 12.2.I is applicable. Indeed, this σ-finiteness of $\tilde{C}_{\mathscr{P}}$ implies the existence of a strictly positive function $h(x, \psi)$ such that, provided $\mathscr{P}(\{\varnothing\}) < 1$,

$$0 < \int_{\mathscr{X}} \int_{\mathscr{M}_{\mathscr{X}}} h(x, \psi) \tilde{C}_{\mathscr{P}}(dx \times d\psi) < \infty$$

(cf. Exercises 12.2.2 and 12.1.7). Define $\alpha(\psi) = \int_{\mathscr{X}} h(x, \psi) dx$, so that $\alpha(\psi) > 0$, and let $g(\cdot)$ be any nonnegative Lebesgue integrable function on $\mathscr{X}$. By using the invariance properties of $\tilde{C}_{\mathscr{P}}$ we obtain

$$\int_{\mathscr{X}} \int_{\mathscr{M}_{\mathscr{X}}} g(x) \alpha(\psi) \tilde{C}_{\mathscr{P}}(dx \times d\psi)$$

$$= \int_{\mathscr{X}} \int_{\mathscr{M}_{\mathscr{X}}} \int_{\mathscr{X}} g(x) h(x + y, \psi) dy \, \tilde{C}_{\mathscr{P}}(dx \times d\psi)$$

$$= \int_{\mathscr{X}} \int_{\mathscr{M}_{\mathscr{X}}} \int_{\mathscr{X}} g(u - y) h(u, \psi) dy \, \tilde{C}_{\mathscr{P}}(du \times d\psi)$$

$$= \int_{\mathscr{X}} g(u - y) dy \int_{\mathscr{X}} \int_{\mathscr{M}_{\mathscr{X}}} h(u, \psi) \tilde{C}_{\mathscr{P}}(du \times d\psi) < \infty.$$

The finiteness of the integral on the left-hand side for all such integrable g shows that the modified measure $\alpha(\psi) \tilde{C}_{\mathscr{P}}(dx \times d\psi)$ takes finite values on products of bounded sets, and indeed on sets $A \times \mathscr{M}_{\mathscr{X}}$ for bounded A. Since the presence of the multiplier $\alpha(\psi)$ does not affect invariance of the measure with respect to shifts in x, Lemma A2.7.II can still be applied and yields

$$\alpha(\psi) \tilde{C}_{\mathscr{P}}(dx \times d\psi) = {}_{\alpha}\hat{C}_{\mathscr{P}}(d\psi) \ell(dx)$$

for some uniquely defined finite measure ${}_{\alpha}\hat{C}_{\mathscr{P}}$ on $\mathscr{B}(\mathscr{M}_{\mathscr{X}})$. We now define the Palm measure being sought by setting

$$\hat{C}_{\mathscr{P}}(d\psi) = (1/\alpha(\psi)) \, {}_{\alpha}\hat{C}_{\mathscr{P}}(d\psi).$$

From (A2.7.5) we obtain, for nonnegative or $C_{\mathscr{P}}$-integrable g,

$$(12.2.3) \qquad E\left(\int_{\mathscr{X}} g(x, \xi) \xi(dx) \right) = \int_{\mathscr{X}} \int_{\mathscr{M}_{\mathscr{X}}} g(x, \xi) C_{\mathscr{P}}(dx \times d\xi)$$

$$= \int_{\mathscr{X}} dx \int_{\mathscr{M}_{\mathscr{X}}} g(x, S_{-x}\psi) \hat{C}_{\mathscr{P}}(d\psi).$$

This is sometimes written more conveniently in the form

$$(12.2.4) \qquad E\left(\int_{\mathscr{X}} g(x, S_{x}\xi) \xi(dx) \right) = \int_{\mathscr{X}} dx \int_{\mathscr{M}_{\mathscr{X}}} g(x, \psi) \hat{C}_{\mathscr{P}}(d\psi).$$

We have now established all but the last part of the following theorem.

Theorem 12.2.II. *Let ξ be a stationary random measure on $\mathscr{X} = \mathbb{R}^d$. Then there exists a unique σ-finite measure $\hat{C}_{\mathscr{P}}$ on $\hat{\mathscr{M}}_{\mathscr{X}}$ such that for any $\mathscr{B}_{\mathscr{X}} \otimes \mathscr{B}(\hat{\mathscr{M}}_{\mathscr{X}})$-measurable, nonnegative or $C_{\mathscr{P}}$-integrable function $g(\cdot)$, (12.2.3) holds. The measure $\hat{C}_{\mathscr{P}}$ is totally finite if and only if ξ has finite mean density m, in which case $m = \hat{C}_{\mathscr{P}}(\hat{\mathscr{M}}_{\mathscr{X}})$ and the measure $m^{-1}\hat{C}_{\mathscr{P}}(\cdot)$ coincides for ℓ-a.e. x with the regular local Palm distribution $\mathscr{P}_0(x, S_{-x}(\cdot))$.*

PROOF. Set $g(x, \xi) = I_A(x)$ for some bounded $A \in \mathscr{B}_{\mathscr{X}}$. Then (12.2.3) yields

$$M(A) = E\xi(A) = \ell(A) \int_{\hat{\mathscr{M}}_{\mathscr{X}}} \hat{C}_{\mathscr{P}}(d\psi),$$

so that if $M(A) < \infty$, $\hat{C}_{\mathscr{P}}$ must be totally finite with $\hat{C}_{\mathscr{P}}(\hat{\mathscr{M}}_{\mathscr{X}}) = M(A)/\ell(A) = m$. Conversely, if $\hat{C}_{\mathscr{P}}(\hat{\mathscr{M}}_{\mathscr{X}}) < \infty$, and equal to m' say, then $M(A) = m'\ell(A) < \infty$.

Furthermore, setting $g(x, \xi) = f(x)h(S_x\xi)$ in (12.1.6) and (12.2.3) yields

$$m \int_{\mathscr{X}} \int_{\hat{\mathscr{M}}_{\mathscr{X}}} f(x)h(S_x\xi)\mathscr{P}_0(x, d\xi)dx = \int_{\mathscr{X}} f(x)dx \int_{\hat{\mathscr{M}}_{\mathscr{X}}} h(\psi)\hat{C}_{\mathscr{P}}(d\psi)$$

for all measurable Lebesgue-integrable f; hence, for all $\hat{C}_{\mathscr{P}}$-integrable h it follows that

$$m \int_{\hat{\mathscr{M}}_{\mathscr{X}}} h(S_x\xi)\mathscr{P}_0(x, d\xi) = \int_{\hat{\mathscr{M}}_{\mathscr{X}}} h(\psi)\hat{C}_{\mathscr{P}}(d\psi) \qquad (\ell\text{-a.e. } x),$$

which in turn implies that $m\mathscr{P}_0(x, S_{-x}d\xi)$ and $\hat{C}_{\mathscr{P}}(d\psi)$ must coincide for ℓ-a.e. x as measures. $\qquad\square$

Definition 12.2.III. The measure $\hat{C}_{\mathscr{P}}(\cdot)$ defined by (12.2.3) is the *Palm measure* associated with the stationary random measure ξ or its distribution $\mathscr{P}$.

Equations (12.2.3) and (12.2.4) yield a range of striking formulae as special cases and corollaries. In particular, they provide the basis for more explicit formulae expressing the Palm measure $\hat{C}_{\mathscr{P}}$ in terms of $\mathscr{P}$ and vice versa. Thus, by setting $g(x, \xi) = I_{\cup^d}(x)h(\xi)$ in (12.2.4), the expression at (12.2.6) below for $\hat{C}_{\mathscr{P}}$ in terms of $\mathscr{P}$ is obtained. For an inverse relation, more subtlety is needed: suppose that $k: \mathscr{X} \times \hat{\mathscr{M}}_{\mathscr{X}} \to \mathbb{R}_+$ is a nonnegative measurable function satisfying

(12.2.5) $$\int_{\mathscr{X}} k(x, \xi)\xi(dx) = 1 \quad \text{for each } \xi \neq \varnothing$$

and set $k(x, \varnothing) = 0$. Substituting $g(x, \xi) = k(x, \xi)f(\xi)$ for some nonnegative $\mathscr{B}(\hat{\mathscr{M}}_{\mathscr{X}})$-measurable $f(\cdot)$ in (12.2.3), Equation (12.2.7) is obtained.

Proposition 12.2.IV. (a) *For any nonnegative $\mathscr{B}(\hat{\mathscr{M}}_{\mathscr{X}})$-measurable function $h(\cdot)$,*

(12.2.6) $$\int_{\hat{\mathscr{M}}_{\mathscr{X}}} h(\psi)\hat{C}_{\mathscr{P}}(d\psi) = E_{\mathscr{P}}\left(\int_{\cup^d} h(S_x\xi)\xi(dx)\right).$$

(b) *For any nonnegative $\mathscr{B}(\mathscr{M}_{\mathscr{X}})$-measurable function $f(\cdot)$ and for $k(\cdot)$ satisfying* (12.2.5),

$$(12.2.7) \quad E_{\mathscr{P}}(f(\xi)) = \int_{\mathscr{M}_{\mathscr{X}}\setminus\{\varnothing\}} \int_{\mathscr{X}} k(x, S_{-x}\psi) f(S_{-x}\psi) \hat{C}_{\mathscr{P}}(d\psi) dx$$
$$+ f(\varnothing)\mathscr{P}\{\xi = \varnothing\},$$

where $\varnothing$ is the null measure.

Specific examples of functions $k(\cdot)$ satisfying (12.2.5) are given in Section 12.3, while a general construction due to Mecke (1967b) is given in Exercise 12.2.2.

For the rest of this section we assume that $\mathscr{P}\{\xi = \varnothing\} = 0$, and hence (see Proposition 10.1.IV) that $\mathscr{P}\{\xi(\mathscr{X}) = \infty\} = 1$.

Both of the formulae (12.2.6) and (12.2.7) can be specialized in various obvious ways. If we take h or f to be the indicator function of a set $U \in \mathscr{B}(\mathscr{M}_{\mathscr{X}})$, we obtain direct expressions for $\hat{C}_{\mathscr{P}}(U)$ in terms of $\mathscr{P}$ and for $\mathscr{P}(U)$ in terms of $\hat{C}_{\mathscr{P}}$. When the mean density m exists, the equations can be put in the more symmetrical forms

$$(12.2.8) \quad E_{\mathscr{P}_0}(h(\psi)) = m^{-1} E_{\mathscr{P}}\left(\int_{\cup^d} h(S_x\xi)\xi(dx)\right),$$

$$(12.2.9) \quad E_{\mathscr{P}}(f(\xi)) = m E_{\mathscr{P}_0}\left(\int_{\mathscr{X}} k(x, S_{-x}\psi) f(S_{-x}\psi) dx\right).$$

We turn next to the use of the theorem to elucidate the nature of the moments of the Palm distribution: note that there is no loss of generality in speaking of moments of the Palm distribution rather than of the Palm measure, because the existence of higher moments implies the existence of the first moment, which in turn is enough to ensure that the Palm measure can be normalized to yield the Palm distribution. Write

$$\mathring{M}_k(A_1 \times \cdots \times A_k) = E_{\mathscr{P}_0}(\psi(A_1)\cdots\psi(A_k)) \qquad (A_1, \ldots, A_k \in \mathscr{B}_{\mathscr{X}})$$

for the kth moment measure for $\mathscr{P}_0$.

Proposition 12.2.V. *For $k = 1, 2, \ldots$ the kth moment measure $\mathring{M}_k$ of the Palm distribution exists if and only if the $(k + 1)$th moment measure of the original random measure exists, in which case it is related to the reduced $(k + 1)$th moment measure $\hat{M}_{k+1}$ by*

$$(12.2.10) \quad \mathring{M}_k(\cdot) = m^{-1} \hat{M}_{k+1}(\cdot).$$

PROOF. The result is a further application of (12.2.3) and Fubini's theorem. For integrable $g(x)$ $(x \in \mathscr{X})$ and measurable $h(\cdot)$ on $\mathscr{X}^{(k)}$, with g, h nonnegative, set

$$g(x, \xi) = g(x) \int_{\mathscr{X}} \cdots \int_{\mathscr{X}} h(y_1 - x, \ldots, y_k - x)\xi(dy_1)\cdots\xi(dy_k).$$

Then the left-hand side of (12.2.3), with the use also of (10.4.6), becomes

$$\int_{\mathcal{X}^{(k+1)}} g(x)h(y_1 - x, \ldots, y_k - x)M_{k+1}(dx \times dy_1 \times \cdots \times dy_k)$$

$$= \int_{\mathcal{X}} g(x)dx \int_{\mathcal{X}^{(k)}} h(u_1, \ldots, u_k)\hat{M}_k(du_1 \times \cdots \times du_k),$$

while using Fubini's theorem with the right-hand side yields

$$mE_{\mathscr{P}_0}\left(\int_{\mathcal{X}} g(x)dx \int_{\mathcal{X}^{(k)}} h(u_1, \ldots, u_k)\psi(du_1)\cdots\psi(du_k)\right)$$

$$= m \int_{\mathcal{X}} g(x)dx \int_{\mathcal{X}^{(k)}} h(u_1, \ldots, u_k)\mathring{M}_k(du_1 \times \cdots \times du_k).$$

Since $h \geq 0$ is arbitrary, (12.2.10) follows, together with finiteness (since m is finite). □

The results of Section 10.4 and as above can be summed up in the following diagram:

$$
\begin{array}{ccc}
\mathscr{P}(d\xi)\xi(dx) & \xrightarrow{\text{moments}} & M_{k+1} \\
\downarrow \text{reduction} & & \downarrow \text{reduction} \\
m\mathscr{P}_0(d\xi) & \xrightarrow{\text{moments}} & m\mathring{M}_k \equiv \hat{M}_{k+1}
\end{array}
$$

A similar situation holds with regard to ergodic limits. In Theorem 10.4.VII, reduced moment measures appeared as the limits of averaged products of random measures: similarly, $\hat{C}_{\mathscr{P}}$ appears as an averaged form of indicator functions. We start with the ergodic case.

Proposition 12.2.VI. *Let ξ be a strictly stationary ergodic random measure on $\mathbb{R}^d$, $\hat{C}_{\mathscr{P}}$ its Palm measure, and g a $\mathcal{B}(\mathcal{M}_{\mathcal{X}})$-measurable nonnegative function on $\mathcal{M}_{\mathcal{X}}$. Then for any convex averaging sequence $\{A_n\}$, as $n \to \infty$,*

$$(12.2.11) \qquad \frac{1}{\ell(A_n)}\int_{A_n} g(S_x\xi)\xi(dx) \to \int_{\mathcal{M}_{\mathcal{X}}} g(\xi)\hat{C}_{\mathscr{P}}(d\xi) \qquad (\mathscr{P}\text{-a.s.}).$$

PROOF. The result is an application of the individual ergodic theorem (Theorem 10.2.II) and the approximation arguments used in deriving Theorem 10.2.IV. Suppose first that $\int_{\mathcal{M}_{\mathcal{X}}} g(\xi)\hat{C}_{\mathscr{P}}(d\xi) < \infty$ ($\mathscr{P}$-a.s.), and introduce the function

$$f(\xi) = \int_{\mathcal{X}} g(S_x\xi)g_\varepsilon(u)\xi(du),$$

where $g_\varepsilon(\cdot)$ is a continuous function "close" to a δ-function as in the proof of Theorem 10.2.IV. As in that proof, we find

$$\int_{A_n^\varepsilon} f(S_x\xi)dx = \int_{\mathcal{X}} g_\varepsilon(y-x)\int_{A_n^\varepsilon} g(S_y\xi)\xi(dy)dx$$

$$\geq \int_{\mathcal{X}} g_\varepsilon(y-x)\int_{A_n^{-\varepsilon}} g(S_y\xi)\xi(dy)dx = \int_{A_n^{-\varepsilon}} f(S_x\xi)dx.$$

From Theorem 10.2.II, using also (12.2.3), we have, as $n \to \infty$,

$$\frac{1}{\ell(A_n)}\int_{A_n} f(S_x\xi)dx \to E(f(\xi)) = \int_{\mathcal{X}} g_\varepsilon(u)du\int_{\mathcal{M}_{\mathcal{X}}} g(\psi)\hat{C}_{\mathscr{P}}(d\psi)$$

$$= \int_{\mathcal{M}_{\mathcal{X}}} g(\psi)\hat{C}_{\mathscr{P}}(d\psi),$$

with similar results if A_n is replaced by A_n^ε or $A_n^{-\varepsilon}$. Since ε is arbitrary, (12.2.11) follows when the limit is finite $\mathscr{P}$-a.s. If not, then replace $g(\cdot)$ by an increasing sequence of functions $\{g_r(\cdot)\}$ for which $g_r(\xi)\uparrow g(\xi)$ ($r \to \infty$), as, for example, $g_r(\xi) = \min(g(\xi), r\alpha(\xi))$, where $\alpha(\cdot)$ is as in the discussion leading to Theorem 12.2.II. Then for every r,

$$\liminf_{n\to\infty} \frac{1}{\ell(A_n)}\int_{A_n} g(S_x\xi)\xi(dx) \geq \int_{\mathcal{M}_{\mathcal{X}}} g_r(\xi)\hat{C}_{\mathscr{P}}(d\xi),$$

and the right-hand side $\to \infty$ as $r \to \infty$.   □

As with Theorem 12.2.II, there are obvious special cases when g reduces to the indicator function of an event $\Gamma \in \mathscr{B}(\mathcal{M}_{\mathcal{X}})$ and when the mean density m is finite. For point processes, the left-hand side of (12.2.11) represents the average density of points of the realization, which, when the origin is transferred to the point in question, are associated with an occurrence of Γ, while the right-hand side is just the expected value of this rate: a detailed exploration of such point process results is deferred to Section 12.3.

We conclude this section by noting in summary form extensions to the nonergodic case, leaving details of the proofs as exercises.

Lemma 12.2.VII. *Let $\mathscr{P}$ be the distribution of a stationary random measure on $\mathbb{R}^d$, $\hat{C}_{\mathscr{P}}$ its Palm measure, and $\mathscr{I}$ the σ-algebra of invariant events. Then there exists an invariant random measure ζ, defined on $(\mathcal{M}_{\mathcal{X}}, \mathscr{B}(\mathcal{M}_{\mathcal{X}}))$, such that for nonnegative $\hat{C}_{\mathscr{P}}$-integrable and $\mathscr{B}(\mathcal{M}_{\mathcal{X}})$-measurable functions $g(x, \xi)$,*

$$(12.2.12) \qquad E\left(\int_{\mathcal{X}} g(x, S_x\xi)\xi(dx)\Big|\mathscr{I}\right) = \int_{\mathcal{X}} dx\int_{\mathcal{M}_{\mathcal{X}}} g(x, \psi)\zeta(d\psi)$$

with

$$(12.2.13) \qquad\qquad\qquad E(\zeta(d\psi)) = \hat{C}_{\mathscr{P}}(d\psi).$$

Theorem 12.2.VIII. *Let ξ be a strictly stationary random measure on $\mathcal{X} = \mathbb{R}^d$, ζ the invariant random measure defined in Lemma 12.2.VII, and $h(\cdot)$ a $\mathscr{B}(\mathcal{M}_{\mathcal{X}})$-*

measurable nonnegative or $\hat{C}_{\mathscr{P}}$-integrable function on $\mathscr{M}_{\mathscr{X}}$. Then for any convex averaging sequence $\{A_n\}$, as $n \to \infty$,

$$(12.2.14) \qquad \frac{1}{\ell(A_n)} \int_{A_n} h(S_x \xi)\xi(dx) \to \int_{\mathscr{M}_{\mathscr{X}}} h(\psi)\zeta(d\psi) \qquad (\mathscr{P}\text{-a.s.}).$$

In particular, for $h(\psi) = I_\Gamma(\psi)$ with $\Gamma \in \mathscr{B}(\mathscr{M}_{\mathscr{X}})$,

$$(12.2.15) \qquad \frac{1}{\ell(A_n)} \int_{A_n} I_\Gamma(S_x \xi)\xi(dx) \to \zeta(\Gamma) \qquad (\mathscr{P}\text{-a.s.}).$$

It is to be noted that the random measure $\zeta(\cdot)$ is associated with the Palm measure rather than the Palm distribution. Thus, it is the conditional Palm measures, rather than the normalized forms, that combine linearly according to (12.2.13).

EXAMPLE 12.2(a) *A mixed Poisson process.* Consider two stationary Poisson processes on $\mathbb{R}$ with parameters λ, μ ($\lambda \neq \mu$), selected with probabilities p and $q = 1 - p$, respectively. The invariant σ-field contains two nontrivial events U_1, U_2 corresponding to the choice of the λ and μ processes, respectively. Let $\Gamma = \{N(0, a] = 0\}$ for some fixed $a > 0$. Then $S_x\Gamma = \{N(x, x + a] = 0\}$, and

$$E(I_\Gamma(\xi)) = pe^{-\lambda a} + qe^{-\mu a},$$

while from (12.2.12), with $g(x, \xi) = I_U(x)I_\Gamma(\xi)$ with U denoting the unit interval,

$$\zeta(\Gamma) = \begin{cases} \lambda e^{-\lambda a} & \text{with probability } p \\ \mu e^{-\mu a} & \text{with probability } q, \end{cases}$$

the multiplier λ or μ representing the average rate of occurrence of points followed by an empty interval of length a. The measure $\hat{C}_{\mathscr{P}}(\Gamma)$, however, represents the overall average rate of occurrence of such points, weighted according to the probabilities of the two processes, and so it is given by

$$\hat{C}_{\mathscr{P}}(\Gamma) = p\lambda e^{-\lambda a} + q\mu e^{-\mu a},$$

corresponding to (12.2.13). This expression is to be contrasted with the situation for the Palm distributions: the Palm probability of Γ on U_1 is $e^{-\lambda a}$ while on U_2 it is $e^{-\mu a}$, whereas the overall Palm probability of Γ equals

$$(p\lambda e^{-\lambda a} + q\mu e^{-\mu a})/(p\lambda + q\mu)$$

and not $pe^{-\lambda a} + qe^{-\mu a}$.

Exercises

12.2.1. Show that Proposition 12.2.I is equivalent to the following statement: $\mathscr{P}$ is stationary if and only if for every nonnegative $\mathscr{B}_{\mathscr{X}} \otimes \mathscr{B}_{\mathscr{X}} \otimes \mathscr{B}(\mathscr{M}_{\mathscr{X}})$-measurable function $g(\cdot)$,

$$\int_{\mathscr{X}} \int_{\mathscr{X}} \int_{\mathscr{M}_{\mathscr{X}}} g(x, y, S_x \xi) C_{\mathscr{P}}(dy \times d\xi) dx$$

$$= \int_{\mathscr{X}} \int_{\mathscr{X}} \int_{\mathscr{M}_{\mathscr{X}}} g(x, y, S_y \xi) C_{\mathscr{P}}(dx \times d\xi) dy.$$

12.2.2. Let $\{A_n\}$ be a covering of $\mathscr{X}$ by disjoint bounded Borel subsets of $\mathscr{X}$. Define the function $a(\cdot)$ on $\mathscr{W} \setminus (\mathscr{X} \times \{\varnothing\})$

$$a(x, \xi) = \sum_{n=1}^{\infty} 2^{-n} I_{A_n}(x)(\xi(A_n))^{-1}$$

with the added convention that $a(x, \xi) = 1$ if $x \in A_n$ and $\xi(A_n) = 0$. Define

$$k(x, \xi) = \frac{a(x, \xi)}{\int_{\mathscr{X}} a(y, \xi)\xi(dy)}$$

for $\xi \neq \varnothing$, and verify that this function $k(\cdot)$ satisfies (12.2.5).

12.2.3. (a) Let the stationary random measure ξ have finite first moment measure. Express the Laplace functional result of Proposition 12.1.V more simply via $L[f; x] = L[S_{-x}f; 0]$.
   (b) Let ξ', ξ'' be stationary random measures with probability measures $\mathscr{P}'$, $\mathscr{P}''$. For nonnegative p, q with $p + q = 1$, the random measure ξ, which equals either ξ' or ξ'' with probabilities p, q, respectively, has probability measure $\mathscr{P} = p\mathscr{P}' + q\mathscr{P}''$. Find its Campbell and Palm measures.
   (c) Let ξ', ξ'' as in (b) be independent random measures, and let $\xi = \xi' + \xi''$. Show that the Palm measure $\mathscr{P}_0$ of ξ is given by

$$\mathscr{P}_0 = \mathscr{P}'_0 * \mathscr{P}'' + \mathscr{P}' * \mathscr{P}''_0,$$

where the asterisk denotes convolution.

12.2.4. Let $\mathscr{P}$ be the probability measure of a stationary infinitely divisible random measure with finite first moment measure, and let $\tilde{Q}$ be its KLM measure. Prove that $\mathscr{P}_0 = \tilde{Q}_0 * \mathscr{P}$, where $\tilde{Q}_0$ is the reduced Campbell measure $\hat{C}_{\tilde{Q}}$. [*Hint:* Let $\mathscr{P}$ and $\tilde{Q}$ have Laplace functionals $L_{\mathscr{P}}$ and $L_{\tilde{Q}}$. Relate $\log L_{\mathscr{P}}[f]$ to $L_{\tilde{Q}}[f]$ and deduce that for $f, g \in BM_+(\mathbb{R}^d)$ (cf. (12.1.9))

$$\int_{\mathbb{R}^d} g(x) L_{\mathscr{P}}[S_{-x}f; 0] m_{\mathscr{P}} \, dx = L_{\mathscr{P}}[f] \int_{\mathbb{R}^d} g(x) L_{\tilde{Q}}[S_{-x}f; 0] m_{\tilde{Q}} \, dx.]$$

12.2.5. Mimic the steps in the proofs of Lemma 10.4.VI and Theorem 12.2.II to establish Lemma 12.2.VII and Theorem 12.2.VIII.

12.2.6. Let the random measure ξ on the integers as in Exercise 12.1.5 be stationary. Describe ξ as a stationary sequence $\{X_n\} \equiv \{\xi\{n\}\}$ of nonnegative r.v.s. What aspects of this sequence are described by $\mathscr{P}$ and $\mathscr{P}_0$, respectively? When ξ is a simple point process, give analogues and simple cases of (12.2.2), (12.2.3), (12.2.6), and (12.2.7).

12.2.7. Let $\{\mathscr{P}_n\}$ be a sequence of probability measures on $\mathscr{M}_{\mathscr{X}}$ and $\mathscr{P}$ a limit measure. If $\{\mathscr{P}_n\}$ and $\mathscr{P}$ are stationary, show that

$$\mathscr{P}_n \to \mathscr{P} \quad \text{(weakly)}$$

if and only if

$$\hat{C}_{\mathscr{P}_n} \to \hat{C}_{\mathscr{P}}.$$

What happens if the requirement that $\mathscr{P}_n$ and $\mathscr{P}$ be probability measures is dropped?

12.3. Palm Theory for Point Processes

When the ideas of Section 12.2 are specialized to point processes, there arise a number of new features, which we review in this section. Looking first at the Campbell measure, observe that it is concentrated on the subspace of $\mathscr{X} \times \mathscr{N}_{\mathscr{X}}$ defined by

$$\mathscr{U} = \{(x, N): N \in \mathscr{N}_{\mathscr{X}}, N(\{x\}) \geq 1\}.$$

Since $\mathscr{N}_{\mathscr{X}}$ is a closed and hence also a Borel subset of $\mathscr{M}_{\mathscr{X}}$, we can assume that for a point process, $C_{\mathscr{P}}$ is carried by the product space $\mathscr{X} \times \mathscr{N}_{\mathscr{X}}$. The following results are also true.

Lemma 12.3.I. (i) $\mathscr{U}$ is a closed and hence a Borel subset of $\mathscr{X} \times \mathscr{N}_{\mathscr{X}}$. (ii) For a point process with distribution $\mathscr{P}$ and Campbell measure $C_{\mathscr{P}}$, $C_{\mathscr{P}}(\mathscr{U}^c) = 0$.

PROOF. Let $\{(x_k, N_k)\}$ be a convergent sequence of points from $\mathscr{U}$ so that $x_k \to x$, $N_k \to N$ for some x, N. To establish (i), we have to show that $(x_k, N_k) \in \mathscr{U}$ (all k) implies $(x, N) \in \mathscr{U}$ also. Now $(x_k, N_k) \in \mathscr{U}$ implies that $N_k(\{x_k\}) \geq 1$ and thus $N_k(S(x_k, \varepsilon)) \geq 1$, and so, for all sufficiently large k, since $x_k \in S(x, \varepsilon)$, $N_k(S(x, \varepsilon)) \geq 1$. Letting $k \to \infty$, we have $N(S(x, \varepsilon)) \geq 1$, and thus letting $\varepsilon \downarrow 0$, $N(\{x\}) \geq 1$; that is, $(x, N) \in \mathscr{U}$.

To establish (ii), take a disjoint covering $\{A_{nm}: m = 1, 2, \ldots\}$ of $\mathscr{X}$ by a sequence of Borel sets of diameter $\leq n^{-1}$, and set

$$\Gamma_{nm} = \{N: N(A_{nm}) \geq 1\}, \qquad V_{nm} = A_{nm} \times \Gamma_{nm}.$$

Clearly, $V_{nm} \in \mathscr{B}(\mathscr{X}) \otimes \mathscr{B}(\mathscr{N}_{\mathscr{X}})$, and we have the representation

$$\mathscr{U} = \bigcap_n \bigcup_m V_{nm}$$

because any (x, N) on the right-hand side must belong, for each n, to exactly one element of $\{V_{nm}\}$, $V_n(x)$ say, so that

$$N(\{x\}) = \lim_{n \to \infty} N(V_n(x)) \geq 1,$$

and thus $(x, N) \in \mathscr{U}$. Conversely, any $(x, N) \in \mathscr{U}$ is a point in some V_{nm} for each n.

It is enough then to show that for each n,

$$C_{\mathscr{P}}\left(\bigcap_{m=1}^{\infty} V_{nm}^c\right) = 0.$$

Using the definition of V_{nm} and Equation (12.1.2) for $C_{\mathscr{P}}(\cdot)$, we have

$$C_{\mathscr{P}}\left(\bigcap_{m=1}^{\infty} V_{nm}^c\right) = E\left[\int_{\mathcal{X}} \prod_{m=1}^{\infty} \{1 - I_{A_{nm}}(x)I_{\Gamma_{nm}}(N)\} N(dx)\right]$$

$$= E\left[\prod_{m=1}^{\infty} \int_{A_{nm}} \{1 - I_{A_{nm}}(x)I_{\Gamma_{nm}}(N)\} N(dx)\right],$$

since for $x \in A_{nm}$, only the term involving A_{nm} can contribute a term different from unity to the infinite product. But now for $N \in \Gamma_{nm}$, the integrand, and hence the integral, vanishes; while if $N \notin \Gamma_{nm}$ then $N(A_{nm}) < 1$, that is, $N(A_{nm}) = 0$ and so, again, the integral vanishes. Since this holds for all m, the desired conclusion follows. $\square$

The converse to part (ii) of the lemma is true: see Exercise 12.3.1.

The important implication of Lemma 12.3.I is that we can and shall treat the Campbell measure $C_{\mathscr{P}}(\cdot)$ as being defined on the set $\mathcal{U}$, with the families of Borel and open sets inherited from $\mathscr{B}_{\mathcal{W}}$.

The lemma also has implications for the discussion of Section 12.2:

(a) The mappings θ_u of Proposition 12.2.I map $\mathcal{U}$ into $\mathcal{U}$ [this is seen directly from taking $(x, N) \in \mathcal{U}$, so that $S_u N\{x - u\} = N\{x\} > 0$ and thus $(x - u, S_u N) \in \mathcal{U}$].

(b) The mapping $D: (x, N) \to (x, S_{-x}N)$ is best considered as a mapping from $\mathcal{U}_0 \equiv \mathcal{X} \times \mathscr{N}_{\mathcal{X}}^0$ into $\mathcal{U}$, where $\mathscr{N}_{\mathcal{X}}^0$ is the subspace of $\mathscr{N}_{\mathcal{X}}$ with a point at the origin, that is, $\mathscr{N}_{\mathcal{X}}^0 = \{N \in \mathscr{N}_{\mathcal{X}}: N(\{0\}) \geq 1\}$, because when $N(\{0\}) \geq 1$, $(S_{-x}N)(\{x\}) = N(\{0\}) \geq 1$ and thus $(x, N) \in \mathcal{U}_0$. The inverse mapping $D^{-1}: (x, N) \to (x, S_x N)$ takes $\mathcal{U}$ into this product space, which we denote $\mathcal{U}_0$ because it is a subspace of $\mathcal{U}$.

(c) The Palm measure of a point process can be treated as a measure on $\mathscr{N}_{\mathcal{X}}^0$.

This last conclusion means that for a point process the basic equations (12.2.3) and (12.2.4) can be formally rewritten with the expectation on the left taken as an integral over $\mathscr{N}_{\mathcal{X}}$ rather than $\mathscr{M}_{\mathcal{X}}$, and the inner integral on the right taken over $\mathscr{N}_{\mathcal{X}}^0$ rather than $\mathscr{M}_{\mathcal{X}}$, with similar changes to the results that follow from these equations. For example, (12.2.3) takes the form

$$(12.3.1) \qquad E\left(\sum_i g(x_i(N), N)\right) = \int_{\mathcal{X}} dx \int_{\mathscr{N}_{\mathcal{X}}^0} g(x, S_{-x}N_0)\hat{C}_{\mathscr{P}}(dN_0),$$

where the summation on the left is over all points x_i of N and on the right we have written N_0 for a generic element of $\mathscr{N}_{\mathcal{X}}^0$. As a simple application, take $A \in \mathscr{B}_{\mathcal{X}}$ and $g(x, N) = I_A(x)I_{\Gamma}(N)$ with

$$\Gamma = \{N: N(A) = k\}.$$

Then (12.3.1) reduces to

$$(12.3.2) \qquad k\mathscr{P}\{N(A) = k\} = \int_A \hat{C}_{\mathscr{P}}(\{N_0: S_{-x}N_0(A) = k\})dx$$

$$= \int_A \hat{C}_{\mathscr{P}}\{N_0(A - x) = k\}dx.$$

Further insight into the character and interpretation of the Palm measure for a point process is provided by the case of a point process on the circle $\mathscr{X} = \mathbb{S}$ and invariant under rotations. There is little difficulty in checking that the preceding theory (developed for shifts on $\mathbb{R}^d$) carries over to addition modulo 2π on $\mathbb{S}$.

EXAMPLE 12.3(a) *Stationary point process on the circle.* Because the state space is compact, the realizations are necessarily a.s. finite so that explicit constructions in terms of the Janossy measures are possible. Thus, by supposing that the realization consists of exactly n points, it can be described by the symmetrized probability measure (conditional on n)

$$\Pi_n(d\theta_1 \times \cdots \times d\theta_n) = J_n(d\theta_1 \times \cdots \times d\theta_n)/J_n(\mathscr{X}^{(n)}).$$

Invariance under rotations implies that for all $0 < \theta < 2\pi$ and $A_1, \ldots, A_n \in \mathscr{B}(\mathbb{S})$,

$$\Pi_n(T_\theta A_1 \times \cdots \times T_\theta A_n) = \Pi_n(A_1 \times \cdots \times A_n)$$

so that we have exactly the invariance under diagonal shifts described for the moment measures. Here it implies that Π_n can be written in terms of a product of the uniform measure on $(0, 2\pi)$ and a reduced probability measure $\hat{\Pi}_n$ on a space of $n - 1$ arguments $\phi_1, \ldots, \phi_{n-1}$ so that

$$(12.3.3) \quad \int_{\mathscr{X}^{(n)}} g(\theta_1, \ldots, \theta_n)\Pi_n(d\theta_1 \times \cdots \times d\theta_n)$$

$$= (2\pi)^{-1} \int_{\mathscr{X}} d\theta \int_{\mathscr{X}^{(n-1)}} g(\theta, \theta + \phi_1, \ldots, \theta + \phi_{n-1})\hat{\Pi}_n(d\phi_1 \times \cdots \times d\phi_{n-1}).$$

The interpretation of this result is quite simple. If the distribution Π_n of n points is rotationally invariant, it can be described by locating one point uniformly around the circle and the other $n - 1$ points relative to it according to the reduced distribution $\hat{\Pi}_n$. The symmetry properties of Π_n imply that it is immaterial which point is designated as the one to be uniformly distributed, while stationarity (i.e., rotational invariance) implies that it is immaterial which point of the circle is chosen to play the role of origin. For example, if $n = 2$ and densities exist, the distribution of the two points is completely described by a symmetrical density function $f(\cdot)$ such that

$$\Pi_2(d\theta_1 \times d\theta_2) = (2\pi)^{-1}f(\theta_2 - \theta_1)d\theta_1\, d\theta_2.$$

Note that here, as in general, the marginal distributions $\Pi_2(\cdot \times \mathscr{X})$ must be uniform on $(0, 2\pi)$, being a necessary consequence of stationarity.

It is obvious that the Palm measure for the process should be closely related to the reduced distributions $\hat{\Pi}_n$. Recall from Chapter 5 that the distribution for a finite point process can be described as a symmetric probability measure on the union [see (5.3.8)]

$$\mathscr{X}^{\cup} = \{\varnothing\} \cup \mathscr{X} \cup \mathscr{X}^{(2)} \cup \cdots .$$

The diagonal decompositions summarized by (12.3.3) for a given value of n can be expressed in portmanteau form via a mapping of $\mathscr{X}^{\cup}\backslash\{\varnothing\} \to \mathscr{X} \times \mathscr{X}^{\cup}$, where on the component $\mathscr{X}^{(n)}$

$$(\theta_1, \ldots, \theta_n) \to (\theta_1; \theta_2 - \theta_1, \ldots, \theta_n - \theta_1).$$

Thus, this mapping is similar to the mapping D at (12.2.2), with any measure $\mathscr{P}$ here on $\mathscr{X}^{\cup}$ satisfying $\mathscr{P}(\{\varnothing\}) = 0$ being mapped into a product of uniform measure on $\mathscr{X}$ and a reduced measure $\hat{\mathscr{P}}$ on $\mathscr{X}^{\cup}$. This measure $\hat{\mathscr{P}}$ consists of the measures $\hat{\Pi}_n$ with weightings $p_n = \mathscr{P}\{\xi(\mathscr{X}) = n\}$, but this is not quite the Palm distribution, as we can see by reference to any of the previous formulae, such as (12.3.1), from which follows [cf. (12.2.6)]

$$\hat{C}_{\mathscr{P}}(\Gamma) = (2\pi)^{-1} E\left(\int_0^{2\pi} I_{\Gamma}(S_\theta N) N(d\theta) \right).$$

Then for a set Γ determined by a realization with n points of the form $(0, \phi_1, \ldots, \phi_{n-1})$,

$$\hat{C}_{\mathscr{P}}(\Gamma) = \frac{p_n}{2\pi} E\left(\sum_{i=1}^n I_{\Gamma}(S_{\theta_i} N) | n \right)$$

$$= \frac{p_n}{2\pi} \int_{\mathscr{X}^{(n)}} \sum_{i=1}^n I_{\Gamma}(S_{\theta_i} N) \Pi_n(d\theta_1 \times \cdots \times d\theta_n)$$

$$= \frac{np_n}{2\pi} \int_{\mathscr{X}} d\theta \int_{\mathscr{X}^{(n-1)}} I_{\Gamma}(N_0) \hat{\Pi}_n(d\phi_1 \times \cdots \times d\phi_{n-1}),$$

where now N_0 is a generic counting measure with points at $0, \phi_1, \ldots, \phi_{n-1}$. The factor n arises because the n terms in the sum give identical integrals on account of the symmetry properties of Π_n. For such Γ we therefore have $\hat{C}_{\mathscr{P}}(\Gamma) = np_n \hat{\Pi}_n(\Gamma)$. Thus, the Palm measure requires a weighting by the factor n, the Palm distribution being obtained by normalizing this weighted form, which of course requires $\sum_{n=1}^\infty np_n = E(N(\mathscr{X})) < \infty$. In terms of the conditional probability interpretation of Palm measure (cf. Chapter 3), the reason for this weighting is clear: a realization with n points has n times the chance that a realization of one point has of locating a point at the origin and must be weighted accordingly in taking the conditional expectation.

Another important interpretation of the Palm measure for a point process comes from (12.2.6), which yields for $\Gamma \in \mathscr{N}_{\mathscr{X}}^0$

(12.3.4) $\qquad \hat{C}_{\mathscr{P}}(\Gamma) = E(\#\{i : x_i \in \mathbb{U}^d \text{ and } S_{x_i} N \in \Gamma\}),$

where on the right-hand side it is to be understood that each x_i is a point of the realization N. Thus, $\hat{C}_{\mathscr{P}}(\Gamma)$ is the expected number in the unit cube (or, since the process is stationary, the expected *rate*) of points of the process, which, when the origin is transferred to the point in question, are associated with the occurrence of Γ. As Matthes and others have suggested, we can regard this as the rate of occurrence of marked points where a point is marked if and only if Γ occurs when the origin is shifted to the point in question. The Palm distribution then appears as a ratio of rates

(12.3.5)
$$\mathscr{P}_0(\Gamma) = m(\Gamma)/m,$$

where $m(\Gamma)$ is the rate of the marked process and m is the rate of the original process.

EXAMPLE 12.3(b) *The Palm factorization of the KLM measure for a stationary infinitely divisible process.* From Proposition 10.1.V we know that an infinitely divisible point process is stationary if and only if its KLM measure is stationary. In that case, a Palm factorization can be applied to the Campbell-type measure

$$C_{\tilde{Q}}(A \times U) = \int_U \tilde{N}(A)\tilde{Q}(d\tilde{N}) \qquad (U \in \mathscr{B}(\hat{N}_{\mathscr{X}}\backslash\{\varnothing\}))$$

just as it can to the underlying probability measure. We obtain, by analogy with (12.3.1),

$$\int_{\mathscr{X}} \int_{\mathscr{N}_{\mathscr{X}}\backslash\{\varnothing\}} g(x, S_x\tilde{N})\tilde{N}(dx)\tilde{Q}(d\tilde{N}) = \int_{\mathscr{X}} dx \int_{\mathscr{N}_0(\mathscr{X})} g(x, \tilde{N}_0)\hat{C}_{\tilde{Q}}(d\tilde{N}_0),$$

where $\hat{C}_{\tilde{Q}}$ is the reduced Campbell measure for $\tilde{Q}$ and $\tilde{N}_0$ is used here to denote a generic element of $\tilde{N}_0(\mathscr{X})$. Let us write for brevity

$$\hat{C}_{\tilde{Q}} = \tilde{Q}_0$$

and note that, as in the probability case, $\tilde{Q}_0$ is defined on $\mathscr{B}(\mathscr{N}_0)$; $\tilde{Q}_0$ may or may not be totally finite.

We can now examine the properties of $\tilde{Q}_0$ for the various types of stationary, infinitely divisible processes.

(i) Suppose that $\mathscr{P}$ is regular and therefore has a representation as the regular version of a stationary Poisson cluster process (Proposition 10.1.VI). Here $\tilde{Q}_0$ is closely related to the symmetrized measures $\tilde{P}_{k-1}$ used in defining the regular representation. Regard $\tilde{P}_{k-1}$ not as a measure on $\mathscr{X}^{(k-1)}$ but as a measure on the set $\mathscr{D}_k$ of counting measures in $\mathscr{N}_0$ containing just $k-1$ points in addition to the point at the origin. Then we have

$$\int_{\mathscr{D}_k} h(\tilde{N}_0)\tilde{Q}(d\tilde{N}_0) = k \int_{\mathscr{X}^{(k-1)}} h\left(\delta_0 + \sum_1^{k-1} \delta_{x_i}\right) \tilde{P}_{k-1}(dx_1 \times \cdots \times dx_{k-1}),$$

the factor k arising here, as in the previous example, from the $\tilde{N}(du)$ integration in the Campbell measure. The normalized measures

$$kp_k\tilde{P}_{k-1}(\cdot)/m, \qquad m = \sum kp_k,$$

where $\{p_k\}$ describes the distribution of the cluster size, can be interpreted loosely as providing the conditional distribution of the other cluster members, given that the point at the origin is arbitrarily chosen from a randomly selected population of i.i.d. families of k members.

We see that in the regular case, the measure $\tilde{Q}_0$ is supported by the set of counting measures in $\mathcal{N}_0$ with finite support.

(ii) If the process is strongly singular (see the discussion following Proposition 10.3.XII), the KLM measure itself is supported on the set of counting measures with positive ergodic limits (asymptotic density), and it follows, as in the discussion of Theorem 12.3.II below, that $\tilde{Q}_0$ is concentrated on the space of sequences that also have positive ergodic limits. This is the situation if, in particular, the process is a Poisson randomization, in which case $\tilde{Q}_0 = \mu\hat{C}_{\mathscr{P}}$, where μ is the parameter of the Poisson distribution and $\mathscr{P}$ is the point process that is being "randomized."

(iii) Finally, the weakly singular processes have $\hat{Q}_0$ measures concentrated on the subset of $\mathcal{N}_0$ counting measures, which have infinite support but are asymptotically sparse in the sense that their asymptotic densities are zero.

Thus, *a stationary infinitely divisible point process is regular, strongly singular, or weakly singular, according to whether the Palm measure $\tilde{Q}_0$ is supported by the finite counting measures, the counting measures with infinite support and positive asymptotic densities, or the counting measures with infinite support but zero asymptotic densities.*

We turn next to a number of results for the very important special case where $\mathscr{X}$ is the real line, and the point process is simple with finite mean rate m. In this case, the support of the Palm measure can further be reduced to the set $\mathcal{N}_0^*$ consisting of the elements N of $\mathcal{N}_{\mathbb{R}}$ for which

(i) $N(\{0\}) = 1$,
(ii) N is simple, and
(iii) $N(-\infty, 0] = N(0, \infty) = \infty$.

It follows as before [cf. Lemma 12.3.I(ii)] that

$$\hat{C}_{\mathscr{P}}(\mathcal{N}_{\mathbb{R}} \backslash \mathcal{N}_0^*) = 0$$

whenever $\mathscr{P}$ is the probability measure of a simple stationary point process [for condition (iii) here, see Proposition 10.1.IV]. For this special case we can therefore replace $\mathcal{N}_{\mathscr{X}}^0$ by $\mathcal{N}_0^*$.

At the same time, it is clear that there is a one-to-one both ways measurable mapping Φ between the space $\mathcal{N}_0^*$ [with the σ-algebra of Borel sets inherited from $\mathscr{B}(\mathcal{N}_{\mathscr{X}})$] and the space $\mathscr{T}^+$ of doubly infinite sequences of positive numbers. Denoting the points of a generic element $N_0 \in \mathcal{N}_0^*$ by $\{\ldots, t_{-1}(N_0), t_0(N_0) = 0, t_1(N_0), \ldots\}$ with $t_i(N_0) < t_{i+1}(N_0)$ $(i = 0, \pm 1, \ldots)$, the mapping Φ associates the points of N_0 with the sequence of intervals $\tau_i \equiv t_i(N_0) - t_{i-1}(N_0)$; that is,

$$\Phi N_0 = \{\tau_i\} \equiv \{t_i(N_0) - t_{i-1}(N_0)\}.$$

Measurability follows as in Exercise 7.1.4. Every measure on $(\mathcal{N}_0^*, \mathscr{B}(\mathcal{N}_0^*))$, and in particular $\hat{C}_{\mathscr{P}}(\cdot)$, then induces a measure on $(\mathscr{T}^+, \mathscr{B}(\mathscr{T}^+))$, $(\hat{C}_{\mathscr{P}}\Phi^{-1})(\cdot)$ say.

These remarks pave the way for the result, already announced in Chapter 1, that there is a one-to-one correspondence between stationary simple point processes and stationary sequences of positive random variables, that is, between counting properties and interval properties. The correspondence is essentially a restatement of the equations representing the Palm measure in terms of its underlying distribution, and vice versa. We state the theorem in its most striking form, for the case of finite mean density m. As may be anticipated from the discussion of the Section 12.2, the theorem can be extended to marked point processes, to processes that need not be simple, and to processes of infinite intensity, but at the expense of the condition that Π should be a probability measure (cf. Proposition 12.3.III).

Theorem 12.3.II (Ryll-Nardzewski, 1961; Slivnyak, 1962, 1966). *There is a one-to-one correspondence between the distributions $\mathscr{P}$ on $\mathscr{B}(\hat{\mathscr{N}}_{\mathscr{X}})$ of simple stationary point processes on the line [i.e., on $\mathscr{B}(\hat{\mathscr{N}}_{\mathbb{R}}^{*})$] with finite mean density m and having $\mathscr{P}\{N(\mathbb{R}) = 0\} = 0$, and the distributions Π on $\mathscr{B}(\mathscr{T}^{+})$ of stationary sequences of positive random variables with finite mean m^{-1}, effected by the equations*

$$(12.3.6) \qquad E_{\mathscr{P}_0}(h(N_0)) = m^{-1} E_{\mathscr{P}}\left(\sum_{i=1}^{N((0,1])} h(S_{t_i}N) \right)$$

for nonnegative $\mathscr{B}(\mathscr{N}_0^{*})$-measurable $h(\cdot)$, and

$$(12.3.7) \quad E_{\mathscr{P}}(g(N)) = m E_{\mathscr{P}_0}\left(\int_0^{t_1(N_0)} g(S_t N_0)dt \right) = m E_{\mathscr{P}_0}\left(\int_{-t_1(N_0)}^0 g(S_{-t}N_0)dt \right)$$

$$= m \int_0^{\infty} E_{\mathscr{P}_0}(g(S_t N_0)I_{\{t_1(N_0)>t\}}(N_0))dt$$

for nonnegative $\mathscr{B}(\hat{\mathscr{N}}_{\mathscr{X}})$-measurable $g(\cdot)$, where $\mathscr{P}_0$ is the image in $\mathscr{B}(\mathscr{N}_0^{*})$ of the measure Π on $\mathscr{B}(\mathscr{T}^{+})$.

PROOF. Equations (12.3.6) and (12.3.7) are adaptations to the present context of Equations (12.2.8) and (12.2.9), but further comments are required. In (12.3.6), the points t_i refer to points of N lying in the unit interval $(0, 1]$; each $S_{t_i}N$ satisfies $(S_{t_i}N)(\{0\}) = N(\{t_i\}) = 1$, and so with probability 1 it can be identified with an element of $\mathscr{U}_0$ whenever $h(S_{t_i}N)$ is well defined. In the exceptional $\mathscr{P}$ null set, where $(t_i, S_{t_i}N) \notin \mathscr{U}_0$, the value of $h(S_{t_i}N)$ can be represented arbitrarily (and set equal to zero, say).

To derive (12.3.7) from (12.2.9) set there

$$(12.3.8) \qquad k(x, N) = \begin{cases} 1 & \text{if } x = t_0(N), \\ 0 & \text{otherwise.} \end{cases}$$

Observe that for a simple counting measure for which $\mathscr{P}\{N(\mathbb{R}) = 0\} = 0$,

$$\int_{\mathbb{R}} k(x, N)N(dx) = N(\{t_0(N)\}) = 1,$$

so that $k(\cdot)$ satisfies (12.2.5) when also $\mathscr{P}$ corresponds to a simple point process [i.e., $\mathscr{P}(\mathscr{N}^*) = 1$]. Now substituting in (12.2.9), the term $k(x, S_{-x}N_0)$ in the integral on the right-hand side of (12.2.9) equals unity provided $x = t_0(S_{-x}N_0)$, which, since the counting measure $S_{-x}N_0$ for $N_0 \in \mathscr{N}_0^*$ consists of atoms of unit mass at $\{x + t_i(N_0): i = 0, \pm 1, \ldots\}$, is true for $x \leq 0 < x + t_1(N_0)$, that is, for $-\tau_1 < x \leq 0$. Changing the variable of integration from x to $-x$ leads to (12.3.7).

We now show that if $\mathscr{P}$ is stationary on $\mathscr{B}(\mathscr{N}_{\mathbb{R}}^*)$ then Π is stationary on $\mathscr{B}(\mathscr{T}^+)$ and conversely. Following Franken et al. (1981), we argue as follows. First, note that (12.3.6) can be extended (using the stationarity of $\mathscr{P}$) to give the form

$$E_\Pi(h(N_0)) = mT^{-1}E_{\mathscr{P}}\left\{\sum_{i=1}^{N(0, T]} h(S_{t_i}N)\right\}$$

so that if $\Theta: \mathscr{N}_0^* \to \mathscr{N}_0^*$ is the image of the shift operator in $\mathscr{T}^+$ [meaning that, if $\vartheta: \mathscr{T}^+ \to \mathscr{T}^+$ is defined by $\{\vartheta\tau_i\} = \{\tau_{i-1}\}$, then $\Theta N_0 = \Phi^{-1}\{\vartheta\tau_i\} = \Phi^{-1}(\vartheta(\Phi N_0))]$, then

$$E_\Pi(h(\Theta N_0)) = mT^{-1}E_{\mathscr{P}}\left\{\sum_{i=1}^{N(0, T]} h(S_{t_{i-1}}N)\right\},$$

from which we have

$$|E_{\mathscr{P}_0}(h(N_0)) - E_{\mathscr{P}_0}h(\Theta N_0)| \leq (m/T)E_{\mathscr{P}}\{|h(S_{t_0}N)| + |h(S_{t_{N'+1}}N)|\},$$

where $N' = N(0, T]$. Then for all bounded h, the right-hand side $\to 0$ as $T \to \infty$. Consequently, the expectations on the left coincide for all bounded measurable h, so that the measures Π and $\Pi \circ \vartheta$, equivalent to $\mathscr{P}_0$ and $\mathscr{P}_0 \circ \Theta$, are therefore equal; that is, Π is invariant under ϑ, and thus also its iterates.

Similarly, when Π is stationary, (12.3.7) can be extended by iteration to the form

$$E_{\mathscr{P}}(g(N)) = (mr)^{-1}E_{\mathscr{P}_0}\left(\int_0^{t_r(N_0)} g(S_t N_0)dt\right), \qquad r = 1, 2, \ldots.$$

Replacing N by $S_t N$, subtracting, and letting $r \to \infty$, we find in an analogous fashion that $\mathscr{P}$ is stationary under shifts S_t.

We come finally to the question of uniqueness. Suppose we are given a stationary measure Π on $\mathscr{T}^+$ and that $\mathscr{P}$ is constructed from Π via (12.3.7). Then $\mathscr{P}$, which is clearly a probability measure, has an associated Palm measure $\hat{C}_{\mathscr{P}}$, which satisfies the equation analogous to (12.3.7); namely,

(12.3.9) $$E_{\mathscr{P}}(g(N)) = \int \hat{C}_{\mathscr{P}}(dN_0) \int_0^{t_1(N_0)} g(S_t N_0)dt.$$

Substituting $g(N) = h(S_{t_0(N)}N)$, the right-hand side of (12.3.9) becomes the expectation of

$$\int_0^{t_1(N_0)} h(S_{t_0(S_t N_0)}S_t N_0)dt.$$

Now for $0 < t < t_1(N_0)$, $S_t N_0$ has points at $t_i(N_0) - t$, with $-t$ the nearest point to the origin lying in $(-\infty, 0)$. In this range of t, therefore, the argument of h reduces to N_0, and (12.3.7) yields for this g

$$E_{\mathscr{P}}(g(N)) = mE_\Pi(t_1(N_0)h(N_0)).$$

Similarly, (12.3.8) yields

$$E_{\mathscr{P}}(g(N)) = \int_{\mathscr{N}_0^*} t_1(N_0)h(N_0)\hat{C}_{\mathscr{P}}(dN_0).$$

These equations both hold for nonnegative $\mathscr{B}(\mathscr{N}_0^*)$-measurable h, so it follows that the measures $mt_1(N_0)\Pi(dN_0)$ and $t_1(N_0)\hat{C}_{\mathscr{P}}(dN_0)$ coincide, implying that $m\Pi$ is nothing other than the Palm measure for $\mathscr{P}$. Thus, not only is $\mathscr{P}$ determined uniquely by Π via (12.3.7), but also Π is determined uniquely by $\mathscr{P}$.

Again, if $\mathscr{P}$ is given and Π is determined by (12.3.6), then we know already that Π is the Palm distribution of $\mathscr{P}$, and hence from (12.3.7) that $\mathscr{P}$ is uniquely determined by Π. Thus, either equation on its own is enough to imply a one-to-one correspondence. □

The intuitive content of (12.3.7) can be expressed as follows. To embed a stationary sequence of intervals into a stationary point process on $\mathbb{R}$, first select a realization $(\ldots, \tau_{-1}, \tau_0, \tau_1, \ldots)$ of the intervals, and then choose a number X uniformly at random on the interval τ_1 say. Then define a realization of the point process on $\mathbb{R}$ by making this X correspond to the origin and laying out the intervals in sequence so that if the $\{t_i\}$ are the points with conventions as above,

$$t_0 = -X, \quad t_1 = \tau_1 - X, \quad t_2 = \tau_1 + \tau_2 - X, \ldots,$$

$$t_{-1} = -\tau_0 - X, \quad t_{-2} = -\tau_1 - \tau_0 - X, \ldots.$$

Theorem 12.3.II is a substantial generalization of the Palm–Khinchin equations of Section 3.4, and it provides the most satisfactory approach to the determination of the point process associated with a given process of intervals. Both these remarks are illustrated in the following example.

EXAMPLE 12.3(c) *Renewal and Wold processes.* Suppose first that $(\ldots, L_{-1}, L_0, L_1, \ldots)$ is a sequence of i.i.d. positive r.v.s., which is therefore stationary and so describes a distribution Π on $\mathscr{T}^+$. Indeed, Π is just the product measure on $(\mathbb{R}_+)^{(\infty)}$ derived from multiple copies of the measure $F(dx)$ associated with each of the L_i. To fit into the framework of the theorem we must have

$$F(0+) = 0, \qquad \int_0^\infty xF(dx) = m^{-1} < \infty.$$

In (12.3.7) take $g(N) = I_\Gamma(N)$, where

$$\Gamma = \Gamma_1 \equiv \{N: t_1(N) > x\}.$$

Then the term $g(S_t N_0)$ on the right of (12.3.7) equals unity for $0 < t < t_1(N_0) - x$

and $t_1(N_0) > x$, and zero otherwise, so that

$$E_{\mathscr{P}}(g(N)) = \mathscr{P}(\Gamma_1) = \mathscr{P}\{t_1(N) > x\} = mE_{\Pi}[(L_1 - x)I_{\{L_1 > x\}}]$$
$$= m \int_x^\infty (y - x)F(dy) = m \int_x^\infty (1 - F(y))dy,$$

which is the first of the Palm–Khinchin equations (3.4.9) and shows in the renewal case that the first interval after a fixed origin (and in view of stationarity the choice of origin is immaterial) has the distribution (4.1.14) of the forward recurrence time.

Next we take

$$\Gamma = \Gamma_2 \equiv \{N: t_1(N) > x, t_2(N) - t_1(N) > y\}.$$

We obtain similarly

$$\mathscr{P}(\Gamma_2) \equiv \mathscr{P}\{t_1(N) > x, t_2(N) - t_1(N) > y\} = mE_{\Pi}[(L_1 - x)I_{\{L_1 > x, L_2 > y\}}]$$
$$= m \int_x^\infty (1 - F(u))du(1 - F(y)),$$

on account of the assumed independence of the $\{L_i\}$. The first equality here is the second of the Palm–Khinchin equations, while the other equality shows that for a stationary renewal process, the length of the second interval after the origin is independent of the first.

In the Wold process example (see Section 4.5), the intervals $\{L_i\}$ form a stationary Markov chain with stationary distribution $\pi(\cdot)$ say and transition kernel $P(x, B) = \Pr\{L_{i+1} \in B | L_i = x\}$. Again we must assume that $\pi(\{0\}) = 0 = \pi((-\infty, 0])$ and $\int_0^\infty x\pi(dx) = m^{-1} < \infty$. For Γ_1 and Γ_2 as above we find that $t_1(N)$ has the same kind of forward recurrence time distribution with $\pi(\cdot)$ in place of $F(\cdot)$, and that $t_1(N)$ and $t_2(N) - t_1(N)$ have the joint distribution

$$F_2(dx \times dy) = m \, dx \int_x^\infty \pi(du)P(u, dy).$$

Thus, the marginal distribution of $t_2(N) - t_1(N)$ is now given by

$$F_2(\mathbb{R}_+ \times dy) = m \int_0^\infty dx \int_x^\infty \pi(du)P(u, dy),$$

and in general neither this interval nor any of the later intervals has exactly the stationary interval distribution.

The analysis of Section 12.2 allows us to construct a Palm measure even for a process with infinite intensity. It is therefore natural to seek a version of Theorem 12.2.II, along the lines of Theorem 12.3.II, and such can be given but only at the expense of requiring Π to be a probability measure. In fact, the proof of Theorem 12.3.II carries over with only notational changes as soon as we replace $m\Pi$ by a measure Π_m (being the measure induced on $\mathscr{T}^+$ by the Palm measure $\hat{C}_{\mathcal{P}}$), which may be allowed to be σ-finite but not necessarily totally finite. The proof is left to the reader.

Proposition 12.3.III. *There is a one-to-one correspondence between distributions $\mathcal{P}$ on $\mathcal{B}(\mathcal{N}_{\mathbb{R}}^*)$ of simple stationary point processes on $\mathbb{R}$ and stationary σ-finite (but not necessarily totally finite) measures Π_m on $\mathcal{B}(\mathcal{T}^+)$ satisfying*

$$(12.3.10) \qquad \int_{\mathcal{N}_0^*} t_1(N_0)\mathcal{P}_0^m(dN_0) = \int_{\mathcal{N}_{\mathbb{R}}^*} \mathcal{P}(dN) = 1,$$

where $\mathcal{P}_0^m$ is the image in $\mathcal{B}(\mathcal{N}_0^*)$ of Π_m, being given by

$$(12.3.11a) \qquad \int_{\mathcal{N}_0^*} h(N_0)\mathcal{P}_0^m(dN_0) = \int_{\mathcal{N}_{\mathbb{R}}^*} \left[\sum_{i=1}^{N(0,1]} h(S_{t_i}N) \right] \mathcal{P}(dN),$$

and

$$(12.3.11b) \qquad \int_{\mathcal{N}_{\mathbb{R}}^*} g(N)\mathcal{P}(dN) = \int_{\mathcal{N}_0^*} \mathcal{P}_0^m(dN_0) \int_0^{t_1(N_0)} g(S_u N_0)du,$$

for nonnegative h and g that are $\mathcal{B}(\mathcal{N}_0^*)$- and $\mathcal{B}(\mathcal{N}_{\mathbb{R}}^*)$-measurable, respectively.

We return now to the more general context of point processes on $\mathbb{R}^d$. In the absence of the total ordering of $\mathbb{R}$, it is not immediately apparent what should be the exact counterpart of the preceding results. Some useful progress can be made by replacing the role of τ_1 above by the point of the realization, $x^*(N)$ say, that is closest to the origin. We first check that this concept is well defined.

Lemma 12.3.IV. *Let N be a stationary simple point process on $\mathcal{X} = \mathbb{R}^d$. Then the set*

$$\{N: \text{there exist } x', x'' \text{ with } \|x'\| = \|x''\| \text{ and } N(\{x'\}) \geq 1, N(\{x''\}) \geq 1\}$$

is $\mathcal{B}(\mathcal{N}_{\mathcal{X}})$-measurable and has $\mathcal{P}$-measure zero.

PROOF. The set $J \subset \mathcal{X}^{(2)}$ defined by

$$J = \{(x, y): \|x\| = \|y\|, x \neq y\}$$

is a measurable set in $\mathcal{B}(\mathcal{X}^{(2)})$ by inspection, and we can write

$$\int_{\mathcal{X}^{(2)}} I_J(x, y)N(dx)N(dy) = \int_{\mathcal{X}} h(x, N)N(dx),$$

where

$$h(x, N) = \begin{cases} 1 & \text{if } N(\{y\}) > 0 \text{ for some } y \text{ with } \|y\| = \|x\| \\ 0 & \text{otherwise} \end{cases}$$

is measurable. Applying (12.3.1), we obtain

$$E\left(\int_{\mathcal{X}} h(x, N)N(dx)\right) = \int_{\mathcal{N}_{\mathcal{X}}^0} \hat{C}_{\mathcal{P}}(dN_0) \int_{\mathcal{X}} h(x, S_{-x}N_0)dx.$$

The function $h(x, S_{-x}N_0)$ equals 1 only on the at most countable set of surfaces

$$\{y: \|y + x_i\| = \|x_i\|, y \neq x_i\}$$

obtained by letting x_i run through the points of N_0. For $d = 1$, the surface consists of the single point $y = -2x_i$; for $d > 1$, it consists of a surface in $\mathbb{R}^d$ of dimension $d - 1$, and so is of zero $\mathbb{R}^d$-Lebesgue measure. In either case, the inner integral vanishes for each N_0, and so the expectation is zero. $\quad\square$

It follows from this lemma that with probability 1 the distances from the origin of the points of a realization of a stationary simple point process in $\mathbb{R}^d$ can be set out in a strictly increasing sequence

$$0 < r_1(N) < r_2(N) < \cdots.$$

In any case the quantities $r_i(N)$ are well-defined random variables because

$$\{r_i(N) < a\} \quad \text{if and only if} \quad \{N(S(0; a)) > i\}.$$

With probability 1, for given i, there is a unique point of the process, $x_i^*(N)$ say, associated with a given distance r_i. In the exceptional set where there is no such unique point, we can put all the $x_i^*(N)$ equal to zero.

The $x_i^*(N)$ also form well-defined random elements in $\mathbb{R}^d$, as follows from the measurability of sets such as

$$\{N: x_i^*(N) \in A\} = \bigcap_n \bigcup_k \{k/n \leq r_i(N) < (k + 1)/n; N(A) > 0\}$$

for $A \in \mathcal{B}(\mathbb{R}^d)$. In the sequel we mostly use the point of a realization N that is closest to the origin, which we denote for brevity by

$$(12.3.12) \qquad\qquad x^*(N) = x_1^*(N).$$

One immediate use for this $x^*(N)$ is to develop an inversion formula extending (12.3.7) to the case $\mathcal{X} = \mathbb{R}^d$. For this we need the concept of a *Voronoi polygon*: for any given realization N of a simple point process, and any point x_i of N, the Voronoi polygon about x_i is the set of points

$$V_{x_i}(N) = \{x: \|x - x_i\| < \|x - x_j\|, j \neq i\};$$

that is, it is the subset of points of $\mathbb{R}^d$ that lie closer to the chosen point x_i than to any other point x_j of N. In particular, if $N_0 \in \mathcal{N}_0^*$, we write $V_0(N_0)$ for the Voronoi polygon about the origin (which is a point of N_0). The required inversion formula then takes the form

$$(12.3.13) \qquad\qquad E_{\mathcal{P}}(g(N)) = mE_{\mathcal{P}_0}\left(\int_{V_0(N_0)} g(S_x N_0)dx\right)$$

for stationary simple point processes with finite mean density m and non-negative $\mathcal{B}(\mathcal{N}_{\mathcal{X}})$-measurable $g(\cdot)$. The proof is similar to that of (12.3.7) and left to Exercise 12.3.5. It is not as useful in $\mathbb{R}^d$ ($d \geq 2$) as is (12.3.7) in $\mathbb{R}$, which is chiefly a reflection of the increased structural complexity of the higher-dimensional Euclidean spaces, but a few simple results can be deduced from it, such as the intuitively obvious fact that the expected hypervolume (i.e., Lebesgue measure) of the Voronoi polygon about the origin equals m^{-1}.

A further use of $x^*(N)$ is in the next theorem which extends to $\mathbb{R}^d$ the conditional probability interpretation of the Palm distribution.

Theorem 12.3.V. *Let N be a simple stationary point process in $\mathbb{R}^d$ with finite mean rate m, distribution $\mathscr{P}$, and Palm distribution $\mathscr{P}_0$. When $\{A_n: n = 1, 2, \dots\}$ is a nested sequence of bounded Borel sets with nonempty interiors satisfying*

$$(12.3.14) \qquad \mathrm{diam}(A_n) \to 0 \qquad (n \to \infty),$$

$$(12.3.15) \qquad \ell(A_n)^{-1}\mathscr{P}\{N(A_n) > 0\} \to m.$$

When moreover the sets $\{A_n\}$ are spheres in $\mathbb{R}^d$ centred at the origin, then for bounded continuous nonnegative Borel functions f on $\mathscr{N}_x$,

$$(12.3.16) \qquad E_{\mathscr{P}}(f(N)|N(A_n) > 0) \to E_{\mathscr{P}_0}(f(N_0)).$$

PROOF. The first assertion (12.3.15) is a corollary to the discussion on intensities in Chapter 7 [see, in particular, (7.2.14) and Exercise 7.2.7]. A further corollary of the same discussion, which we need in the sequel, is that

$$(12.3.17) \qquad \mathscr{P}\{N(A_n) > 1\}/\ell(A_n) \to 0 \qquad (n \to \infty)$$

(see Proposition 7.2.VIII). We approach the assertion at (12.3.16) via the following result, which is of independent interest.

Proposition 12.3.VI. *Let N, $\mathscr{P}$, $\mathscr{P}_0$, m, and $\{A_n\}$ be as in the theorem above, and $x^*(N)$ as at (12.3.12). Then for bounded nonnegative $\mathscr{B}(\mathscr{N}_x)$-measurable $f(\cdot)$,*

$$(12.3.18) \qquad E_{\mathscr{P}}(f(S_{x^*(N)}N)|N(A_n) > 0) \to E_{\mathscr{P}_0}(f(N_0)).$$

PROOF. Note first that

$$|E_{\mathscr{P}}(f(S_{x^*(N)}N)|N(A_n) > 0) - E_{\mathscr{P}_0}(f(N_0))|$$

$$\leq (m\ell(A_n))^{-1}|E_{\mathscr{P}}[f(S_{x^*(N)}N)I_{\{N(A_n)>0\}}] - m\ell(A_n)E_{\mathscr{P}_0}(f(N_0))|$$

$$+ (\ell(A_n))^{-1}E_{\mathscr{P}}[f(S_{x^*(N)}N)I_{\{N(A_n)>0\}}]|m^{-1} - \ell(A_n)/\mathscr{P}\{N(A_n) > 0\}|.$$

In the last term here, the modulus of the difference converges to zero as $n \to \infty$ by (12.3.15), while the multiplier remains finite because

$$E_{\mathscr{P}}[f(S_{x^*(N)}N)I_{\{N(A_n)>0\}}]/\ell(A_n)$$

$$\leq \left(\sup_{N \in \mathscr{N}_x} f(N)\right)\mathscr{P}\{N(A_n) > 0\}/\ell(A_n) \to m(\sup f(N)),$$

where the assumed boundedness of $f(\cdot)$ implies that the supremum is finite, so this last term $\to 0$ as $n \to \infty$. For the other term, we note first from the proof of Theorem 12.2.II and (12.2.8) that

$$m\ell(A_n)E_{\mathscr{P}_0}(f(N_0)) = E_{\mathscr{P}}\left(\int_{A_n} f(S_x N)N(dx)\right) = E_{\mathscr{P}}\left(\sum_{x_i \in A_n} f(S_{x_i} N)\right).$$

It is thus enough to consider the difference

$$\frac{1}{\ell(A_n)}\left|E_{\mathscr{P}}\left[f(S_{x^*(N)} N)I_{\{N(A_n)>0\}} - \sum_{x_i \in A_n} f(S_{x_i} N)\right]\right|,$$

which certainly vanishes when $N(A_n) = 0$. When $N(A_n) > 0$, then we have $x^*(N) \in A_n$, implying that it can be identified with one of the $x_i \in A_n$, so the first term cancels with one of the elements of the sum. Consequently, the difference is dominated by $(\sup f(N))\,\mathscr{P}(N(A_n) \geq 2)/\ell(A_n)$, which tends to zero by (12.3.17). $\square$

Resuming the proof of Theorem 12.3.V, it follows from Proposition 12.3.VI that it is enough to establish the convergence to zero of the difference

$$(12.3.19) \quad |E_{\mathscr{P}}[f(N)|N(A_n) > 0] - E_{\mathscr{P}}[f(S_{x^*(N)} N)|N(A_n) > 0]|$$

$$\leq E_{\mathscr{P}}[|f(N) - f(S_{x^*(N)} N)||N(A_n) > 0]$$

$$\leq E_{\mathscr{P}}\left[\sup_{x \in A_n} |f(S_{x^*(N)} N) - f(S_{x+x^*(N)} N)||N(A_n) > 0\right],$$

since $x^*(N) \in A_n$ under the condition $N(A_n) > 0$. Fixing the set A_n for the supremum as A_{n_0} say, and letting $n \to \infty$ for the conditioning, this last expression converges by Proposition 12.3.VI to

$$E_{\mathscr{P}_0}\left(\sup_{x \in A_{n_0}} |f(N_0) - f(S_x N_0)|\right).$$

Since f is uniformly bounded and continuous, and the shift operation is continuous also, the term under the supremum converges to zero pointwise as $n_0 \to \infty$, and then by dominated convergence the expectation must converge to zero. $\square$

We note that in both Theorem 12.3.V and Proposition 12.3.VI the convergence results are sufficient to imply that $\mathscr{P}\{\cdot|N(A_n) > 0\}$ and $\mathscr{P}\{S_{x^*}(\cdot)|N(A_n) > 0\}$ converge weakly to $\mathscr{P}_0\{\cdot\}$ as $n \to \infty$.

The results just proved also provide some kind of analogue to the differential form of the Palm–Khinchin equations given at (3.4.11) of Chapter 3. Even in the one-dimensional case, however, it is not easy to provide a completely satisfactory account by this differential approach [cf. Exercise 3.4.4 and Leadbetter (1972)]. One approach along these lines was developed by Slivnyak (1962, 1966), who showed that for the operator S_x^0 defined by

$$S_x^0 \Gamma = \{N: N(0, x] = 0, N(0, y_i + x] \leq k_i \quad (i = 1, \ldots, r)\}$$

on sets Γ of the form

$$\Gamma = \{N: N(0, y_i] \leq k_i \quad (i = 1, \ldots, r)\},$$

$\mathscr{P}(S_x^0\Gamma)$ is convex in x so that the right-hand derivative in $x > 0$ necessarily exists finite. Indeed, on sets $\Gamma_x \equiv S_x^0\Gamma$ for $x > 0$,

$$Q(\Gamma_x) = Q(S_x^0\Gamma) \equiv \lim_{h\downarrow 0} h^{-1}(\mathscr{P}(S_x^0\Gamma) - \mathscr{P}(S_{x+h}^0\Gamma)) \leq 1/x.$$

Slivnyak showed that $Q(\cdot)$ can be extended from being finitely additive on the ring of sets generated by such sets Γ_x $(x > 0)$ to being σ-additive on the σ-algebra generated by the ring, and that Q so extended has the requisite shift invariance property.

Exercises

Note: Assume below that $\mathscr{P}\{N = \varnothing\} = 0$.

12.3.1. Let $C_\mathscr{P}$ be the Campbell measure of a random measure ξ for which $C_\mathscr{P}(\mathscr{U}^c) = 0$. Prove that ξ is a point process.

12.3.2. [Compare (12.3.7) and (12.2.4).] Substitute $g(x, N) = h(x, N)k(x, N)$ with $k(\cdot)$ as in (12.3.8) to show that

$$E_\mathscr{P}(h(t_1(N), S_{t_1(N)}N)) = mE_{\mathscr{P}_0}\left(\int_0^{t_1(N_0)} h(x, N_0)dx\right).$$

12.3.3. For simple stationary N use (12.3.7) to find the joint distribution of $X = t_1(N)$ and $\tau_1 \equiv t_1(N) - t_0(N)$ in terms of the d.f. $F(\cdot)$ of τ_1. In particular, show the following:
(a) The joint distribution for (X, τ_1) has a density function representation

$$f(u, v)du\, dv = \begin{cases} mv^{-1}(1 - F(v))du\, dv & (0 \leq u \leq v), \\ 0 & (u > v). \end{cases}$$

(b) The conditional distribution of X given τ_1 is uniform on $(0, \tau_1)$.
(c) The conditional distribution of X given the whole sequence $\{\tau_n: n = 0, \pm 1, \ldots\}$ is uniform on $(0, \tau_1)$.
[*Hint*: Let $A \in \mathscr{B}(\mathscr{N}_x)$ belong to the sub-σ-field generated by the τ_i and start from the definition of conditional expectation, so that, for measurable h,

$$E(h(X)I_A|\sigma\{\tau_i\}) = I_A(\{\tau_i\})\int_0^{\tau_1} h(x)dx.]$$

12.3.4. Use (12.3.7) and Exercises 12.3.1–12.3.3 to provide an alternative derivation of the formulae in Exercise 3.4.4 for $Q(B_k)$ and $\Pr(B_k)$.

12.3.5. Define $k(x, N) = 1$ if $x = x^*(N)$, $= 0$ otherwise. Verify that $k(\cdot)$ so defined satisfies (12.2.5) and establish (12.3.13) from (12.2.9) as in the derivation of (12.3.7).

12.3.6. Supply an alternative derivation of (12.3.15) from (12.3.8) and (12.3.9).

12.3.7. The conclusion of Proposition 12.3.VI can be strengthened to $\|\tilde{\mathscr{P}}_n - \mathscr{P}_0\| \to 0$, where $\tilde{\mathscr{P}}_n$ is the measure on $\mathscr{N}_0^*$ induced by the conditional probabilities

$E_{\mathscr{P}}\{f(S_{x^*(N)}N)|N(A_n) > 0\}$ and convergence is with respect to the variation norm. [*Hint*: the basic inequalities depend on f only through $\|f\|$ and hence hold uniformly in f for $\|f\| \leq 1$ say.]

12.3.8. Use the inversion equation (12.3.13) to deduce that under the conditions of Theorem 12.3.V, $\mathscr{P}\{N(A_n) > 1\} = o(\ell(A_n)) \equiv \ell(A_n)o(1)$ and $\mathscr{P}\{N(A_n) = 1\} = m\ell(A_n)(1 + o(1))$ [cf. Theorem 1.2.12 of Franken et al. (1981)]. For simple stationary point processes on $\mathbb{R}$ as in Theorem 12.3.II, the analogue of (12.3.13) is

$$E_{\mathscr{P}}(g(N)) = mE_{\mathscr{P}_0}\left(\int_{t_{-1}(N_0)/2}^{t_1(N_0)/2} g(S_t N_0)dt \right).$$

12.3.9. Under the assumptions that N is stationary, simple, and has finite mean rate m, show that in Theorem 12.3.V there is a nested sequence $\{A_n\}$ with $\ell(A_n) \to 0$, not satisfying (12.3.14), for which (12.3.15) fails. Investigate whether (12.3.15) holds with (12.3.14) but without $\{A_n\}$ being nested, and whether (12.3.16) holds for more general sets A_n than spheres. [*Hint*: Let the realizations span a lattice, and let A_n be the union of two small spheres with centres at two lattice points.]

12.4. Convergence to Equilibrium

Suppose that a point process with prescribed structure is specified by certain initial conditions "near zero." It is often important to know whether, after the passage of time (when $\mathscr{X} = \mathbb{R}_+$), or more generally as $\|x\| \to \infty$ for processes on $\mathscr{X} = \mathbb{R}^d$, the process observed for such large $\|x\|$ approximates a stationary process. Such behaviour is familiar from the study of renewal processes and Markov chains and is a powerful tool in applications where the stationary distributions are frequently easier to describe and to compute than the transient distributions associated with prescribed initial conditions. Such behaviour is also a manifestation of a "loss of memory" property: after some time, the process has essentially "forgotten" its original configuration and approximates the stationary pattern. It is therefore closely associated with the various forms of mixing—indeed, to a large extent, mixing properties and convergence to equilibrium properties are different names for the same phenomenon.

The concepts of Section 12.3, when coupled with the interpretations of the distribution of a stationary point process as an "arbitrary time" distribution and of the Palm distribution as an "arbitrary point" distribution, provide the framework for important results of the kind outlined in the last paragraph. Specifically, starting from an "arbitrary point" (i.e., with the Palm distribution) and translating through some $x \in \mathbb{R}^d$, we can seek conditions under which the translated distribution converges as $\|x\| \to \infty$. Dually, starting from an "arbitrary time" (i.e., the stationary distribution) and observing the process at the nth point "after" that time, we may seek conditions under which the distribution of the process, relative to that nth point as origin, converges to the Palm distribution as $n \to \infty$. This cycle of ideas, while not dealing with all aspects of the convergence to equilibrium problem, does provide a sufficiently general approach to it so as to yield useful results.

We first restate and extend the main ergodic result of Section 12.2, working for simplicity with the case where the mean density is finite.

Proposition 12.4.I. *Let $\mathscr{P}$ be the distribution of a simple stationary ergodic point process on $\mathbb{R}^d$ with finite density m, $\mathscr{P}_0$ the corresponding Palm distribution, f and g nonnegative $\mathscr{B}(\mathcal{N}_{\mathcal{X}})$-measurable functions such that $E_{\mathscr{P}}(f(N)) < \infty$ and $E_0(g(N_0)) < \infty$, and $\{A_n\}$ a convex averaging sequence in $\mathbb{R}^d$. Then as $n \to \infty$,*

$$(12.4.1) \qquad \frac{1}{\ell(A_n)} \int_{A_n} f(S_{-x} N_0) dx \to E_{\mathscr{P}}(f(N)) \qquad (\mathscr{P}_0\text{-a.s.}),$$

and as $k \to \infty$, with $x_j^* \equiv x_j^*(N)$ as above (12.3.12),

$$(12.4.2) \qquad \frac{1}{k} \sum_{j=1}^{k} g(S_{x_j^*} N) \to E_{\mathscr{P}_0}(g(N_0)) \qquad (\mathscr{P}\text{-a.s.}).$$

PROOF. In the point process context, the result of the ergodic theorem 12.2.VI can be expressed, with $\{A_n\}$ a sequence of spheres, in the form

$$(12.4.3) \qquad \frac{1}{\ell(A_n)} \sum_{j=1}^{N(A_n)} g(S_{x_j^*} N) \to m E_{\mathscr{P}_0}(g(N_0)) \qquad (\mathscr{P}\text{-a.s.})$$

since the points in A_n are precisely those of the process with modulus $r_j = \|x_j^*\|$ less than the radius of A_n. Taking $g \equiv 1$, it follows that

$$(12.4.4) \qquad N(A_n)/\ell(A_n) \to m,$$

so in place of (12.4.3) we have

$$(12.4.5) \qquad \frac{1}{N(A_n)} \sum_{j=1}^{N(A_n)} g(S_{x_j^*} N) \to E_{\mathscr{P}_0}(g(N_0)) \qquad (\mathscr{P}\text{-a.s.}).$$

We can suppose that the $\{A_n\}$ have been so chosen that $\ell(A_n)/\ell(A_{n+1}) \to 1$ as $n \to \infty$, in which case we then have

$$N(A_n)/N(A_{n+1}) \to 1 \qquad (\mathscr{P}\text{-a.s.}).$$

For brevity, write $g_j = g(S_{x_j^*} N)$, and $N_k = N(A_{n(k)})$, where $n(k)$ is chosen to satisfy $x_k^* \notin A_{n(k)}$, $x_k^* \in A_{1+n(k)}$. Then the inequalities

$$N_{k+1}^{-1} \sum_{j=1}^{N_k} g_j \le k^{-1} \sum_{j=1}^{k} g_j \le N_k^{-1} \sum_{j=1}^{N_{k+1}} g_j$$

show that the limit relation (12.4.5) implies (12.4.2).

Equation (12.4.1) is a corollary of the following result.

Lemma 12.4.II. *Let Γ be an invariant set in $\mathscr{B}(\mathcal{N}_{\mathcal{X}})$ with $\mathscr{P}(\Gamma) = 1$, where $\mathscr{P}$ is the distribution of a simple stationary point process. Then $\mathscr{P}_0(\Gamma_0) = 1$, where $\Gamma_0 = \Gamma \cap \mathcal{N}_0^*$.*

PROOF OF LEMMA. From (12.2.8),

$$\mathcal{P}_0(\Gamma_0) = m^{-1} E_{\mathcal{P}}\left(\int_{\mathbb{U}^d} I_{\Gamma_0}(S_x N) N(dx)\right)$$

$$= m^{-1} \int_{\Gamma} \int_{\mathbb{U}^d} I_{\Gamma_0}(S_x N) N(dx)\mathcal{P}(dN)$$

since Γ has $\mathcal{P}$-measure one. Now for $N \in \Gamma$, $S_x N \in \Gamma$ a.s. for all $x \in \mathbb{U}^d$ because Γ is invariant, and hence in particular for the values of x that are points of N in $\mathbb{U}^d$. Now N is simple, $N(\mathcal{X}) = \infty$ a.s. by the assumed ergodicity, and $(S_x N)(\{0\}) = N(\{x\})$, so $S_x N \in \Gamma_0$ if and only if $N(\{x\}) = 1$. The inner integral therefore equals $N(\mathbb{U}^d)$, so

$$\mathcal{P}_0(\Gamma_0) = m^{-1} \int_{\Gamma} N(\mathbb{U}^d)\mathcal{P}(dN) = m^{-1} E_{\mathcal{P}}(N(\mathbb{U}^d)) = 1. \qquad \square$$

Application of (10.2.6) yields, for $n \to \infty$,

(12.4.6) $$\frac{1}{\ell(A_n)} \int_{A_n} f(S_x N)dx \to E_{\mathcal{P}}(f(N)) \qquad (\mathcal{P}\text{-a.s.}).$$

Now an application of the lemma, taking for Γ the set of N on which (12.4.6) holds and Γ_0 its restriction to $\mathcal{N}_0^*$, proves (12.4.1). $\square$

The results in Proposition 12.4.I provide quite a strong statement about convergence to equilibrium: with probability 1, the averages along individual realizations converge to their equilibrium values. In applications, we are more often interested in statements about the distribution or moments of the variables. As an immediate corollary to the proposition we obtain the following.

Corollary 12.4.III. *Suppose that the conditions of Proposition 12.4.I hold, and in addition that f and g are bounded. Then as $n \to \infty$,*

(12.4.7) $$\frac{1}{\ell(A_n)} \int_{A_n} E_{\mathcal{P}_0}(f(S_{-x} N_0))dx \to E_{\mathcal{P}}(f(N)),$$

and as $k \to \infty$,

(12.4.8) $$\frac{1}{k} \sum_{j=1}^{k} E_{\mathcal{P}}(g(S_{x_j^*} N)) \to E_{\mathcal{P}_0}(g(N_0)).$$

PROOF. Take expectations with respect to $\mathcal{P}$ and $\mathcal{P}_0$, respectively, and apply the dominated convergence theorem. $\square$

If an initial distribution $\mathcal{P}_I$ is such that, for any convex averaging sequence $\{A_n\}$,

$$(12.4.9) \qquad \frac{1}{\ell(A_n)} \int_{A_n} \hat{S}_x \mathcal{P}_I(\cdot) dx \to_w \mathcal{P}(\cdot),$$

where the limit holds in the sense of weak convergence, we could describe $\mathcal{P}_I$ as belonging to the weak domain of attraction of the stationary distribution $\mathcal{P}$. For example, (12.4.7) shows that the Palm distribution $\mathcal{P}_0$ belongs to the weak domain of attraction of the distribution $\mathcal{P}$ from which it is derived.

A stronger form of convergence is obtained by dropping the averaging in (12.4.9): say that $\mathcal{P}_I$ belongs to the strong domain of attraction of the stationary distribution $\mathcal{P}$ if, as $\|x\| \to \infty$,

$$(12.4.10) \qquad \hat{S}_x \mathcal{P}_I \to_w \mathcal{P},$$

again in the sense of weak convergence. This form of convergence to equilibrium is closely associated with the concept of mixing. For example, the result of Exercise 10.3.5(b) implies that $\mathcal{P}_I$ is in the strong domain of attraction of $\mathcal{P}$ if $\mathcal{P}_I \ll \mathcal{P}$ and $\mathcal{P}$ is mixing. The absolute continuity condition here is not easy to verify: the main result of this section is the more useful result that when $\mathcal{P}$ is mixing, the Palm distribution $\mathcal{P}_0$ (regarded here as a distribution on $\mathcal{N}_{\mathcal{X}}$, even though it is concentrated on a "thin" subset) belongs to the strong domain of attraction of $\mathcal{P}$.

Theorem 12.4.IV. *Let $\mathcal{P}$ be the distribution of a simple stationary mixing point process on $\mathbb{R}^d$, with finite density, and let $\mathcal{P}_0$ be the corresponding Palm distribution. Then as $\|x\| \to \infty$,*

$$(12.4.11) \qquad \hat{S}_x \mathcal{P}_0 \to_w \mathcal{P}.$$

PROOF. To establish weak convergence we need to show that for all bounded continuous f on $\mathcal{N}_{\mathcal{X}}$,

$$E_{\mathcal{P}_0}(f(S_x N_0)) \to E_{\mathcal{P}}(f(N)) \quad \text{as } \|x\| \to \infty.$$

Proposition 12.3.VI is a convenient starting point for the proof. From that result, for any given $\varepsilon > 0$ and sufficiently small sphere A_n,

$$(12.4.12) \qquad |E_{\mathcal{P}_0}(f(S_x N_0)) - E_{\mathcal{P}}(f(S_x S_{x^*(N)} N)|N(A_n) > 0)| < \varepsilon/2$$

for each fixed $x \in \mathcal{X}$ [replace $f(\cdot)$ by $f(S_x \cdot)$ in (12.3.18)]. Inspect the proof of (12.3.18) and observe that the inequality is uniform in x (cf. Exercise 12.3.7) since the two critical inequalities used in its proof depend only on (12.3.15) and $\sup|f(\cdot)|$, both of which are independent of x. Consequently, we can fix n from (12.4.12) and proceed by simply evaluating the difference

$$|E_{\mathcal{P}}(f(S_x S_{x^*(N)} N)|N(A_n) > 0) - E_{\mathcal{P}}(f(N))|$$
$$= (\mathcal{P}\{N(A_n) > 0\})^{-1} |E_{\mathcal{P}}(f(S_x S_{x^*(N)} N) I_{\{N(A_n)>0\}}(N)$$
$$- E_{\mathcal{P}}(f(N)) E_{\mathcal{P}}(I_{\{N(A_n)>0\}}(N))|.$$

Now it is enough to apply the result of Exercise 10.3.5(a) with

$$X(N) = f(S_{x^*(N)}N), \qquad Y(N) = I_{\{N(A_n) > 0\}}(N)$$

to deduce that this difference can also be made less than $\varepsilon/2$ by taking $\|x\|$ sufficiently large.   □

To illustrate the close connection between these results and the classical renewal theorems, we prove a result for mixing second-order processes attributed by Delasnerie (1977) to Neveu. It asserts that for large $\|x\|$, the reduced second moment measure approximates its form under a Poisson process.

Theorem 12.4.V. *Let N be a stationary second-order point process in $\mathbb{R}^d$ with density m and reduced second moment measure $\hat{M}_2(\cdot)$. If N is mixing then as $\|x\| \to \infty$,*

(12.4.13) $S_x \hat{M}_2(\cdot) \to_w m^2 \ell(\cdot).$

PROOF. The formal connection here lies with the representation of the reduced moment measures as moments of the Palm distribution. However, we do not need to call on the Palm theory as such; it is enough to use the definition of the reduced moment measure, which yields, with $b^*(x) = b(-x)$ as in Chapter 10, and functions $a(\cdot)$, $b(\cdot)$ vanishing outside a bounded set,

$$E\left(\int_{\mathscr{X}} \int_{\mathscr{X}} a(u - x)b(v)N(du)N(dv) \right) = \int_{\mathscr{X}} (a * b^*)(v - x)\hat{M}_2(dv)$$

$$= \int_{\mathscr{X}} (a * b^*)(v)S_x \hat{M}_2(dv).$$

Now when N is mixing, the first expectation converges as $\|x\| \to \infty$ to

$$m^2 \int_{\mathscr{X}} a(u)du \int_{\mathscr{X}} b(v)dv = m^2 \int_{\mathscr{X}} (a * b^*)(v)dv,$$

which by letting $a(\cdot)$ run through bounded continuous functions ensures the weak convergence of $b * (S_x \hat{M}_2)(\cdot)$ to $b * (m^2 \ell(\cdot))$, from which a standard sandwich argument yields (12.4.13).   □

This result assumes a more familiar form in the case that $d = 1$ (i.e., $\mathscr{X} = \mathbb{R}$) when expressed in terms of the generalized renewal function $U(\cdot)$ introduced in Theorem 3.5.III. We have then for a simple second-order stationary point process on $\mathbb{R}$,

$$U(x) = 1 + \lim_{h \downarrow 0} E_{\mathscr{P}}(N(0, x] \mid N(-h, 0] > 0)$$

$$= 1 + E_{\mathscr{P}_0}(N(0, x]) = 1 + \hat{M}_2(0, x]/m,$$

leading to the following corollary to Theorem 12.4.V.

Corollary 12.4.VI. (Generalized Blackwell Theorem). *Let N be a simple stationary mixing point process on $\mathbb{R}$ with finite second moment measure. Then* *as $x \to \infty$, for all $h > 0$,*

$$U(x + h) - U(x) \to mh.$$

Since a renewal process with $m < \infty$ has finite second moment measure and is mixing if its lifetime distribution F is nonlattice, this corollary includes the standard version of Blackwell's theorem (Theorem 4.4.I) as a special case. However, the simplicity of the above argument as compared with the intricacies of Chapter 4 is misleading, because what is obscured here is the fact that to prove that the renewal process is mixing, a result close to Blackwell's theorem must be assumed. For this case, therefore, the corollary would then become the conclusion of a somewhat circular argument. More generally, there is no very simple relation between mixing of the basic process and mixing of the sequence of intervals, in contrast to the case of ergodicity for which the concepts coincide as a corollary to Lemma 12.4.II (see Exercise 12.4.3). For the Wold process, similar questions regarding the lattice structure have to be overcome as in Chapter 4, and, additionally, the function $U(\cdot)$ refers to expectations when the initial interval has the stationary distribution. Consequently, further extensions are needed to cover the case of a process starting with an arbitrary distribution for the initial interval.

The topics discussed so far in this section are a little different in character from the problem of convergence to equilibrium as it commonly arises in applications. Here, one is typically given a "law of evolution" of the process and one seeks to establish, first, whether such a law is compatible with a stationary form for the process, and second, whether the process will converge to that stationary form when started at $t = 0$ from an arbitrary initial distribution.

We do not seek to define too precisely what is meant by a "law of evolution" (beyond noting that it nearly always involves a reduction to a Markovian property), but we do suppose simply that we are given an initial point process, with distribution $\mathcal{P}'$ say, defined on the half-line $[0, \infty)$, and an associated stationary process $\mathcal{P}$ defined on the whole real line. Note that the specification of $\mathcal{P}'$ must include any appropriate initial conditions. Since the distributions for the two processes are ostensibly defined on different spaces, a little care is needed in stating what is meant by convergence of a shifted version of the former to the latter.

In fact, if $\mathcal{P}'$ is defined on the Borel sets of $\hat{\mathcal{M}}([0, \infty)) \equiv \hat{\mathcal{M}}_{\mathbb{R}_+}$, then $\hat{S}_{-x}\mathcal{P}'$, which corresponds to looking at the process from a new time origin at $x > 0$, is defined on the Borel sets of $\hat{\mathcal{M}}([-x, \infty))$. Now $\mathcal{B}(\hat{\mathcal{M}}_{\mathbb{R}_+})$ can be identified with a sub-σ-algebra of $\mathcal{B}(\hat{\mathcal{M}}([-x, \infty)))$, and any measure on the former can be projected onto a measure on the latter. Thus, each of the measures $S_{-x}\mathcal{P}'$, as well as the stationary measure $\mathcal{P}$, induces a measure on $\mathcal{B}(\hat{\mathcal{M}}([0, \infty)))$. By the statement

(12.4.14) $$\hat{S}_{-x}\mathcal{P}' \to \mathcal{P} \quad \text{(weakly)}$$

we understand, for the rest of this section, the weak convergence of these induced measures.

The most familiar approach to these problems, as expounded, for example, in the fundamental paper by W. L. Smith (1955) on regenerative processes and which is by no means restricted to point processes, depends on identifying a renewal process imbedded in the process under consideration and on deducing the convergence to equilibrium of this latter process from an application of the renewal theorems to the imbedded renewal process. [See Kendall (1951) for some comments and earlier references.]

The scope of this approach has been considerably enhanced in recent years by the "splitting techniques" described in connection with the Wold process in Section 4.5. This approach permits the identification of regeneration points even in processes that are governed by Markov chains with continuous state space, for which no initially obvious points of this kind exist. A closely related technique is the use of "coupling" arguments, as in the proof of Blackwell's theorem in Section 4.4. Berbée (1979) reviews such arguments, with applications to general types of point and other processes. We restrict ourselves here to an example of each type of argument, illustrating first how the renewal theorems of Sections 4.4 and 4.5 can be used to establish convergence to equilibrium of the process as a whole.

EXAMPLE 12.4(a) *Convergence to equilibrium of renewal and Wold processes.* The key to these results is the convergence to equilibrium of the associated forward recurrence time processes. Consider first the simpler case of the renewal process, supposing the lifetime distribution to be nonlattice, with finite mean $\mu = \lambda^{-1}$. Let $h(N)$ be a bounded continuous functional defined on $\mathscr{M}(\mathbb{R}_+)$; then to establish the weak convergence at (12.4.14) it is enough to show that, for all such h,

$$(12.4.15) \qquad \int_{\mathscr{M}(\mathbb{R}_+)} h(N)(\hat{S}_{-u}\mathscr{P}')(dN) \to \int_{\mathscr{M}(\mathbb{R}_+)} h(N)\mathscr{P}(dN).$$

With $t_0(N)$ defined as in Chapter 3, and $\mathbf{X} \equiv \{X_i(N)\} = \{t_i(N) - t_{i-1}(N): i = 1, 2, \ldots\}$ an i.i.d. sequence with the given lifetime distribution, the continuous functional $h(N)$ can be written equivalently as a jointly continuous functional, say $\phi_h(t_0, \mathbf{X})$, of the pair t_0, $\mathbf{X}$. Then the left-hand side of (12.4.15) can be rewritten as

$$(12.4.16) \qquad \int_0^\infty \left[\int_{\mathscr{X}_0} \phi(y, \mathbf{X})\Pi_0(d\mathbf{X}) \right] F_u(dy) = \int_0^\infty E(\phi(y, \mathbf{X}))F_u(dy),$$

where Π_0 is the distribution in sequence space $\mathscr{X}_0$ of the sequence $\{X_i\}$ and $F_u(\cdot)$ is the forward recurrence time distribution at time u. The integrand $E(\phi(y, \mathbf{X}))$ is again a continuous function of y, say $\psi(y) = E(\phi(y, \mathbf{X}))$, and the convergence of the right-hand side of (12.4.16) to its equilibrium form is now just a restatement of the weak convergence of the forward recurrence times outlined in Example 4.4(a).

In fact a stronger result is true, for as shown in Exercise 4.4.4, convergence at (12.4.16) holds even under the weaker assumption that ψ, hence in turn ϕ

and then h, is merely bounded and measurable. But (12.4.15) with h bounded and measurable implies strong convergence (i.e., convergence in variation norm) of $\hat{S}_{-u}\mathscr{P}'$ to the limit distribution $\mathscr{P}$ of the stationary renewal process. Thus, *if the lifetime distribution is nonlattice with finite mean, the convergence to equilibrium in* (12.4.14) *holds not only weakly but also in variation norm.*

Similar results for the Wold process can be obtained from the discussion in Section 4.5. Although the process is defined from $t = 0$ onward, it is convenient to describe the initial conditions in terms of the time $t_0(N)$ to the first event and the length $L_0(N) = t_0(N) - t_{-1}(N)$ of an (unobserved) initial interval. By analogy with the previous case we write

$$\int_{\mathscr{M}_{\mathbb{R}_+}} h(N)\mathscr{P}'(dN) = \int_0^\infty \int_0^\infty \phi(y, \mathbf{X})p_0(dx \times dy)\Pi(d\mathbf{X}|x),$$

where p_0 is an initial distribution for the pair $(L_0(N), t_0(N))$ and $\Pi(\cdot|x)$ is the distribution in sequence space of the sequence of intervals $X_1, X_2, \ldots$, given that $L_0(N) = x$. Of course $\Pi(\cdot|x)$ can be written out in terms of the Markov transition kernel:

$$\Pi(dX_1 \times dX_2 \times \cdots |x) = P(x, dX_1)P(X_1, dX_2)\cdots.$$

Denoting by $F_u(dx \times dy)$ the distribution at time u of the pair $(L(t), R(t))$, the left-hand side of (12.4.14) can be rewritten as

$$\int_0^\infty \int_0^\infty \phi(y, \mathbf{X})\Pi(d\mathbf{X}|x)F_u(dx \times dy) = \int_0^\infty \int_0^\infty \psi(x, y)F_u(dx \times dy),$$

where now

$$\psi(x, y) = E(\phi(y, \mathbf{X})|x).$$

If this function is continuous whenever ϕ is continuous—for example, if the transition kernel takes continuous functions into continuous functions, that is, is "weakly Feller"—and the distribution function G of (4.5.10) is nonlattice, then the first assertion of Proposition 4.5.VI implies that weak convergence holds in (12.4.14). If alternatively, G is spread out, and hence in particular if the transition kernel satisfies Condition 4.5.I(ii'), then the second assertion of Proposition 4.5.VI implies that (12.4.14) converges also in variation norm.

The next example can be handled by what is in effect a simple type of coupling argument.

EXAMPLE 12.4(b) *Convergence to equilibrium of the Hawkes process.* This process was introduced in Example 10.4(c) as an example of a Poisson cluster process, from which the existence of a stationary version could immediately by deduced. Such a process is associated with a complete intensity function of the form

(12.4.17)
$$\lambda^+(t) = v + \int_{-\infty}^t \mu(t - u)dN(u)$$

[see Chapter 13 for a general discussion of conditional intensities, and Example 13.1(f) for a discussion of this process in particular]. The only general result concerning conditional intensities that we need to know here is that the form of the conditional intensity over the interval $[0, \infty)$ specifies the process uniquely on that interval (see Proposition 13.1.IV and the discussion following Proposition 13.4.III, with Exercises 13.2.7 and 13.2.8). The restriction of the stationary process to $\mathbb{R}_+$ can be characterized in the following way. At any time t, the conditional intensity $\lambda^+(t)$ has the form

$$\lambda^+(t) = Z_0(t) + v + \int_0^t \mu(t - u)dN(u),$$

where

$$Z_0(t) = \int_{-\infty}^0 \mu(t - u)dN(u)$$

is a random function, evolving deterministically for $t > 0$ [equivalently, for $t > 0$, $Z_0(t)$ is $\mathcal{H}_0$-measurable, where $\mathcal{H}_0$ is the history of the process up to time 0]. Here it is the random process $Z_0(t)$ that defines the "initial distribution" required to make the point process stationary. Note that $Z_0(t)$ is nonnegative, converges a.s. to zero, is integrable a.s. over any finite interval $[0, S]$, and satisfies

$$E(Z_0(t)) = \lambda \int_t^\infty \mu(u)du \to 0 \qquad (t \to \infty).$$

Similarly, we may specify an arbitrary "initial distribution" for the process by specifying the distribution of a process $Z_1(t) \geq 0$ satisfying the same requirements of a.s. local integrability and $E(Z_1(t)) \to 0$.

Let $\mathscr{P}_0$ and $\mathscr{P}_1$ be the distributions on $\mathcal{M}([0, \infty))$ corresponding to the self-exciting processes with initial conditions specified by $Z_0(t)$ and $Z_1(t)$, respectively. In each case we may regard the resulting point process as the superposition of two components, a process that, conditional on $\mathcal{H}_0$, is of Poisson type with rate parameter $Z_0(t)$ [resp. $Z_1(t)$] and a self-exciting process with conditional intensity

$$\lambda^*(t) = v + \int_0^t \mu(t - u)dN(u).$$

Denote the distributions of the Poisson components by $\mathscr{P}_0^*$ ($\mathscr{P}_1^*$) and that of the self-exciting component by $\mathscr{Q}$. Then we have

$$\mathscr{P}_0 = \mathscr{P}_0^* * \mathscr{Q}, \qquad \mathscr{P}_1 = \mathscr{P}_1^* * \mathscr{Q};$$

and similarly,

$$\hat{S}_{-t}\mathscr{P}_0 = \hat{S}_{-t}\mathscr{P}_0^* * \hat{S}_{-t}\mathscr{Q}, \qquad \hat{S}_{-t}\mathscr{P}_1 = \hat{S}_{-t}\mathscr{P}_1^* * \hat{S}_{-t}\mathscr{Q}$$

Now let $[0, S]$ be any finite interval and consider the variation difference between the projections of these measures onto $\mathcal{M}([0, S])$. Using elementary properties of the variation distance, we obtain

$$\|\hat{S}_{-t}\mathcal{P}_1 - \mathcal{P}_0\|_{[0, S]} = \|\hat{S}_{-t}\mathcal{P}_1 - \hat{S}_{-t}\mathcal{P}_0\|_{[0, S]} \le \|\hat{S}_{-t}\mathcal{P}_1^* - \hat{S}_{-t}\mathcal{P}_0^*\|_{[0, S]}$$

$$\le \mathcal{P}_1^*\{N(t, t + S) > 0\} + \mathcal{P}_0^*\{N(t, t + S) > 0\},$$

where both the last probabilities tend to zero.

Since this result clearly implies convergence of the fidi distributions, and hence weak convergence of the point processes, we deduce that (12.4.14) holds.

If the infectivity function $\mu(x)$ satisfies the stronger condition $\int_0^\infty x\mu(x)dx < \infty$, and a similar integrability requirement is imposed on $E(Z_1(t))$, then the restriction to a finite interval $[0, S]$ in the above argument can be dropped, and the convergence in (12.4.14) holds also in variation norm.

Exercises

12.4.1. Let $\mathcal{P}$ be the distribution of a stationary point process on $\mathbb{R}$ for which $\mathcal{P}\{N(\mathbb{R}) = \infty\} = 1$. Restate (12.4.7)–(12.4.9) in terms of integrals on $(0, t_n]$ with $t_n \to \infty$, where t_n is the nth point of the process in $\mathbb{R}_+$ [cf. also (12.3.7)].

12.4.2. Let Γ_0 be an invariant set of $\mathcal{N}_0^*$. Show that there exists an invariant set $\Gamma \in \mathcal{N}_\mathscr{X}$ such that $\Gamma_0 = \Gamma \cap \mathcal{N}_0^*$. Show also that if $\mathcal{P}_0(\Gamma_0) = 1$, then $\mathcal{P}(\Gamma) = 1$. [Hint: What is Γ? If the association of Γ_0 with respect to $\mathcal{P}_0$ is that of the occurrence of a point at the origin, then the association of Γ with respect to $\mathcal{P}$ bears the same relation to its first point after the origin, as Γ_0 to a point at the origin, as, for example, if $\Gamma_0 = \{$all intervals bounded and a point at the origin$\}$, then $\Gamma = \{$all intervals bounded$\}$.]

12.4.3. Show that a stationary point process N is ergodic if and only if the associated Palm distribution $\mathcal{P}_0$ is ergodic (e.g., when $\mathscr{X} = \mathbb{R}$, N is ergodic if and only if the associated interval process is ergodic). [Hint: Ergodicity is equivalent to the requirement that all invariant sets have probability 0 or 1; now use Lemma 12.4.II. A converse to the lemma is also needed: $\mathcal{P}_0(\Gamma_0) = 1$ implies the existence of Γ in $\mathscr{B}(\mathcal{N}_\mathscr{X})$, such that Γ is invariant with $\mathcal{P}(\Gamma) = 1$ and $\Gamma_0 = \Gamma \cap \mathcal{N}_0^*$.]

12.4.4. Let the multivariate point process $N(t) = (N_0(t), N_1(t), \ldots, N_k(t))$ in $t > 0$ be such that the successive points $t_{00} \le 0 < t_{01} < t_{02} < \cdots$ of the component process N_0 are regeneration epochs for $N(t)$ in the sense that, for $u_i \ge 0$, the conditional distributions of $N(t + u_i)$ given $t_{0j} = t$ for some $j \ge 1$ are independent of t, and the interval lengths $\{t_{0,j+1} - t_{0j}\}$ are i.i.d. r.v.s with density function $f(\cdot)$. Define

$$H(t) = E(N_1(t)|t_{00} = 0, t_{01} = t), \qquad V(t) = \text{var}(N_1(t)|t_{00} = 0, t_{01} = t).$$

Assuming the moments are finite, show that

$$\lim_{t \to \infty} \frac{\text{var}(N_1(t))}{E(N_1(t))} \ge \beta \equiv \int_0^\infty V(t)f(t)dt \Big/ \int_0^\infty H(t)f(t)dt$$

with equality holding if and only if $H(t)/t$ is constant a.e. on the support of $f(\cdot)$.

[See Berman (1978) for this and other results concerning such multivariate point processes that are regenerative in the sense of Smith (1955). Results concerning ergodicity and Palm distributions have been extended from regenerative processes to the context of marked point processes; there are details and several examples in Franken et al. (1981).]

CHAPTER 13

Conditional Intensities and Likelihoods

The ideas to be discussed in this chapter have been the subject of intensive development during the last two decades, as much by engineers as by mathematicians and statisticians. The underlying theme is the need for a theory of estimation, prediction, and control for point processes. In the late 1960s and early 1970s engineers, in particular, began to exploit a remarkable analogy between point processes and diffusion processes, with the Poisson process playing a role analogous to that of Brownian motion. Early papers by Yashin (1970) in the Soviet Union and Snyder (1972) and Rubin (1972) in the United States explored the analogy between filtering and detection problems for point processes and the Kalman filtering techniques for signal-from-noise problems in the Gaussian context; the analogy is closest for doubly stochastic (i.e., Cox) processes. The paper by Gaver (1963) may be regarded as some kind of precursor of these developments. These papers were followed by more systematic studies in the theses by Brémaud (1972) and van Schuppen (1973), and papers by Boel, Varaiya, and Wong (1975), Kailath and Segall (1975), and Davis (1976), to mention only a few. On the probabilistic side, the possibility of a powerful link with martingale theory was noted as early as 1964 by Watanabe (1964) who gave a martingale characterization of the Poisson process; the martingale theory was developed further in Kunita and Watanabe (1967). A synthesis of these approaches was presented by Kabanov, Liptser, and Shiryayev (1975) and incorporated in Volume II of Liptser and Shiryayev (1978). Further important reviews are found in Brémaud and Jacod (1977), Brémaud (1981), Shiryayev (1981), and Jacobsen (1982).

On a rather different tack, Cox (1972a,b) explored regression models for life tables where the hazard function may depend on supplementary variables. Taken over to the point process context, this leads to the analysis of situations where the current risk may depend on factors that include aspects of the past of the process. This theory was developed further and linked to martingale theory by Aalen (1975) and Jacobsen (1982).

Our aim in this chapter is to give an introduction to this circle of ideas, stressing the links with other aspects of point process theory rather than the analogy with Gaussian filtering theory. After all, it is only in the one-dimensional situation that a natural *causal* theory of successive conditioning exists, to provide, in turn, a natural context for the martingale approach. The first section of the chapter gives an introduction to point process likelihoods in general, starting from the recognition that the likelihood is nothing other than a Janossy density. Some problems can be dealt with directly by the machinery of cumulant and Khinchin measures developed in Chapter 5. In the one-dimensional case, a simple constructive definition of the conditional intensity can be given, and the fundamental formula for the likelihood in terms of the conditional intensity can be developed from the definition of the likelihood as a Janossy density.

Likelihood functions reappear in the martingale approach outlined in the second section, where we try to give some of the more important results without striving either for the greatest generality or complete detail. A feature of this approach is that it requires a careful examination of the effect of conditioning on the regularity properties of trajectories. The notion of *predictability* plays a key role, alongside other aspects of the so-called general theory of processes as set out in Dellacherie and Meyer (1978), for example. A brief outline of some background material required for this section is set out in Appendix 3. Fuller treatments of the theory exist in Jacod (1975), Liptser and Shiryayev (1978), and Brémaud (1981), and in the books on inference by Kutoyants (1984b) and Karr (1986).

The remaining sections of this chapter look at a variety of applications and extensions of these ideas—to characterization and limit theorems, to a few of the many problems of filtering and estimation, and to the extensions to complete intensities and entropy rates. An auxiliary concept, which appears twice in these discussions, is that of *stable convergence*, which we regard as a form of convergence of conditional distributions; it is particularly useful in handling problems where some kind of nonergodicity is present, and the limit distribution can be represented as a mixture.

13.1. Point Process Likelihood

Suppose there is given a realization $\{x_1, \ldots, x_N\}$ of a point process over a bounded Borel set A in $\mathbb{R}^d$. Our main concern is with the situation where densities (with respect to Lebesgue measure ℓ on $\mathbb{R}^d$) exist, so we make the following definition.

Definition 13.1.I. A point process on $\mathcal{X} = \mathbb{R}^d$ is *regular on A* for a bounded Borel set $A \subseteq \mathbb{R}^d$ if for all integers $k \geq 1$ the local Janossy measures

$$J_k(dx_1 \times \cdots \times dx_k | A)$$

of Section 7.4 are absolutely continuous with respect to ℓ on A. It is *regular* if it is regular on A for all bounded $A \in \mathcal{B}(\mathbb{R}^d)$.

Note that from Proposition 5.4.IV a *regular point process is necessarily simple*. Now let $\{x_1, \ldots, x_N\}$ be a realization of a regular point process over some observation region A, which we take to be a bounded Borel set in $\mathcal{X} = \mathbb{R}^d$. As discussed in Chapter 5, the Janossy density $j_N(x_1, \ldots, x_N)$ has the interpretation that, after multiplication by the volume element $dx_1 \cdots dx_N$, it represents the probability that the realization contains just N points, and that, in some ordering, there is one of these points in each of the infinitesimal regions around each x_i. The local version of this function, regarded as a function of the parameters for fixed N, $x_1, \ldots, x_N$, is the function we regard as the *likelihood* of the realization.

Definition 13.1.II. The *likelihood* of a realization $x_1, \ldots, x_N$ of a regular point process on a bounded Borel set $A \subseteq \mathbb{R}^d$ is the local Janossy density

$$(13.1.1) \qquad L_A(x_1, \ldots, x_N) = j_N(x_1, \ldots, x_N | A).$$

For convenience we often abbreviate L_A to L. Strictly speaking, the likelihood, like any density, is an equivalence class of functions defined up to their values on a set of Lebesgue measure zero. In applications, we are concerned exclusively with the situations where there exists at least a left- or right-continuous version of the density (in $\mathbb{R}$), or more often a continuous and even differentiable version. In these cases we always choose the version of the density that is defined uniquely by the continuity requirement. For the time being we explore some representations of the Janossy measure without making these additional continuity requirements.

In fact, Definition 13.1.II itself does not take us very far in calculating point process likelihoods or exploring their properties. There is, however, one obvious case in which the likelihood can be written down directly from the definition, namely, the Poisson process treated below. Another important general tool is the representation of the Janossy densities in terms of the Khinchin densities as discussed in Chapter 5 around Equation (5.5.28).

EXAMPLE 13.1(a) *Inhomogeneous Poisson process with density.* While the likelihood as below can readily be obtained from the lack of memory property or the form of the probability distribution (see Exercise 13.1.1), it is more instructive, as an introduction to more complex examples, to illustrate its derivation via the p.g.fl. and Khinchin measures. From (7.4.10) and (7.4.17) the p.g.fl. $G_A[\cdot]$ for a Poisson process on A with parameter measure having a density $\mu(\cdot)$ there is given by

$$\log G_A[h] = - \int_A (1 - h(x)) \mu(x) dx \qquad (h \in \mathcal{V}_0).$$

This shows, as we already know from the completely random property, that the process confined to A is unaffected by the process outside A and is again a Poisson process. Only the first Khinchin measure is nonzero, so in the notation of Exercise 5.5.8 we have, say,

$$K_0 = -\log p_0(A) = \int_A \mu(x)\,dx = \mu(A),$$

$$k_1(x|A) = \mu(x).$$

Hence, the Janossy density for the process on A exists and has the form

$$(13.1.2) \qquad L \equiv j_n(x_1, \ldots, x_n|A) = p_0(A) \prod_{i=1}^{n} \mu(x_i)$$

$$= \left[\exp\left(-\int_A \mu(y)\,dy \right) \right] \prod_{i=1}^{n} \mu(x_i),$$

since the symmetrized sum of all other terms vanishes, while

$$(13.1.3) \qquad\qquad \log L = \sum \log \mu(x_i) - \int_A \mu(x)\,dx.$$

An immediate corollary of (13.1.2) is that, conditional on the number n of observations, the likelihood of the Poisson process with density $\mu(\cdot)$ is (apart from the term $n!$) identical with that of n i.i.d. observations having common probability density $\mu(x)/M(A)$, where $M(A) = \int_A \mu(y)\,dy$. The factor $n!$ arises because in the i.i.d. context there are $n!$ different orderings of the variables, which produce the same counting measure.

To obtain a concept of likelihood that can be transferred to more general situations, it is necessary to move from the above definition of likelihood to the concept of *likelihood ratio*. This is also the concept that plays the key role in inference. For this purpose, we need to choose a standard process for the denominator of the ratio and to ascertain conditions under which a general distribution of the class of random objects in view is absolutely continuous with respect to the distribution of the standard. In the context of simple point processes on $\mathbb{R}^d$, the natural standard is the Poisson process with parameter measure equal to Lebesgue measure on $\mathbb{R}^d$. We have then the following characterization of absolute continuity with respect to this standard.

Proposition 13.1.III. *Let N be a point process on $\mathcal{X} = \mathbb{R}^d$, N_A its restriction to the bounded Borel set $A \subseteq \mathbb{R}^d$, and $\mathcal{P}_A$ the distribution of N_A on $\mathcal{N}(A)$. Let $\mathcal{P}_A^*$ be the distribution on $\mathcal{N}(A)$ of the Poisson process with intensity measure equal to Lebesgue measure on $\mathbb{R}^d$. Then*

$$\mathcal{P}_A \ll \mathcal{P}_A^*$$

if and only if N is regular on A.

PROOF. Recalling again the machinery of Chapter 5, regard each of $\mathscr{P}_A$ and $\mathscr{P}_A^*$ as measures on the space $\mathscr{X}^\cup$ at (5.3.8). Clearly, from the definition, $\mathscr{P}_A \ll \mathscr{P}_A^*$ if and only if the restriction of $\mathscr{P}_A$ to each of the components $\mathscr{X}^{(n)}$ of $\mathscr{X}^\cup$ is absolutely continuous with respect to the corresponding restriction of $\mathscr{P}_A^*$. But this just means (in an obvious notation) that $J_n \ll J_n^*$, and since J_n^* reduces to a multiple of Lebesgue measure because the process is Poisson [cf. Example 13.1(a) above], the statement is now obvious.   □

In the situation described by Proposition 13.1.III, the likelihood ratio is given by $L_A/L_A^* = e^{\ell(A)} j_N(x_1, \ldots, x_N | A)$.

Suppose as in (13.1.2) and (13.1.3) that $\mathscr{P}_A$ is the distribution associated with an inhomogeneous Poisson process with intensity $\mu(x)$. Then the log likelihood ratio takes the form

$$(13.1.4) \qquad \log(L_A/L_A^*) = \sum_{i=1}^N \log \mu(x_i) - \int_A (\mu(x) - 1)dx.$$

We shall see later that this representation holds for a much wider class of processes, provided $\mu(x)$ is suitably reinterpreted. One further manipulation of (13.1.4) may be worth pointing out. Suppose that $\mu(x)$ has the form

$$\mu(x) = C\phi(x),$$

where C is a positive scale parameter, and $\phi(x)$ is normalized so that, for example, $\int_A \phi(x)dx = 1$. Then (13.1.4) becomes

$$\log(L_A/L_A^*) = N \log C + \sum \log \phi(x_i) - C + \ell(A).$$

Differentiation with respect to C yields the maximum likelihood estimate

$$\hat{C} = N,$$

and it is clear that here N is a sufficient statistic for C. Moreover, substituting this value back into the log likelihood ratio yields

$$\log(\hat{L}_A/L_A^*) = N \log N - N + \ell(A) + \sum \log \phi(x_i).$$

Apart from a constant term, this is the same expression as would be obtained by first conditioning on N, when the likelihood reduces to that for N independent observations on the distribution with density $\phi(x_i)$. Clearly, in this situation, estimates based on Poisson observations with variable N yield the same results as estimates obtained by first conditioning on N, a statement that is not true with other distributions even asymptotically.

Finally, consider the model

$$\mu(x) = C/\ell(A)$$

with likelihood L_A^0 say. We find as a special case of the above

$$\log \hat{L}_A^0/L_A^* = N \log N - N + \ell(A) - N \log \ell(A),$$

from which

$$\log \hat{L}_A/\hat{L}_A^0 = \sum \log \phi(x_i) + N \log \ell(A).$$

Thus, the term on the right is the increment to the log likelihood ratio achieved by fitting a model with density proportional to $\phi(x)$ over a model with constant density. This elementary observation often provides a useful reduction in the complexity of numerical computations involving Poisson models.

We turn to a few further examples where the likelihood can be written down more or less immediately.

EXAMPLE 13.1(b) *Gauss–Poisson process* (see Example 8.3(c)). Observe first that if $N(\cdot)$ on $\mathscr{X}$ is Gauss–Poisson, so also is $N_A(\cdot)$ though not necessarily with precisely the same parametric functions. For simplicity then, assume that $\mathscr{X} = A$ to obviate the need for any edge corrections (but see Exercise 13.1.2). The log p.g.fl. has two terms in its expansion:

$$-\log G[h] = \int_A (1 - h(x))K_1(dx) + \int_{A^{(2)}} (1 - h(x)h(y))K_2(dx \times dy).$$

Assume that $K_1(dx) = \mu \, dx \equiv \mu\ell(dx)$ and $K_2(dx \times dy) = \frac{1}{2}q(x - y)dx \, dy$ for some symmetric function $q(\cdot)$ so that the Khinchin densities k_r are given by

$$K_0 = -\log p_0(A) = \mu\ell(A) + \frac{1}{2} \int \int_{A^{(2)}} q(x - y)dx \, dy,$$

$$k_1(x) = \mu \quad \text{(all } x\text{)},$$

$$k_2(x, y) = q(x - y),$$

$$k_r(\cdot) = 0 \quad \text{for all } r = 3, 4, \ldots.$$

We turn to the expansion of the Janossy densities in terms of Khinchin densities given by Equation (5.5.28), namely,

$$j_n(x_1, \ldots, x_n | A) = \exp(-K_0) \sum_{r=1}^{n} \sum_{\mathscr{T} \in \mathscr{P}_{rn}} \prod_{i=1}^{r} k_{|S_i(\mathscr{T})|}(x_{i,1}, \ldots, x_{i,|S_i(\mathscr{T})|}),$$

where the inner summation is taken over all partitions $\mathscr{T}$ of $x_1, \ldots, x_n$ into i subsets as described above Lemma 5.2.VI. The only nonzero terms arising in this summation are those relating to partitions into sets of sizes 1 and 2 exclusively. This leads to the form for the Janossy densities

$$(13.1.5) \quad j_n(x_1, \ldots, x_n | A) = p_0(A) \sum_{k=0}^{[n/2]} \mu^{n-2k} \sum{}^* q(x_{i_1} - x_{i_2}) \cdots q(x_{i_{2k-1}} - x_{i_{2k}}),$$

where the summation $\sum^*$ extends over the $n!/((n - 2k)!2^k)$ distinct sets of k pairs of different indices $(i_1, i_2), \ldots, (i_{2k-1}, i_{2k})$ from $1, \ldots, n$ satisfying $i_{2j-1} < i_{2j} \, (j = 1, \ldots, k)$ and $i_1 < i_3 < \cdots < i_{2k-1}$.

Given a realization $x_1, \ldots, x_N$ of a Gauss–Poisson process on a set A, its likelihood is then $j_N(x_1, \ldots, x_N | A)$, which is in principle computable but in practice is somewhat complex as soon as N is of moderate size.

Newman (1970) established (13.1.5) by an induction argument.

In principle, it is possible to write down even more complicated expressions than (13.1.5) for cluster processes with up to 3, 4, ... points in each cluster. Baudin (1981) has developed an equivalent systematic procedure for writing down the likelihood of a Neyman–Scott cluster process, but again it is of extreme combinatorial complexity: see Exercise 13.1.3 for details.

EXAMPLE 13.1(c) *Fermion and boson processes* (see Examples 5.4(b) and 8.5(b)). Each of these processes is completely specified by a covariance function $c(x, y)$ and the Janossy measures appear as either the determinants [for the fermion process: see (5.4.19)] or the permanents [for the boson process: see (8.5.10)], in each case derived from the resolvent kernel of the integral equation with kernel $c(\cdot, \cdot)$.

EXAMPLE 13.1(d) *Pairwise interaction systems* (see Example 5.3(c)). An important class of problems from theoretical physics was introduced in Example 5.3(c), with likelihood of the form

$$L(x_1, \ldots, x_n) = C(\theta)\exp\{-\theta U(x_1, \ldots, x_n)\},$$

where, in the case of pairwise interactions only, $U(x_1, \ldots, x_n)$ has the form

$$U(x_1, \ldots, x_n) = \sum \psi_2(x_i, x_j).$$

The initial attractiveness of this setup as a general model for point process likelihoods is somewhat countered by the difficulty of expressing the partition function (normalizing constant) $C(\theta)$ as a function of any remaining parameters of the process. In fact, exact solutions do not seem to be available in any cases of practical interest. Ogata and Tanemura (1981) have advocated an approximate evaluation using the expansion techniques developed by physicists for this purpose, but even so the computations are extensive and the adequacy of the approximation somewhat uncertain.

If such examples suggest that there are no easy methods for evaluating point process likelihoods on general spaces, it is all the more remarkable, and fortunate, that in the special and important case $\mathscr{X} = \mathbb{R}$ there is available an alternate approach to the problem of considerable power and generality. The essence of this approach is the use of a causal description of the process, through successive conditionings. A full development of this approach is deferred until the later sections of this chapter; here we seek to establish its links to the more general representations in terms of Janossy functions. For simplicity, we suppose observation of the process to occur over the time interval $A = [0, T]$, so that results may be described in terms of a point process on $\mathbb{R}_+$.

Proposition 13.1.IV. *For a regular point process on $\mathscr{X} = \mathbb{R}_+$, there exists a uniquely determined family of conditional probability densities $p_n(t|t_1, \ldots, t_{n-1})$ and associated survivor functions*

$$S_n(t|t_1, \ldots, t_{n-1}) = 1 - \int_{t_{n-1}}^{t} p_n(u|t_1, \ldots, t_{n-1})du \qquad (t > t_{n-1})$$

defined on $0 < t_1 < t_2 < \cdots < t_{n-1} < t$ such that the support of each $p_n(\cdot|t_1, \ldots, t_{n-1})$ is carried by the half-line (t_{n-1}, ∞), and for all $n \geq 1$ and all finite intervals $[0, T]$ with $T > 0$,

(13.1.6a) $J_0(T) = S_1(T),$

(13.1.6b) $j_n(t_1, \ldots, t_n|T) \equiv j_n(t_1, \ldots, t_n|(0, T))$

$$= p_1(u_{(1)})p_2(u_{(2)}|u_{(1)}) \cdots p_n(u_{(n)}|u_{(1)}, \ldots, u_{(n-1)})S_{n+1}(T|u_{(1)}, \ldots, u_{(n)}),$$

where $0 < u_{(1)} < \cdots < u_{(n)} < T$ are the order statistics of the points $\{t_i\}$ of a realization of the point process on $[0, T]$. Conversely, given any such family of conditional densities for all $t > 0$, Equations (13.1.6a) and (13.1.6b) specify uniquely the distribution of a regular point process on $\mathbb{R}_+$.

PROOF. Suppose first that the Janossy measures, and their densities, $j_n(t_1, \ldots, t_n|T)$, are given for all finite intervals $(0, T)$. Since the Janossy measures are symmetric, we may and do suppose the points $t_1, \ldots, t_n$ are given in their natural order. We first note the identity, for $t < T$,

$$J_0(t) = J_0(T) + \sum_{k=1}^{\infty} \frac{1}{k!} \int_t^T \cdots \int_t^T j_k(u_1, \ldots, u_k|T)du_1 \cdots du_k.$$

This result establishes the absolute continuity of $J_0(t)$ as a function of t and allows us to represent its density in the form

$$p_1(t) = j_1(t|T) + \sum_{k=2}^{\infty} \frac{1}{(k-1)!} \int_t^T \cdots \int_t^T j_k(t, u_2, \ldots, u_k|T)du_2 \cdots du_k,$$

an expression that is actually independent of T for $T > t$. Thus, we may take $S_1(t) = J_0(t)$ and $p_1(t)$ as defined above.

The remaining equations follow by an inductive argument: we sketch the next step and leave the rest to the reader. Define $p_2(t|t_1)$ for $0 < t_1 < t < T$ by

$$p_1(t_1)p_2(t|t_1) = j_2(t_1, t|T)$$

$$+ \sum_{k=3}^{\infty} \frac{1}{(k-2)!} \int_t^T \cdots \int_t^T j_k(t_1, t, u_3, \ldots, u_k|T)du_3 \cdots du_k,$$

and verify that if $S_2(t|t_1) = 1 - \int_{t_1}^{t} p_2(u|t_1)du$ (for $t_1 < t < T$),

$$p_1(t_1)S_2(t|t_1)$$

$$= j_1(t_1|T) + \sum_{k=2}^{\infty} \frac{1}{(k-1)!} \int_t^T \cdots \int_t^T j_k(t_1, u_2, \ldots, u_k|T)du_2 \cdots du_k$$

$$= j_1(t_1|t),$$

again establishing the absolute continuity of $S_2(t|t_1)$ and also verifying that with this definition (13.1.6b) holds for $n = 1$. Continuing, (13.1.6b) is established in general. The survivor functions could be defined recursively as ratios; the argument as sketched shows additionally that these survivor functions are absolutely continuous in (t_{r-1}, ∞) and identifies their densities.

Conversely, given such a family of conditional densities, both $J_0(T)$ and symmetric densities $j_k(\cdot \,|\, T)$ can be defined by (13.1.6) and we can verify that they satisfy

$$J_0(T) + \sum_{n=1}^{\infty} \frac{1}{n!} \int_0^T \cdots \int_0^T j_n(t_1, \ldots, t_n | T) dt_1 \cdots dt_n$$

$$= J_0(T) + \sum_{n=1}^{\infty} \int \cdots \int_{0 < t_1 < \cdots < t_n < T} j_n(t_1, \ldots, t_n | T) dt_1 \cdots dt_n = 1.$$

It follows from Proposition 5.3.II that there exists a well-defined point process with these densities. Finally, since the point process is uniquely determined by the Janossy measures and these are equivalent to the conditional densities $p_n(t|t_1, \ldots, t_{n-1})$ for a regular point process, there is a one-to-one correspondence between regular point processes and families $p_n(\cdot\,|\,\cdot)$ as described.   □

From now on we suppose that $0 < t_1 < \cdots < t_n < \cdots$. We now make a seemingly innocuous but critical shift of view. Instead of specifying the conditional densities $p_n(\cdot\,|\,\cdot)$ directly, we express them in terms of their hazard functions

$$h_n(t|t_1, \ldots, t_{n-1}) = p_n(t|t_1, \ldots, t_{n-1})/S_n(t|t_1, \ldots, t_{n-1})$$

so that

(13.1.7)

$$p_n(t|t_1, \ldots, t_{n-1}) = h_n(t|t_1, \ldots, t_{n-1}) \exp\left[-\int_{t_{n-1}}^t h_n(u|t_1, \ldots, t_{n-1}) du \right].$$

Given a sequence $\{t_i\}$ with $0 < t_1 < \cdots < t_n < \cdots$, we define an amalgam of the hazard functions by

(13.1.8) $\lambda^*(t) = \begin{cases} h_1(t) & (0 < t \le t_1), \\ h_n(t|t_1, \ldots, t_{n-1}) & (t_{n-1} < t \le t_n, n \ge 2). \end{cases}$

Definition 13.1.V. The *conditional intensity function* for a regular point process on $\mathbb{R}_+ = [0, \infty)$ is the representative function $\lambda^*(\cdot)$ defined piecewise by (13.1.8).

The function $\lambda^*(t)$ can be interpreted as the conditional risk of the occurrence of an event at t, being conditional on the process over the interval $[0, t)$. Strictly, we should regard $\lambda^*(\cdot)$ as $\lambda^*(\cdot\,|\,t_1, \ldots, t_{N(t)})$ of the point history, or even more generally as a stochastic process $\lambda^*(t, \omega)$ depending on ω through the realization $\{t_1(\omega), \ldots, t_N(\omega)\}$ of the history. The terms *conditional risk* (or *rate* or *hazard*) *function*, or even these terms omitting the word "conditional," have also been used to describe $\lambda^*(\cdot)$ as defined at (13.1.8). It is the key both to likelihood analysis and to solving problems of prediction, filtering, and simulating point processes on a half-line.

Just as the density function of a probability distribution can in principle be specified only up to its values on a set of Lebesgue measure zero, so also a lack of uniqueness arises in defining $\lambda^*(\cdot)$. In all practical situations, the densities $p_n(\cdot \mid \cdot)$ will be at least piecewise continuous, and uniqueness can then be ensured by (for example) taking the left-continuous modification $\lambda^*(t-)$ for $\lambda^*(t)$; the reason for using *left* continuity is connected with predictability, which is discussed in Section 13.2. In the remainder of this section, unless stated otherwise, it is tacitly assumed that a left-continuous version of $\lambda^*(\cdot)$ exists and is used.

Proposition 13.1.VI. *The likelihood L of a regular point process over the interval* $[0, T]$, *for any* $0 < T < \infty$, *is expressible in the form*

$$(13.1.9) \qquad L = \left[\prod_{i=1}^{N(T)} \lambda^*(t_i) \right] \exp\left(- \int_0^T \lambda^*(u)du \right),$$

and its log likelihood ratio relative to a Poisson process on $[0, T]$ *with constant rate 1 is expressible as*

$$(13.1.10) \qquad \log\left(\frac{L}{L_0} \right) = \prod_{i=1}^{N(T)} \log[\lambda^*(t_i)] - \int_0^T [\lambda^*(u) - 1]du.$$

PROOF. To establish (13.1.9) it is enough to express the Janossy density in terms of the conditional densities $p_n(t \mid t_1, \ldots, t_{n-1})$ and then express each of these in terms of their hazard functions and hence of $\lambda^*(\cdot)$. Details are left to the reader. □

EXAMPLE 13.1(e) *Wold process of correlated intervals* (compare Section 4.5). Suppose the Markov process of successive interval lengths $\{I_n\} \equiv \{t_n - t_{n-1}\}$ $(t_0 \equiv 0)$ is governed by the transition kernel with densities $p(y \mid x)$ for length y of the interval I_n given the length of x of the interval I_{n-1}. For $n \geq 3$, the conditional distribution has the density

$$p_n(t \mid t_1, \ldots, t_{n-1}) = p(t - t_{n-1} \mid t_{n-1} - t_{n-2}),$$

so that in terms of the hazard function $h(y \mid x) = p(y \mid x)/S(y \mid x)$, where $S(y \mid x) = 1 - \int_0^y p(u \mid x)du$, we have

$$\lambda^*(t) = h(t - t_{N(t)} \mid t_{N(t)} - t_{N(t)-1}).$$

Here $t_{N(t)}, t_{N(t)-1}$ are the first and second points to the left of t, and it is assumed that $N(t) \geq 2$. To specify $\lambda^*(\cdot)$ at the beginning of the observation period [i.e., in $\{t > 0: N(t) \leq 1\}$], some further description of the initial conditions is needed. If observations are started from an event of the process as origin, it is enough to be given the distribution of the initial interval $(0, t_1)$ [e.g., it may be the stationary density $\pi(\cdot)$ satisfying $\pi(y) = \int_0^\infty p(y|x)\pi(x)dx$, if such $\pi(\cdot)$ exists]. Otherwise, the length of the interval terminating at t_1 may be an additional parameter in the likelihood and we may seek to estimate it, or we may impose further description on both the interval terminating at t_1 and the interval (t_1, t_2). Some special cases are indicated in Exercises 13.1.5 and 13.1.6, including renewal processes.

EXAMPLE 13.1(f) *Hawkes process* (see Examples 10.4(c) and 11.2(e)). Suppose that the infectivity measure $\mu(dx)$ has a density, $\mu(dx) = \mu(x)dx$ say. Then each event at $t_i < t$ contributes an amount $\mu(t - t_i)$ to the risk at t. There is also a risk, λ say, of a new arrival at t. Assuming no contributions to the risk from the negative half-line, $\lambda^*(\cdot)$ is expressible quite simply in the form

$$(13.1.11) \qquad \lambda^*(t) = \lambda + \sum_{0 < t_i < t} \mu(t - t_i) = \lambda + \int_0^t \mu(t - u)N(du).$$

If we assume that $v = \int_0^\infty \mu(x)dx < 1$ so that a unique stationary process exists [see Example 12.4(b)], the process converges toward equilibrium as $t \to \infty$ and the conditional intensity approaches the *complete intensity function*, which is the analogue of $\lambda^*(t)$ for a process defined on $\mathbb{R}$ and not merely $\mathbb{R}_+$; that is, events of the process are no longer confined to $t > 0$. Thus, in place of (13.1.11) we have the function

$$\lambda + \int_{-\infty}^t \mu(t - u)N(du),$$

which is the same form as is obtained from the second-order theory with a linear estimate of the risk. It follows that, *for the Hawkes process, the linear and optimal predictors coincide.*

In applications it is desirable to give $\mu(\cdot)$ some convenient parametric form. Ogata and Akaike (1982) and Vere-Jones and Ozaki (1982) discussed likelihood estimation for this process using a parametrization of the form

$$(13.1.12) \qquad \mu(t) = \begin{cases} \sum_{k=0}^{K} \alpha_k L_k(t)e^{-bt} & (t > 0), \\ 0 & (t \le 0), \end{cases}$$

where the functions $L_k(t)$ are Laguerre polynomials defined on $t > 0$; detailed computations are given in the quoted papers. An extension would be to consider combinations of exponential terms, but pragmatic problems of estimability arise: even estimating b at (13.1.12) can be difficult.

Initial conditions also pose a problem. It is simplest to suppose that the process is initiated by the first observed point so that any influence from the past is excluded. If $K = 0$ in (13.1.12), any contribution to the risk from events in $t < 0$ decays exponentially and can therefore be covered by an additional term $A_0 e^{-bt}$ added to (13.1.11), with A_0 being treated as an additional unknown parameter. Alternatively, if there are grounds for believing the process to be stationary, A_0 may be replaced by its equilibrium value $\lambda v/(1 - v) = \lambda \alpha_0/(b - \alpha_0)$.

The form (13.1.12) taken with (13.1.11) gives an example of a *linearly parameterized intensity*. We now subtly change our point of view on one of some practical importance. Instead of seeking the conditional intensity of a model that is given *a priori*, it may be more convenient, especially for filtering and prediction purposes, to choose a flexible family of models that are readily amenable to processing, in much the way that ARMA models can be used in conventional time series analysis. To this end we look for examples in which the conditional intensity has a convenient parametric form. Two major classes of models are those in which the conditional intensity has either a *linear* or *log-linear form*, that is, corresponding, respectively, to the representations

$$(13.1.13) \qquad\qquad \lambda^*(t) = \sum_k \alpha_k Q_k^*(t),$$

$$(13.1.14) \qquad\qquad \log \lambda^*(t) = \sum_k \alpha_k R_k^*(t).$$

In both cases either the likelihood or the log likelihood is a convex function of the parameter so that, *if it exists, the maximum likelihood estimate of λ^* is unique* [see Exercise 13.1.7 and Ogata (1978)]. The known functions $Q_k^*(\cdot)$ or $R_k^*(\cdot)$ may represent many types of dependency: trends or cyclic effects, linear or nonlinear dependence on the lengths of past intervals as in the Wold process, or linear dependence on the occurrence times of past events as in the Hawkes process. Further examples are given in the exercises along with some indication of the numerical problems of estimation. For a more extended review see Ogata and Katsura (1986), and for a deeper theoretical treatment see Kutoyants (1984b).

EXAMPLE 13.1(g) *Simulation of a point process with bounded conditional intensity.* The Shedler–Lewis thinning technique (see Exercise 2.1.6) is one of several simulation techniques that can be carried over to the point process context when the conditional intensity λ^* is known explicitly as a function of past variables. The thinning technique is particularly useful when λ^* is *conditionally bounded*, by which we mean that for every $n = 1, 2, \ldots$ and all sequences $t_1, \ldots, t_{n-1}$ with $t_1 < \cdots < t_{n-1} < t$, the hazard function $h_n(\cdot | \cdot)$ satisfies

$$h_n(t + u | t_1, \ldots, t_{n-1}) \le M^*(t) \quad \text{(all } u > 0)$$

for some $M^*(t) = M^*(t; t_1, \ldots, t_{n-1}) < \infty$. An algorithm in outline for simulating the points $\{t_i: i = 1, 2, \ldots\}$ of such a process on $(0, \infty)$ can be specified as follows:

(1) set $t = 0, i = 1$;
(2) calculate $M^*(t)$;

(3) generate an exponential r.v. T with mean $1/M^*(t)$ and a r.v. U uniformly distributed on $(0, 1)$;
(4) if $\lambda^*(t + T)/M^*(t) > U$, replace t by $t + T$ and return to step (2); while otherwise,
(5) set $t_i = t + T$, advance i by 1, replace t by t_i, and return to step (2).

See Ogata (1981) for a more extended discussion and variations on the procedure.

We conclude this section with an excursion, which has the incidental advantage of illustrating further the role of the Khinchin density functions, into the realm of hypothesis testing. A commonly occurring need in practice is to test for the null hypothesis of a Poisson process against some appropriate class of alternatives, and it is then pertinent to enquire as to the form of the optimal or at least locally optimal test statistic for this purpose. This question has been examined by Davies (1977), whose general approach we follow.

The locally optimal test statistic is just the derivative of the log likelihood function, calculated at the parameter values corresponding to the null hypothesis. Davies' principal result is that this quantity has a representation as a sum of orthogonal terms, containing contributions from the factional cumulants of successively higher orders. The formal statement is as follows (note that we return here to the general case $\mathscr{X} = \mathbb{R}^d$):

Proposition 13.1.VII. *Let the distributions $\{\mathscr{P}_\theta\}$ correspond to a family of point processes on $\mathbb{R}^d$ indexed by a single real parameter θ such that*

(i) *for $\theta = 0$ the process reduces to a Poisson process with constant intensity μ, and*
(ii) *for all θ in some neighborhood V of the origin, all factorial moment and cumulant densities $m_{[k]}$ and $c_{[k]}$ exist and are differentiable functions of θ and are such that the series*

$$(13.1.15) \qquad \sum_{k=1}^{\infty} \frac{1}{k!} \int \cdots \int_{A^{(k)}} c'_{[k+n]}(x_1, \ldots, x_n, y_1, \ldots, y_k; \theta) dy_1 \cdots dy_k$$

are uniformly convergent for $\theta \in V$, where A is a bounded Borel subset of $\mathbb{R}^d$ and the series

$$(13.1.16) \qquad \sum_{k=1}^{\infty} \frac{1}{k!} (1 + \delta)^k \int \cdots \int_{A^{(k)}} c'_{[k]}(y_1, \ldots, y_k; \theta) dy_1 \cdots dy_k$$

converges for some $\delta > 0$.

Then the efficient score statistic $\partial \log L/\partial \theta|_{\theta=0}$ can be represented as the sum

$$(13.1.17) \qquad D \equiv \frac{\partial \log L}{\partial \theta}\bigg|_{\theta=0} = \sum_{k=1}^{\infty} D_k,$$

where, with $I(y_1, \ldots, y_k) = 1$ if no arguments coincide and $= 0$ otherwise and $Z(dy) = N(dy) - \mu \, dy$,

(13.1.18)

$$D_k = \frac{1}{\mu^k k!} \int \cdots \int_{A^{(k)}} I(y_1, \ldots, y_k) c'_{[k]}(y_1, \ldots, y_k; 0) Z(dy_1) \cdots Z(dy_k).$$

Under the null hypothesis $\theta = 0$ and $j > k \geq 1$,

(13.1.19a) $E(D_k) = E(D_k D_j) = 0,$

(13.1.19b) $\text{var}(D_k) = \dfrac{1}{\mu^k k!} \displaystyle\int \cdots \int_{A^{(k)}} [c'_{[k]}(y_1, \ldots, y_k; 0)]^2 \, dy_1 \cdots dy_k.$

PROOF. We again use the machinery for finite point processes starting with
the expression for the likelihood $L \equiv L_\theta = j_N(x_{1(1)N}; \theta)$ of the realization
$\{x_1, \ldots, x_N\} \equiv \{x_{1(1)N}\}$ on the set A in the form [see (5.5.28)]

(13.1.20) $L = \exp(-K_0(\theta)) \displaystyle\sum_{j=1}^{N} \sum_{\mathcal{T} \in \mathcal{P}_{jN}} \prod_{i=1}^{j} k_{|S_i(\mathcal{T})|}(x_{i,1}, \ldots, x_{i,|S_i(\mathcal{T})|}; \theta),$

where the $k_r(\cdot)$ denote Khinchin densities and the inner summation extends
over the set $\mathcal{P}_{jN}$ of all j-partitions $\mathcal{T}$ of the realization $x_{1(1)N}$. Because $\theta = 0$
corresponds to a Poisson process, $K_0(0) = \mu\ell(A)$ and $k_r(y_{1(1)r}; 0) = 0$ unless
$r = 1$ when $k_1(y; 0) = \mu$. Consequently, for $\theta = 0$ (13.1.20) reduces to $L_0 = \exp(-\mu\ell(A))\mu^N$ as it should. This fact simplifies the differentiation of (13.1.20)
because (assuming that the derivatives

$$k'_r(y_{1(1)r}; 0) \equiv (\partial/\partial\theta) k_r(y_{1(1)r}; \theta)|_{\theta=0}$$

exist, as will be justified later) in differentiating the product term in (13.1.20),
nonzero terms remain on setting $\theta = 0$ only if at most one set $S_i(\mathcal{T})$ has
$|S_i(\mathcal{T})| > 1$, and all other $j - 1$ sets have $|S_i(\mathcal{T})| = 1$. Thus,

$$(\log L)' \equiv \frac{\log L}{\partial\theta}\bigg|_{\theta=0} = -K'_0(0) + \sum_{j=1}^{N} \mu^{j-1} \sum{}^* k'_{N-j+1}(x_{r_1}, \ldots, x_{r_{N-j+1}}; 0)/\mu^N$$

$$= -K'_0(0) + \sum_{i=1}^{N} \mu^{-i} \sum{}^* k'_i(x_{r_1}, \ldots, x_{r_i}; 0),$$

where the sum $\sum^*$ extends over all distinct selections of size i from $\{x_{1(1)N}\}$.
Since this set is a realization of the process $N(\cdot)$ over A, the sum $\sum^*$ is
expressible as the integral (with the i-fold integral over $A^{(i)}$ abbreviated)

$$\frac{1}{i!} \int_{A^{(i)}} I(y_{1(1)i}) k'_i(y_{1(1)i}; 0) N(dy_1) \cdots N(dy_i),$$

where the factor $I(y_{1(1)i})$ avoids repeated indices and division by $i!$ compensates
for the $i!$ recurrences of the same set of indices in different orders. This leads
to the representation

(13.1.21)

$$(\log L)' = -K'_0(0) + \sum_{i=1}^{\infty} \frac{1}{\mu^i i!} \int_{A^{(i)}} I(y_{1(1)i}) k'(y_{1(1)i}; 0) N(dy_1) \cdots N(dy_i)$$

now valid on an infinite range for i as the sum terminates after $N(A)$ terms.

When the Khinchin measures are known explicitly, (13.1.21) can be used directly. Otherwise, use the expansion (5.5.26) of $k(\cdot)$ in terms of factorial cumulant densities

$$k_i(y_{1(1)i}; \theta) = \sum_{j=0}^{\infty} \frac{(-1)^j}{j!} \int_{A^{(j)}} c_{[i+j]}(y_{1(1)i}, u_{1(1)j}; \theta) du_1 \cdots du_j,$$

which, in view of the assumption at (13.1.15), both shows that the $k_i(\cdot)$ are differentiable as assumed earlier and justifies term by term differentiation. Because of (13.1.20) the same is also true of L_θ. Also, since by (5.5.23) $K_0(\theta)$ is a weighted sum of all other Khinchin measures, substitution for $k'_i(\cdot)$ yields

$$K'_0(\theta) = \sum_{i=1}^{\infty} (i!)^{-1} \int_{A^{(i)}} \left(\sum_{j=0}^{\infty} (-1)^j (j!)^{-1} \right.$$

$$\left. \times \int_{A^{(j)}} c'_{[i+j]}(y_{1(1)i}, u_{1(1)j}; \theta) du_1 \cdots du_j \right) dy_1 \cdots dy_j,$$

which on replacing j by $j - i$, inverting the order of summation, and using $\sum_{i=1}^{j}(-1)^{j-i}/i!(j-i)! = -(-1)^j/j!$, gives for $\theta = 0$

$$K'_0(0) = -\sum_{j=1}^{\infty} \frac{(-1)^j}{j!} \int_{A^{(j)}} c'_{[j]}(u_{1(1)j}; 0) du_1 \cdots du_j.$$

Similar substitution after differentiation into (13.1.21), rearrangement of the order of summation, and substitution for $-K'_0(0)$, yields

$$(\log L)' = \sum_{j=1}^{\infty} \frac{1}{\mu^j j!} \sum_{i=0}^{j} \frac{(-\mu)^{j-i} j!}{i!(j-i)!}$$

$$\times \int_{A^{(j)}} c'_{[j]}(y_{1(1)i}, u_{1(1)j-i}; 0) N(dy_1) \cdots N(dy_i) du_1 \cdots du_{j-i}.$$

Here we recognize that the inner sum can arise from an expansion of $\prod_{i=1}^{j} [N(dv_i) - \mu(dv_i)]$, the symmetry of the densities $c_{[j]}(\cdot)$ implying equality of their integrals with respect to any reordering of the indices in a differential expansion such as $N(dv_1) \cdots N(dv_i) dv_{i+1} \cdots dv_j$. Inserting this product form leads to (13.1.17) and (13.1.18).

Verification of (13.1.19a,b) under the null hypothesis is straightforward. $\quad\square$

EXAMPLE 13.1(h) *Poisson cluster processes with bounded cluster size.* Suppose the size of the clusters is limited to M, so that only the first M terms are present in the expansions in terms of Khinchin or cumulant densities; the Gauss–Poisson case corresponds to $M = 2$. Then for $\theta > 0$ we may define the process as the superposition of a stationary Poisson process with parameter μ and a Poisson cluster process with clusters of size $2, \ldots, M$ with Khinchin measures with densities $\theta k_j(y_1, \ldots, y_j)$ taken from the p.g.fl. representation (8.3.23) [i.e., k_j is the density of the measure K_j at (8.3.23)]. Then the Khinchin densities in the resultant process have the form (identifying the state space $\mathscr{X}$ with the set A)

$$K_0(\theta) = \theta\ell(A) + \theta \sum_{j=1}^{M} \frac{1}{j!} \int \cdots \int_{A^{(j)}} k_j(x_1, \ldots, x_j)dx_1 \cdots dx_j,$$

$$k_1(x; \theta) = \mu + \theta k_1(x),$$

$$k_j(x_1, \ldots, x_j; \theta) = \theta k_j(x_1, \ldots, x_j) \qquad (j = 2, \ldots, M).$$

From (13.1.21) we have the expansion

$$\frac{\partial \log L}{\partial \theta}\bigg|_{\theta=0} = \sum_{j=1}^{M} \frac{1}{\mu^j} \int \cdots \int_{A^{(j)}} I(y_1, \ldots, y_j)k_j(y_1, \ldots, y_j)N(dy_1) \cdots N(dy_j)/j!$$

$$= \sum_{j=1}^{M} \frac{1}{\mu^j} \sum{}^* k_j(x_{r_1}, \ldots, x_{r_j}).$$

This expression exhibits the efficient score $\partial \log L/\partial\theta|_{\theta=0}$ as the sum of first-, second-, ..., Mth-order statistics in the observed points $x_1, \ldots, x_N$. In the Gauss–Poisson case, only the first- and second-order terms are needed.

The derivation here implies that the form of the cluster process, up to and including the detailed specification of the K_j, is known *a priori*. The situation if the structure is not known is much more complex but would in effect involve taking a supremum over an appropriate family of functions K_j.

An alternative representation is available through (13.1.17) and (13.1.18). This has the advantage that the cumulant densities can be specified globally, so that no implicit assumptions about boundary effects are needed. It follows from (8.3.23) (see Exercise 8.3.13) that only the first M factorial cumulant densities $c_{[j]}$ need be considered and (since the $c_{[j]}$ are derived from linear combinations of the k_j) that the same kind of structure holds for the $c_{[j]}$, namely,

$$c_{[1]}(x; \theta) = \mu + \theta c_{[1]}(x),$$

$$c_{[j]}(x_1, \ldots, x_j; \theta) = \theta c_{[j]}(x_1, \ldots, x_j) \qquad (j = 2, \ldots, M).$$

Then (13.1.17) leads to a similar expansion in terms of linear, quadratic, ... statistics; namely,

$$D_k = \frac{1}{k!\mu^k} \int \cdots \int_{A^{(k)}} I(y_1, \ldots, y_k)c_{[k]}(y_1, \ldots, y_k)Z(dy_1) \cdots Z(dy_k).$$

For further examples, asymptotic behaviour in the stationary case, and the possibility of representing the D_k in terms of spectral measures, see Davies (1977) and Exercises 13.1.11–13.1.13.

Exercises

13.1.1. An inhomogeneous Poisson process with density $\mu(\cdot)$ on a bounded Borel set A has

$$\Pr\{N(A) = n\} = e^{-M(A)}(M(A))^n/n!,$$

where $M(A) = \int_A \mu(x)dx$, and conditional on $N(A) = n$, the points $x_1, \ldots, x_n$ are i.i.d. on A with probability density function $\mu(x)/M(A)$. Write down the likelihood for a realization $x_1, \ldots, x_n$ direct from Definition 13.1.II.

13.1.2. Suppose that a stationary Gauss–Poisson process is observed on a bounded Borel set A. To find the Janossy density express the densities $k(\cdot)$ of the Khinchin measures for the process as observed on A in terms of the factorial and reduced factorial cumulant densities:

$$k_1(x) \equiv k_1(x|A) = c_{[1]}(x) + \sum_{j=1}^{\infty} \frac{(-1)^j}{j!}$$

$$\times \int \cdots \int_{A^{(j)}} c_{[1+j]}(x, y_1, \ldots, y_j)dy_1 \cdots dy_j$$

$$= c_{[1]}(x) - \int_A \hat{c}_{[2]}(x - y)dy,$$

$$k_2(x_1, x_2) \equiv k_2(x_1, x_2|A) = \hat{c}_{[2]}(x_1 - x_2) \qquad (x_1, x_2 \in A).$$

Now use Equation (5.5.28) much as in Example 13.1(b).

13.1.3. (a) Use the relations in Equation (5.5.28) between Janossy and Khinchin densities to provide a representation of the likelihood of a Poisson cluster process in terms of the Janossy densities of the cluster member process. [*Hint*: Suppose first that the whole process is a.s. finite. Expand $\log G[h] = \int (G[h|x] - 1)\mu(dx)$ $(h \in \mathscr{V})$ and obtain

$$k_n(x_1, \ldots, x_n) = \int j_n(x_1, \ldots, x_n|y)\mu(dy).$$

In the general case, proceed from the p.g.fl. expansion of the local process on A as at (7.4.18) and (7.4.19).]

(b) When the cluster structure is that of a stationary Neyman–Scott process with $\mu(dx) = \mu\,dx$ [Example 8.3(a)] so that

$$G[h|x] = \sum_{j=0}^{\infty} p_j \left(\int h(x + u)F(du) \right)^j \equiv Q\left(\int h(x + u)f(u)du \right)$$

say, deduce that

$$j_n(x_1, \ldots, x_n|A) = \exp\left(\mu \int [Q(1 - F(A - x)) - 1]dx \right) \sum_{b \in \mathscr{B}_{01}} \prod_{i=1}^{2^n - 1}$$

$$\times \left(\mu \int Q^{(|a_i|)}(1 - F(A - x)) \prod_{j=1}^{n} (f(x_j - x))^{a_{ij}}\,dx \right)^{b(a_i)},$$

where $a_i = (a_{i1}, \ldots, a_{in})$ is the binary expansion of $i = 1, \ldots, 2^n - 1$, $|a_i| = \#\{j: a_{ij} = 1\}$, and $\mathscr{B}_{01}$ is the class of all $\{0, 1\}$-valued functions $b(\cdot)$ defined on $\{a_i: i = 1, \ldots, 2^n - 1\}$ such that $\sum_i b(a_i)a_i = (1, \ldots, 1)$. [Thus, any $b(\cdot)$ has $b(a) = 0$ except for the at most n subsets of a partition of $\{1, \ldots, n\}$, and $\sum_b \prod_i$ here is equivalent to $\sum_j \sum_{\mathscr{J}} \prod_x$ in Equation (5.5.28). Baudin (1981) used a combinatorial lemma in Ammann and Thall (1979) to deduce the expression above and commented on the impracticality of its use for even a moderate number of points!]

13.1.4. Complete the details of the proof of Proposition 13.1.VI starting from (13.1.6b), (13.1.7), and (13.1.8).

13.1.5. (a) Write h for the hazard function of the d.f. F with density f. Show that a renewal process with lifetime d.f. F on $\mathbb{R}_+$, with realization $0 = t_0 < t_1 < \cdots < t_n < \cdots$ and $N(t) = \sup\{n: t_n < t\}$, has $\lambda^*(t) = h(t - t_{N(t)})$; also show that its likelihood equals

$$(N(t)!)f(t_1)f(t_2 - t_1)\cdots f(t_{N(t)} - t_{N(t)-1})(1 - F(t - t_{N(t)})).$$

[Compare Example 5.3(b).]

(b) Now let $N(t)$ be the counting function on $(0, t)$ of a stationary renewal process with lifetime d.f. F with mean λ^{-1} as in (a). Show that on $\{N(t) = 0\}$, $\lambda^*(t) = \lambda(1 - F(t))$ and otherwise is as before, and that the likelihood function is much as before with $\lambda(1 - F(t_1))$ in place of $f(t_1)$ on $\{N(t) > 0\}$. [Note that $N(t)$ as defined here is left-continuous.]

(c) Simplify the expressions in (a) and (b) when $F(x) = 1 - e^{-\lambda x}$ $(x > 0)$.

13.1.6. Let $0 = t_0 < t_1 < \cdots$ be a realization on $(0, t]$ of the Wold process detailed in Exercise 4.5.8. Write down its likelihood function and its hazard function. Investigate these functions when the process is stationary (so that then $t_0 < 0$ in general). [For another example see Lai (1978).]

13.1.7. (a) For each of the models implied by (13.1.13) and (13.1.14) with r parameters $\alpha_1, \ldots, \alpha_r$,

$$\sum_{j=1}^{r} \sum_{k=1}^{r} v_j v_k \frac{\partial^2 \log L}{\partial \alpha_j \partial \alpha_k} \leq 0 \quad \text{(all real } v_j, j = 1, \ldots, k).$$

Deduce that if a solution of the equations $\partial L/\partial \alpha_j = 0$ $(j = 1, \ldots, k)$ is found, then it is unique.

(b) For the log-linear model, show that along any ray $\{(\rho\alpha_1, \ldots, \rho\alpha_k): -\infty < \rho < \infty\}$, $\log L \to -\infty$ for $|\rho| \to \infty$, so that a maximum on the ray exists, and hence a global maximum for $\log L$ exists. [For an example, see Ogata and Vere-Jones (1984). In the linear model, there is no guarantee that with any parameters $\{\hat{\alpha}_j\}$ so determined, the likelihood of any other set of observations will necessarily have positive likelihood, nor is it even necessarily the case that the intensity at every point in the realization is positive! In general, it is necessary to treat the problem as one of constrained optimization: for example, see Ogata (1983) and related comment by Berman (1983).]

13.1.8. The likelihood of a *cyclic Poisson process* with rate parameter of the form

$$\mu(t) = \exp\{\alpha + \beta \sin(\omega_0 t + \theta)\}$$

has been discussed in Exercise 2.1.9 with a slightly different parametric form [e^α here equals $\lambda/I_0(\kappa)$ there] and the nature of maximum likelihood estimators exhibited when ω_0 is known.

(a) When ω_0 is not known, the supremum of the likelihood function in general will be approached by a sequence of arbitrarily large values of ω_0 for which $\sin \omega_0 t_i \approx$ constant and $\cos \omega_0 t_i \approx$ constant for every t_i of a given realization. A global maximum of the likelihood is attainable if the parameters are constrained to a compact set.

(b) Envisage the observation interval $T \to \infty$. Then if ω_0 is constrained to an interval $[0, \omega_T]$, where $\omega_T/T^{1-\varepsilon} \to 0$ $(T \to \infty)$ for some $\varepsilon > 0$, the sequence of estimators $\hat{\omega}_0(T)$ is consistent [see Vere-Jones (1982) for details].

13.1.9. Another model for a cyclic Poisson process assumes that $\mu(t) = \alpha + \beta(1 + \sin(\omega_0 t + \theta))$. Investigate the practicality of constructing maximum likelihood estimators for the parameters [cf. earlier references and Chapter 4 of Kutoyants (1980, 1984b)].

13.1.10. For another possible family of models to describe realizations of an inhomogeneous Poisson process on the unit interval (or rectangle or cuboid, etc.), suppose that the density $\mu(\cdot)$ can be expanded as a finite series of polynomials orthogonal with respect to some weight function $w(\cdot)$ so that

$$\mu(x) = \alpha w(x)\left(1 + \sum_{j=1}^{r} \beta_j v_j(x)\right) \equiv \alpha w(x)\psi(x),$$

where $\int w(x)dx = 1$, $\int w(x)v_j(x)dx = 0$, $\int w(x)v_j(x)v_k(x)dx = \delta_{jk}$ $(j, k = 1, \ldots, r)$. Show that the problem of maximizing the log likelihood ratio $\log(L/L_0)$, where L_0 refers to a Poisson process with density $w(x)$, is equivalent to the problem of maximizing the value of $\sum_{i=1}^{N} \log \psi(x_i)$ subject to the constraint that $\psi(x) \geq 0$ on the interval (rectangle, etc.). This maximization has to be done numerically; the main difficulty arises from the nonnegativity constraint.

13.1.11. (a) In the context of Proposition 13.1.III and Example 13.1(h), a stationary Gauss–Poisson process, for which $c_{[1]}(u) = \mu + \theta$ and $c_{[2]}(u, v) = \theta\gamma(u - v)$ for some symmetric probability density function $\gamma(\cdot)$ representing the distribution of the signed distance between the points of a two-point cluster, has its efficient score statistic D expressible as $D = D_1 + D_2$, where

$$D_1 = N(A) - \mu\ell(A) \equiv Z(A),$$

$$D_2 = \int\int_{A^{(2)}} \gamma(x - y)Z(dx)Z(dy).$$

(b) In practice, $\hat{\mu}$ is estimated by $N(A)/\ell(A)$, so D_1 vanishes, and in the second term Z is replaced by $\hat{Z}(\cdot) = N(\cdot) - \hat{\mu}\ell(\cdot)$. Davies (1977) showed that the asymptotic results remain valid with this modification, so the efficiency of other second-order statistics can be compared with the locally optimum form D_2. Write the variance estimator as $(r - 1)\sum_{j=1}^{r}(N(\Delta_j) - \hat{\mu}\ell(\Delta_j))^2$, where $\Delta_1 \cup \cdots \cup \Delta_r$ is a partition of the observation region A into subregions of equal Lebesgue measure, in a similar form to D_2, and investigate the variance-to-mean ratio as a test for the Gauss–Poisson alternative to a Poisson process. (Davies suggested that the asymptotic local efficiency is bounded by 2/3.)

13.1.12. (Continuation) In the case of a Neyman–Scott process with Poisson cluster size distribution, all terms D_k in the expansion at (13.1.17) are present, and D_2 dominates D only if the cluster dimensions are small compared with the mean distance between cluster centres.

13.1.13. When the Poisson cluster process of Example 13.1(h) for $\mathscr{X} = \mathbb{R}$ is stationary and $A = (0, t]$,

$$D_j \approx \frac{1}{t^{j+1} j! \mu^j} \sum_{l_1 + \cdots + l_j = 0} \cdots \sum \phi_j(l_1/t, \ldots, l_j/t) g_j(\lambda_1, \ldots, \lambda_j),$$

where

$$\phi_j(\lambda_1, \ldots, \lambda_j) = \int_{\mathbb{R}^{j-1}} k_j'(t_1, \ldots, t_j) \exp\left(2\pi i \sum_{r=1}^{j} \lambda_r t_r\right) dt_2 \cdots dt_j$$

with $\lambda_1 + \cdots + \lambda_j = 0$, and

$$g_j(\lambda_1, \ldots, \lambda_j) = \int \cdots \int_{[0, t]^{(j)}} I(t_1, \ldots, t_j) \exp\left(2\pi i \sum_{r=1}^{j} \lambda_r t_r\right) Z(dt_1) \cdots Z(dt_j).$$

[*Hint*: $t^{-1} E|\bar{D}_j - D_j|^2 \to 0$ as $t \to \infty$ using Parseval-type relations. See also Theorem 3.1 of Davies (1977).]

13.2. Compensators and Martingales

The aim of this section is to give a brief introduction to the martingale approach to the study of point processes on the open half-line $\mathbb{R}_+ \equiv (0, \infty)$ with many of the technicalities relegated to Appendix 3 so as to allow scope here to stress connections with other aspects of point process theory. In much of the discussion we are concerned with a random measure on $\mathbb{R}_+$, for while the case of point processes is of paramount importance, the more general theory finds applications, for example, in marked point processes with little extra effort. Thus, general results are stated in terms of the *cumulative process*

$$\xi(t) \equiv \xi(t, \omega) \equiv \xi((0, t], \omega)$$

for some random measure $\xi(\cdot, \omega)$ (the abuse of notation should not lead to difficulties). Observe that such processes have trajectories that are a.s. monotonic increasing and right-continuous, as are the *counting processes*

$$N(t) \equiv N(t, \omega) \equiv N((0, t], \omega)$$

of a point process $N(\cdot, \omega)$ on $\mathbb{R}_+$.

The "information available at time t" is represented mathematically by a σ-algebra $\mathscr{F}_t$ of sets from the underlying probability space $(\Omega, \mathscr{E}, \mathscr{P})$. The accumulation of information with time is reflected in $\mathscr{F}_t$ being a member of an increasing family $\mathscr{F} = \{\mathscr{F}_s : 0 \leq s < \infty\}$ of σ-algebras; that is, $\mathscr{F}_s \subseteq \mathscr{F}_t$ for $0 \leq s \leq t < \infty$. $\mathscr{F}$ is called a *history* for the process ξ provided $\xi(t)$ is $\mathscr{F}_t$-measurable for all $0 \leq t < \infty$ (i.e., ξ is *adapted* to $\mathscr{F}$). The history $\mathscr{H}$ consisting of the σ-algebras $\mathscr{H}_t$ generated for each t by $\{\xi(s) : 0 < s \leq t\}$ plays a special role: we call it the *internal history* (it is also called the *natural* or *minimal* history, reflecting the fact that $\mathscr{H}$ is the smallest family of nested σ-algebras to which ξ is adapted). $\mathscr{F}_0$ plays the special role of subsuming all prior information, that is, information available to us before we commence observations at $0+$, while the σ-algebra $\mathscr{F}_\infty \equiv \bigvee_{t \geq 0} \mathscr{F}_t$ subsumes all information available in the history $\mathscr{F}$. Note that $\mathscr{H}_0 = \{\varnothing, \Omega\}$, while histories $\mathscr{F}$ with the particular structure $\mathscr{F}_t = \mathscr{F}_0 \vee \mathscr{H}_t$, with $\mathscr{F}_0$ in general nontrivial, allow us to handle doubly stochastic processes.

A history $\mathscr{F}$ for which $\mathscr{F}_t = \bigcap_{s > t} \mathscr{F}_s \equiv \mathscr{F}_{t+}$ is called right-continuous. Counting processes N, being right-continuous and boundedly finite by assumption, necessarily yield internal histories that are right-continuous. In general, right-continuity represents a mild constraint on the admissible forms of conditioning information; in any case, whenever the process is adapted to the history $\mathscr{F}$, it is adapted to the right-continuous history $\mathscr{F}_{(+)} \equiv \{\mathscr{F}_{t+}: 0 \leq t < \infty\}$ (see also Exercise 13.2.9).

We assume that the realizations of the process are a.s. finite for finite t, reflecting the assumption that our trajectories a.s. lie in the space $\mathscr{\hat{M}}$ of boundedly finite random measures. This rules out the possibility of explosions and imposes the constraint on the sequence $\{T_n\}$ of $\mathscr{F}$-stopping times defined (see Lemma A3.3.III) for $n = 0, 1, \ldots$ by

$$(13.2.1) \quad T_n \equiv T_n(\omega) = \sup\{t: \xi(t, \omega) < n\}$$

$$= \begin{cases} \infty & \text{if } \xi(t, \omega) < n \text{ for all } 0 < t < \infty, \\ \inf\{t: \xi(t, \omega) \geq n\} & \text{otherwise,} \end{cases}$$

that $T_n \to \infty$ a.s. as $n \to \infty$ (but see Exercise 13.2.6).

In the general theory of processes, the family $\xi(t, \omega)$ is regarded as a single real-valued mapping $\xi: \mathbb{R}_+ \times \Omega \to \mathbb{R}_+$ rather than as an indexed family of r.v.s. There is an hierarchy of sub-σ-algebras of the product σ-algebra $\mathscr{B}(\mathbb{R}_+) \otimes \mathscr{E}$ of this product space $\mathbb{R}_+ \times \Omega$, together with corresponding classes of processes, namely, measurable, progressively measurable, and predictable; these are discussed briefly in Section A3.3. For our present purposes we need the concept of an $\mathscr{F}$-*predictable* process X, which is a process measurable with respect to the $\mathscr{F}$-predictable σ-algebra, which in turn is the sub-σ-algebra of $\mathscr{B}(\mathbb{R}_+) \otimes \mathscr{E}$ generated by all product sets of the form $(s, t] \times U$ for $U \in \mathscr{F}_s$ and $0 < s < t < \infty$.

The main result of this section is a theorem that asserts that, for every $(\xi, \mathscr{F})$ consisting of a cumulative process and history $\mathscr{F}$ for ξ, there exists an integrated form of the conditional intensity function described in Section 13.1. In the general case it is not easy to describe the appropriate concept directly in terms of conditional distribution functions; furthermore, it must be borne in mind that the function generally depends both on the history $\mathscr{F}$ and on the probability structure of the process itself. The key idea is an extension of the fact (to be proved shortly) that if $\lambda^*(\cdot)$ is a conditional intensity as in Section 13.1 and the first moments exist, the process $\xi(t) - \int_0^t \lambda^*(u)du$ is a martingale. Here, what must be subtracted from the process ξ to yield a martingale is called a *compensator*, being formally defined as follows.

Definition 13.2.I. Let $\xi(t)$ be a cumulative process on $\mathbb{R}_+$ and $\mathcal{F}$ a history for ξ. An $\mathcal{F}$-*compensator* for ξ is a monotonic nondecreasing right-continuous predictable process $A(\cdot)$, such that for each n and stopping time T_n at (13.2.1), the stopped process $\{\xi(t \wedge T_n) - A(t \wedge T_n): 0 \le t < \infty\}$ is a martingale with respect to $\mathcal{F}$.

For the rest of this section, "the pair $(\xi, \mathcal{F})$" or "process $(\xi, \mathcal{F})$" always means a cumulative process ξ and history $\mathcal{F}$ to which ξ is adapted.

In passing, we note (but shall not use the fact) that a process $\{D(t): 0 \le t < \infty\}$ such that $\{D(t \wedge T_n): 0 \le t < \infty\}$ is a martingale for some sequence of stopping times $\{T_n\}$ for which $E|D(t \wedge T_n)| < \infty$ (all $t \ge 0$, $n = 1, 2, \ldots$) is a *local martingale*.

Example 13.2(a) below, while trivial, illustrates the fact that the compensator is effectively of interest only for jump-type processes: indeed, the compensator may be regarded as a device for smoothing out jumps and producing a diffuse measure from an atomic measure that has no fixed atoms.

EXAMPLE 13.2(a) *Cumulative process with density.* Suppose $\xi(\cdot)$ is the cumulative process of an absolutely continuous random measure, with density $x(t, \omega)$ some $\mathcal{F}$-progressively measurable nonnegative process. Then $\xi(t) = \int_0^t x(u)du$ is its own compensator, for since $x(\cdot, \omega) \ge 0$, ξ is monotonic nondecreasing and continuous, and for this reason predictable, since it is both $\mathcal{F}$-adapted and left-continuous.

Given a pair $(\xi, \mathcal{F})$ as in Definition 13.2.I, the first problem is to give conditions that ensure that a compensator for ξ exists. We start by considering a *one-point process*, here meaning a point process consisting of a single point whose location can be defined by a positive r.v. X with d.f. F: the counting process is defined by

$$(13.2.2) \qquad N(t, \omega) = I_{(0, t)}(X(\omega)) \qquad (0 < t < \infty, \omega \in \Omega).$$

For this simple example, and in the simplest case that $\mathcal{F}$ coincides with the internal history of the process, that is, $\mathcal{H}_t \in \mathcal{H}$ is the σ-algebra generated by the sets $\{\{\omega: X(\omega) \le s\}: 0 < s \le t\}$, we can give a direct construction of the $\mathcal{H}$-compensator, which, subtracted from $N(\cdot)$, yields a martingale as required. We do not here need to appeal to the deeper theorems of the general theory of processes, while at the same time we establish a link between the conditional intensity, its integrated form, and the martingale property.

Observe first that N is monotonic nondecreasing, right-continuous, and even uniformly bounded so there is no problem about the existence of moments. Observe next that, since $N(t, \omega) = 1$ implies $N(t', \omega) = 1$ for all $t' \ge t$, the compensator, for the same ω, must also be constant for such $t' \ge t$. On the other hand, if $N(t, \omega) = 0$, then we know that $X(\omega) > t$, and thus, in a small interval $(t, t + dt)$, we can expect

(13.2.3)　　　　　　　　　$E(dN(t, \omega)) \approx (1 - F(t))^{-1} dF(t)$

$$= h(t)dt$$

if the d.f. has a density and therefore a hazard function h.

These heuristics are approximately correct: there are certain niceties that change the factor $(1 - F(t))^{-1}$ to $(1 - F(t-))^{-1}$: the precise statement follows (see Definition 4.6.III for the integrated hazard function—IHF).

Proposition 13.2.II. *The one-point process N at (13.2.2) generated by the positive r.v. X has $\mathcal{H}$-compensator*

(13.2.4)　　　　$A(t, \omega) = H(t \wedge X(\omega))$　　　$(0 < t < \infty, \omega \in \Omega)$,

where H is the IHF for the d.f. F of the r.v. X.

PROOF. Note that for each $\mathcal{H}_t$ the set $\{\omega: X(\omega) > t\}$ constitutes a large "atom" (i.e., a subset of Ω that cannot be decomposed by the σ-algebra). Of course, $\mathcal{H}_0 = \{\varnothing, \Omega\}$, while $\mathcal{H}_\infty$ is the σ-algebra generated by the r.v. X.

By inspection, $H(t \wedge X(\omega))$ is monotonic increasing and right continuous in t. To verify that it is predictable, we first check that $X(t, \omega) \equiv t \wedge X(\omega)$ is predictable, so we study

$$\{(t, \omega): X(t, \omega) > x\} = \{t > x\} \times \{\omega: X(\omega) > x\}.$$

The second set $\in \mathcal{H}_x$ by definition, and so the set in (t, ω) has the form of a generating set for the predictable σ-algebra. Thus, $X(t, \omega)$ is predictable.

Now the function $H(x)$ is monotonic increasing and right-continuous in x and thus has a uniquely defined inverse H^{-1} for which $H(x) \geq y$ if and only if $x \geq H^{-1}(y)$. In particular, $\{X(t, \omega) \geq H^{-1}(y)\}$ is a predictable set, so $H(X(t, \omega))$ is a predictable process.

It remains to verify the martingale property that for fixed s, t with $0 \leq s < t$,

(13.2.5)　$E(N(t \wedge X) - H(t \wedge X)|\mathcal{H}_s) = N(s \wedge X) - H(s \wedge X)$　a.s.

Note first that, because of the special structure of $\mathcal{H}_t$ here, we have for any bounded function $g(\cdot)$,

(13.2.6)　$E(g(X)|\mathcal{H}_t) = \begin{cases} g(X) & \text{on } \{X(\omega) \leq t\}, \\ E(g(X)I_{\{x>t\}})/E(I_{\{x>t\}}) & \text{on } \{X(\omega) > t\}. \end{cases}$

The latter form can be written in terms of the d.f. $F(\cdot)$ of X as

$$E(g(X)|\mathcal{H}_t) = \frac{1}{1 - F(t)} \int_t^\infty g(u)F(du) \quad \text{on } \{t < X(\omega)\}.$$

On $\{X(\omega) \leq s\}$, $N(t \wedge X) = N(s \wedge X) = 1$ and $H(t \wedge X) = H(s \wedge X) = H(X)$, which for $X \leq s$ is $\mathcal{H}_s$-measurable, so (13.2.5) holds in this case. On the complement where $\{s < X(\omega)\}$, using (13.2.6),

$$E(N(t \wedge X)|\mathcal{H}_s) = \frac{1}{1 - F(s)} \int_s^t F(du) = \frac{F(t) - F(s)}{1 - F(s)},$$

and from Lemma 4.6.I, which embodies the critical property of the IHF for this purpose,

$$(1 - F(s))[E(H(t \wedge X)|\mathcal{H}_s) - H(s)] = \int_s^t (H(u) - H(s))F(du)$$

$$+ (H(t) - H(s))(1 - F(t))$$

$$= F(t) - F(s).$$

Thus, $E(N(t \wedge X) - H(t \wedge X)|\mathcal{H}_s) = -H(s)$ on $\{s < X(\omega)\}$, so (13.2.5) holds generally as asserted. $\qquad\square$

EXAMPLE 13.2(b) *One-point process with prior σ-algebra.* An important extension of the last result can be given when the history $\mathcal{F}$ consists of σ-algebras of the form $\mathcal{F}_t = \mathcal{F}_0 \vee \mathcal{H}_t$, that is, when $\mathcal{F}$ is an intrinsic history for the one-point process. At least in the case that X has a regular conditional probability distribution given $\mathcal{F}_0$, a version of which we denote by $F(\cdot|\mathcal{F}_0)$, the influence of $\mathcal{F}_0$ can be described very simply: all we need to do in Proposition 13.2.II is to replace the distribution of X and its IHF by this conditional distribution $F(\cdot|\mathcal{F}_0)$ and its associated conditional IHF.

To see this more formally, note first that since $\mathcal{F}_t \supseteq \mathcal{F}_0$, $E[\cdot|\mathcal{F}_0] = E[E(\cdot|\mathcal{F}_t)|\mathcal{F}_0]$. We now claim that for nonnegative measurable functions $g: \mathbb{R} \to \mathbb{R}$,

$$(13.2.7) \quad E(g(X)|\mathcal{F}_t) = \begin{cases} g(X) & \text{on } \{X(\omega) \le t\}, \\ (1 - F(t|\mathcal{F}_0))^{-1} \int_t^\infty g(u)F(du|\mathcal{F}_0) & \text{on } \{X(\omega) > t\}. \end{cases}$$

The first part of (13.2.7) is obvious, while on $\{X(\omega) > t\}$, $\mathcal{F}_t$ consists entirely of sets of the form $U \cap \{X(\omega) > t\}$ for some $U \in \mathcal{F}_0$. In this case we can write

$$(13.2.8) \quad \int_{U \cap \{X > t\}} g(X(\omega))\mathcal{P}(d\omega)$$

$$= \int_U I_{\{X > t\}} g(X(\omega))\mathcal{P}(d\omega)$$

$$= \int_U E(g(X)I_{\{X > t\}}|\mathcal{F}_0)\mathcal{P}(d\omega)$$

$$= \int_U [I_{\{X > t\}}/E(I_{\{X > t\}}|\mathcal{F}_0)]E(g(X)I_{\{X > t\}}|\mathcal{F}_0)\mathcal{P}(d\omega)$$

$$= \int_{U \cap \{X > t\}} [E(g(X)I_{\{X > t\}}|\mathcal{F}_0)/E(I_{\{X > t\}}|\mathcal{F}_0)]\mathcal{P}(d\omega).$$

The first expression in this chain reduces to the left-hand side of (13.2.7), while from the assumption of $F(\cdot|\mathscr{F}_0)$ as a version of the regular conditional distribution, the last expression reduces to the right-hand side of (13.2.7) as asserted on $\{X(\omega) > t\}$.

This result can now be used in place of (13.2.6) to establish the compensator property of the IHF, provided at least that we can manipulate the conditional distributions in the same way as the unconditional distributions, which will certainly be the case if we can choose a regular version of the conditional distribution.

EXAMPLE 13.2(c) *One-point process with randomized hazard function.* To take a specific example, suppose that X has a negative exponential distribution with parameter λ, where λ itself is a positive random variable determined by $\mathscr{F}_0$ (i.e., λ is $\mathscr{F}_0$-measurable). Then the $\mathscr{F}$-compensator, $A^{\mathscr{F}}(t, \omega)$ say, can be represented in terms of the IHF of the exponential (λ) distribution, namely,

$$A^{\mathscr{F}}(t, \omega) = \lambda(t \wedge X(\omega)).$$

On the other hand, to find the $\mathscr{H}$-compensator we must first evaluate the survivor function for the resultant mixed exponential distribution. If, for example, λ itself has a unit negative exponential distribution with density $e^{-\lambda} \, d\lambda$, then the unconditional survivor function is

$$H(t) = E[H(t)|\mathscr{F}_s] = \int_0^\infty e^{-\lambda t} e^{-\lambda} \, d\lambda$$

$$= (1 + t)^{-1}.$$

The IHF is therefore equal to $\log(1 + t)$, and for the $\mathscr{H}$-compensator we obtain

$$A^{\mathscr{H}}(t, \omega) = \log(1 + t \wedge X(\omega)).$$

Such examples show that the choice of prior σ-algebra can drastically affect the form of the compensator.

We are now in a position to construct the compensator for a simple point process with respect to the *intrinsic history* $\mathscr{F} = \{\mathscr{F}_0 \vee \mathscr{H}_t : 0 < t < \infty\}$; that is, we allow some initial conditioning as in the last example. The structure of the history $\mathscr{F}$ is completely described by the initial σ-algebra $\mathscr{F}_0$ and the family of stopping times $\{T_n\}$ as at (13.2.1): in view of the assumed simplicity, $\{T_n\}$ is a.s. a strictly increasing sequence. Given

$$\mathscr{F}_{(n-1)} \equiv \mathscr{F}_{T_{n-1}},$$

which means we are given $\mathscr{F}_0$ and $T_1, \ldots, T_{n-1}$, choose a family of regular conditional distributions $G_n(x|\mathscr{F}_{(n-1)})$ for the distributions of the successive differences

$$D_n = T_n - T_{n-1}, \qquad n = 1, 2, \ldots \quad (T_0 \equiv 0).$$

Writing, say,

$$N(t) = \sum_{n=1}^{\infty} [N(t \wedge T_n) - N(t \wedge T_{n-1})]$$

$$= \sum_{n=1}^{\infty} N^{(n)}(t),$$

each $N^{(n)}(\cdot)$ is a one-point process with a single point of increase at T_n. Defining the IHFs $H_n(\cdot) \equiv H_n(\cdot | \mathcal{F}_{(n-1)})$ from the conditional d.f.s. $G_n(x | \mathcal{F}_{(n-1)})$ by $H_n(x | \mathcal{F}_{(n-1)}) = \int_0^x [1 - G_n(u - | \mathcal{F}_{(n-1)})]^{-1} G_n(du | \mathcal{F}_{(n-1)})$, we assert that the $\mathcal{F}$-compensator for $N^{(n)}(\cdot)$ has the form

$$(13.2.9) \qquad A^{(n)}(t, \omega) = \begin{cases} 0 & t < T_{n-1}(\omega), \\ H_n(t - T_{n-1}) & T_{n-1}(\omega) \le t < T_n(\omega), \\ H_n(T_n - T_{n-1}) & T_n(\omega) \le t. \end{cases}$$

[By additivity, $N(\cdot)$ then has the $\mathcal{F}$-compensator

$$A(t, \omega) = \sum_{n=1}^{\infty} A^{(n)}(t, \omega).]$$

To establish (13.2.9), note that predictability of $A^{(n)}(\cdot)$ is established as in Proposition 13.2.II, so it remains to show that each difference

$$Z^{(n)}(t, \omega) \equiv N^{(n)}(t, \omega) - A^{(n)}(t, \omega)$$

is an $\mathcal{F}$-martingale. We establish the requisite equality

$$(13.2.10) \qquad\qquad E(Z^{(n)}(t) | \mathcal{F}_s) = Z^{(n)}(s)$$

for $0 < s \le t$ separately on the sets $B_n = \{\omega \colon T_{n-1} \le s\}$ and B_n^c, observing that B_n and $B_n^c \in \mathcal{F}_{(n-1)}$. Considering first the subsets of B_n, we have

$$(13.2.11) \quad \mathcal{F}_s \cap \{T_{n-1}(\omega) \le s < T_n(\omega)\} = \mathcal{F}_{(n-1)} \cap \{T_{n-1}(\omega) \le s < T_n(\omega)\}$$

which means that, given any $C \in \mathcal{F}_s$, there exists $C' \in \mathcal{F}_{(n-1)}$ such that $C \cap B_n = C' \cap B_n$ and conversely: that this is so is clear from the structure of the σ-algebra $\mathcal{F}_s$ (since $\mathcal{F}_s \supset \mathcal{H}_s$) and a consideration of basic sets such as $\{\omega \colon N(s, \omega) = k\}$. Now on B_n, the stopping time D_n plays the same role for $N^{(n)}(\cdot)$ as X plays for the one-point process $N(\cdot)$ of Example 13.2(b), with $\mathcal{F}_{(n-1)}$ here playing the role of $\mathcal{F}_0$ there. In particular, on B_n we have

$$E(f(D_n) | \mathcal{F}_s) = E(f(D_n) I_{\{D_n > x_n\}} | \mathcal{F}_{(n-1)}) / E(I_{\{D_n > x_n\}} | \mathcal{F}_{(n-1)})$$

$$= \int_{x_n}^{\infty} f(u) G_n(du | \mathcal{F}_{(n-1)}) / [1 - G_n(x_n | \mathcal{F}_{(n-1)})],$$

where $x_n = s - T_{n-1}$, necessarily ≥ 0 on B_n. In principle, this evaluation of the conditional expectation involves the extension of (13.2.7a) to the case where t there (equals x_n here) is a r.v. measurable with respect to the prior

σ-algebra $\mathscr{F}_0$ there (which is $\mathscr{F}_{(n-1)}$ here). However, scrutiny of (13.2.8) and the surrounding argument shows that nothing need be altered there, with (13.2.7a) remaining $\mathscr{F}_0$-measurable, so (13.2.8b) is still valid. Thus, on B_n, proof of the martingale equality (13.2.10) follows as in Example 13.2(b).

On the sets $\{s < t < T_{n-1}(\omega)\}$ and $\{s \geq T_n(\omega)\}$ the equality is trivial because all terms are zero. There remains the case $\{s < T_{n-1}(\omega) \leq t\}$. Here we proceed by conditioning first on $\mathscr{F}_{(n-1)}$, when equality follows as a special case of the above, because this equality is not affected by further conditioning on $\mathscr{F}_s$. We can summarize the discussion as follows.

Theorem 13.2.III. *Let N be the counting process of a simple point process on $(0, \infty)$, $\mathscr{F}$ a history for N of the form $\{\mathscr{F}_0 \vee \mathscr{H}_t\}$, and $\{T_n\}$ the sequence of stopping times at (13.2.1), and suppose there exist regular versions $G_n(\cdot \,|\, \mathscr{F}_{(n-1)})$ of the conditional d.f.s of the intervals $D_n = T_n - T_{n-1}$, given $\mathscr{F}_{(n-1)}$, such that $1 - G_n(x-) > 0$ for $x > 0$. Then a version of the $\mathscr{F}$-compensator for N is given by*

$$(13.2.12) \qquad A(t, \omega) = \sum_{n=1}^{\infty} A^{(n)}(t, \omega),$$

where

$$(13.2.13) \quad A^{(n)}(t, \omega) = \begin{cases} 0 & (t \leq T_{n-1}(\omega)), \\ \displaystyle\int_{T_{n-1}(\omega)}^{t \wedge T_n(\omega)} \frac{G_n(du \,|\, \mathscr{F}_{(n-1)})}{1 - G_n(u - |\, \mathscr{F}_{(n-1)})} & (t > T_{n-1}(\omega)). \end{cases}$$

The following special case ties in the result of Theorem 13.2.III with the discussion of Section 13.1.

Corollary 13.2.IV. *The $\mathscr{F}$-compensator $A(\cdot)$ at (13.2.12) is absolutely continuous a.s. if and only if the conditional d.f.s $G_n(\cdot \,|\, \mathscr{F}_{(n-1)})$ have absolutely continuous versions, with densities $g_n(\cdot \,|\, \mathscr{F}_{(n-1)})$ say, in which case one version of the $\mathscr{F}$-compensator is given by*

$$A(t, \omega) = \int_0^t \lambda^*(u, \omega) \, du,$$

where

$$\lambda^*(t, \omega) = \sum_{n=1}^{\infty} \lambda_n^*(t, \omega)$$

and

$$\lambda_n^*(t, \omega) = [1 - G_n(t - |\, \mathscr{F}_{(n-1)})]^{-1} g_n(t \,|\, \mathscr{F}_{(n-1)}) I_{\{T_{n-1} < t < T_n\}}.$$

In particular, the compensator has this form when N is regular and a.s. $\lambda^*(t, \omega)$ coincides t-a.e. with the function denoted $\lambda^*(t, \omega)$ in Definition 13.1.V.

We now turn to the general case of a cumulative process ξ with history $\mathscr{F}$: the result below also establishes the uniqueness of the compensator.

Theorem 13.2.V. *Let $\{\xi(t): t > 0\}$ be a cumulative process with history $\mathscr{F}$ for which $\mathscr{F}_t$ is right continuous. Then $\xi(\cdot)$ admits an $\mathscr{F}$-compensator $A(t, \omega)$, which is uniquely defined $\mathscr{P}$-a.e. in the sense that for any other compensator $\tilde{A}(t, \omega)$, $\mathscr{P}\{A(t, \omega) = \tilde{A}(t, \omega) \text{ (all } t)\} = 1$.*

PROOF. We again use the stopped process

$$\xi_n(t) = \xi(t \wedge T_n),$$

where the stopping times $\{T_n\}$ are as at (13.2.1). Each $\xi_n(\cdot)$ is uniformly bounded and uniformly integrable in t. The trajectories of each $\xi_n(t)$ are a.s. nondecreasing in t, so for $0 < s < t$,

$$E(\xi_n(t)|\mathscr{F}_s) = E(\xi_n(t) - \xi_n(s)|\mathscr{F}_s) + E(\xi_n(s)|\mathscr{F}_s) \geq \xi_n(s).$$

Thus, $\{\xi_n(t): 0 < t < \infty\}$ is a right-continuous submartingale with respect to the history $\mathscr{F}$, and the Doob–Meyer decomposition (Definition A3.3.II) can be applied. It implies that there exists an $\mathscr{F}$-martingale $M_n(\cdot)$ and a right-continuous nondecreasing $\mathscr{F}_{(n)}$-predictable process such that

$$\xi_n(t) = M_n(t) + A_n(t).$$

Moreover the processes A_n, M_n are uniquely defined $\mathscr{P}$-a.s. as functions on $(0, \infty)$. From this last remark it follows that the functions $\{A_n(t)\}$ are a.s. nested in the sense that for $m > n$,

$$A_n(t, \omega) \leq A_m(t, \omega) \quad \text{a.s. for } t \leq T_n(\omega).$$

Now the definition of a cumulative process in terms of a boundedly finite random measure requires $T_n \to \infty$ a.s., so there exists a uniquely defined process $A(t, \omega)$ such that

$$A(t, \omega) = A_n(t, \omega) \quad \text{for } t \leq T_n(\omega).$$

Clearly, $A(t, \omega)$ inherits the monotonicity and right-continuity properties from each member of the sequence $\{A_n(t, \omega)\}$. For predictability, we observe that because $T_n \to \infty$, the left-continuous $\mathscr{F}_{(n)}$-adapted processes generate left-continuous $\mathscr{F}$-adapted processes, so $A(t, \omega)$, which is $\mathscr{F}_{(n)}$-predictable for each n, is also $\mathscr{F}$-predictable. Finally, uniqueness of the overall decomposition $\xi(t) = M(t) + A(t)$ follows from the uniqueness on each of the sets $t \leq T_n$. $\square$

Even in the point process case, it is not possible to provide a general representation for the $\mathscr{F}$-compensator analogous to that of Theorem 13.2.III, which was established for histories of the form $\{\mathscr{F}_0 \vee \mathscr{H}_t: 0 < t < \infty\}$: there are too many different ways in which the conditioning information can affect the duration of the interval lengths. In specific situations such as the next example, it may not be too difficult to identify the appropriate distributional form.

EXAMPLE 13.2(d) *Simple and modulated renewal processes.* In Exercise 13.1.5 we found that for a renewal process whose lifetime distribution has a density and hazard function $h(\cdot)$, the conditional intensity has the form $h(t - T_{N(t)})$. Evidently, the corresponding compensator has the form

$$A(t) = \sum_{n=1}^{N(t)} H(T_n - T_{n-1}) + H(t - T_{N(t)}),$$

where $H(\cdot)$ is the IHF corresponding to h. From Theorem 13.2.III it is easy to see that this form holds for a general renewal process whose lifetime r.v.s are positive a.s.

Suppose that in addition to the stopping times $\{T_n\}$ we also observe a family (vector) of stochastic processes

$$\{X(t): 0 < t < \infty\} \equiv \{X_1(t), \ldots, X_k(t): 0 < t < \infty\},$$

and suppose that the σ-algebras $\mathcal{F}_t$ of the history $\mathcal{F}$ have the form

$$\mathcal{F}_t = \mathcal{H}_t^N \vee \mathcal{H}_t^X,$$

where on the right-hand side there are denoted σ-algebras of the internal histories of $\{N(t): 0 < t < \infty\}$ and $\{X(t): 0 < t < \infty\}$. Returning to the absolutely continuous case for ease of exposition, suppose that the hazard function in successive intervals is modified in a multiplicative fashion by some nonnegative function $\psi(X_1(\cdot), \ldots, X_k(\cdot))$; that is, we take

$$\lambda^*(t) = h(t - T_{N(t)})\psi(X_1(t), \ldots, X_k(t)).$$

In this setup, the $\mathcal{F}$-compensator would be found by integrating $\lambda^*(t)$ over successive intervals. The problem posed by Cox (1972a) was that of estimating parameters $\beta_1, \ldots, \beta_k$ when $\psi(\cdot)$ has the "log-linear" form

$$\log \psi(X_1, \ldots, X_k) = \sum_{j=1}^{k} \beta_j X_j.$$

There is a close analogy with the problem of estimating the parameters in a model for lifetime distributions when the lifetimes of different individuals may be affected by different values of concomitant variables $X_1, \ldots, X_k$: this is the Cox regression model described in Cox (1972b) and now the subject of a considerable literature. Other variations are described by Aalen (1975, 1978) and Jacobsen (1982); in particular, the same multiplicative modification can be introduced for other types of underlying process $X(\cdot)$.

If the processes $X_j(\cdot)$ can be treated as known functions, or if $X(t)$ is stochastic and evolves independently of the point process (i.e., $\mathcal{H}_t^N$ and $\mathcal{H}_t^X$ are independent for each t), the likelihood of a realization can be written out explicitly in terms of $\lambda^*(\cdot)$ as in Section 13.1. In other cases, the full likelihood for X and N together should be used, which tends to be an unmanageable procedure. Alternatives such as Cox's partial likelihoods may yield more tractable models while retaining some desirable properties (e.g., see Cox, 1975).

The properties of a compensator are closely tied up with predictability and related concepts from the general theory of processes. This connection can be examined more closely via a Campbell-type measure on $\mathbb{R}_+ \times \Omega$ defined on product sets $B \times U$ for $B \in \mathscr{B}(\mathbb{R}_+)$, $U \in \mathscr{E}$, by

$$(13.2.14) \qquad C_\xi(B \times U) = \int_U \xi(B, \omega)\mathscr{P}(d\omega).$$

When Ω is the canonical space $\mathscr{M}$ or $\mathscr{N}$, C_ξ reduces to Campbell measure itself; here we allow the possibility that Ω is a more general space because this gives us greater flexibility in the choice of a history $\mathscr{F}$.

As in Chapter 12, the set function C_ξ can be extended to a σ-finite measure on the product σ-algebra $\mathscr{B}(\mathbb{R}_+) \otimes \mathscr{E}$. This done, we focus attention on its restriction to the sets of the $\mathscr{F}$-predictable σ-algebra $\Psi^\mathscr{F}$. In particular, for $U \in \mathscr{F}_s$ and $B = (s, t]$ for $0 \le s < t < \infty$, we have from the defining relation

$$C_\xi((s, t] \times U) = \int_U \mathscr{P}(d\omega) \int_{(s,t]} \xi(dx, \omega).$$

On the other hand, the martingale relation of Theorem 13.2.V implies that for $U \in \mathscr{F}_s$ and $n = 1, 2, \ldots$

$$\int_U [\xi(t \wedge T_n, \omega) - A(t \wedge T_n, \omega)]\mathscr{P}(d\omega)$$

$$= \int_U [\xi(s \wedge T_n, \omega) - A(s \wedge T_n, \omega)]\mathscr{P}(d\omega),$$

which on rearranging gives

$$\int_U \mathscr{P}(d\omega) \int_{s \wedge T_n}^{t \wedge T_n} \xi(dx, \omega) = \int_U \mathscr{P}(d\omega) \int_{s \wedge T_n}^{t \wedge T_n} A(dx, \omega).$$

Then monotone convergence can be used to let $n \to \infty$ and we conclude that

$$\int_U \mathscr{P}(d\omega) \int_s^t \xi(dx, \omega) = \int_U \mathscr{P}(d\omega) \int_s^t A(dx, \omega),$$

or, equivalently,

$$(13.2.15) \quad E \int_{\mathbb{R}_+} I_{(s,t] \times U}(x, \omega)\xi(dx, \omega) = E \int_{\mathbb{R}_+} I_{(s,t] \times U}(x, \omega)A(dx, \omega).$$

Comparison with (12.1.2) shows that this is just the assertion that on $\Psi^\mathscr{F}$ the Campbell-type measure induced by ξ coincides with the Campbell-type measure induced by the predictable process A. More generally, the indicator function in (13.2.15) can be replaced by any $\Psi^\mathscr{F}$-measurable function $Y(\cdot)$. But such a function is just an $\mathscr{F}$-predictable process. Since the argument can be reversed, we are led to the following alternative characterization of the compensator, equivalent to the martingale characterization, but couched here in terms of the general theory of processes.

Proposition 13.2.VI. *Given a cumulative process ξ adapted to the history $\mathscr{F}$, its compensator A is the unique $\mathscr{F}$-predictable cumulative process satisfying*

$$(13.2.16) \qquad E \int_{\mathbb{R}_+} Y(x, \omega)\xi(dx, \omega) = E \int_{\mathbb{R}_+} Y(x, \omega)A(dx, \omega)$$

for every nonnegative predictable process $Y(\cdot)$.

It is on account of this relation that the compensator is referred to as the *dual predictable projection* in literature that adheres to the terminology of the general theory of processes.

This point of view also helps to clarify the role of predictability in defining an intensity function when the compensator is absolutely continuous. It is desirable, if possible, to choose a version of the intensity that is predictable, since the intensity is used to calculate risks before rather than after the occurrence of points. Regard the absolute continuity as referring not to the a.s. properties of the compensator for fixed ω but rather to the Campbell measure on the product space with respect to the product of $\mathscr{P}$ with Lebesgue measure on $\mathbb{R}_+$; then the Radon–Nikodym derivative on the product space provides us with the predictable version that we want. These remarks are formalized in the following definition and proposition.

Definition 13.2.VII. An $\mathscr{F}$-*intensity* for a cumulative process $(\xi, \mathscr{F})$ with compensator A is any $\mathscr{F}$-measurable process λ^* such that a.s. for all t

$$A(t, \omega) = \int_0^t \lambda^*(u, \omega)du.$$

In other words, we require $\int_0^t \lambda^*(u, \omega)du$ to be $\mathscr{P}$-indistinguishable from $A(t, \omega)$. This then yields the following statement concerning the existence of a predictable version of the intensity.

Proposition 13.2.VIII. *Let $(\xi, \mathscr{F})$ be a cumulative process with $\mathscr{F}$-compensator A. A necessary and sufficient condition for the existence of an $\mathscr{F}$-intensity λ^* for A is that the Campbell measure at (13.2.14) is absolutely continuous with respect to $\ell \times \mathscr{P}$ on $\Psi^{\mathscr{F}}$. When this condition is satisfied, the Radon–Nikodym derivative $dC_\xi(t, \omega)/d(\ell \times \mathscr{P}) = \lambda^*(t, \omega)$ provides an $\mathscr{F}$-predictable version of the conditional intensity, with this version coinciding except possibly on a set of $\ell \times \mathscr{P}$ measure zero with any $\mathscr{F}$-intensity satisfying Definition 13.2.VII.*

PROOF. Consider any basic set $(s, t] \times U$ ($U \in \mathscr{F}_s, s < t$) for the predictable σ-algebra. Since $\lambda^*(\cdot)$ must be a Radon–Nikodym derivative we can write

$$\int_{(s, t] \times U} \lambda^*(u, \omega)du\, \mathscr{P}(d\omega) = E[I_U(N(t) - N(s))] = C((s, t] \times U).$$

Rearrangement leads to

$$\int_U \left[N(t) - \int_s^t \lambda^*(u, \omega) du \right] \mathscr{P}(d\omega) = N(s),$$

which, writing $A(t) = \int_0^t \lambda^*(u) du$, is just the requirement that $N(t) - A(t)$ should form a martingale, or that $A(t)$, which by inspection is monotonic and continuous, and hence predictable, should be a compensator. Conversely, if the compensator is absolutely continuous and admits an $\mathscr{F}$-predictable intensity, then reversing the chain of equalities shows that the intensity plays the role of the Radon–Nikodym derivative. Finally, any Radon–Nikodym derivative is unique up to its values on a subset of measure zero in the parent measure, here $\ell \times \mathscr{P}$. □

Corollary 13.2.IX. *Suppose that $\tilde{\lambda}(t, \omega)$ is any $\mathscr{G}$-measurable intensity for ξ, where $\mathscr{G}$ is a σ-algebra on $\mathbb{R}_+ \times \Omega$ containing the $\mathscr{F}$-predictable σ-algebra $\Psi^{\mathscr{F}}$. Then ξ admits an $\mathscr{F}$-conditional intensity $\lambda^*(t, \omega)$, given (up to values on an $\mathscr{F}$-predictable subset of $\ell \times \mathscr{P}$ measure zero) by the Radon–Nikodym derivative of $\int_V \tilde{\lambda}(t, \omega) dt \, \mathscr{P}(d\omega) (V \in \Psi^{\mathscr{F}})$ with respect to $\ell \times \mathscr{P}$ on $\Psi^{\mathscr{F}}$.*

Exercises

13.2.1. Consider a simple point process N on $\mathscr{X} = \mathbb{Z}_+ \equiv \{0, 1, \ldots\}$ adapted to a history $\mathscr{F} = \{\mathscr{F}_n : n \in \mathbb{Z}_+\}$. Show the following:
  (a) A process $\{X_n : n \in \mathbb{Z}_+\}$ is $\mathscr{F}$-adapted if X_n is $\mathscr{F}_n$-measurable for each $n = 0, 1, \ldots$.
  (b) $\{X_n\}$ is $\mathscr{F}$-predictable if each X_n is $\mathscr{F}_{n-1}$-measurable for $n = 1, 2, \ldots$.
  (c) An $\mathscr{F}$-adapted simple point process N on $\mathbb{Z}_+$ has $\mathscr{F}$-compensator A_n given by

$$A_n = \sum_{k=1}^n E(N(\{k\})|\mathscr{F}_{k-1}).$$

13.2.2. (Continuation) Suppose that N is a discrete time renewal process with interval distribution $\{f_r\} = \{\Pr\{X = r\} : r = 1, 2, \ldots\}$ (so $f_0 = 0$). Then if

$$N(n) = \#\{j = 1, \ldots, n : \text{renewal at } j\}$$
$$= \#\{1 \le j \le n : N(\{j\}) = 1\},$$

and $T(k) = \inf\{j : N(k) = j\}$,

$$\Delta A_n = \begin{cases} f_{n-T(N(n-1))}/q_{n-T(N(n-1))} & \text{on } \{N(n-1) \ge 1\}, \\ f_{n-1}^{(0)} & \text{on } \{N(n-1) = 0\}, \end{cases}$$

where $q_r = 1 - f_1 - \cdots - f_{r-1}$ and $\{f_r^{(0)}\}$ is the distribution of the initial length. Deduce that if $\{f_r\}$ is the geometric distribution $\{(1 - \rho)\rho^{r-1} : r = 1, 2, \ldots\}$, then $A_n = n(1 - \rho)$, representing the discrete analogue of the Poisson process.

13.2.3. Show that if $\xi(t)$ is an $\mathscr{F}$-adapted cumulative process with compensator $A(t)$, and if $Y(t)$ is any bounded $\mathscr{F}$-predictable process, then with $Z(t) = \xi(t) - A(t)$,

$$\eta(t) \equiv \int_0^t Y(u) Z(du)$$

is an $\mathscr{F}$-local martingale [i.e., $\eta(t \wedge T_n)$ is an $\mathscr{F}$-martingale for each stopping time T_n as at (13.2.1)]. [*Hint:* The case $Y(t, \omega) = I_{\{(s,t] \times B\}}$, for $B \in \mathscr{F}_s$ and $s < t$, reduces to the defining requirement of the compensator. An extension argument completes the proof.]

13.2.4. Let N be a point process with internal history $\mathscr{H}$. A process $X(t, \omega)$ on $\mathbb{R}_+$ is $\mathscr{H}$-predictable if and only if there exist $(\mathscr{B}(\mathbb{R}_+) \otimes \mathscr{H}_{T_n})$-measurable functions $f_n(t, \omega)$ such that, for $n = 0, 1, \ldots$,

$$X(t, \omega) = f_n(t, \omega) \quad \text{on } T_n < t \le T_{n+1}.$$

[*Hint:* First write $X(t, \omega) = \sum_{n=0}^{\infty} X(t, \omega) I_{\{T_n < t \le T_{n+1}\}}(t, \omega)$. Then argue as around (13.2.7) that, on each such set, the predictability requirement implies that $X(t, \omega)$ must be $\mathscr{H}_{T_n}$-measurable.]

13.2.5. (a) For the one-point process of Example 13.2(b), $Z(t, \omega) \equiv N(t, \omega) - A(t, \omega)$ is an $\mathscr{H}$-martingale if and only if it has a representation as in Exercise 13.2.3.
   (b) Extend the result of (a) to processes with a prior σ-algebra, first for the case of a one-point process and then for the case of a general simple point process. [*Hint:* Compare Theorem 13.2.II.]

13.2.6. Suppose that the sequence of stopping times at (13.2.1) can have $T_\infty \equiv \lim_{n \to \infty} T_n < \infty$. Show that (a) T_∞ is a stopping time, and (b) the conclusions of Proposition 13.2.II and Theorem 13.2.III continue to hold under the constraint that $0 \le t < T_\infty$.

13.2.7. Let $\{Q_0(x), Q_k(x; t_1, \ldots, t_k); (k = 1, 2, \ldots)\}$ be a family of nonnegative functions defined on $0 \le x < \infty$, $0 < t_1 < \cdots < t_k < \cdots$, satisfying the following conditions:
   (i) $Q_k(x; t_1, \ldots, t_k)$ is measurable in $t_1, \ldots, t_k$ for fixed x, and monotonic nondecreasing and right-continuous in x for fixed $t_1, \ldots, t_k$.
   (ii) $Q_0(0) = Q_k(0; t_1, \ldots, t_k) = Q_k(x; t_1, \ldots, t_k) = 0$ for $x \le t_k$.
   (iii) At any discontinuities $\{x_i\}$ of Q_k,

$$\Delta Q_k(x_i) \equiv Q_k(x_i) - Q_k(x_i-) \le 1,$$

   with $\Delta Q_k(x_i) = 1$ possible only if

$$Q_k(x; t_1, \ldots, t_k) = Q_k(x_i; t_1, \ldots, t_k) \quad \text{for all } x > \text{ such } x_i.$$

   Interpret $Q_k(\cdot)$ as the IHFs for the successive intervals of a simple point process N on $(\mathscr{N}(\mathbb{R}_+), \mathscr{B}(\mathscr{N}(\mathbb{R}_+)))$ by showing that for given Q_k the corresponding d.f.s are determined uniquely from the results in Section 4.6. Deduce that N has $\mathscr{H}$-compensator $A(\cdot)$ given by $A(t) = Q_k(t; t_1, \ldots, t_k)$ for $t_k < t \le t_{k+1}$, and that only finitely many points can occur in any finite interval, provided also that
   (iv) the Janossy measures corresponding to the IHFs $Q_k(\cdot)$ are proper.
   Thus, the $\mathscr{H}$-compensator A determines the distribution of N (cf. Boel et al., 1975; Davis, 1976; Brémaud, 1981).

13.2.8. (Continuation) Let the functions $Q_k(\cdot)$ be replaced by a family of regular conditional IHFs given a prior σ-algebra $\mathscr{F}_0$. Extend the uniqueness statement to a point process N with history $\{\mathscr{F}_0 \vee \mathscr{H}_t\}$. Finally, find an extension to the case where the given process N is conditioned by a point process N'

evolving simultaneously with N. [*Hint*: Use a history with $\mathscr{F}_t = \mathscr{F}_t^{(N)} \vee \mathscr{F}_t^{(N')}$; no essential differences arise, but the functions Q_k are now functions of the points t_i', say, of the process N' as well as the points t_i of N, and may therefore change at both t_i and t_i'.]

13.2.9. Show that the history generated by a cumulative process or random measure need not necessarily be right-continuous. Investigate whether the origin is the only possible exceptional time. [*Hint*: Consider Lebesgue measure multiplied by a nondegenerate r.v.]

13.3. Filtering, Likelihood Ratios, and a Central Limit Theorem

Important applications of the preceding ideas are to be found mainly in the electrical engineering context, where the transfer of information by a pulsed signal rather than by a continuously modulated signal has become the rule rather than the exception. In the simplest case of a "telegraph signal," for example, the signal to be transmitted can be modelled by a $\{0, 1\}$-valued process, with the transmission taking the form of high-frequency Poisson pulses emitted during the "1" sections of the signal and no transmission during the "0" sections. Noise pulses arising at various stages of the transmission process contaminate the received signal, which is typically a Poisson process with two components—namely, the original signal and the noise. A similar pattern also occurs frequently in optical communication problems. The practical question to be resolved concerns the estimation of the original signal on the basis of the point process observed at the receiving end of the transmission line.

It is not surprising to find that in modelling these situations key roles are played by doubly stochastic or Cox processes and by techniques for estimating the stochastic rate function of such a process given observations consisting of the points of a realization of the process. It is also not surprising to find strong emphasis in the engineering literature, in marked contrast to the statistical literature, on estimators that are of the recursive type since these are more readily applied in a real-time situation.

In this section we introduce some of the issues that have their origin and motivation in these fields. More substantial introductions to the engineering literature have been given by Snyder (1975) and Brémaud (1981).

We return in this section to the absolutely continuous context of Section 13.1, that is, point processes regular as at Definition 13.1.I, but now a critical role is played by the conditioning σ-algebras. For example, in the case of a Cox process the stochastic properties are relatively trivial if the (random) rate function $\mu(t)$ is known *a priori* for all t: in particular, the conditional intensity λ^* is then just the function μ; that is, $\lambda^*(t) = \mu(t)$ (all t). This situation is much altered if the only information available is the sequence of observed points of the process, when the relevant conditional intensity is then the $\mathcal{H}$-conditional intensity, $\lambda^{\mathcal{H}}(\cdot)$ say, and we must then determine the relation between $\mu(\cdot)$ and $\lambda^{\mathcal{H}}(\cdot)$ and the part these quantities play in estimation problems. The concept of predictability is again important, largely because a version it supplies of the conditional expectation of the future, given the past, has the measurability properties needed for its use in integral relations and recursive formulae.

The first result concerns the existence of predictable versions of a stochastic process and is a parallel of the dual predictable projection results around Definition 13.2.VII.

Proposition 13.3.I. *Let $X(t, \omega)$ be a measurable stochastic process on the probability space $(\Omega, \mathscr{E}, \mathscr{P})$ satisfying*

$$E\left(\int_0^t |X(s, \omega)|\,ds\right) < \infty \quad (all\ 0 < t < \infty),$$

and let $\mathscr{F}$ be a history for X. Then there exists an $\mathscr{F}$-predictable process $X^{\mathscr{F}}(t, \omega)$ such that for all bounded $\mathscr{F}$-predictable functions $Y(t, \omega)$,

(13.3.1)

$$E\left(\int_0^t Y(u, \omega)X(u, \omega)\,du\right) = E\left(\int_0^t Y(u, \omega)X^{\mathscr{F}}(u, \omega)\,du\right) \quad (all\ 0 < t < \infty).$$

Moreover, $X^{\mathscr{F}}(\cdot)$ is uniquely defined up to its values on a predictable set of $\ell \times \mathscr{P}$ measure zero.

PROOF. Let $\tilde{X}(t, \omega)$ be the Radon–Nikodym derivative of the measure $X(t, \omega)dt\,\mathscr{P}(d\omega)$ with respect to the measure $dt\,\mathscr{P}(d\omega)$ on the $\mathscr{F}$-predictable σ-algebra $\Psi^{\mathscr{F}}$ on $\mathbb{R}_+ \times \Omega$. If $Y(u, \omega)$ is the indicator function of the generating set $(s, t] \times U\ (0 \le s < t < \infty,\ U \in \mathscr{F}_s)$ of $\Psi^{\mathscr{F}}$, then (13.3.1) takes the form of the defining relation for the Radon–Nikodym derivative

$$\int_{(s,t]\times U} X(u, \omega)du\,\mathscr{P}(d\omega) = \int_{(s,t]\times U} \tilde{X}(u, \omega)du\,\mathscr{P}(d\omega).$$

The extension to (13.3.1) is now routine, with $X^{\mathscr{F}} = \tilde{X}$ and the uniqueness assertion the usual uniqueness statement for Radon–Nikodym derivatives.   □

The process $X^{\mathscr{F}}$ can be called the $\mathscr{F}$-*predictable projection* of X, or predictable projection for short. Note that the technique of proof is exactly that used in the study of conditional expectation, except that here the measure on $\mathbb{R}_+ \times \Omega$ is no longer finite nor is X necessarily integrable on $\mathbb{R}_+ \times \Omega$.

The most important case for us is where X is a conditional intensity, in which case its predictable projection we define to be a density for the compensator as follows.

Definition 13.3.II. An $\mathscr{F}$-*intensity* for a cumulative process ξ with $\mathscr{F}$-compensator A is any $\mathscr{F}$-progressively measurable process $\lambda^{\mathscr{F}}$ such that

$$A(t, \omega) = \int_0^t \lambda^{\mathscr{F}}(u, \omega)du.$$

The restriction to a progressively measurable version of the intensity is no major restriction and is done to ensure that integrals with respect to the intensity are well-defined r.v.s. (see Section A3.3). For purposes like martingale representations a predictable version of the intensity may be needed, in which case Proposition 13.3.I guarantees its existence as the predictable projection $\tilde{\lambda}^{\mathscr{F}}$ of $\lambda^{\mathscr{F}}$.

Indeed, more is true, because from the relation of the compensator to the Campbell-type measure C_ξ defined by (13.2.14), $\tilde{\lambda}^{\mathscr{F}}$ is identified directly as the Radon–Nikodym derivative of C_ξ with respect to $\ell \times \mathscr{P}$ on $\Psi^{\mathscr{F}}$. This leads to the following characterization.

Proposition 13.3.III. *Let* $(\xi, \mathscr{F})$ *be a cumulative process with* $\mathscr{F}$-*compensator A. A necessary and sufficient condition for the existence of an* $\mathscr{F}$-*intensity is that the Campbell measure* C_ξ *defined at (13.2.14) be absolutely continuous with respect to* $\ell \times \mathscr{P}$ *on the* $\mathscr{F}$-*predictable σ-algebra* $\Psi^{\mathscr{F}}$. *When this condition is satisfied, the Radon–Nikodym derivative* $dC_\xi(t, \omega)/d(\ell \times \mathscr{P})$ *provides a predictable version of the conditional intensity.*

PROOF. Let $\lambda^{\mathscr{F}}(t, \omega)$ be any $\mathscr{F}$-intensity, so that for any $s < t$ the integral

$$\int_s^t \lambda^{\mathscr{F}}(u, \omega)du = A(t, \omega) - A(s, \omega)$$

is a well-defined r.v. Integrating with respect to $\mathscr{P}$ over any $B \in \mathscr{E}$ yields

$$\int_B \mathscr{P}(d\omega) \int_s^t \lambda^{\mathscr{F}}(u, \omega)du = C_\xi((s, t] \times B) = E(I_B(\omega)(\xi(t, \omega) - \xi(s, \omega))),$$

which exhibits $\lambda^{\mathscr{F}}$ as a version of the Radon–Nikodym derivative $dC_\xi(t, \omega)/d(\ell \times \mathscr{P})$. By a similar argument but with B restricted to $B \in \mathscr{F}_s$, it follows that the predictable projection $\tilde{\lambda}^{\mathscr{F}}$ of $\lambda^{\mathscr{F}}$ is a version of the Radon–Nikodym derivative of the same two measures restricted to the σ-algebra $\Psi^{\mathscr{F}}$.

Conversely, if C_ξ is absolutely continuous with respect to $\ell \times \mathscr{P}$ on $\Psi^{\mathscr{F}}$, the derivative $\tilde{\lambda}$, say, will satisfy the above equation for $B \in \mathscr{F}_s$. Rearrangement leads to

$$\int_B \left(\xi(t, \omega) - \int_s^t \tilde{\lambda}(u, \omega)du \right) \mathscr{P}(d\omega) = \xi(s),$$

which, writing $A(t, \omega) = \int_0^t \tilde{\lambda}(u, \omega)du$, is just the requirement that $\xi(t) - A(t)$ should form a martingale. Clearly, $A(t, \omega)$ is a cumulative process, and being continuous it is $\mathscr{F}$-predictable. Thus, $A(t)$ must be the $\mathscr{F}$-compensator for ξ, and $\tilde{\lambda}$ must be its density, and thus a predictable version of the $\mathscr{F}$-intensity. ☐

Let $\mathscr{F}$ and $\mathscr{G}$ be two histories for a process $(\xi, \mathscr{F})$ with $\mathscr{G} \subseteq \mathscr{F}$ in the sense that $\mathscr{G}_t \subseteq \mathscr{F}_t$ for every $t \geq 0$. A typical *filtering* problem is to find the $\mathscr{G}$-intensity for ξ given its $\mathscr{F}$-intensity. Again, this problem is readily solved in principle by appeal to Proposition 13.3.I: the $\mathscr{G}$-predictable projection of the $\mathscr{F}$-intensity is a $\mathscr{G}$-intensity. However, while the question of existence of a $\mathscr{G}$-intensity has been resolved, the solution does not give an easy route to the computation of this intensity because it is hard to work directly from the Radon–Nikodym derivatives in the product space $\mathbb{R}_+ \times \Omega$. A relation like

(13.3.2) $$\tilde{\lambda}^{\mathscr{G}}(t, \omega) = E(\lambda^{\mathscr{F}}(t)|\mathscr{G}_{t-})(\omega)$$

is intuitively plausible, but the difficulty is that there is no guarantee in general that the right-hand side has a version that is even measurable, let alone predictable. Fortunately, this is more of a theoretical difficulty than a practical drawback because, when an appropriate version does exist, as is usual in practice, (13.3.2) then provides a convenient form for computing the $\mathscr{G}$-intensity.

Lemma 13.3.IV. *Suppose that the conditional intensities at* (13.3.2) *admit a version that has a.s. left-continuous trajectories, or more generally is $\mathscr{G}$-predictable. Then this version is also a version of the $\mathscr{G}$-predictable intensity.*

PROOF. Suppose such a version as described exists, $\mu(t, \omega)$ say, so that it necessarily satisfies

$$\int_B \mu(u, \omega)\mathscr{P}(d\omega) = \int_B \lambda^{\mathscr{F}}(u, \omega)\mathscr{P}(d\omega) \quad \text{(all } B \in \mathscr{G}_s \subseteq \mathscr{F}_s, \text{ all } u > s)$$

by definition of the $\mathscr{F}$-intensity and the inclusion $\mathscr{G}_u \supseteq \mathscr{G}_s \, (u \geq s)$. By assumption, the left-hand side is measurable and can be integrated on $(s, t]$ to give

$$\int_{(s,t] \times B} \mu(u, \omega)du \, \mathscr{P}(d\omega) = \int_{(s,t] \times B} \lambda^{\mathscr{F}}(u, \omega)du \, \mathscr{P}(d\omega).$$

Since these sets $(s, t] \times B$ with $B \in \mathscr{G}_s$ generate $\Psi^{\mathscr{G}}$, this is just the assertion that μ is a version of the $\mathscr{G}$-predictable projection of $\lambda^{\mathscr{F}}$. ☐

Most commonly, the coarser σ-algebra $\mathscr{G}$ is the internal history $\mathscr{H}$, and the problem is to find the intensity for the internal history in terms of a larger history, such as some intrinsic history, for which the intensity is more easily calculated. The computation is effectively a form of Bayes' theorem, and the following example is a convenient introduction.

EXAMPLE 13.3(a) *Intensities for a mixed Poisson process.* Suppose there is given a realization $t_1, \ldots, t_N$ on $(0, t]$ of a mixed Poisson process with rate parameter μ that is to be treated as a random variable with d.f. F on $(0, \infty)$. Take $\mathscr{F}$ as the intrinsic history, so $\mathscr{F}_t = \sigma\{\mu\} \vee \mathscr{H}_t$. Then the $\mathscr{F}$-intensity is just μ itself. To find the $\mathscr{H}$-intensity we investigate the form of

$$E(\mu|\mathscr{H}_{t-}),$$

and assume for simplicity that F has a density f. The point about the internal history is that it has a simple structure and we can appeal to the existence of regular conditional distributions expressed in the form of densities. Bayes' theorem here implies for the conditional density of μ given $\mathscr{H}_t$

$$p(\mu|\mathscr{H}_{t-}) = \frac{p(\mathscr{H}_{t-}|\mu)f(\mu)}{\int_0^\infty p(\mathscr{H}_{t-}|\mu)f(\mu)d\mu}$$

$$= \frac{(\mu t)^{N'}e^{-\mu t}f(\mu)}{\int_0^\infty (\mu t)^{N'}e^{-\mu t}f(\mu)d\mu},$$

where $N' = N(t-, \omega)$, and

$$E(\mu|\mathscr{H}_{t-}) = \int_0^\infty \mu^{N'+1}e^{-\mu t}f(\mu)d\mu \bigg/ \int_0^\infty \mu^{N'}e^{-\mu t}f(\mu)d\mu.$$

If, for example, μ has the exponential density $\alpha e^{-\alpha\mu}$, then

(13.3.3) $E(\mu|\mathscr{H}_{t-}) = (N' + 1)/(t + \alpha) \equiv (N(t-, \omega) + 1)/(t + \alpha)$

and since this function is a.s. left-continuous in t, it can be taken as a version of the $\mathscr{H}$-intensity.

EXAMPLE 13.3(b) *Cox process directed by a finite state Markov process.* This relatively simple example stimulated much of the early discussion of filtering for point processes (e.g., see Yashin, 1970; Galchuk and Rosovskii, 1971; Snyder, 1972; Jowett and Vere-Jones, 1972; Rudemo, 1972, 1973; Vere-Jones, 1975b; Brémaud, 1981, Chap. 4). Our treatment follows most closely the exposition in Rudemo (1972).

Suppose we have a Markov process $\{X(t): t \geq 0\}$ on the finite state space $\{1, \ldots, K\}$ with Q-matrix $Q = (q_{ij})$ so that $\sum_{j=1}^K q_{ij} = 0$ $(i = 1, \ldots, K)$, $q_i \equiv -q_{ii}$ governs the exponential holding times in state i, q_{ij}/q_i represents the probability that when a jump occurs from state i it is into state $j \neq i$, and the matrix of transition probabilities $P(t) \equiv (p_{ij}(t))$ satisfies the forward and backward equations

$$dP/dt = QP(t) = P(t)Q$$

with solution [with $P(0) = I$] $P(t) = \exp(tQ)$. Suppose further that when this Markov process is in state j, points of a Poisson process at rate λ_j are emitted and that the observational data consist purely of these emitted points. The simplest nontrivial case of this setup occurs with a process $X(\cdot)$ on two states with $\lambda_2 \approx 0$ and λ_1 somewhat larger: we then have a model of a "telegraph signal" process sketched at the beginning of this section.

Several estimation problems arise in connection with this process. Given the observations, one aim may be to "track" the unobserved Markov process $X(\cdot)$ directing the point process. This would require maintaining and updating the family of probabilities

$$\pi_i(t) \equiv \mathscr{P}(\{X(t) = i\} | \mathscr{H}_t).$$

A second object of interest could be the $\mathscr{H}$-intensity $\lambda^{\mathscr{H}}$, which is given here by

$$\lambda^{\mathscr{H}}(t) = \sum_{i=1}^{K} \lambda_i \pi_i(t).$$

Finally, both the Poisson process rates λ_i and the Markov process transition rates q_{ij} may depend on some unknown parameter(s) and the aim may be to estimate such parameter(s) from the point process observations.

Suppose the points observed on $(0, t]$ are $t_1 < t_2 < \cdots < t_N \leq t < t_{N+1}$. Consider the evolution of the "joint statistics"

$$\hat{p}_i(t; t_1, \ldots, t_N) dt_1 \cdots dt_N$$
$$= \Pr\{X(t) = i \text{ and points occur in } (t_j, t_j + dt_j), j = 1, \ldots, N\}.$$

Call "either $X(\cdot)$ changes state or there is a point at t" an event at t. Then, conditional on $X(t+) = i$, the time τ elapsing until the next event is exponentially distributed with $\Pr\{\tau > u\} = \exp(-(q_i + \lambda_i)u)$, and, independent of τ, the event is a point with probability $\lambda_i/(q_i + \lambda_i)$ and is a transition of $X(\cdot)$ from i to j with probability $q_{ij}/(q_i + \lambda_i)$. Between observed points, therefore, the joint statistics evolve in a similar manner to the basic transition probabilities but with the matrix $Q - \Lambda$ in place of Q, where $\Lambda \equiv \mathrm{diag}(\lambda_1, \ldots, \lambda_K)$. It then follows that the vector $\hat{p}(\cdot) \equiv (\hat{p}_1(\cdot), \ldots, \hat{p}_K(\cdot))^T$ of joint statistics can be expressed as the matrix product

(13.3.4) $\hat{p}(t)^T \equiv \hat{p}(t; t_1, \ldots, t_N)^T$

$$= \hat{p}(0)^T J(t_1) \Lambda J(t_2 - t_1) \Lambda \cdots \Lambda J(t_N - t_{N-1}) \Lambda J(t - t_N),$$

where $\hat{p}(0) = (\hat{p}_1(0), \ldots, \hat{p}_k(0))^T$ is the vector of initial probabilities for the process $X(\cdot)$ and

$$J(t) = \exp((Q - \Lambda)t).$$

From (13.3.4) we can immediately write down the likelihood in the form

$$L(t_1, \ldots, t_N) = \hat{p}(t)^T \mathbf{1},$$

where $\mathbf{1}$ is the column vector of 1's, while the probability $\pi_i(t)$ that the process is in state i, given the observations $t_1, \ldots, t_N$ and the initial distribution, is the ratio

(13.3.5) $$\pi_i(t) = \hat{p}_i(t)/\hat{p}(t)^T \mathbf{1}.$$

Hence, the right-continuous version of the conditional intensity estimator in matrix form is

(13.3.6) $$\lambda^{\mathscr{H}}(t) = \hat{p}(t)^T \Lambda \mathbf{1} / \hat{p}(t)^T \mathbf{1}.$$

Here the elements $\hat{p}_i(t)$ are continuous between the observations so $\hat{p}_i(t)$ has left limits, and so also therefore has $\lambda^{\mathscr{H}}(t)$: a predictable version of the conditional intensity estimator is therefore $\lambda^{\mathscr{H}}(t-)$. [Note that in defining $\hat{p}_i(t)$ we allowed $t_N = t$, thereby making $\hat{p}_i(t)$ right-continuous. By inspection, $\hat{p}(t_N+)^T = \hat{p}(t_N-)^T \Lambda$.]

Although (13.3.4) gives an explicit representation of the joint statistics, it may be just as convenient, particularly if an updating procedure is envisaged, to represent their evolution in terms of the differential equations they satisfy between events and the discrete jumps that occur when the trajectory passes through an event. In terms of the $\hat{p}_i(t)$ these equations are linear in form as below, with $D_t \equiv \partial/\partial t$:

(13.3.7) $$D_t \hat{p}_i(t) = -(\lambda_i + q_i)\hat{p}_i(t) + \sum_{j \neq i} \hat{p}_j(t)q_{ji},$$

(13.3.8) $$\Delta \hat{p}_i(t_n) = \hat{p}_i(t_n+) - \hat{p}_i(t_n-) = (\lambda_i - 1)\hat{p}_i(t_n-).$$

Similar equations can also be written down for the conditional probabilities $\pi_i(t)$ but in view of the ratio involved in $\lambda^{\mathscr{H}}(t)$ these are nonlinear, having the form

(13.3.9) $$D_t \pi_i(t) = -\pi_i(t)(\lambda_i + q_i - \lambda^{\mathscr{H}}(t)) + \sum_{j \neq i} \pi_j(t)q_{ji},$$

(13.3.10) $$\Delta \pi_i(t_n) = (\lambda_i/\lambda^{\mathscr{H}}(t) - 1)\pi_i(t_n-).$$

This last example contains in embryonic form most of the features of the general problem of filtering for point processes. In particular, note the appearance of estimates of the current state as ratios involving the likelihood at (13.3.5) and (13.3.6), and the possibility of developing a succinct system of equations for updating such estimates at (13.3.7)–(13.3.10). It is the latter concern that predominates in most of the published literature. Both the differential equations that hold between observed points and the difference equations that hold at such points can be incorporated into a single set of integral equations, and such integral equations then form the main object of study.

The martingale representations fit naturally into this discussion, where two main approaches can be identified, the "innovations" approach, in which the martingale representations are studied directly, and the method of "reference probabilities," in which they enter via the likelihoods. We give in outline an introduction to the second approach, based on Brémaud (1981), which may be consulted for a more extended account.

We start by extending Proposition 13.1.VI concerning the structure of likelihood ratios when densities exist [for this structure in more general situations see Liptser and Shiryayev (1978), Boel, Varaiya, and Wong (1975), and Jacod (1975)].

Proposition 13.3.V. *Let N be a point process on $\mathbb{R}_+$ defined on a measure space $(\Omega, \mathcal{E})$, $\mathcal{P}_0$ and $\mathcal{P}_1$ two probability distributions on $(\Omega, \mathcal{E})$, and for each $t > 0$, let $\mathcal{P}_0^t, \mathcal{P}_1^t$ be the distributions induced by $\mathcal{P}_0$ and $\mathcal{P}_1$ on the restrictions of $\mathcal{B}(\mathcal{N})$ to $\mathcal{B}(\mathcal{N}(0, t])$. Suppose also that N has boundedly finite first moment measure under both $\mathcal{P}_0$ and $\mathcal{P}_1$ and that $\mathcal{P}_0$ has a predictable $\mathcal{H}$-intensity $\lambda_0^{\mathcal{H}}(t, \omega)$. The necessary and sufficient condition for $\mathcal{P}_1^t \ll \mathcal{P}_0^t$ for $0 < t \le \infty$ is the existence of a nonnegative predictable process $\mu(t, \omega)$, such that N admits a predictable intensity $\lambda_1^{\mathcal{H}}(t, \omega) = \mu(t, \omega)\lambda_0^{\mathcal{H}}(t, \omega)$ under $\mathcal{P}_1$. When this condition is satisfied, the likelihood ratio*

$$L_t(\omega) = d\mathcal{P}_1^t(N(\omega))/d\mathcal{P}_0^t(N(\omega))$$

has a right-continuous version with left limits given $\mathcal{P}_0$-a.s. for $t_1(\omega) \le t$ by

$$(13.3.11) \quad L_t(\omega) = \left(\prod_{0 < t_i(\omega) \le t} \mu(t_i, \omega)\right)\exp\left(-\int_0^t [\mu(t, \omega) - 1]\lambda_0^{\mathcal{H}}(t, \omega)dt\right),$$

and $L_t(\omega) = 1$ for $t < t_1(\omega)$, and for each $T > 0$, $L_t(\omega)$ is the unique such solution of the integral equation

$$(13.3.12) \quad L_t(\omega) = 1 + \int_0^t L_{s-}(\omega)[\mu(s, \omega) - 1]dZ_0(s) \quad (0 \le t \le T),$$

where $Z_0(s) = N(s) - \int_0^s \lambda_0^{\mathcal{H}}(u, \omega)du$ is the $\mathcal{H}$-martingale arising in the Doob–Meyer decomposition of N under $\mathcal{P}_0$.

PROOF. Since we are concerned here only with the internal history intensities, a straightforward proof of (13.3.11) can be written down in terms of Janossy densities, restating the absolute continuity requirement in terms of the absolute continuity of these densities under $\mathcal{P}_1$ with respect to the corresponding densities under $\mathcal{P}_0$, then restating this condition in terms of the corresponding hazard functions and hence the $\mathcal{H}$-intensities, and finally substituting these expressions into the expressions for likelihoods and hence the likelihood ratio. The details are essentially as in the special case treated earlier and are again left to the reader.

The fact that the conditional hazard functions are measurable functions of $t_i(\omega)$ for $t_i \le t$ implies that, as a function on $(0, t] \times \Omega$, $\mu(s, \omega)$ is $\mathcal{B}((0, t]) \otimes \mathcal{H}_{t-}$-measurable and hence that $\mu(t, \omega)$ is $\mathcal{H}$-progressively measurable and therefore, from the projection theorem, possesses an $\mathcal{H}$-predictable version. Use of this version in (13.3.11) leaves the likelihood unaltered except possibly on a set of $\ell \times \mathcal{P}_0$-measure zero.

Finally, the equivalence of (13.3.11) and (13.3.12) is a consequence of the exponential formula (Lemma 4.6.II). The boundedness requirement on $\mu(\cdot)$ here follows from the equation

$$E_0\left(\int_0^t \mu(s)dN(s)\right) = E_0\left(\int_0^t \mu(s)\lambda_0^{\mathcal{H}}(s)ds\right) = E_1 N(0, t] < \infty,$$

where E_i denotes expectation with respect to $\mathcal{P}_i$ $(i = 0, 1)$. $\qquad\square$

Corollary 13.3.VI. *Under the conditions stated there exists a sequence of stopping times* $S_n \to \infty$ $(n \to \infty)$ *a.s. such that for each n,* $L_{t \wedge S_n}$ *is an* $\mathcal{H}$*-martingale under* $\mathcal{P}_0$.

PROOF. Since $L(t) \equiv L_t$ is left-continuous and nonnegative in each finite interval $(0, t]$, it is also bounded a.s. on such intervals. Furthermore, with T_n as at (13.2.1),

$$E_0\left(\int_0^{t \wedge T_n} \mu(s)\lambda^{\mathcal{H}}(s)ds\right) = E_1(N(t \wedge T_n)) \leq n < \infty,$$

and

$$E_0\left(\int_0^{t \wedge T_n} \lambda^{\mathcal{H}}(s)ds\right) = E_0(N(t \wedge T_n)) \leq n < \infty.$$

Defining

$$S_n = T_n \wedge \inf\{t: L(t) \geq n\},$$

we necessarily have $S_n \to \infty$ and thus

$$E_0\left(\int_0^{t \wedge S_n} |L(s-)[\mu(s) - 1]|\lambda^{\mathcal{H}}(s)ds\right) \leq n^2.$$

Thus, the quantity $L(s-)(\mu(s) - 1)$ on the right-hand of the integral relation (13.3.12) is predictable, and since $Z_0(\cdot)$ is an $\mathcal{H}$-martingale under $\mathcal{P}_0$, it follows from Exercise 13.2.3 that the likelihoods $L(t \wedge S_n)$ also form a martingale.   □

This corollary can also be rephrased as stating that *under* $\mathcal{P}_0$, *the likelihood ratios* L_t *form an* $\mathcal{H}$*-local martingale.*

The form of the likelihood ratio prompts the following more general question. Given a point process on $\mathbb{R}_+$ with measure $\mathcal{P}$ and $\mathcal{F}$-intensity $\lambda^{\mathcal{F}}$ under $\mathcal{P}$, and some further nonnegative $\mathcal{F}$-predictable function $\mu(\cdot)$, does the product $\mu(t, \omega)\lambda^{\mathcal{F}}(t, \omega)$ represent the $\mathcal{F}$-intensity of the point process under the new measure $\mathcal{P}_1(d\omega) = L_t(\omega)\mathcal{P}(d\omega)$? The answer in general is no, because under the new measure there is no guarantee, without some further constraints on $\mu(\cdot)$, that the new trajectories will be a.s. boundedly finite. In other words, the new measure may not necessarily be a probability measure, the possible mass deficiency corresponding to the probability that the realizations no longer lie within $\mathcal{N}((0, t])$. It seems rather difficult to find conditions directly on μ that will avert this possibility; while it is obvious that boundedness of $\mu(t, \omega)\lambda^{\mathcal{H}}(t, \omega)$ on $(0, t]$ is sufficient, this is too restrictive to be generally useful. An alternative stratagem is simply to require $\mathcal{P}_1$ to form a probability measure, and this leads to the following result.

Proposition 13.3.VII. *Let N be a point process on* $\mathbb{R}_+$ *defined on the probability space* $(\Omega, \mathcal{E}, \mathcal{P})$, $\mathcal{F}$ *a right-continuous history for N such that N admits the* *intensity $\lambda^{\mathscr{F}}(t, \omega)$, and $\mu(t, \omega)$ a nonnegative $\mathscr{F}$-predictable process satisfying for some $t > 0$*

$$\int_0^t \mu(s, \omega)\lambda^{\mathscr{F}}(s, \omega)ds < \infty \quad a.s.$$

Then for $L_t(\omega)$ defined by (13.3.11), the necessary and sufficient condition for $\mathscr{P}_1(d\omega) = L_t(\omega)\mathscr{P}(d\omega)$ to be a probability measure on $(\Omega, \mathscr{E})$ is that

$$(13.3.13) \qquad E(L_t(\omega)) = \int_\Omega L_t(\omega)\mathscr{P}(d\omega) = 1,$$

in which case N has, for $0 \le s \le t$, an $\mathscr{F}$-intensity under $\mathscr{P}_1$ equal to $\mu(s, \omega)\lambda^{\mathscr{F}}(s, \omega)$.

PROOF. The relation at (13.3.13) is clearly necessary and sufficient for $\mathscr{P}_1$ to be a probability measure, since it is simply the statement $\int_\Omega \mathscr{P}_1(d\omega) = 1$. The substantial part is to show that when it is satisfied, $\mu(s, \omega)\lambda^{\mathscr{F}}(s, \omega)$ is the $\mathscr{F}$-intensity on $(0, t]$ for N under $\mathscr{P}_1$, for which it is sufficient to show that for every nonnegative $\mathscr{F}$-predictable process $Y(s, \omega)$ on $(0, t]$,

$$E_1\left(\int_0^t Y(s)dN(s)\right) = E_1\left(\int_0^t Y(s)\mu(s)\lambda^{\mathscr{F}}(s)ds\right).$$

By definition of $\mathscr{P}_1$, these expectations $E_1(\cdots)$ under $\mathscr{P}_1$ can be rewritten as expectations $E(\cdots)$ with respect to $\mathscr{P}$, writing $L(t) = L_t(\omega)$,

$$E\left(L(t)\int_0^t Y(s)dN(s)\right) \quad \text{and} \quad E\left(L(t)\int_0^t Y(s)\mu(s)\lambda^{\mathscr{F}}(s)ds\right),$$

respectively. Now under condition (13.3.13), $L(s, \omega)$ is not merely a local martingale but is in fact a martingale [this follows from the defining relation (13.3.11), where it is necessarily a submartingale, and the relation $E_1(L_t) = E_1(L_0) = 1$ then shows it to be a martingale]. From the results in Section A3.3 concerning the Doob–Meyer decomposition and natural increasing functions, these expectations $E(\cdots)$ can now be rewritten as

$$E\left(\int_0^t L(s)Y(s)dN(s)\right) \quad \text{and} \quad E\left(\int_0^t L(s)Y(s)\mu(s)\lambda^{\mathscr{F}}(s)ds\right),$$

respectively. But then from the definition of $L(s)$ and the fact that $\lambda^{\mathscr{F}}(\cdot)$ is the $\mathscr{F}$-intensity of N under $\mathscr{P}$, the first of these integrals equals

$$E\left(\int_0^t L(s-)Y(s)\mu(s)dN(s)\right) = E\left(\int_0^t L(s-)Y(s)\mu(s)\lambda^{\mathscr{F}}(s)ds\right)$$

$$= E\left(\int_0^t L(s)Y(s)\mu(s)\lambda^{\mathscr{F}}(s)ds\right),$$

where the last equality comes from the natural increasing property of $\int_0^s Y(u)\mu(u)\lambda^{\mathscr{F}}(u)du$. $\qquad\square$

Next, we formulate a general version of the Bayesian type of formulae as appeared in Examples 13.3(a) and 13.3(b). In this version, the role of the likelihood itself (i.e., the density with respect to Lebesgue measure) is taken by the likelihood ratio with respect to a "reference probability" $\mathscr{P}_0$, which we discuss shortly.

Proposition 13.3.VIII. *Let $\mathscr{G} \subseteq \mathscr{F}$ be two histories for the point process N on $\mathbb{R}_+$, and $\mathscr{P}_0$, $\mathscr{P}_1$ two probability measures, all defined on the measurable space $(\Omega, \mathscr{E})$. Suppose that, for t in some interval $(0, T]$, the restrictions $\mathscr{P}_i^t$ of $\mathscr{P}_i$ to $\mathscr{F}_t$ $(i = 0, 1)$ satisfy $\mathscr{P}_1^t \ll \mathscr{P}_0^t$, and let $L_t = d\mathscr{P}_1^t / d\mathscr{P}_0^t$ be the likelihood ratio. Then for any real-valued bounded $\mathscr{F}$-adapted process Z_t,*

$$(13.3.14) \qquad E_1(Z_t | \mathscr{G}_t) = E_0(Z_t L_t | \mathscr{G}_t) / E_0(L_t | \mathscr{G}_t) \qquad (\mathscr{P}_0 \text{ a.s.}).$$

PROOF. First we show that the product $E_0(L_t | \mathscr{G}_t) E_1(Z_t | \mathscr{G}_t)$ can be taken as a version of the conditional expectation $E_0(Z_t L_t | \mathscr{G}_t)$. By definition, for $B \in \mathscr{G}_t$,

$$\int_B E_0(Z_t L_t | \mathscr{G}_t) \mathscr{P}_0(d\omega) = \int_B Z_t L_t \mathscr{P}_0(d\omega) = \int_B Z_t \mathscr{P}_1(d\omega),$$

and, similarly, since $E_1(Z_t | \mathscr{G}_t)$ is $\mathscr{G}_t$-measurable,

$$\int_B E_1(Z_t | \mathscr{G}_t) E_0(L_t | \mathscr{G}_t) \mathscr{P}_0(d\omega) = \int_B E_1(Z_t | \mathscr{G}_t) \mathscr{P}_1(d\omega)$$

$$= \int_B Z_t \mathscr{P}_1(d\omega),$$

implying the desired $\mathscr{P}_0$-a.s. equality.

Now the set D, where $E_0(L_t | \mathscr{G}_t) = 0$, is $\mathscr{G}_t$-measurable and satisfies

$$\mathscr{P}_1(D) = \int_D L_t \mathscr{P}_0(d\omega) = \int_D E_0(L_t | \mathscr{G}) \mathscr{P}_0(d\omega) = 0,$$

so the $\mathscr{P}_0$-a.s. equality remains true when put in the ratio form (13.3.14) whatever particular definition is used for the conditional expectations when the denominator of (13.3.14) is zero.   □

These results form the starting point of a general attack on the problem of filtering for point processes. The reference probability $\mathscr{P}_0$ is generally the distribution of a Poisson process at unit rate, this process being assumed to be independent of the other random variables of interest, and in particular of those governing the signal process. The smaller history $\mathscr{G}$ will commonly be the internal history $\mathscr{H}$, in which case the ratios at (13.3.14) are quite analogous to the ratios occurring earlier. Thus, in Example 13.3(a), the $\mathscr{F}$-likelihood ratio is equal to $(\mu t)^{N'} e^{-(\mu-1)t}$, and similarly the quantity under the expectation sign in the numerator at (13.3.14) equals $\mu^{N'+1} t^{N'} e^{-(\mu-1)t}$, which, on taking conditional expectations, cancelling the factor $t^{N'} e^t$, and noting that μ is independent of $\mathcal{H}_t$ under $\mathcal{P}_0$, leads back to the expression for the $\mathcal{H}$-intensity obtained earlier.

We now quote some more general results, which can be obtained by this method. Essentially, we follow the development in Brémaud (1981), which gives more detail.

Updating formulae can be developed for both numerator and denominator of (13.3.14), essentially as corollaries to the integral equation (13.3.11) already obtained for the likelihood. The denominator requires the conditional expectation of the $\mathcal{F}$-likelihood ratio defined in terms of the $\mathcal{F}$-intensity. At first sight it may seem surprising that the result of this is simply to replace the $\mathcal{F}$-intensity by the $\mathcal{G}$-intensity in the expression for the likelihood ratio, which in the language of the engineers implies the "separation of estimation and detection." This is most easily proved by first reverting to the integral equation form, taking conditional expectations, replacing $\lambda^{\mathcal{F}}$ by $\lambda^{\mathcal{G}}$, and then returning to the basic form via a second application of the exponential formula. See Exercise 13.3.5 for details.

Updating the numerator at (13.3.14) when $\mathcal{G} = \mathcal{H}$ is effected by again writing down the integral equation for the likelihood ratio, multiplying through by Z_t, and taking conditional expectations with respect to $\mathcal{H}$. In particular, if $\mathcal{F}_t = \mathcal{F}_0 \vee \mathcal{H}_t$, where $\mathcal{F}_0 \supseteq \sigma\{X_t : 0 \le t < \infty\}$ for a prior or signal process $\{X_t\}$, and we use the $\mathcal{F}$-predictable version of the intensity, then under $\mathcal{P}_0$, since N is independent here of $\sigma\{X_t\}$,

$$(13.3.15) \quad E_0(Z_t L_t | \mathcal{H}_t) = E_0(Z_t) + \int_0^t E_0(Z_s L_{s-} (\lambda^{\mathcal{F}}(s) - 1) | \mathcal{H}_s)(dN(s) - ds).$$

Suppose, in particular, that N is a Cox process directed by some nonnegative measurable function of $X(t) \equiv X_t$, say

$$\lambda(t) = \mu(X(t)) \ge 0 \quad \text{a.s.},$$

and that $X(t)$ is Markovian on $\mathbb{R}$ with transition semigroup P^t. For any bounded continuous function $f : \mathbb{R} \to \mathbb{R}$ we have, from the Markov property,

$$E_0(L_t f(X_t)) = E_0(f(X_t))$$
$$+ \int_0^t E_0\{L(s-)(\lambda(s) - 1)P^{t-s}f(X_s) | \mathcal{H}_s\}(dN(s) - ds).$$

Moreover, if the transition probabilities $P^t(x, B)$ $(x \in \mathbb{R}, B \in \mathcal{B}(\mathbb{R}))$ are continuous functions of x for $t > 0$, this expression can be written explicitly in terms of these probabilities and the associated distributions $P_t(B) = \mathcal{P}\{X(t) \in B\}$ and $\Pi_t(B) \equiv \Pi_t(B|N) \equiv E(L_t I_B(X_t) | \mathcal{H}_t)$, the latter being a regular version of the conditional probability expressed as a function of the realization N. It then takes the form

$$(13.3.16) \quad \Pi_t(B) = P_t(B) + \int_{\mathbb{R}} \int_0^t \Pi_s(dx)(\mu(x) - 1)P^{t-s}(x, B)(dN(s) - ds),$$

from which the updating character is more readily apparent. The updating equations for Example 13.3(b) can now be recovered, as we illustrate further with an example based on a diffusion process.

EXAMPLE 13.3(c) *Cox process directed by a Markov diffusion process.* Suppose there is given a diffusion process on $\mathbb{R}_+$, whose densities $p_t(y)$ satisfy the forward equation (with $D_t = \partial/\partial t$, $D_y = \partial/\partial y$, $D_y^2 = \partial^2/\partial y^2$):

$$D_t p_t(y) = -D_y(\beta(y)p_t(y)) + \tfrac{1}{2}D_y^2(\alpha(y)p_t(y)) \equiv \mathcal{L}(p_t(y)).$$

Denoting the density of Π_t at (13.3.16) by π_t and differentiating (13.3.16) between jumps, we obtain [recalling $p^0(x, y) = \delta(x - y)$ and using the linearity of $\mathcal{L}$]

$$D_t \pi_t(y) = \mathcal{L}(p_t(y)) + \int_{\mathbb{R}} \int_0^t \pi_s(x)(\mu(x) - 1)\mathcal{L}(p^{t-s}(x, y))dx(dN(s) - ds)$$

$$\qquad - \pi_s(y)(\mu(y) - 1)$$

$$\qquad = \mathcal{L}(\pi_t(y)) - \pi_s(y)(\mu(y) - 1),$$

while at any jump t of N we have

$$\pi_{t+}(y) = \pi_{t-}(y)\mu(y).$$

From these equations explicit results for the likelihood or the conditional intensity can be obtained by arguments similar to those used in Example 13.3(b).

If the Bayesian approach, with its close links with updating formulae, has been the main focus of attention in the engineering literature, there has also been a substantial development in the application of "classical" statistical procedures to inference problems for point processes. In particular, the monograph of Kutoyants (1980), especially in its revised edition in English (Kutoyants, 1984b), develops the asymptotic results for maximum likelihood estimates based on the representations given earlier in this section. An important part of this development is establishing asymptotic normality for the likelihood derivatives $D_\theta \log L_t$ (as usual, $D_\theta \equiv \partial/\partial\theta$), where θ is the parameter under study. From the representation at (13.1.9) or (13.3.11) it is readily seen that under suitable regularity conditions these take the form

$$\int_0^t (D_\theta \lambda^{\mathcal{H}}(s)/\lambda^{\mathcal{H}}(s))(dN(s) - \lambda^{\mathcal{H}}(s)ds).$$

Evaluated at the true parameters, such integrals then reduce to integrals with respect to the point process martingale $Z(s) = N(s) - A(s)$, and hence they are themselves martingales. It is then possible to apply to them general central limit theorems for martingales, as, for example, did Rebolledo (1980), or else to develop versions of such theorems specially tailored for the point process context, as did Kutoyants (1979, 1984b). We follow the latter approach and give a slight extension to Kutoyants' work to allow for the possibility of a random variance term that leads to a mixed normal distribution. A convenient framework for this extension is the concept of stable convergence in distribution, as described in Section A3.2. However, we do not use the full strength of stable convergence with respect to the σ-algebra $\mathscr{F}_\infty$ but only stable convergence with respect to the σ-algebra generated by the limit r.v. itself, since this is all that is needed here to discuss the convergence to mixtures of normals. Stronger forms, requiring further conditions, were obtained by Jarupskin (1984).

Theorem 13.3.IX. *Let N be a simple point process on $\mathbb{R}_+$, $\mathscr{F}$-adapted and with continuous $\mathscr{F}$-compensator A. Suppose that for each $T > 0$ an $\mathscr{F}$-predictable process $f_T(t)$ is given and that there exists a positive $\mathscr{F}_0$-measurable random variable η, such that*

(i) $E[\int_0^T f_T(u)^2 \, dA(u)] < \infty$;
(ii) *as $T \to \infty$, $\int_0^T f_T(u)^2 \, dA(u) \to \eta^2$ in probability;*
(iii) *there exists $\delta > 0$ such that as $T \to \infty$,*

$$E\left[\int_0^T |f_T(u)|^{2+\delta} \, dA(u)\right] \to 0.$$

Then the random integral

$$X_T = \int_0^T f_T(x)[dN(x) - dA(x)]$$

converges $\mathscr{F}_0$-stably in distribution to a limit random variable $U\eta$, where U is independent of $\mathscr{F}_0$ and has a normal $N(0, 1)$ distribution.

PROOF. It is most convenient to make use of the form (A3.2.10) for stable convergence, since the exponential formula can again be used to good effect to simplify the limiting form of expectations $E(Z \exp(iyX_T))$.

To this end, consider the process, for fixed real y,

$$\zeta_T(t, y) = \exp\left\{iy \int_0^t f_T(u)[dN(u) - dA(u)] + \frac{1}{2}y^2 \int_0^t f_T(u)^2 \, dA(u)\right\}.$$

Since $A(t)$ is a continuous and $N(t)$ a purely jump process, $\zeta_T(t, y)$ can be written in terms of its continuous and jump components as

(13.3.17) $\qquad \zeta_T(t, y) = \exp\left\{\int_0^t \left[\frac{1}{2}y^2 f_T(u)^2 - iyf_T(u)\right] dA(u)\right\}$

$$\times \prod_i [1 + (\exp(iyf_T(t_i)) - 1)\Delta N(t_i)],$$

where the product is taken over the jump points t_i of the realization of N over the interval $(0, t]$, and since N is assumed simple, $\Delta N(t_i) = 1$ a.s. for all i. Comparing this expression for $\zeta_T(t, y)$ with the exponential formula at (4.6.2), it can be deduced that $\zeta_T(t, y)$ is the unique solution, bounded in $[0, T]$, of the integral equation

$$\zeta_T(t, y) = 1 + \int_0^t \zeta_T(u-, y) \left\{ \left[\frac{1}{2} y^2 f_T(u)^2 - iy f_T(u) \right] dA(u) \right.$$

$$\left. + [\exp(iy f_T(u)) - 1] dN(u) \right\}$$

$$= 1 + \int_0^t \zeta_T(u-, y) [\exp(iy f_T(u)) - 1][dN(u) - dA(u)]$$

$$+ \int_0^t \zeta_T(u-, y) \left[\exp(iy f_T(u)) - 1 - iy f_T(u) + \frac{1}{2} y^2 f_T(u)^2 \right] dA(u).$$

Now let τ denote the stopping time (recall that η is $\mathscr{F}_0$-measurable)

$$\tau = \inf \left\{ t: \int_0^t f_T(u)^2 \, dA(u) \geq \eta^2 \right\}$$

and let Z be any $\mathscr{F}_0$-measurable, essentially bounded random variable. Setting $t = T \wedge \tau$ in the integral equation, multiplying by Z, and taking conditional expectations with respect to $\mathscr{F}_0$, we have from the optional sampling theorem that

$$E\left\{ Z \int_0^{T \wedge \tau} \zeta_T(u-, y) [\exp(iy f_T(u)) - 1][dN(u) - dA(u)] | \mathscr{F}_0 \right\} = 0;$$

since both $Z\zeta_T(u-, s)$ (left-continuous) and $Z[\exp(iy f_T(u)) - 1]$ are $\mathscr{F}$-predictable, the latter function is bounded, and the integral to t is an $\mathscr{F}$-martingale. Thus, we obtain the estimate

$$|E([Z\zeta_T(T \wedge \tau)|\mathscr{F}_0] - Z)|$$

$$\leq E\left\{ |Z| \int_0^{T \wedge \tau} [|\zeta_T(u-, y)| |R(f_T(u), y)| dA(u)] | \mathscr{F}_0 \right\},$$

where

$$R(f_T(u), y) = \exp(iy f_T(u)) - 1 - iy f_T(u) + \tfrac{1}{2} y^2 f_T(u)^2.$$

If $\delta > 0$ is chosen as in condition (iii) of the theorem, then there exists some $C(\delta) < \infty$ such that

$$|R(f_T(u), y)| \leq C(\delta)|y|^{2+\delta} |f_T(u)|^{2+\delta}.$$

Furthermore, on $0 < u < T \wedge \tau$,

$$|\zeta_T(u-, y)| \leq \exp\left\{ \frac{1}{2} y^2 \int_0^{T \wedge \tau} f_T(u)^2 \, dA(u) \right\} \leq \exp\left(\frac{1}{2} y^2 \eta^2 \right).$$

Making use of these inequalities, we obtain the further estimate (writing $\|Z\| = \text{ess sup} |Z(\omega)|$),

$$|E[Z\zeta_T(T \wedge \tau)|\mathscr{F}_0] - Z|$$

$$\leq \|Z\| C(\delta) |y|^{2+\delta} e^{y^2\eta^2/2} E\left[\int_0^{T\wedge\tau} |f_T(u)|^{2+\delta} dA(u)|\mathscr{F}_0\right].$$

Multiplying through by the $\mathscr{F}_0$-measurable function $\exp(-\frac{1}{2}y^2\eta^2)$ yields

(13.3.18) $$|E\{Z[\rho_T e^{iyX_T} - e^{-y^2\eta^2/2}]|\mathscr{F}_0\}|$$

$$\leq \|Z\| C(\delta) |y|^{2+\delta} E\left[\int_0^{T\wedge\tau} |f_t(u)|^{2+\delta} dA(u)|\mathscr{F}_0\right],$$

where

$$\rho_T = \exp\left\{iy \int_{T\wedge\tau}^T f_T(u)[dN(u) - dA(u)]\right.$$

$$\left. -\frac{1}{2}y^2\left[\eta^2 - \int_0^T f_T(u)^2 \, dA(u)\right]_+\right\}.$$

Taking expectations in (13.3.18), the right-hand side converges to zero from assumption (iii). Also, since $|\rho_T| \leq 1$ and $\rho_T \to 1$ in probability from assumption (ii), $E[Z(\rho_T - 1)e^{iyX_T}] \to 0$, so that from (13.3.18) we obtain the limit relation

$$E[Ze^{iyX_T}] \to E[Ze^{-y^2\eta^2/2}].$$

It now follows from Proposition A3.2.IV that there exists a random variable X such that $X_T \to X$ ($\mathscr{F}_0$-stably) and for each bounded, $\mathscr{F}_0$-measurable Z,

$$E[Ze^{iyX}] = E[Ze^{-y^2\eta^2/2}].$$

This equality is equivalent to

$$E[e^{isX}|\mathscr{F}_0] = e^{-s^2\eta^2/2}$$

and hence to

$$E[e^{iyX/\eta}|\mathscr{F}_0] = e^{-y^2/2}.$$

We deduce that $X/\eta = U$ is independent of $\mathscr{F}_0$ and has a unit normal distribution.   □

Corollary 13.3.X. *Under the conditions of the theorem, the distributions of the random integrals X_T converge weakly to the mixed normal distribution with characteristic function $\phi(y) = E[e^{-y^2\eta^2/2}]$. In particular, if η is a.s. constant, the X_T converge weakly in distribution to the normal distribution $N(0, \eta^2)$.*

This corollary merely restates the fact that $\mathscr{F}_0$-stable convergence implies weak convergence.

Corollary 13.3.XI. *If $B_T^2 = \int_0^T f_T(u)^2 \, dA(u) > 0$, then the randomly normed integrals X_T/B_T converge $\mathscr{F}_0$-stably in distribution to the unit normal variable U.*

PROOF. We use the result from Proposition A3.2.IV that if $X_n \to X$ ($\mathcal{F}$-stably) then $g(X_n, Y) \to g(X, Y)$ ($\mathcal{F}$-stably) for bounded continuous functions $g(\cdot)$. Supposing first that Y is bounded away from zero and X is essentially bounded, we can take $g(x, y) = x/y$ so that $X_n/Y \to X/Y$ ($\mathcal{F}$-stably). The constraint on X is immaterial in that it is given that $\mathcal{P}\{|X| < \infty\} = 1$ (because X is a well-defined r.v.). Now suppose also that $Y_n \to Y$ in probability, where each Y_n is a.s. positive and $\mathcal{F}$-measurable. Then $(X_n, Y_n) \to (X, Y)$ in distribution and thus, again, $X_n/Y_n \to X/Y$ ($\mathcal{F}$-stably). Finally, by approximating to Y by a sequence of r.v.s bounded away from zero, the result extends to the case $Y > 0$ a.s. Taking $Y_n = B_{T_n}$ and $X_n = X_{T_n}$ for some sequence $T_n \to \infty$, and $\mathcal{F} = \mathcal{F}_0$, the result follows. $\qquad\square$

The form of condition (iii) is not the most general possible. As Kutoyants (1984b) pointed out, it may be replaced by a Lindeberg type of condition, although the Liapounov type of condition given suffices for most applications. Multivariate versions of the theorem can be given (see Kutoyants, 1984a,b).

The major application of the theorem is to the proof of the asymptotic normality of parameter estimates. This application is discussed and illustrated at length in Kutoyants (1980) for the case of inhomogeneous Poisson processes, and in Kutoyants (1984b) for more general processes. The next two examples may also help illustrate the range of applications for the theorem.

EXAMPLE 13.3(d) *Poisson and mixed Poisson processes.* As the simplest possible example, let N be a simple Poisson process with rate μ. Successful application of the theorem relies on identifying the appropriate norming function $f_T(\cdot)$ for the quantity of interest. Here, to study $N(t)$, recall first that its $\mathcal{H}$-compensator is μt. Thus, we need $f_T(\cdot)$ to satisfy

$$\int_0^T f_T(u)^2 \mu \, dt \to \text{constant} \qquad (T \to \infty),$$

so $f_T(u) = T^{-1/2}$ is the simplest choice here, with the constant $= \mu$ and non-random. Then the left-hand side of (iii) reduces to $\mu T^{-\delta/2} \to 0$ ($T \to \infty$) as required. Thus,

$$(N(T) - \mu T)/T^{1/2} \to \mu^{1/2} U \quad \text{in distribution}$$

with U a standard normal r.v. as in the theorem.

If in fact the process is mixed Poisson with μ a r.v. as in Example 13.3(a), the same conclusion holds provided we use the $\mathcal{F}$-compensator with $\mathcal{F}_t = \mathcal{F}_0 \vee \mathcal{H}_t$. Indeed, from Corollary 13.3.XI we should have

$$(N(T) - \mu T)/(\mu T)^{1/2} \to U \quad \text{in distribution}.$$

If the aim is to devise a result concerning an estimate of μ, it would be preferable to express the left-hand side here as $(N(T)/T - \mu)/(\mu/T)^{1/2}$ and then observe that, as $T \to \infty$, we have $N(T)/T \to \mu$ a.s. As a result of this, we can replace μ in the denominator and deduce further that

$$(N(T)/T - \mu)/[(N(T))^{1/2}/T] \to U \quad \text{in distribution}$$

with all quantities on the left-hand side apart from μ known at T.

A final possibility would be to use the $\mathcal{H}$-compensator, which in the special case given in Example 13.3(a) has the form

$$dA(t) = [(N(t-) + 1)/(t + \alpha)]dt,$$

and leads to virtually the same conclusions.

In examples of this kind, where $\mathcal{F}_0$ is either trivial or very simple, there is little advantage in using the extensions to random norming. Only weak convergence is asserted and the theorem sheds no light on whether the estimates converge $\mathcal{H}_\infty$-stably, for example. For detail on this question see Jarupskin (1984). It also underlies the next example.

EXAMPLE 13.3(e) *Simple birth process.* This is a standard example (e.g., see Keiding, 1975; Basawa and Scott, 1983), which shows "nonergodic" behaviour in the sense that the asymptotic distribution of the maximum likelihood estimate is not normal but a mixture of normals. If the probability of an individual producing offspring in time $(t, t + dt)$ is $\lambda \, dt$, and all individuals reproduce independently, it is known that with $N(t)$ denoting the sum of the initial number n_0 and the number of individuals born in $(0, t]$,

$$(13.3.19) \quad \mathcal{P}\{N(t) = n\} = q_t^{n_0} p_t^{n-n_0} \frac{(n-1)!}{(n_0 - 1)!(n - n_0)!} \quad (p_t = 1 - e^{-\lambda t}),$$

that

$$(13.3.20) \qquad\qquad N(t)e^{-\lambda t} \to W,$$

and that the maximum likelihood estimate of λ is given by

$$\hat{\lambda}_t = \frac{N(t) - n_0}{\int_0^t N(u)du},$$

where W is a random variable which, if $n_0 = 1$, has the unit exponential distribution. Clearly, the process may be treated as a point process, and it is then of interest to see what light the present methods show on the behaviour of the likelihood estimate.

The conditional intensity of the process with respect to the internal history $\mathcal{H}$ generated by the $N(t)$ themselves is just equal to $\lambda N(t-)$. If we use this history, the first derivative of the likelihood for the process on $(0, T]$ is proportional to

$$N(T) - \lambda \int_0^T N(t-)dt,$$

which has variance function

$$\lambda \int_0^T N(t)dt \sim We^{\lambda T}.$$

This suggests that the norming factor $k(T) = e^{-\lambda T/2}$ is appropriate, but since W is not $\mathscr{F}_0$-measurable with this choice of history, further discussion is required. In fact, what is needed is the $\mathscr{F}$-intensity when $\mathscr{F}_0 = \sigma\{W\}$ and $\mathscr{F}_t = \mathscr{F}_0 \vee \mathscr{H}_t^{(N)}$. The history $\mathscr{F}$ is a refinement of the internal history, and to find the $\mathscr{F}$-compensator we have to discuss the behaviour of the process conditional on the value of W. This can be computed by writing down from (13.3.19) the joint distribution of $N(s)$ and $N(t)$ for $s > t$, conditioning on $N(s)$, and letting $s \to \infty$, taking into account (13.3.20) and using Stirling's formula (cf. Keiding, 1975). The result can be stated as follows: given $N(t)$ and W, the conditional distribution of $N(s) - N(t)$ is Poisson with parameter

$$\lambda(s|t, W) = We^{\lambda t}(e^{\lambda(s-t)} - 1).$$

Hence, the $\mathscr{F}$-intensity is

$$\lambda^{\mathscr{F}}(t) = \lambda We^{\lambda t}.$$

Note that $E(\lambda^{\mathscr{F}}(t)|\mathscr{H}_t) = \lambda e^{\lambda t}E(W|N(t-)) = \lambda e^{\lambda t}N(t-)e^{-\lambda t} = \lambda N(t-)$, which is just the $\mathscr{H}$-compensator if a predictable version of $N(t)$ is taken.

We now consider the asymptotic behaviour of the scaled difference

$$(13.3.21) \quad \Delta(T) = e^{-\lambda T/2}(\hat{\lambda}_T - \lambda)$$

$$= \left\{e^{-\lambda T/2}\left[N(T) - \lambda \int_0^T N(u)du\right]\right\}\Big/\left\{\lambda e^{-\lambda T}\int_0^T N(u)du\right\}.$$

Applying the theorem, we find after some simple computations that the pair

$$e^{-\lambda T/2}\int_0^T [dN(u) - \lambda We^{\lambda u}\,du] = e^{-\lambda T/2}[N(T) - n_0 - W(e^{\lambda T} - 1)]$$

and

$$e^{-\lambda T/2}\int_0^T \lambda(T - u)[dN(u) - \lambda We^{\lambda u}\,du]$$

$$= e^{-\lambda T/2}\left[\int_0^T N(u)du - n_0 T - W(e^{\lambda T} - 1 - \lambda T)\right]$$

converges $\mathscr{F}_0$-stably to the pair $Z_1 W^{1/2}, Z_2 W^{1/2}$, where Z_1, Z_2 are independent of $\mathscr{F}_0$ and jointly normally distributed with covariance matrix $\begin{pmatrix} 1 & 1 \\ 1 & 2 \end{pmatrix}$, so that in fact we can write $Z_2 = Z_1 - Z_1'$, where Z_1, Z_1' are independent unit normal variates. Thus, the numerator in the term on the right-hand side of (13.3.21) converges $\mathscr{F}_0$-stably to $Z_1' W^{1/2}$ while from (13.3.20) the denominator converges a.s. to W. Hence,

$$\Delta(t) \sim Z'W^{-1/2} \quad (\mathscr{F}_0\text{-stably}).$$

But an exponential variable W has just the form $\chi_{(2)}^2/2$, where $\chi_{(2)}^2$ denotes a chi-square r.v. on two degrees of freedom, and so the ratio has a t-distribution on two degrees of freedom [see again Keiding (1975)].

Exercises

13.3.1. (a) Extend Example 13.3(b) to the context where the underlying Markov process is bivariate, $(X(t), Y(t))$ say, with $X(t)$ $\{1, \ldots, K\}$-valued as before and unobserved, and $Y(t)$ observed with values $\{\alpha, \beta, \ldots\}$, so that $\{(X(t), Y(t))\}$ has Q-matrix $(q_{(i, \alpha)(j, \beta)})$ say. Write $\mathscr{H} = \{\mathscr{H}_t\} \equiv \{\sigma(\{Y(s): 0 \le s \le t\})\}$ for the internal history of the observed process $Y(\cdot)$.

By analogy with (13.3.4) set $\hat{p}_X(t) \equiv (\hat{p}_1(t), \ldots, \hat{p}_K(t))^T$ with $\hat{p}_i(t) = \mathscr{P}\{X(t) = i,$ observed $Y(s)$ $(0 \le s \le t)\}$, so that [cf. (13.3.7) and (13.3.8)], on intervals of constancy for $Y(\cdot)$, $Y(t) = \alpha$ say,

$$D_t \hat{p}_i(t) = -q_{(i, \alpha)(j, \alpha)} \hat{p}_i(t) + \sum_{k \ne i} q_{(k, \alpha)(i, \alpha)} \hat{p}_k(t),$$

while where $Y(t-) = \alpha$, $Y(t) = \beta \ne \alpha$,

$$\hat{p}_i(t) = \hat{p}_i(t-) q_{(i, \alpha)(i, \beta)} / |q_{(i, \alpha)(i, \alpha)}|.$$

(b) Recover Example 13.3(b) by taking $X(t)$ as in that example and $Y(t) = N(t)$.

(c) As another special case, derive the corresponding equations for the process in which $Y(t)$ simply counts the jumps in the process $X(\cdot)$, which is otherwise unobserved. [For further details and special cases see Rudemo (1972, 1973).]

13.3.2. Consider a Neyman–Scott cluster process with Poisson cluster centre process at rate μ and clusters of random size v located at independent exponentially distributed distances, mean $1/\lambda$, from the cluster centre. The observed process $N(t)$ consists of both the cluster centres and the points of the cluster, without distinction, lying in the interval $(0, t]$.

Write $X(t)$ for the numbers of points generated from centres $t_j' < t$ at locations $t_i \ge t$. Then $X(\cdot)$ is an unobserved Markov process on $\{0, 1, \ldots\}$ governing the observed points, and $\lambda^*(t) = \mu + \lambda X(t-)$. Show that the process fits the context of Exercise 13.3.1 [albeit a countable state space for $X(\cdot)$] when $Y(t) = N(t)$ and the nonzero off-diagonal transition rates are given (for all $i, j, r = 0, 1, \ldots$) by

$$q_{(i, r), (i+j, r+1)} = \mu q_j, \qquad q_{(i, r), (i-1, r+1)} = \lambda i.$$

Deduce that the joint p.g.f. $P_t(w, z) = E(w^{X(t)} z^{N(t)} | X(0))$ is given by

$$P_t(w, z) = (z + (w - z)e^{-\lambda t})^{X(0)} \exp\left\{-\mu \int_0^t [1 - zQ(z + (w - z)e^{-\lambda u})] du\right\},$$

and that

$$\lim_{t \to \infty} E(w^{X(t)}) = \exp\left\{\frac{\mu}{\lambda} \int_0^1 [Q(1 - (1 - w)v) - 1]v^{-1} dv\right\}.$$

See also Jowett and Vere-Jones (1972).

13.3.3. To complete the proof of Proposition 13.3.V, suppose that $\mathscr{P}_1 \ll \mathscr{P}_0$, where $\mathscr{P}_0$ has $\mathscr{H}$-intensity $\lambda_0(\cdot)$. Arguing as in Proposition 13.1.III, this implies that $\mathscr{P}_1$

is absolutely continuous with respect to a Poisson process at unit rate, and thus has $\mathcal{H}$-intensity $\lambda_1(\cdot)$ say. Set $\mu(t, \omega) = \lambda_1(t, \omega)/\lambda_0(t, \omega)$ if $\lambda_0(t, \omega) \neq 0$, $= 1$ otherwise, and let $\tilde{\mu}$ be the predictable projection of μ. Show that μ defined by (13.3.11) has the properties of the Radon–Nikodym derivative $d\mathcal{P}_1/d\mathcal{P}_0$.

13.3.4. Prove that if $X(\cdot)$ is an $\mathcal{F}$-submartingale and $E(X(t)) = E(X(0))$ for some $t > 0$, then the process $Y(s, \omega) = X(s \wedge t, \omega)$ is an $\mathcal{F}$-martingale.

13.3.5. (a) Let L_t be a likelihood ratio relative to a unit rate Poisson process for a process with $\mathcal{F}$-intensity $\lambda^{\mathcal{F}}$. When the history $\mathcal{G}$ has $\mathcal{G}_t \subseteq \mathcal{F}_t$ (all $t \geq 0$), $E(L_t|\mathcal{G}_t)$ has the same form as L_t but with the $\mathcal{G}$-intensity $E(\lambda_t^{\mathcal{F}}|\mathcal{G}_{t-})$ in place of $\lambda^{\mathcal{F}}$. [*Hint:* From the integral equation for L_t construct $E(L_t|\mathcal{G}_t)$: since N_s is $\mathcal{G}_t$-measurable for $t > s$,

$$E_0\left(\int_0^t L_{s-}(1 - \lambda^{\mathcal{F}}(s))(dN(s) - ds)|\mathcal{G}_t\right)$$

$$= \int_0^t E_0(L_{s-}(1 - \lambda^{\mathcal{F}}(s))|\mathcal{G}_t)(dN(s) - ds).$$

L_{s-} and $1 - \lambda^{\mathcal{F}}(s)$ are $\mathcal{G}_{s-}$-measurable so the integrand on the right equals $E_0(L_{s-}|\mathcal{G}_{s-})E_1(1 - \lambda^{\mathcal{F}}(s)|\mathcal{G}_{s-})$ $\mathcal{P}_1$-a.s.]

(b) Use a similar argument to show that (13.3.15) holds [cf. also Chapter VI, Section 3, of Brémaud (1981)].

13.3.6. (a) Derive the updating equations (13.3.7) and (13.3.8) of Example 13.3(b) from Equation (13.3.16) by using standard Chapman–Kolmogorov equations for the derivatives of transition probabilities and considering (13.3.16) between jumps of $N(\cdot)$ and at jumps of $N(\cdot)$.

(b) Convert these equations into updating equations for the conditional probabilities $\Pi_t(\cdot)/L_t$, so that with $\hat{\pi}_i(t) = \mathcal{P}\{X(t) = i|\mathcal{H}_t\}$, $\hat{\pi}_i(t) = (\lambda_i/\hat{\lambda})\pi_i(t-)$ if t is a point of the realization in $\mathcal{H}_t$ and otherwise

$$\frac{\partial \hat{\pi}_i(t)}{\partial t} = \sum_{j \neq i} q_{ji}\hat{\pi}_j(t) - (\lambda_i - \hat{\lambda})\hat{\pi}_i(t).$$

13.3.7. (a) Suppose in Example 13.3(b) that the transition rates (q_{ij}) and the rates λ_i are functions of some parameter α, and give α some prior distribution. Extend the updating equations [cf. Example 13.3(a) also] to obtain the integral equation for the joint statistic $h_i(\alpha, t)$ for $X(t)$, α, $N(\cdot)$, corresponding to (13.3.16),

$$h_i(\alpha, t) = \sum_j \int_0^t h_j(\alpha, s)[\mu_j(\alpha) - 1]p_{ji}(t - s; \alpha)dZ(s).$$

(b) Consider the special case where $X(\cdot)$ is $\{1, 2\}$-valued, with unknown emission rates λ_1, λ_2 but known exponential holding times in each state. Investigate the consequences of assuming prior distributions for λ_1, λ_2 that are independent gamma distributions.

13.3.8. For the self-correcting or stress-release model of Isham and Westcott (1979) for which $\lambda(t) = \exp[\alpha + \beta(t - \rho N(t))]$, show that conditions for estimators of β and ρ to have central limit theorem properties hold for $\beta > 0$, $\rho > 0$ but fail when $\beta = 0$. [*Hint:* When $\beta > 0$, $\rho > 0$, the process $X(t) = t - \rho N(t)$ is

Markovian and the law of large numbers implies that condition (ii) of Theorem 13.3.IX holds, while it fails when $\beta = 0$. See also Vere-Jones and Ogata (1984).]

13.3.9. If the process $X(t, \omega)$ is left-continuous and integrable and the history $\mathscr{F}_t$ is also left-continuous, then there exists a predictable version of the conditional expectation $E(X(t)|\mathscr{F}_t)$ (see Mertens, 1972).

13.4. Some Applications of Point Process Compensators

The variety of problems discussed in this section continues the application of the ideas of Section 13.2. The first result is the earliest in the application of martingale ideas to point process theory, namely, Watanabe's (1964) characterization of the Poisson process. Following Brémaud (1981) and Brown (1978), we present it here in an extended form, which applies to doubly stochastic processes and not just Poisson processes. The derivation involves an elegant application of the exponential formula of Section 4.6.

Theorem 13.4.I. *Let N be a simple point process on $\mathbb{R}_+$ adapted to the history $\mathscr{F}$. If the $\mathscr{F}$-compensator A of N is continuous and $\mathscr{F}_0$-measurable, then N is a Cox process directed by A.*

PROOF. For fixed θ set

$$M_\theta(t) = e^{i\theta N(t)}/\exp\{(e^{i\theta} - 1)A(t)\}$$

and identify this function with the solution (4.6.3) of the integral equation (4.6.2) by setting

$$G(x) = N(x) - A(x) \qquad (x > 0),$$

$$u(x) = e^{i\theta} - 1 \quad \text{(independent of } x).$$

Thus, $M_\theta(\cdot)$ satisfies

$$M_\theta(t) = 1 + \int_0^t M_\theta(s-)(e^{i\theta} - 1)(dN(s) - dA(s)).$$

The integrand on the right-hand side is left-continuous and $\mathscr{F}$-adapted, and therefore (see the discussion following Lemma A3.3.I) $\mathscr{F}$-predictable. It now follows from Exercise 13.2.3 that the integral is an $\mathscr{F}$-martingale, so that on taking conditional expectations with respect to $\mathscr{F}_0$, $E(M_\theta(t)|\mathscr{F}_0) = 1$. By assumption the compensator A is $\mathscr{F}_0$-measurable, so this last equation can be rewritten as

$$E(e^{i\theta N(t)}|\mathscr{F}_0) = \exp\{(e^{i\theta} - 1)A(t)\},$$

which we recognize as the characteristic function of a Poisson distribution with mean $A(t)$. A similar argument leads to the result, for $0 < s < t$, that

$$E(e^{i\theta N(t)}|\mathscr{F}_s) = \exp\{(e^{i\theta} - 1)(A(t) - A(s))\}e^{i\theta N(s)}.$$

This relation can be used repeatedly to establish the conditional independence increment property required to show that, given $\mathscr{F}_0$, $N(\cdot)$ is a Poisson process with parameter measure $A(\cdot)$. The result of the theorem now follows from the definition of a Cox process (cf. Proposition 8.5.I). □

Corollary 13.4.II. *Let N be a simple point process with internal history $\mathscr{H}$ and let its $\mathscr{H}$-intensity be the deterministic function $\mu(\cdot)$. Then N is a Poisson process with density function $\mu(\cdot)$.*

Watanabe discussed the special case $\mu(t) = \mu$ (all $t > 0$). Both his result and its generalization are closely related to a theorem of Papangelou (1972b) to the effect that any simple point process with continuous compensator is locally Poisson in character, in the sense that there exists a local transformation of the time axis that converts the process into a Poisson process. The form of the time change is given by the inverse of the compensator, namely,

(13.4.1) $$A^{-1}(x) = \inf\{t: A(t) \geq x\}.$$

If A is continuous, then A^{-1} is right-continuous (and monotonic, like A), with jumps at the at most countable set of values x of constancy of A, and $A(A^{-1}(x)) = x$ for all $x > 0$. Such continuity of A implies its $\mathscr{F}$-progressive measurability, and thus (see Lemma A3.3.III) for every x, $A^{-1}(x)$ is an $\mathscr{F}$-stopping time. The σ-algebra

$$\tilde{\mathscr{F}}_x \equiv \mathscr{F}_{A^{-1}(x)}$$

is well-defined (Definition A3.4.V), with $\tilde{\mathscr{F}}_x \subseteq \tilde{\mathscr{F}}_y$ for $x \leq y$ (Theorem A3.4.VII), and thus $\tilde{\mathscr{F}} \equiv \{\tilde{\mathscr{F}}_x: 0 < x < \infty\}$ constitutes a history for the process $A^{-1}(\cdot)$.

Proposition 13.4.III. *Let N be a simple point process adapted to the history $\mathscr{F}$ with continuous $\mathscr{F}$-compensator A that is not a.s. bounded. Under the random time change $t \to A(t)$, the transformed process*

$$\tilde{N}(x) = N(A^{-1}(x))$$

is $\tilde{\mathscr{F}}$-adapted and is a Poisson process with unit rate.

PROOF. Because $A^{-1}(x)$ is an $\mathscr{F}$-stopping time, $\tilde{N}(x)$ is $\tilde{\mathscr{F}}_x$-adapted by Lemma A3.4.VI. Clearly, $\tilde{N}(x)$ inherits from $N(\cdot)$ and $A(\cdot)$ the properties of monotonicity, of increasing only by integer-valued jumps, which where $A^{-1}(\cdot)$ is continuous are necessarily unit jumps. $A^{-1}(\cdot)$ is càdlàg, and the only jumps in $A^{-1}(x)$ are stretches where $A(t)$ is constant, such as the interval $(a, b]$ say. But then $E(N(a, b]|\mathscr{F}_a) = A(b) - A(a) = 0$, so $N(a, b]|\mathscr{F}_a = 0$ a.s. Letting a, b range over a countable set of rationals, we have $\mathscr{P}\{\tilde{N}$ has only unit jumps$\} = 1$; that is, $\tilde{N}$ is simple.

To complete the proof, we apply Corollary 13.4.II by showing that $\tilde{N}$ has $\mathscr{F}$-compensator x. Since $A^{-1}(x)$ is a stopping time for each x, it follows from the optional stopping theorem (A3.4.VII) that, for $y \geq x \geq 0$,

$$E(\tilde{N}(y) - y|\mathscr{F}_x) = E(N(A^{-1}(y)) - A(A^{-1}(y))|\mathscr{F}_{A^{-1}(x)})$$
$$= N(A^{-1}(x)) - A(A^{-1}(x)) = \tilde{N}(x) - x.$$

Thus, $\tilde{N}(x) - x$ is an $\tilde{\mathscr{F}}$-martingale; hence, from the uniqueness theorem 13.2.V, x must be the $\tilde{\mathscr{F}}$-compensator for $\tilde{N}$. □

The unboundedness constraint can be relaxed via use of a randomization argument.

When $A(t)$ has density $\lambda^*(t)$ say, Papangelou (1974a) describes the intuitive content of the above theorem in essentially the following way (we have altered Papangelou's text slightly to allow for the fact that his paper discussed stationary processes on $\mathbb{R}$): "Suppose that, starting at 0 say, we trace $\mathbb{R}_+$ in such a way that at the time we are passing position t our speed is $1/\lambda^*(t)$, which can be ∞. (The value of $\lambda^*(t)$ is determined by observation of the past, i.e., by what happened up to t.) Then the time instants at which we shall meet all the points in $\mathbb{R}_+$ of the process form a homogeneous Poisson process."

Theorem 13.4.I and its corollary are particular instances of a general type of uniqueness theorem: given a history $\mathscr{F}$ and a point process with $\mathscr{F}$-compensator A, the point process (i.e., its fidi distributions) is uniquely specified by the process A. While there is a loose sense in which a general theorem of this kind is true, it is not easy to formulate such a general result in precise terms because of the immense variety of possible interactions between a family $\mathscr{F}$ and a cumulative process A [recall Example 13.2(b)].

There is, however, one circumstance in which specific results can be formulated, namely, when $\mathscr{F}$ is the internal history $\mathscr{H}$ of the point process, with the proviso that "knowing the $\mathscr{H}$-compensator A" means being given an explicit representation of A as a function of t and the jump times prior to t of the process. Armed with this information, the conditional distributions and hence the whole set of fidi distributions for the point process can be recovered from the relations outlined in Section 4.6 between a distribution and its hazard measure.

Similarly, given a sufficiently simple joint dependence of the hazard rates on the prior jump times and some external variables (i.e., some $\mathscr{F}_0$-measurable variables), it may again be possible to write down a family of conditional fidi distributions, given the values of both these prior jump times and the external variables. The details of some of these remarks are amplified in Exercise 13.2.7 and 13.2.8.

The other substantive theoretical application of compensators we illustrate is in establishing limit theorems, particularly (see Proposition 13.4.VI) where the operation inducing the limit may incorporate some form of dependence on the process itself. We first give a theorem by Brown (1978, 1982, 1983) on convergence to Poisson and Cox processes.

Theorem 13.4.IV. *Let $\{\mathscr{F}^{(n)}: n = 1, 2, \ldots\}$ be a sequence of histories defined on a common probability space $(\Omega, \mathscr{E}, \mathscr{P})$, $\{N_n\}$ a sequence of simple point processes with N_n $\mathscr{F}^{(n)}$-adapted for each n, and $\{A_n\}$ a sequence of compensators with A_n the $\mathscr{F}^{(n)}$-compensator of N_n. Suppose $A(\cdot)$ is a cumulative process defined on $(\Omega, \mathscr{E}, \mathscr{P})$ with continuous trajectories and such that for each $t > 0$,*

(i) $A(t)$ is $\mathscr{F}_0^{(n)}$-measurable for every $n = 1, 2, \ldots$;
(ii) $A_n(t) \to A(t)$ $(n \to \infty)$ in probability.

Then N_n converges weakly (i.e., in distribution) to a Cox process directed by A.

PROOF. We first show that conditions (i) and (ii) imply the tightness of the distributions on $\mathscr{N}_{\mathbb{R}_+}$ induced by $\{N_n\}$, so that subsequences converge weakly to the distribution of some point process N, and then stable convergence is used to help in identifying the limit distribution.

Tightness in the present context amounts to showing that for each $t \in \mathbb{R}_+$, given $\varepsilon > 0$, we can find some a_0 and some subsequence $\{n_k\}$ such that for all n in the subsequence

$$(13.4.2) \qquad\qquad \mathscr{P}\{N_n(t) > a\} < \varepsilon \quad \text{(all } a > a_0\text{)};$$

mostly, we take "n in a subsequence $\{n_k\}$" as understood. Now for any event $U \in \mathscr{E}$,

$$|\mathscr{P}(U | \{A(t) \le M\}) - \mathscr{P}(U)| \le \mathscr{P}\{A(t) > M\}/\mathscr{P}\{A(t) \le M\},$$

$$\le \varepsilon/3 \quad \text{for } M \text{ sufficiently large.}$$

Consequently, (13.4.2) will be established if we can show that, for all n,

$$(13.4.3) \qquad \mathscr{P}(\{N_n(t) > a\} | \{A(t) \le M\}) < 2\varepsilon/3 \quad \text{(all } a > a_0\text{)}.$$

Write $N_n'(\cdot) = I_B N_n(\cdot)$, $A_n'(\cdot) = I_B A_n(\cdot)$, $A'(\cdot) = I_B A(\cdot)$, where I_B is the indicator function of the set $\{A(t) \le M\}$. Equation (13.4.3) will be established if we can show that $\mathscr{P}(\{N_n'(t) > a\}) < 2\varepsilon/3$ (all $a > a_0$).

From condition (ii) of the theorem we have immediately the property

(ii)' $A_n'(\cdot) \to A'(\cdot)$ in probability,

so by a diagonal selection argument we can find a subsequence $\{n_k'\}$ such that $A_{n_k'}'(s) \to A'(s)$ a.s. for a countable set of values of s dense in $(0, t]$, and thus by the a.s. continuity of $A'(\cdot)$, and hence a.s. uniform continuity, we have

$$\sup_{0 \le s \le t} |A_{n_k'}'(s) - A'(s)| \to 0 \quad \text{a.s.,}$$

so, identifying $\{n_k\} = \{n_k'\}$,

$$(13.4.4) \qquad\qquad \sup_{0 \le s \le t} |A_n'(s) - A'(s)| \to 0 \quad \text{in probability.}$$

By the continuity and $\mathscr{F}_0^{(n)}$-measurability of $A'(\cdot)$,

$$T_n \equiv \inf\{s: A'_n(s) > A'(t) + 1\}$$

is an extended $\mathscr{F}_{(-)}^{(n)}$-stopping time, with the property implied by (13.4.4) that $\mathscr{P}\{T_n \geq t\} \to 1$ as $n \to \infty$. Consequently, there exists Δ such that, for all n, $\mathscr{P}\{|N'_n(t \wedge T_n) - N'_n(t)| > \Delta\} < \varepsilon/3$. Now

$$\mathscr{P}\{N'_n(t \wedge T_n) > a + \Delta\} \leq E(N'_n(t \wedge T_n))/(a + \Delta)$$
$$= E(A'_n(t \wedge T_n))/(a + \Delta)$$
$$\leq (M + 1)/(a + \Delta) < \varepsilon/3$$

for a sufficiently large and all n. Equation (13.4.3), and hence (13.4.2), now follows.

Assume there is given a subsequence $\{n_k\}$ for which the distributions induced by $N_n(\cdot)$ converge weakly to those of some limit point process $N(\cdot)$: our aim is to show that all such limit distributions coincide with those of a Cox process directed by $A(\cdot)$. This will follow from the characterization result in Theorem 13.4.I if we can show that there exists a version of $N(\cdot)$ having $A(\cdot)$ as its $\mathscr{F}$-compensator, where $\mathscr{F} = \{\mathscr{F}_t\}$, $\mathscr{F}_t = \mathscr{F}_0 \vee \mathscr{F}_t^{(N)}$, and $\mathscr{F}_0 = \sigma\{A(s): 0 < s < \infty\}$.

As in the first part of the proof, it is enough to fix some $t < \infty$ and to assume that the subsequence is so chosen and the point process so modified that $A_n(s) \to A(s)$ uniformly a.s. on $(0, t]$ and that the compensators $A_n(t)$ are a.s. uniformly bounded by (say) $M < \infty$. Referring to the properties of $\mathscr{F}$-stable convergence of distributions, with the space $\mathscr{X}$ of Definition A3.2.III taken to be $\mathscr{N}_{(0,t]}$ and $\mathscr{F} = \{\mathscr{F}_t\}$ as above, it follows from Proposition A3.2.VI that a version of N can be defined on the (possibly enlarged) space $(\Omega, \mathscr{E}, \mathscr{P})$ in such a way that if $U \in \mathscr{F}_s$, $0 < s \leq t$,

(13.4.5) $$\int_U N_n(s)\mathscr{P}(d\omega) \to \int_U N(s)\mathscr{P}(d\omega)$$

[see condition (iv) of Proposition A3.2.IV]. Since the convergence of the compensators $\{A_n(\cdot)\}$ implies a result corresponding to (13.4.5) with A_n and A replacing N_n and N, we have further that

(13.4.6) $$\int_U (N_n(s) - A_n(s))\mathscr{P}(d\omega) \to \int_U (N(s) - A(s))\mathscr{P}(d\omega).$$

Before we can invoke the martingale property for the left-hand side here, we have to show that (13.4.6) continues to hold when U on the left-hand side is replaced by some approximating set U_n from $\mathscr{F}_s^{(n)}$. It is enough to take U to be a generating set $V \cap W$, where $V \in \mathscr{F}_0$, $W = \{\omega: N(\cdot, \omega) \in B, B \in \mathscr{B}(\mathscr{N}_{(0,s]})\}$. Define $U_n = V \cap W_n$, where W_n is defined like W with N replaced by N_n. The properties of $\mathscr{F}$-stable convergence imply that $\mathscr{P}(U \triangle U_n) \to 0$ (see Proposition A3.2.IV). Furthermore, the integrands at (13.4.6) are uniformly integrable because of the boundedness of their second moments as follows from

$$E(N_n^2(s)) \leq E(N_n^2(t)) = E[(\sum \Delta N_n(t_i))^2]$$

$$= E\left[\sum_i (\Delta N_n(t_i))^2 + 2 \sum_i \Delta N_n(t_i) \sum_{t_j < t_i} \Delta N_n(t_j)\right]$$

$$= E\left[N_n(t) + 2 \int_0^t N_n(s-)dN_n(s)\right]$$

$$= E\left[A_n(t) + 2 \int_0^t N_n(s-)dA_n(s)\right]$$

$$\leq E[A_n(t) + 2N_n(t)A_n(t)] \leq M + 2M^2.$$

Using these two facts, we may replace (13.4.6) by

$$(13.4.7) \qquad \int_{U_n} (N_n(s) - A_n(s))\mathscr{P}(d\omega) \to \int_U (N(s) - A(s))\mathscr{P}(d\omega).$$

Take $s = t$ in this equation, but in the definition of W_n, and hence of U_n, take $B \in \mathscr{B}(\mathscr{N}_{(0,s)})$ with $s < t$. Then the martingale property of N_n implies

$$\int_{U_n} (N_n(t) - A_n(t))\mathscr{P}(d\omega) = \int_{U_n} (N_n(s) - A_n(s))\mathscr{P}(d\omega).$$

Using (13.4.7), the same equality holds with N_n and A_n replaced by N and A, which is just the conditional expectation property identifying $N(\cdot) - A(\cdot)$ as a martingale, and hence $A(\cdot)$ as the $\mathscr{F}$-compensator for $N(\cdot)$.   □

We illustrate this result below by applying it to "dependent thinnings" where the probability of a point being deleted is allowed to depend on either or both of the past of the original (unthinned) point process and of the history of previous deletions. We start by giving a lemma which is of some independent interest.

Lemma 13.4.V. *Let $\mathscr{F}$ be a history, $N(\cdot)$ a simple point process that is $\mathscr{F}$-predictable, and $X(\cdot)$ a nonnegative $\mathscr{F}$-adapted process with finite first moment. Then the cumulative process*

$$(13.4.8) \qquad \eta(t) = \sum_{i:\, t_i \leq t} X(t_i),$$

where $N(\cdot)$ has jump points $\{t_i\}$, is $\mathscr{F}$-adapted with $\mathscr{F}$-compensator

$$(13.4.9) \qquad \alpha(t) = \sum_{i:\, t_i \leq t} \zeta(t_i) \equiv \sum_{i:\, t_i \leq t} E(X(t_i)|\mathscr{F}_{t_i-}).$$

PROOF. Before embarking on the substance of the proof, note the assumption that N be $\mathscr{F}$-predictable. This holds, for example, if $\mathscr{F}_0 \supseteq \sigma(\{N(s): 0 < s < \infty\}) = \mathscr{H}$, in which case the randomness of N is concentrated in $\mathscr{F}_0$ and allows the marks (e.g., thinning) to be left to "the rest" of the history $\mathscr{F}$. Recall that in general $N(t) < \infty$ a.s. for $t < \infty$, so that we can and shall interpret $t_i = t_i(\omega) \equiv \inf\{t: N(t, \omega) \geq i\}$ for $i = 1, 2, \ldots$. Then, being $\mathscr{F}$-predictable, N is certainly $\mathscr{F}_{(-)}$-adapted (Lemma A3.3.I).

All the processes N, η, and α are clearly right-continuous and monotonic increasing, with their points of increase confined to $\{t_i\}$ (or a subset of these jump points of N), where the sizes of their jumps are 1, $X(t_i)$, and $\zeta(t_i)$, respectively. N is $\mathscr{F}$-adapted by assumption, and it is easily checked that so too are η and α. Note that had we used in place of (13.4.9) the definition

$$\alpha(t) = \int_0^t \zeta(s)dN(s),$$

we should have been led into concerns of the existence of an $\mathscr{F}$-progressively measurable version of the conditional expectation $E(X(t)|\mathscr{F}_{t-}) \equiv \zeta(t)$. When such a version does exist, the lemma can be extended to a general cumulative process ξ and integral in place of N and the summation at (13.4.8) and (13.4.9) (see Exercise 13.4.1).

Two steps are needed to prove the lemma: we must show first that $\alpha(\cdot)$ is $\mathscr{F}$-predictable, and then that $\eta(\cdot) - \alpha(\cdot)$ is an $\mathscr{F}$-local martingale. Since $\alpha(\cdot)$ can be written in the form

$$\alpha(t, \omega) = \sum_{i=1}^{\infty} \zeta(t_i)V_{t_i}^+(t, \omega),$$

where $V_T^+(t, \omega) \equiv I_{\{\omega: T(\omega) \leq t\}}(t, \omega)$ is the right-continuous indicator process of the stopping time T (see the end of Appendix A3.3 for discussion), we limit ourselves here to establishing these steps in the special case of a one-point process, that is, where

(13.4.10) $\eta(t, \omega) = X(T)V_T^+(t, \omega)$

and

(13.4.11) $\alpha(t, \omega) = \zeta(T)V_T^+(t, \omega),$

where $\zeta(T) = E(X(T)|\mathscr{F}_{T-})$, for some $\mathscr{F}$-stopping time T such that $V_T^+(\cdot)$ is predictable. The extension to the general case is left to Exercise 13.4.1.

Let Y be any $\mathscr{F}_{T-}$-measurable r.v., and consider the process $YV_T^+(t)$. Indeed, taking Y first to be an indicator r.v. of some basic $\mathscr{F}_{T-}$-measurable set of the form $B_s \cap \{T(\omega) > s\}$ for some $B_s \in \mathscr{F}_s$ and $s \in \mathbb{R}_+$, $\alpha(t, \omega) = 1$ on the intersection of the sets

$$\{(t, \omega): T(\omega) \leq t\} \quad \text{and} \quad \{(t, \omega): t > s, \omega \in B_s \cap \{\omega: T(\omega) > s\}\}.$$

The first set here is in the predictable σ-algebra $\Psi^{\mathscr{F}}$ by assumption, while the second is of the form of a generating set for $\Psi^{\mathscr{F}}$ and is therefore predictable also. A similar argument holds when Y is the indicator r.v. of the other type of generating set for $\Psi^{\mathscr{F}}$, namely, an element of $\mathscr{F}_0$. Since the class of predictable processes is closed under the formation of nonnegative linear combinations and monotone limits, it follows that $YV_T^+(\cdot)$ is a predictable process whenever

Y is $\mathscr{F}_{T-}$ measurable and nonnegative, and hence in particular when it has the form $E(X(T)|\mathscr{F}_{T-})$.

For the second part of the proof we have to show that, for every $A_s \in \mathscr{F}_s$ and $s < t$,

$$\int_{A_s} (\eta(t, \omega) - \alpha(t, \omega))\mathscr{P}(d\omega) = \int_{A_s} (\eta(s, \omega) - \alpha(s, \omega))\mathscr{P}(d\omega),$$

with η and α as at (13.4.10) and (13.4.11), so that

$$\eta(t, \omega) - \alpha(t, \omega) = (X(T) - E(X(T)|\mathscr{F}_{T-}))I_{\{T(\omega) \leq t\}}(t, \omega).$$

The indicator function vanishes on $\{T(\omega) \leq s\}$, for $s < t$, and on $\{\omega: T(\omega) > t\}$, so it is enough to consider $\{\omega: s < T(\omega) \leq t\}$, and hence to show that, for $T > s$,

$$(13.4.12) \qquad \int_{A_s \cap \{T > s\}} (X(T) - E(X(T)|\mathscr{F}_{T-}))\mathscr{P}(d\omega) = 0.$$

Since the set $A_s \cap \{\omega: T(\omega) > s\}$ is an element of both $\mathscr{F}_s$ and $\mathscr{F}_{T-}$, the integrand can be replaced by its conditional expectation with respect to $\mathscr{F}_{T-}$, and thus (13.4.12) holds. □

The special case that X is a $\{0, 1\}$-valued process leads to η as a thinning of the process N, with

$$\zeta(t_i) = \Pr\{t_i \text{ from } N \text{ retained in } \eta\}.$$

Combining the lemma with the earlier proposition leads to the result below, illustrated in the example.

Proposition 13.4.VI. *Let $\{N_n, \mathscr{F}^{(n)}: n = 1, 2, \ldots\}$ be a sequence of simple point processes and associated histories, all defined on a common probability space $(\Omega, \mathscr{E}, \mathscr{P})$ and such that N_n is $\mathscr{F}^{(n)}$-predictable for each n. Let $\{X_n(\cdot)\}$ be a family of $\{0, 1\}$-valued processes with X_n $\mathscr{F}^{(n)}$-adapted, and let $\eta_n(\cdot)$, $\zeta_n(\cdot)$, and $\alpha_n(\cdot)$ be defined as at (13.4.8) and (13.4.9). If for all $t > 0$,*

$$(13.4.13) \qquad \alpha_n(t) \to A(t) \qquad (n \to \infty) \text{ in probability,}$$

where $A(\cdot)$ has continuous paths and is $\mathscr{F}_0^{(n)}$-measurable for each n, then the thinned processes $\eta_n(\cdot)$ converge in distribution to a Cox process directed by $A(\cdot)$.

EXAMPLE 13.4(a) *A point process with controlled thinning.* In quality control and similar contexts, the detection and elimination of errors may be regarded as a thinning operation on an original stream of errors. The error rate in production may vary between batches, so that in order to achieve a uniform low level of errors in the output, screening may need to be intensified according to current estimates of the error rate.

As a crude model, suppose the actual error rate to be some quantity $\lambda \equiv \lambda(\omega)$ per item produced; here, λ is constant within a batch but may vary between batches, and $\omega \in \Omega$ for some probability space $(\Omega, \mathscr{E}, \mathscr{P})$. Suppose that probabilistic screening of items occurs, the $\{0, 1\}$-valued r.v. $X(t_i)$ indicating elimination of $(X(t_i) = 0)$ or failure to detect $(X(t_i) = 1)$ an error at t_i, and $E(X(t_i)|\mathscr{F}_{t_i-}) = \zeta(t_i)$ for some process $\zeta(\cdot)$. Denote by $Y(t)$ and $Z(t)$ the numbers of errors detected and undetected, respectively, in $(0, t)$, so that, assuming the time-scale unit is chosen according to the rate of production of items (whether faulty or not), $(Y(t) + Z(t))/t \approx \lambda$ for large t assuming ergodicity. The aim is to choose $\zeta(\cdot)$ (and this choice is assumed to be available to the producer) in such a way that $Z(t)/t \lesssim \gamma$, asymptotically in t ($=$ long batch run), for some small residual error rate γ per item produced. One such possibility is to have

(13.4.14)
$$1 - \zeta(t, \omega) = \gamma t/(\gamma t + Y^*(t-, \omega)),$$

$$\text{where } Y^*(t, \omega) \equiv \max(1, Y(t, \omega)),$$

noting that this implies that $\zeta(t, \omega) \to 1$ as $t \to 0$ and that $\zeta(t, \omega)$ remains closer to 1 until (if ever) $Y^*(t-, \omega)/\gamma t$ is no longer significantly larger than 1: if $\lambda \gg \gamma$ we expect intuitively that this would not occur, since the aim is to make $Z(t, \omega)/\gamma t$ asymptotically about 1 and so $Y^*(t, \omega)/\gamma t$ is like $(\lambda - \gamma)/\gamma$.

We therefore study the asymptotic behaviour in $Z(\cdot)$ for $\gamma \to 0$ by considering a sequence of schemes, indexed by γ, and show how Proposition 13.4.VI may be applicable. Suppose that the realizations $N(\cdot)$ are kept fixed and that each of a sequence of thinning operations is applied to the same realizations, so that $N_\gamma(t) = N(t)$ and $Y_\gamma(t)$ and $Z_\gamma(t)$ are the result of a dependent thinning via a $\{0, 1\}$-valued process $X_\gamma(t)$ for which $E(X_\gamma(t_i)|\mathscr{F}_{T_i-}) = \zeta_\gamma(t)$ and $\zeta_\gamma(\cdot)$ is related to $Y_\gamma(\cdot)$ as at (13.4.14). Finally, change the time scale by setting $\tau = \gamma t$ and defining the processes

$$\tilde{Y}_\gamma(\tau) = Y_\gamma(\tau/\gamma), \qquad \tilde{Z}_\gamma(\tau) = Z_\gamma(\tau/\gamma),$$

$$\tilde{\zeta}_\gamma(\tau) = \zeta_\gamma(\tau/\gamma) = 1 - \tau/(\tau + \tilde{Y}_\gamma(\tau/\gamma-, \omega)).$$

Set up a scheme of histories $\mathscr{F}^{(\gamma)}$ as follows. Take $\mathscr{F}_0^{(\gamma)}$ to include the information on $\tilde{N}_\gamma(\tau) = N_\gamma(\tau/\gamma)$ for every $\gamma > 0$, and define $\mathscr{F}_\tau^{(\gamma)} = \mathscr{F}_0^{(\gamma)} \vee \sigma\{\tilde{X}_\gamma(s): 0 < s < \tau\}$. This choice ensures that for each γ we have $\mathscr{F}^{(\gamma)}$-predictability of $\tilde{N}_\gamma$ for each γ and that $\tilde{X}_\gamma$ is $\mathscr{F}^{(\gamma)}$-adapted, leading to the expression for the $\mathscr{F}^{(\gamma)}$-compensator for the thinned (output) process $\tilde{Z}_\gamma$,

$$\tilde{A}_\gamma(\tau) = \int_0^\tau (1 - \tilde{\zeta}_\gamma(u))d\tilde{N}_\gamma(u) = \int_0^{\tau/\gamma} (1 - \zeta_\gamma(u))dN(u).$$

We must now determine whether the processes $\tilde{A}_\gamma(\cdot)$ converge in probability as $\gamma \to 0$, and whether the limit function is the compensator of a Poisson process (since this is the plausible limit process under thinning). The triangle inequality gives

$$
\text{(13.4.15)} \qquad |\tilde{A}_\gamma(\tau) - \tau| \le \left| \frac{\gamma}{\lambda} \int_0^\tau d\tilde{N}_\gamma(v) - \tau \right| + \left| \frac{\gamma}{\lambda} \int_0^{\tau'} d\tilde{N}_\gamma(v) \right|
$$

$$
+ \left| \int_0^{\tau'} (1 - \tilde{\zeta}_\gamma(v)) d\tilde{N}_\gamma(v) \right|
$$

$$
+ \int_{\tau'}^\tau \left| (1 - \tilde{\zeta}_\gamma(v)) - \frac{\gamma}{\lambda} \right| d\tilde{N}_\gamma(v),
$$

and as indicated in Exercise 13.4.2, provided $N(t, \omega)/t \to \lambda$ a.s. ($t \to \infty$), τ' can be chosen here to make each of these four terms converge to zero in probability as $\gamma \to 0$.

We therefore conclude that, in the asymptotic sense indicated by change of time scale, the thinning procedure will be effective in reducing the output error rate to the required low level γ, irrespective of λ, and that the resultant process will be asymptotically Poisson in character.

Observe that while conceptually we regarded N as being known a priori [i.e., $\sigma(N) \subseteq \mathscr{F}_0^{(\gamma)}$], $\zeta(\cdot)$ is in fact $\mathscr{H}_{(-)}^{(Y)}$-adapted, where $\mathscr{H}^{(Y)}$ is the internal history of the observed process of errors.

Exercises

13.4.1. (a) Extend Lemma 13.4.V from the one-point case to a general point process N.
   (b) Let $\mathscr{F}$ be a history, ξ an $\mathscr{F}$-predictable cumulative process, and X a nonnegative $\mathscr{F}$-adapted process with finite first moment. Show that if there exists an $\mathscr{F}$-predictable version of the conditional expectation $\zeta(t) \equiv E(X(t)|\mathscr{F}_{t-})$, then the process $v(t) \equiv \int_0^t X(t) d\xi(t)$ has $\mathscr{F}$-compensator $\alpha(t) \equiv \int_0^t \zeta(t) d\xi(t)$.
   [*Hint*: The required measurability and predictability properties are preserved in (a) because only linear combinations and a.s. limits are involved. To establish the compensator property in (b), use Fubini's theorem and the argument in the text to show that
$$
\int_{A_s} \mathscr{P}(d\omega) \int_s^t [X(u) - E(X(u)|\mathscr{F}_{u-})] du = 0.]
$$

13.4.2. In Example 13.4(a), show that each of the four terms on the right-hand side of (13.4.15) converges in probability to zero as $\gamma \to 0$ on the assumption that $N(t)/t$ converges a.s. to some limit $\lambda \equiv \lambda(\omega) \in \mathscr{F}_0^{(\gamma)}$ for all γ. [*Hint*: The convergence is shown directly for the first three terms, while for the last, investigate $\sup_{\tau' < v < t} |1 - \tilde{\zeta}_\gamma(v) - \gamma/\lambda|$ via $Y_\gamma(t)/t \le N(t)/t$ a.s. in one direction and $\liminf_{t \to \infty} Y_\gamma(t)/t$ in the other direction.]

13.5. Complete Intensities and Point Process Entropy

This section and much of Chapter 14 give an introduction to a circle of ideas stemming from the work of Papangelou (1972b, 1974a, b, 1976) on the Davidson conjecture on the structure of line processes [see Example 10.6(b)]. Among the unexpected and fruitful by-products of this research has been the development of a notion of conditional intensity, which is not dependent on the order structure of the real line (Papangelou, 1974b, 1976; Kallenberg, 1978) and the discovery of fundamental links between the resulting theory and statistical mechanical concepts such as Gibbs potentials. We defer an account of these aspects to Chapter 14, contenting ourselves in this section with an account of Papangelou's earlier work on the complete intensity function for stationary processes on $\mathbb{R}$. This is illustrated by a discussion of the entropy rate for a stationary point process, a topic of interest in its own right.

For stationary point processes on $\mathbb{R}$ it is natural to use a form of conditional intensity that depends on the entire past rather than on the past since a fixed origin. Throughout this section we are concerned only with the internal histories of point processes, so that we can and shall take for $(\Omega, \mathscr{E})$ the canonical space $(\mathscr{N}, \mathscr{B}(\mathscr{N})) \equiv (\mathscr{N}_{\mathbb{R}}, \mathscr{B}(\mathscr{N}_{\mathbb{R}}))$ and the history $\mathscr{H}^*$ consisting of the σ-algebras $\mathscr{H}_t^* = \sigma\{N(u) - N(s): -\infty < s < u \le t\}$ for $-\infty < t < \infty$. (Note that $\mathscr{H}^*$ is on $\mathbb{R}$, whereas each $\mathscr{H}_t$ in the internal history $\mathscr{H}$ of Sections 13.2–13.4 is a σ-algebra of events on $(0, t] \subseteq \mathbb{R}_+$.) Throughout this section A^* denotes the $\mathscr{H}^*$-compensator for a point process N with state space $\mathbb{R}$, and λ^* denotes an $\mathscr{H}^*$-conditional intensity for N.

Definition 13.5.I. A *complete intensity function* for the simple point process N defined on $\mathbb{R}$ is any $\mathscr{H}^*$-predictable version of an $\mathscr{H}^*$-conditional intensity for N.

As in the earlier discussion around Proposition 13.3.VIII, we can always obtain a predictable version from any $\mathscr{H}^*$-conditional intensity by projection onto the predictable σ-algebra $\Psi^{\mathscr{H}^*}$ of $\mathbb{R} \times \mathscr{N}_{\mathbb{R}}$. (If any distinction needs to be made, $\tilde{\lambda}^*$ can be used to denote a complete intensity function, that is, a predictable version of λ^*.)

EXAMPLE 13.5(a) *The Hawkes process* (continued from Example 10.4(c), 11.2(e), and 13.1(f)). This process is a stationary Poisson cluster process with clusters that are finite branching processes described by an offspring intensity measure with support in $\mathbb{R}_+$ and having density function $\mu(\cdot)$ of total mass $v < 1$. Because of this Poisson character and the support of μ being contained by the half-line, the conditional behaviour of the process is very simple: given the history up to time t, the process of births in $[t, \infty)$ to individuals themselves born before t is conditionally a Poisson process with intensity at time $t + u$ given by $\lambda + \sum_{t_i < t} \mu(t - t_i + u)$. Of course, any individuals born in $[t, t + u)$ will also contribute to the total birth rate. However, knowing from Example 10.4(c) that the expected number of births on a finite interval is finite, it follows from the above remark that

$$(13.5.1) \qquad \lim_{u \to 0} u^{-1} E(N(t + u) - N(t)|\mathscr{H}_t^*) = \lambda + \sum_{t_i \le t} \mu(t - t_i),$$

which suffices to establish the right-hand side as a version of the $\mathscr{H}^*$-conditional intensity. In practice, μ is usually continuous apart from a possible jump at zero, so either by defining $\mu(0) = 0$ or restricting the summation at (13.5.1) to birth epochs $t_i < t$, we can then obtain a left-continuous version that can therefore be taken as the complete intensity function.

It is noteworthy that the linear representation here has exactly the same form as that derived from the second-order theory of Chapter 11 [see Examples 11.2(c) and 11.4(c)]. In other words, it shows that for the Hawkes process, as for Gaussian processes, the "best" predictors are linear, at least where prediction of the intensity is in view.

EXAMPLE 13.5(b) *Renewal process with density* (continued from Example 13.2(d)). Here and for the Wold process, the complete intensity function has the form of the hazard function given in Example 13.2(d) but without the correction term due to the choice of a fixed origin; that is, for the renewal process, $\lambda^*(t) = h(t - t_{N^*(t-)})$, where $t_{N^*(t-)} = \sup\{t_i: t_i(\omega) < t\}$. This illustrates the fact that the complete intensity function is frequently simpler analytically, as well as necessarily being amenable in principle to probabilistic study.

Since the hazard function here is not linear in the sense of Chapter 11 and Example 13.5(a), it also illustrates the fact that, in general, nonlinear predictors must be used for optimal prediction of point processes.

We proceed to a more detailed study of the complete intensity function, starting from the observation in Proposition 13.2.VIII that the conditional intensity (here the complete intensity) can be characterized as the Radon–Nikodym derivative of the Campbell-type measure $C(\cdot)$ with respect to the product measure $\ell \times \mathscr{P}$ on the restriction of these latter measures to the predictable σ-algebra $\Psi^{\mathscr{H}^*}$. In the ensuing discussion that relates intensities and Palm distributions, the particular case where N has a stationary distribution is of especial interest.

In general, start by assuming that N has a boundedly finite first moment measure $M(\cdot)$ and let $\mathscr{P}_0(\cdot, \cdot)$ be the associated regular family of local Palm distributions (Proposition 12.1.IV). Then the Campbell measure relation can be put in the form, for $-\infty < t < u < \infty$ and $U \in \mathscr{H}_t^*$,

$$(13.5.2) \qquad \int_t^u \mathscr{P}_0(s, U)M(ds) = C((t, u] \times U) = \int_U \int_t^u dA^*(s, N)\mathscr{P}(dN).$$

Suppose that a complete intensity $\lambda^*(t, N)$ exists. Taking $B = \Omega$ in (13.5.2), we see first that $M(\cdot) \ll \ell(\cdot)$ with M having density

$$(13.5.3) \qquad\qquad m(s) = E\lambda^*(s, N).$$

Taking t rational with $t < s$, it follows from Fubini's theorem again that, for almost all $s > t$,

$$m(s)\mathscr{P}_0(s, U) = \int_U \lambda^*(s, N)\mathscr{P}(dN)$$

for all U in any countable family generating $\mathcal{H}_t^*$. But this implies that $m(s)\mathcal{P}_0(s, \cdot)$ is absolutely continuous with respect to $\mathcal{P}$ on $\mathcal{H}_t^*$. Since the rationals form a countable set, we can assume this absolute continuity to hold for all rational $t < s$ excluding s in an exceptional set of zero Lebesgue measure. For all such s, $m(s)\mathcal{P}_0(s, \cdot) \ll \mathcal{P}$ on $\bigvee_{t<s} \mathcal{H}_t^* = \mathcal{H}_{s-}^*$.

In the particular case that N is simple and stationary, so that $m(s) = m$ (all s) and $\mathcal{P}_0(s, U) = \mathcal{P}_0(0, S_s U) = \mathcal{P}_0((S_s U) \cap \mathcal{N}_0^*)$, where $\mathcal{P}_0(\cdot)$ is the Palm measure on $\mathcal{B}(\mathcal{N}_0^*)$, the results are more conveniently restated in terms of this Palm measure $\mathcal{P}_0$ of Theorem 12.3.II. Since $U \in \mathcal{H}_{s-}^*$ if and only if $S_s U \in \mathcal{H}_{0-}^*$, the identification of $\mathcal{P}_0(\cdot, \cdot)$ with $\mathcal{P}_0(\cdot)$ made possible by stationarity and simplicity implies that (with an abuse of terminology) $\mathcal{P}_0(\cdot) \ll \mathcal{P}(\cdot)$ on $\mathcal{H}_{0-}^*$ in the sense that for $U \in \mathcal{H}_{0-}^*$, $\mathcal{P}(U) = 0$ implies $\mathcal{P}_0(U \cap \mathcal{N}_0^*) = 0$ [and recall that $\mathcal{P}_0(\mathcal{N}_0^*) = 1$]. This then is a necessary condition for the existence of a complete intensity function in this case of simple stationary N with finite mean density m.

Conversely, when $\mathcal{P}_0 \ll \mathcal{P}$ on $\mathcal{H}_{0-}^*$, denote any $\mathcal{H}_{0-}^*$-measurable version of the Radon–Nikodym derivative $(d\mathcal{P}_0/d\mathcal{P})(N)$ on $\mathcal{H}_{0-}^*$ by $X(N)$. Then from (13.5.2), for a simple stationary point process with mean density m, for $U \in \mathcal{H}_t^*$ and $u > t$,

$$C((t, u] \times U) = \int_t^u \mathcal{P}_0(s, U) M(ds)$$

$$= m \int_t^u \mathcal{P}_0(S_s U) ds$$

$$= m \int_t^u \int_{S_s U} X(N) \mathcal{P}(dN) ds$$

$$= m \int_t^u \int_U X(S_s N) \mathcal{P}(dN) ds.$$

This shows that $C(\cdot)$ has a Radon–Nikodym derivative $mX(S_s N)$ with respect to $\ell \times \mathcal{P}$, so by Proposition 13.2.VIII we can conclude that a complete intensity exists. In order to identify $mX(S_s N)$ as a complete intensity function, it must be established that it is measurable with respect to the predictable σ-algebra: this is a consequence of the following lemma.

Lemma 13.5.II. Let $Y: \hat{\mathcal{N}}_{\mathbb{R}} \to \mathbb{R}_+$ be $\mathcal{H}_{0-}^*$-measurable. Then $h(s, N) \equiv Y(S_s N)$ is $\mathcal{H}^*$-predictable.

PROOF. Since Y is $\mathcal{H}_{0-}^*$-measurable, $Y(S_s N)$ is $\mathcal{H}_{s-}^*$-measurable, so $h(\cdot, \cdot)$ is $\mathcal{H}_{(-)}^*$-adapted. Because Y is defined on the canonical space $(\hat{\mathcal{N}}_{\mathbb{R}}, \mathcal{B}(\hat{\mathcal{N}}_{\mathbb{R}}))$, it follows from the remarks in Section A3.3 concerning conditions for the converse of Lemma A3.3.I to hold that h is $\mathcal{H}^*$-predictable. $\qquad\square$

All this discussion can now be summarized as follows.

Proposition 13.5.III. *Let N be a simple point process in $\mathbb{R}$ with first moment measure M, distribution $\mathscr{P}$ on $\mathscr{B}(\mathscr{N})$, and a regular family of Palm distributions $\mathscr{P}_0(\cdot, \cdot)$. If a complete intensity function λ^* exists, then $M \ll \ell$, with density $m(s) = E(\lambda^*(s, N))$ a.e., and for ℓ-a.e. s for which $m(s) > 0$, $\mathscr{P}_0(s, \cdot) \ll \mathscr{P}_0(\cdot)$ on $\mathscr{H}^*_{s-}$ with density $\lambda^*(s, N)/m(s)$.*

If in particular N is stationary, then $\mathscr{P}_0 \ll \mathscr{P}$ on $\mathscr{H}^*_{0-}$ if and only if a complete intensity exists, in which case a stationary version of the complete intensity is given by

$$(13.5.4) \qquad\qquad \lambda^*(s, N) = mX(S_s N),$$

where X is an $\mathscr{H}^*_{0-}$-measurable version of the Radon–Nikodym derivative $d\mathscr{P}_0/d\mathscr{P}$ on $\mathscr{H}^*_{0-}$.

We next establish a hazard function representation for λ^* analogous to the representation obtained in Section 13.2 for the intrinsic intensities. The important point here is that for a stationary process the conditioning is with respect to the Palm distribution of intervals. Note also that since the past of the process can be represented as a point in a c.s.m.s., we can and shall assume the existence of regular conditional probabilities.

Lemma 13.5.IV. *For a simple stationary point process on $\mathbb{R}$, a version of the $\mathscr{H}^*$-compensator is given by*

$$dA(u) = F(T_u + du|\tau(u))/[1 - F(T_u - |\tau(u))],$$

where T_u is the backward recurrence time at u, $\tau(u) = \{\tau_{-1}(u), \tau_{-2}(u), \ldots\}$ is the vector of intervals between consecutive points prior to u, and $F(T|\tau)$ is the conditional distribution under the stationary Palm probability for the current interval T given the vector τ of intervals preceding the current interval.

PROOF. We may suppose $u = 0$ without loss of generality, and consider the problem of determining the conditional distribution of $t_1(N)$, the first point in $\mathbb{R}_+$, given the backward recurrence time T and the vector of intervals τ. Let $h(t_1, T, \tau)$ be any jointly measurable function of these variables on the product space $\mathbb{R}_+ \times \mathbb{R}_+ \times (\mathbb{R}_+)^{(\infty)}$, where the last term is the space of interval sequences $(\tau_{-1}, \tau_{-2}, \ldots)$, and the space is given the usual Borel σ-algebra. From the basic relation (12.3.7) we have

$$E_{\mathscr{P}}(h(t_1, T, \tau)) = mE_{\mathscr{P}_0}\left(\int_0^{\tau_0} h(x, \tau_o - x, \tau)dx \right)$$

$$= mE_{\mathscr{P}_0}\left(\int_0^\infty dx \int_0^\infty h(x, y, \tau)F(x + dy|\tau) \right),$$

where τ_0 is the length of the current interval and $F(u|\tau)$ is its conditional distribution under $\mathscr{P}_0$ given the vector $\tau = (\tau_{-1}, \tau_{-2}, \ldots)$. From this relation it can be seen that the joint distribution of (t_1, T, τ) has the form (in infinitesimal notation)

$$m \, dx \, d_t F(x + t|\tau) M_0(d\tau),$$

where M_0 is the measure induced by $\mathscr{P}_0$ on $(\mathbb{R}_+)^{(\infty)}$, and that the conditional distribution of t_1, given T and τ, is equal to

$$d_t F(T + t|\tau)/[1 - F(T - t|\tau)].$$

Appealing to the properties of regular conditional probabilities, it now follows from the arguments used in Example 13.2(b) in establishing the form of the compensator there that the $\mathscr{H}^*$-compensator here has the form asserted. $\square$

Corollary 13.5.V. *A complete intensity for a simple stationary point process exists if and only if the conditional distribution $F(\cdot|\tau) \ll \ell(\cdot)$, in which case, using $f(\cdot|\tau)$ for a density for $F(\cdot|\tau)$, a version of the $\mathscr{H}^*$-conditional intensity is given by*

(13.5.5) $$\lambda^*(u) = f(T_u|\tau(u))/[1 - F(T_u|\tau(u))]$$

In examples, it is usually the case that either $f(\cdot|\tau)$ is continuous or it can be chosen to be left-continuous, and in either circumstance (13.5.5) then gives a predictable version of the $\mathscr{H}^*$-intensity provided that at a point of the process, T_u is interpreted as the length of the preceding interval and not as zero.

As an application of the complete intensity function, we consider the notion of an *entropy rate* for stationary point processes, essentially following Papangelou (1978), but starting from some elementary facts about entropy. Given a finite probability distribution $\{p_1, \ldots, p_k\}$, its *entropy*, measuring in some sense the information conveyed by taking one observation of a finite-valued random variable having the given distribution, is defined to be

$$H = -\sum_{j=1}^{k} p_j \log p_j.$$

(Note that for convenience, we take natural logarithms here rather than logarithms to base 2 as would be more appropriate in an information theory context; also, we use the usual convention that $0 \log 0 = 0$.) A seemingly natural analogue for an absolutely continuous distribution with density $f(\cdot)$ is the integral

$$H_1 = -\int_{-\infty}^{\infty} f(x) \log f(x) dx,$$

with a similar definition for multivariate densities, but there are difficulties with such extensions. In particular, they are not approximated as the limit of the entropies of approximating discrete distributions. For example, the H_1 entropy of the uniform distribution on an interval of length L equals $\log L$ by the above definition, whereas the entropy of the approximating discrete distribution with mass $1/n$ at each point $(k - \frac{1}{2})/nL$ $(k = 1, \ldots, n)$ equals log n, which $\to \infty$ as $n \to \infty$. For uniform distributions on cubes in $\mathbb{R}^d$ with side-length L, the H_1 entropy equals $d \log L$ and the H entropy equals $d \log n = \log(n^d) = \log(\# \text{ points used in discrete approximation})$.

Intuitively, this lack of agreement between H and its "limit" H_1 can be regarded as stemming from the unreasonable requirement that the real-valued random variable is specified exactly in the sense that all digits in its decimal representation are known, thus conveying infinite information. Formally, the difficulty can be resolved by considering *relative* or *generalized entropies*, an approach that also permits the definition of the entropy of a distribution on a general probability space. Suppose that $(\Omega, \mathscr{E}, \mu)$ is a measure space, and $\mathscr{P} \ll \mu$ is a probability distribution on this space. Then the generalized entropy of $\mathscr{P}$ with respect to the reference measure μ is given by

$$(13.5.6) \qquad H(\mathscr{P}; \mu) = -\int_\Omega \Lambda(\omega) \log \Lambda(\omega)\, \mu(d\omega) = -E_\mathscr{P}(\log \Lambda),$$

where $\Lambda(\omega) = (d\mathscr{P}/d\mu)(\omega)$ is the Radon–Nikodym derivative of $\mathscr{P}$ with respect to μ. If $\mathscr{P}$ is singular with respect to μ, we set $\mathscr{H}(\mathscr{P}; \mu) = \infty$. Clearly, the entropy H_1 defined earlier is the generalized entropy of the distribution with density f with respect to Lebesgue measure on $\mathbb{R}$. However, if we take the generalized entropy of the approximating discrete distribution with respect to the corresponding discrete approximation to the reference measure μ, the offending terms involving $\log n$ cancel, and the limit $H(\mathscr{P}; \mu)$ is the limit of the sequence of discrete approximations $H(\mathscr{P}_n; \mu_n)$.

Consider now the entropy of a finite point process. Observation of the process conveys information of two kinds: the actual number of points observed and the location of these points given their number. This suggests defining the entropy of a realization $\{x_1, \ldots, x_N\}$ as

$$(13.5.7) \quad H = H(N) + E(H(x_1, \ldots, x_N | N))$$

$$= -\sum_{k=0}^{\infty} p_k \log p_k$$

$$\quad - \sum_{k=1}^{\infty} p_k \int \pi_k^{(\text{sym})}(x_1, \ldots, x_k) \log(k!\,\pi_k^{(\text{sym})}(x_1, \ldots, x_k))\, dx_1 \cdots dx_k.$$

Here we have used the notation of Section 5.3, with the factor $k!$ arising, just as in the discussion of likelihoods, from the fact that only unordered point sets can be distinguished. Rudemo (1964) and McFadden (1965) introduced point process entropy effectively in this form. Note that, from this definition,

$$H = -E\{\log[p_N N!\,\pi_N^{(\text{sym})}(x_1, \ldots, x_N)]\}$$

$$= -E\{\log[j_N(x_1, \ldots, x_N)]\} = -E(\log L),$$

where L is the likelihood defined in Section 13.1. When the point process has as its state space a finite interval $(0, T]$ of $\mathbb{R}$, the results of the same section can be used to represent the likelihood L in terms of the internal conditional intensity here denoted λ^+ to distinguish it from the complete intensity function λ^*. We obtain

(13.5.8) $$H \equiv H_{(0,T]} = -E\left(\sum_{i=1}^{N(T)} \log \lambda^+(t_i) - \int_0^T \lambda^+(t)dt\right).$$

Since the first term can be written in the form

$$\int_0^T \log \lambda^+(t)dN(t),$$

and $\lambda^+(t)$ can be assumed to be $\mathcal{H}$-predictable, (13.5.8) simplifies to

(13.5.9) $$H_{(0,T]} = -E_{\mathcal{P}}\left[\int_0^T \lambda^+(t)\log(\lambda^+(t))dt\right] + \int_0^T m(t)dt.$$

When the process is Poisson with constant intensity μ we have in particular

(13.5.10) $$H_{(0,T]}^P = -\mu T \log T + \mu T.$$

It can be checked that (13.5.10) gives the maximum entropy for a given mean rate μ (see Exercise 13.5.2).

For the purpose of defining the generalized entropy of a point process, the Poisson process provides a convenient reference measure. Let $\mathcal{P}_T$ and $\mathcal{P}_{\mu,T}$ denote the measures induced on the space $\mathcal{N}_{(0,T]}$ by a general point process (with distribution $\mathcal{P}$) and the Poisson process with rate μ, respectively. By noting that when $\mathcal{P}_T \ll \mathcal{P}_{\mu,T}$

$$H(\mathcal{P}_T; \mathcal{P}_{\mu,T}) = -E_{\mathcal{P}}(\log(L_1/L_0)) = -E_{\mathcal{P}}(\log L_1) + E_{\mathcal{P}}(\log L_0),$$

where L_1 and L_0 refer to the likelihoods under $\mathcal{P}_T$ and $\mathcal{P}_{\mu,T}$, respectively, it follows that

$$H(\mathcal{P}_T; \mathcal{P}_{\mu,T}) = -E_{\mathcal{P}}\left[\int_0^T \lambda^+(t)\log(\lambda^+(t)/\mu)dt\right] + \int_0^T m(t)dt - \mu T.$$

This expression simplifies still further if we take $\mu = 1$ and replace the probability measure $\mathcal{P}_{1,T}$ by the renormalized measure $\mathcal{Q}_T = e^T \mathcal{P}_{1,T}$, since it then reduces to (13.5.9), a result we record more formally below.

Proposition 13.5.VI. *Let N be a simple point process on $(0, T]$, with finite mean rate $m(t)$ and $\mathcal{H}$-intensity $\lambda^+(t)$, and let $\mathcal{P}_T$ denote the distribution of N on $(\mathcal{N}_{(0,T]}, \mathcal{B}(\mathcal{N}_{(0,T]}))$ and $\mathcal{Q}_T$ the renormalized measure of the Poisson process at unit rate on $(0, T]$. Then the entropy $H_{(0,T]}$ at (13.5.9) equals the generalized entropy $H(\mathcal{P}_T; \mathcal{Q}_T)$.*

The benefit we gain from viewing (13.5.9) as a generalized entropy is that it suggests other possibilities such as discrete approximations. One method is based on partitioning the state space rather than the probability space. Let

$$\{\mathcal{T}_n\} = \{\{A_{ni}: i = 1, \ldots, k_n\}: n = 1, 2, \ldots\}$$

be a dissecting system of nested partitions of $\mathcal{X}$. Then for each n we can compute the entropies of the joint distributions of the discrete random variables $\{Z_{ni}\} \equiv \{N(A_{ni})\}$, first for the given point process, and second for the Poisson process at unit rate. From these in turn we can compute the generalized entropy of the distribution of the given point process with respect to that of the second, renormalizing the latter by the same factor e^T. Then, as Fritz (1973) has shown more generally, these discrete generalized entropies converge to (13.5.9) in the limit as $n \to \infty$. Indeed, for a simple point process a similar result holds for the corresponding indicator variables $Y_{ni} = I_{\{N(A_{ni})>0\}}$ (see Exercise 13.5.4).

We return to the question of defining an entropy rate that here is a question of determining the limit, if any, of the averages $T^{-1}H_{(0, T]}$ with $H_{(0, T]}$ defined as in (13.5.9). Stronger statements, analogous to MacMillan's theorem for a discrete ergodic source with finite alphabet (e.g., see Billingsley, 1965) can also be made. Here, the basic statements assert the convergence not only of the expectation in (13.5.9) but also of the log likelihoods $T^{-1} \log L_{(0, T]}$, either a.s. or in L_1 norm. We follow Papangelou (1978) in deriving the L_1 version of the result, from which the convergence of the entropies follows as a simple corollary.

As in the classical theory there are two main steps in the proof: first, establish the convergence of pseudo-likelihoods in which the complete intensity plays the role of the intrinsic intensity, and second, show that the difference between the true and pseudo-likelihood is asymptotically negligible. These two steps are set out in the next two lemmas.

Lemma 13.5.VII. *Suppose $E(\lambda^*(0) \log \lambda^*(0)) < \infty$ for a simple stationary point process N. Then as $T \to \infty$,*

$$(13.5.11) \qquad T^{-1} \int_0^T \log \lambda^*(t)dN(t) \to E(\lambda^*(0)\log \lambda^*(0)|\mathscr{I})$$

a.s. and in L_1 norm, where $\mathscr{I}$ is the σ-algebra of invariant events.

PROOF. Because N is stationary, the process $\lambda^*(t)$ is stationary. Also, $\lambda^*(t)$ is $\mathscr{H}^*$-predictable so the set function

$$\xi(A) = \int_A \log \lambda^*(u)N(du) \quad (\text{bounded } A \in \mathscr{B})$$

may be regarded as a stationary random signed measure with mean density $m = E(\lambda^*(0)\log \lambda^*(0))$. The result (13.5.11) then follows from the a.e. and L_1-ergodic results of Proposition 10.2.II [this involves noting that the two processes

$$\xi_+(A) = \int_A (\log \lambda^*(u))_+ N(du),$$

$$\xi_-(A) = \int_A (\log \lambda^*(u))_- N(du)$$

are both nonnegative measures to which the theorems apply directly, with the finiteness of $E|\lambda^*(0)\log \lambda^*(0)|$ following from $x \log x \geq -e^{-1}$ $(x \geq 0)$ and the finiteness assumption in the lemma]. $\qquad\square$

In the next result the monotone family of σ-algebras $\{\mathcal{H}_{(-T,0)}\}$ generated by $\{N(t): -T < t < 0\}$, which increase as $T \to \infty$ to $\mathcal{H}_{0-}^*$, plays a key role. First, the nonnegativity of $\lambda \equiv \lambda^*(0)$ and assumed finiteness of $E(\lambda \log \lambda)$ ensure that $E(\lambda) < \infty$. Next, the family $\{\lambda_T: 0 < T < \infty\}$, where

(13.5.12) $$\lambda_T = E(\lambda^*(0)| \mathcal{H}_{(-T,0)}),$$

constitutes a martingale, which by definition and the finiteness of $E(\lambda)$ is uniformly integrable, so $\lambda_T \to \lambda$ both a.e. and in L_1 norm by the martingale convergence theorem. Furthermore, since the function $x \log x$ is convex in x, we have by Jensen's inequality that

$$\infty > E(\lambda \log \lambda) = E(E(\lambda \log \lambda | \mathcal{H}_{(-T,0)}))$$
$$\geq E(\lambda_T \log \lambda_T),$$

and since $x \log x \geq -e^{-1}$ (all $x \geq 0$), it follows that $E(\lambda_T \log \lambda_T)$ is well defined and finite.

Lemma 13.5.VIII. *Under the conditions of Lemma 13.5.VII, with λ_T as at (13.5.12),*

(13.5.13) $\quad E|\lambda^*(0)\log \lambda^*(0) - \lambda^*(0)\log \lambda_T| \to 0 \quad$ *as $T \to \infty$.*

PROOF. Since $\lambda_T \to \lambda$ in distribution and $\infty > E(\lambda \log \lambda) \geq E(\lambda_T \log \lambda_T)$, and since $0 \leq \lambda \log(\lambda_T/\lambda)I\{\lambda_T > \lambda\} \leq \lambda(\lambda_T/\lambda - 1) = \lambda_T - \lambda$ for which $\lambda_T \to \lambda$ in L_1 norm, it is enough to show that $E(\lambda_T \log \lambda_T) \to E(\lambda \log \lambda)$. Let $x \geq 1$ be a continuity point of the distribution of λ; then for sufficiently large x we can certainly make

$$E(\lambda \log \lambda\, I\{\lambda > x\}) < \varepsilon$$

for arbitrary $\varepsilon > 0$. Now

$$E(\max(x \log x, \lambda_T \log \lambda_T))$$
$$= E(\max\{x \log x, E(\lambda|\mathcal{H}_{(-T,0)})\log(E(\lambda|\mathcal{H}_{(-T,0)}))\})$$
$$\leq E(\max\{x \log x, \lambda \log \lambda\})$$

by Jensen's inequality because $\max(x \log x, y \log y)$ is convex in $y > 0$ for $x \geq 0$. Since x is a continuity point for λ with $x \geq 1$,

$$0 \leq E(\lambda_T \log \lambda_T\, I\{\lambda_T > x\})$$
$$= E(\max\{x \log x, \lambda_T \log \lambda_T\}) - x \log x\, \Pr\{\lambda_T \leq x\}$$
$$\leq E(\max\{x \log x, \lambda \log \lambda\}) - x \log x\, \Pr\{\lambda_T \leq x\}$$

$$\to E(\max\{x \log x, \lambda \log \lambda\}) - x \log x \operatorname{Pr}\{\lambda \le x\}$$
$$= E(\lambda \log \lambda I\{\lambda > x\}) < \varepsilon$$

with the convergence holding uniformly for T sufficiently large. $\square$

Theorem 13.5.IX. *Let the simple stationary point process N admit $\mathcal{H}^*$-predictable complete intensity $\lambda^*(t)$ and $\mathcal{H}$-predictable conditional intensity $\lambda^+(t)$ on $t \ge 0$ and be such that*

$$H = -E[\lambda^*(0)(\log \lambda^*(0) - 1)]$$

is finite, so that $m = E(\lambda^*(0))$ is finite also. Then

(13.5.14) $$T^{-1}H_{(0, T]} \to H \quad as \ T \to \infty,$$

and

(13.5.15) $$T^{-1} \log L_{(0, T)} \to E(Z|\mathcal{I}) \quad in \ L_1 \ norm,$$

where $Z = \lambda^*(0)(\log \lambda^*(0) - 1)$ and $\mathcal{I}$ denotes the σ-algebra of invariant events for N.

PROOF. Convergence as in (13.5.14) follows from the definition of $H_{(0, T]}$, H, and the conditions and results of the last two lemmas. To prove (13.5.15) consider the difference

(13.5.16) $$E|T^{-1} \log L_{(0, T)} - E(Z|\mathcal{I})|,$$

which by virtue of the triangle inequality is dominated by $T_1 + T_2 + T_3 + T_4$, where

$$T_1 = T^{-1}E\left| \int_0^T \log \lambda^+(t)dN(t) - \int_0^T \log \lambda^*(t)dN(t) \right|,$$

$$T_2 = T^{-1}E\left| \int_0^T \lambda^+(t)dt - \int_0^T \lambda^*(t)dt \right|,$$

$$T_3 = E\left| T^{-1} \int_0^T \log \lambda^*(t)dN(t) - E(\lambda^*(0) \log \lambda^*(0)|\mathcal{I}) \right|,$$

$$T_4 = E\left| T^{-1} \int_0^T \lambda^*(t)dt - E(\lambda^*(0)|\mathcal{I}) \right|.$$

Here, $T_3 \to 0$ by Lemma 13.5.VII, while applying the ergodic theorem to the stationary process $\lambda^*(t)$ implies that $T_4 \to 0$. Since $\lambda^+(t)$ and $\lambda^*(t)$ are respectively $\mathcal{H}$- and $\mathcal{H}^*$-predictable by assumption, both are $\mathcal{H}^*$-predictable, and thus T_1 is dominated by

$$T^{-1}E \int_0^T |\log \lambda^+(t) - \log \lambda^*(t)| \lambda^*(t)dt.$$

Recall from Proposition 13.3.I that $\lambda^+(t)$ can be replaced by a suitably chosen version of $E(\lambda^*(t)|\mathscr{H}_{t-})$ without altering the value of the integrals in T_1 and T_2. Using stationarity, replace $(0, T)$ by $(-T, 0)$, which leads to

$$T_1' = T^{-1}E \int_{-T}^{0} |\log E(\lambda^*(t)|\mathscr{H}_{(-T,t)}) - \log \lambda^*(t)|\lambda^*(t)dt,$$

$$T_2' = T^{-1}E \int_{-T}^{0} |E(\lambda^*(t)|\mathscr{H}_{(-T,t)}) - \lambda^*(t)|dt.$$

For each fixed t, the expectation of the first integrand $\to 0$ as $T \to \infty$ by Lemma 13.5.VIII and stationarity, so the $(C, 1)$ mean also converges to zero. In the proof of the same lemma, the expectation of the second integrand also converges to zero, so the $(C, 1)$ mean does also. $\qquad\square$

The result of this theorem justifies the definition of entropy rate as follows.

Definition 13.5.X. The *entropy rate* of a stationary point process satisfying the conditions of Theorem 13.5.IX is the quantity

$$H = -E(\lambda^*(0)(\log \lambda^*(0) - 1)).$$

Clearly, H as so defined is a rate per unit time. In view of Proposition 13.5.VI, it can also be regarded as a rate for the generalized entropy of the given point process relative to the renormalized version of the Poisson process. Indeed, it is straightforward to prove from that proposition that under the conditions of Theorem 13.5.IX,

$$T^{-1}H(\mathscr{P}_T; \mathscr{Q}_T) \to H \qquad (T \to \infty).$$

More generally, if $\mathscr{P}_\mu$ is the probability measure on $\mathscr{N}_{\mathbb{R}_+}$ induced by the Poisson process with rate parameter μ,

$$H(\mathscr{P}; \mathscr{P}_\mu) \equiv \lim_{T\to\infty} T^{-1}H(\mathscr{P}_T; \mathscr{P}_{\mu,T}) = H + m \log \mu - \mu.$$

A different approach is to ask for entropy rates associated with the point process on $\mathbb{R}$ in its dual form as a stationary process of intervals. Extensions of McMillan's theorem from its original context of a discrete time finite-alphabet source (i.e., a finite state space stochastic process) to stationary sequences of random variables with arbitrary distributions have been given by Perez (1959) and can be applied directly to the process of intervals. In particular, Perez showed that if $\{X_n: n = 0, \pm 1, \ldots\}$ is a stationary sequence of r.v.s taking their values on the c.s.m.s. $\mathscr{X}$, if Π is a fixed totally finite or σ-finite measure on $\mathscr{X}$, and if the fidi distributions F_k of order k of the sequence are absolutely continuous with respect to the k-fold product measure $\Pi^{(k)} = \Pi \times \cdots \times \Pi$ on $(\mathscr{X}^{(k)}, \mathscr{B}(\mathscr{X}^{(k)}))$, then

$$-n^{-1} \log[dF_k(X_1, \ldots, X_n)/d\Pi^{(k)}(X_1, \ldots, X_n)] \to E(Z|\mathscr{I}),$$

where the invariant r.v. Z has expectation (finite or infinite)

$$E(Z) = E\left\{\int_0^\infty \frac{dF(x|\mathcal{H}^*_{(-1)})}{\Pi(dx)} \log\left(\frac{dF(x|\mathcal{H}^*_{(-1)})}{\Pi(dx)}\right)\Pi(dx)\right\}$$

$$= E\int_0^\infty \log(dF(x|\mathcal{H}^*_{(-1)})/\Pi(dx))dF(x|\mathcal{H}^*_{(-1)}),$$

where $dF(x|\mathcal{H}^*_{(-1)})$ is a regular version of the conditional distribution of X_0 given the sequence of past values $\{X_{-1}, X_{-2}, \ldots\}$ which generate $\mathcal{H}^*_{(-1)}$. This result can be applied directly to our context if we take $\Pi(dx) = \mu e^{-\mu x}\,dx$ ($x \ge 0$), that is, the stationary interval distribution on $\mathbb{R}_+$ associated with the Poisson process with constant mean rate μ. This leads to the result that

$$H_I(\mathcal{P}; \mathcal{P}_\mu) = -E_0\left(\int_0^\infty f(x|\tau)\log f(x|\tau)dx\right) + \log\mu - \frac{\mu}{m},$$

where $f(\cdot|\tau)$ is the conditional density introduced in Corollary 13.5.V and H_I is used to denote an "interval entropy rate." If, in particular, we take $\mu = 1$ and use $\mathcal{Q}$ to denote the measure corresponding to $\Pi(dx) = e^{-x+1/m}\,dx$, we have similarly that

$$H_I \equiv H_I(\mathcal{P}; \mathcal{Q}) = -E_0\left(\int_0^\infty f(x|\tau)\log f(x|\tau)dx\right).$$

This interval entropy rate is easily related to the entropy rate H by appealing to Corollary 13.5.V. As in the proof of Lemma 13.5.IV, for any function $h(T, \tau)$ of the backward recurrence time T and the past sequence τ,

$$Eh(T, \tau) = mE_0\int_0^{\tau_0} h(\tau_0 - x, \tau)dx$$

$$= mE_0\int_0^\infty f(y|\tau)dy\int_0^y h(x, \tau)dx$$

$$= mE_0\int_0^\infty h(x, \tau)[1 - F(x|\tau)]dx.$$

Now by taking for $h(T, \tau)$ the function

$$f(T|\tau)[1 - F(T|\tau)]^{-1}\log\{f(T|\tau)[1 - F(T|\tau)]^{-1}\},$$

it follows from Corollary 13.5.V that

$$E(\lambda^*(0)\log\lambda^*(0)) = mE_0\left(\int_0^\infty f(x|\tau)\log f(x|\tau)dx\right.$$

$$\left. -\int_0^\infty \log(1 - F(x|\tau))f(x|\tau)dx\right)$$

$$= mE_0\left(\int_0^\infty f(x|\tau)\log f(x|\tau)dx + 1\right).$$

and hence

$$H = -E(\lambda*(0)\log \lambda*(0) - \lambda*(0))$$

$$= -mE_0\left(\int_0^\infty f(x|\tau)\log f(x|\tau)dx\right) = mH_I.$$

Thus, $H(\mathscr{P}; \mathscr{P}_\mu) = mH_I(\mathscr{P}; \mathscr{P}_\mu)$, which leads to the following statement.

Proposition 13.5.XI. *For a simple stationary point process with mean rate m, the entropy rate per unit time equals m times the entropy rate per interval.*

Exercises

13.5.1. Find explicitly the form of the complete intensity function for a Wold process with transition kernel $P(x, A)$.

13.5.2. (a) Show that the Poisson distribution maximizes the sum

$$-\sum_{k=0}^\infty p_k \log(k! \, p_k)$$

subject to the conditions

$$\sum_{k=0}^\infty p_k = 1, \qquad \sum_{k=0}^\infty kp_k = \mu, \qquad p_k \geq 0.$$

(b) Deduce that for a regular point process on a bounded interval $D \subset \mathbb{R}^d$ with $E(N(D)) = \mu = $ constant, the point process entropy (13.5.7) is maximized when the process is Poisson with uniform mean rate over D. [*Hint*: Start by writing (13.5.7) in the form

$$-H = \sum p_k \log(k!p_k) + \sum p_k \int_{D^{(k)}} \pi_k(\mathbf{y})\log \pi_k(\mathbf{y})d\mathbf{y}.$$

Now use (a) together with the fact that, conditional on k, the integral is maximized, subject to $\int \pi_k(\mathbf{y})d\mathbf{y} = 1$, when $\pi_k(\mathbf{y})$ reduces to a uniform distribution over $D^{(k)}$.]

13.5.3. Let $(\Omega, \mathscr{E}, \mu)$ be a measure space and $\mathscr{P}$ a probability measure on $(\Omega, \mathscr{E})$ with $\mathscr{P} \ll \mu$. Let $\{\mathscr{A}_\alpha\}$ be a family of finite or countable subalgebras of $\mathscr{E}$. Define the generalized entropies $H(\mathscr{P}; \mu)$, $H(\mathscr{P}_\alpha; \mu_\alpha)$ by

$$-H(\mathscr{P}; \mu) = \int \frac{d\mathscr{P}}{d\mu} \log \frac{d\mathscr{P}}{d\mu}\mu(d\omega) = \int \log \frac{d\mathscr{P}}{d\mu}\mathscr{P}(d\omega),$$

$$-H(\mathscr{P}_\alpha; \mu_\alpha) = \sum_j \mathscr{P}(U_{\alpha j})\log \frac{\mathscr{P}(U_{\alpha j})}{\mu(U_{\alpha j})},$$

where $\{U_{\alpha j}\}$ is an irreducible (and countable) partition generating $\mathscr{A}_\alpha$.
(i) If $\mathscr{A}_\alpha \subseteq \mathscr{A}_\beta$ then $H(\mathscr{P}_\alpha; \mu_\alpha) \geq H(\mathscr{P}_\beta; \mu_\beta)$.
(ii) If $\{\mathscr{A}_\alpha\}$ generates $\mathscr{E}$, then

$$-H(\mathscr{P}; \mu) = \inf_\alpha \{-H(\mathscr{P}_\alpha; \mu_\alpha)\}.$$

(iii) Let $\mathscr{P}_T$, $\mathscr{Q}_T$ be defined as in Proposition 13.5.VI, and suppose that $\{\mathscr{T}_\alpha\}$ is a family of finite or countable partitions of the interval $(0, T]$, so that

$\mathcal{T}_\alpha = \{A_{\alpha i}: i = 1, \ldots, K_\alpha\}$ such that $\{\mathcal{T}_\alpha\}$ generates $\mathcal{B}((0, T])$. Let $\mathcal{A}_\alpha$ be the algebra of events generated by $Z_{\alpha i} = N(A_{\alpha i})$. Show that

$$-H(\mathcal{P}_T; \mathcal{Q}_T) = \inf_\alpha \{-H(\mathcal{P}_{\alpha T}; \mathcal{Q}_{\alpha T})\},$$

where

$$-H(\mathcal{P}_{\alpha T}; \mathcal{Q}_{\alpha T}) = \sum_{\mathbf{n}} p_{\alpha \mathbf{n}} \log\left(\frac{p_{\alpha \mathbf{n}}}{q_{\alpha \mathbf{n}}}\right),$$

$\mathbf{n} = (n_1, \ldots, n_{K_\alpha})$, $p_{\alpha \mathbf{n}} = \mathcal{P}\{Z_{\alpha i} = n_i, i = 1, \ldots, K_\alpha\}$, $q_{\alpha \mathbf{n}} = \prod_{i=1}^{K_\alpha} \ell(A_{\alpha i})^{n_i}$. [This result provides a discrete approximation to generalized entropy. See Csiszar (1969) and Fritz (1969).]

13.5.4. (a) Show that $H(\mathcal{P}_T; \mathcal{Q}_T)$ can also be characterized as

$$-H(\mathcal{P}_T; \mathcal{Q}_T) = \inf_\alpha \{\textstyle\sum p_{\alpha \mathbf{n}} \log p_{\alpha \mathbf{n}} - T \log \delta_\alpha\},$$

where $\delta_\alpha = \max_i \mu(A_{\alpha i})$.
(b) Show also that

$$-H(\mathcal{P}_T; \mathcal{Q}_T) = \inf_\alpha \left[\pi_{\alpha \mathbf{n}} \log\left(\frac{\pi_{\alpha \mathbf{n}}}{q_{\alpha \mathbf{n}}}\right) + \sum_{i=1}^{K_\alpha} \mathcal{P}\{Z_{\alpha i} \geq 1\} \log \mu(A_{\alpha i}) \right],$$

where $\pi_{\alpha \mathbf{n}} = \mathcal{P}\{Y_{\alpha i} = n_i, i = 1, \ldots, K_\alpha\}$ for $n_i = 0$ or 1 and $Y_{\alpha i} = I_{\{N(A_{\alpha i}) > 0\}}$. [Hint: Show first that if $\mathcal{T}_\alpha \subseteq \mathcal{T}_\beta$ and each set $A_{\alpha i}$ of $\mathcal{T}_\alpha$ is a union of no more than r sets of $\mathcal{T}_\beta$, then

$$\textstyle\sum p_{\alpha \mathbf{n}} \log p_{\alpha \mathbf{n}} \leq \sum p_{\beta \mathbf{n}} \log p_{\beta \mathbf{n}} \leq \sum p_{\alpha \mathbf{n}} \log p_{\alpha \mathbf{n}} + T \log r.$$

See Fritz (1973) for further details. This result shows that in some sense $E(N(0, T])$ plays the role of a dimension for the process, as in Renyi's (1959) discussion of "dimensional entropy."]

13.5.5. Generalize the results of the last two exercises to the case of a general space $\mathcal{X}$ with Poisson distribution having nonatomic parameter measure $\mu(\cdot)$.

13.5.6. Calculate the entropy rate for stationary renewal processes when the lifetime d.f. has unit mean and is (a) exponential on $(0, \infty)$; (b) uniform on $(0, 2)$; (c) piecewise uniform on (a, b) and (b, c); and (d) triangular.

13.5.7. The entropy rate of a stationary renewal process with absolutely continuous lifetime d.f. with density $f(\cdot)$ equals $m \int_0^\infty f(x) \log f(x) dx$, where $m^{-1} = \int_0^\infty x f(x) dx$. One technique used in approximating the behaviour of a stationary point process N on $\mathbb{R}$ (e.g., for simulation purposes) is to replace N by the renewal process whose lifetime d.f. coincides with the stationary interval distribution. Use Proposition 13.5.XI to show that the entropy rate of such an approximating stationary renewal process is larger than that of N.

CHAPTER 14

Exterior Conditioning

In this last chapter we introduce what is perhaps the most recent intertwining of the strands of point process theory. Here it is a combination of ideas from statistical mechanics on the one hand with those of Palm theory and conditional intensities on the other. By exterior conditioning we mean conditioning of the point process on its behaviour outside a bounded set. In this sense the theory forms a kind of dual to the Palm theory, which is concerned with conditioning on the behaviour within a bounded set.

The first of the three sections provides background and motivation from the physical setting, while the other two sections give a more rigorous account of some of the principal results under some simplifying assumptions.

14.1. Motivation

A very simple statistical mechanical process was described in Example 5.3(c), where it was specified through Janossy densities of the form

$$(14.1.1) \qquad j_k(x_1, \ldots, x_k) = C \exp \left\{ \sum_{i=1}^{k} \psi_1(x_i) + \sum_{i=2}^{k} \sum_{j=1}^{i-1} \psi_2(x_i, x_j) \right\}.$$

The functions $\psi_1(\cdot)$, $\psi_2(\cdot)$ here were interpreted as *interaction potentials* and the expression in the exponent as some measure of *energy* of the system, under equilibrium conditions, when it happens that k particles of the system are located at points $x_1, \ldots, x_k$. Although the process here involves only first- and second-order potentials, in principle one can consider a.s. finite processes defined similarly in terms of potentials of arbitrary order: all that is needed to ensure that the process is well defined is an integrability condition sufficient both for the Janossy measures $J_k(\mathscr{X}^{(k)})$ to be finite and for their weighted sum over all k to be finite also. Conversely, given a process specified through a family of positive Janossy densities, Equations (14.1.1) can be solved successively for the functions $\psi_1(\cdot)$, $\psi_2(\cdot)$, ... to produce an alternative description in terms of interaction potentials (see Exercise 5.3.7).

In the finite case, therefore, no essentially new point process ideas are involved, and the main interest lies in developing further properties of particular processes specified through interactions of physically relevant form. The situation changes radically, however, if we try to specify the distribution of an *infinite* particle system in terms of interaction potentials. Certainly, (14.1.1) can no longer be used to describe the distribution because the Janossy densities, while existing in a local sense, no longer exist in a global sense, and in any case sums such as those in the exponent of (14.1.1) will diverge in general for $k \to \infty$.

The approach adopted by physicists in this situation has been to take a bounded subset, B say, of the state space, and to suppose that the particles in B are in equilibrium with both the "external" interaction forces exerted on them by the particles outside B and the "internal" interaction forces generated among themselves. Equations such as (14.1.1) can then be used to describe the conditions for local equilibrium, conditional on the configuration of particles outside B. Taking expectations over all possible exterior configurations leads to a family of balance equations that must be satisfied by the overall equilibrium distribution of the process, if in fact such a distribution exists (and this last proviso is an important qualifier).

For example, suppose that exactly one particle lies in B and that the process is to be specified through the given functions ψ_1 and ψ_2 as in (14.1.1). Then, conditional on the external configuration, which we denote by $B^c N$, the local Janossy densities for the process on B must be of the form

$$(14.1.2) \quad j_1^B(y|B^c N) = C_B \exp\left\{\psi_1(y) + \sum_{x_i \in \text{supp}(B^c N)} \psi_2(y, x_i)\right\} \qquad (y \in B),$$

where the normalization constant is now C_B, and we must require $\int_{B^c} \psi_2(y, x) dN(x)$ to converge for all $N \in \mathscr{N}(B^c)$. To obtain a convenient form for the balance equations, multiply by a function $f(y, \eta)$ mapping $(y, \eta) \in B \times \mathscr{N}(B^c)$ into $\mathbb{R}$ and take expectations over $B^c N$. This leads to

$$(14.1.3) \qquad \int_{\mathscr{N}(B^c)} \int_B f(y, \eta) j_1^B(y|\eta) \mathscr{P}_{B^c}(d\eta)$$

$$= \int_{\mathscr{N}(\mathscr{X})} \int_B f(y, B^c N) N(dy) I_{\{N(B)=1\}}(N) \mathscr{P}(dN),$$

where $\mathscr{P}$ is the equilibrium distribution assumed to exist for the process as a whole, and $\mathscr{P}_{B^c}$ is its projection onto the space of boundedly finite point processes with support in B^c.

Whether or not, given functions $\psi_i(\cdot)$, there exists an equilibrium distribution $\mathscr{P}$ satisfying (14.1.3) and related equations, is far from obvious. Indeed, it is nothing other than a general version of the *Ising problem*, which in its original and special form referred to the existence of an equilibrium distribution for a process on a one-dimensional lattice specified by interactions of pairs of points involving only nearest neighbours. The general problem, even in the lattice case, is still unsolved, although many partial results are available [e.g., see Preston (1976) for a general formulation of the Ising problem and a review of results known then]. In particular, it is known that even when an equilibrium distribution exists, it may not be unique (leading to the possibility of "phase transitions"), and that even when the interaction potentials are spatially stationary in character (i.e., they depend only on the relative positions of the particles), the resulting solutions may not be stationary (this is known as "symmetry breakdown"). It is not our intention, however, to pursue the Ising problem as such, but rather to pursue the question of *how the description of a point process model in terms of conditional Janossy densities of the form* (14.1.3) *can be related to other characteristics of the point process.*

One special feature of (14.1.2) is worth noting at this stage. For given location y and $\{x_i: i = 1, 2, \ldots\}$, the function at (14.1.2) is dependent on the set B only through the normalization constant C_B and the requirements that $y \in B$, $x_i \in B^c$ $(i = 1, 2, \ldots)$. We are therefore led to let $B \downarrow \{y\}$ to obtain an expression for what we call the *Papangelou intensity*, namely, the conditional intensity for the occurrence of a particle at y given the realization of the process throughout the remainder of the state space, that is, in $\mathscr{X} \setminus \{y\}$. Physically, the term in the exponent at (14.1.2) can be related to the work required to introduce a new particle into the position y keeping the locations of the existing particles fixed. Given this function, it seems plausible (though in fact it is not true without some further conditions) that the general form for the equilibrium configuration inside a set B could be built up by successively introducing new particles, one at a time, each time making use of the Papangelou intensity. This leads to a multiplicative form for the local Janossy densities, which indeed is already implicit in expressions like (14.1.2) and its higher-order analogues.

Before considering such questions in general, we illustrate the nature of the results by returning to the a.s. finite case and setting out the most important properties of the Papangelou intensity when the process is specified in terms of its Janossy densities. In this case the required conditional density is just the ratio

$$(14.1.4) \qquad \rho(y|x_1, \ldots, x_k) = j_{k+1}(y, x_1, \ldots, x_k)/j_k(x_1, \ldots, x_k),$$

provided that the denominator is positive. Indeed,

$$\Pr\{\text{realization contains } k + 1 \text{ particles in } (y, y + dy), (x_i, x_i + dx_i)$$

$$(i = 1, \ldots k)\}$$

$$= (1 + o(1))j_{k+1}(y, x_1, \ldots, x_k)dy\, dx_1 \cdots dx_k,$$

with a similar interpretation for j_k, so in heuristic terms it is clear that (14.1.4) represents the required conditional density.

Higher-order Papangelou intensities can be defined in a similar fashion, representing the conditional intensities of finding particles inside B at $y_1, \ldots, y_l$ given particles outside B at locations $x_1, \ldots, x_k$, and again these are given by ratios of the Janossy densities, supposing as always that the denominators are positive:

$$(14.1.5) \quad p(y_1, \ldots, y_l | x_1, \ldots, x_k) = j_{k+l}(y_1, \ldots, y_l, x_1, \ldots, x_k) / j_k(x_1, \ldots, x_k).$$

These ratios have a number of interesting properties, which are quite elementary to establish from the defining relation (14.1.5) and which indicate the main results to be expected in the general case. For compactness here we write $x_1, \ldots, x_n$ as $x_{1(1)n}$ in stating these properties:

(i) *Multiplicative Relation*

$$(14.1.6) \quad p(u_{1(1)l}, v_{1(1)m} | x_{1(1)k}) = p(u_{1(1)l} | v_{1(1)m}, x_{1(1)k}) p(v_{1(1)m} | x_{1(1)k}).$$

(ii) *Conditional Probability Interpretation*

For any bounded Borel set B with $y_{1(1)l} \in B$ and $x_{1(1)k} \in B^c$,

$$(14.1.7) \qquad p(y_{1(1)l} | x_{1(1)k}) \prod_{j=1}^{l} dy_j$$

$$= \frac{\Pr\{N(dy_j) = 1 \, (j = 1(1)l) | B^c N = \{x_{1(1)k}\}\}}{\Pr\{N(B) = 0 | B^c N = \{x_{1(1)k}\}\}}.$$

(iii) *Relation to Palm densities*

$$(14.1.8) \qquad p(y_{1(1)l} | x_{1(1)k}) = q(x_{1(1)k} | y_{1(1)l}) / q(\emptyset | y_{1(1)l}),$$

where $q(x_{1(1)k} | y)$ is the density on $(\mathcal{X} - \{y\})^{(k)}$ of the corresponding component of the local Palm distribution $\mathscr{P}_0(y, dN)$, and $q(x_{1(1)k} | y_{1(1)l})$ is defined similarly on $(\mathcal{X} - \{y_{1(1)l}\})^{(k)}$ from the higher-order Palm distribution $\mathscr{P}_0(y_{1(1)l}, dN)$ such as in Exercise 12.1.2 for the case $l = 2$. Here it is assumed that $E(N(\mathcal{X}^{(k)})) < \infty$, although in fact an identical expression will hold for any Palm measure (Kallenberg, 1983a, Chap. 12). To understand (14.1.8) first note that for any $y, x_{1(1)k}$ with $y \notin \{x_{1(1)k}\}$, we have for the simple (first-order) Palm density

$$q(x_{1(1)k} | y) = j_{k+1}(x_{1(1)k}, y) / h_1(y),$$

where

$$h_1(y) = \sum_{k=1}^{\infty} (k!)^{-1} \int_{\mathcal{X}^{(k)}} j_{k+1}(x_{1(1)k}, y) \prod_{i=1}^{k} dx_i$$

is the marginal or "coincidence" density for the probability of finding a point at y irrespective of the remainder of the configuration. Since we have also

$$q(\varnothing|y) = j_1(y)/h_1(y),$$

Equation (14.1.8) in the case $l = 1$ follows. The higher-order expressions are shown in a similar way.

(iv) *Integral Relations*

For bounded Borel functions $f(y_{1(1)l}, x_{1(1)k})$,

$$(14.1.9) \quad \int_{\mathscr{X}^{(l)}} \int_{\mathscr{X}^{(k)}} f(y_{1(1)l}, x_{1(1)k}) \rho(y_{1(1)l}|x_{1(1)k}) j_k(x_{1(1)k}) \prod_{i=1}^{k} dx_i \prod_{j=1}^{l} dy_j$$

$$= \int_{\mathscr{X}^{(l+k)}} f(y_{1(1)l}, x_{1(1)k}) j_{l+k}(y_{1(1)l}, x_{1(1)k}) \prod_{i=1}^{k} dx_i \prod_{j=1}^{l} dy_j.$$

This relation, like (14.1.6) and (14.1.7), follows trivially from the definition (14.1.5).

In the general case considered shortly, recognizing that conditional intensities or probabilities or expectations are stochastic quantities, it is necessary to distinguish three different random measures, each of which embodies some aspect of the conditional intensities $\rho(\cdot)$ above. These quantities are as follows:

(i) *Papangelou kernels* defined by integral relations extending (14.1.9).
(ii) A random measure $\pi(\cdot)$ describing, loosely speaking, the *atomic part of these kernels*.
(iii) The *Papangelou intensity measures* $\zeta(\cdot)$ as originally introduced by Papangelou (1974b) in terms of the limit

$$(14.1.10) \qquad \zeta(B) = \lim_{n \to \infty} \sum_{i=1}^{k_n} E(N(B_{ni})|B_{ni}^c N),$$

where $\{B_{ni}: i = 1, \ldots, k_n\}$ for $n = 1, 2, \ldots$ is a fixed dissecting system of partitions of B.

Our aim in the next two sections is to define these quantities precisely and exhibit links between them.

14.2. Modified Campbell Measures and Papangelou Kernels

What follows may be regarded as an introduction to the general theory to be found, for example, in Chapter 9 of the 1982 edition in Russian of MKM and subsequent developments in Kallenberg (1983a, Chaps. 12–14) (some misprints are corrected in the 1986 reprinting). Connections with statistical mechanics are explored in Nguyen and Zessin (1979), Matthes, Warmuth, and Mecke (1979), and Rauchenschwandtner (1980), among other papers. Our treatment has been much influenced by Kallenberg's work, especially the informal account in Kallenberg (1984).

Throughout, we assume that the point process is simple, and we consider the results indicated at the end of Section 14.1 in detail only for the first-order case.

Condition Σ below plays a fundamental role in all approaches to this topic, and we work under it unless explicitly stated otherwise.

Definition 14.2.I. The simple point process on the c.s.m.s. $\mathcal{X}$ satisfies Condition Σ if for all bounded Borel sets B,

$$(14.2.1) \qquad\qquad \mathcal{P}\{N(B) = 0 | B^c N\} > 0 \quad \text{a.s.}$$

This requirement generalizes the assumption of Section 14.1 that the Janossy densities be positive everywhere. Its essential role is to preclude situations where the behaviour inside B is deterministically controlled by the behaviour outside B.

In order to set down a general form of the integral equation (14.1.9) for the Papangelou kernel, introduce the *modified Campbell measure*[†] denoted $C^*_{\mathcal{P}}$ and defined for point processes by the equation

$$(14.2.2) \quad C^*_{\mathcal{P}}(A \times U) = E\left(\int_A I_U(N - \delta_y)N(dy)\right) \qquad (A \in \mathcal{B}_{\mathcal{X}}, U \in \mathcal{B}(\hat{\mathcal{N}}_{\mathcal{X}}))$$

[cf. (12.1.1)]. We write the Papangelou kernel itself as $\rho(A|N)$ for $A \in \mathcal{B}_{\mathcal{X}}$, $N \in \mathcal{N}_{\mathcal{X}}$, and derive it from a distintegration of the second component of $C^*_{\mathcal{P}}$ with respect to $\mathcal{P}$, namely,

$$(14.2.3) \quad \int_U \rho(A|N)\mathcal{P}(dN) = C^*_{\mathcal{P}}(A \times U) \quad \text{(all bounded } A \in \mathcal{B}_{\mathcal{X}}, U \in \mathcal{B}(\hat{\mathcal{N}}_{\mathcal{X}})).$$

To see the connection with (14.1.9), first think of the second argument of $\rho(y|x_1, \ldots, x_k)$ as a particular realization of N with k points, and then amalgamate the various equations (14.1.9) for $l = 1$ and different k into the single equation

$$(14.2.4) \quad \int\int f(y, N)\rho(y|N)dy\, \mathcal{P}(dN) = \int\int f(y, N - \delta_y)N(dy)\mathcal{P}(dN)$$

$$= \int\int f(y, N)C^*_{\mathcal{P}}(dy \times dN).$$

This exhibits the function ρ at (14.1.9) as coming from a disintegration of $C^*_{\mathcal{P}}$ in the special case and leads us to seek such a disintegration in general.

For such a relation to hold in general we need the absolute continuity condition that, for each fixed $A \in \mathcal{B}_{\mathcal{X}}$,

---

[†] Kallenberg (1983a, §12.3) uses the term "reduced Campbell measure," which we avoid here to eliminate any confusion with the term "reduced moment measure" used, for example, in Section 10.4.

(14.2.5) $$C_{\mathscr{P}}^*(A \times \cdot) \ll \mathscr{P}(\cdot).$$

The proof below of (14.2.5) gives us immediately a typical example of the role that Condition Σ plays. The proof also makes use of the following simple results.

Lemma 14.2.II. (a) *For any* $U \in \sigma\{N\} \subseteq \mathscr{B}(\mathscr{N}_{\mathscr{X}})$, *and any* $B \in \mathscr{B}_{\mathscr{X}}$,

(14.2.6) $U \cap \{N(B) = 0\} = U^* \cap \{N(B) = 0\}$ *for some* $U^* \in \sigma\{B^c N\}$.

(b) *For any* $\sigma\{N\}$-*measurable function* $g(N)$, *and any* $B \in \mathscr{B}_{\mathscr{X}}$,

(14.2.7) $$g(N)I_{\{N(B)=0\}}(N) = g_0(N)I_{\{N(B)=0\}}(N)$$

for some $\sigma\{B^c N\}$-*measurable function* $g_0(N)$, *and when* $E|g(N)| < \infty$, *for any bounded* $\sigma\{B^c N\}$-*measurable* Y,

(14.2.8) $E(Y(N)g(N)I_{\{N(B)=0\}}(N)) = E(Y(N)g_0(N)\mathscr{P}\{N(B) = 0|B^c N\}).$

PROOF. Any $U^* \in \sigma\{B^c N\}$ is generated by sets of the form $\{N(A_i) = j_i:$ $A_i \in \mathscr{B}(B^c)$, nonnegative integers $j_i\}$, and for any $U \in \sigma\{N\}$, $U \cap \{N(B) = 0\}$ is generated by sets of the form $\{N(B) = 0, N(A_i) = j_i: A \in \mathscr{B}(B^c), j_i = 0, 1,$ $\ldots\}$. This proves (a). (b) follows from (a) by the usual extension argument starting from indicator functions $I_U(N)$ for $U \in \sigma\{N\}$, for which $I_{U \cap \{N(B)=0\}} = I_{U^*}I_{\{N(B)=0\}}$ with $I_{U^*} \sigma\{B^c N\}$-measurable. $\qquad \square$

Proposition 14.2.III. *Let N be a simple point process on the c.s.m.s. $\mathscr{X}$ satisfying Condition Σ. Then for all bounded $A \in \mathscr{B}_{\mathscr{X}}$; the absolute continuity condition (14.2.5) holds.*

PROOF. We have to show that for any $U \in \mathscr{B}(\mathscr{N}_{\mathscr{X}})$ such that $\mathscr{P}(U) = 0$, $C_{\mathscr{P}}^*(A \times U) = 0$ (all bounded $A \in \mathscr{B}_{\mathscr{X}}$).

Suppose first that $U \subseteq \{N(A) = 0\}$, so that $U = U \cap \{N(A) = 0\}$, so by Lemma 14.2.II(a), $I_U(N) = I_{U^*}(N)I_{\{N(A)=0\}}(N)$ for some $U^* \in \sigma\{A^c N\}$. Noting that for $y \in A, N - \delta_y \in U^*$ if and only if $N \in U^*$ (i.e., the behaviour of N inside A is irrelevant to whether or not $N \in U^*$),

$$C_{\mathscr{P}}^*(A \times U) = \int_{\mathscr{N}_{\mathscr{X}}} \int_A I_U(N - \delta_y)N(dy)\mathscr{P}(dN)$$

$$= \int_{\mathscr{N}_{\mathscr{X}}} \int_A I_{\{N(A)=0\}}(N - \delta_y)N(dy)I_{U^*}(N)\mathscr{P}(dN)$$

$$= \int_{\mathscr{N}_{\mathscr{X}}} I_{\{N(A)=1\}}(N)I_{U^*}(N)\mathscr{P}(dN) \le \mathscr{P}(U^*).$$

Equally, using (14.2.8),

$$0 = \mathscr{P}(U) = E(I_{U^*}(N)\mathscr{P}\{N(A) = 0|A^c N\}).$$

By Condition Σ, the coefficient of the bounded function $I_{U^*}(N)$ is positive a.s., so we have a contradiction unless $I_{U^*}(N) = 0$ a.s.; that is, $\mathcal{P}(U^*) = 0$, and hence $C_{\mathscr{P}}^*(A \times U) = 0$ for such U.

Suppose next that $\mathcal{P}(U) = 0$ for some $U \subseteq \{N: N(A) \le k\}$ for some given integer $k \ge 1$, and let $\mathscr{T} = \{\{A_{ni}: i = 1, \ldots, k_n\}: n = 1, 2, \ldots\}$ be a dissecting family of partitions for A. Write also

$$U_{ni} = U \cap \{N(A_{ni}) = 0\} \quad \text{and} \quad U'_{ni} = U \setminus U_{ni}.$$

Then for $n = 1, 2, \ldots$ we have

$$C_{\mathscr{P}}^*(A \times U) = \sum_{i=1}^{k_n} C_{\mathscr{P}}^*(A_{ni} \times U) = \sum_{i=1}^{k_n} [C_{\mathscr{P}}^*(A_{ni} \times U_{ni}) + C_{\mathscr{P}}^*(A_{ni} \times U'_{ni})]$$

$$= \sum_{i=1}^{k_n} C_{\mathscr{P}}^*(A_{ni} \times U'_{ni})$$

because by the earlier argument, $C_{\mathscr{P}}^*(A_{ni} \times U_{ni}) = 0$. For the second sum we can write

$$\sum_{i=1}^{k_n} C_{\mathscr{P}}^*(A_{ni} \times U'_{ni}) = \sum_{j=1}^{k_n} \int_{\mathscr{N}_{\mathscr{X}}} \int_{A_{ni}} I_{U \setminus U_{ni}}(N - \delta_y) N(dy) \mathcal{P}(dN)$$

$$\le k \sum_{i=1}^{k_n} \mathcal{P}\{N(A_{ni}) \ge 2, N(A) \le k\}$$

[for this last step, $N(A_{ni}) \le N(A) \le k$ for $N \in U$, while any $y \in A_{ni}$ that is an atom of N can contribute to the integral only if also $(N - \delta_y)(A_{ni}) \ge 1$, and thus $N(A_{ni}) \ge 2$ for such y].

The assumption that N is simple implies that the last sum $\to 0$ as $n \to \infty$, and hence that $C_{\mathscr{P}}^*(A \times U) = 0$.

To complete the proof, use monotone convergence to deduce that, whenever $\mathcal{P}(U) = 0$,

$$C_{\mathscr{P}}^*(A \times U) = \lim_{k \to \infty} C_{\mathscr{P}}^*(A \times (U \cap \{N: N(A) \le k\})) = 0. \qquad \square$$

Standard arguments based on this result can now be used to establish the existence and uniqueness properties of the Papangelou kernel defined as follows.

Definition 14.2.IV. For a simple point process defined on the c.s.m.s. $\mathscr{X}$ and satisfying Condition Σ, the *Papangelou kernel* $\rho(A|N)$ is the $\mathcal{P}$-a.s. unique function satisfying

(i) for each bounded $A \in \mathscr{B}_{\mathscr{X}}$, $\rho(A|\cdot)$ is a Borel-measurable function on $\mathscr{N}_{\mathscr{X}}$;
(ii) for each $N \in \mathscr{N}_{\mathscr{X}}$, $\rho(\cdot|N)$ is a bounded finite Borel measure on $\mathscr{B}(\mathscr{N}_{\mathscr{X}})$;
(iii) for all bounded $A \in \mathscr{B}_{\mathscr{X}}$ and $U \in \mathscr{B}(\mathscr{N}_{\mathscr{X}})$, (14.2.3) holds.

Strictly speaking, this function $\rho(\cdot|\cdot)$ is a *first-order* Papangelou kernel, because kernels of higher order can be defined via higher-order modified Campbell measures $C_{\mathscr{P},k}^*$. These we now introduce and briefly discuss, setting

(14.2.9) $C_{\mathscr{P}}^*(A_1 \times \cdots \times A_k \times U)$

$$= \int_{\mathcal{N}_{\mathscr{X}}} \int_{A_1 \times \cdots \times A_k} I_U\left(N - \sum_{i=1}^{k} \delta_{y_i}\right) N_{[k]}(dy_1 \times \cdots \times dy_k)\mathscr{P}(dN)$$

for bounded $A_1, \ldots, A_k \in \mathscr{B}_{\mathscr{X}}$, $U \in \mathscr{B}(\mathcal{N}_{\mathscr{X}})$, where $N_{[k]}(\cdot)$ denotes the k-fold factorial product measure defined by $N(\cdot)$. [$N_{[k]}(\cdot)$ was introduced explicitly in the proof of Proposition 7.4.III; the factorial moment measure $M_{[k]}(\cdot)$ is its expectation measure. For simple point processes, integration with respect to $N_{[k]}(dy_1 \times \cdots \times dy_k)$ is the same as integration with respect to $N(dy_1) \cdots N(dy_k)$ if we add the restriction that $y_1, \ldots, y_k$ must all be distinct: hence, the integral at (13.1.21) could have been written without the coincidence annihilating function $I(\cdot)$ there, if instead we had replaced the product measure by the factorial product measure.] Much as in Proposition 14.2.III, it can be shown that under Condition Σ, $C_{\mathscr{P},k}^*(A_1 \times \cdots \times A_k \times \cdot) \ll \mathscr{P}(\cdot)$, and hence a kth-order Papangelou kernel $\rho_k(A_1 \times \cdots \times A_k | N)$ is well-defined $\mathscr{P}$-a.s. for bounded $A_1, \ldots, A_k \in \mathscr{B}_{\mathscr{X}}$ by

(14.2.10) $\displaystyle\int_U \rho_k(A_1 \times \cdots \times A_k | N)\mathscr{P}(dN)$

$$= C_{\mathscr{P},k}^*(A_1 \times \cdots \times A_k \times U) \quad \text{(all } U \in \mathscr{B}(\mathcal{N}_{\mathscr{X}})\text{)}.$$

Furthermore, regarding $C_{\mathscr{P},k+l}^*$ as a measure on $\mathscr{X}^{(l)} \times (\mathscr{X}^{(k)} \times \mathcal{N}_{\mathscr{X}})$, it can be shown that $C_{\mathscr{P},k+l}^* \ll C_{\mathscr{P},k}^*$ with respect to subsets of $\mathscr{X}^{(k)} \times \mathcal{N}_{\mathscr{X}}$. The corresponding kernel can be identified, up to the usual equivalence, with the kernel function

$$\rho_l\left(A_1 \times \cdots \times A_l | N + \sum_{i=1}^{k} \delta_{x_i}\right),$$

thus justifying the extension of the multiplicative relation (14.1.6) to the form (using the simplicity of N in an essential way)

(14.2.11) $\displaystyle\rho_l\left(dy_1 \times \cdots \times dy_l | N + \sum_{i=1}^{k} \delta_{x_i}\right)\rho_k(dx_1 \times \cdots \times dx_k | N)$

$$= \rho_{k+l}(dy_1 \times \cdots \times dy_l \times dx_1 \times \cdots \times dx_k | N).$$

Finally, defining $\rho_0(\cdot | N) = 1$ for $N(\mathscr{X}) = 0$ and zero otherwise, the Papangelou kernels of all orders can be combined into a portmanteau kernel on the space $\mathscr{X}^{\cup}$, where $N(\mathscr{X}) < \infty$ by means of the equation

(14.2.12) $\displaystyle G(V|N) = \sum_{k=0}^{\infty} \rho_k(V \cap \mathscr{X}^{(k)} | N)/k! \quad (V \in \mathscr{B}(\mathscr{X}^{\cup}))$.

Under Condition Σ, this *Gibbs kernel* $G(\cdot | \cdot)$ is a density for the compound Campbell measure with respect to the distribution of N. Many properties of the Papangelou kernels can be assumed under a general treatment of the Gibbs kernel: see Kallenberg (1983a, Chap. 13) for details.

We return to other properties of the (first-order) Papangelou kernel, of which perhaps the most important is the following extension of the conditional probability relation (14.1.7).

Proposition 14.2.V. *Let N be a simple point process defined on the c.s.m.s. $\mathcal{X}$ satisfying Condition Σ. Then for any bounded $A, B \in \mathcal{B}_{\mathcal{X}}$ with $A \subseteq B$, we have, a.s. on $\{N: N(B) = 0\}$,*

$$(14.2.13) \quad \rho(A|N) = \mathscr{P}\{N(A) = N(B) = 1 | B^c N\} / \mathscr{P}\{N(B) = 0 | B^c N\}.$$

PROOF. In (14.2.4) substitute

$$f(y, N) = I_A(y) I_{\{N(B)=0\}}(N) I_U(N + \delta_y),$$

where $U \in \sigma\{B^c N\}$. Then if $y \in A \subseteq B$, $N + \delta_y \in U$ if and only if $N \in U$, so (14.2.4) yields

$$\int_U \rho(A|N) I_{\{N(B)=0\}}(N) \mathscr{P}(dN) = \int_U N(A) I_{\{N(B)=1\}}(N) \mathscr{P}(dN)$$

$$= \int_U E(N(A) I_{\{N(B)=1\}} | B^c N) \mathscr{P}(dN)$$

$$= \int_U \mathscr{P}\{N(A) = N(B) = 1 | B^c N\} \mathscr{P}(dN).$$

On the other hand, using Lemma 14.2.II(b), noting that $U \in \sigma\{B^c N\}$, we can write

$$E(\rho(A|N) I_{\{N(B)=0\}}(N)) = E(\rho_0(A|N) \mathscr{P}\{N(B) = 0 | B^c N\}),$$

where $\rho_0(A|N)$ is $\sigma\{B^c N\}$-measurable. Since we have equality for all U on $\{N(B) = 0\}$,

$$\rho_0(A|N) \mathscr{P}\{N(B) = 0 | B^c N\} = \mathscr{P}\{N(A) = N(B) = 1 | B^c N\}.$$

Moreover, by Condition Σ, the coefficient of $\rho_0(A|N) > 0$ a.s., while on $N(B) = 0$, $\rho_0(A|N) = \rho(A|N)$, so (14.2.13) follows. $\square$

Thus far, we have considered $\rho(\cdot|N)$ as a kernel on the canonical space $\mathscr{N}_{\mathcal{X}}$. It is more convenient for the sequel to regard $\rho(A|N)$ as constituting a random measure on the probability space $(\Omega, \mathscr{E}, \mathscr{P})$ itself. By an abuse of notation we write

$$\rho(A) = \rho(A, \omega) = \rho(A|N(\omega))$$

for the random measure so defined. Note that $\rho(\cdot, \cdot)$ *is* a random measure, from the measurability of $\rho(A|N)$ as a function of N, which immediately implies that $\rho(A)$ is a random variable for each $A \in \mathcal{B}_{\mathcal{X}}$ and hence that the requirements of Proposition 6.1.II are satisfied.

This changed point of view is appropriate as we turn to consider relations between the random measures ρ, π, and ζ as outlined around (14.1.10). To do so, we suppose there is given a fixed dissecting system of partitions for $\mathscr{X}$, namely,

$$\mathscr{T} = \{\{I_{nj}: j = 1, \ldots, k_n\}, n = 1, 2, \ldots\}.$$

We also need the following Lemma.

Lemma 14.2.VI. *For bounded Borel sets A, B with $A \subseteq B$,*

$$(14.2.14) \quad \mathscr{P}\{\cdot \,|A^c N\} = \mathscr{P}\{\cdot \cap \{N(B \backslash A) = 0\} | B^c N\} / \mathscr{P}\{N(B \backslash A) = 0 | B^c N\}$$

$$\textit{a.s. on } \{N(B) = 0\},$$

the denominator being a.s. positive on $\{N(B) = 0\}$.

PROOF. $E[I_{\{N(B)=0\}}(N)\mathscr{P}\{N(B) = 0 | B^c N\}] = E[\mathscr{P}\{N(B) = 0 | B^c N\}]$ a.s. If $N \in \{N(B) = 0\}$, then either N is in a set of measure zero, or else $\mathscr{P}\{N(B) = 0 | B^c N\} > 0$, so that in either case the last probability is a.s. positive on $\{N(B) = 0\}$, and therefore the denominator in (14.2.14) is a.s. positive on $\{N(B) = 0\}$. The relation itself is just a version of $P(U | V \cap W) = P(U | W) / P(V | W)$ for $V \subseteq W$, where since $A \subseteq B$, we can take P to be $\mathscr{P}(\cdot | B^c N)$ and W to be $\{N(B \backslash A) = 0\}$. $\qquad\square$

In what follows, we take A, B to be elements of $\mathscr{T}$ and note that, since $\mathscr{T}$ is countable, we can assume that (14.2.14) holds simultaneously a.s. for all such choices of A, $B \in \mathscr{T}$.

Proposition 14.2.VII. *Let N be a simple point process on the c.s.m.s. $\mathscr{X}$. Let $\mathscr{T}$ be a dissecting system of partitions of $\mathscr{X}$, x a general point of $\mathscr{X}$, and $\{I_n(x)\}$ a sequence of elements of $\mathscr{T}$ with $I_n(x) \downarrow \{x\}$ $(n \to \infty)$. Then the limit*

$$(14.2.15) \qquad \pi\{x\} = \lim_{n \to \infty} \mathscr{P}\{N(I_n(x)) \geq 1 | I_n^c(x)N\}$$

exists a.s., is independent of $\mathscr{T}$, and can be identified a.s. on the set $\{N(I_n(x)\backslash\{x\}) = 0\}$ with the ratio

$$(14.2.16) \qquad \pi\{x\} = \frac{\mathscr{P}\{N\{x\} = N(I_n(x)) = 1 | I_n^c(x)N\}}{\mathscr{P}\{N(I_n(x)\backslash\{x\}) = 0 | I_n^c(x)N\}},$$

the ratio being interpreted as unity when both numerator and denominator vanish.

The equation

$$(14.2.17) \qquad \pi(A) = \pi(A, N) \equiv \sum_{x_i \in (\mathrm{supp}(N)) \cap A} \pi\{x_i\} = \sum \pi\{x_i\}\delta_{x_i}(A)$$

defines a random measure on $\mathscr{X}$.

When Condition Σ holds, $\pi\{x\} < 1$ for all x, the atoms of π include the atoms of ρ, and

(14.2.18) $\rho\{x\} = \pi\{x\}/(1 - \pi\{x\})$

unless $N\{x\} = 1$, in which case $\rho\{x\} = 0$.

PROOF. In Lemma 14.2.VI take $A = I_n(x)$, $B = I_m(x)$ with $n > m$. Dropping the dependence on x for notational brevity, (14.2.14) implies that a.s. on $\{N(I_m) = 0\}$,

(14.2.19) $\mathscr{P}\{N(I_n) > 0 | I_n^c N\} = 1 - \mathscr{P}\{N(I_n) = 0 | I_n^c N\}$

$$= 1 - \mathscr{P}\{N(I_m) = 0 | I_m^c N\}/\mathscr{P}\{N(I_m \backslash I_n) = 0 | I_m^c N\}.$$

For increasing n, the numerator here remains fixed, while the denominator decreases monotonically to the limit $\mathscr{P}\{N(I_m \backslash \{x\}) = 0 | I_m^c N\}$. We deduce that the limit exists a.s. on the set $\{N(I_m \backslash I_n) = 0\}$ for every $n > m$, hence a.s. on $\{N(I_m \backslash \{x\}) = 0\}$, and hence a.s. since $N(I_m \backslash \{x\}) \to 0$ a.s. as $m \to \infty$. Also the ratio equals (14.2.16) except possibly for realizations where the denominator vanishes. If the latter holds, the ratio for finite n will tend to ∞ unless in the limit the numerator also vanishes. In this case, we have $\mathscr{P}\{N(I_n) = 0 | I_n^c N\} \to 0$; that is, $\mathscr{P}\{N(I_n) \geq 1 | I_n^c N\} \to 1$, implying that $\pi\{x\} = 1$, in accordance with the interpretation here that "$0/0 = 1$."

Next, let $\mathscr{T}_1$ and $\mathscr{T}_2$ be dissecting systems with $\mathscr{T}_1 \subseteq \mathscr{T}_2$. Then the limits $\pi_1\{x\}, \pi_2\{x\}$ say exist for each system, and since $\{I_{n_1}(x)\} \subseteq \mathscr{T}_1 \subseteq \mathscr{T}_2$, it follows that $\pi_1\{x\} = \pi_2\{x\}$ because we can always find $I_{n'}(x) \downarrow \{x\}$ with successive terms taken alternately from $\{I_{n_1}\}$ and $\{I_{n_2}\}$. In general, any two systems $\mathscr{T}_1$, $\mathscr{T}_2$ generate by their intersection a third system $\mathscr{T}_3$ with $\mathscr{T}_3 \supseteq \mathscr{T}_1$ and $\mathscr{T}_3 \supseteq \mathscr{T}_2$, so $\pi\{x\}$ is independent of $\mathscr{T}$.

For bounded $A \in \mathscr{B}_{\mathscr{X}}$, $N(A) < \infty$, so the defining sum at (14.2.17) can be expressed as a finite sum of limits as at (14.2.15) over disjoint sets I_{nj} for sufficiently large n, and thus it is a random variable. From Proposition 6.1.III this implies that $\pi(A, N(\omega))$ as defined is a random measure.

When Condition Σ holds, if $\pi\{x\} = 1$ for some x, then for this x and all n

$$\mathscr{P}\{N(I_n(x)) \geq 1 | I_n^c(x)N\} = 1 \quad \text{a.s.}$$

on account of the monotonicity of the denominator in (14.2.19). Consequently, $\mathscr{P}\{N(I_n(x)) = 0 | I_n^c(x)N\} = 0$ a.s., contradicting Condition Σ. Thus, $\pi\{x\} < 1$.

To demonstrate (14.2.18), refer to (14.2.13) and deduce by putting $A = I_m(x)$, $B = I_n(x)$, that on $\{N(I_n) = 0\}$,

$$\rho(I_m(x)|N) = \mathscr{P}\{N(I_m) = 1 = N(I_n) | I_n^c N\}/\mathscr{P}\{N(I_n) = 0 | I_n^c N\}.$$

$\rho(\cdot|N)$ is a measure and $I_m(x) \downarrow \{x\}$ as $m \to \infty$, so the left-hand side $\to \rho\{x\}$. On the right-hand side, $\{N: N(I_m) = 1 = N(I_n)\} \downarrow \{N: N\{x\} = 1 = N(I_n)\}$, so on $\{N(I_n) = 0\}$

$$\rho\{x\} = \mathscr{P}\{N\{x\} = 1 = N(I_n) | I_n^c N\}/\mathscr{P}\{N(I_n) = 0 | I_n^c N\}.$$

The numerator here coincides with that of (14.2.16), while the denominator equals

$$\mathscr{P}\{N(I_n\setminus\{x\}) = 0|I_n^c N\} - \mathscr{P}\{N(I_n) = N\{x\} \ge 1|I_n^c N\}.$$

Since N is simple, the last term equals $\mathscr{P}\{N(I_n) = N\{x\} = 1|I_n^c N\}$. Then (14.2.18) follows from (14.2.16) whenever $\{N(I_n) = 0\}$ for sufficiently large n. On the complementary event, x is an atom of N because

$$\bigcap_n \{N(I_n) \ge 1\} = \{N\{x\} \ge 1\}.$$

In this case, we choose some positive integer k and substitute

$$f(y, N) = I_A(y)I_{\{N(B) \le k\}}(N)I_{\{N(A) \ge 1\}}(N)$$

in the relation (14.2.4) with $B = I_n(x)$, $A = I_m(x)$ with $m \ge n$. The left-hand side yields

$$E(\rho(I_m)I_{\{N(I_n) \le k\}}(N)I_{\{N(I_m) \ge 1\}}(N)),$$

while the right-hand side is bounded above by $(k + 1)\mathscr{P}\{N(I_m) \ge 2, N(I_n) \le k + 1\}$. Now repeat this with I_m replaced by a dissecting partition I_{nj} for I_m, and sum over j. Proceeding to the limit, the sum $\to 0$ by simplicity, while the sum of the left-hand side converges to $\sum \rho\{x\} N\{x\}$, the sum being taken over all atoms lying in I_m. Consequently, $\rho\{x\} = 0$ whenever $N\{x\} > 0$. ☐

The following simple examples may help illustrate the nature of atoms of ρ and N, and especially the role played by $\pi(\cdot)$.

EXAMPLE 14.2(a) *Processes violating Condition Σ.* Let N be a point process on $\mathscr{X}$ for which $\mathscr{P}\{N(\mathscr{X}) = n\} = 1$ for some fixed integer n. Then for any nonempty set $A \in \mathscr{B}_{\mathscr{X}}$, $\mathscr{P}\{N(A) = 0|N(A^c) < n\} = 0$, and thus Condition Σ is violated.

For such a process, suppose $x \in \text{supp}(N)$, and for a given dissecting system $\mathscr{T}$ let $\{I_n\} \equiv \{I_n(x)\}$ be a sequence of elements of $\mathscr{T}$ contracting to $\{x\}$. Then

$$\mathscr{P}\{N(I_n) \ge 1|N(I_n^c) \le n - 1\} = 1 = \lim_{n \to \infty} \mathscr{P}\{N(I_n) \ge 1|N(I_n^c) \le n - 1\}$$

$$= \pi\{x\}.$$

The set $\{N: N(I_n - \{x\}) = 0\} \cap \{N(I_n^c) \le n - 1\}$ consists precisely of those realizations N for which $N(I_n^c) = n - 1$, $N(I_n) = N\{x\} = 1$. If we assume that the points of N are n points i.i.d. over $\mathscr{X}$, which is a bounded Borel subset of $\mathbb{R}^d$—for example, the interior of a circle or a sphere—then assuming the sets I_n have positive Lebesgue measure, we should have

$$\mathscr{P}\{N(I_n) = 1|N(I_n^c) = n - 1\} = 1$$

$$\ne \mathscr{P}\{N(I_n) = 1 = N\{x\}|N(I_n^c) = n - 1\} = 0$$

$$= \mathscr{P}\{N(I_n - \{x\}) = 0|N(I_n^c) = n - 1\}.$$

We thus have an example of the justification for interpreting $\pi\{x\} = \pi(\{x\}, N)$ as unity when the expression at (14.2.16) equals "0/0."

Now let N_1 denote such a process with exactly one point uniformly distributed over the bounded state space $\mathscr{X} \in \mathscr{B}(\mathbb{R}^d)$—for example, a circle of unit area. Let N_2 be a Poisson process at unit rate on $\mathscr{X}$ with N_2 independent of N_1. Then the point process $N = N_1 + N_2$ violates Condition Σ because for any Borel set $A \subseteq \mathscr{X}$ of positive Lebesgue measure,

$$\mathscr{P}\{N(A) = 0 | N(A^c) = 0\} = 0.$$

On the other hand, the process N equal to N_1 with probability p and to N_2 with probability $q = 1 - p$, with $pq > 0$, satisfies Condition Σ (details are left to the reader).

EXAMPLE 14.2(b) *A particular Gauss–Poisson process.* Suppose there is given a Gauss–Poisson process in the plane, which, in its Poisson cluster process representation, consists of a cluster centre process that is Poisson at unit rate, and for which any point x in the centre process produces clusters of either 0 or 1 additional points, with probability p for there being one point, which is then located at $x + a$ for some fixed position a relative to the cluster centre. Consider such a process on a bounded subset $\mathscr{X} \in \mathscr{B}(\mathbb{R}^2)$. It can be checked that this process satisfies Condition Σ.

For some $x \in \mathscr{X}$ for which both $x - a$ and $x + a \in \mathscr{X}$ also, consider realizations N for which $N\{x\} = 1$, and let $\{I_n\} \equiv \{I_n(x + a)\}$ be a sequence of sets of positive Lebesgue measure $\downarrow \{x + a\}$ and belonging to some dissecting system for $\mathscr{X}$. On realizations N for which $N\{x\} = 1 = N\{x - a\}$ and $N(\mathscr{X}\backslash(\{x\} \cup \{x - a\} \cup I_n)) = 0$, $\mathscr{P}\{N(I_n) \geq 1 | I_n^c N\} = \ell(I_n)(1 + o(1))$, so the ratio at (14.2.16) $\to 0$. On realizations for which $N\{x\} = 1 = N(I_n^c)$,

$$\mathscr{P}\{N(I_n) \geq 1 | I_n^c N\} = p + \ell(I_n)(1 + o(1))$$

and

$$\mathscr{P}\{N(I_n\backslash\{x + a\}) = 0 | I_n^c N\} = 1 - \ell(I_n)(1 + o(1)),$$

so the ratio at (14.2.16) $\to p = \pi\{x\} \equiv \pi(\{x\}, N)$.

EXAMPLE 14.2(c) *Binomial lattice process.* Consider a process on $\mathscr{X} = \{x_1, \ldots, x_n\}$, and, independently for each point, $N\{x_i\} = 0$ or 1 with probabilities q and $p = 1 - q$, respectively. The Janossy measures are purely atomic, with $J_0 = q^n$ and

$$J_k(x_{r_1}, \ldots, x_{r_k}) \equiv J_k(\{x_{r_1}\}, \ldots, \{x_{r_k}\}) = p^k q^{n-k}$$

for any subset S_k of k distinct points in $\mathscr{X}$. Observe that

$$\sum_{\text{all } S_k} J_k(S_k) = \binom{n}{k} p^k q^{n-k}.$$

The integral equation defining ρ reduces to a definition as a ratio,

$$\rho(y | x_1, \ldots, x_k) = J_{k+1}(y, x_1, \ldots, x_k) / J_k(x_1, \ldots, x_k) = p/q.$$

Also, if $B = \{y, x_1, \ldots, x_k\}$,

$$\mathscr{P}\{N\{y\} = N(\{y, x_1, \ldots, x_k\}) = 1 | B^c N\} / \mathscr{P}\{N(\{y, x_1, \ldots, x_k\}) = 0 | B^c N\}$$
$$= pq^k / q^{k+1} = p/q,$$

consistent with (14.2.13). On the other hand, $\pi\{y\}$ equals

$$\mathscr{P}\{N\{y\} = N(\{y, x_1, \ldots, x_k\}) = 1 | B^c N\} / \mathscr{P}\{N(\{x_1, \ldots, x_k\}) = 0 | B^c N\}$$
$$= pq^k / q^k = p,$$

and $\pi\{y\} / (1 - \pi\{y\}) = p/(1 - p) = p/q$.

Finally, if $N\{y\} = 1$, $\pi\{y\}$ is unchanged, but for $\rho\{y\}$ we should have a ratio of Janossy measures with the argument y repeated in the numerator, which is zero on account of the process being simple.

14.3. The Papangelou Intensity Measure and Exvisibility

The last of the three quantities mentioned at the end of Section 14.1 is arguably the one with the most important applications. Papangelou (1974b) devised it primarily as a means of tackling certain problems in stochastic geometry quite distinct from the present context [e.g., see Kallenberg (1983b) and related discussion for an informal account and references]. It is in fact a conditional intensity *measure*, to which we here attach Papangelou's name to distinguish it from the various conditional intensity *functions* of Chapter 13. Another approach is possible, namely, via the compound Campbell measure, which on disintegration via its two coordinates leads to the Palm measures and the Gibbs and Papangelou kernels respectively (see Kallenberg, 1983a).

We start by establishing its existence under Condition Σ, relating it to the Papangelou kernel $\rho(\cdot)$ and atomic measure $\pi(\cdot)$ discussed already.

Proposition 14.3.I. *Let N, $\mathscr{X}$, $\mathscr{T}$ be as in Proposition 14.2.VII, and suppose that Condition Σ holds. Then as $n \to \infty$, the limit*

$$(14.3.1) \quad \zeta(B) = \lim_{n \to \infty} \sum_{j=1}^{k_n} \mathscr{P}\{N(B_{nj}) = 1 | B_{nj}^c N\}, \quad B_{nj} \equiv B \cap I_{nj},$$

exists a.s. for all bounded $B \in \mathscr{B}_{\mathscr{X}}$ and defines a random measure given a.s. by

$$(14.3.2) \quad \zeta(\cdot) = \pi(\cdot) + \rho_d(\cdot),$$

where $\rho_d(\cdot)$ is the diffuse (i.e., nonatomic) component of the random measure $\rho(\cdot)$.

PROOF. Without loss of generality assume that $B \in \mathscr{T}$; then each $B_{nj} = I_{nj} \in \mathscr{T}$ (though we continue to write B_{nj}). We can write

$$\sum_{j=1}^{k_n} \mathscr{P}\{N(B_{nj}) = 1 | B_{nj}^c N\} = \sum_{j=1}^{k_n} [\mathscr{P}\{N(B_{nj}) = 1 | B_{nj}^c N\} I_{\{N(B_{nj})=0\}}$$

$$+ \mathscr{P}\{N(B_{nj}) \geq 1 | B_{nj}^c N\} I_{\{N(B_{nj}) \geq 1\}}$$

$$- \mathscr{P}\{N(B_{nj}) \geq 2 | B_{nj}^c N\} I_{\{N(B_{nj}) \geq 1\}}]$$

$$\equiv \Sigma_0(n) + \Sigma_1(n) - \Sigma_2(n), \quad \text{say}.$$

For $\Sigma_0(n)$, observe from (14.2.13) that

$$\mathscr{P}\{N(B_{nj}) = 1 | B_{nj}^c N\} = \rho(B_{nj}) \mathscr{P}\{N(B_{nj}) = 0 | B_{nj}^c N\},$$

so we can rewrite $\Sigma_0(n)$ in the form

$$\Sigma_0(n) = \int_B I_{B_n}(x) h_n(x) \rho(dx),$$

where, for fixed N, B_n is the union of those B_{nj} where $N(B_{nj}) = 0$, and $h_n(x) = \mathscr{P}\{N(B_{nj}) = 0 | B_{nj}^c N\}$ on B_{nj}. $\{B_n\}$ is a monotonic increasing sequence of sets, with limit $B \setminus \{\text{supp } N\}$, while $h_n(x) \uparrow 1 - \pi\{x\}$ a.s. by Proposition 14.2.VII. By monotone convergence, therefore,

$$\Sigma_0(n) \to \int_{B \setminus \{\text{supp } N\}} (1 - \pi\{x\})(\rho_a(dx) + \rho_d(dx))$$

with ρ_a denoting the atomic component of ρ. By using (14.2.15), $\rho_a \ll \pi_a$ a.s., so the first term here equals $\pi(B \setminus \{\text{supp } N\})$, while since $\pi\{x\} = 0$ ρ_d-a.s., and $\rho\{x\} = 0$ for $x \in \{\text{supp } N\}$, the second term equals $\rho_d(B)$.

For $\Sigma_1(n)$, for given N, the sum reduces for n sufficiently large to a sum over sets B_{nj} containing exactly one of the atoms of $N(\cdot)$ in B. By Proposition 14.2.VII again, the limit as $n \to \infty$ reduces to $\pi(B \cap \{\text{supp } N\})$. Thus,

$$\Sigma_0(n) + \Sigma_1(n) \to \rho_d(B) + \pi(B) = \zeta(B) \quad \text{a.s.},$$

and it remains to prove that $\Sigma_2(n) \to 0$ a.s. Just as for $\Sigma_1(n)$, the sum reduces for n sufficiently large to a sum, $\sum'$ say, over precisely $N(B)$ sets B_{nj}, where $N(B_{nj}) = 1$; that is,

$$\Sigma_2(n) = \sum{}' \mathscr{P}\{N(B_{nj}) \geq 2 | B_{nj}^c N\} = \sum{}' \frac{\mathscr{P}\{N(B_{nj}) \geq 2, N(B \setminus B_{nj}) = 0 | B^c N\}}{\mathscr{P}\{N(B \setminus B_{nj}) = 0 | B^c N\}}$$

on using Lemma 14.2.VI. As n increases, each of the $N(B)$ terms in the numerator $\to 0$ because N is simple, while for the denominator, which is decreasing to $\mathscr{P}\{N(B - \{x\}) = 0 | B^c N\}$ for some $x \in \{\text{supp } N\}$, Condition Σ implies that

$$0 < \mathscr{P}\{N(B) = 0 | B^c N\} \leq \mathscr{P}\{N(B - \{x\}) = 0 | B^c N\}. \qquad \square$$

The Papangelou intensity measure is related to a first moment in much the way that the first moment and intensity measures coincide (Proposition 7.2.IV).

Corollary 14.3.II. *Suppose the first moment measure $EN(\cdot)$ exists. Then for all bounded $B \in \mathcal{B}_{\mathcal{X}}$, (14.3.1) extends to*

$$(14.3.3) \qquad \sum_{j=1}^{k_n} E(N(B_{nj})|B_{nj}^c N) \to \zeta(B) \quad \text{a.s. and in } L_1 \text{ mean.}$$

PROOF. For the a.s. convergence, write

$$E(N(B_{nj})|B_{nj}^c N) = \mathscr{P}\{N(B_{nj}) = 1|B_{nj}^c N\} + E(N(B_{nj})I_{\{N(B_{nj}) \geq 2\}}(N)|B_{nj}^c N),$$

and use an extension of Lemma 14.2.VI to write

$$\sum_{j=1}^{k_n} E(N(B_{nj})I_{\{N(B_{nj}) \geq 2\}}(N)|B_{nj}^c N)$$

$$= \sum_{j=1}^{k_n} \frac{E(N(B_{nj})I_{\{N(B_{nj}) \geq 2\}}I_{\{N(B \setminus B_{nj}) = 0\}}|B^c N)}{\mathscr{P}\{N(B \setminus B_{nj}) = 0|B^c N\}}$$

$$\leq (\mathscr{P}\{N(B) = 0|B^c N\})^{-1} E\left(\sum_{j=1}^{k_n} N(B_{nj})I_{\{N(B_{nj}) \geq 2\}}(N)|B^c N\right).$$

This conditional expectation is bounded by $E(N(B)|B^c N) < \infty$ a.s., and N being simple implies that each term in the sum $\to 0$ a.s. (cf. also Exercise 7.2.7), so by dominated convergence we have the required result.

To establish L_1 convergence, refer to the proof of the Proposition and observe that $\Sigma_0(n)$ increases monotonically to its limit, which has expectation bounded by $E(N(B))$, so its a.s. convergence implies its L_1 convergence. Also,

$$\Sigma_1(n) - \Sigma_2(n) = \sum_{j=1}^{k_n} \mathscr{P}\{N(B_{nj}) = 1|B_{nj}^c N\}I_{\{N(B_{nj}) \geq 1\}}$$

$$\leq \sum_{j=1}^{k_n} I_{\{N(B_{nj}) \geq 1\}} \leq N(B),$$

so here the a.s. convergence of $\Sigma_1(n) - \Sigma_2(n)$ implies its L_1 convergence by the dominated convergence theorem. Finally,

$$E\left(\sum_{j=1}^{k_n} E(N(B_{nj})I_{\{N(B_{nj}) \geq 2\}}(N)|B_{nj}^c N)\right) = E\left(\sum_{j=1}^{k_n} N(B_{nj})I_{\{N(B_{nj}) \geq 2\}}\right)$$

$$\to 0 \qquad (n \to \infty)$$

from simplicity and the assumption that $EN(B) < \infty$. $\square$

So far the development in this chapter has been based mainly on disintegrations and limits, having much in common with the material of Chapter 12. It is possible to base the derivation of the Papangelou intensity measure on arguments much closer to those used in the discussion of the compensator and its density, the conditional intensity $\lambda(\cdot, \omega)$. With a state space $\mathcal{X}$ more general than $\mathbb{R}$ or $\mathbb{R}_+$ as in Chapter 13, the concept of predictability used there is replaced by that of *exvisibility* due to Van der Hoeven (1982) [we follow the terminology of Kallenberg (1983a)].

Write $\bar{\sigma}\{B^c N\}$ for the completion of the B-external σ-algebra $\sigma\{B^c N\}$ with respect to the null sets of $\sigma\{N\}$ of the process N. Then on the product space $\mathscr{X} \times \Omega$ (or, more specifically, $\mathscr{X} \times \hat{\mathcal{N}}_{\mathscr{X}}$ in the canonical setup), define the *exvisible σ-algebra* $\mathscr{Z}$ to be the σ-algebra generated by sets of the form $B \times U$, where $B \in \mathscr{B}_{\mathscr{X}}$, $U \in \bar{\sigma}\{B^c N\}$. A stochastic process on $(\Omega, \mathscr{E}, P)$ is then *exvisible* if it is measurable with respect to $\mathscr{Z}$ on $\mathscr{X} \times \Omega$.

Given a random measure ξ, a "dual exvisible projection" of ξ can be introduced as the unique random measure satisfying conditions (i)–(iii) of Proposition 14.3.III. A direct proof of this assertion requires arguments from the general theory of processes analogous to those needed to give a direct proof of the properties of the compensator $A(\cdot)$ in Section 13.2 (see Van der Hoeven, 1982, 1983). However, when ξ is a point process satisfying the special conditions assumed in this chapter (namely, it is simple and satisfies Condition Σ), it is not too difficult to see that the dual exvisible projection is nothing other than the Papangelou intensity measure ζ itself: we conclude with a formal statement and proof of this result.

Proposition 14.3.III. *Under the conditions of Proposition 14.3.I, and assuming $EN(\cdot)$ exists, the Papangelou intensity measure ζ is the unique (up to equivalences) random measure satisfying the following conditions:*

(i) ζ *is determined by the point process N (i.e., $\zeta(B)$ is $\sigma\{N\}$-measurable for every $B \in \mathscr{B}_{\mathscr{X}}$).*
(ii) *The process $Z(x) \equiv \zeta\{x\}$ is exvisible.*
(iii) *For every nonnegative exvisible process Y, and bounded $B \in \mathscr{B}_{\mathscr{X}}$,*

$$(14.3.4) \qquad E\left(\int_B Y(x)\zeta(dx)\right) = E\left(\int_B Y(x)N(dx)\right).$$

PROOF. ζ as defined at (14.3.2) is the limit of a $\sigma\{N\}$-measurable r.v., and therefore (i) holds for ζ.

Suppose x is an atom of ζ. Then in the notation used in the proof of Proposition 14.3.I,

$$\zeta\{x\} = 1 - \pi\{x\} = \lim_{n\to\infty} (1 - h_n(x)) \quad \text{a.s.,}$$

where $h_n(x) = \sum_{j=1}^{k_n} \mathscr{P}\{N(B_{nj}) = 0 | B_{nj}^c N\} I_{B_{nj}}(x)$ is clearly exvisible. The limit is thus a.s. equal to an exvisible process, and if the σ-fields are complete we can allow modifications on sets of measure zero without upsetting measurability, so all versions are exvisible.

Finally, take Y in (14.3.4) to have the special form

$$Y(x, \omega) = I_B(x)I_U(\zeta) \quad \text{for } U \in \sigma\{B^c N\}.$$

Then Corollary 14.3.II implies that since $U \in \sigma\{B_{nj}^c N\}$ for every B_{nj},

$$E(I_U N(B)) = E\left(I_U \sum_{j=1}^{k_n} E(N(B_{nj})| B_{nj}^c N)\right) \to E(I_U \zeta(B)).$$

Since the left-hand side here is fixed, (14.3.4) follows for this particular function Y, and then for processes Y as described by standard extension arguments.

Thus, ζ satisfies (i)–(iii): suppose η is some other random measure satisfying the conditions. Whenever $U \in \sigma\{B_{nj}^c N\}$, (14.3.4) implies that

$$E(I_U E(\eta(B_{nj})| B_{nj}^c N)) = E(I_U \eta(B_{nj})) = E(I_U N(B_{nj}))$$
$$= E(I_U E(N(B_{nj})| B_{nj}^c N)),$$

from which it follows that

$$E(\eta(B_{nj})| B_{nj}^c N) = E(N(B_{nj})| B_{nj}^c N) \quad \text{a.s.},$$

and hence that

$$\lim_{n \to \infty} \sum_{j=1}^{k_n} E(\eta(B_{nj})| B_{nj}^c N) = \lim_{n \to \infty} \sum_{j=1}^{k_n} E(N(B_{nj})| B_{nj}^c N) = \zeta(B) \quad \text{a.s.}$$

Each of the two sums here may be further analysed by the same procedure as used in forming the sums $\Sigma_0(n)$, $\Sigma_1(n)$, $\Sigma_2(n)$ in the proof of Proposition 14.3.I. In particular, using the $\sigma\{B_{nj}^c N\}$-measurability of $\eta(\cdot)$ on $\{N(B_{nj}) = 0\}$,

$$\sum_{j=1}^{k_n} E(\eta(B_{nj}) I_{\{N(B_{nj})=0\}}(N)| B_{nj}^c N) I_{\{N(B_{nj})=0\}}$$

$$= \sum_{j=1}^{k_n} \eta(B_{nj}) \mathscr{P}\{N(B_{nj}) = 0| B_{nj}^c N\} I_{\{N(B_{nj})=0\}}$$

$$\to \int_{B \setminus \{\text{supp } N\}} (1 - \pi\{x\})\eta(dx) = \eta_d(B) + \sum (1 - \pi\{x_i\})\eta\{x_i\},$$

where in the second step we have used the limit behaviour of the function $h_n(x)$ as in the proof of the earlier result, and $\eta_d(\cdot)$ denotes the diffuse component of η and summation is over the atoms of $\eta(\cdot)$. Thus, we have a.s.

$$(14.3.5) \quad \eta_d(B) + \sum (1 - \pi\{x_i\})\eta\{x_i\} = \eta_d(B) + \sum (1 - \pi\{x_i\})\zeta\{x_i\}.$$

Now it follows from conditions (ii) and (iii) that the atomic parts of η and ζ must be equal, because if we let $V = \{(x, \omega) \in \mathscr{X} \times \Omega: Z(x, \omega) > \zeta(\{x\}, \omega)\}$, then V is an exvisible set and from (14.3.1)

$$\int_V (Z(x, \omega) - \zeta(\{x\}, \omega))(\eta(dx, \omega) - \zeta(dx, \omega))\mathscr{P}(dx) = 0.$$

Only atoms of η and ζ contribute to this integral, and indeed only those for which $\eta\{x_i\} - \zeta\{x_i\} > 0$. This leads to a contradiction unless $\eta\{x_i\} \le \zeta\{x_i\}$ a.s., and by reversing the argument we deduce that $\eta\{x_i\} = \zeta\{x_i\}$ a.s. for all atoms; that is, η and ζ have the same atoms and the atoms are of the same size a.s. Then (14.3.5) implies that the diffuse components agree a.s.; that is, η and ζ coincide except possibly on a set of measure zero. $\qquad\square$

A Review of Some Basic Concepts of Topology and Measure Theory

In this appendix we summarize, mainly without proof, some standard results from topology and measure theory. The aims are to establish terminology and notation, to set out results needed at various stages in the text in some specific form for convenient reference, and to provide some brief perspectives on the development of the theory. For proofs and further details the reader should refer, in particular, to Kingman and Taylor (1966), Chapters 1–6, whose development and terminology we have followed rather closely.

A1.1. Set Theory

A set A of a space $\mathscr{X}$ is a collection of *elements* or *points* of $\mathscr{X}$. When x is an element of the set A, we write $x \in A$ (x *belongs to* or *is included in* A). The set of points of $\mathscr{X}$ not included in A is the complement of A, written A^c. If A, B are two sets of points from $\mathscr{X}$ their *union*, written $A \cup B$, is the set of points in either A or B or both; their *symmetric difference*, written $A \triangle B$, is the set of points in A or B but *not* both; and their *intersection*, written $A \cap B$, is the set of points in both. If every element of B is also an element of A we say B is *included* in A ($B \subseteq A$), or A *contains* B ($A \supseteq B$). In this case the *proper difference* of A and B, written either $A - B$ or $A \backslash B$, is the set of points of A but not B. More generally, we use $A - B$ for $A \cap B^c$, but $A - B = A \triangle B$ only when $A \supseteq B$.

The operations $\cap$ and $\triangle$ on subsets of $\mathscr{X}$ are commutative, associative, and distributive. The class of all such subsets thus forms an *algebra* with respect to these operations, where $\varnothing$, the empty set, plays the role of identity for $\triangle$, and $\mathscr{X}$ the role of identity for $\cap$. The special relation

$$A \cap A = A$$

implies that the algebra is *Boolean*. More generally, any class of sets closed under the operations of $\cap$ and $\triangle$ is called a *ring*, or an *algebra* if $\mathscr{X}$ itself is a member of the class. A *semiring* is a class of sets $\mathscr{A}$ with the properties (i) $\mathscr{A}$ is closed under intersections, and (ii) every symmetric difference of sets in $\mathscr{A}$ can be represented as a finite union of disjoint sets in $\mathscr{A}$. The ring generated by an arbitrary family of sets $\mathscr{F}$ is the smallest ring containing $\mathscr{F}$, or, equivalently, the intersection of all rings containing $\mathscr{F}$. Every element in the ring generated by a semiring $\mathscr{A}$ can be represented as a union of disjoint sets of $\mathscr{A}$. If $\mathscr{R}$ is a finite ring, there exists a *basis* of disjoint elements of $\mathscr{R}$ such that every element in $\mathscr{R}$ can be represented uniquely as a union of disjoint elements of the basis.

The notions of union and intersection can be extended to arbitrary classes of sets. If $\{A_n; n = 1, 2, \ldots\}$ is a sequence of sets, we write $A_n \uparrow A = \lim A_n$ if $A_n \subseteq A_{n+1}, n = 1, 2, \ldots$, and $A = \bigcup_1^\infty A_n$; similarly, if $A_n \supseteq A_{n+1}, n = 1, 2, \ldots$, we write $A_n \downarrow A = \lim A_n$ if $A = \bigcap_1^\infty A_n$. A *monotone class* is a class of sets closed under monotone increasing sequences. A ring (algebra) that is closed under countable as well as finite unions is called a *σ-ring* (*σ-algebra*). The σ-ring generated by a class of sets $\mathscr{C}$, written $\sigma(\mathscr{C})$, is the smallest σ-ring containing $\mathscr{C}$. A σ-ring is *countably generated* if it can be generated by a countable class of $\mathscr{C}$. The following result, linking σ-rings to monotone classes, is useful in identifying the σ-ring generated by certain classes of sets.

Proposition A1.1.I (Monotone Class Theorem). *If $\mathscr{R}$ is a ring, and $\mathscr{C}$ is a monotone class containing $\mathscr{R}$, then $\mathscr{C}$ contains $\sigma(\mathscr{R})$.*

A closely related result uses the concept of a *Dynkin system*: $\mathscr{D}$ is a Dynkin system if

(i) $\mathscr{X} \in \mathscr{D}$;
(ii) $\mathscr{D}$ is closed under proper differences; and
(iii) $\mathscr{D}$ is closed under monotone increasing limits.

Proposition A1.1.II (Dynkin System Theorem). *If $\mathscr{S}$ is a class of sets closed under finite intersections, and $\mathscr{D}$ is a Dynkin system containing $\mathscr{S}$, then $\mathscr{D}$ contains $\sigma(\mathscr{S})$.*

A1.2. Topologies

A topology $\mathscr{U}$ on a space $\mathscr{X}$ is a class of subsets of $\mathscr{X}$ that is closed under arbitrary unions and finite intersections and that includes the empty set $\varnothing$ and the whole space $\mathscr{X}$; the members of $\mathscr{U}$ are *open sets*, while their complements are *closed sets*. The pair $(\mathscr{X}, \mathscr{U})$ is a *topological space*. The *closure* of an arbitrary set A from $\mathscr{X}$, written $\bar{A}$, is the smallest closed set (equivalently, the intersection of all closed sets) containing A. The *interior* of A, written A°, is the largest open set (equivalently, the union of all open sets) contained within A. The *boundary* of A, written ∂A, is the difference $\bar{A} \backslash A^{\circ}$. The following elementary properties of boundaries are needed in the discussion of weak convergence of measures.

Proposition A1.2.1. (a) $\partial(A \cup B) \subseteq \partial A \cup \partial B$;

(b) $\partial(A \cap B) \subseteq \partial A \cup \partial B$;

(c) $\qquad \partial A^{c} = \partial A$.

A *neighbourhood* of the point $x \in \mathscr{X}$ with respect to the topology $\mathscr{U}$ (or, more briefly, a $\mathscr{U}$-*neighbourhood* of x) is an open set from $\mathscr{U}$ containing x. $\mathscr{U}$ is a *Hausdorff* or T_2 *topology* if the open sets separate points, that is, if for $x \neq y$, x and y possess disjoint neighbourhoods. A family of sets $\mathscr{F}$ forms a *base* for the topology $\mathscr{U}$ if every $U \in \mathscr{U}$ can be represented as a union of sets in $\mathscr{F}$, and $\mathscr{F} \subseteq \mathscr{U}$. $\mathscr{U}$ is *second countable* if it has a *countable base*, that is, if there exists a countable family $\mathscr{F}$ with these properties. The topology $\mathscr{U}_1$ generated by the base $\mathscr{F}_1$ has the same open sets as, and hence coincides with, the topology $\mathscr{U}_2$ generated by the base $\mathscr{F}_2$ if every set in $\mathscr{F}_1$ can be represented as a union of sets in $\mathscr{F}_2$, and vice versa. In this case the topological spaces $(\mathscr{X}, \mathscr{U}_1)$ and $(\mathscr{X}, \mathscr{U}_2)$ are said to be *equivalent*.

Given a topology $\mathscr{U}$ on $\mathscr{X}$, a notion of convergence of sequences (or more generally nets, but we do not need the latter concept) can be introduced by saying $x_n \to x$ in the topology $\mathscr{U}$ if, given any $\mathscr{U}$-neighbourhood of x, $\mathscr{U}_x$, there exists an integer N (depending on the neighbourhood in general) such that $x_n \in U_x$ for $n \geq N$. Conversely, nearly all the important types of convergence can be described in terms of a suitable topology. In this book, the overwhelming emphasis is on *metric topologies*, where the open sets are defined in terms of a *metric* or *distance function* $\rho(\cdot)$ satisfying for arbitrary $x, y, z \in \mathscr{X}$ the conditions

(i) $\rho(x, y) = \rho(y, x)$;

(ii) $\rho(x, y) \geq 0$ and $\rho(x, y) = 0$ if and only if $x = y$;

(iii) (triangle inequality) $\rho(x, y) + \rho(y, z) \geq \rho(x, z)$.

With respect to a given distance function ρ, the *open sphere* $S(x, \varepsilon)$ is the set $\{y \colon \rho(x, y) < \varepsilon\}$, being defined for any $\varepsilon > 0$. The *metric topology* generated by ρ is the smallest topology containing the open spheres; it is necessarily Hausdorff. A set is open in this topology if and only if every point in the set can be enclosed by an open sphere lying wholly within the set. A sequence of points $\{x_n\}$ converges to x in this topology if and only if $\rho(x_n, x) \to 0$. A *limit point* y of a set A is a limit of a sequence of points $x_n \in A$, with $x_n \neq y$; y need not necessarily be in A. The closure of A in the metric topology is the union of A and its limit points. A space $\mathscr{X}$ with topology $\mathscr{U}$ is *metrizable* if a distance function ρ can be found such that $\mathscr{U}$ is equivalent to the metric topology generated by ρ. Two metrics on the same space $\mathscr{X}$ are *equivalent* if they each generate the same topology on $\mathscr{X}$.

A sequence of points $\{x_n : n \geq 1\}$ in a metric space is a *Cauchy sequence* if $\rho(x_n, x_m) \to 0$ as $n, m \to \infty$. The space is *complete* if every Cauchy sequence has a limit, that is, if for every Cauchy sequence $\{x_n\}$ there exists a point $x \in \mathscr{X}$ such that $\rho(x_n, x) \to 0$. A set $\mathscr{D}$ is *dense* in $\mathscr{X}$ if, for every $\varepsilon > 0$, every point in $\mathscr{X}$ can be approximated by points in $\mathscr{D}$, that is, given $x \in \mathscr{X}$, there exists $d \in \mathscr{D}$ such that $\rho(x, d) < \varepsilon$. The space $\mathscr{X}$ is *separable* if there exists a *countable dense set*, also called a *separability set*. If $\mathscr{X}$ is a separable metric space, the spheres with rational radii and centres on a countable dense set form a countable basis for the topology.

Given two topological spaces $(\mathscr{X}_1, \mathscr{U}_1)$ and $(\mathscr{X}_2, \mathscr{U}_2)$, a mapping $f(\cdot)$ from $(\mathscr{X}_1, \mathscr{U}_1)$ into $(\mathscr{X}_2, \mathscr{U}_2)$ is continuous if the inverse image $f^{-1}(U)$ of every open set U in $\mathscr{U}_2$ is an open set in $\mathscr{U}_1$. If both spaces are metric spaces, the mapping is continuous if and only if for every $x \in \mathscr{X}_1$ and every $\varepsilon > 0$, there exists $\delta > 0$ such that $\rho_2(f(x'), f(x)) < \varepsilon$ whenever $\rho_1(x', x) < \delta$, where ρ_1, ρ_2 are the metrics in $\mathscr{X}_1, \mathscr{X}_2$, respectively, a statement we can more loosely express by saying $f(x') \to f(x)$ whenever $x' \to x$. A *homeomorphism* is a $1:1$ continuous-both-ways mapping between two topological spaces. A famous theorem of Urysohn asserts that any *complete separable metric space* (*c.s.m.s.*) can be mapped homeomorphically into a countable product of unit intervals. A space that can be mapped homeomorphically into an open subset of a c.s.m.s. is called a *Polish space*. The theory we develop in Appendix 2 can be carried through for an arbitrary Polish space with only minor changes, but we do not seek this greater generality.

A set K in a topological space $(\mathscr{X}, \mathscr{U})$ is *compact* if every covering of K by a family of open sets contains a finite subcovering ($K \subseteq \bigcup_\alpha U_\alpha$, $U_\alpha \in \mathscr{U}$, implies the existence of $\alpha_1, \ldots, \alpha_N$ such that $K \subseteq \bigcup_1^N U_{\alpha_i}$). It is *relatively compact* if its closure is compact. In a separable space every open covering contains a countable subcovering and consequently it is sufficient to check the compactness property for sequences of open sets rather than general families. More generally, for a c.s.m.s. the following important characterizations of compact sets are equivalent.

Proposition A1.2.II (Metric Compactness Theorem). *Let $\mathscr{X}$ be a c.s.m.s. Then the following properties of a subset K of $\mathscr{X}$ are equivalent, and each is equivalent to the compactness of K.*

(i) (Heine–Borel property) *Every countable open covering of K contains a finite subcovering.*

(ii) (Bolzano–Weierstrass property) *Every infinite sequence of points in K contains a convergent subsequence with its limit in K.*

(iii) (Total boundedness and closure) K *is closed, and for every $\varepsilon > 0$, K can be covered by a finite number of spheres of radius ε.*

(iv) *Every sequence $\{F_n\}$ of closed subsets of K with nonempty finite intersections ($\bigcap_1^N F_n \neq \emptyset$: the finite intersection property) has nonempty total
intersection ($\bigcap_1^\infty F_n \neq \emptyset$).*

The space $\mathcal{X}$ itself is compact if the compactness criterion applies with $\mathcal{X}$
in place of K. It is *locally compact* if every point of $\mathcal{X}$ has a neighbourhood
with compact closure. A space with a locally compact second countable
topology is always metrizable. In a c.s.m.s. local compactness implies σ-
compactness: the whole space can be represented as a countable union of
compact sets (take the compact closures of the neighbourhoods of any countable dense set). Any finite-dimensional Euclidean space is σ-compact, but the
same does not apply to infinite-dimensional spaces such as $C[0, 1]$ or the
infinite-dimensional Hilbert space ℓ_2.

A useful corollary of Proposition A1.2.II is that any closed subset F of a
compact set in a complete metric space is again compact; for by (ii) any infinite
sequence of points of F has a limit point in K, and by closure the limit point
is also in F—hence, F is compact.

A1.3. Finitely and Countably Additive Set Functions

Let $\mathcal{A}$ be a class of sets in $\mathcal{X}$, and $\xi(\cdot)$ a real- or complex-valued function
defined on $\mathcal{A}$. $\xi(\cdot)$ is *finitely additive* on $\mathcal{A}$ if for finite families $\{A_1, \ldots, A_N\}$
of disjoint sets from $\mathcal{A}$, with their union also in $\mathcal{A}$, there holds

$$\xi\left(\bigcup_1^N A_i\right) = \sum_1^N \xi(A_i).$$

If a similar result holds for *sequences* of sets $\{A_i: i = 1, 2, \ldots\}$ then ξ is
countably additive (equivalently, σ-*additive*) on $\mathcal{A}$. A countably additive set
function on $\mathcal{A}$ is a *measure* if it is nonnegative; a *signed measure* if it is
real-valued but not necessarily nonnegative; and a *complex measure* if it is not
necessarily real-valued.

A *determining class* for a particular type of set function is a class of sets
with the property that if two set functions of the given type agree on the
determining class, then they coincide. In this case we can say that the set
function is determined by its values on the determining class in question. The
following proposition gives two simple results on determining classes. The
first is a consequence of the representation of any element in a ring of sets as
a disjoint union of the sets in any generating semiring; the second can be
proved using a monotone class argument and the continuity lemma A1.3.II
immediately following.

Proposition A1.3.I. (a) *A finitely additive, real- or complex-valued set function
defined on a ring $\mathcal{A}$ is determined by its values on any semiring generating $\mathcal{A}$.*

(b) *A countably additive real- or complex-valued set function defined on a σ-ring $\mathscr{S}$ is determined by its values on any ring generating $\mathscr{S}$.*

Proposition A1.3.II (Continuity Lemma). *Let $\mu(\cdot)$ be a finite real- or complex-valued, finitely additive set function defined on a ring $\mathscr{A}$. Then μ is countably additive on $\mathscr{A}$ if and only if for every decreasing sequence $\{A_n: n = 1, 2, \ldots\}$ of sets with $A_n \downarrow \varnothing$,*

$$\mu(A_n) \to 0.$$

So far we have assumed the set functions to take finite values on all the sets for which they are defined. It is frequently convenient to allow a nonnegative set function to take the value $+\infty$; this leads to few ambiguities and simplifies many statements. We then say that a finitely additive set function $\xi(\cdot)$ defined on an algebra or σ-algebra $\mathscr{A}$ is *totally finite* if, for all finite unions of disjoint sets $A_1, \ldots, A_N$ in $\mathscr{A}$, there exists $M < \infty$ such that

$$\sum_1^N |\xi(A_i)| \le M.$$

In particular, a nonnegative, additive set function $\mathscr{A}$ is totally finite if and only if $\mu(\mathscr{X}) < \infty$. A finitely additive set function is *σ-finite* if there exists a sequence of sets $\{A_n; n = 1, 2, \ldots\} \in \mathscr{A}$ such that $\mathscr{X} \subseteq \bigcup_1^\infty A_n$ and for each n the *restriction of ξ to A_n*, defined by the equation

$$\hat{\xi}(A) = \xi(A \cap A_n), \qquad A \in \mathscr{A},$$

is totally finite, a situation we describe more briefly by saying that ξ is totally finite on each A_n. The continuity lemma extends to σ-finite set functions with the proviso that we consider only sequences for which $|\mu(A_n)| < \infty$ for some $n < \infty$. (This simple condition, extending the validity of Proposition A1.3.II to σ-finite set functions, fails in the general case, however, and it is then better to refer to continuity from below.)

We next state the basic extension theorem used to establish the existence of measures on σ-rings. Note that it follows from Proposition A1.3.I that when such an extension exists, it must be unique.

Theorem A1.3.III (Extension Theorem). *A finitely additive, nonnegative set function defined on a ring $\mathscr{R}$ can be extended to a measure on $\sigma(\mathscr{R})$ if and only if it is countably additive on $\mathscr{R}$.*

As an example of the use of this theorem we cite the well-known result that a right-continuous monotonic increasing function $F(\cdot)$ on $\mathbb{R}$ can be used to define a measure on the Borel sets of $\mathbb{R}$ (the sets in the smallest σ-ring containing the intervals) through the following sequence of steps:

(i) define a nonnegative set function on the semiring of half-open intervals $(a, b]$ by setting $\mu_F(a, b] = F(b) - F(a)$;

(ii) extend μ_F by additivity to all sets in the ring generated by such intervals (this ring consisting, in fact, of all finite disjoint unions of such half-open intervals);

(iii) establish countable additivity on this ring by appealing to compactness properties of finite closed intervals; and

(iv) use the extension theorem to assert the existence of a measure extending the definition of μ_F to the σ-ring generated by the half-open intervals, that is, the Borel sets.

The intrusion of the topological notion of compactness into this otherwise measure-theoretic sequence is a reminder that in most applications there is a close link between open and measurable sets. Generalizing the corresponding concept for the real line, the *Borel sets* in a topological space are the sets in the smallest σ-ring (necessarily a σ-algebra) $\mathcal{B}_{\mathcal{X}}$ containing the open sets. A *Borel measure* is any measure defined on the Borel sets. The properties of such measures when $\mathcal{X}$ is a c.s.m.s. are explored in Appendix 2.

Returning to the general discussion, we note that no simple generalization of the extension theorem is known for signed measures. However, there is an important result, which shows that in some respects the study of signed measures can always be reduced to the study of measures.

Theorem A1.3.IV (Jordan–Hahn Decomposition). *Let ξ be a signed measure defined on a σ-algebra $\mathcal{S}$. Then ξ can be written as the difference*

$$\xi = \xi^+ - \xi^-$$

of two measures ξ^+, ξ^-, on $\mathcal{S}$ and $\mathcal{X}$ can be written as the union of two disjoint sets U^+, U^-, in $\mathcal{S}$ such that for all $E \in \mathcal{S}$

$$\xi^+(E) = \xi(E \cap U^+)$$

and

$$\xi^-(E) = -\xi(E \cap U^-),$$

and hence in particular $\xi^+(U^-) = \xi^-(U^+) = 0$.

The measures ξ^+ and ξ^- appearing in this theorem are called the upper and lower variations of ξ, respectively. The total variation of ξ is their sum

$$V_\xi(A) \equiv \xi^+(A) + \xi^-(A).$$

It is clear from the theorem that

$$V_\xi(A) = \sup_{\mathbb{P}(A)} \sum_1^{n(\mathbb{P})} |\xi(A_i)|,$$

where the supremum is taken over all finite partitions $\mathbb{P}$ of A into disjoint measurable sets. Thus, ξ is totally bounded if and only if $V_\xi(\mathcal{X}) < \infty$. In this case $V_\xi(A)$ acts as a norm on the space of totally bounded signed measures ξ on $\mathcal{S}$; it is referred to as the *variation norm* and sometimes written $V_\xi(\mathcal{X}) = \|\xi\|$.

A1.4. Measurable Functions and Integrals

A measurable space is a pair $(\mathscr{X}, \mathscr{F})$, where $\mathscr{X}$ is the space and $\mathscr{F}$ a σ-ring of sets defined on it. A mapping f from a measurable space $(\mathscr{X}_1, \mathscr{F}_1)$ into a measurable space $(\mathscr{X}_2, \mathscr{F}_2)$ is itself *measurable* if, for all $A \in \mathscr{F}_2$, $f^{-1}(A) \in \mathscr{F}_1$. Note that the inverse images in $\mathscr{X}_1$ of sets in $\mathscr{F}_2$ form a σ-ring $\mathscr{G}_f$, say, and the requirement for measurability is that $\mathscr{G}_f \subseteq \mathscr{F}_1$.

By specializing to the case that $\mathscr{X}_2$ is the real line $\mathbb{R}$ with $\mathscr{F}_2$ the σ-algebra of Borel sets generated by the intervals, the criterion for measurability simplifies as follows.

Proposition A1.4.I. *A real-valued function* $f : (\mathscr{X}, \mathscr{F}) \to \mathbb{R}$ *is measurable if and only if the set* $\{x : f(x) \leq c\}$ *is a set in* $\mathscr{F}$ *for every real* c.

The family of real-valued measurable functions on a measurable space $(\mathscr{X}, \mathscr{F})$ has many striking properties. It is closed under the operations of addition, subtraction, multiplication, and (with due attention to zeros) division. Moreover, any monotone limit of measurable functions is measurable. If $\mathscr{X}$ is also a topological space, and $\mathscr{F}$ the Borel σ-field on $\mathscr{X}$, then every continuous function on $\mathscr{X}$ is measurable.

The next proposition provides an important approximation result for measurable functions. Here a *simple function* is a finite linear combination of indicator functions of measurable sets, that is, a function of the form

$$ s(x) = \sum_1^N c_k I_{A_k}(x), $$

where $c_1, \dots, c_N$ are real and $A_1, \dots, A_N$ are measurable sets.

Proposition A1.4.II. *A nonnegative function* $f : (\mathscr{X}, \mathscr{F}) \to \mathbb{R}_+$ *is measurable if and only if it can be represented as the limit of a monotonic increasing sequence of simple functions.*

Now let μ be a measure on $\mathscr{F}$. We call the triple $(\mathscr{X}, \mathscr{F}, \mu)$ a finite or σ-finite measure space according to whether μ has the corresponding property; in the special case of a *probability space*, when μ has total mass unity, the triple is more usually written $(\Omega, \mathscr{E}, \mathscr{P})$, where the sets of the σ-algebra $\mathscr{E}$ are interpreted as *events*, a measurable function on $(\Omega, \mathscr{E})$ is a *random variable*, and $\mathscr{P}$ is a *probability measure*.

We turn to the problem of defining an *integral* (or in the probability case an *expectation*) with respect to the measure μ. If $s = \sum_1^N c_k I_{A_k}$ is a nonnegative simple function, set

$$ \int_{\mathscr{X}} s(x)\mu(dx) = \int_{\mathscr{X}} s\, d\mu = \sum_1^N c_k \mu(A_k), $$

where we allow $+\infty$ as a possible value of the integral. Next, for any nonnegative measurable function f, and any sequence of simple functions $\{s_n\}$ approximating f from below, set

$$\int_{\mathcal{X}} f\, d\mu = \lim_{n \to \infty} \int_{\mathcal{X}} s_n\, d\mu,$$

and prove that the limit is independent of the particular sequence of simple functions used. Finally, for any measurable function f, write

$$f_+(x) = [f(x)]^+ = \max(f(x), 0),$$

$$f_-(x) = f_+(x) - f(x),$$

and, if $\int f_+ \, d\mu$ and $\int f_- \, d\mu$ are both finite (equivalently, $\int_{\mathcal{X}} |f|\, d\mu$ is finite), say that f is *integrable* and then define, for any integrable function f,

$$\int_{\mathcal{X}} f\, d\mu = \int_{\mathcal{X}} f_+\, d\mu - \int_{\mathcal{X}} f_-\, d\mu.$$

The resulting *abstract Lebesgue integral* is well defined, additive, linear, order preserving, and enjoys strikingly elegant continuity properties. These last are set out in the theorem below, where we say $f_n \to f$ μ-almost everywhere (μ-a.e., or a.e. μ) if the (necessarily measurable) set $\{x: f_n(x) \nrightarrow f(x)\}$ has μ-measure zero. [In the probability case we refer to *almost sure* (a.s.) rather than a.e. convergence.]

Theorem A1.4.III (Lebesgue Convergence Theorems). *The following results hold for a sequence of measurable functions $\{f_n; n = 1, 2, \ldots\}$ defined on the measure space $(\mathcal{X}, \mathcal{F}, \mu)$:*

(a) (Fatou's lemma) *If $f_n \geq 0$,*

$$\int_{\mathcal{X}} \liminf_{n \to \infty} f_n(x)\, d\mu(x) \leq \liminf_{n \to \infty} \int_{\mathcal{X}} f_n(x)\, d\mu(x)$$

(b) (Monotone convergence theorem) *If $f_n \geq 0$, $f_n \uparrow f$ (a.e. μ) then f is measurable and*

$$\lim_{n \to \infty} \int_{\mathcal{X}} f_n\, d\mu = \int_{\mathcal{X}} f\, d\mu$$

in the sense that either both sides are finite, and then equal, or both are infinite.

(c) (Dominated convergence theorem) *If $|f_n(x)| \leq g(x)$, where $g(\cdot)$ is integrable, and $f_n \to f$ (a.e. μ), then*

$$\lim_{n \to \infty} \int_{\mathcal{X}} f_n\, d\mu = \int_{\mathcal{X}} f\, d\mu.$$

If f is an integrable function, the *indefinite integral* of f over any measurable subset A can be defined by

$$\xi_f(A) \overset{\text{def}}{=} \int_A f\, d\mu \overset{\text{def}}{=} \int_{\mathcal{X}} I_A f\, d\mu,$$

where I_A is the indicator function of A. It is clear that ξ_f is totally finite and finitely additive on $\mathcal{S}$. Moreover, it follows from the dominated convergence theorem that if $A_n \in \mathcal{S}$, $A_n \downarrow \varnothing$, then $I_{A_n} f \to 0$ and hence $\xi_f(A_n) \to 0$. Thus, ξ_f is also countably additive, that is, a signed measure on $\mathcal{S}$. This raises the question of which signed measures can be represented as indefinite integrals with respect to a given μ. The essential feature is that the ξ-measure of a set should tend to zero with the μ-measure. More specifically, ξ is *absolutely continuous* with respect to μ wherever $\mu(A) = 0$ implies $\xi(A) = 0$; we then have the following theorem.

Theorem A1.4.IV (Radon–Nikodym Theorem). *Let $(\mathcal{X}, \mathcal{F}, \mu)$ be a σ-finite measure space and ξ a totally finite measure or signed measure on $\mathcal{F}$. Then there exists a measurable integrable function f, such that*

(A1.4.1) $$\xi(A) = \int_A f(x)\, d\mu(x) \quad (all\ A \in \mathcal{F}),$$

if and only if ξ is absolutely continuous with respect to μ; moreover f is a.e. uniquely determined by (A1.4.1), in the sense that any two functions satisfying (A1.4.1) for all $A \in \mathcal{F}$ must be equal (a.e. μ).

The function f appearing in (A1.4.1) is usually referred to as a *Radon–Nikodym derivative* of ξ with respect to μ, written $d\xi/d\mu$.

There is an obvious extension of Theorem A1.4.IV to the case where ξ is σ-finite; in this extension (A1.4.1) holds for subsets A of each of the denumerable family of measurable sets on which ξ is totally finite.

Finally, we consider the relation between a fixed σ-finite measure μ and an arbitrary σ-finite signed measure ξ. ξ is said to be *singular* with respect to μ if there is a set E in $\mathcal{F}$ such that

$$\mu(E) = 0$$

and for all $A \in \mathcal{F}$,

$$\xi(A) = \xi(E \cap A)$$

[so that also $\xi(E^c) = 0$ and $\mu(A) = \mu(A \cap E^c)$]. We then have the following theorem.

Theorem A1.4.V (Lebesgue Decomposition Theorem). *Let $(\mathcal{X}, \mathcal{F}, \mu)$ be a σ-finite measure space and $\xi(\cdot)$ a finite or σ-finite signed measure on $\mathcal{F}$. Then there exists a unique decomposition of ξ,*

$$\xi = \xi_s + \xi_{ac},$$

into components that are, respectively, singular and absolutely continuous with respect to μ.

A1.5. Product Spaces

If $\mathcal{X}, \mathcal{Y}$ are two spaces, the *Cartesian product* $\mathcal{X} \times \mathcal{Y}$ is the set of ordered pairs $\{(x, y): x \in \mathcal{X}, y \in \mathcal{Y}\}$. If $\mathcal{X}$ and $\mathcal{Y}$ are either topological or measure spaces, there is a natural way of combining the original structures to produce a structure in the product space. Let us consider first the topological case. If U, V are neighbourhoods of the points $x \in \mathcal{X}$, $y \in \mathcal{Y}$ with respect to topologies $\mathcal{U}, \mathcal{V}$, define a neighbourhood of the pair (x, y) as the product set $U \times V$. The class of product sets of this kind is closed under finite intersections as a consequence of the relation

$$(U \times V) \cap (A \times B) = (U \cap A) \times (V \cap B).$$

It can therefore be taken as the basis of a topology in $\mathcal{X} \times \mathcal{Y}$, which is called the *product topology* and denoted $\mathcal{U} \otimes \mathcal{V}$ [we follow Brémaud (1981), for example, in using a distinctive product sign as a reminder that the product entity here is generated by the elements of the factors]. Most properties enjoyed by the component (or coordinate) topologies are passed on to the product topology. In particular, if $\mathcal{X}, \mathcal{Y}$ are both c.s.m.s, then $\mathcal{X} \times \mathcal{Y}$ is also a c.s.m.s. with respect to any one of a number of equivalent metrics, of which perhaps the simplest is

$$\rho((x, y), (u, v)) = \max\{\rho_{\mathcal{X}}(x, u), \rho_{\mathcal{Y}}(y, v)\}.$$

More generally, if $\{\mathcal{X}_t, t \in \mathcal{T}\}$ is a family of spaces, the Cartesian product

$$\mathcal{X} = \underset{t \in \mathcal{T}}{\times} (\mathcal{X}_t)$$

may be defined as the set of all functions $x: \mathcal{T} \to \bigcup_t \mathcal{X}_t$, such that $x(t) \in \mathcal{X}_t$. A *cylinder set* in this space is a set in which restrictions are placed on a finite subset of the coordinates, say on $x(t_1), \ldots, x(t_N)$, the values of the other coordinates being unrestricted in their appropriate spaces. A family of basic open sets in $\mathcal{X}$ can be defined by choosing open sets $\{U_i \subseteq \mathcal{X}_{t_i}, i = 1, \ldots, N\}$ and requiring $x(t_i) \in U_i$, $i = 1, \ldots, N$. The topology generated by the class of cylinder sets of this form is called the *product topology* in $\mathcal{X}$. A remarkable property of this topology is that if the coordinate spaces $\mathcal{X}_t$ are individually compact in their respective topologies, then $\mathcal{X}$ is compact in the product topology. On the other hand, if the individual $\mathcal{X}_t$ are metric spaces, there are again many ways in which $\mathcal{X}$ can be made into a metric space [e.g., by using the supremum of the distances $\rho_t(x(t), y(t))$], but the topologies they generate are not in general equivalent among themselves, or to the product topology defined earlier.

Turning now to the measure context, let $(\mathcal{X}, \mathcal{F}, \mu)$ and $(\mathcal{Y}, \mathcal{G}, \nu)$ be two measure spaces. The product σ-ring $\mathcal{F} \otimes \mathcal{G}$ is the σ-ring generated by the semiring of measurable rectangles $A \times B$, with $A \in \mathcal{F}$, $B \in \mathcal{G}$. The *product measure* $\mu \times \nu$ is the extension to the σ-ring of the countably additive set function defined on such rectangles by

$$(\mu \times v)(A \times B) = \mu(A)v(B)$$

and extended by additivity to the ring of all finite disjoint unions of such rectangles. If μ, v are both finite, then so is $\mu \times v$; similarly, if μ, v are σ-finite so is $\mu \times v$. The *product measurable space* is the space $(\mathcal{X} \times \mathcal{Y}, \mathcal{F} \otimes \mathcal{G})$, and the *product measure space* is the space $(\mathcal{X} \times \mathcal{Y}, \mathcal{F} \otimes \mathcal{G}, \mu \times v)$. All the definitions extend easily to the products of finite families of measure spaces. In the probability context, they form the natural framework for the discussion of *independence*. In the context of integration theory, the most important results pertain to the evaluation of *double integrals*, the question we take up next.

Let $\mathcal{H} = \mathcal{F} \otimes \mathcal{G}$ and $\pi = \mu \times v$. If C is $\mathcal{H}$-measurable, its *sections*

$$A_x = \{y \colon (x, y) \in A\} \quad \text{and} \quad A^y = \{x \colon (x, y) \in A\}$$

are, respectively, $\mathcal{G}$-measurable for each fixed x and $\mathcal{F}$-measurable for each fixed y. (The converse to this result, that a set whose sections are measurable is $\mathcal{H}$-measurable, is false, however.) Similarly, if $f(x, y)$ is $\mathcal{H}$-measurable, then regarded as a function of y, it is $\mathcal{G}$-measurable for each fixed x, and regarded as a function of x, it is $\mathcal{F}$-measurable for each fixed y. Introducing integrals with respect to μ, v, write

$$s(x) = \begin{cases} \displaystyle\int_{\mathcal{Y}} f(x, y)dv(y) & \text{if the integrand is } v\text{-integrable,} \\ +\infty & \text{otherwise;} \end{cases}$$

$$t(y) = \begin{cases} \displaystyle\int_{\mathcal{X}} f(x, y)d\mu(x) & \text{if the integrand is } \mu\text{-integrable,} \\ +\infty & \text{otherwise.} \end{cases}$$

We then have the following theorem.

Theorem A1.5.I (Fubini's Theorem). *Let* $(\mathcal{X}, \mathcal{F}, \mu)$ *and* $(\mathcal{Y}, \mathcal{G}, v)$ *be* σ-*finite measure spaces, and let* $(\mathcal{Z}, \mathcal{H}, \pi)$ *denote the product measure space.*

(a) *If* f *is* $\mathcal{H}$-*measurable and* π-*integrable, then* $s(x)$ *is* $\mathcal{F}$-*measurable and* μ-*integrable,* $t(y)$ *is* $\mathcal{G}$-*measurable and* v-*integrable, and*

$$\int_{\mathcal{Z}} f \, d\pi = \int_{\mathcal{X}} s \, d\mu = \int_{\mathcal{Y}} t \, dv.$$

(b) *If* f *is* $\mathcal{H}$-*measurable and* $f \geq 0$, *it is necessary and sufficient for* f *to be* π-*integrable that either* s *be* μ-*integrable or* t *be* v-*integrable.*

Not all the important measures on a product space are product measures; in the probability context, in particular, it is necessary to study general bivariate probability measures and their relations to the marginal and conditional measures they induce. Thus, if π is a probability measure on $(\mathcal{X} \times \mathcal{Y}, \mathcal{F} \otimes \mathcal{G})$, we define the *marginal probability measures* $\pi_{\mathcal{X}}$ and $\pi_{\mathcal{Y}}$ to be the *projections* of π onto $(\mathcal{X}, \mathcal{F})$ and $(\mathcal{Y}, \mathcal{G})$, respectively, that is, the measures defined by

$$\pi_{\mathscr{X}}(A) = \pi(A \times \mathscr{Y}) \quad \text{and} \quad \pi_{\mathscr{Y}}(B) = \pi(\mathscr{X} \times B).$$

We next investigate the possibility of writing a measure on the product space as an integral (or a mixture of conditional probabilities), say

(A1.5.1) $$\pi(A \times B) = \int_A d\pi_{\mathscr{X}}(x)Q(B|x),$$

where $Q(B|x)$ may be regarded as the conditional probability of observing the event B given the occurrence of x. Such a family is also known as a dis-integration of π.

Proposition A1.5.II. *Given a family $\{Q(\cdot|x), x \in \mathscr{X}\}$ of probability measures on $(\mathscr{Y}, \mathscr{G})$, and a probability measure $\pi_{\mathscr{X}}$ on $(\mathscr{X}, \mathscr{F})$, the necessary and sufficient condition that (A1.5.1) should define a probability measure on the product space $(\mathscr{Z}, \mathscr{H})$ is that as a function of x, $Q(B|x)$ be $\mathscr{F}$-measurable for each fixed $B \in \mathscr{G}$. When this condition is satisfied, for every $\mathscr{H}$-measurable, nonnegative function $f(\cdot, \cdot)$,*

(A1.5.2) $$\int_{\mathscr{Z}} f \, d\pi = \int_{\mathscr{X}} d\pi_{\mathscr{X}}(x) \int_{\mathscr{Y}} f(x, y)Q(dy|x).$$

Indeed, the integral at (A1.5.1) is not defined unless $Q(B|\cdot)$ is $\mathscr{F}$-measurable. When it is, the right side of (A1.5.2) can be extended to a finitely additive set function on the ring of finite disjoint unions of rectangle sets. Countable additivity and the extension to a measure for which (A1.5.2) holds then follow along standard lines using monotone approximation arguments.

The projection of π onto the space $(\mathscr{Y}, \mathscr{G})$, that is, the measure defined by

$$\pi_{\mathscr{Y}}(B) = \int_{\mathscr{X}} d\pi_{\mathscr{X}}(x)Q(B|x),$$

is known as the *mixture* of $Q(\cdot|x)$ with respect to $\pi_{\mathscr{X}}$.

The converse problem, of establishing the existence of a family of measures satisfying (A1.5.1) from a given measure and its marginal, is a special case of the problem of *regular conditional probabilities* [e.g., see Ash (1972, §6.6)]. For any *fixed* $B \in \mathscr{G}$, $\pi(\cdot \times B)$ may be regarded as a measure on $(\mathscr{X}, \mathscr{F})$, which is clearly absolutely continuous with respect to the marginal $\pi_{\mathscr{X}}$. Hence, there exists a Radon–Nikodym derivative, $Q_R(B|x)$ say, that is $\mathscr{F}$-measurable, satisfies (A1.5.1), and should therefore be a candidate for the disintegration of π. The difficulty is that we can guarantee the behaviour of Q_R only for fixed sets B, and it is not clear whether, for x fixed and B varying, the family $Q_R(B|x)$ will have the additivity and continuity properties of a measure. If $\{A_1, \ldots, A_N\}$ is a *fixed* family of disjoint sets in $\mathscr{G}$ or if $\{B_n; n \geq 1\}$ is a fixed sequence in $\mathscr{G}$ with $B_n \downarrow \varnothing$, then it is not difficult to show that

$$Q_R\left(\bigcup_1^N A_i \Big| x\right) = \sum_1^N Q_R(A_i|x) \quad \text{(a.e } \pi_{\mathcal{X}}\text{)},$$

$$Q_R(B_n|x) \to 0 \qquad \qquad \text{(a.e. } \pi_{\mathcal{X}}\text{)},$$

respectively, but because there are nondenumerably many such relations to be checked, it is not obvious that the exceptional sets of measure zero can be combined into a single such set. The problem, in fact, is formally identical to that considered in Chapter 6, Theorem 6.1.VI, and the arguments developed there can be applied equally here. They rest, however, on the assumption of additional topological properties for $\mathcal{Y}$, and we therefore obtain only the following partial converse to Proposition A1.5.II.

Proposition A1.5.III (Existence of Regular Conditional Probabilities). *Let $(\mathcal{Y}, \mathcal{G})$ be a c.s.m.s. with its associated σ-algebra of Borel sets, $(\mathcal{X}, \mathcal{F})$ an arbitrary measurable space, and π a probability measure on the product space $(\mathcal{Z}, \mathcal{H})$. Then there exists a family $Q(B|x)$ such that*

(i) $Q(\cdot|x)$ *is a probability measure on $\mathcal{G}$ for each fixed $x \in \mathcal{X}$*;
(ii) $Q(B|\cdot)$ *is an $\mathcal{F}$-measurable function on $\mathcal{X}$ for each fixed $B \in \mathcal{G}$*;
(iii) *(A1.5.1) is satisfied for all $A \in \mathcal{F}, B \in \mathcal{G}$.*

For details of the proof of this proposition, together with variants of it, we refer to the exercises in Chapter 6.

We consider finally the product of a general family of measurable spaces, say $\{(\mathcal{X}_t, \mathcal{F}_t): t \in \mathcal{T}\}$, where $\mathcal{T}$ is an arbitrary (finite, countable, or uncountable) indexing set. Once again the cylinder sets play a basic role. A *measurable cylinder set* in $\mathcal{X} = \bigtimes_{t \in \mathcal{T}} (\mathcal{X}_t)$ is a set of the form

$$C(t_1, \ldots, t_N; B_1, \ldots, B_N) = \{x(t): x(t_i) \in B_i, i = 1, \ldots, N\},$$

where $B_i \in \mathcal{F}_{t_i}$ is measurable for each $i = 1, \ldots, N$. Such sets form a semiring; their finite disjoint unions form a ring; and the generated σ-ring we denote by

$$\mathcal{F}_\infty = \bigotimes_{t \in \mathcal{T}} \mathcal{F}_t.$$

This construction can be used to define a product measure on $\mathcal{F}_\infty$, but greater interest centres on the *extension problem*: given a system of measures $\pi_{(\sigma)}$ defined on finite subfamilies $\mathcal{F}_{(\sigma)} = \mathcal{F}_{t_1} \otimes \mathcal{F}_{t_2} \otimes \cdots \otimes \mathcal{F}_{t_N}$, where $(\sigma) = \{t_1, \ldots, t_N\}$ is a finite selection of indices from $\mathcal{T}$, when can they be extended to a measure on $\mathcal{F}_\infty$? It follows from the extension theorem A1.3.III that the necessary and sufficient condition for this to be possible is that the given measures must give rise to a countably additive set function on the ring generated by the measurable cylinder sets. As with the previous result, countable additivity cannot be established without some additional assumptions; again it is convenient to put these in topological form by requiring each of the $\mathcal{X}_t$ to be a c.s.m.s. Countable additivity then follows by a variant of the usual compactness argument, and the only remaining requirement is that the given measures should satisfy the obviously necessary consistency conditions stated in the theorem below.

Theorem A1.5.IV (Kolmogorov Extension Theorem). *Let $\mathcal{T}$ be any arbitrary index set, and for $t \in \mathcal{T}$ suppose $(\mathcal{X}_t, \mathcal{F}_t)$ is a c.s.m.s. with its associated Borel σ-algebra. Suppose further that for each finite subfamily $(\sigma) = \{t_1, \ldots, t_N\}$ of indices from $\mathcal{T}$, there is given a probability measure $\pi_{(\sigma)}$ on $\mathcal{F}_{(\sigma)} = \mathcal{F}_{t_1} \otimes \cdots \otimes \mathcal{F}_{t_N}$. In order that there exist a measure π on $\mathcal{F}_\infty$ such that for all (σ), $\pi_{(\sigma)}$ is the projection of π onto $\mathcal{F}_{(\sigma)}$, it is necessary and sufficient that for all (σ), (σ_1), (σ_2),*

(i) *$\pi_{(\sigma)}$ depends only on the choice of indices in (σ), not on the order in which they are written down; and*

(ii) *if $(\sigma_1) \subseteq (\sigma_2)$, then $\pi_{(\sigma_1)}$ is the projection of $\pi_{(\sigma_2)}$ onto $\mathcal{F}_{(\sigma_1)}$.*

Written out more explicitly in terms of distribution functions, condition (i) becomes (in an obvious notation) the condition of *invariance under simultaneous permutations*: if $p_1, \ldots, p_N$ is a permutation of the integers $1, \ldots, N$, then

$$F^{(N)}_{t_1, \ldots, t_N}(x_1, \ldots, x_N) = F^{(N)}_{t_{p_1}, \ldots, t_{p_N}}(x_{p_1}, \ldots, x_{p_N}).$$

Similarly, condition (ii) becomes the condition of *consistency of marginal distributions*, namely, that

$$F^{(N+k)}_{t_1, \ldots, t_N, s_1, \ldots, s_k}(x_1, \ldots, x_N, \infty, \ldots, \infty) = F^{(N)}_{t_1, \ldots, t_N}(x_1, \ldots, x_N).$$

The measure π induced on $\mathcal{F}_\infty$ by the fidi distributions is called their projective limit. Clearly, if stochastic processes have the same fidi distributions, they must also have the same projective limit. Such processes may be described as being *equivalent* or *versions* one of the other.

Theorem A1.5.IV is discussed in a slightly more general form in Parthasarathy (1967, §§5.1–5.5) to which reference may be made for proof and further detail.

Measures on Metric Spaces

A2.1. Borel Sets, Dissecting Systems, and Atomic and Diffuse Measures

If $(\mathcal{X}, \mathcal{U})$ is a topological space, the smallest σ-algebra containing the open sets is called the *Borel σ-algebra*. If $f: \mathcal{X} \to \mathbb{R}$ is any real-valued continuous function, then the set

$$\{x: f(x) < c\}$$

is open in $\mathcal{U}$ and hence measurable. It follows that f is measurable. Thus, every continuous function is measurable with respect to the Borel σ-algebra.

It is necessary to clarify the relation between the Borel sets and various other candidates for useful σ-algebras that suggest themselves, such as

(a) the *Baire sets*, belonging to the smallest σ-field with respect to which the continuous functions are measurable;
(b) the *Borelian sets*, generated by the compact sets in $\mathcal{X}$; and
(c) if $\mathcal{X}$ is a metric space, the σ-algebra generated by the open spheres.

We show that, with a minor reservation concerning (b), all four concepts coincide when $\mathcal{X}$ is a c.s.m.s. More precisely, we have the following result.

Proposition A2.1.I. *Let $\mathcal{X}$ be a metric space and $\mathcal{U}$ the topology induced by the metric. Then*

(i) *the Baire sets and the Borel sets coincide;*
(ii) *if $\mathcal{X}$ is separable, then the Borel σ-algebra is the smallest σ-algebra containing the open spheres;*
(iii) *a Borel set is Borelian if and only if it is σ-compact, that is, if it can be*

*covered by a countable union of compact sets. In particular, the Borel sets
and the Borelian sets coincide if and only if the whole space is σ-compact.*

The proof of (i) depends on the lemma below, of importance in its own
right; (ii) depends on the fact that when $\mathscr{X}$ is separable, every open set can be
represented as a countable union of open spheres; (iii) follows from the fact
that all closed subsets of a compact set are compact and hence Borelian.

Lemma A2.1.II. *Let F be a closed set in the metric space $\mathscr{X}$, U an open set
containing F, and $I_F(\cdot)$ the indicator function of F. Then there exists a sequence
of continuous functions $\{f_n(x)\}$ such that*

(i) $0 \le f_n(x) \le 1$ $(x \in \mathscr{X})$;
(ii) $f_n(x) = 0$ *outside* U;
(iii) $f_n(x) \downarrow I_F(x)$ *as* $n \to \infty$.

PROOF. Let $f_n(x) = \rho(x, U^c)/[\rho(x, U^c) + 2^n \rho(x, F)]$, where for any set C

$$\rho(x, C) = \inf_{y \in C} \rho(x, y)$$

Then the sequence $f_n(x)$ has the required properties.   □

It is clear that in a separable metric space the Borel sets are countably
generated. The next lemma exhibits a simple example of a countable semiring
of open sets generating the Borel sets.

Lemma A2.1.III. *Let $\mathscr{X}$ be a. c.s.m.s., $\mathscr{D}$ a countable dense set in $\mathscr{X}$, and $\mathscr{S}_0$ the
class of all finite intersections of open spheres $S(d, r)$ with centres $d \in \mathscr{D}$ and
rational radii. Then*

(i) $\mathscr{S}_0$ *and the ring $\mathscr{A}_0$ generated by $\mathscr{S}_0$ are countable; and*
(ii) $\mathscr{S}_0$ *generates the Borel σ-algebra in $\mathscr{X}$.*

It is also a property of the Borel sets in a separable metric space, and of
considerable importance in the analysis of sample-path properties of point
processes, that they include a *dissecting system* defined as follows.

Definition A2.1.IV. The sequence $\mathscr{T} = \{\mathscr{T}_n\}$ of finite partitions $\mathscr{T}_n = \{A_{ni} : i = 1, \ldots, k_n\}$ $(n = 1, 2, \ldots)$ consisting of Borel sets in the space $\mathscr{X}$ is a
dissecting system for $\mathscr{X}$ when, in addition to the partition properties that
$A_{ni} \cap A_{nj} = \varnothing$ for $i \ne j$ and $A_{n1} \cup \cdots \cup A_{nk_n} = \mathscr{X}$, the sequences are nested
(meaning that $A_{n-1,i} \cap A_{nj} = A_{nj}$ or $\varnothing$) and separate points of $\mathscr{X}$ (meaning
that for any given distinct points $x, y \in \mathscr{X}$, there exists an integer n such that
$x \in A_{ni}$ implies $y \notin A_{ni}$).

Proposition A2.1.V. *Every separable metric space $\mathscr{X}$ contains a dissecting system.*

PROOF. Let $\{d_1, d_2, \ldots\} = \mathscr{D}$ be a separability set for $\mathscr{X}$ (i.e., $\mathscr{D}$ is a countable dense set in $\mathscr{X}$). Take any pair of distinct points $x, y \in \mathscr{X}$; their distance apart equals $\delta \equiv \rho(x, y) > 0$. We can then find d_m, d_n in $\mathscr{D}$ such that $\rho(d_m, x) < \delta/2$, $\rho(d_n, y) < \delta/2$, and so the spheres $S(d_m, \delta/2)$, $S(d_n, \delta/2)$, which are Borel sets, certainly separate x and y. We have essentially to embed such separating spheres into a sequence of sets covering the whole space.

For the next part of the proof it is convenient to identify one particular element in each $\mathscr{T}_n$ (or it may possibly be a null set for all n sufficiently large) as A_{n0}: this entails no loss of generality.

Definite the initial partition $\{A_{1i}\}$ by $A_{11} = S(d_1, 1)$, $A_{10} = \mathscr{X} \setminus A_{11}$. Observe that $\mathscr{X}$ is covered by the countably infinite sequence $\{S(d_n, 1)\}$, so the sequence of sets $\{A'_{n0}\}$ defined by

$$A'_{n0} = \mathscr{X} \setminus \left(\bigcup_{r=1}^{n} S(d_r, 1) \right)$$

converges to the null set. For $n = 2, 3, \ldots$ and $i = 1, \ldots, n$, define

$$B_{ni} = S(d_i, 2^{-(n-i)}), \quad \text{and set} \quad B_{n0} = \left(\bigcup_{i=1}^{n} B_{ni} \right)^c$$

so that $\{B_{ni}: i = 0, \ldots, n\}$ covers $\mathscr{X}$. By setting $C_{n0} = B_{n0}$, $C_{n1} = B_{n1}$, and $C_{ni} = B_{ni} \setminus (B_{n1} \cup \cdots \cup B_{n,i-1})$, it is clear that $\{C_{ni}: i = 0, 1, \ldots, n\}$ is a partition of $\mathscr{X}$. Let the family $\{A_{ni}\}$ consist of all nonempty intersections of the form $A_{n-1,j} \cap C_{nk}$, setting in particular $A_{n0} = A_{n-1,0} \cap C_{n0} = A'_{n0}$. Then $\{\{A_{ni}\}: n = 1, 2, \ldots\}$ clearly consists of nested partitions of $\mathscr{X}$ by Borel sets, and only the separation property has to be established.

Take distinct points $x, y \in \mathscr{X}$, and write $\delta = \rho(x, y)$ as before. Fix the integer $r \geq 0$ by $2^{-r} \leq \min(1, \delta/2) < 2^{-r+1}$, and locate a separability point d_m such that $\rho(d_m, x) < 2^{-r}$. Then $x \in S(d_m, 2^{-r}) = B_{m+r,m}$, and consequently $x \in C_{m+r,j}$ for some $j = 1, \ldots, m$. But by the triangle inequality,

$$\rho(x, z) < 2, \qquad 2^{-(m+r-j)} < \delta = \rho(x, y),$$

for any $z \in C_{m+r,j}$, and therefore the partition $\{C_{m+r,i}\}$, and hence also $\{A_{m+r,i}\}$, separates x and y. $\square$

Trivially, if $\mathscr{T}$ is a dissecting system for $\mathscr{X}$, the nonempty sets of $\mathscr{T} \cap A$ (in an obvious notation) constitute a dissecting system for any $A \in \mathscr{B}_{\mathscr{X}}$. If A is also compact, the construction of a dissecting system for A is simplified by applying the Heine–Borel theorem to extract a finite covering of A from the countable covering

$$\{S(d_r, 2^{-n}): r = 1, 2, \ldots\}.$$

Definition A2.1.VI. The ring of sets generated by finitely many intersections and unions of elements of a dissecting system is a *dissecting ring*.

The chief motivation for introducing the concept of a dissecting system is that it facilitates the discussion of atomic and nonatomic components of a measure μ (i.e., nonnegative σ-finite countably additive set function) on a metric space $\mathcal{X}$. Call $x \in \mathcal{X}$ an *atom* of μ if $\mu(\{x\}) > 0$, and call the measure δ_x defined on Borel sets A by

$$\delta_x(A) = 1 \quad \text{if } x \in A, \quad = 0 \quad \text{otherwise,}$$

Dirac measure (at x). A measure with only atoms is *purely atomic*, while a measure with no atoms is *diffuse*.

Given a dissecting system $\mathcal{T}$ for $\mathcal{X}$, there is a well-defined nested sequence $\{T_n(x)\} \subset \mathcal{T}$ such that

$$\bigcap_{n=1}^{\infty} T_n(x) = \{x\}, \quad \text{so } \mu(T_n(x)) \to \mu(\{x\}) \quad \text{for } n \to \infty,$$

and it follows that x is an atom of μ if and only if $\mu(T_n(x)) \geq \varepsilon$ (all n) for some $\varepsilon > 0$; indeed, any ε in $0 < \varepsilon \leq \mu(\{x\})$ will do.

Given $\varepsilon > 0$, we can identify all atoms of μ of mass $\mu(\{x\}) \geq \varepsilon$, and then using a sequence $\{\varepsilon_j\}$ with $\varepsilon_j \downarrow 0$ as $j \to \infty$, all atoms of μ can be identified. Note that, because μ is σ-finite, it can have at most countably many atoms, so identifying them as $\{x_j : j = 1, 2, \ldots\}$ say, and writing $b_j = \mu(\{x_j\})$, the measure

$$\sum_{j=1}^{\infty} b_j \delta_{x_j}(\cdot),$$

which clearly consists only of atoms, is the *atomic component* of the measure μ. The measure

$$\mu_d(\cdot) \equiv \mu(\cdot) - \sum_{j=1}^{\infty} b_j \delta_{x_j}(\cdot)$$

has no atoms and is the *diffuse component* of μ. It is thus clear that any measure μ as above has a unique decomposition into atomic and diffuse components. [For further details, see Kallenberg (1975, pp. 10–11).]

A2.2. Regular and Tight Measures

In this section we examine the extent to which the values of a finitely or countably generated set function defined on some class of sets can be approximated by their values on either closed or compact sets.

Definition A2.2.I. (i) A finite or countably additive, nonnegative set function μ defined on the Borel sets is *regular* if, given any Borel set A and $\varepsilon > 0$, there exist open and closed sets G and F, respectively, such that $F \subseteq A \subseteq G$ and

$$\mu(G - A) < \varepsilon \quad \text{and} \quad \mu(A - F) < \varepsilon.$$

(ii) It is *compact regular* if, given any Borel set A and $\varepsilon > 0$, there exists a compact set C such that $C \subseteq A$ and $\mu(A - C) < \varepsilon$.

We first establish the following.

Proposition A2.2.II. *If $\mathscr{X}$ is a metric space, then all totally finite measures on $\mathscr{B}_{\mathscr{X}}$ are regular.*

PROOF. Let μ be a totally finite, additive, nonnegative set function defined on $\mathscr{B}_{\mathscr{X}}$. Call any $A \in \mathscr{B}_{\mathscr{X}}$ μ-regular if it can be approximated by its values on open and closed sets in the manner of Definition A2.2.I. The class of μ-regular sets is obviously closed under complementation. It then follows from the inclusion relations

(A2.2.1a)
$$\bigcup_{\alpha} G_{\alpha} - \bigcup_{\alpha} F_{\alpha} \subseteq \bigcup_{\alpha} (G_{\alpha} - F_{\alpha})$$

and

(A2.2.1b)
$$\bigcap_{\alpha} G_{\alpha} - \bigcap_{\alpha} F_{\alpha} \subseteq \bigcup_{\alpha} \left(\bigcap_{\alpha} G_{\alpha} - F_{\alpha} \right) \subseteq \bigcup_{\alpha} (G_{\alpha} - F_{\alpha})$$

that the class is an algebra if μ is finitely additive and a σ-algebra if μ is countably additive. [In the latter case, the countable union $\bigcup_{\alpha} F_{\alpha}$ in (A2.2.1a) may not be closed, but we can approximate $\mu(\bigcup_{\alpha} F_{\alpha})$ by $\mu(\bigcup_{i=1}^{N} F_{\alpha_i})$ to obtain a set that is closed and has the required properties; similarly, in (A2.2.1b) we can approximate $\mu(\bigcap_{\alpha} G_{\alpha})$ by $\mu(\bigcap_{i=1}^{N} G_{\alpha_i})$.] Moreover, if μ is σ-additive, the class also contains all closed sets, for if F is closed, the *halo sets*

(A2.2.2)
$$F^{\varepsilon} = \bigcup_{x \in F} S(x, \varepsilon) = \{x : \rho(x, F) < \varepsilon\}$$

form, for a sequence of values of ε tending to zero, a family of open sets with the property $F^{\varepsilon} \downarrow F$; hence, it follows from the continuity Lemma A1.3.II that $\mu(F^{\varepsilon}) \to \mu(F)$. In summary, if μ is countably additive the μ-regular sets form a σ-algebra containing the closed sets, and therefore the class must coincide with the Borel sets themselves. □

Note that this proof does not require either completeness or separability.

Compact regularity is a corollary of this result and the notion of a *tight measure*.

Definition A2.2.III. A finite or countably additive set function μ is *tight* if, given $\varepsilon > 0$, there exists a compact set K such that $\mu(\mathscr{X} - K)$ is defined and

$$\mu(\mathscr{X} - K) < \varepsilon.$$

Lemma A2.2.IV. *If $\mathscr{X}$ is a complete metric space, a Borel measure is compact regular if and only if it is tight.*

PROOF. Given any Borel set A it follows from Proposition A2.2.II that there exists a closed set $C \subseteq A$ with $\mu(A - C) < \varepsilon/2$. If μ is tight, choose K so that $\mu(\mathcal{X} - K) < \varepsilon/2$. Then the set $C \cap K$ is a closed subset of the compact set K and hence is itself compact; it also satisfies

$$\mu(A - C \cap K) \le \mu(A - C) + \mu(A - K) < \varepsilon,$$

which establishes the compact regularity of μ. If, conversely, μ is compact regular, tightness follows on taking $\mathcal{X} = K$.   □

Proposition A2.2.V. *If $\mathcal{X}$ is c.s.m.s., every Borel measure μ is tight and hence compact regular.*

PROOF. Let $\mathcal{D}$ be a separability set for $\mathcal{X}$; then for fixed n,

$$\bigcup_{d \in \mathcal{D}} S(d, n^{-1}) = \mathcal{X},$$

and so by the continuity lemma, we can find a finite set $d_1, \dots, d_{k(n)}$ such that

$$\mu\left(\mathcal{X} - \bigcup_{i=1}^{k(n)} S(d_i, n^{-1}) \right) < \varepsilon/2^n.$$

Now consider

$$K = \bigcap_n \left[\bigcup_{i=1}^{k(n)} S(d_i, n^{-1}) \right].$$

It is not difficult to see that K is closed and totally bounded, and hence compact, by Proposition A1.2.II and that $\mu(\mathcal{X} - K) < \varepsilon$. Hence, μ is tight.   □

The above results establish compact regularity as a necessary condition for a finitely additive set function to be countably additive. The next proposition asserts its sufficiency. The method of proof provides a pattern that is used with minor variations at several important points in the further development of the theory.

Proposition A2.2.VI. *Let $\mathcal{A}$ be a ring of sets from the c.s.m.s. $\mathcal{X}$ and μ a finitely additive, nonnegative set function defined and finite on $\mathcal{A}$. A sufficient condition for μ to be countably additive on $\mathcal{A}$ is that, for every $A \in \mathcal{A}$ and $\varepsilon > 0$, there exists a compact set $C \subseteq \mathcal{A}$ such that $\mu(A - C) < \varepsilon$.*

PROOF. Let $\{A_n\}$ be a decreasing sequence of sets in $\mathcal{A}$ with $A_n \downarrow \varnothing$; to establish countable additivity for μ it is enough to show that $\mu(A_n) \to 0$ for every such sequence. Suppose to the contrary that $\mu(A_n) \ge \alpha > 0$. By assumption, there exists for each n a compact set C_n for which $C_n \subseteq A_n$ and $\mu(A_n - C_n) < \alpha/2^{n+1}$. By (A2.2.1),

$$A_n - \bigcap_k C_k \subseteq \bigcup_k (A_k - C_k).$$

Since $\mathscr{A}$ is a ring, every finite union $\bigcup_{k=1}^{n} (A_k - C_k)$ is an element of $\mathscr{A}$, and so from the finite additivity of μ

$$\mu\left(A_n - \bigcap_{k=1}^{n} C_k\right) \leq \sum_{k=1}^{n} \alpha/2^{k+1} < \alpha/2.$$

Thus, the intersection $\bigcap_{k=1}^{n} C_k$ is nonempty for each n, and it follows from the finite intersection part of Proposition A1.2.II that $\bigcap_{k=1}^{\infty} C_k$ is nonempty. This gives us the required contradiction to the assumption $A_n \downarrow \emptyset$. □

Corollary A2.2.VII. *A finite, finitely additive, nonnegative set function defined on the Borel sets of $\mathscr{X}$ is countably additive if and only if it is compact regular.*

We now prove an extension of Proposition A2.2.VI, which plays on important role in developing the existence theorems of Chapter 6. It is based on the notion of a self-approximating ring and is a generalization of the concept of a covering ring given in Kallenberg (1975).

Definition A2.2.VIII. *A ring $\mathscr{A}$ of sets of the c.s.m.s. $\mathscr{X}$ is a self-approximating ring if, for every $A \in \mathscr{A}$ and $\varepsilon > 0$, there exists a sequence of closed sets $\{F_k(A; \varepsilon)\}$ such that*

(i) $F_k(A; \varepsilon) \in \mathscr{A}$ $(k = 1, 2, \ldots)$;
(ii) *each set $F_k(A; \varepsilon)$ is a contained within a sphere of radius ε;*
(iii) $\bigcup_1^{\infty} F_k(A; \varepsilon) = A$.

Kallenberg was concerned with the case when $\mathscr{X}$ is locally compact, in which case it is possible to require the covering to be finite, so that the lemma below effectively reduces to Proposition A2.2.VI. The general version is based on an argument in Harris (1968). The point is that it allows checking for countable additivity to be reduced to a denumerable set of conditions.

Lemma A2.2.IX. *Let $\mathscr{A}$ be a self-approximating ring of subsets of the c.s.m.s. $\mathscr{X}$ and μ a finitely additive, nonnegative set function defined on $\mathscr{A}$. In order that μ have an extension as a measure on $\sigma(A)$ it is necessary and sufficient that for each $A \in \mathscr{A}$,*

(A2.2.3) $$\lim_{m \to \infty} \mu\left(\bigcup_{i=1}^{m} F_i(A; \varepsilon)\right) = \mu(A),$$

where the notation of Definition A2.2.VIII is to be understood.

PROOF. Necessity follows from the continuity lemma. We establish sufficiency by contradiction: suppose that μ is finitely additive and satisfies (A2.2.3) but that μ cannot be extended to a measure on $\sigma(\mathscr{A})$. From the continuity lemma again it follows that there exists $\alpha > 0$ and a sequence of sets $A_n \in \mathscr{A}$, with $A_n \downarrow \emptyset$, such that

(A2.2.4) $$\mu(A_n) \geq \alpha.$$

For each k, use (A2.2.3) to choose a set

$$F_k = \bigcup_{i=1}^{m_k} F_i(A_k; 1/k)$$

that is closed, can be covered by a finite number of k^{-1} spheres, and satisfies

$$\mu(A_k - F_k) \le \alpha/2^{k+1}.$$

From (A2.2.1) we have

$$\left(A_k - \bigcap_1^k F_j\right) \subseteq \bigcup_1^k (A_j - F_j),$$

which, using the additivity of μ, implies that

$$\mu\left(\bigcap_1^k F_j\right) \ge \alpha/2 > 0.$$

Thus, the sets F_j have the finite intersection property.

To show that their complete intersection is nonempty, choose any $x_k \in \bigcap_1^k F_j$. Since F_1 can be covered by a finite number of 1-spheres, there exists a subsequence $\{x_k'\}$ that is wholly contained within a sphere of radius 1. Turning to F_2, we can select a further subsequence x_k'', which for $k \ge 2$ lies wholly within a sphere of radius $\frac{1}{2}$. Proceeding in this way by induction, we finally obtain by a diagonal selection argument a subsequence $\{x_{k_j}\}$ such that for $j \ge j_0$ all terms are contained within a sphere of radius $1/j_0$. This is enough to show that $\{x_{k_j}\}$ is a Cauchy sequence that, since $\mathcal{X}$ is complete, has a limit point $\bar{x}$, say. For each k the x_j are in $\bigcap_1^k F_n$ for all sufficiently large j. Since the sets are closed this implies $\bar{x} \in F_k$ for every k. But this implies also that $\bar{x} \in A_k$ and hence $\bar{x} \in \bigcap_1^\infty A_k$, which contradicts the assumption $A_n \downarrow \varnothing$. The contradiction shows that (A2.2.4) cannot hold, and so completes the proof of the lemma. $\qquad\square$

Let us observe finally that self-approximating rings do exist. A standard example, which is denumerable and generating as well as self-approximating, is the ring $\mathcal{C}$ generated by the *closed* spheres with rational radii and centres on a countable dense set. To see this, consider the class $\mathcal{D}$ of all sets that can be approximated by finite unions of closed sets in $\mathcal{C}$ in the sense required by condition (iii) of Definition A2.2.VIII. This class contains all open sets because any open set G can be written as a denumerable union of closed spheres, with their centres at points of the countable dense set lying within G, and rational radii bounded by the nonzero distance from the given point of the countable dense set to the boundary of G. $\mathcal{D}$ also contains all closed spheres in $\mathcal{C}$; for example, suppose ε is given, choose any positive rational $\delta < \varepsilon$, and take the closed spheres with centres at points of the countable dense set lying within the given sphere and having radii δ. These are all elements of $\mathcal{C}$, and therefore so are their intersections with the given closed sphere. These intersections form a countable family of closed sets satisfying (iii) of Definition A2.2.VIII for the given closed sphere. It is obvious that $\mathscr{D}$ is closed under finite unions, and that, from the relation

$$\left(\bigcup_{j=1}^{\infty} F_j \right) \cap \left(\bigcup_{k=1}^{\infty} F_k' \right) = \bigcup_{j=1}^{\infty} \bigcup_{k=1}^{\infty} (F_j \cap F_k'),$$

$\mathscr{D}$ is also closed under finite intersections. Since $\mathscr{D}$ contains all closed spheres and also their complements (which are open), $\mathscr{D}$ contains $\mathscr{C}$. Thus every set in $\mathscr{C}$ can be approximated by closed spheres in $\mathscr{C}$, and so $\mathscr{C}$ is self-approximating as required.

A2.3. Weak Convergence of Measures

We make reference to the following notions of convergence of a sequence of measures on a metric space.

Definition A2.3.I. Let $\{\mu_n : n \geq 1\}$, μ, be totally finite measures in the metric space $\mathscr{X}$. Then

(i) $\mu_n \to \mu$ *weakly* if $\int f \, d\mu_n \to \int f \, d\mu$ for all bounded continuous functions f on $\mathscr{X}$;

(ii) $\mu_n \to \mu$ *vaguely* if $\int f \, d\mu_n \to \int f \, d\mu$ for all bounded continuous functions f on $\mathscr{X}$, which vanish outside a compact set;

(iii) $\mu_n \to \mu$ *strongly* (or *in variation norm*) if $\|\mu_n - \mu\| \to 0$.

The last definition corresponds to strong convergence in the Banach space of all totally finite signed measures on $\mathscr{X}$, for which the total variation constitutes a genuine norm. The first definition does not correspond exactly to weak convergence in the Banach space sense, but it reduces to weak star (weak*) convergence when $\mathscr{X}$ is compact (say, the unit interval) and the space of signed measures on $\mathscr{X}$ can be identified with the adjoint space to the space of all bounded continuous functions on $\mathscr{X}$. Vague convergence is particularly useful in the discussion of locally compact spaces; in our discussion a somewhat analogous role is played by the notion of weak hat convergence (i.e., $\hat{w}$-convergence) to be introduced in Section A2.6: it is equivalent to vague convergence when the space is locally compact.

Undoubtedly, the central concept for our purposes is the concept of weak convergence. Not only does it lead to a convenient and internally consistent topologization of the space of realizations of a random measure, but it also provides an appropriate framework for discussing the convergence of random measures conceived as probability distributions on this space of realizations. In this section we give a brief treatment of some basic properties of weak convergence, following closely the discussion in Billingsley (1968) to which we refer for further details.

Theorem A2.3.II. *Let $\mathcal{X}$ be a metric space, $\{\mu_n, n \geq 1\}$, μ, measures on $\mathcal{B}_{\mathcal{X}}$. Then the following statements are equivalent:*

(i) $\mu_n \to \mu$ *weakly*;
(ii) $\mu_n(\mathcal{X}) \to \mu(\mathcal{X})$ *and* $\limsup_{n \to \infty} \mu_n(F) \leq \mu(F)$ *for all closed* $F \in \mathcal{B}_{\mathcal{X}}$;
(iii) $\mu_n(\mathcal{X}) \to \mu(\mathcal{X})$ *and* $\liminf_{n \to \infty} \mu_n(G) \geq \mu(G)$ *for all open* $G \in \mathcal{B}_{\mathcal{X}}$;
(iv) $\mu_n(A) \to \mu(A)$ *for all Borel sets* A *with* $\mu(\partial A) = 0$ *(i.e., all μ-continuity sets).*

PROOF. We shall show that (i) $\Rightarrow$ (ii) $\Leftrightarrow$ (iii) $\Rightarrow$ (iv) $\Rightarrow$ (i).

Given a closed set F, choose any fixed $v > 0$ and construct a $[0, 1]$-valued continuous function f that equals 1 on F and vanishes outside F^v [see (A2.2.2) and Lemma A2.1.II]. We have for each $n \geq 1$

$$\mu_n(F) \leq \int f\, d\mu_n \leq \mu_n(F^v);$$

hence, if (i) holds,

$$\limsup_{n \to \infty} \mu_n(F) \leq \int f\, d\mu \leq \mu(F^v).$$

But $F^v \downarrow F$ as $v \downarrow 0$, and by the continuity lemma we can choose v so that, given any $\varepsilon > 0$, $\mu(F^v) \leq \mu(F) + \varepsilon$. Since ε is arbitrary, the second statement in (ii) follows, while the first is trivial if we take $f = 1$.

Taking complements shows that (ii) and (iii) are equivalent.

When A is a μ-continuity set, $\mu(A^0) = \mu(\bar{A})$, and so supposing (iii) holds, and hence (ii) also, we have on applying (ii) to $\bar{A}$ and (iii) to A° that

$$\limsup \mu_n(A) \leq \limsup \mu_n(\bar{A}) \leq \mu(\bar{A}) = \mu(A^\circ) \leq \liminf \mu_n(A^\circ)$$

$$\leq \liminf \mu_n(A).$$

Thus, equality holds throughout and $\mu_n(A) \to \mu(A)$, so that (iv) holds.

Finally, suppose that (iv) holds. Let f be any bounded continuous function on $\mathcal{X}$, and let the bounded interval $[\alpha', \alpha'']$ be such that $\alpha' < f(x) < \alpha''$ for all $x \in \mathcal{X}$. Call $\alpha \in [\alpha', \alpha'']$ a regular value of f if $\mu\{x : f(x) = \alpha\} = 0$. At most a countable number of values of α can be irregular, while for any α, β that are regular values, $\{x : \alpha < f(x) \leq \beta\}$ is a μ-continuity set. From the boundedness of f on $\mathcal{X}$, given any $\varepsilon > 0$, we can partition $[\alpha', \alpha'']$ by a finite set of points $\alpha_0 = \alpha', \ldots, \alpha_N = \alpha''$ with $\alpha_i < \alpha_{i+1} \leq \alpha_i + \varepsilon$ for $i = 0, \ldots, N-1$, and from the countability of the set of irregular points (if any), we can moreover assume that these α_i are all regular points of f. Defining $A_i = \{x : \alpha_{i-1} < f(x) \leq \alpha_i\}$ for $i = 1, \ldots, N$, and then

$$f_L(x) = \sum_{i=1}^{N} \alpha_{i-1} I_{A_i}(x), \qquad f_U(x) = \sum_{i=1}^{N} \alpha_i I_{A_i}(x),$$

each A_i is a μ-continuity set, $f_L(x) \leq f(x) \leq f_U(x)$, and by (iv),

$$\int f_L d\mu = \sum_{i=1}^{N} \alpha_{i-1}\mu(A_i) = \lim_{n\to\infty} \sum_{i=1}^{N} \alpha_{i-1}\mu_n(A_i) = \lim_{n\to\infty} \int f_L d\mu_n$$

$$\leq \lim_{n\to\infty} \int f_U d\mu_n = \int f_U d\mu,$$

the extreme terms here differing by at most $\varepsilon\mu(\mathcal{X})$. Since ε is arbitrary and $\int f_L d\mu_n \leq \int f d\mu_n \leq \int f_U d\mu_n$, it follows that we must have $\int f d\mu_n \to \int f d\mu$ for all bounded continuous f, that is, $\mu_n \to \mu$ weakly. $\qquad\square$

Since the functions used in the proof that (i) implies (ii) are uniformly continuous, we can extract from the proof the following useful condition for weak convergence.

Corollary A2.3.III. $\mu_n \to \mu$ *weakly if and only if $\int f\, d\mu_n \to \int f\, d\mu$ for all bounded and uniformly continuous functions $f: \mathcal{X} \to \mathbb{R}$.*

A class $\mathscr{C}$ of sets with the property that

(A2.3.1) $\mu_n(C) \to \mu(C)$ (all $C \in \mathscr{C}$)   implies $\mu_n \to \mu$ weakly,

is called by Billingsley a *convergence-determining class*. Adapting this terminology, (iv) of the theorem above asserts that the μ-continuity sets form a convergence-determining class. Any convergence-determining class is necessarily a determining class, but the converse need not be true. In particular circumstances, it may be of considerable importance to find a convergence-determining class that is smaller than the classes in Theorem A2.3.II. While such classes often have to be constructed to take advantage of particular features of the metric space in question, the general result below is also of value. In this proposition a *covering semiring* is a semiring with the property that every open set can be represented as a finite or countable union of sets from the semiring. If $\mathcal{X}$ is separable, an important example of such a semiring is obtained by first taking the open spheres $S(d_k, r_j)$ with centres at the points $\{d_k\}$ of a countable dense set and radii $\{r_j\}$ forming a countable dense set in $(0, 1)$, then forming finite intersections, and finally taking proper differences.

Proposition A2.3.IV. *Any covering semiring, together with the whole space $\mathcal{X}$, forms a convergence-determining class.*

PROOF. Let G be an open set, so that by assumption we have

$$G = \bigcup_{1}^{\infty} C_i \quad \text{for some } C_i \in \mathscr{S},$$

where $\mathscr{S}$ is a generating semiring. Since the limit μ in (A2.3.1) is a measure, given $\varepsilon > 0$, we can choose a finite integer K such that

$$\mu\left(G - \bigcup_{i=1}^{K} C_i\right) \leq \varepsilon/2;$$

that is,

$$\mu(G) \le \mu\left(\bigcup_{i=1}^{K} C_i\right) + \varepsilon/2.$$

Furthermore, since $\mathscr{C}$ is a semiring, $\bigcup_{i=1}^{K} C_i$ can be represented as a finite union of disjoint sets in $\mathscr{C}$. From (A2.3.1) it therefore follows that there exists N such that for $n \ge N$

$$\mu\left(\bigcup_{1}^{K} C_i\right) \le \mu_n\left(\bigcup_{1}^{K} C_i\right) + \varepsilon/2.$$

Hence, we obtain

$$\mu(G) \le \liminf_{n\to\infty} \mu_n\left(\bigcup_{1}^{K} C_i\right) + \varepsilon \le \liminf_{n\to\infty} \mu_n(G) + \varepsilon.$$

Since ε is arbitrary, (iii) of Theorem A2.3.II is satisfied, and therefore $\mu_n \to \mu$ weakly.   □

We investigate next the preservation of weak convergence under mappings from one metric space into another. Let $\mathscr{X}$, $\mathscr{Y}$ be two metric spaces with associated Borel σ-algebras $\mathscr{B}_{\mathscr{X}}$, $\mathscr{B}_{\mathscr{Y}}$, and f a measurable mapping from $(\mathscr{X}, \mathscr{B}_{\mathscr{X}})$ into $(\mathscr{Y}, \mathscr{B}_{\mathscr{Y}})$. Any measure μ on $\mathscr{B}_{\mathscr{X}}$ induces a measure μf^{-1} on $\mathscr{B}_{\mathscr{Y}}$, where for $B \in \mathscr{B}_{\mathscr{Y}}$,

$$(\mu f^{-1})(B) = \mu(f^{-1}(B)).$$

Now let μ_n be any sequence of measures on $\mathscr{B}_{\mathscr{X}}$ such that $\mu_n \to \mu$ weakly. Does it follow that $\mu_n f^{-1} \to \mu f^{-1}$ weakly? The answer is no in general; a sufficient condition is given in the next proposition, where D_f is the set of points of discontinuity of f [recall that f is continuous at x if $\rho_{\mathscr{Y}}(f(x'), f(x)) \to 0$ whenever $\rho_{\mathscr{X}}(x', x) \to 0$].

Proposition A2.3.V. *Let* $(\mathscr{X}, \mathscr{B}_{\mathscr{X}})$, $(\mathscr{Y}, \mathscr{B}_{\mathscr{Y}})$ *be metric spaces and* f *a measurable mapping of* $(\mathscr{X}, \mathscr{B}_{\mathscr{X}})$ *into* $(\mathscr{Y}, \mathscr{B}_{\mathscr{Y}})$. *Suppose* $\mu_n \to \mu$ *weakly on* $\mathscr{X}$ *and* $\mu(D_f) = 0$; *then* $\mu_n f^{-1} \to \mu f^{-1}$ *weakly.*

PROOF. Let B be any Borel set in $\mathscr{B}_{\mathscr{Y}}$ and x any point in the closure of $f^{-1}(B)$. For any sequence of points $x_n \in f^{-1}(B)$, such that $x_n \to x$, either $x \in D_f$ or $f(x_n) \to f(x)$, in which case $x \in f^{-1}(\bar{B})$. Arguing similarly for the complement, we find that

(A2.3.2) $\partial\{f^{-1}(B)\} \subseteq f^{-1}(\partial B) \cup D_f.$

Now suppose $\mu_n \to \mu$ weakly on $\mathscr{B}_{\mathscr{X}}$, and consider the image measures $\mu_n f^{-1}$, μf^{-1} on $\mathscr{B}_{\mathscr{Y}}$. Let B be any continuity set for μf^{-1}. It follows from (A2.3.2) and the assumption of the proposition that $f^{-1}(B)$ is a continuity set for μ. Hence, for all such B, $(\mu_n f^{-1})(B) = \mu_n(f^{-1}(B)) \to \mu(f^{-1}(B)) = (\mu f^{-1})(B)$, that is, $\mu_n f^{-1} \to \mu f^{-1}$ weakly.   □

A2.4. Compactness Criteria for Weak Convergence

In this section we call a set $\mathcal{M}$ of totally finite Borel measures on $\mathcal{X}$ *relatively compact* for weak convergence if every sequence of measures in $\mathcal{M}$ contains a weakly convergent subsequence. It is shown in Section A2.5 that weak convergence is equivalent to convergence with respect to a certain metric, and that if $\mathcal{X}$ is a c.s.m.s., the space of all totally finite Borel measures on $\mathcal{X}$ is itself a c.s.m.s. with respect to this metric. We can then appeal to Proposition A1.2.II and conclude that a set of measures is compact (or relatively compact) if and only if it satisfies any of the criteria (i)–(iv) of that proposition.

Our aim in this section is to establish the following criterion for compactness.

Theorem A2.4.I (Prohorov's Theorem). *Let $\mathcal{X}$ be a c.s.m.s. Necessary and sufficient conditions for a set $\mathcal{M}$ of totally finite Borel measures on $\mathcal{X}$ to be relatively compact for weak convergence are*

(i) *the total masses $\mu(\mathcal{X})$ are uniformly bounded for $\mu \in \mathcal{M}$; and*
(ii) *$\mathcal{M}$ is uniformly tight—namely, given $\varepsilon > 0$, there exists a compact K such that, for all $\mu \in \mathcal{M}$,*

$$(A2.4.1) \qquad\qquad \mu(\mathcal{X} - K) < \varepsilon.$$

PROOF. We first establish that the uniform tightness condition is necessary, putting it in the following alternative form.

Lemma A2.4.II. *A set $\mathcal{M}$ of measures is uniformly tight if and only if, for all $\varepsilon > 0$ and $\delta > 0$, there exists a finite family of δ-spheres (i.e., of radius δ) $S_1, \ldots, S_N$ such that*

$$(A2.4.2) \qquad\qquad \mu\left(\mathcal{X} - \bigcup_1^N S_k\right) \le \varepsilon \quad (\text{all } \mu \in \mathcal{M}).$$

PROOF OF LEMMA. If the condition holds, we can find, for every $k = 1, 2, \ldots$, a finite union A_k of spheres of radius $1/k$ such that $\mu(\mathcal{X} - A_k) \le \varepsilon/2^k$ for all $\mu \in \mathcal{M}$. Then the set

$$K = \bigcap_{k=1}^{\infty} A_k$$

is totally bounded and hence compact, and for every $\mu \in \mathcal{M}$,

$$\mu(\mathcal{X} - K) \le \sum_{k=1}^{\infty} \mu(\mathcal{X} - A_k) < \varepsilon.$$

Thus, $\mathcal{M}$ is uniformly tight. Conversely, if $\mathcal{M}$ is uniformly tight and, given ε, we choose a compact K to satisfy (A2.4.1), then for any $\delta > 0$, K can be covered by a finite set of δ-spheres, and so (A2.4.2) holds. $\square$

Returning now to the main theorem, suppose if possible that $\mathcal{M}$ is relatively compact but (A2.4.2) fails for some $\varepsilon > 0$ and $\delta > 0$. Since we assume $\mathcal{X}$ is separable we can write $\mathcal{X} = \bigcup_1^\infty S_k$, where each S_k is a δ-sphere. On the other hand, for every finite n, we can find a measure $\mu_n \in \mathcal{M}$ such that

(A2.4.3a) $$\mu_n\left(\mathcal{X} - \bigcup_1^n S_k\right) \geq \varepsilon.$$

If in fact $\mathcal{M}$ is relatively compact, there exists a subsequence μ_{n_j} that converges weakly to some limit μ^*. From (A2.4.3a) we obtain via (ii) of Theorem A2.3.II that for all $N > 0$

$$\mu^*\left(\mathcal{X} - \bigcup_1^N S_k\right) \geq \limsup_{n_j \to \infty} \mu_{n_j}\left(\mathcal{X} - \bigcup_1^N S_k\right) \geq \varepsilon.$$

This contradicts the requirement that, because $\mathcal{X} - \bigcup_1^N S_k \downarrow \emptyset$, we must have $\mu^*(\mathcal{X} - \bigcup_1^N S_k) \to 0$. Thus, the uniform tightness condition is necessary. As it is clear that no sequence $\{\mu_n\}$ with $\mu_n(\mathcal{X}) \to \infty$ can have a weakly convergent subsequence, condition (i) is necessary also.

Turning to the converse, we again give a proof based on separability, although in fact the result is true without this restriction. Let us start by constructing a countable ring $\mathcal{R}$ from the open spheres with rational radii and centres in a countable dense set, by taking first finite intersections and then proper differences, thus forming a semiring, and finally taking all finite disjoint unions of such differences.

Now suppose that $\{\mu_n : n \geq 1\}$ is any sequence of measures from $\mathcal{M}$. We have to show that $\{\mu_n\}$ contains a weakly convergent subsequence. For any $A \in \mathcal{R}$, condition (i) implies that $\{\mu_n(A)\}$ is a bounded sequence of real numbers and therefore contains a convergent subsequence. Using a diagonal selection argument, we can proceed to extract subsequences $\{\mu_{n_j}\}$ for which the $\mu_{n_j}(A)$ approach a finite limit for each of the countable number of sets $A \in \mathcal{R}$. Let us write $\mu^*(A)$ for the limit, and for brevity of notation set $\mu_{n_j} = \mu_j'$. Thus, we have

(A2.4.3b) $$\mu_j'(A) \to \mu^*(A) \quad (\text{all } A \in \mathcal{R}).$$

This might seem enough to set up a proof, for it is easy to see that μ^* inherits finite additivity from the μ_j', and one might anticipate that the uniform tightness condition could be used to establish countable additivity. The difficulty is that we have no guarantee that the sets $A \in \mathcal{R}$ are continuity sets for μ^*, so that (A2.4.3b) cannot be relied on to give the correct value to the limit measure. To get over this difficulty, we have to develop a more elaborate argument incorporating the notion of a continuity set.

For this purpose we introduce the class $\mathcal{C}$ of Borel sets, which are μ^*-regular in the following sense: given $C \in \mathcal{C}$, we can find a sequence $\{A_n\}$ of sets in $\mathcal{R}$ and an associated sequence of open sets G_n such that $A_n \supseteq G_n \supseteq C$, and similarly a sequence of sets $B_n \in \mathcal{R}$ and closed sets F_n with $C \supseteq F_n \supseteq B_n$, the two sequences $\{A_n\}$, $\{B_n\}$ having the property

(A2.4.4) $$\liminf \mu^*(A_n) = \limsup \mu^*(B_n), = \mu(C), \quad \text{say.}$$

We establish the following properties of the class $\mathscr{C}$.

(1) $\mathscr{C}$ *is a ring*: Let C, C' be any two sets in $\mathscr{C}$, and consider, for example, the difference $C - C'$. If $\{A_n\}$, $\{G_n\}$, $\{B_n\}$, $\{F_n\}$ and $\{A'_n\}$, $\{G'_n\}$, $\{B'_n\}$, $\{F'_n\}$ are the sequences for C and C', respectively, then $A_n - B'_n \supseteq G_n - F'_n \supseteq C - C' \supseteq F_n - G'_n \supseteq B_n - A'_n$, with $G - F'_n$ open, $F_n - G'_n$ closed, and the outer sets elements of $\mathscr{R}$ since $\mathscr{R}$ is a ring. From the inclusion

$$(A_n - B'_n) - (B_n - A'_n) \subseteq (A_n - B_n) \cup (A'_n - B'_n),$$

we find that $\mu^*(A_n - B'_n)$ and $\mu^*(B_n - A'_n)$ have common limit values, which we take to be the value of $\mu(C - C')$. Thus, $\mathscr{C}$ is closed under differences, and similar arguments show that $\mathscr{C}$ is closed also under finite unions and intersections.

(2) $\mathscr{C}$ *is a covering ring*: Let d be any element in the countable dense set used to construct $\mathscr{R}$, and for rational values of r define

$$h(r) = \mu^*(S(d, r)).$$

Then $h(r)$ is monotonic increasing, bounded above, and can be uniquely extended to a monotonic increasing function defined for all positive values of r and continuous at all save a countable set of values of r. It is clear that if r is any continuity point of $h(r)$, the corresponding sphere $S(d, r)$ belongs to $\mathscr{C}$. Hence, for each d, we can find a sequence of spheres $S(d, \varepsilon_n) \in \mathscr{C}$ with radii $\varepsilon_n \to 0$. Since any open set in $\mathscr{X}$ can be represented as a countable union of these spheres, $\mathscr{C}$ must be a covering class.

(3) *For every* $C \in \mathscr{C}$, $\mu'_j(C) \to \mu(C)$: Indeed, with the usual notation we have

$$\mu^*(A_n) = \lim_{j \to \infty} \mu'_j(A_n) \geq \limsup_{j \to \infty} \mu'_j(C) \geq \liminf_{j \to \infty} \mu'_j(C)$$

$$\geq \lim_{j \to \infty} \mu'_j(B_n) = \mu^*(B_n).$$

Since the two extreme members can be made as close as we please to $\mu(C)$, the two inner members must coincide and equal $\mu(C)$.

(4) μ *is finitely additive on* $\mathscr{C}$: This follows from (3) and the finite additivity of μ'_j.

(5) *If* $\mathscr{M}$ *is uniformly tight, then* μ *is countably additive on* $\mathscr{C}$: Suppose that $\{C_k\}$ is a sequence of sets from $\mathscr{C}$, with $C_k \downarrow \varnothing$, but $\mu(C_k) \geq \alpha > 0$. From the definition of $\mathscr{C}$, we can find for each C_k a set $B_k \in \mathscr{R}$ and a closed set F_k such that $C_k \supseteq F_k \supseteq B_k$ and $\mu^*(B_k) > \mu(C_k) - \alpha/2^{k+1}$; then

$$\liminf_{j \to \infty} \mu'_j(F_k) \geq \lim_{j \to \infty} \mu'_j(B_k) = \mu^*(B_k) \geq \alpha - \alpha/2^{k+1}.$$

We then have

$$\mu(C_k) = \liminf_{j \to \infty} \mu'_j\left(\bigcap_1^k F_n\right) + \limsup_{j \to \infty} \mu'_j\left(C_k - \bigcap_1^k F_n\right)$$

$$\leq \liminf_{j \to \infty} \mu'_j\left(\bigcap_1^k F_n\right) + \sum_{n=1}^k \limsup_{j \to \infty} \mu'_j(C_n - F_n)$$

$$\leq \liminf_{j\to\infty} \mu'_j\left(\bigcap_1^k F_n\right) + \sum_{n=1}^k \left[\mu(C_n) - \liminf_{j\to\infty} \mu'_j(F_n)\right]$$

$$\leq \liminf_{j\to\infty} \mu'_j\left(\bigcap_1^k F_n\right) + \alpha/2;$$

hence, for all k

$$\liminf_{j\to\infty} \mu'_j\left(\bigcap_1^k F_n\right) \geq \alpha/2.$$

If now $\mathcal{M}$ is uniformly tight, there exists a compact set K such that $\mu(\mathcal{X} - K) < \alpha/4$ for all $\mu \in \mathcal{M}$. In particular, therefore,

$$\mu'_j\left(\bigcap_1^k F_n\right) - \mu'_j\left(\bigcap_1^k (F_n \cap K)\right) < \alpha/4$$

and so

$$\liminf_{j\to\infty} \mu'_j\left(\bigcap_1^k (F_n \cap K)\right) \geq \alpha/4.$$

But this is enough to show that for each k, the sets $(\bigcap_1^k F_n) \cap K$ are nonempty, and since (if $\mathcal{X}$ is complete) each is a closed subset of the compact set K, it follows from Theorem A1.2.II that their total intersection is nonempty. Since their total intersection is contained in $\bigcap_1^\infty C_n$, this set is also nonempty, contradicting the assumption that $C_n \downarrow \varnothing$.

We can now complete the proof of the theorem without difficulty. From the countable additivity of μ on $\mathcal{C}$, it follows that there is a unique extension of μ to a measure on $\mathcal{B}_{\mathcal{X}}$. Since $\mathcal{C}$ is a covering class, and $\mu'_j(C) \to \mu(C)$ for $C \in \mathcal{C}$, it follows from Proposition A2.3.III that $\mu'_j \to \mu$ weakly, or in other words that the original sequence μ_n contains a weakly convergent subsequence, as required.   □

A2.5. Metric Properties of the Space $\mathcal{M}_{\mathcal{X}}$

Denote by $\mathcal{M}_{\mathcal{X}}$ the space of all totally finite measures on $\mathcal{B}_{\mathcal{X}}$, and consider the following candidate (the Prohorov distance) for a metric on $\mathcal{M}_{\mathcal{X}}$, where F^ε is a halo set as at (A2.2.2):

(A2.5.1) $d(\mu, v) = \inf\{\varepsilon: \varepsilon \geq 0$, and for all closed $F \subseteq \mathcal{X}$,

$$\mu(F) \leq v(F^\varepsilon) + \varepsilon \text{ and } v(F) \leq \mu(F^\varepsilon) + \varepsilon\}.$$

If $d(\mu, v) = 0$, then $\mu(F) = v(F)$ for all closed F, so $\mu(\cdot)$ and $v(\cdot)$ coincide. If $d(\lambda, \mu) = \delta$ and $d(\mu, v) = \varepsilon$, then

$$\lambda(F) \leq \mu(F^\delta) + \delta \leq \mu(\overline{F^\delta}) + \delta$$

$$\leq v((\overline{F^\delta})^\varepsilon) + \delta + \varepsilon \leq v(F^{\delta+\varepsilon}) + \delta + \varepsilon,$$

with similar inequalities holding when λ and ν are interchanged. Thus, the triangle inequality holds for d, showing that d is indeed a metric.

The main objects of this section are to show that the topology generated by this metric coincides with the topology of weak convergence and to establish various properties of $\mathcal{M}_{\mathcal{X}}$ as a metric space in its own right. We start with an extension of Theorem A2.3.II.

Proposition A2.5.I. *Let $\mathcal{X}$ be a c.s.m.s. and $\mathcal{M}_{\mathcal{X}}$ the space of all totally finite measures on $\mathcal{B}_{\mathcal{X}}$. Then each of the following families of sets in $\mathcal{M}_{\mathcal{X}}$ is a basis, and the topologies generated by these four bases coincide:*

(i) *The sets $\{\nu: d(\nu, \mu) < \varepsilon\}$ for all $\varepsilon > 0$ and $\mu \in \mathcal{M}_{\mathcal{X}}$.*
(ii) *The sets $\{\nu: \nu(F_i) < \mu(F_i) + \varepsilon$ for $i = 1, \ldots, k$, $|\nu(\mathcal{X}) - \mu(\mathcal{X})| < \varepsilon\}$ for all $\varepsilon > 0$, finite families of closed sets $F_1, \ldots, F_k$, and $\mu \in \mathcal{M}_{\mathcal{X}}$.*
(iii) *The sets $\{\nu: \nu(G_i) > \mu(G_i) - \varepsilon$ for $i = 1, \ldots, k$, $|\nu(\mathcal{X}) - \mu(\mathcal{X})| < \varepsilon\}$ for all $\varepsilon > 0$, finite families of open sets $G_1, \ldots, G_k$, and $\mu \in \mathcal{M}_{\mathcal{X}}$.*
(iv) *The sets $\{\nu: |\nu(A_i) - \mu(A_i)| < \varepsilon$ for $i = 1, \ldots, k$, $|\nu(\mathcal{X}) - \mu(\mathcal{X})| < \varepsilon\}$ for all $\varepsilon > 0$, finite families of Borel sets $A_1, \ldots, A_k$ with $\mu(\partial A_i) = 0$, and $\mu \in \mathcal{M}_{\mathcal{X}}$.*

PROOF. Each of the four families is specified as a family of neighbourhoods of an element $\mu \in \mathcal{M}_{\mathcal{X}}$. Each family is closed under intersections and so satisfies the defining property of a basis. To show that the four bases are equivalent, it is enough to show that every neighbourhood of μ in one family contains a neighbourhood of μ in each of the others. Taking the families in the order (iv), (iii), (ii), (i), (iv), we show that each neighbourhood in one family contains a neighbourhood of the next family.

Suppose there is given a neighbourhood of μ as at (iv). Take as open set G_i the interiors A_i° of A_i, together with the complements $(\bar{A}_i)^c$ of their closures, and consider any measure ν in the neighbourhood as at (iii) specified by

$$\nu(A_i^\circ) > \mu(A_i^\circ) - \varepsilon/2, \quad \nu((\bar{A}_i)^c) > \mu((\bar{A}_i)^c) - \varepsilon/2, \quad \text{and} \quad |\nu(\mathcal{X}) - \mu(\mathcal{X})| < \varepsilon/2.$$

Then since $\mu(\partial A_i) = 0$, it follows that for each i we have $\nu(A_i) \geq \nu(A_i^\circ) > \mu(A_i^\circ) - \varepsilon/2 > \mu(A_i) - \varepsilon$ and

$$\mu(A_i) = \mu(\bar{A}_i) = \mu(\mathcal{X}) - \mu((\bar{A}_i)^c) > \nu(\mathcal{X}) - \nu((\bar{A}_i)^c) - \varepsilon/2 - \varepsilon/2$$
$$= \nu(\bar{A}_i) - \varepsilon \geq \nu(A_i) - \varepsilon,$$

showing that ν lies within the given neighbourhood of μ.

Suppose next there is given a neighbourhood as at (iii); set $F_i = G_i^c$, and consider any measure ν in the neighbourhood as at (ii) with $\varepsilon/2$ in place of ε. Then $\nu(G_i) = \nu(\mathcal{X}) - \nu(G_i^c) > \mu(\mathcal{X}) - \mu(G_i^c) - \varepsilon/2 - \varepsilon/2 = \mu(G_i) - \varepsilon$, showing that ν lies within the given neighbourhood of μ.

Given a neighbourhood as at (ii), the F_i being closed, we can find a δ in $0 < \delta < \varepsilon/2$ for which, for $i = 1, \ldots, k$,

$$\mu(F_i^\delta) < \mu(F_i) + \varepsilon/2.$$

Consider the sphere $S(\mu, \delta)$ with centre μ and radius δ in the metric d. For any $v \in S(\mu, \delta)$, $v(F_i) < \mu(F_i^\delta) + \delta < \mu(F_i) + \varepsilon/2 + \varepsilon/2 = \mu(F_i) + \varepsilon$, so that v also lies in the given neighbourhood (i).

Finally, suppose there is given a neighbourhood as at (i). Use the separability of $\mathscr{X}$ to cover $\mathscr{X}$ with a countable number of spheres $S_1, S_2, \ldots$ of radius $\varepsilon/3$ or less. For any given $x \in \mathscr{X}$, the quantities $\mu(S(x, r))$ are monotonic increasing in r, and therefore continuous in r except for a countable set of values; so we can choose $r < \varepsilon/3$ such that $S(x, r)$ is a continuity set for μ. We can therefore suppose without loss of generality that the S_i are also μ-continuity sets. Since

$$\mu\left(\bigcup_{i=1}^{N} S_i\right) \uparrow \mu(\mathscr{X}) \qquad (N \to \infty),$$

we can choose N so that $\mu(\bigcup_{i=1}^{N} S_i) > \mu(\mathscr{X}) - \varepsilon/3$. Now consider any v in the neighbourhood as at (iv) specified by

$$|v(A_i) - \mu(A_i)| < \varepsilon/3,$$

where the finite number of sets A_i consists of the spheres $S_1, \ldots, S_N$, all possible finite unions of these spheres, and the set $\mathscr{X} \setminus \bigcup_{i=1}^{N} S_i$, noting that all these sets are μ-continuity sets.

For any closed set F, denote by F' the union of those spheres S_i that intersect F, so that

$$F \subseteq F' \cup \left(\mathscr{X} \setminus \bigcup_{i=1}^{N} S_i\right) \quad \text{and} \quad F' \subseteq F^\varepsilon,$$

and for v in the neighbourhood as described,

$$v(F) \le v(F') + v\left(\mathscr{X} \setminus \bigcup_{i=1}^{N} S_i\right) < \mu(F') + \mu\left(\mathscr{X} \setminus \bigcup_{i=1}^{N} S_i\right) + \varepsilon/3 + \varepsilon/3$$

$$< \mu(F^\varepsilon) + \varepsilon,$$

and

$$\mu(F) \le \mu(F') + \mu\left(\mathscr{X} \setminus \bigcup_{i=1}^{N} S_i\right) < v(F') + \varepsilon/3 + \varepsilon/3 < v(F^\varepsilon) + \varepsilon.$$

Thus, $v \in S(\mu, \varepsilon)$, completing the proof of the proposition. $\qquad \square$

The weak convergence of μ_n to μ is equivalent by Theorem A2.3.II to $\mu_n \to \mu$ in each of the topologies (ii), (iii), and (iv), and hence by the proposition to $d(\mu_n, \mu) \to 0$. The converse holds, so we have the following.

Corollary A2.5.II. *For $\mu_n, \mu \in \mathscr{M}_{\mathscr{X}}$, $\mu_n \to \mu$ weakly if and only if $d(\mu_n, \mu) \to 0$.*

Having established the fact that the weak topology is a metric topology, it makes sense to ask whether $\mathscr{M}_{\mathscr{X}}$ is separable or complete with this topology.

Proposition A2.5.III. *If $\mathscr{X}$ is a c.s.m.s. and $\mathcal{M}_{\mathscr{X}}$ is given the topology of weak convergence, then $\mathcal{M}_{\mathscr{X}}$ is also a c.s.m.s.*

PROOF. We first establish completeness by using the compactness criteria of the preceding section. Let $\{\mu_n\}$ be a Cauchy sequence in $\mathcal{M}_{\mathscr{X}}$; we show that it is uniformly tight. Let positive ε and δ be given, and choose positive $\eta < \min(\varepsilon/3, \delta/2)$. From the Cauchy property there is an N for which $d(\mu_n, \mu_N) < \eta$ for $n \geq N$. Since μ_N itself is tight, $\mathscr{X}$ can be covered by a sequence of spheres $S_1, S_2, \ldots$ of radius η and there is a finite K for which

$$\mu_N(\mathscr{X}) - \mu_N\left(\bigcup_{i=1}^{K} S_i\right) < \eta.$$

For $n > N$, since $d(\mu_n, \mu_N) < \eta$, $\mu_n(\mathscr{X}) - \mu_N(\mathscr{X}) < \eta$ and

$$\mu_N\left(\bigcup_{i=1}^{K} S_i\right) < \mu_n\left(\left(\bigcup_{i=1}^{K} S_i\right)^{\eta}\right) + \eta,$$

so that

$$\mu_n(\mathscr{X}) - \mu_n\left(\left(\bigcup_{i=1}^{K} S_i\right)^{\eta}\right)$$

$$< \mu_n(\mathscr{X}) - \mu_N\left(\bigcup_{i=1}^{K} S_i\right) + \eta$$

$$\leq |\mu_n(\mathscr{X}) - \mu_N(\mathscr{X})| + |\mu_N(\mathscr{X}) - \mu_N\left(\bigcup_{i=1}^{K} S_i\right)| + \eta \leq 3\eta < \varepsilon.$$

It follows that for every ε and δ we can find a finite family of δ spheres whose union has μ_n measure within ε of $\mu_n(\mathscr{X})$, uniformly in n. Hence, the sequence $\{\mu_n\}$ is uniformly tight by Lemma A2.4.II and relatively compact by Theorem A2.4.I [since it is clear that the quantities $\mu_n(\mathscr{X})$ are bounded when $\{\mu_n\}$ is a Cauchy sequence]. Thus, there exists a limit measure such that $\mu_n \to \mu$ weakly, which implies by Corollary A2.5.II that $d(\mu_n, \mu) \to 0$.

Separability is rather easier to establish, as a suitable dense set is ready to hand in the form of the measures with finite support, that is, those that are purely atomic with only a finite set of atoms. Restricting the atoms to the points of a separability set $\mathscr{D}$ for $\mathscr{X}$ and their masses to rational numbers, we obtain a countable family of measures, $\mathscr{D}'$ say, which we now show to be dense in $\mathcal{M}_{\mathscr{X}}$ by proving that any sphere $S'(\mu, \varepsilon) \subseteq \mathcal{M}_{\mathscr{X}}$ contains an element of $\mathscr{D}'$. To this end, first choose a compact set K such that $\mu(\mathscr{X} \setminus K) < \varepsilon/2$, which is possible because μ is tight. Now cover K with a finite family of disjoint sets $A_1, \ldots, A_n$, each with nonempty interior and radius ε or less. [One way of constructing such a covering is as follows. First cover K with a finite family of open spheres, $S_1, \ldots, S_m$ say, each of radius ε. Take $A_1 = \bar{S}_1$, $A_2 = \bar{S}_2 \cap A_1^c$, $A_3 = \bar{S}_3 \cap (A_1 \cup A_2)^c$, and so on, retaining only the nonempty sets in this construction. Then $S_2 \cap A_1^c$ is open, and either empty, in which case $S_2 \subseteq A_1$

so $\bar{S}_2 \subseteq A_1$ and A_2 is empty, or else has nonempty interior. It is evident that each A_i has radius ε or less and that they are disjoint.] For each i, since A_i has nonempty interior, we can choose an element x_i of the separability set for $\mathcal{X}$ with $x_i \in A_i$; give x_i rational mass μ_i such that

$$\mu(A_i) \geq \mu_i \geq \mu(A_i) - \varepsilon/2N,$$

and let μ' denote a purely atomic measure with atoms at x_i of mass μ_i. Then for an arbitrary closed set F, with $\sum'$ denoting $\sum_{i:x_i \in F}$,

$$\mu'(F) = \sum' \mu_i \leq \sum' \mu(A_i) < \mu(F^\varepsilon) + \varepsilon,$$

where we have used the fact that $\bigcup_{i:x_i \in F} A_i \subseteq F^\varepsilon$ because A_i has radius at most ε. Furthermore,

$$\mu(F) < \mu(K \cap F) + \varepsilon/2 \leq \sum'' \mu(F \cap A_i) + \varepsilon/2,$$

where $\sum''$ denotes $\sum_{i:A_i \cap F \neq \varnothing}$, so

$$\mu(F) \leq \sum'' \mu'(A_i) + \varepsilon/2 + \varepsilon/2 \leq \mu(F^\varepsilon) + \varepsilon.$$

Consequently, $d(\mu, \mu') < \varepsilon$, or equivalently, $\mu' \in S'(\mu, \varepsilon)$ as required.   □

Denote the Borel σ-algebra on $\mathcal{M}_{\mathcal{X}}$ by $\mathcal{B}(\mathcal{M}_{\mathcal{X}})$, so that from the results just established it is the smallest σ-algebra containing any of the four bases listed in Proposition A2.5.I. We use this fact to characterize $\mathcal{B}(\mathcal{M}_{\mathcal{X}})$.

Proposition A2.5.IV. *Let $\mathcal{S}$ be a semiring generating the Borel sets $\mathcal{B}_{\mathcal{X}}$ of $\mathcal{X}$. Then $\mathcal{B}(\mathcal{M}_{\mathcal{X}})$ is the smallest σ-algebra of subsets of $\mathcal{M}_{\mathcal{X}}$ with respect to which the mappings $\Phi_A: \mathcal{M}_{\mathcal{X}} \to \mathbb{R}$ defined by*

$$\Phi_A(\mu) = \mu(A)$$

are measurable for $A \in \mathcal{S}$. In particular, $\mathcal{B}(\mathcal{M}_{\mathcal{X}})$ is the smallest σ-algebra with respect to which the Φ_A are measurable for all $A \in \mathcal{B}_{\mathcal{X}}$.

PROOF. Start by considering the class $\mathcal{C}$ of subsets A of $\mathcal{X}$ for which Φ_A is $\mathcal{B}(\mathcal{M}_{\mathcal{X}})$-measurable. Since $\Phi_{A \cup B} = \Phi_A + \Phi_B$ for disjoint A and B, and the sum of two measurable functions is measurable, $\mathcal{C}$ is closed under finite disjoint unions. Similarly, since $\Phi_{A \setminus B} = \Phi_A - \Phi_B$ for $A \supseteq B$, $\mathcal{C}$ is closed under proper differences and hence in particular under complementation. Finally, since a monotone sequence of measurable functions has a measurable limit, and $\Phi_{A_n} \uparrow \Phi_A$ whenever $A_n \uparrow A$, it follows that $\mathcal{C}$ is a monotone class.

Let F be any closed set in $\mathcal{X}$ and y any positive number. Choose $\mu \in \mathcal{M}_{\mathcal{X}}$ such that $\mu(F) < y$ and set $\varepsilon = y - \mu(F)$. We can then write

$$\{v: \Phi_F(v) < y\} = \{v: v(F) < y\} = \{v: v(F) < \mu(F) + \varepsilon\},$$

showing that this set of measures is an element of the basis (i) of Proposition A2.5.I, hence an open set in $\mathcal{M}_{\mathcal{X}}$, and therefore an element of $\mathcal{B}(\mathcal{M}_{\mathcal{X}})$. Thus, Φ_F is an element of $\mathcal{C}$ whenever F is a closed set, and therefore also $\Phi_G \in \mathcal{C}$

whenever G is open. From the properties established for $\mathscr{C}$, it now follows that $\mathscr{C}$ contains the ring of all finite disjoint unions of differences of open sets in $\mathscr{X}$, and since $\mathscr{C}$ is a monotone class, it must contain all sets in $\mathscr{B}_{\mathscr{X}}$. This shows that Φ_A is $\mathscr{B}(\mathcal{M}_{\mathscr{X}})$-measurable for all Borel sets A, and hence *a fortiori* for all sets in any semiring $\mathscr{S}$ generating the Borel sets.

It remains to show that $\mathscr{B}(\mathcal{M}_{\mathscr{X}})$ is the smallest σ-algebra in $\mathcal{M}_{\mathscr{X}}$ with this property. Let $\mathscr{S}$ be given, and let $\mathscr{R}$ be any σ-ring with respect to which Φ_A is measurable for all $A \in \mathscr{S}$. By arguing as above, it follows that Φ_A is also $\mathscr{R}$ measurable for all A in the σ-ring generated by $\mathscr{S}$, which by assumption is $\mathscr{B}_{\mathscr{X}}$. Now suppose we are given $\varepsilon > 0$, a measure $\mu \in \mathcal{M}_{\mathscr{X}}$, and a finite family $F_1, \dots, F_n$ of closed sets. Then the set

$$\{v: v(F_i) < \mu(F_i) + \varepsilon \text{ for } i = 1, \dots, n, \, |\mu(\mathscr{X}) - v(\mathscr{X})| < \varepsilon\}$$

is an intersection of sets of $\mathscr{R}$, and hence is an element of $\mathscr{R}$. But this shows that $\mathscr{R}$ contains a basis for the open sets of $\mathcal{M}_{\mathscr{X}}$. Since $\mathcal{M}_{\mathscr{X}}$ is separable, every open set can be represented as a countable union of basic sets, and thus all open sets are in $\mathscr{R}$. Thus, $\mathscr{R}$ contains $\mathscr{B}(\mathcal{M}_{\mathscr{X}})$, and the proposition is proved. $\qquad\square$

A2.6. Boundedly Finite Measures and the Space $\hat{\mathcal{M}}_{\mathscr{X}}$

For applications to random measures, we need to consider not only totally finite measures on $\mathscr{B}_{\mathscr{X}}$ but also σ-finite measures with the strong local finiteness condition contained in the following definition.

Definition A2.6.I. A Borel measure μ on the c.s.m.s. $\mathscr{X}$ is *boundedly finite* if $\mu(A) < \infty$ for every bounded Borel set A.

We write $\hat{\mathcal{M}}_{\mathscr{X}}$ for the space of boundedly finite Borel measures on $\mathscr{X}$, and generally use the $\hat{\ }$ notation for concepts taken over from finite to boundedly finite measures. The object of this section is to extend to $\hat{\mathcal{M}}_{\mathscr{X}}$ the results previously obtained for $\mathcal{M}_{\mathscr{X}}$: while most of these extensions are routine, they are given here for the sake of completeness.

Consider first the extension of the concept of weak convergence. Taking a fixed origin $x_0 \in \mathscr{X}$, let $S(r) = S(r, x_0)$ for $0 < r < \infty$, and introduce a distance function $\hat{d}$ on $\hat{\mathcal{M}}_{\mathscr{X}}$ by setting

(A2.6.1) $$\hat{d}(\mu, v) = \int_0^\infty e^{-r} d_r(\mu^{(r)}, v^{(r)})[1 + d_r(\mu^{(r)}, v^{(r)})]^{-1} \, dr,$$

where $\mu^{(r)}, v^{(r)}$ are the totally finite restrictions of μ, v to $S(r)$, and d_r is the Prohorov distance between the restrictions. Examining (A2.5.1) where this distance is defined, we see that the infimum cannot decrease as r increases when the number of closed sets to be scrutinized increases, so as a function of r, d_r is monotonic and thus a measurable function. Since the ratio $d_r/(1 + d_r)$ is bounded by one, the integral at (A2.6.1) is thus defined and finite for all μ, v. The triangle inequality is preserved under the mapping $x \to x/(1 + x)$, while $\hat{d}(\mu, v) = 0$ if and only if $\mu^{(r)}$ and $v^{(r)}$ coincide for almost all r. This can happen only if μ and v coincide on a sequence of spheres expanding to the whole of $\mathcal{X}$, in which case they are identical.

We call the metric topology generated by $\hat{d}$ the $\hat{w}$-topology ("weak hat" topology) and write $\mu_k \to_{\hat{w}} \mu$ for convergence with respect to this topology. Some equivalent conditions for $\hat{w}$-convergence are as in the next result.

Proposition A2.6.II. *Let $\{\mu_k : k = 1, 2, \ldots\}$ and μ be measures in $\mathcal{M}_{\mathcal{X}}$; then the following conditions are equivalent:*

(i) $\mu_k \to_{\hat{w}} \mu$;
(ii) *$\int_{\mathcal{X}} f(x)\mu_k(dx) \to \int_{\mathcal{X}} f(x)\mu(dx)$ for all bounded continuous functions $f(\cdot)$ on $\mathcal{X}$ vanishing outside a bounded set;*
(iii) *there exists a sequence of spheres $S^{(n)} \uparrow \mathcal{X}$ such that if $\mu_k^{(n)}$, $\mu^{(n)}$ denote the restrictions of the measures μ_k, μ to subsets of $S^{(n)}$, then $\mu_k^{(n)} \to_w \mu^{(n)}$ as $k \to \infty$ for $n = 1, 2, \ldots$;*
(iv) *$\mu_k(A) \to \mu(A)$ for all bounded $A \in \mathcal{B}_{\mathcal{X}}$ for which $\mu(\partial A) = 0$.*

PROOF. We show that (i) $\Rightarrow$ (iii) $\Rightarrow$ (ii) $\Rightarrow$ (iv) $\Rightarrow$ (i). Write the integral at (A2.6.1) for the measures μ_k and μ as

$$\hat{d}(\mu_k, \mu) = \int_0^\infty e^{-r} g_k(r) dr,$$

so that for each k, $g_k(r)$ increases with r and is bounded above by 1. Thus, there exists a subsequence $\{k_n\}$ and a limit function $g(\cdot)$ such that $g_{k_n}(r) \to g(r)$ at all continuity points of g [this is just a version of the compactness criterion for vague convergence on $\mathbb{R}$: regard each $g_k(r)$ as the distribution function of a probability measure, so that there exists a vaguely convergent subsequence; see Corollary A2.6.V or any standard proof of the Helly–Bray results]. By dominated convergence, $\int_0^\infty e^{-r} g(r) dr = 0$ and hence, since $g(\cdot)$ is monotonic, $g(r) = 0$ for all finite $r > 0$. This being true for all convergent subsequences, it follows that $g_k(r) \to 0$ for such r, and thus, for these r,

$$d_r(\mu_k^{(r)}, \mu^{(r)}) \to 0 \quad \text{as } k \to \infty.$$

In particular, this is true for an increasing sequence of values r_n, corresponding to spheres $\{S(r_n)\} \equiv \{S_n\}$ say, on which therefore $\mu_k^{(r_n)} \to \mu^{(r_n)}$ weakly. Thus, (i) implies (iii).

Suppose next that (iii) holds and that f is bounded, continuous, and vanishes outside some bounded set. Then the support of f is contained in some $S(r)$, and hence $\int f d\mu_k^{(r)} \to \int f d\mu^{(r)}$, which is equivalent to (ii).

When (ii) holds, the argument used to establish (iv) of Theorem A2.3.II shows that $\mu_k(C) \to \mu(C)$ whenever C is a bounded Borel set with $\mu(\partial C) = 0$.

Finally, if (iv) holds and $S(r)$ is any sphere that is a continuity set for μ, then by the same theorem $\mu_k^{(r)} \to \mu^{(r)}$ weakly in $S(r)$. But since $\mu(S(r))$ increases monotonically in r, $S(r)$ is a continuity set for almost all r, so the convergence to zero of $\hat{d}(\mu_k, \mu)$ follows from the dominated convergence theorem.

Note that we cannot find a universal sequence of spheres, $\{S^n\}$ say, for which (i) and (ii) are equivalent, because the requirement of weak convergence on S^n that $\mu_k(S_n) \to \mu(S_n)$ cannot be guaranteed unless $\mu(\partial S_n) = 0$. $\qquad \square$

While the distance function $\hat{d}$ of Definition A2.6.I depends on the centre x_0 of the family $\{S(r)\}$ of spheres used there, *the $\hat{w}$-topology does not depend on the choice of x_0.* To see this, let $\{S_n'\}$ be any sequence of spheres expanding to $\mathscr{X}$, so that to any S_n' we can first find n' for which $S_n' \subseteq S(r_{n'})$, and then find n'' for which $S(r_{n'}) \subseteq S_{n''}'$. Now weak convergence within a given sphere is subsumed by weak convergence in a larger sphere containing it, from which the asserted equivalence follows.

It should also be noted that for locally compact $\mathscr{X}$, $\hat{w}$-convergence coincides with vague convergence.

The next theorem extends to $\hat{w}$-convergence the results in Propositions A2.5.III and A2.5.IV.

Theorem A2.6.III. (i) $\hat{\mathcal{M}}_{\mathscr{X}}$ *with the $\hat{w}$-topology is a c.s.m.s.*

(ii) *The Borel σ-algebra $\mathcal{B}(\hat{\mathcal{M}}_{\mathscr{X}})$ is the smallest σ-algebra with respect to which the mappings $\Phi_A: \hat{\mathcal{M}}_{\mathscr{X}} \to \mathbb{R}$ given by*

$$\Phi_A(\mu) = \mu(A)$$

are measurable for all sets A in a semiring $\mathscr{S}$ of bounded Borel sets generating $\mathcal{B}_{\mathscr{X}}$, and in particular for all bounded Borel sets A.

PROOF. To prove separability, recall first that the measures with rational masses on finite support in a separability set $\mathscr{D}$ for $\mathscr{X}$ form a separability set $\mathscr{D}'$ for the totally finite measures on each S_n under the weak topology. Given $\varepsilon > 0$, choose R so that $\int_R^\infty e^{-r} dr < \varepsilon/2$. For any $\mu \in \hat{\mathcal{M}}_{\mathscr{X}}$, choose an atomic measure μ_R from the separability set for S_R such that μ_R has support in S_R and $d_R(\mu_R, \mu^{(R)}) < \varepsilon/2$. Clearly, for $r < R$, we also have

$$d_r(\mu_R^{(r)}, \mu^{(r)}) < \varepsilon/2.$$

Substitution in the expression for $\hat{d}$ shows that $\hat{d}(\mu_R, \mu) < \varepsilon$, establishing that the union of separability sets is a separability set for measures in $\hat{\mathcal{M}}_{\mathscr{X}}$.

To show completeness, let $\{\mu_k\}$ be a Cauchy sequence for $\hat{d}$. Then each sequence of restrictions $\{\mu_k^{(r)}\}$ forms a Cauchy sequence for d_r and so has a limit ν_r by Proposition A2.5.III. The sequence $\{\nu_r\}$ of measures so obtained is clearly consistent in the sense that $\nu_r(A) = \nu_s(A)$ for $s \leq r$ and Borel sets A of S_s. Then the set function

$$\mu(A) = \nu_r(A)$$

is uniquely defined on Borel sets A of S_r and is nonnegative and countably additive on the restriction of $\mathcal{M}_{\mathcal{X}}$ to each S_r. We now extend the definition of μ to all Borel sets by setting

$$\mu(A) = \lim_{r \to \infty} \nu_r(A \cap S_r),$$

the sequence on the right being monotonic increasing and hence providing a limit (finite or infinite) for all A. It is then easily checked that $\mu(\cdot)$ is finitely additive and continuous from below, and therefore countably additive and so a boundedly finite Borel measure. Finally, it follows from (ii) of Proposition A2.6.II that $\mu_k \to_{\hat{w}} \mu$.

To establish part (ii) of the theorem examine the proof of Proposition A2.5.IV. Let $\mathcal{C}'$ be the class of sets A for which Φ_A is a $\mathcal{B}(\hat{\mathcal{M}}_{\mathcal{X}})$-measurable mapping into $[0, \infty)$. Again, $\mathcal{C}'$ is a monotone class containing all bounded open and closed sets on $\mathcal{X}$, and hence $\mathcal{B}_{\mathcal{X}}$ as well as any ring or semiring generating $\mathcal{B}_{\mathcal{X}}$. Also, if $\mathcal{S}$ is a semiring of bounded sets generating $\mathcal{B}_{\mathcal{X}}$, and Φ_A is $\mathcal{B}_{\mathbb{R}}$-measurable for $A \in \mathcal{S}$ and some σ-ring $\mathcal{R}$ of sets on $\hat{\mathcal{M}}_{\mathcal{X}}$, then Φ_A is $\mathcal{R}$-measurable for $A \in \mathcal{B}_{\mathcal{X}}$. The proposition now implies that $\mathcal{A}^{(r)}$, the σ-algebra formed by projecting the measures in sets of $\mathcal{A}$ onto S_r, contains $\mathcal{B}(\mathcal{M}_{S_r})$. Equivalently, $\mathcal{A}$ contains the inverse image of $\mathcal{B}(\mathcal{M}_{S_r})$ under this projection. The definition of $\mathcal{B}(\hat{\mathcal{M}}_{\mathcal{X}})$ implies it is the smallest σ-algebra containing each of these inverse images. Hence, $\mathcal{A}$ contains $\mathcal{B}(\hat{\mathcal{M}}_{\mathcal{X}})$.   □

The final extension is of the compactness criterion of Theorem A2.4.I.

Proposition A2.6.IV. *A family of measures $\{\mu_\alpha\}$ in $\hat{\mathcal{M}}_{\mathcal{X}}$ is relatively compact in the $\hat{w}$-topology on $\hat{\mathcal{M}}_{\mathcal{X}}$ if and only if their restrictions $\{\mu_\alpha^{(n)}\}$ to a sequence of closed spheres $\bar{S}_n \uparrow \mathcal{X}$ are relatively compact in the weak topology on $\mathcal{M}_{\bar{S}_n}$, in which case the restrictions $\{\mu_\alpha^F\}$ to any closed bounded F are relatively compact in the weak topology on $\mathcal{M}_F$.*

PROOF. Suppose first that $\{\mu_\alpha\}$ is relatively compact in the $\hat{w}$-topology on $\hat{\mathcal{M}}_{\mathcal{X}}$ and that F is a closed bounded subset of $\mathcal{X}$. Given any sequence of the μ_α^F, there exists by assumption a $\hat{w}$-convergent subsequence, $\mu_{\alpha_k} \to_{\hat{w}} \mu$ say. From Proposition A2.6.II, arguing as in the proof of A2.3.II, it follows that for all bounded closed sets C, $\limsup_{k \to \infty} \mu_{\alpha_k}(C) \leq \mu(C)$. Hence, in particular, the values of $\mu_{\alpha_k}(F)$ are bounded above. Moreover, the restrictions $\{\mu_{\alpha_k}^F\}$ are uniformly tight, this property being inherited from their uniform tightness on a closed bounded sphere containing F. Therefore, the restrictions are relatively compact as measures on F, and there exists a further subsequence converging weakly on F to some limit measure, $\hat{\mu}$ say, on F. This is enough to show that the μ_α^F themselves are relatively compact.

Conversely, suppose that there exists a family of spheres S_n, closed or otherwise, such that $\{\mu_\alpha^{(n)}\}$ are relatively compact for each n. By diagonal selection, we may choose a subsequence α_k such that $\mu_{\alpha_k}^{(n)} \to \mu^{(n)}$ weakly for every n. It then follows that, if f is any bounded continuous function vanishing outside a bounded set, then $\int f \, d\mu_{\alpha_k}^{(n)} \to \int f \, d\mu^{(n)}$. It is then easy to see that the $\mu_\alpha^{(n)}$ form a consistent family (i.e., $\mu_\alpha^{(n)}$ coincides with $\mu_\alpha^{(m)}$ on S_m for $n \geq m$) and so define a unique element μ of $\mathcal{M}_{\mathcal{X}}$ such that $\mu_{\alpha_k} \to_{\hat{w}} \mu$. □

The criterion for weak compactness on each S_n can be spelled out in detail from Prohorov's theorem A2.4.I. A particularly neat result obtains in the case that $\mathcal{X}$ is locally (and hence countably) compact, when the following terminology is standard. A *Radon measure* in a locally compact space is a measure taking finite values on compact sets. A sequence $\{\mu_k\}$ of such measures converges *vaguely* to μ if $\int f \, d\mu_k \to \int f \, d\mu$ for each continuous f vanishing outside a compact set. Now any locally compact space with a countable base is metrizable, but the space is not necessarily complete in the metric so obtained. If, however, the space is both locally compact and a c.s.m.s., it can be represented as the union of a sequence of compact sets K_n with $K_n \subseteq K_{n+1}^\circ$, and then by changing to an equivalent metric if necessary, we can ensure that the spheres S_n are compact as well as closed [e.g., see Proposition 2.61 of Hocking and Young (1961)]; we assume this is so. Then a Borel measure is a Radon measure if and only if it is boundedly finite, and vague convergence coincides with $\hat{w}$-convergence. The discussion around (A2.6.1) shows that the vague topology is metrizable and suggests one form for a suitable metric. Finally, Proposition A2.6.IV takes the following form.

Corollary A2.6.V. *If $\mathcal{X}$ is a locally compact c.s.m.s., then the family $\{\mu_\alpha\}$ of Radon measures on $\mathcal{B}_{\mathcal{X}}$ is relatively compact in the vague topology if and only if the values $\{\mu_\alpha(A)\}$ are bounded for each bounded Borel set A.*

PROOF. Assume the metric is so chosen that closed bounded sets are compact. Then if the $\mu_\alpha(\cdot)$ are relatively compact on each S_n, it follows from condition (i) of Theorem A2.4.I that the $\mu_\alpha(S_n)$ are bounded and hence that the $\mu_\alpha(A)$ are bounded for any bounded Borel set A.

Conversely, suppose the boundedness condition holds. Then, in particular, it holds for S_n, which is compact so the tightness condition (ii) of Theorem A2.4.I is satisfied trivially. Thus, the $\{\mu_\alpha\}$ are relatively compact on each S_n and so by Proposition A2.6.IV are relatively compact in the $\hat{w}$- (i.e., vague) topology. □

A2.7. Measures on Topological Groups

A group $\mathcal{G}$ is a set on which is defined a binary relation $\mathcal{G} \times \mathcal{G} \to \mathcal{G}$ with the following properties:

(i) For all $g_1, g_2, g_3 \in \mathcal{G}$, $(g_1 g_2) g_3 = g_1 (g_2 g_3)$ (*associative law*);
(ii) There exists an *identity element* e (necessarily unique) such that for for all $g \in \mathcal{G}$, $ge = eg = g$;

(iii) For every $g \in \mathcal{G}$ there exists a unique *inverse* g^{-1} such that $g^{-1}g = gg^{-1} = e$. The group is *Abelian* if it also has the following property:

(iv) For all $g_1, g_2 \in \mathcal{G}$, $g_1 g_2 = g_2 g_1$ (*commutative law*).

A *homomorphism* between groups is a mapping $\mathcal{T}$ that preserves the group operations, in the sense that $(\mathcal{T}g_1)(\mathcal{T}g_2) = \mathcal{T}(g_1 g_2)$ and $(\mathcal{T}g)^{-1} = \mathcal{T}g^{-1}$. If the mapping is also one-to-one it is an *isomorphism*. An *automorphism* is an isomorphism of the group onto itself.

A *subgroup* $\mathcal{H}$ of $\mathcal{G}$ is a subset of $\mathcal{G}$ that is closed under the group operations and so forms a group in its own right. If $\mathcal{H}$ is *nontrivial* (i.e., neither $\{e\}$ nor the whole of $\mathcal{G}$), its action on $\mathcal{G}$ splits $\mathcal{G}$ into equivalence classes, where $g_1 \equiv g_2$ if there exists $h \in \mathcal{H}$ such that $g_2 = g_1 h$. These classes form the *left cosets* of $\mathcal{G}$ relative to $\mathcal{H}$; they may also be described as the (left) quotient space $\mathcal{G}/\mathcal{H}$ of $\mathcal{G}$ with respect to $\mathcal{H}$. Similarly, $\mathcal{H}$ splits $\mathcal{G}$ into *right cosets*, which in general will not be the same as the left cosets. If $\mathcal{G}$ is Abelian, however, or more generally if $\mathcal{H}$ is a *normal* (or *invariant*) subgroup, which means that for every $g \in \mathcal{G}, h \in \mathcal{H}, g^{-1}hg \in \mathcal{H}$, then the right and left cosets coincide, and moreover the products of two elements, one from each of any two given cosets, fall into a uniquely defined third coset. With this definition of multiplication, the cosets then form a group in their own right, namely, the *quotient group*. The natural map taking an element from $\mathcal{G}$ into the coset to which it belongs is then a homomorphism of $\mathcal{G}$ into $\mathcal{G}/\mathcal{H}$, of which $\mathcal{H}$ is the *kernel*, that is, the inverse image of the identity in the image space $\mathcal{G}/\mathcal{H}$.

The *direct product* of two groups $\mathcal{G}$ and $\mathcal{H}$, written $\mathcal{G} \times \mathcal{H}$, consists of the Cartesian products of $\mathcal{G}$ and $\mathcal{H}$ with the group operation

$$(g_1, h_1)(g_2, h_2) = (g_1 g_2, h_1 h_2),$$

identity $(e_{\mathcal{G}}, e_{\mathcal{H}})$, and inverse $(g, h)^{-1} = (g^{-1}, h^{-1})$. In particular, if $\mathcal{G}$ is a group and $\mathcal{H}$ a normal subgroup, then $\mathcal{G}$ is isomorphic to the direct product $\mathcal{H} \times \mathcal{G}/\mathcal{H}$.

$\mathcal{G}$ is a *topological group* if it has a topology $\mathcal{U}$ with respect to which the mapping $(g_1, g_2) \to g_1 g_2^{-1}$ from $\mathcal{G} \times \mathcal{G}$ (with the product topology) into $\mathcal{G}$ is continuous. This condition makes the operations of left (and right) multiplication by a fixed element of $\mathcal{G}$, and of inversion, continuous. A theory with wide applications results if the topology $\mathcal{U}$ is taken to be locally compact and second countable. It is then metrizable, but not necessarily complete in the resulting metric. In keeping with our previous discussion, however, we frequently assume that $\mathcal{G}$ is a *complete separable metric group* (c.s.m.g.), as well as being locally compact. If, as may always be done by a change of metric, the closed bounded sets of $\mathcal{G}$ are compact, we refer to $\mathcal{G}$ as a σ-group.

Definition A2.7.I. A σ-group is a locally compact, complete separable metric group, with the metric so chosen that closed bounded sets are compact.

In this context boundedly finite measures are Radon measures and the concepts of weak and vague convergence coincide. A boundedly finite measure

μ on the σ-group is *left-invariant* if (writing $gA = \{gx: x \in A\}$)

(A2.7.1) $\mu(gA) = \mu(A)$ $(g \in \mathscr{G}, A \in \mathscr{B}_{\mathscr{G}})$,

or equivalently,

(A2.7.2) $\int_{\mathscr{G}} f(g^{-1}x)\mu(dx) = \int_{\mathscr{G}} f(x)\mu(dx)$

for all $f \in BC(\mathscr{G})$, the class of continuous functions vanishing outside a
bounded (in this case, compact) set. Right-invariance is defined similarly. A
fundamental theorem for locally compact groups asserts that up to scale
factors they admit unique left- and right-invariant measures, called *Haar
measures*. If the group is Abelian, the left and right Haar measures coincide,
as they do also when the group is compact, in which case the Haar measure
is totally finite and is uniquely specified when normalized so as to have total
mass unity. On the real line, or more generally on $\mathbb{R}^d$, the Haar measure is
just Lebesgue measure $\ell(\cdot)$, and the uniqueness referred to above is effectively
a restatement of results on the Cauchy functional equation (see also Exercise
10.1.8).

If $\mathscr{G}$ is a topological group and $\mathscr{H}$ a subgroup, the *quotient topology* on
$\mathscr{G}/\mathscr{H}$ is the largest topology on $\mathscr{G}/\mathscr{H}$ making the natural map from $\mathscr{G}$ into
$\mathscr{G}/\mathscr{H}$ continuous. It is then also an *open map* (i.e., takes open sets into open
sets). If it is closed, then the quotient topology for $\mathscr{G}/\mathscr{H}$ inherits properties
from the topology for $\mathscr{G}$: it is Hausdorff, or compact, or locally compact, if
and only if $\mathscr{G}$ has the same property.

These concepts extend to the more general context where $\mathscr{X}$ is a c.s.m.s.
and $\mathscr{H}$ defines a group of one-to-one bounded continuous maps T_h of $\mathscr{X}$ onto
itself, such that

$$T_{h_1}(T_{h_2}(x)) = T_{h_1 h_2}(x).$$

Again we assume that $\mathscr{H}$ is a σ-group and that the $\{T_h\}$ act continuously on
$\mathscr{X}$, meaning that the mapping $(h, x) \to T_h(x)$ is continuous from $\mathscr{H} \times \mathscr{X}$ into
$\mathscr{X}$. The action of $\mathscr{H}$ splits $\mathscr{X}$ into equivalence classes, where $x_1 \equiv x_2$ if there
exists $h \in \mathscr{H}$ such that $x_2 = T_h(x_1)$. It acts *transitively* on $\mathscr{X}$ if for every x_1,
$x_2 \in \mathscr{X}$ there exists an h such that T_h maps x_1 into x_2. In this case the
equivalence relation is trivial: there exists only one equivalence class, the whole
space $\mathscr{X}$. In general, the equivalence classes define a quotient space $\mathscr{Q}$, which
may be given the quotient topology; with this topology the natural map taking
x into the equivalence class containing it is again both continuous and open.
If the original topology on $\mathscr{H}$ is not adjusted to the group action, however,
the quotient topology may not be adequate for a detailed discussion of
invariant measures.

EXAMPLE A2.7(a). Consider $\mathbb{R}^1$ under the action of scale changes: $x \to \alpha x$
$(0 < \alpha < \infty)$. Here $\mathscr{H}$ may be identified with the positive half-line $(0, \infty)$
with multiplication as the group action. There are three equivalence classes,

$(-\infty, 0)$, $\{0\}$, and $(0, \infty)$, which we may identify with the three-point space $\mathcal{Q} = \{-1, 0, 1\}$. The quotient topology is trivial (only $\varnothing$ and the whole of $\mathcal{Q}$), whereas the natural topology for further discussion is the discrete topology on $\mathcal{Q}$, making each of the three points both open and closed in $\mathcal{Q}$. With this topology the natural map is open but not continuous. It does have, however, a continuous (albeit trivial) restriction to each of the three equivalence classes and therefore defines a Borel mapping of $\mathcal{X}$ into $\mathcal{Q}$.

An important problem is to determine the structure of boundedly finite measures on $\mathcal{X}$, which are invariant under the group of mappings $\{T_h\}$. In many cases, some or all of the equivalence classes of $\mathcal{X}$ under $\mathcal{H}$ can be identified with replicas of $\mathcal{H}$, so that we may expect the restriction of the invariant measure to such cosets to be proportional to Haar measure. When such an identification is possible, the following simple lemma can be used; it allows us to deal with most of the situations arising from concrete examples of invariant measures [for further background see, e.g., Bourbaki (1963)].

Lemma A2.7.II. *Let $\mathcal{X} = \mathcal{H} \times \mathcal{Y}$, where $\mathcal{H}$ is a σ-group and $\mathcal{Y}$ is a c.s.m.s., and suppose that $\mu \in \mathcal{M}_{\mathcal{X}}$ is invariant under left multiplication by elements of $\mathcal{H}$, in the sense that for $A \in \mathcal{B}_{\mathcal{X}}$, $B \in \mathcal{B}_{\mathcal{Y}}$,*

$$\text{(A2.7.3)} \qquad\qquad \mu(hA \times B) = \mu(A \times B).$$

Then $\mu = \ell \times \kappa$, where ℓ is a multiple of left Haar measure on $\mathcal{H}$ and $\kappa \in \mathcal{M}_{\mathcal{Y}}$ is essentially uniquely determined.

PROOF. Consider the set function $\mu_B(\cdot)$ defined on $\mathcal{B}_{\mathcal{H}}$ for fixed $B \in \mathcal{B}_{\mathcal{Y}}$ by

$$\mu_B(A) = \mu(A \times B).$$

Then μ_B inherits from μ the properties of countable additivity and bounded finiteness, and so defines an element of $\mathcal{M}_{\mathcal{H}}$. But then, from (A2.7.3),

$$\mu_B(hA) = \mu(hA \times B) = \mu(A \times B) = \mu_B(A),$$

implying that μ_B is invariant under left multiplication by elements of $\mathcal{H}$. It therefore reduces to a multiple of left Haar measure on $\mathcal{H}$, say

$$\mu_B(A) = \kappa(B)\ell(A).$$

Now the family of constants $\kappa(B)$ may be regarded as a set function on $\mathcal{B}_{\mathcal{Y}}$, and, as for μ_B, this function is both countably additive and boundedly finite. Consequently, $\kappa(\cdot) \in \mathcal{M}_{\mathcal{Y}}$, and it follows that

$$\mu(A \times B) = \mu_B(A) = \ell(A)\kappa(B).$$

In other words, μ reduces to the required product form on product sets, and since these generate $\mathcal{B}_{\mathcal{X}}$, μ and the product measure $\ell \times \kappa$ coincide. $\square$

To apply this result to specific examples it is often necessary to find a suitable product representation for the space on which the transformations act. The situation is formalized in the following statement.

Proposition A2.7.III. *Let $\mathcal{X}$ be a c.s.m.s. acted on measurably by a group of transformations $\{T_h: h \in \mathcal{H}\}$, where $\mathcal{H}$ is a σ-group. Suppose, furthermore, that there exists a mapping $\psi: \mathcal{H} \times \mathcal{Y} \to \mathcal{X}$, where $\mathcal{Y}$ is a c.s.m.s. and ψ is one-to-one, both ways measurable, takes bounded sets into bounded sets, and preserves the transformations $\{T_h\}$ in the sense that*

$$(A2.7.4) \qquad\qquad T_{h'}\psi(h, y) = \psi(h'h, y).$$

Let μ be a measure on $\mathcal{M}_{\mathcal{X}}$ which is invariant under the transformation T_h. Then there exists a unique measure $\kappa \in \mathcal{M}_{\mathcal{Y}}$ such that, for $\mathcal{B}_{\mathcal{X}}$-measurable nonnegative functions f,

$$(A2.7.5) \qquad\qquad \int_{\mathcal{X}} f(x)\mu(dx) = \int_{\mathcal{Y}} \kappa(dy) \int_{\mathcal{H}} f(\psi(h, y))\ell(dh).$$

PROOF. Let $\tilde{\mu}$ be the image of μ induced on $\mathcal{H} \times \mathcal{Y}$ by the mapping ψ; that is, $\tilde{\mu}(A \times B) = \mu(\psi(A \times B))$. Then

$$\tilde{\mu}(hA \times B) = \mu(\psi(hA \times B)) = \mu(T_h\psi(A \times B)) = \mu(\psi(A \times B))$$

$$= \tilde{\mu}(A \times B),$$

so that $\tilde{\mu}$ is invariant under the action of $h \in \mathcal{H}$ on the first argument. Moreover, if A and B are bounded sets in $\mathcal{H}$ and $\mathcal{Y}$, respectively, then by assumption $\psi(A \times B)$ is bounded in $\mathcal{X}$, so that $\tilde{\mu}$ is boundedly finite whenever μ is boundedly finite. Lemma A2.7.II can now be applied and yields the result that

$$\tilde{\mu}(A \times B) = \ell(A)\kappa(B)$$

for some unique boundedly finite measure κ in $\mathcal{M}_{\mathcal{Y}}$. This relation establishes the truth of (A2.7.5) for indicator functions $I_{\psi(A \times B)}(x)$ for $A \in \mathcal{B}_{\mathcal{H}}$ and $B \in \mathcal{B}(\mathcal{M}_{\mathcal{Y}})$. Using the usual approximation arguments, the result extends to simple functions f, and thence to limits of these. It therefore holds for all nonnegative f such that $f \circ \psi$ is measurable on $\mathcal{H} \times \mathcal{Y}$. But this is true for any f that is $\mathcal{B}_{\mathcal{X}}$-measurable, and so proves (A2.7.5). $\qquad\square$

EXAMPLE A2.7(b). Let μ be a measure on $\mathbb{R}^2$, which is invariant under rotations about the origin. These may be written T_θ for $\theta \in \mathbb{S}$, $\mathbb{S}$ being the circumference of the unit disk with addition modulo 2π. The equivalence classes consist of circles of varying radii centred on the origin, together with the isolated point $\{0\}$. The mapping $(r, \theta) \to (r \cos \theta, r \sin \theta)$ takes the product space $\mathbb{S} \times \mathbb{R}_+$ into $\mathbb{R}^2 \backslash \{0\}$ and is a representation of the required kind for $\mathbb{R}^2 \backslash \{0\}$. We therefore write μ as the sum of a point mass at the origin and a measure on $\mathbb{R}^2 \backslash \{0\}$, which is invariant under rotations and can therefore be represented as the image of the uniform distribution around the circle and a measure κ on the positive half-line. Integration with respect to μ takes the form [cf. (A2.7.5)]

$$\int_{\mathbb{R}^2} f(x)\mu(dx) = f(0)\mu\{0\} + \int_{0+}^{\infty} \kappa(dr) \int_0^{2\pi} f(r \cos \theta, r \sin \theta)(2\pi)^{-1} d\theta.$$

A2.8. Fourier Transforms

In this section we collect together a few basic facts from classical Fourier transform theory. For brevity, most results are stated for Fourier transforms of functions on $\mathbb{R} \equiv \mathbb{R}^1$; the corresponding results for $\mathbb{R}^d$ can be obtained by no more than changes in the domain of integration and appropriate book-keeping with multiples of 2π. Both the $\mathbb{R}^d$ theory and the theory of Fourier series, which can be regarded as Fourier transforms of functions defined on the unit circle, are subsumed under the concluding comments concerned with Fourier transforms of functions defined on locally compact Abelian groups. We refer to texts such as Titchmarsh (1937) for more specific material on these topics.

For any real- or complex-valued measurable (Lebesgue) integrable function $f(\cdot)$, its Fourier transform $\tilde{f}(\cdot)$ is defined by

$$(A2.8.1) \qquad \tilde{f}(\omega) = \int_{-\infty}^{\infty} e^{i\omega x} f(x)\,dx \qquad (\omega \in \mathbb{R}).$$

If f is real and symmetric then so is $\tilde{f}$. In any case, $\tilde{f}$ is bounded and continuous, while the Riemann–Lebesgue lemma asserts that $f(\omega) \to 0$ as $|\omega| \to \infty$. Furthermore, if $\tilde{f}$ is integrable then the inverse relation

$$(A2.8.2) \qquad f(\omega) = (2\pi)^{-1} \int_{-\infty}^{\infty} e^{ix\omega} \tilde{f}(\omega)\,d\omega$$

holds. The theory is not symmetric with respect to f and $\tilde{f}$: for example, see Titchmarsh (1937) for a more detailed account of the representation of a function by its inverse Fourier transform.

A symmetrical theory results if we consider (real- or complex-valued) functions that are square integrable. We have the *Plancherel identities* for square integrable functions f and g:

$$(A2.8.3) \qquad \int_{-\infty}^{\infty} f(x)\overline{g(x)}\,dx = \frac{1}{2\pi} \int_{-\infty}^{\infty} \tilde{f}(\omega)\tilde{g}(\omega)\,d\omega,$$

and, with $g = f$,

$$(A2.8.4) \qquad \int_{-\infty}^{\infty} |f(x)|^2\,dx = \frac{1}{2\pi} \int_{-\infty}^{\infty} |\tilde{f}(\omega)|^2\,d\omega.$$

Here the Fourier transform cannot be obtained directly from (A2.8.1) but can be represented as a mean square limit

$$(A2.8.5) \qquad \tilde{f}(\omega) = \operatorname*{l.i.m.}_{T \to \infty} \int_{-T}^{T} e^{i\omega x} f(x)\,dx,$$

the existence of the finite integral following readily from the Schwarz inequality. Since the limit is defined only up to an equivalence, the theory is strictly between equivalence classes of functions, that is, elements of the Hilbert space $L_2(\mathbb{R})$, rather than a theory between individual functions.

An important version for probability theory is concerned with the Fourier transforms of totally finite measures (or signed measures). If G is such a measure, its *Fourier–Stieltjes transform* $\tilde{g}$ is the bounded uniformly continuous function

$$(A2.8.6) \qquad \tilde{g}(\omega) = \int_{-\infty}^{\infty} e^{i\omega x} G(dx).$$

If G is a probability measure, $\tilde{g}(\omega)$ is its characteristic function and $\tilde{g}$ is then a *positive-definite* function: for arbitrary finite families of real numbers $\omega_1, \ldots, \omega_r$ and complex numbers $\alpha_1, \ldots, \alpha_r$,

$$(A2.8.7) \qquad \sum_{i=1}^{r} \sum_{j=1}^{r} \alpha_i \bar{\alpha}_j \tilde{g}(\omega_i - \omega_j) \geq 0.$$

Conversely, *Bochner's theorem* asserts that any function continuous at $\omega = 0$ and satisfying (A2.8.7) can be represented as the Fourier transform of a totally finite measure G on $\mathbb{R}$, with $G(\mathbb{R}) = \tilde{g}(0)$. If we take any real or complex integrable function f with any totally finite signed measure G and apply Fubini's theorem to the double integral

$$\int_{-\infty}^{\infty} \int_{-\infty}^{\infty} e^{i\omega x} f(\omega) G(dx) d\omega,$$

which is certainly well defined, we obtain *Parseval's identity*

$$(A2.8.8) \qquad \int_{-\infty}^{\infty} \tilde{f}(x) G(dx) = \int_{-\infty}^{\infty} f(\omega) \tilde{g}(\omega) d\omega.$$

This identity is of basic importance, since it shows that G is uniquely determined by $\tilde{g}$. Various more specific inversion theorems can be obtained by taking suitable choices of f followed by a passage to the limit: this approach is outlined in Chapter XV, Section 3, of Feller (1966), for example. In particular, the following two forms are traditional:

(i) for continuity intervals (a, b) of G,

$$G((a, b)) = \lim_{T \to \infty} \int_{-T}^{T} (i\omega)^{-1} (e^{-i\omega a} - e^{-i\omega b}) \tilde{g}(\omega) d\omega;$$

(ii) for an atom a of G,

$$G(\{a\}) = \lim_{T \to \infty} (2T)^{-1} \int_{-T}^{T} e^{-i\omega a} \tilde{g}(\omega) d\omega.$$

Much of the preceding theory can be extended without difficulty from $\mathbb{R}$ to the case of a locally compact Abelian topological group $\mathscr{G}$. The *characters* of such a group are the continuous homomorphisms of the group onto the complex numbers of modulus 1. If χ_1, χ_2 are characters, then so are $\chi_1 \chi_2$ and

χ_1^{-1}. Thus, the characters form a group in their own right, $\tilde{\mathscr{G}}$ say, the *dual group* for $\mathscr{G}$. There is a natural topology on $\tilde{\mathscr{G}}$, namely, the smallest making the evaluation mapping $e_g(\chi) \equiv \chi(g)$ continuous for each $g \in \mathscr{G}$, and with this topology $\tilde{\mathscr{G}}$ also is a locally compact Abelian topological group. If $\mathscr{G} = \mathbb{R}$, the characters are of the form $e^{i\omega x}$ ($\omega \in \mathbb{R}$), and $\tilde{\mathscr{G}}$ can be identified with another version of $\mathbb{R}$. If $\mathscr{G} = \mathbb{Z}$, the group of integers, $\tilde{\mathscr{G}}$ is the circle group, and vice versa. In any case, the original group reappears as the dual of the dual group $\tilde{\mathscr{G}}$, and if $\mathscr{G}$ is compact, $\tilde{\mathscr{G}}$ is discrete and conversely.

Now let H and $\tilde{H}$ denote Haar measure on $\mathscr{G}$ and $\tilde{\mathscr{G}}$, respectively. If $f: \mathscr{G} \to \mathbb{R}$ is measurable and H-integrable, its Fourier transform $\tilde{f}$ is the function defined on $\tilde{\mathscr{G}}$ by

$$(A2.8.9) \qquad \tilde{f}(\chi) = \int_{\mathscr{G}} \chi(g) f(g) H(dg).$$

If also $\tilde{f}$ is $\tilde{H}$-integrable, then the inverse relation

$$(A2.8.10) \qquad f(x) = \int_{\tilde{\mathscr{G}}} \overline{\chi(g)} \tilde{f}(\chi) \tilde{H}(d\chi)$$

holds, provided that $\tilde{H}$ is normed appropriately [otherwise, a normalizing constant such as $(2\pi)^{-1}$ in (A2.8.2) is needed]. Assuming that such a norming has been adopted, the appropriate analogues of (A2.8.4)–(A2.8.8) remain true. In particular, we note the generalized Plancherel identity

$$(A2.8.11) \qquad \int_{\mathscr{G}} |f(g)|^2 H(dg) = \int_{\tilde{\mathscr{G}}} |\tilde{f}(x)|^2 \tilde{H}(dx).$$

Conditional Expectations, Stopping Times, and Martingales

This appendix contains mainly background material for Chapter 13. For further discussion and most proofs we refer the reader to Ash (1972), Chung (1974), and Brémaud (1981) and to various references cited in the text.

A3.1. Conditional Expectations

Let $(\Omega, \mathscr{E}, \mathscr{P})$ be a probability space (see Section A1.4), X a random variable (r.v.) with $E|X| = \int_\Omega |X| \mathscr{P}(d\omega) < \infty$, and $\mathscr{G}$ a sub-σ-algebra of events from $\mathscr{E}$. The *conditional expectation* of X with respect to $\mathscr{G}$, written $E(X|\mathscr{G})$ or else $E_{X|\mathscr{G}}(\omega)$, is the $\mathscr{G}$-measurable function (i.e., a random variable) defined up to values on a set of $\mathscr{G}$ of $\mathscr{P}$-measure zero as the Radon–Nikodym derivative

$$E(X|\mathscr{G}) = E_{X|\mathscr{G}}(\omega) = \xi_X^{(\mathscr{G})}(d\omega)/\mathscr{P}^{(\mathscr{G})}(d\omega),$$

where $\xi_X(A) = \int_A X(\omega)\mathscr{P}(d\omega)$ is the indefinite integral of X and the superscript $(\mathscr{G})$ indicates that the set functions are to be restricted to $\mathscr{G}$. It is clear that $\xi_X^{(\mathscr{G})} \ll \mathscr{P}^{(\mathscr{G})}$ so that the Radon–Nikodym derivative exists as a $\mathscr{G}$-measurable function. Since, in general, $\mathscr{G}$ is by assumption a coarser σ-algebra than $\mathscr{E}$, the r.v. $E_{X|\mathscr{G}}(\omega)$ represents a smoothed version of the original r.v. $X(\omega)$.

The $\mathscr{G}$-measurability of $E(X|\mathscr{G})$ implies that

$$(A3.1.1) \qquad \int_U X(\omega)\mathscr{P}(d\omega) = \int_U E_{X|\mathscr{G}}(\omega)\mathscr{P}(d\omega) \quad \text{(all } U \in \mathscr{G}),$$

an equation that determines the conditional expectation uniquely and is usually taken as the defining relation. Extending (A3.1.1) from $\mathscr{G}$-measurable indicator functions $I_U(\omega)$ to more general $\mathscr{G}$-measurable functions Y, we have, whenever $E|X|$ and $E|XY|$ exist,

$$(A3.1.2) \quad E(XY) = \int_\Omega Y(\omega)X(\omega)\mathcal{P}(d\omega) = \int_\Omega Y(\omega)E_{X|\mathcal{G}}(\omega)\mathcal{P}(d\omega)$$
$$= E(YE(X|\mathcal{G})).$$

Now replacing Y by $I_U Y$ $(U \in \mathcal{G})$ and using (A3.1.1), there follows the factorization property of conditional expectations, that for $\mathcal{G}$-measurable r.v.s Y, for which both $E|X|$ and $E|XY|$ exist,

$$(A3.1.3) \qquad\qquad E(XY|\mathcal{G}) = YE(X|\mathcal{G}) \quad \text{a.s.}$$

Conditional expectations inherit many standard properties of ordinary expectations:

$(A3.1.4) \quad$ *linearity:* $\quad E\left(\sum_{j=1}^{k} \alpha_j X_j | \mathcal{G}\right) = \sum_{j=1}^{k} \alpha_j E(X_j|\mathcal{G});$

$(A3.1.5) \quad$ *monotonicity:* $\quad X \leq Y$ a.s. implies $E(X|\mathcal{G}) \leq E(Y|\mathcal{G})$ a.s.;

$(A3.1.6) \quad$ *monotone convergence:* $\quad X_n \geq 0, X_n \uparrow Y$ a.s. implies
$\qquad\qquad E(X_n|\mathcal{G}) \uparrow E(Y|\mathcal{G})$ a.s.;

$(A3.1.7) \quad$ *Jensen's inequality:* For convex measurable functions
$\qquad\qquad f: \mathbb{R} \to \mathbb{R}$ with $E|f(X)| < \infty$, $f(E(X|\mathcal{G})) \leq E(f(X)|\mathcal{G})$ a.s.
$\qquad\qquad$ [convexity here means that $f((x + y)/2) \leq (f(x) + f(y))/2$].

If $\mathcal{G}_1$ and $\mathcal{G}_2$ are two sub-σ-algebras with $\mathcal{G}_1 \subseteq \mathcal{G}_2 \subseteq \mathcal{E}$ and $E|X| < \infty$ as before, the *repeated conditioning* theorem holds:

$$(A3.1.8) \qquad E[E(X|\mathcal{G}_1)|\mathcal{G}_2] = E[E(X|\mathcal{G}_2)|\mathcal{G}_1] = E(X|\mathcal{G}_1),$$

yielding as the special case when $\mathcal{G}_1 = \{\varnothing, \Omega\}$,

$$(A3.1.9) \qquad\qquad E[E(X|\mathcal{G})] = EX.$$

Two σ-algebras $\mathcal{G}$ and $\mathcal{H}$ are *independent* if, for all $A \in \mathcal{G}$ and $B \in \mathcal{H}$, $\mathcal{P}(A \cap B) = \mathcal{P}(A)\mathcal{P}(B)$. Given such $\mathcal{G}$ and $\mathcal{H}$, if X is $\mathcal{G}$-measurable and we seek $E(X|\mathcal{H})$, we may expect it to reduce to yield

$$(A3.1.10) \qquad\qquad E(X|\mathcal{H}) = EX.$$

This is a special case of the principle of *redundant conditioning*: if the r.v. X is independent of $\mathcal{H}$ [i.e., $\sigma(X)$ and $\mathcal{H}$ are independent σ-algebras] and $\mathcal{G}$ is independent of $\mathcal{H}$, then

$$(A3.1.11) \qquad\qquad E(X|\mathcal{G} \vee \mathcal{H}) = E(X|\mathcal{G}),$$

reducing to (A3.1.10) for trivial $\mathcal{G}$.

Let $\mathcal{X}$ be a c.s.m.s. and X an $\mathcal{X}$-valued r.v. on $(\Omega, \mathcal{E}, \mathcal{P})$. Given a sub-$\sigma$-algebra $\mathcal{G}$ of $\mathcal{E}$, the *conditional distribution* of X given $\mathcal{G}$ is defined by analogy with (A3.1.1) by

$$(A3.1.12) \qquad \mathcal{P}(X \in A|\mathcal{G}) = E(I_A(X)|\mathcal{G}) \qquad (A \in \mathcal{B}(\mathcal{X})).$$

As in Section A1.5, the question of the existence of *regular* conditional distributions arises. In our present context, we seek a kernel function

$$Q(A, \omega) \qquad (A \in \mathcal{B}(\mathcal{X}), \omega \in \Omega)$$

such that for fixed A, $Q(A, \cdot)$ is a $\mathcal{G}$-measurable function of ω [and we identify this with (A3.1.12)], while for fixed ω, we want $Q(\cdot, \omega)$ to be a probability measure on $\mathcal{B}(\mathcal{X})$. Introduce the set function $\pi(\cdot)$ defined initially for product sets $A \times U$ for $A \in \mathcal{B}(\mathcal{X})$, $U \in \mathcal{G}$, by

$$(A3.1.13) \qquad \pi(A \times U) = \int_U I_A(X(\omega))\mathcal{P}(d\omega).$$

Since $\pi(\cdot)$ is countably additive on such sets, it can be extended to a measure, clearly a probability, on $(\mathcal{X} \times \Omega, \mathcal{B}(\mathcal{X}) \otimes \mathcal{G})$. Then Proposition A1.5.III can be applied and yields the following formal statement, in which we identify the kernel function $Q(\cdot, \cdot)$ sought above with $\mathcal{P}(X \in A | \mathcal{G})$.

Proposition A3.1.I. *Let $\mathcal{X}$ be a c.s.m.s., $(\Omega, \mathcal{E}, \mathcal{P})$ a probability space, and X an $\mathcal{X}$-valued r.v. defined on $(\Omega, \mathcal{E}, \mathcal{P})$. If $\mathcal{G}$ is a sub-σ-algebra of $\mathcal{E}$, then there exists a regular version of the conditional distribution $\mathcal{P}_{X \in \cdot | \mathcal{G}}(\omega)$ such that*

(i) *$\mathcal{P}_{X \in \cdot | \mathcal{G}}(\omega)$ is a probability measure on $\mathcal{B}(\mathcal{X})$ for each fixed ω;*
(ii) *$\mathcal{P}_{X \in A | \mathcal{G}}(\cdot)$ is a $\mathcal{G}$-measurable function of ω for fixed $A \in \mathcal{B}(\mathcal{X})$;*
(iii) *for each $U \in \mathcal{G}$ and $A \in \mathcal{B}(\mathcal{X})$,*

$$(A3.1.14) \qquad \int_U \mathcal{P}_{X \in A | \mathcal{G}}(\omega)\mathcal{P}(d\omega) = \int_U I_A(X(\omega))\mathcal{P}(d\omega).$$

Observe that if $\mathcal{G} = \mathcal{E}$, then the conditional distribution $\mathcal{P}_{X \in \cdot | \mathcal{G}}(\omega)$ is the degenerate distribution concentrated on the point $X(\omega)$. In general, the conditional distribution represents a blurred image of this degenerate distribution, the blurring arising as a result of the incomplete information concerning X carried by the sub-σ-algebra $\mathcal{G}$.

Consider the following question, which is of the nature of a converse to the proposition. Given $(\mathcal{X}, \mathcal{B}(\mathcal{X}))$, $(\Omega, \mathcal{E}, \mathcal{P})$, and a regular kernel $Q(A, \omega)$, can we find a refinement $\mathcal{E}' \supseteq \mathcal{E}$ and an $\mathcal{E}'$-measurable $\mathcal{X}$-valued r.v. X such that $Q(A, \omega)$ coincides with $\mathcal{P}_{X \in A | \mathcal{G}}(\omega)$? If we confine ourselves to the original space this may not necessarily be possible, but by extending Ω we can accomplish our aim. Take the probability space $(\Omega', \mathcal{E}', \mathcal{P}')$ given by $\Omega' = \mathcal{X} \times \Omega$, $\mathcal{E}' = \mathcal{B}(\mathcal{X}) \otimes \mathcal{E}$, $\mathcal{P}' = \pi$ as constructed via (A3.1.13) (identifying $\mathcal{G}$ there with $\mathcal{E}$ here), and consider the r.v. $X: \mathcal{X} \times \Omega \to \mathcal{X}$ for which $X(\omega') = X(x, \omega) = x$. With the mapping $T: \Omega' \to \Omega$ for which $T(\omega') = T(x, \omega) = \omega$, so that $T^{-1}(\mathcal{E})$ is a sub-σ-algebra of $\mathcal{E}'$, we then have, for $A \in \mathcal{B}(\mathcal{X})$,

$$(A3.1.15) \qquad \mathcal{P}'_{X \in A | T^{-1}(\mathcal{E})}(\omega') = Q(A, T(\omega')) = Q(A, \omega).$$

Often the conditioning σ-algebra $\mathcal{G}$ is itself generated by some real or (more generally) c.s.m.s.-valued r.v. Y. Then $E(X | \mathcal{G})$ is called the conditional expectation of X given Y, and $\mathscr{P}(X \in A|\mathscr{G})$ the conditional distribution of X given Y, together with the suggestive notation $E(X|Y)$ or $E_{X|Y}(\omega)$ and $\mathscr{P}(X \in A|\mathscr{G})$ or $\mathscr{P}_{X \in A|\mathscr{G}}(\omega)$. Equation (A3.1.3) then implies, for any Borel-measurable function $h(\cdot)$ such that the unconditional expectations exist,

$$(A3.1.16) \qquad E(Xh(Y)|Y) = h(Y)E(X|Y).$$

The terminology suggests that, although $E(X|Y)$ is defined as a r.v., its value should depend on ω only through $Y(\omega)$. Thus, if Y takes its values in a c.s.m.s. $\mathscr{Y}$, we should look for a real-valued $\mathscr{B}(\mathscr{Y})$-measurable function $h_{X|Y}(y)$ such that

$$(A3.1.17) \qquad E_{X|Y}(\omega) = h_{X|Y}(Y(\omega)) \quad \text{a.s.}$$

That such a function exists is the assertion of the *Doob representation theorem* (e.g., see Doob, 1953). It can be established by applying the argument around (A3.1.1) to the measures induced on $\mathscr{B}(\mathscr{Y})$ by the equations

$$\mathscr{P}_Y(B) = \mathscr{P}(Y^{-1}(B)) \qquad (B \in \mathscr{B}(\mathscr{Y})),$$

$$\xi_X(B) = \int_{Y^{-1}(B)} X(\omega)\mathscr{P}(d\omega),$$

and, noting that $\xi_X \ll \mathscr{P}_Y$ on $\mathscr{B}(\mathscr{Y})$, by applying the Radon–Nikodym theorem. Since the product of a finite or denumerably infinite number of c.s.m.s.s can itself be regarded as a c.s.m.s., we state the theorem in the following general form.

Proposition A3.1.II. *Let $(\Omega, \mathscr{E}, \mathscr{P})$ be a probability space, X an integrable real-valued r.v. on Ω, and $\mathscr{G}$ a sub-σ-algebra of $\mathscr{E}$ generated by a countable family of r.v.s. $Y = \{Y_1, Y_2, \ldots\}$ taking their values in the c.s.m.s.s $\mathscr{Y}_1, \mathscr{Y}_2, \ldots$, respectively. Then there exists a Borel measurable function $h_{X|Y}(\cdot)$: $\mathscr{Y}_1 \times \mathscr{Y}_2 \times \cdots \to \mathbb{R}$, such that*

$$(A3.1.18) \qquad E_{X|\mathscr{G}}(\omega) = h_{X|Y}(Y_1(\omega), Y_2(\omega), \ldots) \quad \mathscr{P}\text{-a.s.}$$

The proposition concerning regular conditional distributions can be transformed in a similar way, yielding a kernel $\mathscr{P}_{X \in A|Y}(y_1, y_2, \ldots)$, which is a probability distribution in A for each vector $(y_1, y_2, \ldots)$, a Borel-measurable function of the family $(y_1, y_2, \ldots)$ for each A, and satisfies

$$\mathscr{P}_{X \in A|\mathscr{G}}(\omega) = \mathscr{P}_{X \in A|Y}(Y_1(\omega), Y_2(\omega), \ldots) \quad \mathscr{P}\text{-a.s.}$$

When densities exist with respect to some underlying measure μ such as Lebesgue measure on $\mathbb{R}^d$, the conditional distributions have the form

$$\mathscr{P}_{X \in A|Y}(y_1, y_2, \ldots) = \frac{\int_A f_{X,Y}(x, y_1, y_2, \ldots)\mu(dx)}{\int_{\mathscr{X}} f_{X,Y}(x, y_1, y_2, \ldots)\mu(dx)},$$

where $f_{X,Y}(\cdot)$ is the joint density function for $X, Y_1, Y_2, \ldots$ in the product space $\mathscr{X} \times \mathscr{Y}_1 \times \mathscr{Y}_2 \times \cdots$, and a similar representation holds for the conditional expectation $h_{X|Y}(\cdot)$.

A3.2. Convergence Concepts

Most of the different notions of convergence and of uniform integrability mentioned below are standard. Stable convergence is less familiar and is discussed in more detail.

A sequence of r.v.s $\{X_n: n = 1, 2, \ldots\}$ on a common probability space $(\Omega, \mathscr{E}, \mathscr{P})$ *converges in probability* to a limit r.v. X, also defined on $(\Omega, \mathscr{E}, \mathscr{P})$, if for all $\varepsilon > 0$,

$$(A3.2.1) \qquad \mathscr{P}\{|X_n - X| > \varepsilon\} \to 0 \quad \text{as } n \to \infty.$$

The sequence *converges almost surely* to X if

$$(A3.2.2) \quad 1 = \mathscr{P}\{\omega: X_n(\omega) \to X(\omega)\,(n \to \infty)\}$$

$$= \mathscr{P}\left(\bigcap_{r=1}^{\infty} \bigcup_{n=1}^{\infty} \bigcap_{m \geq n} \{\omega: |X_m(\omega) - X(\omega)| < r^{-1}\}\right)$$

$$= \mathscr{P}\left(\bigcap_{r=1}^{\infty} \bigcup_{n=1}^{\infty} \bigcap_{m \geq n} \{\omega: |X_m(\omega) - X_n(\omega)| < r^{-1}\}\right).$$

Both these concepts readily generalize to the case where the r.v.s X and X_n are $\mathscr{X}$-valued for some c.s.m.s. $\mathscr{X}$ by simply replacing the Euclidean distance $|X - Y|$ by the metric $\rho(X, Y)$ for $X, Y \in \mathscr{X}$. The a.s. convergence as at (A3.2.2) implies convergence in probability; convergence in probability implies the existence of a subsequence $\{X_{n_k}\}$ that converges a.s. to the same limit.

Returning to the real-valued case, for any given real $p \geq 1$, $\{X_n\}$ *converges in the mean of order p* (or *in pth mean*, or *in L_p norm*), if the pth moments exist and

$$(A3.2.3) \qquad \|X_n - X\|_p \equiv (E|X_n - X|^p)^{1/p} \to 0 \qquad (n \to \infty),$$

the norm here denoting the norm in the Banach space $L_p(\Omega, \mathscr{E}, \mathscr{P})$ of equivalence classes of r.v.s with finite pth moments. For $p = \infty$, the space $L_\infty(\Omega, \mathscr{E}, \mathscr{P})$ consists of $\mathscr{P}$-*essentially bounded* r.v.s X, that is, r.v.s X for which $|X| \leq M$ a.s. for some $M < \infty$; then

$$(A3.2.4) \qquad \|X\|_\infty = \text{ess sup}|X(\omega)| = \inf\{M: |X(\omega)| \leq M \text{ a.s.}\}.$$

If $X_n \to X$ in pth mean, then $E(X_n^p) \to E(X^p)\,(n \to \infty)$.

Chebyshev's inequality, in the form for an L_p r.v. X,

$$(A3.2.5) \qquad \mathscr{P}\{|X - a| > \varepsilon\} \leq \varepsilon^{-p}E(|X - a|^p) \quad \text{(real } a, \varepsilon > 0),$$

implies that convergence in L_p norm implies convergence in probability. The converse requires the additional condition of *uniform integrability*.

Definition A3.2.I. A family of real-valued r.v.s $\{X_t: t \in \mathscr{T}\}$ defined on the common probability space $(\Omega, \mathscr{E}, \mathscr{P})$ is *uniformly integrable* if, given $\varepsilon > 0$, there exists $M < \infty$ such that

$$(A3.2.6) \qquad \int_{|X_t| > M} |X_t(\omega)|\mathscr{P}(d\omega) < \varepsilon \quad \text{(all } t \in \mathscr{T}).$$

Proposition A3.2.II. *Let the r.v.s* $\{X_n: n = 1, 2, \ldots\}$ *and* X *be defined on a common probability space* $(\Omega, \mathscr{E}, \mathscr{P})$ *and be such that* $X_n \to X$ *in probability. Then a necessary and sufficient condition for the means to exist and for* $X_n \to X$ *in* L_1 *norm is that the sequence* $\{X_n\}$ *be uniformly integrable.*

Applied to the sequence $\{X_n^p\}$ and noting the inequality $E|X_n - X|^p \leq 2^p(E|X_n|^p + E|X|^p)$ $(1 \leq p < \infty)$, the proposition extends in an obvious way to convergence in L_p norm for $1 \leq p < \infty$.

A weaker concept than convergence in L_p norm [i.e., strong convergence in the Banach space $L_p(\Omega, \mathscr{E}, \mathscr{P})$] is that of *weak* L_p *convergence*; namely, that if X_n, $X \in L_p$, then $E(X_n Y) \to E(XY)$ $(n \to \infty)$ for all $Y \in L_q$, where $p^{-1} + q^{-1} = 1$.

When X_n is $\mathscr{X}$-valued for a c.s.m.s. $\mathscr{X}$ with metric ρ, X_n *converges to* X *in distribution* if $\mathscr{P}\{X_n \in A\} \to \mathscr{P}\{X \in A\}$ for all $A \in \mathscr{B}(\mathscr{X})$ for which $\mathscr{P}\{X \in \partial A\} = 0$. This type of convergence is not a constraint on the r.v.s so much as a constraint on the distributions they induce on $\mathscr{B}(\mathscr{X})$: indeed, it is precisely the weak convergence of their induced distributions. If $X_n \to X$ in probability (or, a fortiori, if $X_n \to X$ a.s. or in L_p norm), then from the inequalities

$$\mathscr{P}\{X_n \in A\} - \mathscr{P}\{X \in A\}$$

$$\leq \mathscr{P}(\{X_n \in A\} \cap \{X \in A^c\})$$

$$\leq \mathscr{P}(\{X_n \in A\} \cap \{X \in (A^\varepsilon)^c\}) + \mathscr{P}\{X \in A^\varepsilon\} - \mathscr{P}\{X \in A\}$$

$$\leq \mathscr{P}\{\rho(X_n, X) > \varepsilon\} + \mathscr{P}\{X \in A^\varepsilon\} - \mathscr{P}\{X \in A\},$$

it follows that $X_n \to X$ in distribution, also written $X_n \to_d X$. No general converse statement is possible except when X is degenerate, that is, $X = a$ a.s. for some $a \in \mathscr{X}$. For this exceptional case, $X_n \to_d a$ means that $\mathscr{P}\{\rho(X_n, a) < \varepsilon\} = \mathscr{P}\{X_n \in S(a; \varepsilon)\} \to 1$ $(n \to \infty)$, where $S(a; \varepsilon)$ is the sphere with centre a and radius ε, which is the same as $X_n \to a$ in probability.

A hybrid concept, in the sense that it depends partly on the r.v.s X_n themselves and partly on their distributions, is that of *stable convergence*.

Definition A3.2.III. *If* $\{X_n: n = 1, 2, \ldots\}$ *and* X *are* $\mathscr{X}$-*valued r.v.s on* $(\Omega, \mathscr{E}, \mathscr{P})$ *and* $\mathscr{F}$ *is a sub-σ-algebra of* $\mathscr{E}$, *then* $X_n \to X$ ($\mathscr{F}$-*stably*) *in distribution if for all* $U \in \mathscr{F}$ *and all* $A \in \mathscr{B}(\mathscr{X})$ *with* $\mathscr{P}\{X \in \partial A\} = 0$,

$$(A3.2.7) \qquad \mathscr{P}(\{X_n \in A\} \cap U) \to \mathscr{P}(\{X \in A\} \cap U) \qquad (n \to \infty).$$

The hybrid nature of stable convergence is well illustrated by the facts that when $\mathscr{F} = \{\varnothing, \Omega\}$, $\mathscr{F}$-stable convergence is convergence in distribution whereas when $\mathscr{F} \supseteq \sigma(X)$, we have a.s. convergence in probability, because the regular version $\mathscr{P}_{X \in \cdot | \mathscr{F}}(\omega)$ of the conditional distribution appearing in $\mathscr{P}(\{X \in A\} \cap U) = \int_U \mathscr{P}_{X \in A | \mathscr{F}}(\omega) \mathscr{P}(d\omega)$ can be taken as being $\{0, 1\}$-valued, and when such degenerate distributions for the limit r.v. occur the concepts of convergence in distribution and in probability coincide as already noted.

In general, stable convergence always implies weak convergence, and it may be regarded as a form of weak convergence of the conditional distributions $\mathscr{P}(X_n \in A|\mathscr{F})$. Just as weak convergence can be expressed in equivalent ways, so also can stable convergence, as set out below (see Aldous and Eagleson, 1978).

Proposition A3.2.IV. *Let* $\{X_n\}$, X, $\mathscr{F}$ *be as in Definition A3.2.III. Then the following conditions are equivalent:*

(i) $X_n \to X$ *($\mathscr{F}$-stably) [i.e., (A3.2.7) holds].*
(ii) *For all $\mathscr{F}$-measurable $\mathscr{P}$-essentially bounded r.v.s Z and all bounded continuous $h: \mathscr{X} \to \mathbb{R}$,*

$$(A3.2.8) \qquad E(Zh(X_n)) \to E(Zh(X)) \qquad (n \to \infty).$$

(iii) *For all real-valued $\mathscr{F}$-measurable r.v.s Y, the pair (X_n, Y) converges jointly in distribution to the pair (X, Y).*
(iv) *For all bounded continuous functions $g: \mathscr{X} \times \mathbb{R} \to \mathbb{R}$ and all real-valued $\mathscr{F}$-measurable r.v.s Y,*

$$(A3.2.9) \qquad g(X_n, Y) \to g(X, Y) \qquad (\mathscr{F}\text{-stably}).$$

If $\mathscr{X} = \mathbb{R}^d$ then any of (i)–(iv) is equivalent to condition (v):
(v) *For all real vectors $t \in \mathbb{R}^d$ and all $\mathscr{P}$-essentially bounded $\mathscr{F}$-measurable r.v.s Z,*

$$(A3.2.10) \qquad E(Z \exp(it' X_n)) \to E(Z \exp(it' X)).$$

PROOF. Equation (A3.2.7) is the special case of (A3.2.8) with $Z = I_U(\omega)$ and $h(x) = I_A(x)$ for $U \in \mathscr{F}$ and $A \in \mathscr{B}(\mathscr{X})$, except that such $h(\cdot)$ is not in general continuous: as in the continuity theorem for weak convergence, (A3.2.8) can be extended to the case where h is bounded and Borel measurable and $\mathscr{P}\{X \in \partial h\} = 0$, where ∂h is the set of discontinuities of h. When $\mathscr{X} = \mathbb{R}^d$, (A3.2.10) extends the well-known result that joint convergence of characteristic functions is equivalent to weak convergence of distributions. Note that all of (A3.2.7), (A3.2.8), and (A3.2.10) are contracted versions of the full statement of weak convergence in L_1 of the conditional distributions, namely, that

$$(A3.2.11) \qquad E(ZE(h(X_n)|\mathscr{F})) \to E(ZE(h(X)|\mathscr{F})) \qquad (n \to \infty)$$

for arbitrary (not necessarily $\mathscr{F}$-measurable) r.v.s Z. However, (A3.2.11) can immediately be reduced to the simpler contracted forms by using the repeated conditioning theorem, which shows, first, that it is enough to consider Z $\mathscr{F}$-measurable, and second, that when Z is $\mathscr{F}$-measurable the conditioning on $\mathscr{F}$ can be dropped.

If Y is real-valued and $\mathscr{F}$-measurable and in (A3.2.7) we set $U = Y^{-1}(B)$ for $B \in \mathscr{B}(\mathbb{R})$, we obtain

$$\mathscr{P}\{(X_n, Y) \in A \times B\} \to \mathscr{P}\{(X, Y) \in A \times B\},$$

from which (iii) follows. Conversely, taking $Y = I_U$ in (iii) yields (A3.2.7).

Finally, for any two real-valued $\mathscr{F}$-measurable r.v.s Y, Z, repeated application of (iii) shows that (X_n, Y, Z) converges weakly in distribution to the triple (X, Y, Z). Applying the continuous mapping theorem (Proposition A2.2.VII) yields the result that the pairs $(g(X_n, Y), Z)$ converge weakly in distribution to $(g(X, Y), Z)$, which is equivalent to the stable convergence of $g(X_n, Y)$ to $g(X, Y)$ by (iii). Since stable convergence implies weak convergence, (iv) implies (iii).   □

When the limit r.v. is independent of the conditioning σ-algebra $\mathscr{F}$, we have a special case of some importance. Then, (A3.2.7) and (A3.2.10) reduce to the forms

(A3.2.12) $\mathscr{P}(X_n \in A | U) \to \mathscr{P}\{X \in A\}$ $(\mathscr{P}(U) > 0)$

and

(A3.2.13) $E(Z \exp(it'X_n)) \to (EZ)E(\exp(it'X))$,

respectively. In this case the X_n are said to *converge $\mathscr{F}$-mixing* to X.

In applications it is often the case that the left-hand sides of relations like (A3.2.7) converge as $n \to \infty$, but it is not immediately clear that the limit can be associated with the conditional distribution of a well-defined r.v. X. Indeed, in general there is no guarantee that such a limit r.v. will exist, but we can instead extend the probability space in such a way that on the extended space a new sequence of r.v.s can be defined, with effectively the same conditional distributions as for the original r.v.s, and for which there is $\mathscr{F}$-stable convergence in the limit to a proper conditional distribution.

Lemma A3.2.V. *Suppose that for each $U \in \mathscr{F}$ and for A in some covering ring generating $\mathscr{B}(\mathscr{X})$, the sequences $\{\mathscr{P}(\{X_n \in A\} \cap U)\}$ converge. Then there exists a probability space $(\Omega', \mathscr{E}', \mathscr{P}')$, a measurable mapping $T: (\Omega', \mathscr{E}') \to (\Omega, \mathscr{E})$, and a r.v. X' defined on $(\Omega', \mathscr{E}')$ such that if $\mathscr{F}' = T^{-1}\mathscr{F}$ and $X'_n(\omega') = X_n(T\omega')$, then $X'_n \to X'$ ($\mathscr{F}'$-stably).*

PROOF. Set $\Omega' = \mathscr{X} \times \Omega$ and let $\mathscr{E}'$ be the smallest σ-algebra of subsets of Ω' containing both $\mathscr{B}(\mathscr{X}) \otimes \mathscr{F}$ and also $\mathscr{X} \times \mathscr{E}$. Defining T by $T(x, \omega) = \omega$, we see that T is measurable. Also, for each $A \in \mathscr{B}(\mathscr{X})$ and $U \in \mathscr{F}$, the limit $\pi(A \times U) = \lim_{n \to \infty} \mathscr{P}(\{X_n \in A\} \cap U)$ exists by assumption and defines a countably additive set function on such product sets. Similarly, we can set $\pi(\mathscr{X} \times B) = \lim_{n \to \infty} \mathscr{P}(\{X_n \in \mathscr{X}\} \cap B) = \mathscr{P}(B)$ for $B \in \mathscr{E}$. Thus, π can be extended to a countably additive set function, $\mathscr{P}'$ say, on $\mathscr{E}'$. Observe that $\mathscr{F}' = T^{-1}\mathscr{F}$ consists of all sets $\mathscr{X} \times U$ for $U \in \mathscr{F}$. Define also $X'(x, \omega) = x$. Then for $U' = \mathscr{X} \times U \in \mathscr{F}'$,

$$\mathscr{P}'(\{X'_n \in A\} \cap U') = \mathscr{P}(\{X_n \in A\} \cap U) \to \mathscr{P}'(A \times U)$$

$$= \mathscr{P}'(\{X' \in A\} \cap U')$$

so that X'_n converges to X', $\mathscr{F}'$-stably.   □

Each of the conditions (i)–(v) of Proposition A3.2.IV consists of a family of sequences, involving r.v.s X_n converging in some sense, and the family of the limits is identified with a family involving a limit r.v. X. It is left to the reader to verify via Lemma A3.2.V that if we are given only the convergence parts of any of these conditions, then the conditions are still equivalent, and it is possible to extend the probability space and construct a new sequence of r.v.s X_n' with the same joint probability distributions as the original X_n, together with a limit r.v. X', such that $X_n' \to X'$, $\mathscr{F}'$-stably, and so on.

In a similar vein, there exists the following selection theorem for stable convergence.

Proposition A3.2.VI. *Let $\{X_n\}$ be a sequence of $\mathscr{X}$-valued r.v.s on $(\Omega, \mathscr{E}, \mathscr{P})$, and $\mathscr{F}$ a sub-σ-algebra of $\mathscr{E}$. If*

(i) *either $\mathscr{F}$ is countably generated, or $\mathscr{F} \supseteq \sigma(X_1, X_2, \ldots)$; and*
(ii) *the distributions of the $\{X_n\}$ converge weakly on $\mathscr{B}(\mathscr{X})$;*

then there exists an extended probability space $(\Omega', \mathscr{E}', \mathscr{P}')$, elements T, $\mathscr{F}'$, X_n' defined as in Lemma A3.2.V, a sequence $\{n_k\}$, and a limit r.v. X', such that $\{X_{n_k}'\}$ converges to X', $\mathscr{F}'$-stably, as $k \to \infty$.

PROOF. Suppose first that $\mathscr{F}$ is countably generated, and denote by $\mathscr{R}$ some countable ring generating $\mathscr{F}$. For each $U \in \mathscr{R}$ the measures on $\mathscr{B}(\mathscr{X})$ defined by

$$Q_n(A; U) = \mathscr{P}(\{X_n \in A\} \cap U)$$

are uniformly tight because they are strictly dominated by the uniformly tight measures $\mathscr{P}(\{X_n \in A\})$. Thus, they contain a weakly convergent subsequence. Using a diagonal selection argument, the subsequence can be so chosen that convergence holds simultaneously for all $U \in \mathscr{R}$. Therefore, we can assume that the sequence $\{Q_{n_k}(A; U)\}$ converges as $k \to \infty$ to some limit $Q(A; U)$ for all A that are continuity sets of this limit measure and for all $U \in \mathscr{R}$.

Given $\varepsilon > 0$ and $B \in \mathscr{F}$, there exist $U_\varepsilon, V_\varepsilon \in \mathscr{R}$ such that $U_\varepsilon \subseteq B \subseteq V_\varepsilon$ and $\mathscr{P}(U_\varepsilon) \geq \mathscr{P}(V_\varepsilon) - \varepsilon$. Then the two extreme terms in the chain of inequalities

$$\lim_{k \to \infty} Q_{n_k}(A; U_\varepsilon) \leq \liminf_{k \to \infty} \mathscr{P}(\{X_{n_k} \in A\} \cap B)$$

$$\leq \limsup_{k \to \infty} \mathscr{P}(\{X_{n_k} \in A\} \cap B) \leq \lim_{k \to \infty} Q_{n_k}(A; V_\varepsilon)$$

differ by at most ε, so the sequence $\{\mathscr{P}(\{X_{n_k} \in A\} \cap B)\}$ also converges. The construction of an extended probability space $(\Omega', \mathscr{E}', \mathscr{P}')$ and a limit r.v. X' now follows as in the lemma, establishing the proposition in the case that $\mathscr{F}$ is countably generated.

To treat the case that $\mathscr{F} \supseteq \sigma(X_1, X_2, \ldots)$, consider first the case that $\mathscr{F} = \mathscr{F}_0 \equiv \sigma(X_1, X_2, \ldots)$. This is countably generated because $\mathscr{X}$ is separable and only a countable family of r.v.s is involved. Applying the selection argument and extension of the probability space, we can conclude from (A3.2.10) that

(A3.2.14) $E(Zh(X'_{n_k})) \to E(Zh(X'))$ for any $\mathcal{F}'_0$-measurable Z.

Now let Z' be any $\mathcal{F}'$-measurable r.v. (where $\mathcal{F}' \supset \mathcal{F}'_0$). Because $h(X'_{n_k})$ is $\mathcal{F}'_0$-measurable, we can write

$$E(Z'h(X'_{n_k})) = E(E(Z'|\mathcal{F}'_0)h(X'_{n_k})),$$

and the convergence follows from (A3.2.14) by the $\mathcal{F}'_0$-measurability of $E(Z'|\mathcal{F}'_0)$. Thus, for any such Z', $E(Z'h(Z'_{n_k})) \to E(Z'h(X'))$, implying that $X'_{n_k} \to X'$ ($\mathcal{F}'$-stably).   □

A systematic account of the topology of stable convergence when $\mathcal{F} = \mathcal{E}$ but no limit r.v. is assumed is given by Jacod and Memin (1984).

A3.3. Processes and Stopping Times

This section is primarily intended as background material for Chapter 13 where the focus is on certain real-valued stochastic processes denoted $\{X_t(\omega)\} = \{X(t, \omega)\} = \{X(t)\}$ on the positive time axis, $t \in (0, \infty) \equiv \mathbb{R}_+$. Other time domains—finite intervals, or $\mathbb{R}$, or (subsets of) the integers $\mathbb{Z} = \{0, \pm 1, \ldots\}$—can be considered: it is left to the reader to supply appropriate modifications to the theory as needed. Our aim here is to give just so much of the measure-theoretic framework as we hope will make our text intelligible.

For a detailed discussion of this framework, texts like Dellacherie (1972) or Dellacherie and Meyer (1978) or Elliott (1982) should be consulted. Condensed accounts of selected results, such as given here, are also given in Brémaud (1981), Kallianpur (1980), and Liptser and Shiryayev (1977).

While a stochastic process $X(t, \omega)$ may be regarded as an indexed family of random variables on a common probability space $(\Omega, \mathcal{E}, \mathcal{P})$, with index set here taken to be $\mathbb{R}_+$, it is more appropriate for our purposes, as in the general theory, to regard it as a function on the product space $\mathbb{R}_+ \times \Omega$. The stochastic process $X: \mathbb{R}_+ \times \Omega \to \mathcal{B}(\mathbb{R}_+) \otimes \mathcal{E}$ is *measurable* when this mapping is measurable; that is, for all $A \in \mathcal{B}(\mathbb{R})$,

(A3.3.1) $\{(t, \omega): X(t, \omega) \in A\} \in \mathcal{B}(\mathbb{R}_+) \otimes \mathcal{E},$

where the right-hand side denotes the product σ-algebra of the two σ-algebras there. As a consequence of this measurability and Fubini's theorem, $X(\cdot, \omega): \mathbb{R}_+ \to \mathbb{R}$ is a.s. measurable, while for measurable functions $h: \mathbb{R} \to \mathbb{R}$,

$$Y(\omega) \equiv \int_{\mathbb{R}_+} h(X(t, \omega))dt$$

is a random variable provided the integral exists. A stochastic process on $\mathbb{R}_+$, if defined merely as an indexed family of r.v.s on a common probability space, is necessarily measurable if, for example, the trajectories are either a.s. continuous or a.s. monotonic and right-continuous.

The main topic we treat concerns the evolution of a stochastic process; that is, we observe $\{X(s, \omega): 0 < s \le t\}$ for some (unknown) ω and finite time interval $(0, t]$. It is then natural to consider the σ-algebra

$$\mathcal{F}_t^{(X)} \equiv \sigma\{X(s, \omega): 0 < s \le t\}$$

generated by all possible such evolutions. Clearly,

$$\mathcal{F}_s^{(X)} \subseteq \mathcal{F}_t^{(X)}$$

for $0 < s < t < \infty$. Of course, we may also have some foreknowledge of the process X, and this we represent by a σ-algebra $\mathcal{F}_0$. Quite generally, an expanding family $\mathcal{F} = \{\mathcal{F}_t: 0 \le t \le \infty\}$ of sub-σ-algebras of $\mathcal{E}$ is called a *filtration* or a *history*, and we concentrate on those histories that incorporate information on the process X. For this purpose, we want the r.v. $X(t, \omega)$ to be $\mathcal{F}_t$-measurable (all t); we then say that X is $\mathcal{F}$-*adapted*. We adopt the special notation

$$\mathcal{H} = \{\mathcal{F}_t^{(X)}: 0 \le t \le \infty\} \equiv \{\mathcal{H}_t: 0 \le t \le \infty\},$$

where $\mathcal{F}_0^{(X)} = \lim\inf_{t>0} \mathcal{F}_t^{(X)} = \{\emptyset, \Omega\}$ and $\mathcal{F}_\infty^{(X)} = \bigcap_{t>0} \mathcal{F}_t^{(X)}$, and call $\mathcal{H}$ the *internal* or *minimal* or *natural* history of the process X, both of these last two names reflecting the fact that $\mathcal{H}$ is the smallest family of nested σ-algebras to which X is adapted. Any history of the form $\mathcal{F} = \{\mathcal{F}_0 \vee \mathcal{H}_t: 0 \le t \le \infty\}$ is called an *intrinsic* history.

Suppose X is measurable and $\mathcal{F}$-adapted. An apparently stronger condition to impose on X is that of *progressive measurability* with respect to $\mathcal{F}$, meaning that for every $t \in \mathbb{R}_+$ and any $A \in \mathcal{B}(\mathbb{R})$,

(A3.3.2) $\{(s, \omega): 0 < s \le t, X(s, \omega) \in A\} \in \mathcal{B}((0, t]) \otimes \mathcal{F}_t.$

Certainly, (A3.3.2) is more restrictive on X than (A3.3.1), and while (A3.3.2) implies (A3.3.1), the converse is not quite true. What can be shown, however, is that given any measurable $\mathcal{F}$-adapted $\mathbb{R}$-valued process X, we can find an $\mathcal{F}$-progressively measurable process Y (that is therefore measurable and $\mathcal{F}$-adapted) that is a *modification* of X in the sense of being defined (like X) on $(\Omega, \mathcal{E}, \mathcal{P})$ and satisfying

(A3.3.3) $\mathcal{P}\{\omega: X(t, \omega) = Y(t, \omega)\} = 1$ (all t)

[e.g., see Theorems 29 and 30 of Chapter IV of Dellacherie and Meyer (1978)].

The sets of the form $[s, t] \times U$, $0 \le s < t$, $U \in \mathcal{F}_t$, $t \ge 0$, generate a σ-algebra on $\mathbb{R}_+ \times \Omega$, which may be called the $\mathcal{F}$-*progressive σ-algebra*. Then the requirement that the process X be $\mathcal{F}$-progressively measurable may be rephrased as the requirement that $X(t, \omega)$ be measurable with respect to the $\mathcal{F}$-progressive σ-algebra.

A more restrictive condition to impose on X is that it be $\mathcal{F}$-*predictable* (the term $\mathscr{F}$-*previsible* is also used). Call the sub-σ-algebra of $\mathscr{B}(\mathbb{R}_+) \otimes \mathscr{E}$ generated by product sets of the form $(s, t] \times U$, where $U \in \mathscr{F}_s$, $t \geq s$, and $0 \leq s < \infty$, the *predictable σ-algebra*, denoted $\Psi^{\mathscr{F}}$. (The terminology is well chosen, because it reflects what can be predicted at some "future" time t given the evolution of the process—as revealed by sets $U \in \mathscr{F}_s$—up to the "present" time s). Then X is $\mathscr{F}$-predictable when it is $\Psi^{\mathscr{F}}$-measurable; that is, for any $A \in \mathscr{B}(\mathbb{R})$,

$$\{(t, \omega): X(t, \omega) \in A\} \in \Psi^{\mathscr{F}}.$$

The archetypal $\mathscr{F}$-predictable process is left-continuous, and this is reflected in Lemma A3.3.I below, in which the left-continuous history $\mathscr{F}_{(-)} \equiv \{\mathscr{F}_{t-}\}$ associated with $\mathscr{F}$ appears: here, $\mathscr{F}_{0-} = \mathscr{F}_0$ and $\mathscr{F}_{t-} = \limsup_{s<t} \mathscr{F}_s = \bigvee_{s<t} \mathscr{F}_s$. Note that if $X(t, \omega)$ is $\mathscr{F}_{t-}$-measurable, its value at t is in fact determined by information at times *prior* to t.

Lemma A3.3.I. *An $\mathscr{F}$-predictable process is $\mathscr{F}_{(-)}$-adapted.*

PROOF. Consider first a process of the form

(A3.3.4) $X(t, \omega) = I_{(a, b]}(t) I_U(\omega)$ $(0 < a < b < \infty, U \in \mathscr{F}_a)$,

which is $\mathscr{F}$-predictable by construction of $\Psi^{\mathscr{F}}$. For given t, $\{\omega: X(t, \omega)) = 1\} = \varnothing$ if $a \geq t$ or $b < t$, $= U$ if $a < t \leq b$, so $X(t, \omega)$ is $\mathscr{F}_{t-}$-measurable. Since an arbitrary $\mathscr{F}$-predictable function can be approximated by a linear combination of functions of this type, and since the class of $\mathscr{F}_{(-)}$-adapted processes is closed under linear combinations and monotone limits, standard extension arguments complete the proof. $\square$

Indicator functions as at (A3.3.4), and linear combinations of them, can be used to show that the $\mathscr{F}$-predictable σ-algebra $\Psi^{\mathscr{F}}$ above can be characterized as the σ-algebra generated by the class of bounded left-continuous $\mathscr{F}$-adapted processes [e.g., see Lemma 3.1.1 of Kallianpur (1980)].

It is often important to examine the behaviour of a process not at a fixed time t but rather a random time $T = T(\omega)$. Here the definition of a *stopping time* is fundamental.

Definition A3.3.II. Given a history $\mathscr{F}$, a nonnegative r.v. $T: \Omega \to [0, \infty]$ is an *$\mathscr{F}$-stopping time* if

$$\{\omega: T(\omega) \leq t\} \in \mathscr{F}_t   (0 \leq t < \infty).$$

If S, T are stopping times, then so are $S \wedge T$ and $S \vee T$. Indeed, given a family $\{T_n: n = 1, 2, \ldots\}$ of stopping times, $\sup_{n \geq 1} T_n$ is an $\mathscr{F}$-stopping time, while $\inf_{n \geq 1} T_n$ is an $\mathscr{F}_{(+)}$-stopping time.

Since $\{T(\omega) = \infty\} = \bigcap_n \{T(\omega) > n\} \in \mathscr{F}_\infty$, we can also consider extended stopping times as those for which $\mathscr{P}\{T(\omega) < \infty\} < 1$.

While stopping times can be generated in various ways, the most common method is as a first passage time, which for a nondecreasing process usually arises as a level crossing time.

Lemma A3.3.III. *Let X be an $\mathcal{F}$-adapted monotonic increasing right-continuous process and let Y be an $\mathcal{F}_0$-measurable r.v. Then $T(\omega) \equiv \inf\{t: X(t, \omega) \geq Y(\omega)\}$ is an $\mathcal{F}$-stopping time, possibly extended, while if X is $\mathcal{F}$-predictable then T is an (extended) $\mathcal{F}_{(-)}$-stopping time.*

PROOF. If Y is constant, $X(t) \geq Y$ if and only if $T \leq t$, and since $\{\omega: X(t, \omega) \geq Y\} \in \mathcal{F}_t$, we also have $\{T(\omega) \leq t\} \in \mathcal{F}_t$. More generally, $X(t, \omega) - Y(\omega)$ is monotonic increasing, right-continuous, and $\mathcal{F}$-adapted (because Y, being $\mathcal{F}_0$-measurable, is necessarily $\mathcal{F}_t$-measurable for every $t > 0$). Then by the same argument, $\{T(\omega) \leq t\} = \{\omega: X(t, \omega) - Y(\omega) \geq 0\} \in \mathcal{F}_t$. Finally, when X is $\mathcal{F}$-predictable, it is $\mathcal{F}_{(-)}$-adapted, and thus we can replace $\mathcal{F}_t$ by $\mathcal{F}_{t-}$ throughout. □

The next result shows that a process stopped at an $\mathcal{F}$-stopping time T inherits some of the regularity properties of the original process. Here we use the notation

$$X(t \wedge T) = \begin{cases} X(t) & (t \leq T), \\ X(T) & (t > T). \end{cases}$$

Proposition A3.3.IV. *Let $\mathcal{F}$ be a history, T an $\mathcal{F}$-stopping time, and X a process. Then $X(t \wedge T)$ is measurable, $\mathcal{F}$-progressive, or $\mathcal{F}$-predictable, according to whether $X(t)$ itself is measurable, $\mathcal{F}$-progressive, or $\mathcal{F}$-predictable. In all these cases, if $T < \infty$ a.s., then $X(T)$ is an $\mathcal{F}_\infty$-measurable r.v.*

PROOF. The product σ-algebra $\mathcal{B}(\mathbb{R}_+) \otimes \mathcal{E}$ is generated by sets of the form $(a, \infty) \times B$ for real finite a and $B \in \mathcal{E}$. Since

$$\{(t, \omega): (t \wedge T(\omega), \omega) \in (a, \infty) \times B\} = (a, \infty) \times (B \cap \{T(\omega) > a\})$$

and $B \cap \{T(\omega) > a\} \in \mathcal{E}$, if X is measurable, so is $Y(t, \omega) \equiv X(t \wedge T(\omega), \omega)$.

The $\mathcal{F}$-predictable σ-algebra $\Psi^{\mathcal{F}}$ is generated by sets of a similar product form but with $B \in \mathcal{F}_a$. Since $\{T(\omega) > a\} \in \mathcal{F}_a$, $(a, \infty) \times (B \cap \{T(\omega) > a\})$ is also a set generating $\Psi^{\mathcal{F}}$, and thus if X is $\mathcal{F}$-predictable, so is Y as before.

Suppose now that X is $\mathcal{F}$-progressive, so that for given t in $0 < t < \infty$, $\{X(s, \omega): 0 < s \leq t\}$ is measurable as a process on $(0, t]$ with probability space $(\Omega, \mathcal{F}_t, \mathcal{P})$. Then the first argument shows that $Y(s) \equiv X(s \wedge T)$ is a measurable process on this space, that is, $X(t \wedge T)$ is $\mathcal{F}$-progressive.

On the set $\{T < \infty\}$, $X(t \wedge T) \to X(T)$ as $t \to \infty$, so provided $\mathcal{P}\{T < \infty\} = 1$, $X(T)$ is a r.v. as asserted. □

As an important corollary to this result, observe that if X is $\mathcal{F}$-progressive and a.s. integrable on finite intervals, then

$$Y(t, \omega) = \int_0^t X(s, \omega)ds$$

is $\mathscr{F}$-progressive, $Y(T)$ is a r.v. if $T < \infty$ a.s., and $Y(t \wedge T)$ is again $\mathscr{F}$-progressive.

We conclude this section with some remarks about the possibility of a converse to Lemma A3.3.I. In the case of a quite general history, no such result of this kind holds, as is shown by the discussion in Dellacherie and Meyer (1978), especially around Chapter IV, Section 97. On the other hand, it is shown in the same reference that when X is defined on the canonical measure space $(\mathcal{M}_{[0, \infty)}, \mathscr{B}(\mathcal{M}_{[0, \infty)}))$ the two concepts of being $\mathscr{F}_{(-)}$-adapted and $\mathscr{F}$-predictable can be identified, a fact exploited in the treatment by Jacobsen (1982).

The situation can be illustrated further by the two indicator processes

$$V_T^+ (t, \omega) \equiv I_{\{T(\omega) \leq t\}}(t, \omega),$$

$$V_T^- (t, \omega) \equiv I_{\{T(\omega) < t\}}(t, \omega),$$

generated by an $\mathscr{F}$-stopping time T. The trajectories of V_T^+ are right-continuous while those of V_T^- are left-continuous. Since $\mathscr{F}_t \ni \{\omega: T(\omega) \leq t\} = \{\omega: V_T^+ (t) = 1\}$, it follows that V_T^+ is $\mathscr{F}$-adapted; so too is V_T^- because

$$\{\omega: V_T^- (t) = 1\} = \{\omega: T(\omega) < t\} = \bigcup_{n=1}^{\infty} \{\omega: T(\omega) \leq t - 1/n\} \in \mathscr{F}_t.$$

Hence, both V_T^+ and V_T^- are $\mathscr{F}$-progressively measurable [see the earlier comments or Brémaud (1981), Theorem A1.T33)].

Being left-continuous, V_T^- is $\mathscr{F}$-predictable [e.g., Theorem 1.T9 of Brémaud (1981)] and hence also $\mathscr{F}_{(-)}$-adapted. No such statement can be made in general about V_T^+. However, suppose further that T is not only an $\mathscr{F}$-stopping time but also an $\mathscr{F}_{(-)}$-stopping time, so that from the above V_T^+ is $\mathscr{F}_{(-)}$-adapted. Can we assert that it is $\mathscr{F}$-predictable?

Suppose that T is a countably-valued r.v.; that is,

$$T^{-1}(\{t_k: k = 1, 2, \ldots\}) = \bigcup_{k=1}^{\infty} T^{-1}(t_k) = \bigcup_{k=1}^{\infty} U_k, \quad \text{say,} = \Omega \text{ for some } t_k \geq 0.$$

Then

$$\{(t, \omega): V_T^+ (t, \omega) = 1\} = \bigcup_{k=1}^{\infty} [t_k, \infty) \times U_k.$$

By assumption, T being an $\mathscr{F}_{(-)}$-stopping time, $U_k \in \mathscr{F}_{t_k-}$, so $U_k \in \sigma\{\bigcup_n \mathscr{F}_{t_k-1/n}\}$ and hence V_T^+ is $\mathscr{F}$-predictable.

While it can be proved that any $\mathscr{F}$-stopping time can be approximated from above by a sequence of stopping times taking only a countable set of values, this is not enough to treat the general case—indeed, the counter-example considered by Dellacherie and Mayer is just of this indicator function type.

A3.4. Martingales

Definition A3.4.I. Let $(\Omega, \mathscr{E}, \mathscr{P})$ be a probability space, $\mathscr{F}$ a history on $(\Omega, \mathscr{E})$, and $X(\cdot) \equiv \{X(t): 0 \leq t < \infty\}$ a real-valued process adapted to $\mathscr{F}$ and such that $E|X(t)| < \infty$ for $0 \leq t < \infty$. Then X is an $\mathscr{F}$-*martingale* if for $0 \leq s < t < \infty$,

(A3.4.1) $E(X(t)|\mathscr{F}_s) = X(s)$ a.s.;

it is an $\mathscr{F}$-*submartingale* if

(A3.4.2) $E(X(t)|\mathscr{F}_s) \geq X(s)$ a.s.,

and it is an $\mathscr{F}$-*supermartingale* if the reverse inequality at (A3.4.2) holds.

Strictly, we should speak of X as a $\mathscr{P}$-$\mathscr{F}$-martingale: mostly, it is enough to call it a martingale since both $\mathscr{P}$ and $\mathscr{F}$ are clear from the context.

While the concept of a martingale had its origins in gambling strategies, it has come to play a dominant role in the modern theory of stochastic processes. In our text we need only a small number of the many striking results concerning martingales and their relatives, principally those connected with stopping times and the Doob–Meyer decomposition.

An important example of a martingale is formed from an $\mathscr{F}_\infty$-measurable r.v. X_∞ with finite mean by taking successive conditional expectations with respect to $\mathscr{F}$: define

(A3.4.3) $X(t) = E(X_\infty|\mathscr{F}_t).$

Such a martingale is uniformly integrable. The converse statement is also true [e.g., Theorem 3.6 of Liptser and Shiryayev (1977)].

Proposition A3.4.II. *Let $X(\cdot)$ be a uniformly integrable $\mathscr{F}$-martingale. Then there exists on $\mathscr{F}_\infty$-measurable r.v. X_∞ such that (A3.4.3) holds.*

The following form of the well-known convergence theorem can be found at Theorem 3.3 of Liptser and Shiryayev.

Theorem A3.4.III. *Let $X(\cdot)$ be an $\mathscr{F}$-submartingale with a.s. right-continuous trajectories. If $\sup_{0 \leq t < \infty} E(\max(0, X(t))) < \infty$, then there exists an $\mathscr{F}_\infty$-measurable r.v. X_∞ such that*

$$X(t, \omega) \to X_\infty(\omega) \qquad (t \to \infty) \text{ a.s.}$$

If also $X(\cdot)$ is uniformly integrable, then $E|X_\infty| < \infty$ and $E|X(t) - X_\infty| \to 0$ as $t \to \infty$; that is, $X(t) \to X_\infty$ in L_1 norm.

This theorem can be applied to the example at (A3.4.3) whether the family of σ-algebras $\{\mathscr{F}_t\}$ is increasing (as with a history $\mathscr{F}$) or decreasing.

For convenience, we state the result in terms of a two-sided history $\mathscr{G} = \{\mathscr{G}_t: -\infty < t < \infty\}$, defining $\mathscr{G}_\infty$ as usual and $\mathscr{G}_{-\infty} = \bigcap_{-\infty < t < \infty} \mathscr{G}_t = \lim_{t \to \infty} \mathscr{G}_t$.

Corollary A3.4.IV. *If the r.v. Y is $\mathscr{G}_\infty$-measurable, has finite first moment, and $Y(t) \equiv E(Y|\mathscr{G}_t)$ has a.s. right-continuous trajectories on $-\infty < t < \infty$ for some two-sided history $\mathscr{G}$, then*

$$(A3.4.4) \qquad E(Y|\mathscr{G}_t) \to \begin{cases} Y & (t \to \infty) \\ E(Y|\mathscr{G}_{-\infty}) & (t \to -\infty) \end{cases}$$

a.s. and in L_1 norm.

In most point process applications, the processes concerned are right-continuous by definition, so the sample-path conditions for the convergence results above are automatically satisfied. In the general theory of processes, it is shown that, if the history $\mathscr{F}$ is right-continuous and the σ-algebras are $\mathscr{P}$-complete in the strong sense that $\mathscr{F}_0$ (and hence $\mathscr{F}_t$ for all $t > 0$) contains all $\mathscr{P}$-null sets from $\mathscr{F}_\infty$, there always exists a right-continuous modification of an $\mathscr{F}$-submartingale, with the additional property that this modification also has left limits at each $t > 0$; that is, the (modified) process is càdlàg [e.g., see Liptster and Shiryayev (1977, pp. 55–59) or Dellacherie and Meyer (1980); Elliott (1982) uses corlol, the acronym of the English equivalent, continuous on right, limits on left].

In turning to properties of martingales with fixed times s, t replaced by stopping times S, T say, we need the notion of σ-algebras consisting of events prior to (and including) the time T and also strictly prior to T.

Definition A3.4.V. *Let $\mathscr{F}$ be a history and T an $\mathscr{F}$-stopping time. The T-prior σ-algebra $\mathscr{F}_T$ is the sub-σ-algebra of $\mathscr{F}_\infty$*

$$\mathscr{F}_T = \{A: A \in \mathscr{F}_\infty \text{ and } A \cap \{T \le t\} \in \mathscr{F}_t \text{ for every } t\},$$

and the strict T-prior σ-algebra $\mathscr{F}_{T-}$ is generated by the sets

$$\{A: A \in \mathscr{F}_0\} \cup \{A \cap \{T > t\} \text{ for } A \in \mathscr{F}_t \text{ and for } t \ge 0\}.$$

Clearly, $\mathscr{F}_T$ and $\mathscr{F}_{T-}$ are somewhat different entities [cf. Dellacherie and Meyer (1978, p. 117)]. It can be checked that T is both $\mathscr{F}_T$- and $\mathscr{F}_{T-}$-measurable. A contrast is provided in the next result.

Lemma A3.4.VI. *Let $\mathscr{F}$ be a history, T an $\mathscr{F}$-stopping time, and $X(\cdot)$ an $\mathscr{F}$-progressive process. Then $X(T)$ is $\mathscr{F}_T$-measurable. Furthermore, if $X(\cdot)$ is $\mathscr{F}$-predictable, then $X(T)$ is $\mathscr{F}_{T-}$-measurable.*

PROOF. Suppose $X(\cdot)$ is $\mathscr{F}$-progressive. Setting for any $x \in \mathbb{R}$,

$$A_x = \{\omega: X(T(\omega), \omega) \le x\},$$

$X(T)$ is $\mathscr{F}_T$-measurable if $A_x \cap \{T \le t\} \in \mathscr{F}_t$. But from Proposition A3.3.IV, $X(t \wedge T)$ is $\mathscr{F}$-progressive, and therefore $\mathscr{F}$-adapted, so that $\{\omega: X(t \wedge T(\omega), \omega) \le x\} \in \mathscr{F}_t$ (all x); hence,

$$A_x \cap \{T \le t\} = \{\omega: X(t \wedge T(\omega), \omega) \le x\} \cap \{T \le t\} \in \mathscr{F}_t.$$

Now suppose that $X(\cdot)$ is $\mathscr{F}$-predictable. To show the $\mathscr{F}_{T-}$-measurability of $X(T)$, look at the inverse image under $X(T): \omega \to X(T(\omega), \omega) \in \mathbb{R}$ of a generating set

$$(t, \infty) \times A \qquad (A \in \mathscr{F}_t)$$

of the $\mathscr{F}$-predictable σ-algebra $\Psi^{\mathscr{F}}$, namely,

$$\{\omega: t < T(\omega) < \infty\} \cap \{\omega: \omega \in A\},$$

which is a generating set for $\mathscr{F}_{T-}$. $\qquad\square$

The *optional sampling theorem* for martingales follows [e.g., see Liptser and Shiryayev (1977, pp. 60–61)].

Theorem A3.4.VII. *Let $\mathscr{F}$ be a history, S and T the $\mathscr{F}$-stopping times with $S \le T$ a.s., and $X(\cdot)$ an $\mathscr{F}$-submartingale that is uniformly integrable and has right-continuous trajectories. Then $\mathscr{F}_S \subseteq \mathscr{F}_T$ and*

$$E(X(T)|\mathscr{F}_S) \ge X(S) \quad a.s.,$$

where equality holds if X is an $\mathscr{F}$-martingale.

Corollary A3.4.VIII. *Let T be an $\mathscr{F}$-stopping time. If $X(\cdot)$ is a uniformly integrable $\mathscr{F}$-martingale (resp. submartingale) then so is $X(t \wedge T)$.*

PROOF. For fixed s, t with $s < t$, $s \wedge T$ and $t \wedge T$ are two stopping times satisfying the conditions of the theorem, so

$$E(X(t \wedge T)|\mathscr{F}_{s \wedge T}) \ge X(s \wedge T),$$

and thus $\{X(t \wedge T)\}$ is a $\{\mathscr{F}_{t \wedge T}\}$-martingale. To show the stronger property that it is an $\mathscr{F}$-martingale, note that $\mathscr{F}_{t \wedge T} \subseteq \mathscr{F}_t$ so $\{X(t \wedge T)\}$ is $\mathscr{F}$-adapted, and it remains to show that

$$(A3.4.5) \qquad \int_A X_{t \wedge T} \mathscr{P}(d\omega) \ge \int_A X_{s \wedge T} \mathscr{P}(d\omega) \quad (\text{all } A \in \mathscr{F}_s),$$

knowing that it holds for all $A \in \mathscr{F}_{s \wedge T}$. Express the left-hand side as the sum of integrals over $A_1 = A \cap \{T > s\}$ and $A_2 = A \cap \{T \le s\}$. Certainly, $A_1 \in \mathscr{F}_s$, while

$$A_1 \cap \{s \wedge T \le u\} = A \cap \{T > s\} \cap \{s \wedge T \le u\}.$$

This equals $\varnothing \in \mathscr{F}_u$ for $u < s$, and for $u \ge s$ it equals $A_1 \in \mathscr{F}_s \subseteq \mathscr{F}_u$, so by definition of $\mathscr{F}_{s \wedge T}$, we have $A_1 \in \mathscr{F}_{s \wedge T}$, and (A3.4.5) holds for A_1. On A_2,

$t \geq s \geq T$ so $X(t \wedge T) = X(s \wedge T)$ there, and (A3.4.5) holds for A_2. By addition, we have shown (A3.4.5).   □

Finally, we quote the form of the Doob–Meyer decomposition theorem used in Section 13.2, referring the reader to Liptser and Shiryayev (1977), for example, for proof.

Theorem A3.4.IX. *Let $\mathscr{F}$ be a history and $X(\cdot)$ a bounded $\mathscr{F}$-submartingale with right-continuous trajectories. Then there exists a unique (up to equivalence) uniformly integrable $\mathscr{F}$-martingale $Y(\cdot)$ and a unique $\mathscr{F}$-predictable cumulative process $A(\cdot)$ such that*

$$(A3.4.6) \qquad\qquad X(t) = Y(t) + A(t).$$

For nondecreasing processes $A(\cdot)$ with right-continuous trajectories, it can be shown that $\mathscr{F}$-predictability is equivalent to the property that for every bounded $\mathscr{F}$-martingale $Z(\cdot)$ and positive u,

$$E \int_0^u Z(t) A(dt) = E \int_0^u Z(t-) A(dt).$$

Since for any $\mathscr{F}$-adapted cumulative process ξ and any $\mathscr{F}$-martingale Z, $E[Z(u) \int_0^u \xi(dt)] = E[\int_0^u Z(t) \xi(dt)]$, the above property is equivalent to

$$E[Z(u) A(u)] = E \int_0^u Z(t-) A(dt).$$

A cumulative process with this property is referred to in many texts as a *natural increasing process*. The theorem can then be paraphrased thus: every bounded submartingale has a unique decomposition into the sum of a uniformly integrable martingale and a natural increasing function. The relation between natural increasing and predictable processes is discussed in Dellacherie and Meyer (1980).

The boundedness condition in Theorem A3.4.IX is much stronger than is really necessary, and it is a special case of of Liptser and Shiryayev (1977)'s "Class D" condition for supermartingales, namely, that the family $\{X(T)\}$ is uniformly integrable for all $\mathscr{F}$-stopping times. More general results, of which the decomposition for point processes described in Chapter 13 is in fact a special case, relax the boundedness or uniform integrability conditions but weaken the conclusion by requiring $Y(\cdot)$ to be only a local martingale [i.e., the stopped processes $Y(\cdot \wedge T_n)$ are martingales for a suitable increasing sequence $\{T_n\}$ of $\mathscr{F}$-stopping times].

The Doob–Meyer theorem is commonly stated for supermartingales, in which case the natural increasing function should be subtracted from the martingale term, not added to it.

Given an $\mathscr{F}$-martingale X, it is *square integrable* on $[0, \tau]$ for some $\tau \leq \infty$ if $\sup_{0 < t \leq \tau} EX^2(t) < \infty$. The process $\{X^2(t)\}$ is then an $\mathscr{F}$-submartingale on

$[0, \tau]$. When it is a bounded submartingale, the Doob–Meyer theorem as quoted above implies that we have the decomposition

(A3.4.7) $X^2(t) = Y_2(t) + A_2(t)$ $(0 \le t \le \tau)$

for some $\mathscr{F}$-martingale $Y_2(\cdot)$ and $\mathscr{F}$-predictable process $A_2(\cdot)$. It is readily checked that for $0 \le s < t \le \tau$,

$$A_2(t) - A_2(s) = E((X_t - X_s)^2 | \mathscr{F}_s),$$

hence, the name quadratic variation process for $A_2(\cdot)$. The equation (A3.4.7) can be established for any square-integrable martingale via the general Doob–Meyer theorem [e.g., see Liptser and Shiryayev (1977, Chap. 5)], and a significant calculus for such processes can be constructed (e.g., see Kunita and Watanabe, 1967) including applications to point processes (see also Brémaud, 1981), but this mostly lies beyond the discussion of this book.

References and Author Index

[Pages on which authors are cited are given in brackets. A bibliography of about 600 references up to about 1970, although excluding much of the historical material of Chapter 1 of this book, is given in D. J. Daley and R. K. Milne (1972), The theory of point processes: A bibliography, *Int. Statist. Rev.* **41**, 183–201.]

Aalen, O.O. (1975). *Statistical Inference for a Family of Counting Processes.* Ph.D. thesis, Statistics Department, University of California, Berkeley.   [496,523]

Aalen, O.O. (1978). Non-parametric inference for a family of counting processes. *Ann. Statist.* **6**, 701–726.   [523]

Abbé, E. (1879). Über Blutkörper-Zahlung. *Jena Z. Med. Naturwiss.* **13** (New Series 6), 98–105.   [8]

Aldous, D. and Eagleson, G.K. (1978). On mixing and stability of limit theorems. *Ann. Probab.* **6**, 325–331.   [645]

Ambartzumian, R.V. (1972). Palm distributions and superpositions of independent point processes in R^n. In *Stochastic Point Processes* (P.A.W. Lewis, ed.), Wiley, New York, pp. 626–645.   [253]

Ammann, L.P. and Thall, P.F. (1979). Count distributions, orderliness and invariance of Poisson cluster processes. *J. Appl. Probab.* **16**, 261–273.   [511]

Andrews, G.E. (1976). *The Theory of Partitions.* Addison-Wesley, Reading, MA.   [119]

Argabright, L. and de Lamadrid, J.G. (1974). Fourier analysis of unbounded measures on locally compact abelian groups. *Mem. Am. Math. Soc.* **145**.   [399,401]

Arjas, E., Nummelin, E. and Tweedie, R.L. (1978). Uniform limit theorems for non-singular renewal and Markov renewal processes. *J. Appl. Probab.* **15**, 112–125.   [87]

Ash, R.B. (1972). *Real Analysis and Probability.* Academic Press, New York.   [166, 604,639]

Athreya, K. and Ney, P.E. (1972). *Branching Processes.* Springer-Verlag, New York.   [144]

Athreya, K. and Ney, P.E. (1978). A new approach to the limit theory of recurrent Markov chains. *Trans. Am. Math. Soc.* **245**, 493–501.   [93–94]

Athreya, K., Tweedie, R.L. and Vere-Jones, D. (1980). Asymptotic behaviour of point-processes with Markov-dependent intervals. *Math. Nachr.* **99**, 301–313.   [99]

Barbour, A.D. and Hall, P. (1984). On the rate of Poisson convergence. *Math. Proc. Cambridge Philos. Soc.* **95**, 473–480. [297]

Barndorff-Nielsen, O. and Yeo, G.F. (1969). Negative binomial processes. *J. Appl. Probab.* **6**, 633–647. [156]

Bartlett, M.S. (1954). Processus stochastiques ponctuels. *Ann. Inst. Henri Poincaré* **14**, 35–60. [14]

Bartlett, M.S. (1955). *An Introduction to Stochastic Processes.* Cambridge University Press, Cambridge [2nd ed. 1966; 3rd ed. 1978]. [13]

Bartlett, M.S. (1963). The spectral analysis of point processes. *J. R. Statist. Soc. Ser. B* **29**, 264–296. [16,246,364,397,399,412]

Bartlett, M.S. (1964). The spectral analysis of two-dimensional point processes. *Biometrika* **51**, 299–311. [16,399]

Bartlett, M.S. (1967). The spectral analysis of line processes. *Proc. Fifth Berkeley Symp. Math. Statist. Probab.* **3**, 135–153. [378]

Bartlett, M.S. and Kendall, D.G. (1951). On the use of the characteristic functional in the analysis of some stochastic processes in physics and biology. *Proc. Cambridge Philos. Soc.* **47**, 65–76. [15,142]

Basawa, I.V. and Scott, D.J. (1983). *Asymptotic Inference for Non-ergodic Models* (Springer Lecture Notes Statist. **17**). Springer-Verlag, New York. [545]

Bateman, H. (1910). Note on the probability distribution of α-particles. *Philos. Mag.* **20** (6), 704–707. [Note to E. Rutherford and H. Geiger, The probability variations in the distribution of α-particles, *Philos. Mag.* **20** (6), 698–704.] [9]

Baudin, M. (1981). Likelihood and nearest neighbour distance properties of multidimensional Poisson cluster processes. *J. Appl. Probab.* **18**, 879–888. [501,511]

Benard, C. and Macchi, O. (1973). Detection and emission processes of quantum particles in a chaotic state. *J. Math. Phys.* **14**, 155–167. [137]

Berbée, H. (1983). A bound on the size of point clusters of a random walk with stationary increments. *Ann. Probab.* **11**, 414–418. [373]

Berbée, H.C.P. (1979). *Random Walks with Stationary Increments and Renewal Theory* (Mathematical Centre Tracts 112). Mathematisch Centrum, Amsterdam. [490]

Berman, M. (1978). Regenerative multivariate point processes. *Adv. Appl. Probab.* **10**, 411–430. [494]

Berman, M. (1983). Discussion of Ogata's paper. *Bull. Int. Statist. Inst.* **50** (3), 412–422. [512]

Bhabha, H.J. (1950). On the stochastic theory of continuous parametric systems and its application to electron-photon cascades. *Proc. R. Soc. London Ser. A* **202**, 301–332. [15,109,122,133]

Billingsley, P. (1965). *Ergodic Theory and Information.* Wiley, New York. [331,566]

Billingsley, P. (1968). *Convergence of Probability Measures.* Wiley, New York. [153, 167,279,615]

Bloom, W.R. (1984). Translation bounded measures and the Orlicz–Paley–Sidon theorem. *Springer Lecture Notes Math.* **1064**, 1–9. [410]

Bochner, S. (1947). Stochastic processes. *Ann. Math.* **48**, 1014–1061. [15]

Bochner, S. (1955). *Harmonic Analysis and the Theory of Probability.* University of California Press, Berkeley. [15,416]

Boel, R., Varaiya, P. and Wong, E. (1975). Martingales on jump processes, I: Representation results, and II: Applications. *SIAM J. Control* **13**, 999–1021 and 1022–1061. [495,527,534]

Bogoliubov, N.N. (1946). *Problems of a Dynamical Theory in Statistical Physics* (in Russian). Gostekhizdat, Moscow. [Translated by E.K. Gora in *Studies in Statistical Mechanics* Vol. 1 (J. de Boer and G.E. Uhlenbeck, eds.) North Holland, Amsterdam, 1962, pp. 5–116.] [15,109,122]

Bol'shakov, I.A. (1969). *Statistical Problems in Isolating a Stream of Signals from Noise* (in Russian). Sovyetskoye Radio, Moscow. [145,233,247]

Boltzmann, L. (1868). Studien über das Gleichgewicht der lebendigen Kraft zwischen bewegten materiellen Punkten. *Sitzungsber. Math. Naturwiss. Kl. Kais. Akad. Wiss., Wien* **58**, 517–560.   [9]

Bourbaki, N. (1963). *Éléments de Mathématique, Fasc. XXIX (Livre VI, Intégration, Chaps. 7 et 8)* (Actual. Sci. Industr. 1306). Hermann, Paris.   [634]

Breiman, L. (1963). The Poisson tendency in traffic distribution. *Ann. Math. Statist.* **34**, 308–311.   [307]

Breiman, L. (1965). Some probabilistic aspects of the renewal theorem. *Trans. Fourth Prague Conf. Inf. Theory Statist. Dec. Func. Random Proc.*, 255–261.   [85]

Brémaud, P. (1972). *A Martingale Approach to Point Processes.* Ph.D. thesis, Electrical Engineering Department, University of California, Berkeley.   [495]

Brémaud, P. (1981). *Point Processes and Queues: Martingale Dynamics.* Springer-Verlag, New York.   [14,16,104–105,495–496,527–528,532,539,548–549,602,639,648, 652,657]

Brémaud, P. and Jacod, J. (1977). Processus ponctuels et martingales: résultats récents sur le modélisation et le filtrage. *Adv. Appl. Probab.* **9**, 362–416.   [495]

Bretagnolle, J. and Dacunha-Castelle, D. (1967). Sur une classe de marches aléatoires. *Ann. Inst. Henri Poincaré.* **3**, 403–431.   [87]

Brillinger, D.R. (1972). The spectral analysis of stationary interval functions. *Proc. Sixth Berkeley Symp. Math. Statist. Probab.* **1**, 483–513.   [15,399,416,418,427]

Brillinger, D.R. (1978). Comparative aspects of the study of ordinary time series and point processes. In *Developments in Statistics*, Vol. I, (P.R. Krishnaiah, ed.), Academic Press, New York, pp. 33–133.   [399]

Brillinger, D.R. (1981). *Time Series: Data Analysis and Theory,* 2nd ed. Holden-Day, San Francisco.   [399]

Brown, T.C. (1978). A martingale approach to the Poisson convergence of simple point processes. *Ann. Probab.* **6**, 615–628.   [549,551]

Brown, T.C. (1982). Poisson approximations and exchangeable random variables. In *Exchangeability in Probability and Statistics* (G. Koch and F. Spizzichino, eds.), North-Holland, Amsterdam, pp. 177–183.   [551]

Brown, T.C. (1983). Some Poisson approximations using compensators. *Ann. Probab.* **11**, 726–744.   [551]

Byth, K. (1981). θ-stationary point processes and their second order analysis. *J. Appl. Probab.* **18**, 864–878.   [378,385]

Campbell, N.R. (1909). The study of discontinuous phenomena. *Proc. Cambridge Philos. Soc.* **15**, 117–136.   [188,455]

Cane, V.R. (1974). The concept of accident proneness. *Izv. Mat. Inst. Bulgar. Akad. Sci.* **15**, 183–189.   [11]

Cane, V.R. (1977). A class of non-identifiable stochastic models. *J. Appl. Probab.* **14**, 475–482.   [11]

Carlsson, H. and Nerman, O. (1986). An alternative proof of Lorden's renewal inequality. *Adv. Appl. Probab.* **18**, 1015–1016.   [89]

Chernick, M.R., Daley, D.J. and Littlejohn, R.P. (1988). A time-reversibility relationship between two Markov chains with exponential stationary distributions. *J. Appl. Probab.* **25** (to appear).   [103]

Chong, F.S. (1981). A point process with second order Markov dependent intervals. *Math. Nachr.* **103**, 155–163.   [103,383]

Chung, K.L. (1972). Crudely stationary point processes. *Am. Math. Monthly* **79**, 867–877.   [41]

Chung, K.L. (1974). *A Course in Probability Theory,* 2nd ed. Academic Press, New York.   [212,281,343,639]

Copson, E.C. (1935). *An Introduction to the Theory of Functions of a Complex Variable.* Oxford University Press, Oxford.   [424,449]

Cox, D.R. (1955). Some statistical methods connected with series of events (with Discussion). *J. R. Statist. Soc. Ser. B* **17**, 129–164.   [16,102,107,261]

Cox, D.R. (1962). *Renewal Theory.* Methuen, London.   [63]

Cox, D.R. (1972a). Regression models and life tables (with Discussion). *J. R. Statist. Soc. Ser. B* **34**, 187–220.   [495,523]

Cox, D.R. (1972b). The statistical analysis of dependencies in point processes. In *Stochastic Point Processes* (P.A.W. Lewis, ed.), Wiley, New York, pp. 55–66.   [495, 523]

Cox, D.R. (1975). Partial likelihood. *Biometrika* **62**, 269–276.   [523]

Cox, D.R. and Isham, V. (1980). *Point Processes.* Chapman and Hall, London.   [63, 102,364]

Cox, D.R. and Lewis, P.A.W. (1966). *The Statistical Analysis of Series of Events.* Methuen, London.   [16,19,63,364,399]

Cramér, H. and Leadbetter, M.R. (1967). *Stationary and Related Stochastic Processes.* Wiley, New York.   [14,156,294,420,430]

Csiszar, I. (1969). On generalized entropy. *Stud. Sci. Math. Hungar.* **4**, 401–419.   [572]

Daley, D.J. (1965). On a class of renewal functions. *Proc. Cambridge Philos. Soc.* **61**, 519–526.   [76]

Daley, D.J. (1971). Weakly stationary point processes and random measures. *J. R. Statist. Soc. Ser. B* **33**, 406–428.   [58,340,366,373,397,400,411,418]

Daley, D.J. (1972). A bivariate Poisson queueing process that is not infinitely divisible. *Proc. Cambridge Philos. Soc.* **72**, 449–450.   [250]

Daley, D.J. (1973). Poisson and alternating renewal processes with superposition a renewal process. *Math. Nachr.* **57**, 359–369.   [79]

Daley, D.J. (1974). Various concepts of orderliness for point processes. In *Stochastic Geometry* (E.J. Harding and D.G. Kendall, eds.), Wiley, Chichester, pp. 148–161. [45,49,211,214]

Daley, D.J. (1981). The absolute convergence of weighted sums of dependent sequences of random variables. *Z. Wahrs.* **58**, 199–203.   [267]

Daley, D.J. (1982a). Stationary point processes with Markov-dependent intervals and infinite intensity. In *Essays in Statistical Science* (J. Gani and E.J. Hannan, eds.) (*J. Appl. Probab.* Special Vol. **19A**), pp. 313–320.   [91,102,214]

Daley, D.J. (1982b). Infinite intensity mixtures of point processes. *Math. Proc. Cambridge Philos. Soc.* **92**, 109–114.   [214]

Daley, D.J. (1987). The variation distance between Poisson distributions. (Unpublished). [300,314]

Daley, D.J. and Milne, R.K. (1975). Orderliness, intensities and Palm–Khinchin equations for multivariate point processes. *J. Appl. Probab.* **12**, 383–389.   [385]

Daley, D.J. and Narayan, P. (1980). Series expansions of probability generating functions and bounds for the extinction probability of a branching process. *J. Appl. Probab.* **17**, 939–947.   [117,120]

Daley, D.J. and Vere-Jones, D. (1972). A summary of the theory of point processes. In *Stochastic Point Processes* (P.A.W. Lewis, ed.), Wiley, New York, pp. 299–383. [57]

Daley, D.J. and Vere-Jones, D. (1984). A note on orderliness of point processes. (Unpublished)   [214]

Daley, D.J. and Vere-Jones, D. (1987). The extended probability generating functional, with application to mixing properties of cluster point processes. *Math. Nachr.*

131, 311–319.   [232,347]

Daniels, H.E. (1945). The statistical theory of the strength of bundles of threads, I. *Proc. R. Soc. London Ser. A* **183**, 405–435.   [7]

Darwin, J.H. (1957). The power of the Poisson index of dispersion. *Biometrika* **44**, 286–289.   [22]

David, F.N. and Barton, D.E. (1962). *Combinatorial Chance.* Griffin, London.   [112–113,119]

Davidson, R. (1974a). *Stochastic processes of flats and exchangeability* (Part II, Ph.D. thesis, Cambridge University, 1968). In *Stochastic Geometry* (E.J. Harding and D.G. Kendall, eds.), Wiley, Chichester, pp. 13–45.   [392]

Davidson, R. (1974b). Construction of line processes: second-order properties. In *Stochastic Geometry* (E.J. Harding and D.G. Kendall, eds.), Wiley, Chichester, pp. 55–75. [Original publication (1970), *Izv. Akad. Nauk Armen. SSR Ser. Mat.* **5**, 219–234.]   [395,415]

Davidson, R. (1974c). Exchangeable point-processes. In *Stochastic Geometry* (E.J. Harding and D.G. Kendall, eds.), Wiley, Chichester, pp. 46–51.   [228]

Davies, R.B. (1977). Testing the hypothesis that a point process is Poisson. *Adv. Appl. Probab.* **9**, 724–746.   [507,510,513,514]

Davis, M.H.A. (1976). The representation of martingales of jump processes. *SIAM J. Control* **14**, 623–638.   [495,527]

Debes, H., Kerstan, J., Liemant, A. and Matthes, K. (1971). Verallgemeinerungen eines Satzes von Dobruschin, III. *Math. Nachr.* **50**, 99–139.   [315]

Delasnerie, M. (1977). Flots mélangements et mesures de Palm. *Ann. Inst. Henri Poincaré, Sec. B* **8**, 357–369.   [452,488]

Dellacherie, C. (1972). *Capacités et Processus Stochastiques.* Springer, Berlin.   [648]

Dellacherie, C. and Meyer, P.-A. (1978). *Probabilities and Potential.* Hermann, Paris, and North-Holland, Amsterdam.   [496,648,649,652,654]

Dellacherie, C. and Meyer, P.-A. (1980). *Probabilités et Potential, Chap. V-VIII, Théorie des Martingales.* Hermann, Paris.   [654,656]

Derman, C. (1955). Some contributions to the theory of denumerable Markov chains. *Trans. Am. Math. Soc.* **79**, 541–555.   [242,315]

Diggle, P.J. (1983). *Statistical Analysis of Spatial Point Patterns.* Academic Press, London.   [363,383]

Diggle, P.J. and Milne, R.K. (1984). Negative binomial quadrat counts and point processes. *Scand. J. Statist.* **10**, 257–267.   [228]

Dobrushin, R.L. (1956). On the Poisson law for distributions of particles in space (in Russian). *Ukr. Mat. Zh.* **8**, 127–134.   [307]

Doksum, K. (1974). Tailfree and neutral random probabilities and their posterior distributions. *Ann. Probab.* **2**, 183–201.   [165]

Doob, J.L. (1948). Renewal theory from the point of view of the theory of probability. *Trans. Am. Math. Soc.* **63**, 422–438.   [452]

Doob, J.L. (1949). Time series and harmonic analysis. *Proc. Berkeley Symp. Math. Statist. Probab.*, 303–343.   [418]

Doob, J.L. (1953). *Stochastic Processes.* Wiley, New York.   [58,420,425,642]

Doob, J.L., Snell, J.L. and Williamson, R.E. (1960). Application of boundary theory to sums of independent random variables. In *Contributions to Probability and Statistics (Essays in Honor of H. Hotelling)*, Stanford University Press, Stanford, pp. 182–197.   [70]

Dubins, L.E. and Freedman, D.A. (1967). Random distribution functions. *Proc. Fifth Berkeley Symp. Math. Statist. Probab.* **2** (Pt.1), 183–214.   [166]

Dudley, R.M. (1969). Random linear functionals. *Trans. Am. Math. Soc.* **136**, 1–24.   [183]

Dwass, M. and Teicher, H. (1957). On infinitely divisible random vectors. *Ann. Math. Statist.* **28**, 461–470.   [249]

Eggenberger, F. and Pólya, G. (1923). Über die Statistik verketteter Vorgänge. *Z. Angew. Math. Mech.* **3**, 279–289.   [11]

Elliott, R.J. (1982). *Stochastic Calculus and Applications.* Springer-Verlag, New York. [648,654]

Ellis, R.L. (1844). On a question in the theory of probabilities. *Cambridge Math. J.* **4** (21), 127–133. [Reprinted in W. Walton (ed.) (1863) *The Mathematical and Other Writings of Robert Leslie Ellis,* Deighton Bell, Cambridge, pp. 173–179.]   [4]

Erlang, A.K. (1909). The theory of probabilities and telephone conversations. *Nyt. Tidsskr. Mat. B* **20**, 33–41. [Reprinted in E. Brockmeyer, H.L. Halstrom and Arne Jensen (1948), *The Life and Works of A.K. Erlang,* Copenhagen Telephone Company, Copenhagen, pp. 131–137.]   [9]

Feller, W. (1950). *An Introduction to Probability Theory and its Applications.* Wiley, New York (2nd ed. 1957; 3rd ed. 1968.)   [13,27–29]

Feller, W. (1966). *An Introduction to Probability Theory and its Applications,* Vol.2. Wiley, New York [2nd ed. 1971].   [42,59,61,63,67,70,81,84–85,88,158,166,281,328, 637]

Feller, W. (1968). *An Introduction to Probability Theory and its Applications,* 3rd ed. Wiley, New York.   [27–29]

Feller, W. (1971). *An Introduction to Probability Theory and its Applications,* Vol. 2, 2nd ed. Wiley, New York.   [294]

Ferguson, T.S. (1973). A Bayesian analysis of some nonparametric problems. *Ann. Statist.* **1**, 209–230.   [165]

Fieger, W. (1971). Die Anzahl der γ-Niveau-Kreuzungspunkte von stochastische Prozessen. *Z. Wahrs.* **18**, 227–260.   [56]

Fleischmann, K. (1978). Mixing properties of cluster-invariant distributions. *Litovsk. Mat. Sb.* **18**(3), 191–199.   [312]

Fleischmann, K. and Prehn, U. (1974). Ein Grenzwersatz für subkritische Verzweigungsprozesse mit endlich vielen Typen von Teilchen. *Math. Nachr.* **64**, 357–362.   [313]

Fleischmann, K. and Prehn, U. (1975). Subkritische räumlich homogene Verzweigungsprozesse. *Math. Nachr.* **70**, 231–250.   [313]

Franken, P. (1963). Approximation durch Poissonsche Prozesse. *Math. Nachr.* **26**, 101–114.   [285]

Franken, P. (1975). Einige Anwendungen der Theorie zufälliger Punktprozesse in der Bedienungstheorie, I. *Math. Nachr.* **70**, 303–319.   [453]

Franken, P., König, D., Arndt, U., and Schmidt, V. (1981). *Queues and Point Processes.* Akademie-Verlag, Berlin.   [14,452,476,484,494]

Fréchet, M. (1940). *Les probabilités associées à un système d'événements compatibles et dépendants* (Actual. Sci. Industr. 859). Hermann, Paris.   [117]

Fritz, J. (1969). Entropy of point processes. *Stud. Sci. Math. Hungar.* **4**, 389–399. [572]

Fritz, J. (1973). An approach to the entropy of point processes. *Period. Math. Hungar.* **3**, 73–83.   [566,572]

Galambos, J. (1975). Methods for proving Bonferroni inequalities. *J. London Math. Soc.* **9** (2), 561–564.   [117]

Galambos, J. and Kotz, S. (1978). *Characterizations of Probability Distributions* (Springer Lecture Notes Math. 675). Springer-Verlag, Berlin.   [23,74]

Galchuk, L.I. and Rosovskii, B.L. (1971). The "disorder" problem for a Poisson process. *Teor. Veroyat. Primen.* **16**, 729–734. [Translation in *Theory Probab. Appl.* **16**, 712–717.]   [532]

Galton, F. and Watson, H.W. (1874). On the probability of extinction of families. *J. R. Anthropol. Inst.* **4**, 138–144.   [9]

Gaver, D.P. (1963). Random hazard in reliability problems. *Technometrics* **5**, 211–216. [495]

Gaver, D.P. and Lewis, P.A.W. (1980). First-order autoregressive gamma sequences and point processes. *Adv. Appl. Probab.* **12**, 727–745.   [90]

Gel'fand, I.M. and Vilenkin, N.Ya. (1964). *Generalized Functions*, Vol.4. Academic Press, New York.   [184]

Glass, L. and Tobler, W.R. (1971). Uniform distribution of objects in a homogeneous field: Cities on a plain. *Nature* **233**, 67–68.   [365,383]

Goldman, J.R. (1967). Stochastic point processes: Limit theorems. *Ann. Math. Statist.* **38**, 771–779.   [30]

Goodman, N.R. and Dubman, M.R. (1969). The theory of time-varying spectral analysis and complex Wishart matrix processes. In *Multivariate Analysis II*, (P.R. Krishnaiah, ed.), Academic Press, New York, pp. 351–366.   [266]

Grandell, J. (1976). *Doubly Stochastic Poisson Processes* (Springer Lecture Notes Math. 529). Springer-Verlag, New York.   [266,268]

Greenwood, M. and Yule, G.U. (1920). An enquiry into the nature of frequency distributions of multiple happenings, with particular reference to the occurrence of multiple attacks of disease or repeated accidents. *J. R. Statist. Soc.* **83**, 255–279.   [10]

Grégoire, G. (1984). Negative binomial distribution for point processes. *Stoch. Proc. Appl.* **16**, 179–188.   [228]

Greig-Smith, P. (1964). *Quantitative Plant Ecology,* 2nd ed. Butterworth, London. [366]

Griffiths, R.C., Milne, R.K. and Wood, R. (1979). Aspects of correlation in bivariate Poisson distributions and processes. *Aust. J. Statist.* **21**, 238–255.   [249]

Grigelionis, B. (1963). On the convergence of sums of random step processes to a Poisson process (in Russian). *Teor. Veroyat. Primen.* **8**, 189–194. [Translation in *Theory Probab. Appl.* **8**, 177–182.]   [285]

Häberlund, E. (1975). Infinitely divisible stationary recurrent point processes. *Math. Nachr.* **70**, 259–264.   [79]

Haight, F.A. (1967). *Handbook of the Poisson Distribution.* Wiley, New York.   [9]

Hannan, E.J. (1970). *Multiple Time Series.* Wiley, New York.   [432]

Harding, E.J. and Kendall, D.G. (eds.) (1974). *Stochastic Geometry.* Wiley, Chichester. [17,375,386]

Harris, T.E. (1956). The existence of stationary measures for certain Markov processes. *Proc. Third Berkeley Symp. Math. Statist. Probab.* **2**, 113–124.   [90,94]

Harris, T.E. (1963). *The Theory of Branching Processes.* Springer-Verlag, Berlin.   [15, 144,308,312]

Harris, T.E. (1968). Counting measures, monotone random set functions. *Z. Wahrs.* **10**, 102–119.   [15,613]

Harris, T.E. (1971). Random measures and motions of point processes. *Z. Wahrs.* **18**, 85–115.   [15]

Hawkes, A.G. (1971a). Spectra of some self-exciting and mutually exciting point processes. *Biometrika* **58**, 83–90.   [367]

Hawkes, A.G. (1971b). Point spectra of some mutually exciting point processes. *J. R. Statist. Soc. Ser. B* **33**, 438–443.   [367,414,443–444]

Hawkes, A.G. (1972). Spectra of some mutually exciting point processes with associated variables. In *Stochastic Point Processes* (P.A.W. Lewis, ed.), Wiley, New York, pp. 261–271.   [367,443]

Hawkes, A.G. and Adamopoulos, L. (1973). Cluster models for earthquakes – regional comparisons. *Bull. Int. Statist. Inst.* **45**(3), 454–461.   [414]

Hawkes, A.G. and Oakes, D. (1974). A cluster representation of a self-exciting process. *J. Appl. Probab.* **11**, 493–503.   [367]

Hewitt, E. and Zuckerman, H.S. (1969). Remarks on the functional equation $f(x+y) = f(x) + f(y)$. *Math. Mag.* **42**, 121–123.   [61]

Heyde, C.C. and Seneta, E. (1977). *I.J. Bienaymé: Statistical Theory Anticipated.* Springer-Verlag, New York.   [9]

Hille, E. and Phillips, R.S. (1957). *Functional Analysis and Semi-Groups.* American Mathematics Society, Providence, RI.   [60–62]

Hocking, T.G. and Young, G.S. (1961). *Topology.* Addison-Wesley, Reading, MA, and London.   [631]

Holgate, P. (1964). Estimation for the bivariate Poisson distribution. *Biometrika* **51**, 241,245.   [249]

Hunter, J.J. (1974a). Renewal theory in two dimensions: Basic results. *Adv. Appl. Probab.* **6**, 376–391.   [69]

Hunter, J.J. (1974b). Renewal theory in two dimensions: Asymptotic results. *Adv. Appl. Probab.* **6**, 546–562.   [69]

Ibragimov, I.A. and Linnik, Yu.V. (1971). *Independent and Stationary Sequences of Random Variables.* Wolters-Noordhoff, Gröningen. [Translated from original in Russian (1965), Nauka, Moscow.]   [301]

Isham, V. and Westcott, M. (1979). A self-correcting point process. *Stoch. Proc. Appl.* **8**, 335–347.   [548]

Ito, Y. (1980). Renewal processes decomposable into i.i.d. components. *Adv. Appl. Probab.* **12**, 672–688.   [79]

Jacobsen, M. (1982). *Statistical Analysis of Counting Processes* (Springer Lecture Notes Statist. 12). Springer-Verlag, New York.   [16,495,496,523,652]

Jacod, J. (1975). Multivariate point processes: Predictable projections, Radon-Nikodym derivatives, representation of martingales. *Z. Wahrs.* **31**, 235–253.   [496,534]

Jacod, J. and Memin, J. (1984). Sur un type de convergence intermédiaire entre la convergence en loi et la convergence en probabilité. *Springer Lecture Notes Math.* **850**, 529–540.   [648]

Jagers, P. (1974). Aspects of random measures and point processes. In *Advances in Probability and Related Topics*, Vol. 3 (P. Ney, ed.), Marcel Dekker, New York, pp. 179–239.   [15]

Jagers, P. (1975). *Branching Processes with Biological Applications.* Wiley, London.   [144]

Janossy, L. (1948). *Cosmic Rays.* Oxford University Press, Oxford.   [15]

Janossy, L. (1950). On the absorption of a nucleon cascade. *Proc. R. Irish Acad. Sci. Sec. A* **53**, 181–188.   [109,122]

Jarupskin, B.D.S. (1984). *Maximum Likelihood and Related Estimation Methods in Point Processes.* Ph.D. thesis, University of California, Berkeley.   [541,545]

Jirina, M. (1966). Asymptotic behaviour of measure-valued branching processes. *Rozpr. Cesk. Adad. Ved., Rada Mat. Prir. Ved* **75**, no.3.   [15]

Johnson, N.L and Kotz, S. (1969). *Distributions in Statistics, Vol.I: Discrete Distributions.* Houghton Mifflin, Boston. [Reprinted by Wiley, New York.]   [10]

Johnson, N.L and Kotz, S. (1970). *Distributions in Statistics, Vol.II: Continuous Univariate Distributions*–1. Houghton Mifflin, Boston.   [7]

Jolivet, E. (1978). Caractérisation et test du caractère agrégatif des processus ponctuels stationnaires sur R^2. In *Journées de Statistiques des Processus Stochastiques* (Springer Lecture Notes Math. 636), Springer-Verlag, Berlin, pp. 1–25.   [363]

Jowett, J. and Vere-Jones, D. (1972). The prediction of stationary point processes. In *Stochastic Point Processes* (P.A.W. Lewis, ed.), Wiley, New York, pp. 405–435. [418,532,547]

Kabanov, Yu.M., Liptser, R.G. and Shiryayev, A.N. (1975). Martingale methods in point process theory (in Russian). *Trudy Shkoly-seminara no teorii sluchainikh protsessov II.* Druskeninkai, Vilnius, pp. 296–353.   [495]

Kailath, T. and Segall, I. (1975). The modelling of random modulated jump processes. *IEEE Trans. Inf. Theory* **IT-21**(2), 135–142.   [495]

Kallenberg, O. (1973). Characterization and convergence of random measures and point processes. *Z. Wahrs.* **27**, 9–21.   [215]

Kallenberg, O. (1975). *Random Measures.* Akademie-Verlag, Berlin, and Academic Press, London. [3rd ed. 1983, reprinted with corrections as 4th ed. 1986].   [15,186,215, 281,288,317,455,610,613]

Kallenberg, O. (1977). A counterexample to R. Davidson's conjecture on line processes. *Math. Proc. Cambridge Philos. Soc.* **82**, 301–307.   [395]

Kallenberg, O. (1977). Stability of critical cluster fields. *Math. Nachr.* **77**, 7–43. [310-311]

Kallenberg, O. (1978). On conditional intensities of point processes. *Z. Wahrs.* **41**, 205–220.   [559]

Kallenberg, O. (1983a). *Random Measures*, 3rd ed. Akademie-Verlag, Berlin, and Academic Press, London.   [455,576–578,581,587,589]

Kallenberg, O. (1983b). On random processes of flats with special emphasis on the invariance problem. *Bull. Int. Statist. Inst.* **50**(2), 854–862, and **50**(3), 383–392.   [587]

Kallenberg, O. (1984). An informal guide to the theory of conditioning in point processes. *Int. Statist. Review* **52**, 151–164.   [578]

Kallianpur, G. (1980). *Stochastic Filtering Theory.* Springer-Verlag, New York.   [648, 650]

Kaplan, E.L. (1955). Transformations of stationary random sequences. *Math. Scand.* **3**, 127–149.   [452]

Karbe, W. (1973). *Konstruction einfacher zufälliger Punktfolgen.* Diplomarbeit, Friedrich-Schiller-Universität Jena, Sektion Mathematik.   [215]

Karr, A.F. (1986). *Point Processes and Their Statistical Inference.* Marcel Dekker, New York.   [496]

Kathirgamatamby, N. (1953). Note on the Poisson index of dispersion. *Biometrika* **40**, 225–228.   [22]

Keiding, N. (1975). Maximum likelihood estimation in birth and death processes. *Ann. Statist.* **3**, 363–372.   [545-547]

Kendall, D.G. (1949). Stochastic processes and population growth. *J. R. Statist. Soc. Ser. B* **11**, 230–264.   [15]

Kendall, D.G. (1951). Some problems in the theory of queues (with Discussion). *J. R. Statist. Soc. Ser. B* **13**, 151–185.   [490]

Kendall, D.G. (1963). Extreme-point methods in stochastic analysis. *Z. Wahrs.* **1**, 295–300.   [181]

Kendall, D.G. (1974). Foundations of a theory of random sets. In *Stochastic Geometry* (E.J. Harding and D.G. Kendall, eds.), Wiley, New York, pp. 322–376.   [215,375]

Kerstan, J. (1964). Verallgemeinerung eines Satzes von Prochorov und Le Cam. *Z. Wahrs.* **2**, 173–179.   [297]

Kerstan, J. and Debes, H. (1969). Zufällige Punktfolgen und Markoffsche Übergangsmatrizen ohne stationäre Verteilungsgesetze. *Wiss. Z. Friedrich-Schiller-Universität Jena* **18**, 349–359.   [315]

Kerstan, J. and Matthes, K. (1964). Stationäre zufällige Punktfolgen II. *Jber. Deutsch. Math.-Verein.* **66**, 106–118.   [258]

Kerstan, J. and Matthes, K. (1967). Ergodische unbegrenzt teilbare stationäre Punkt-folgen. *Trans. Fourth Prague Conf. Inf. Theory Stat. Dec. Functions Random Proc.*, 399–415.   [349]

Kerstan, J., Matthes, K., and Mecke, J. (1974). *Unbegrenzt Teilbare Punktprozesse.* Akademie-Verlag, Berlin.   [14,452]

Kerstan, J., Matthes, K., and Mecke, J. (1982). Infinitely Divisible Point Processes (in Russian). Nauka, Moscow [This is the 3rd ed. of Kerstan, Mathes, and Mecke (1974).]   [14,269,314,347,352–354,452,577]

Khinchin, A.Ya. (1955). *Mathematical Methods in the Theory of Queueing* (in Russian). *Trudy Mat. Inst. Steklov* **49**. [Translated (1960) Griffin, London.]   [14,28,43–44, 51,211,285,452]

Khinchin, A.Ya. (1956). On Poisson sequences of chance events. *Teor. Veroyat. Primen.* **1**, 320–327. [Translation in *Theory Probab. Appl.* **1**, 291–297.]   [49]

Kingman, J.F.C. (1964). On doubly stochastic Poisson processes. *Proc. Cambridge Philos. Soc.* **60**, 923–930.   [265,267]

Kingman, J.F.C. and Taylor, S.J. (1966). *Introduction to Measure and Probability.* Cambridge University Press, Cambridge.   [419,592]

Kolmogorov, A.N. (1935). La transformation de Laplace dans les espaces linéaires. *C. R. Acad. Sci. Paris* **200**, 1717–1718.   [14]

König, D. and Matthes, K. (1963). Verallgemeinerung der Erlangschen Formeln,I. *Math. Nachr.* **26**, 45–56.   [452]

König, D., Matthes, K. and Nawrotzki, K. (1967). *Verallgemeinerung der Erlangschen und Engsetschen Formeln (Eine Methode in der Bedienungstheorie).* Akademie-Verlag, Berlin.   [452]

Kotz, S. and Shanbhag, D. (1980). Some new approaches to probability distributions. *Adv. Appl. Probab.* **12**, 903–921.   [106]

Kraft, C.H. (1964). A class of distribution function processes which have derivatives. *J. Appl. Probab.* **1**, 385–388.   [166]

Krickeberg, K. (1974a). Invariance properties of the correlation measure of line-processes. In *Stochastic Geometry* (E.J. Harding and D.G. Kendall, eds.), Wiley, New York, pp. 76–88.   [392]

Krickeberg, K. (1974b). Moments of point processes. In *Stochastic Geometry* (E.J. Harding and D.G. Kendall, eds.), Wiley, New York, pp. 89–113.   [139,355,386,390,392]

Krickeberg, K. (1980). Statistical problems on point processes. In *Mathematical Statistics* (Banach Centre Publ. 6), PWN, Warsaw, pp. 197–223.   [363]

Kummer, G. and Matthes, K. (1970). Verallgemeinerung eines Satzes von Sliwnjak, II. *Rev. Roumaine Math. Pures Appl.* **15**, 845–870.   [452,455]

Kunita, H. and Watanabe, S. (1967). On square-integrable martingales. *Nagoya Math. J.* **30**, 209–245.   [495,657]

Kurtz, T.G. (1974). Point processes and completely monotone set functions. *Z. Wahrs.* **31**, 57–67.   [215–216]

Kutoyants, Y. (1979). Local asymptotic normality for Poisson type processes. *Izv. Akad. Nauk Arm. SSR Ser. Mat.* **14**(1), 3–20 and 72.   [540]

Kutoyants, Y. (1980). *Estimation of Parameters of Stochastic Processes* (in Russian). Armenian Academy of Science, Erevan.   [513,540]

Kutoyants, Y. (1984a). Parameter estimation for processes of Poisson type. *Izv. Akad. Nauk Arm. SSR Ser. Mat.* **19**, 233–241   [544]

Kutoyants, Yu.A. (1984b). *Parameter Estimation for Stochastic Processes.* Heldermann, Berlin. [Translated by B.L.S. Prakasa Rao and Revised from Kutoyants (1980).] [25,496,506,513,540,544]

Lai, C.D. (1978). An example of Wold's point processes with Markov-dependent intervals. *J. Appl. Probab.* **15**, 748–758.   [93,101–102,512]

Lampard, D.G. (1968). A stochastic process whose successive intervals between events form a first order Markov chain-I. *J. Appl. Probab.* **5**, 648–668.   [93,103]

Lancaster, H.O. (1963). Correlations and canonical forms of bivariate distribution functions. *Ann. Math. Statist.* **34**, 532–538.   [92]

Lanford, O.E. and Ruelle, D. (1969). Observables at infinity and states with short range correlations in statistical mechanics. *Comm. Math. Phys.* **13**, 194–215.   [353]

Laplace, P.S. (1814). *Essai Philosophique des Probabilités.* Introduction (pp. i–cvi), Théorie Analytique des Probabilités, 2nd ed. [English Translation (1951), *A Philosophical Essay on Probabilities,* Dover, New York.]   [3]

Lawrance, A.J. (1970). Selective interaction of a stationary point process and a renewal process. *J. Appl. Probab.* **7**, 483–489.   [41]

Lawrance, A.J. (1971). Selective interaction of a Poisson and a renewal process: The dependancy structure of the intervals between the responses. *J. Appl. Probab.* **8**, 170–183.   [368]

Le Cam, L. (1947). Un instrument d'étude des fonctions aléatoires: la fonctionelle caractéristique. *C. R. Acad. Sci. Paris* **224**, 710–711.   [15]

Le Cam, L. (1960). An approximation theorem for the Poisson binomial distribution. *Pacific J. Math.* **10**, 1181–1197.   [299]

Le Cam, L. (1961). A stochastic theory of precipitation. *Proc. Fourth Berkeley Symp. Math. Statist. Probab.* **3**, 165–186.   [242]

Leadbetter, M.R. (1968). On three basic results in the theory of stationary point processes. *Proc. Amer. Math. Soc.* **19**, 115–117.   [171]

Leadbetter, M.R. (1972). On basic results of point process theory. *Proc. Sixth Berkeley Symp. Math. Statist. Probab.* **3**, 449–462.   [14,45,49,171,457,482]

Leadbetter, M.R., Lindgren, G. and Rootzen, H. (1983). *Extremes and Related Properties of Random Sequences and Processes.* Springer-Verlag, New York.   [14,294]

Lee, P.M. (1964). A structure theorem for infinitely divisible point processes. Address to I.A.S.P.S., Berne (unpublished) (cf. Lee, P.M. 1964), The superposition of point processes (Abstract), *Ann. Math. Statist.* **35**, 1406–1407).   [258]

Lee, P.M. (1967). Infinitely divisible stochastic processes. *Z. Wahrs.* **7**, 147–160.   [258]

Lee, P.M. (1968). Some aspects of infinitely divisible point processes. *Stud. Sci. Math. Hungar.* **3**, 219–224.   [30–31]

Lewis, P.A.W. (1964a). A branching Poisson process model for the analysis of computer failure patterns (with Discussion). *J. R. Statist. Soc. Ser. B* **26**, 398–456.   [16, 246,253]

Lewis, P.A.W. (1964b). The implications of a failure model for the use and maintenance of computers. *J. Appl. Probab.* **1**, 347–368.   [246]

Lewis, P.A.W. (1970). Remarks on the theory, computation and application of the spectral analysis of series of events. *J. Sound Vib.* **12** (3), 353–375.   [25]

Lewis, P.A.W. (ed.) (1972). *Stochastic Point Processes.* Wiley, New York.   [vii]

Lewis, P.A.W. and Shedler, G.S. (1976). Simulation of nonhomogeneous Poisson processes with log linear rate function. *Biometrika* **63**, 501–506.   [23]

Liemant, A. (1969). Invariante zufällige Punktfolgen. *Wiss. Z. Friedrich-Schiller-Universität Jena* **18**, 361–372.   [311]

Liemant, A. (1975). Verallgemeinerungen eines Satzes von Dobruschin, V. *Math. Nachr.* **70**, 387–390.   [311]

Lin, V.Ya. (1965). On equivalent norms in the space of square summable entire functions of exponential type (in Russian). *Mat. Sb. (N.S.)* **67**(109), 586–608. [Translation (1969) *Am. Math. Soc. Transl.* **79**(2), 53–76.]   [401,407]

Lindvall, T. (1977). A probabilistic proof of Blackwell's renewal theorem. *Ann. Probab.* **5**, 482–485.   [80]

Liptser, R.S. and Shiryayev, A.N. (1974). *Statistics of Random Processes* (in Russian). Nauka, Moscow. [Translation (1977, 1978).]   [16]

Liptser, R.S. and Shiryayev, A.N. (1977). *Statistics of Random Processes, I: General Theory.* Springer-Verlag, New York.   [648,653–657]

Liptser, R.S. and Shiryayev, A.N. (1978). *Statistics of Random Processes, II: Applications.* Springer-Verlag, New York.   [495,496,534]

Loève, M. (1963). *Probability Theory,* 3rd ed. Van Nostrand, New York.   [28,31, 37,281]

Lotka, A.J. (1939). A contribution to the theory of self-renewing aggregates, with especial reference to industrial replacement. *Ann. Math. Statist.* **10**, 1–25.   [5]

Lüders, R. (1934). Die Statistik der seltenen Ereignisse. *Biometrika* **26**, 108–128.   [11]

Lukacs, E. (1970). *Characteristic Functions,* 2nd Ed. Griffin, London.   [76]

Lyon, J.F. and Thoma, R. (1881). Ueber die Methode der Blutkörperzählung. *Virchows Arch. Path. Anat. Physiol.* **84**, 131–154.   [9]

Macchi, O. (1971a). Distribution statistique des instants d'émission des photoélectrons d'une lumière thermique. *C. R. Acad. Sci. Paris Ser. A* **272**, 437–440.   [136,265–268]

Macchi, O. (1971b). Stochastic processes and multicoincidences. *IEEE Trans.* **IT-17**, 1:1–7.   [140]

Macchi, O. (1975). The coincidence approach to stochastic point processes. *Adv. Appl. Probab.* **7**, 83–122.   [122,127,129,133–134,136–137,265,267]

MacMahon, P.A. (1915). *Combinatory Analysis,* Vol. 1. Cambridge University Press, Cambridge.   [268]

Maistrov, L.E. (1967). *Probability Theory—A Historical Sketch* (in Russian). Izdat. Nauka, Moscow. [Translated by S. Kotz (ed.) (1974), Academic Press, New York.]   [3]

Mandelbrot, B. (1975). Limit theorems on the self-normalized range for weakly and strongly dependent processes. *Z. Wahrs.* **31**, 271–285.   [326]

Maruyama, G. (1955). On the Poisson distribution derived from independent random walks. *Nat. Sci. Rep. Ochanomiza Univ.* **6**, 1–6.   [307]

Matérn, B. (1960). *Spatial Variation.* Meddelanded Stat. Skogsforsk. **49**(5), 1–144. [2nd ed. (1986) *(Springer Lecture Notes Statist.* **36**), Springer-Verlag, New York].   [16, 366]

Matthes, K. (1972). Infinitely divisible point processes. In *Stochastic Point Processes* (P.A.W. Lewis, ed.), Wiley, New York, pp. 384–404.   [188]

Matthes, K., Kerstan, J. and Mecke, J. (1978). *Infinitely Divisible Point Processes.* Wiley, Chichester. [This is the 2nd. ed. of Kerstan, Matthes, and Mecke (1974).]   [*See* MKM]

Matthes, K., Warmuth, W. and Mecke, J. (1979). Bemerkungen zu einer Arbeit von Nguyen Xuan Xanh und Hans Zessin. *Math. Nachr.* **88**, 117–127.   [577]

McFadden, J.A. (1956). The axis-crossing intervals of random functions, I. *Trans. Inst. Radio Engs.* **PGIT-2**, 146–150.   [14]

McFadden, J.A. (1958). The axis-crossing intervals of random functions, II. *Trans. Inst. Radio Engs.* **PGIT-4**, 14–24.   [14]

McFadden, J.A. (1965a). The mixed Poisson process. *Sankhya A* **27**, 83–92.   [228]

McFadden, J.A. (1965b). The entropy of a point process. *J. SIAM* **13**, 988–994.   [564]

McFadden, J.A. and Weissblum, W. (1963). Higher-order properties of a stationary point process. *J. R. Statist. Soc. Ser. B* **25**, 413–431.   [79]

McKendrick, A.G. (1914). Studies on the theory of continuous probabilities with special reference to its bearing on natural phenomena of a progressive nature. *Proc. London Math. Soc.* **13**(2), 401–416.   [9–10]

McKendrick, A.G. (1926). The application of mathematics to medical problems. *Proc. Edinburgh Math. Soc.* **44**, 98–130.   [9]

McMillan, B. (1953). Absolutely monotone functions. *Ann. Math.* **60**, 467–501. [215]

Mecke, J. (1967a). Zum Problem der Zerlegbarkeit stationärer rekurrenter zufälliger Punktfolgen. *Math. Nachr.* **35**, 311–321.   [79]

Mecke, J. (1967b). Stationäre zufällige Masse auf lokal-kompakten abelschen Gruppe. *Z. Wahrs.* **9**, 36–58.   [459,464]

Mecke, J. (1968). Eine charakteristische Eigenschaft der doppelt stochastischen Poissonsche Prozesse. *Z. Wahrs.* **11**, 74–81.   [300]

Mecke, J. (1969). Verschärfung eines Satzes von McFadden. *Wiss. Z. Friedrich-Schiller-Universität Jena* **18**, 387–392.   [79]

Mecke, J. (1979). An explicit description of Kallenberg's lattice type point process. *Math. Nachr.* **89**, 185–195.   [395]

Mertens, J.-F. (1972). Théorie des processus stochastiques généraux: applications aux martingales. *Z. Wahrs.* **22**, 45–68.   [549]

Métivier, M. (1971). Sur la construction de mesures aléatoires presque sûrement absolument continues par rapport á une mesure donnée. *Z. Wahrs.* **20**, 332–344.   [166]

Miles, R.E. (1969). Poisson flats in Euclidean spaces, Part I: A finite number of random uniform flats. *Adv. Appl. Probab.* **1**, 211–237.   [390]

Miles, R.E. (1971). Poisson flats in Euclidean spaces, Part II: Homogeneous Poisson flats and the complementary theorem. *Adv. Appl. Probab.* **3**, 1–43.   [390]

Miles, R.E. (1974). On the elimination of edge effects in planar sampling. In *Stochastic Geometry* (E.J. Harding and D.G. Kendall, eds.), Wiley, New York, pp. 228–247. [374,390]

Milne, R.K. (1971). *Stochastic analysis of multivariate point processes*. Ph.D. thesis, Australian National University.   [256]

Milne, R.K. (1974). Infinitely divisible bivariate Poisson processes (Abstract). *Adv. Appl. Probab.* **6**, 226–227.   [249]

Milne, R.K. and Westcott, M. (1972). Further results for Gauss-Poisson processes. *Adv. Appl. Probab.* **4**, 151–176.   [247–248,418]

Milne, R.K. and Westcott, M. (1988). Generalized multivariate Hermite distributions and related point processes. *J. Appl. Probab.* **25** (to appear).   [121,249]

Minc, H. (1978). *Permanents*. Addison-Wesley, Reading, MA.   [266]

MKM (1978). [= Matthes, Kerstan and Mecke (1978).]   [14,144,188,214–215,269, 281,296,307,314–315,317,334,349,352–354,452–453]

MKM (1982). See Kerstan, Matthes and Mecke (1982).

Mönch, G. (1971). Verallgemeinerung eines Satzes von A. Rényi. *Stud. Sci. Math. Hungar.* **6**, 81–90.   [215]

Moran, P.A.P. (1967). A non-Markovian quasi-Poisson process. *Stud. Sci. Math. Hungar.* **2**, 425–429.   [30]

Moran, P.A.P. (1968). *An Introduction to Probability Theory*. Clarendon Press, Oxford.   [31,120,162,188]

Moran, P.A.P. (1976a). A quasi-Poisson point process in the plane. *Bull. London Math. Soc.* **8**, 69–70.   [30]

Moran, P.A.P. (1976b). Another quasi-Poisson plane point process. *Z. Wahrs.* **33**, 269–272.   [30]

Moyal, J.E. (1962a). The general theory of stochastic population processes. *Acta Math.* **108**, 1–31.   [15,109,127,142,198]

Moyal, J.E. (1962b). Multiplicative population chains. *Proc. R. Soc. London Ser. A* **266**, 518–526.   [142,144]

Neveu, J. (1968). Sur la structure des processus ponctuels stationnaires. *C. R. Acad. Sci. Paris Sér. A* **267**, 561–564.   [452]

Neveu, J. (1976). Processus ponctuels. In *Springer Lecture Notes Math.* **598**, 249–445. [452]

Newman, D.S. (1970). A new family of point processes characterized by their second moment properties. *J. Appl. Probab.* **7**, 338–358.   [247,500]

Newton, Sir Isaac (1728). *The Chronology of Ancient Kingdoms Amended.* [Published Posthumously. See H. Zeitlinger (1927) A Newton Bibliography, in W.J. Greenstreet (Ed.), *Isaac Newton 1642–1727*, Bell and Sons, London, pp. 148–170.]   [5]

Neyman, J. (1939). On a new class of "contagious" distributions applicable in entomology and bacteriology. *Ann. Math. Statist.* **10**, 35–57.   [11]

Neyman, J. and Scott, E.L. (1958). Statistical approach to problems of cosmology (with Discussion). *J. R. Statist. Soc. Ser. B* **20**, 1–43.   [11,245]

Neyman, J. and Scott, E.L. (1972). Processes of clustering and applications. In *Stochastic Point Processes* (P.A.W. Lewis, ed.), Wiley, New York, pp. 646–681. [245]

Nguyen, X.X. and Zessin, H. (1976). Punktprozesse mit Wechselwirkung. *Z. Wahrs.* **37**, 91–126.   [359]

Nguyen, X.X. and Zessin, H. (1979). Ergodic theorems for spatial point processes. *Z. Wahrs.* **48**, 133–158.   [334,577]

Nummelin, E. (1978). A splitting technique for Harris recurrent Markov chains. *Z. Wahrs.* **43**, 309–318.   [93–94]

Oakes, D. (1974). A generalization of Moran's quasi-Poisson process. *Stud. Sci. Math. Hungar.* **9**, 433–437.   [30]

Ogata, Y. (1978). The asymptotic behaviour of maximum likelihood estimates for stationary point processes. *Ann. Inst. Statist. Math.* **30**, 243–261.   [506]

Ogata, Y. (1981). On Lewis' simulation method for point processes. *IEEE Trans. Inf. Theory* **IT-27**, 23–31.   [507]

Ogata, Y. (1983). Likelihood analysis of point processes and its applications to seismological data. *Bull. Int. Statist. Inst.* **50** (2), 943–961.   [512]

Ogata, Y. and Akaike, H. (1982). On linear intensity models for mixed doubly stochastic Poisson and self-exciting point processes. *J. R. Statist. Soc. Ser. B* **44**, 102–107. [414–415,505]

Ogata, Y. and Katsura, K. (1986). Point-process models with linearly parametrized intensity for the application to earthquake catalogue. *J. Appl. Probab.* **23A**, 231–240.   [506]

Ogata, Y. and Tanemura, M. (1981). Estimation of interaction potentials of spatial point patterns through the maximum likelihood procedure. *Ann. Inst. Statist. Math.* **33B**, 315–338.   [501]

Ogata, Y. and Tanemura, M. (1984). Likelihood analysis of spatial point patterns. *J. R. Statist. Soc. Ser. B* **46**, 496–518.   [125]

Ogata, Y. and Vere-Jones, D. (1984). Inference for earthquake models: A self-correcting model. *Stoch. Proc. Appl.* **17**, 337–347.   [512,549]

Ogata, Y., Akaike, H. and Katsura, K. (1982). The application of linear intensity models to the investigation of causal relations between a point process and another stochastic process. *Ann. Inst. Statist. Math.* **34**, 373–387.   [414]

Ohser, H. and Stoyan, D. (1981). On the second-order and orientation analysis of planar stationary point processes. *Biom. J.* **23**, 523–533.   [383]

Orey, S. (1971). *Limit Theorems for Markov Chain Transition Probabilities.* Van Nostrand-Reinhold, London.   [90]

Ososkov, G.A. (1956). A limit theorem for flows of similar events (in Russian). *Teor. Veroyat. Primen.* **1**, 274–282. [Translation in *Theory Probab. Appl.* **1**, 248–255.] [285]

Ozaki, T. (1979). Maximum likelihood estimation of Hawkes' self-exciting point processes. *Ann. Inst. Statist. Math.* **31**, 145–155.   [414]

Palm, C. (1943). Intensitätsschwankungen im Fernsprechverkehr. *Ericsson Techniks* **44**, 1–189.   [13,285,378,452]

Paloheimo, J.E. (1971). On a theory of search. *Biometrika* **58**, 61–75.   [253]

Papangelou, F. (1970). The Ambrose–Kakutani theorem and the Poisson process. In *Springer Lecture Notes Math.* **160**, 234–240.   [452]

Papangelou, F. (1972a). Summary of some results on point and line processes. In *Stochastic Point Processes* (P.A.W. Lewis, ed.), Wiley, New York, pp. 522–532.   [22,452]

Papangelou, F. (1972b). Integrability of expected increments of point processes and a related random change of scale. *Trans. Amer. Math. Soc.* **165**, 483–506.   [550,558]

Papangelou, F. (1974a). On the Palm probabilities of processes of points and processes of lines. In *Stochastic Geometry* (E.J. Harding and D.G. Kendall, eds.), Wiley, New York, pp. 114–147.   [452,551,558]

Papangelou, F. (1974b). The conditional intensity of general point processes and an application to line processes. *Z. Wahrs.* **28**, 207–226.   [558–559,577,587]

Papangelou, F. (1976). Point processes on spaces of flats and other homogeneous spaces. *Math. Proc. Cambridge Philos. Soc.* **80**, 297–314.   [558–559]

Papangelou, F. (1978). On the entropy rate of stationary point processes and its discrete approximation. *Z. Wahrs.* **44**, 191–211.   [563,566]

Parthasarathy, K.R. (1967). *Probability Measures on Metric Spaces*. Academic Press, New York.   [153,185,218,281,606]

Perez, A. (1959). Information theory with an abstract alphabet (Generalized forms of McMillan's limit theorems for the case of discrete and continuous time). *Teor. Veroyat. Primen.* **4**, 105–109. (Translation in *Theory Probab. Appl.* **4**, 99–102.)   [569]

Pogorzelski, W.A. (1966). *Integral Equations and Their Applications*. Pergamon Press, Oxford, and PWN, Warsaw.   [137–138]

Poisson, S.D. (1837). *Recherches sur la Probabilité des Jugements en Matière Criminelle et en Matière Civile, Précédées des Règles Générales du Calcul des Probabilités*. Bachelier, Paris.   [8]

Pólya, G. (1931). Sur quelques points de la théorie des probabilités. *Ann. Inst. Henri Poincaré* **1**, 117–162.   [11]

Prekopa, A. (1957a). On the compound Poisson distribution. *Acta Sci. Math. Szeged.* **18**, 23–28.   [35]

Prekopa, A. (1957b). On Poisson and composed Poisson stochastic set functions. *Stud. Math.* **16**, 142–155.   [35]

Preston, C.J. (1976). *Random Fields* (Springer Lecture Notes Math. 534). Springer-Verlag, New York.   [125,575]

Prohorov, Yu.V. (1956). Convergence of random processes and limit theorems in probability theory (in Russian). *Teor. Veroyat. Primen.* **1**, 177–238. [Translation in *Theory Probab. Appl.* **1**, 157–214.]   [15]

Ramakrishnan, A. (1950). Stochastic processes relating to particles distributed in a continuous infinity of states. *Proc. Cambridge Philos. Soc.* **46**, 595–602.   [15,109,133]

Rao, C.R. and Shanbhag, D.N. (1986). Recent results on characterizations of probability distributions: A unified approach through extensions of Deny's theorem. *Adv. Appl. Probab.* **18**, 660–678.   [70]

Rauchenschwandtner, B. (1980). Gibbsprozesse und Papangeloukerne. *Verb. Wiss. Gesellsch. Österreichs, Wien.*   [577]

Rebolledo, R. (1980). Central limit theorem for local martingales. *Z. Wahrs.* **51**, 269–286.   [540]

Renyi, A. (1956). A characterization of Poisson processes (in Hungarian; Russian and English summaries). *Magyar Tud. Akad. Mat. Kutato Int. Kozl.* **1**, 519–527. [Translation in (1976) *Selected Papers of Alfred Renyi*, Vol.1, (P. Turan, ed.), pp. 622–628, Akadémiai Kiadó, Budapest.]   [240]

Renyi, A. (1959). On the dimension and entropy of probability distributions. *Acta Math. Acad. Sci. Hungar.* **10**, 193–215.   [572]

Renyi, A. (1967). Remarks on the Poisson process. *Stud. Sci. Math. Hungar.* **5**, 119–123.   [29]

Resnick, S.I. (1986). Point processes, regular variation and weak convergence. *Adv. Appl. Probab.* **18**, 66–138. [See also S.I. Resnick (1987), *Extreme Values, Regular Variation, and Point Processes,* Springer-Verlag, New York.]   [295]

Rice, S.O. (1944). Mathematical analysis of random noise. *Bell Syst. Tech. J.* **23**, 282–332 and **24**, 46–156. [Reprinted in N. Wax (ed.) (1954), *Selected Papers on Noise and Stochastic Processes,* Dover, New York, pp. 133–294.]   [14]

Ripley, B.D. (1976). The second-order analysis of spatial point processes. *J. Appl. Probab.* **13**, 255–266.   [329,363,383,399]

Ripley, B.D. (1977). Modelling spatial patterns (with Discussion). *J. R. Statist. Soc. Ser. B* **39**, 172–212.   [125,383]

Ripley, B.D. (1981). *Spatial Statistics.* Wiley, New York.   [16,363,399]

Robertson, A.P. and Thornett, M.L. (1984). On translation bounded measures. *J. Aust. Math. Soc. Ser. A* **37**, 139–142.   [401,410]

Rolski, T. (1981). *Stationary Random Processes Associated with Point Processes* (Springer Lecture Notes Statist. 5). Springer-Verlag, New York.   [453]

Romanowska, M. (1978). Poisson approximation of some probability distributions. *Bull. Acad. Polon. Sci., Ser. Sci. Math. Astr. Phys.* **26**, 1023–1026.   [297]

Rubin, I. (1972). Regular point processes and their detection. *IEEE Trans. Inf. Theory* **IT-18**, 547–557.   [495]

Rudemo, M. (1964). Dimension and entropy for a class of stochastic processes. *Magyar Tud. Akad. Mat. Kutato Int. Kozl.* **9**, 73–87.   [564]

Rudemo, M. (1972). Doubly stochastic Poisson processes and process control. *Adv. Appl. Probab.* **4**, 318–338.   [532,547]

Rudemo, M. (1973). Point processes generated by transitions of Markov chains. *Adv. Appl. Probab.* **5**, 262–286.   [532,547]

Ruelle, D. (1969). *Statistical Mechanics: Rigorous Results.* Benjamin, New York. [125]

Ryll-Nardzeweki, C. (1961). Remarks on processes of calls. *Proc. Fourth Berkeley Symp. Math. Statist. Probab.* **2**, 455–465.   [14,452,475]

Sampath, G. and Srinivasan, S.K. (1977). *Stochastic Models for Spike Trains of Single Neurons* (Springer Lecture Notes Biomath. 16). Springer-Verlag, Berlin.   [368]

Samuels, S.M. (1965). On the number of successes in independent trials. *Ann. Math. Statist.* **36**, 1272–1278.   [297]

Schäl, M. (1971). Über Lösungen einer Erneuerungsgleichung. *Abh. Math. Sem. Univ. Hamburg* **36**, 89–98.   [87]

Schwarz, L. (1951). *Théorie des Distributions*, Vol. II. Hermann, Paris.   [400]

Seidel, H. (1876). Über die Probabilitäten solcher Ereignisse welche nur seiten vorkommen, obgleich sie unbeschränkt oft möglich sind. *Sitzungsber. Math. Phys. Cl. Akad. Wiss. München* **6**, 44–50.   [8]

Shiryayev, A.N. (1981). Martingales: Recent developments and applications. *Int. Statist. Rev.* **49**, 199–233.   [495]

Sinai, Ya.G. (1976). Self-similar probability distributions. *Teor. Veroyat. Primen.* **21**, 63–80. [Translation in *Theory Probab. Appl.* **21**, 64–80.]   [326]

Slivnyak, I.M. (1962). Some properties of stationary flows of homogeneous random events. *Teor. Veroyat. Primen.* **7**, 347–352. [Translation in *Theory Probab. Appl.* **7**, 336–341.]   [57,452,459,475,482]

Slivnyak, I.M. (1966). Stationary streams of homogeneous random events. *Vest. Harkov. Gos. Univ. Ser. Mech. Math.* **32**, 73–116.   [57,452,475,482]

Smith, W.L. (1955). Regenerative stochastic processes. *Proc. R. Soc. London Ser. A* **232**, 6–31.   [490,494]

Smith, W.L. (1962). On necessary and sufficient conditions for the convergence of the renewal density. *Trans. Am. Math. Soc.* **104**, 79–100.   [88]

Snyder, D.L. (1972). Filtering and detection for doubly stochastic Poisson processes. *IEEE Trans. Inf. Theory* **IT-18**, 97–102.   [495,532]

Snyder, D.L. (1975). *Random Point Processes*. Wiley, New York.   [16,528]

Solomon, H. and Wang, P.C.C. (1972). Nonhomogeneous Poisson fields of random lines with applications to traffic flow. *Proc. Sixth Berkeley Symp. Math. Statist. Probab.* **3**, 383–400.   [378]

Srinivasan, S.K. (1969). *Stochastic Theory and Cascade Processes*. American Elsevier, New York.   [15,122]

Srinivasan, S.K. (1974). *Stochastic Point Processes and Their Applications*. Griffin, London.   [15]

Stam, A.J. (1967a). On shifting iterated convolutions, I. *Compositio Math.* **17**, 268–280.   [307]

Stam, A.J. (1967b). On shifting iterated convolutions, II. *Compositio Math.* **18**, 201–228.   [307]

Stone, C. (1966). On absolutely continuous components and renewal theory. *Ann. Math. Statist.* **37**, 271–275.   [85,87]

Stone, C. (1968). On a theorem of Dobrushin. *Ann. Math. Statist.* **39**, 1391–1401.   [303]

Stoyan, D. (1983). *Comparison Methods for Queues and Other Stochastic Models*. Wiley, Chichester.   [7]

Stoyan, D. and Mecke, J. (1983). *Stochastische Geometrie*. Akademie-Verlag, Berlin.   [375,386,453]

Stoyan, D., Kendall, W.S. and Mecke, J. (1987). *Stochastic Geometry*. Wiley, Chichester, and Akademie-Verlag, Berlin.   [17,375]

Straf, M. (1972). Weak convergence of stochastic processes with several parameters. *Proc. Sixth Berkeley Symp. Math. Statist. Probab.* **2**, 187–222.   [279,281]

"Student" (1907). On the error of counting with a haemacytometer. *Biometrika* **5**, 351–360.   [9–10]

Szasz, D.O.H. (1970). Once more on the Poisson process. *Stud. Sci. Math. Hungar.* **5**, 441–444.   [30]

Takacs, L. (1965). A moment problem. *J. Aust. Math. Soc.* **5**, 487–490.   [120]

Takacs, L. (1967). On the method of inclusion and exclusion. *J. Am. Statist. Assoc.* **62**, 102–113.   [117]

Takacs, L. (1976). Some remarks on a counter process. *J. Appl. Probab.* **13**, 623–627.   [103]

Taqqu, M. (1978). A representation for self-similar processes. *Stoch. Proc. Appl.* **7**, 55–64.   [326]

Tempel'man, A.A. (1972). Ergodic theorems for general dynamical systems. *Trudy Moskov. Mat. Obsc.* **26**, 95–132. [Translation in *Trans. Moscow Math. Soc.* **26**, 94–132.]   [332,339]

Thedeen, T. (1964). A note on the Poisson tendency in traffic distribution. *Ann. Math. Statist.* **35**, 1823–1824.   [307,378]

Thompson, H.R. (1955). Spatial point processes with applications to ecology. *Biometrika* **42**, 102–115.   [245]

Thornett, M.L. (1979). A class of second-order stationary random measures. *Stoch. Proc. Appl.* **8**, 323–334.   [400,401,409,410,415,425,429]

Titchmarsh, E.C. (1937). *Introduction to the Theory of Fourier Integrals*. Oxford University Press, Oxford.   [636]

Tyan, S. and Thomas, J.B. (1975). Characterization of a class of bivariate distribution functions. *J. Multivariate Anal.* **5**, 227–235.   [93]

Van der Hoeven, P.C.T. (1982). Une projection de processus ponctuels. *Z. Wahrs.* **61**, 483–499.   [589–590]

Van der Hoeven, P.C.T. (1983). *On Point Processes* (Mathematical Centre Tracts 167). Mathematisch Centrum, Amsterdam.   [590]

Van Harn, K. (1978). *Classifying Infinitely Divisible Distributions by Functional Equations* (Mathematical Centre Tract 103). Mathematisch Centrum, Amsterdam.   [76]

Van Schuppen, J. (1973). *Estimation Theory for Continuous Time Processes: A Martingale Approach.* Ph.D. thesis, University of California, Berkeley.   [495]

Vasil'ev, P.I. (1965). On the question of ordinariness of a stationary stream. *Kisinev. Gos. Univ. Ucen. Zap.* **82**, 44–48.   [49]

Vere-Jones, D. (1968). Some applications of probability generating functionals to the study of input/output streams. *J. R. Statist. Soc. Ser. B* **30**, 321–333.   [308]

Vere-Jones, D. (1970). Stochastic models for earthquake occurrences (with Discussion). *J. R. Statist. Soc. Ser. B* **32**, 1–62.   [253,377,423]

Vere-Jones, D. (1971). The covariance measure of a weakly stationary random measure. *J. R. Statist. Soc. Ser. B* **33**, 426–428. [Appendix to Daley (1971).]   [355]

Vere-Jones, D. (1974). An elementary approach to the spectral theory of stationary random measures. In *Stochastic Geometry* (E.J. Harding and D.G. Kendall, eds.), Wiley, New York, pp. 307–321.   [400,418,421–422,430]

Vere-Jones, D. (1975a). A renewal equation for point processes with Markov-dependent intervals. *Math.Nachr.* **68**, 133–139.   [92,101]

Vere-Jones, D. (1975b). On updating algorithms and inference for stochastic point processes. In *Perspectives in Probability and Statistics*, (J. Gani, ed.), Applied Probability Trust, Sheffield, and Academic Press, London, pp. 239–259.   [532]

Vere-Jones, D. (1978). Space time correlations for microearthquakes – a pilot study. Supplement to *Adv. Appl. Probab.* **10**, 73–87.   [363–365,374,383]

Vere-Jones, D. (1982). On the estimation of frequency in point-process data. In *Essays in Statistical Science* (J. Gani and E.J. Hannan, eds.) (*J. Appl. Probab.* Special Vol. 19A), pp. 383–394.   [513]

Vere-Jones, D. (1984). An identity involving permanents. *Linear Alg. Appl.* **63**, 267–270.   [268]

Vere-Jones, D. and Davies, R.B. (1966). A statistical survey of earthquakes in the main seismic region of New Zealand. Part II, Time Series Analysis. *N.Z. J. Geol. Geophys.* **9**, 251–284.   [263,423]

Vere-Jones, D. and Ogata, Y. (1984). On the moments of a self-correcting process. *J. Appl. Probab.* **21**, 335–342.   [548]

Vere-Jones, D. and Ozaki, T. (1982). Some examples of statistical inference applied to earthquake data. *Ann. Inst. Statist. Math.* **34**, 189–207.   [415,505]

Volkonski, V.A. (1960). An ergodic theorem on the distribution of fades. *Teor. Veroyat. Primen.* **5**, 357–360. [Translation in *Theory Probab. Appl.* **5**, 323–326.]   [210]

Von Bortkiewicz, L. (1898). *Das Gesetz der kleinen Zahlen.* G. Teubner, Leipzig. [See M.P. Quine and E. Seneta (1987), Bortkiewicz's data and the law of small numbers, *Int. Statist. Review* **55**, 173–181.]   [9]

Warren, W.G. (1962). *Contributions to the study of spatial point processes.* Ph.D. thesis, University of North Carolina, Chapel Hill (Statist. Dept. Mimeo Series 337).   [245]

Warren, W.G. (1971). The centre-satellite concept as a basis for ecological sampling. In *Statistical Ecology* Vol.2 (G.P. Patil, E.C. Pielou, and W.E. Waters, eds.), Pennsylvania State University Press, University Park, PA, 87–118.   [245]

Watanabe, S. (1933). On the theory of durability. *Geophys. Mag. (Tokyo)* **7**, 307–317.   [7]

Watanabe, S. (1964). On discontinuous additive functionals and Lévy measures of a Markov process. *Japanese J. Math.* **34**, 53–70.   [495,549]

Wegmann, H. (1977). Characterization of Palm distributions and infinitely divisible random measures. *Z. Wahrs.* **39**, 257–262.   [460]

Weibull, W. (1939a). A statistical theory of the strength of materials. *Ing. Vetensk. Akad. Hanal. Stockholm*, No.**151**.   [4]

Weibull, W. (1939b). The phenomenon of rupture in solids. *Ing. Vetensk. Akad. Hanal. Stockholm*, No.**153**.   [4]

Westcott, M. (1970). Identifiability in linear processes. *Z. Wahrs.* **16**, 39–46.   [196]

Westcott, M. (1971). On existence and mixing results for cluster point processes. *J. R. Statist. Soc. Ser. B* **33**, 290–300.   [347]

Westcott, M. (1972). The probability generating functional. *J. Aust. Math. Soc.* **14**, 448–466.   [220,223,344]

Westcott, M. (1976). Simple proof of a result on thinned point processes. *Ann. Probab.* **4**, 89–90.   [291]

Wold, H. (1948). On stationary point processes and Markov chains. *Skand. Aktuar.* **31**, 229–240.   [14,89,102,107]

Wold, H. (1949). Sur les processes stationnaires ponctuels. *Coll. Int. CNRS* **13**, 75–86.   [14]

Yaglom, A.Ya. (1961). Second-order homogeneous random fields. *Proc. Fourth Berkeley Symp. Math. Statist. Probab.* **2**, 593–622.   [184]

Yashin, A. (1970). Filtering of jump processes. Avtomat. i Telemekh. **1970**(5), 52–58. [Translation in *Automation and Remote Control* **1970**, 725–730.]   [495,532]

Yule, G.U. (1924). A mathematical theory of evolution, based on the conclusions of Dr. J.C. Willis. *Philos. Trans. B* **213**, 21–87.   [9]

Yvon, J. (1935). *La Théorie Statistique des Fluides et l'Équation d'État* (Actual. Sci. Industr. **203**). Hermann, Paris.   [12,109,122]

Zygmund, A. (1968). *Trigonometric Series*, 2nd ed. Cambridge University Press, Cambridge.   [428]

Subject Index